## DATE DUE

| | | | |
|---|---|---|---|
| | | | |
| | | | |
| | | | |
| | | | |
| | | | |
| | | | |
| | | | |
| | | | |
| | | | |
| | | | |
| | | | |
| | | | |
| | | | |
| | | | |
| | | | |
| | | | |
| | | | |

DEMCO 38-297

# ANNUAL REVIEW OF PHYSIOLOGY

# ANNUAL REVIEW OF PHYSIOLOGY

VOLUME 58, 1996

JOSEPH F. HOFFMAN, *Editor*

Yale University School of Medicine

PAUL De WEER, *Associate Editor*

University of Pennsylvania School of Medicine

http://annurev.org                 science@annurev.org                 415-493-4400

ANNUAL REVIEW INC.    4139 EL CAMINO WAY,    P.O. BOX 10139    PALO ALTO, CALIFORNIA 04303-0139

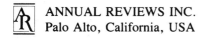 ANNUAL REVIEWS INC.
Palo Alto, California, USA

*International Standard Serial Number: 0066–4278*
*International Standard Book Number: 0–8243–0358-X*
*Library of Congress Catalog Card Number: 39-15404*

Annual Review and publication titles are registered trademarks of Annual Reviews Inc.

♾ The paper used in this publication meets the minimum requirements of
American National Standard for Information Sciences—Permanence of Paper
for Printed Library Materials, ANSI Z39.48-1984.

Annual Reviews Inc. and the Editors of its publications assume no responsibility for the
statements expressed by the contributors to this *Review*.

Typesetting by Kachina Typesetting Inc., Tempe, Arizona; John Olson, President;
Marty Mullins, Typesetting Coordinator; and by the Annual Reviews Inc. Editorial Staff

PRINTED AND BOUND IN THE UNITED STATES OF AMERICA

# PREFACE

While a student in the very early 1950s, I attended a lecture at which Linus Pauling, with arms raised high, began by jubilantly exclaiming, "*This* is the most exciting time in biology." He dealt with a host of new developments but none more prominent than the implications of his own laboratory's recent report that the electrophoretic mobility of sickle cell hemoglobin was different from normal. My purpose here is not to highlight this particular work but to say that Pauling's exclamation is as true today as at any time in the intervening years. There is also no doubt that physiology has contributed to, and benefited from, the rich harvest of fundamental discoveries that emerged during this time; and while the future holds perhaps even more promise, it is not particularly clear to this observer that the science of physiology has been or will be in a position to optimally exploit or initiate new advances. So we come to the real subject of this preface. The problem is more than one of simple funding, although the current (and changing) attitudes of the providers toward basic (biomedical) science is cause enough for concern. In my view, the growth of insight and understanding of physiological processes is also becoming limited by the inabilities of our colleagues at all levels to utilize expeditiously developments in other and related fields, regardless of the degree of sophistication and/or specialization, e.g. three-dimensional structure of transport proteins, control of transcription and gene expression, analysis of knock-out and transgenic animals. Studies of these sorts, perhaps approached with complementary collaborations, represent in a real sense a "new physiology" linking whole-animal functions to their molecular counterparts. The question can also be raised as to what extent are we, as responsible educators, training scientists who are conversant with and who can perfect this new physiology. The nature of the articles that appear in the *Annual Review of Physiology* have and will continue to reflect these changing aspects of our field.

JOSEPH F. HOFFMAN
EDITOR

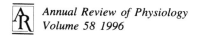

*Annual Review of Physiology*
*Volume 58 1996*

# CONTENTS

# OTHER REVIEWS OF INTEREST TO PHYSIOLOGISTS

From the *Annual Review of Biochemistry*, Volume 64 (1995):

*Human Carbonic Anhydrases and Carbonic Anhydrase Deficiencies*, W. S. Sly and P. Y. Hu

*Structure and Function of Voltage-Gated Ion Channels*, W. Catterall

*Metabolic Coupling Factors in Pancreatic β-Cell Signal Transduction*, C. B. Newgard and J. D. McGarry

*6-Phosphofructo-2-Kinase/Fructose-2,6-Bisphosphatase: A Metabolic Signaling Enzyme*, S. J. Pilkis, T. H. Claus, I. J. Kurland, and A. J. Lange

From the *Annual Review of Medicine*, Volume 46 (1995):

*The Nuclear Hormone Receptor Gene Superfamily*, R. C. J. Ribeiro, P. J. Kushner, and J. D. Baxter

From the *Annual Review of Neuroscience*, Volume 19 (1996):

*Sodium Channel Defects in Myotonia and Periodic Paralysis*, S. C. Cannon

*The* Drosophila *Neuromuscular Junction: A Model System for Studying Synaptic Development and Function*, H. Keshishian, K. Broadie, A. Chiba, and M. Bate

*Structure and Function of Cyclic Nucleotide-Gated Channels*, W. N. Zagotta and S. A. Siegelbaum

*Intracellular Signaling Pathways Activated by Neurotrophic Factors*, R. A. Segal and M. E. Greenberg

*Physiology of Neutrotrophins*, G. Lewin and Y.-A. Barde

*Information Coding in the Vertebrate Olfactory System*, L. B. Buck

*Neuotransmitter Release*, G. Matthews

From the *Annual Review of Nutrition*, Volume 15 (1995):

*Regulation of Tight Junction Permeability During Nutrient Absorption Across the Intestinal Epithelium*, S. T. Ballard, J. H. Hunter, and A. E. Taylor

*Lactoferrin: Molecular Structure and Biological Function*, B. Lonnerdal and S. Iyer

*Roles of Ubiquitinylation in Proteolysis and Cellular Regulation*, K. D. Wilkinson

*Regulation of Iron Metabolism: Translational Effects Mediated by Iron, Hemin, and Cytokines*, D. P. Mascotti, D. Rup, and R. E. Thach

For the convenience of readers, a detachable order form/envelope is bound into the back of this volume.

Hugh E. Huxley

*Annu. Rev. Physiol. 1996. 58:1–19*

# A PERSONAL VIEW OF MUSCLE AND MOTILITY MECHANISMS

## H. E. Huxley

Rosensteil Center and Department of Biology, Brandeis University, Waltham, Massachusetts 02254

KEY WORDS:    molecular structure, contraction mechanism, X-ray, electron microscopy, autobiography

### ABSTRACT

This is a personal account of some of the successive steps in our understanding of the structural mechanism of muscle contraction during the last 45 years. It describes how I, as an ex-physicist, came to be studying muscle by X-ray diffraction in 1949; how the concepts of the double array of actin and myosin filaments and, later, the overlapping filament model and the sliding filament mechanism were developed; and how further electron microscope findings of the structural polarity of muscle filaments led to the suggestion that analogous structures and mechanisms might be involved in cellular motility. The article describes briefly how synchrotron radiation has made it possible to obtain detailed structural information about contracting muscle with millisecond time resolution and discusses some of the recent major advances in the field and the prospects of reaching a full understanding of the contraction mechanism.

## Introduction

In 1995 the muscle and cell motility field is in a very exciting state, as can be seen from several articles in this volume. There have been major advances in the last few years, including the publication of high resolution X-ray structures of actin and myosin subfragment 1 (16, 37, 43, 44), the observations stemming from the development of various types of in vitro motile systems (36, 38, 40, 46, 50), and the use of laser tweezers to measure the forces and displacements produced by single working molecules (4, 9), that have greatly sharpened our perceptions of the underlying molecular events. Although these experiments have amply confirmed the general picture of sliding filaments driven by crossbridges, there is still sufficient uncertainty about the detailed molecular mechanism to leave open the possibility that Nature may be using crossbridges in a

1

0066–4278/96/0315–0001$08.00

very subtle and unexpected way. This adds a further touch of drama to an already intriguing and significant chase. It is just over 40 years since the the original papers about the overlapping filament model and the sliding filament mechanisms were published in 1953 and 1954 (11, 17, 30), and I have been invited to write a more personal review of some of the developments in the field and some account of how I came to be involved in this work in the first place.

My first involvement in muscle work was in 1949 as a research student in a small group supported by the Medical Research Council, at the Cavendish Laboratory in Cambridge. This was the group that eventually grew into the MRC Laboratory of Molecular Biology, but at that stage it consisted of Max Perutz, John Kendrew (my PhD supervisor), Francis Crick, and myself. I was supposed to be working on the X-ray analysis of crystalline proteins, but I had grown restive at the lack of concrete results in that field (this was several years before Perutz showed that the heavy atom technique could work on proteins), and as a sideline, I was exploring the use of a microcamera that Kendrew had suggested to me, a device employing a narrow glass capillary to collimate down an X-ray beam to allow patterns to be recorded from very small selected areas of biological specimens. Reading through Perutz's reprint collection during long night vigils over water-cooled X-ray generators, I became intrigued by the problem of muscle structure and the contraction mechanism. I previously had no biological training, as I will explain presently, and was amazed to find out that the structural changes involved in contraction were still completely unknown. At first I planned to obtain X-ray patterns from individual A-bands, to identify the additional material present there. I hoped to do this using some arthropod or insect muscles that have particularly long A-bands, or even using the organism *Anoplodactylus lentus* Wilson, which my literature search revealed had A-bands up to 50 μm in length! However, getting the microcamera built was a lengthy process, and in the meantime I also became very interested by Schmitt et al's early work on muscle ultrastructure in the mid-1940s (10), and the X-ray diffraction patterns that Bear (2, 3) had obtained from air-dried specimens. He had used such material because of the very long exposure times necessary, so as to get more protein into the X-ray beam than a fully hydrated muscle would allow. But I had learned from Perutz that the whole secret of getting good high-resolution X-ray diagrams from protein crystals was to maintain them in their native fully hydrated state, in their mother-liquor. So I wondered whether a whole host of new details might not spring to light if one could obtain a low-angle X-ray diffraction pattern from a live, fully hydrated muscle. I knew from the earlier work on dried material that the size of the structural units present was likely to be in the hundreds of Angstroms range, and so I set about constructing a slit camera with the necessary high resolution.

The key to success in this endeavor lay in the use of a microfocus X-ray generator, developed by Ehrenberg in Bernal's laboratory (7). With its 50 μm spot size, this generator gave a gain in brilliance (i.e. X-ray intensity per unit area of the source) by about 120 times over the sealed-off fixed anode X-ray tubes of that period. Kendrew, who knew Bernal well from wartime days, had first been interested in this generator in connection with microcamera work, for which it was well-suited, and through his good offices, I was able to obtain an early prototype of the device. I built a high-voltage supply from surplus parts, using the Van der Graf principle, and soon had an X-ray source that (viewed at a 10:1 angle) was ideal for a miniature low-angle-camera using 5–10 μm-wide slits, a film distance of a few centimeters, and a medium power microscope to view (hopefully) the resultant patterns.

And patterns there were! As soon as I had overcome the elementary technical problems of keeping an isolated frog sartorious muscle in good condition for the duration of the X-ray exposures (hours and sometimes days), I was able to see a number of equatorial reflections based on a hexagonal unit cell of 400–450 Å spacing. I took this lattice to represent a continuous array of contractile filaments spaced out across the myofibrils. A little later, using the Szent-Györgyi glycerinated muscle preparation, I found that muscles in rigor showed the same hexagonal reflections, but with greatly altered relative intensities. This showed that there must be some lateral redistribution of material within the same hexagonal lattice, leading to additional concentrations of material around the trigonal points in the lattice.

I then arrived at the correct interpretation of the overall lateral structure, but by somewhat faulty reasoning. I supposed that the actin and myosin must be present in separate filaments, with myosin probably occupying the hexagonal lattice points (because there was more of it) and actin filaments lying in between, more or less randomly in resting, relaxed muscle, but becoming fixed at the trigonal points of the lattice in rigor (i.e. no ATP) by symmetrically arranged crosslinks to the myosin filaments. The idea of an actomyosin complex forming in the absence of ATP was common at that time from the work of Szent-Györgyi and of HH Weber and Portzehl, but the concept of the two proteins being in separate filaments interacting via crosslinks was new. However, at that time I visualized the crosslinks as relatively thin structures and did not consider the possibility that their mass distribution might be the major factor affecting the intensity of the X-ray reflections, rather than the temperature factor of the actin filaments. And, of course, I also assumed that the array of filaments was continuous throughout the length of each sarcomere.

Some time later (in 1951) I found that the muscles from frogs caught in the wild from Fens around Cambridge (on very early morning bicycle expeditions) gave much better X-ray patterns than muscles from the cold-room frogs. Their patterns showed clear reflections in the meridional area, some corresponding to the series already identified by Astbury (1) and by Bear (3) as arising from actin (the 59, 51 Å pair of reflections and the 27 Å repeat), and also others at high spacings, greater than 400 Å, with a strong third order repeat, which originally I supposed probably also came from actin. However, the most remarkable thing about these reflections was that all their spacings remained unchanged when the relaxed muscle was stretched. I reasoned that the contractile material itself must be extended by the stretch (rather than some separate elastic component) because the large passive compliance disappeared immediately when the muscle was activated. I supposed that in the dissociated, relaxed state, actin and myosin filaments could move independently in response to the extension. I envisaged that the actin filaments remained constant in structure, that the myosin filaments were extensible and were responsible for passive tension, and that there was overlap between filaments throughout the sarcomere. Upon activation the rigid actin filaments became crosslinked to myosin, making the whole structure immediately much less extensible, and shortening was produced by partial depolymerization of actin combined with rearrangement of myosin subunits during their interaction. I supposed that the myosin filaments, unlike actin, did not have a very regular internal structure and therefore did not show up in the X-ray diagram.

With hindsight, one can wonder why I did not then entertain the possibility that the very low-angle set of reflections at the higher spacings might come not from actin but from myosin. I can only plead that I was confused both by the numerology of the spacings, by somewhat inaccurate values of their relative values (recorded on two different cameras and relying on micrometer eyepiece measurements on grainy film), and by not knowing which if any reflections were off meridional. This was in the very early days of helical diffraction theory, and reflections at about 59 and 51 Å seemed consistent with a 410 Å fundamental period, approximately (since the seventh and eighth orders would occur at 58.57 and 51.25 Å), whereas the 27 Å reflection seemed to index on either 405 or 432 Å. My long-period repeat seemed to measure around 420 Å, and my failure to pursue these discrepancies cost me the opportunity to have predicted the whole structure and its behavior from the X-ray patterns alone!

I have described this matter in some detail because it added considerably to the sense of revelation some two years later when Jean Hanson and I, working together at Massachusetts Institute of Technology, discovered that the myosin filaments were present only in the A-bands and that it was the actin filaments that were attached to the Z-lines. However, more of that later.

Toward the end of my time as a research student in Cambridge, during 1951 and 1952, the first version of a rotating-anode X-ray generator built at the MRC by Tony Broad began to function. I was able to reduce the exposure on some of the axial patterns to a few hours, short enough to at least begin to contemplate some heroic experiments involving many many frogs in order to obtain the crucial patterns from contracting muscle, but still too long to actually carry them out. I did, however, perform one heroic experiment, by repeatedly pouring an actin preparation (supplied by Andrew Szent-Györgyi through John Kendrew's good offices) down a thin capillary for 24 h in an effort to record the much sought after low-angle pattern from pure oriented actin—but to no avail!

My PhD viva, in June 1952, with Sir Lawrence Bragg and Dorothy Hodgkin as examiners, produced one exchange that later aroused some interest, and which I recounted at a Royal Society muscle meeting in 1964 (although it was not recorded). Dorothy had been impressed by the large increase in intensity of the equatorial (11) reflection that I had shown occurred when a muscle went into rigor. Being unfamiliar with the preparations in question (live and glycerinated rabbit psoas muscle), she had assumed that the muscles shortened considerably during the onset of rigor, and therefore wondered whether the increase could be due in some way to increased overlap between the filaments. I responded that I had taken great care not to allow the fiber bundles to shorten and to check that they had not done so. I had done this in order be sure that the intensity changes that I saw were produced by the lateral rearrangements during crosslinking of actin and myosin filaments on their own, without extraneous factors. Indeed, as later work showed (25), this was in fact precisely the case. Nevertheless, her intuition, although based on a misunderstanding and lacking a realistic model of the sarcomere structure, had considerable elements of truth in it. However, at the time I was slightly irritated by what I considered was her failure to read my "Methods" section carefully, and I took her suggestion much less seriously than (as I gathered some years later) she had done! Indeed, I quite dismissed it, and it was not until Gerald Elliott and his colleagues (8) showed in 1963 that changes in sarcomere length in a relaxed muscle do indeed also produce intensity changes, in the way she had envisaged, that I appreciated how close she had been.

But in 1952, these were early days still, and I was off to MIT as a post-doc on a Commonwealth Fund Fellowship to learn electron microscopy in Frank Schmitt's lab and to see the New World. This all proved so exciting that there was never any time to write up the X-ray work properly (except as brief conference abstracts) (19, 21), and that work was overtaken by the microscopy results that Jean Hanson and I obtained at MIT. However, perhaps now I should explain a little more why my approach to biological problems has always had a mainly physical orientation and how I came to be in the MRC Group in the first place, at such a crucial time in scientific history.

I was born in 1924, in Birkenhead, Cheshire, of Welsh parentage; families who had moved to Merseyside from North Wales in the previous generation but who still had strong ties to the Welsh countryside. They were schoolteachers and shopkeepers and government employees— my father was a Post Office accountant who later became Head of the Accounts Branch in Liverpool, but in the 1920s and 30s we were fairly poor—it was the Depression, and Merseyside was a particularly depressed area. However, both my parents were people of remarkable intellect, great readers, lovers of music, and with great moral strength and power of judgment. With the help of extremely good local secondary schools (i.e. State schools), they instilled in my sister and me the idea that if we worked hard and tried hard enough we could win scholarships to University, perhaps even to Cambridge. My sister, who is about seven years my senior, was the first to succeed (she got a first in both parts of the English Tripos at Newnham, the first woman, I believe, to do so) and of course that spurred me on to greater efforts. My main interest was in atomic and nuclear physics, enthralling subjects for a 12-year-old schoolboy in the 1930s, and when I gradually realized that the main center for experimental research was in Rutherford's laboratory in Cambridge, my course was set.

My scientific and technical inclinations had started in the usual way with the Meccano constructions and chemistry sets, electric motors and shocking coils, and continued into building short-wave radio receivers and getting up very early in the morning when ionospheric conditions were best for receiving amateur stations from the Pacific, using a directional aerial system. My most ambitious experiment had been an attempt—unsuccessful—to make diamonds by dissolving carbon in molten metals in a home-made electric furnace. I was fortunate in having excellent schoolteachers in physics and chemistry and seven years of instruction by each of them in high school. Those were the days! One piece of advice was particularly memorable: "Always look very closely at what is happening in an experiment—you may see something that no one has ever noticed before!" Biology was not taught at all in school—it was a subject considered more suitable for girls—and perhaps that was just as well.

Atomic physics, relativity and quantum theory—or what little I knew of it—were to me then subjects of magical interest, offering glimpses of the ultimate nature of reality, and perhaps the opportunity to make some significant contribution oneself, to one of man's supreme intellectual endeavors. Moreover, my social conscience was persuaded that this would not be a purely abstract and selfish activity by my belief (around 1940) that nuclear power would be needed eventually to replace other sources of fuel, even if it took hundreds of years to discover how to do so.

But by that time, Merseyside was being bombed quite heavily, and I learned to recognize the terrifying hiss of the parachute on a descending landmine and have vivid memories of cycling through the smoking ruins of the center of Liverpool with sagging tangles of wires from the overhead tramcar cables making a quite apocalyptic spectacle. However, after two years in the sixth form, one of them as school captain (not in recognition of my athletic ability, although I was quite good at cross-country running, probably helped by 100 mile Sunday cycle rides through the North Wales mountains), I managed to get to Cambridge, in 1941.

Cambridge, even in wartime, was everything I had ever dreamed of, and when I was able to go on directly to Part II Physics in my second year, i.e. to do nothing else but advanced physics (plus electronics as a wartime training program), my heaven was complete. However, although my greatest ambition was to do research in nuclear physics, preferably in Cambridge, I felt very restive at playing no direct part in, nor even being very near to, the great wartime events that were taking place. So in 1943 I chose to join the Royal Air Force as a radar officer and to come back after the war to finish my degree, rather than spend the war inside some research laboratory. Basically, I suppose I wanted to have some adventure first. I was not successful in getting myself into Europe at the opening of the Second Front, but I did have an extremely interesting time doing flight trials on experimental radar systems, at Malvern and with Bomber Command, (often as it turned out, not far from Cambridge), as well as spending some time on an operational bomber station. I was scheduled to go as liaison with the first RAF Bomber Command Groups in the Far East, after the war ended in Europe.

Other events intervened. I heard the radio announcement of the dropping of the first atomic bomb on Japan with qualified surprise because the nature of such a chain reaction had been published in the popular science magazine *Discovery* several years previously, and during the war I had heard leaks of the enormous scientific and technical effort that was being put into the project in the United States. However, it was not until some time later that I realized the effect the bomb had on my idealistic attitude towards nuclear physics. I remember reading a magazine, *Life* probably, in the Officer's Mess at RAF Marham, with a full page picture spread giving a brief history of the physics involved. It included a gallery of photographs of all the distinguished faces who were my great heroes— Curie, Planck, Einstein, Bohr, Rutherford, Millikan, Compton, Heisenberg, Schrodinger, Pauli, DeBroglie, Chadwick, Dirac, who had done all those marvelous experiments and dreamed up those elegant theories—followed by a line of photographs of some of the survivors from Hiroshima. It was devastating.

At first I thought very seriously about switching to economics, but eventually it seemed to make more sense to at least finish a degree in a subject for which I had shown some aptitude. So, resisting some inducements to stay in the Air Force and help develop high altitude navigation systems, I went back to Cambridge in October 1947 when I was finally demobilized, back to Part II Physics again. I was sure, for a start anyway, that I wanted to do scientific research involving physics, but far away from its wartime uses, and I felt hopeful that interesting applications must exist in some form of medical research. The first task, however, was to be sure of getting a good enough degree to be eligible and desirable as a research student, and it was hard work because my memorizing capacity seemed to have deteriorated sadly in the intervening years.

I was very fortunate in my supervisors, one of whom, Dr. David Shoenberg, had worked with Kapitza and happened to know Kendrew and Perutz through a college connection. They had been given some space in the new Austin Wing of the Cavendish Laboratory, where Sir Lawrence Bragg was Head of the Physics Department and very interested in this new application of X-ray diffraction to more complicated molecules, i.e. proteins. I knew nothing about proteins, and I had not been particularly enamored by what I had learned about crystallography and space groups, but it sounded as though it might lead somewhere interesting. However, I felt pessimistic about my performance in the Tripos exams and went off cycling in the south of France to await the worst. However, when I received my sister's telegram "Congratulations: First: Idiot." in Perpignan, I knew that my ambition of doing research in Cambridge was to be realized. But it took a year or two to find my own direction, as I have described earlier. After getting my PhD, I went to MIT.

Even in those early days of electron microscopy, it was apparent to me that the combination of that technique (which gave one real tangible images, but with all sorts of artifacts) and X-ray diffraction of intact specimens (which gave one true data but in an enigmatic form) would together provide a very powerful means of deciphering these hitherto hidden but very important biological structures and organelles. I knew I had the ideal material for this task and that was what brought me to Frank Schmitt's lab at MIT, where Dick Bear and Cecil Hall were also working at that time. After some months of work and the joint development of a new microtome with Alan Hodge and Dave Spiro, I was able to obtain convincing electron micrographs of the double array of filaments as seen in cross-sections, and I believed I could also see the cross-bridges between thick and thin filaments. However, at that time I still assumed that both types of filament were present throughout the sarcomere—otherwise, how could muscle shorten over such a wide range of lengths? The A-substance seemed to be just some mysterious extra material.

Jean Hanson's arrival in MIT (also to learn electron microscopy) focused my thinking much more sharply on the significance of the striations in skeletal muscles and on the various contradictory data in the literature about the changes in them during contraction. Up to that time, I had never actually seen what the striations looked like in the light microscope, but Jean had taken many beautiful photographs of rabbit and insect myofibrils, as seen in phase contrast—a relatively new technique then—and we wondered whether the A-substance diffused throughout the sarcomere in some way upon activation, and how it would change with muscle length. We drew up a long list of experiments to compare corresponding images as seen in phase-contrast light microscopy and in thin-section electron microscopy while exposing the muscle to various relaxing, activating, and extracting solutions. Almost immediately, we obtained some very startling results. After several initial problems with unbuffered pyrophosphate, we found that the solutions standardly used to extract myosin from whole minced muscle would, when applied to myofibrils, selectively extract the A-band material. At first, still thinking in terms of my earlier model with myosin connected to the Z-lines and actin filaments floating in between, we wondered if perhaps it was actin that was first extracted from this very finely minced muscle. However, we soon convinced ourselves that that was not the case (we could see the same effect in coarsely minced muscle, in electron microscope sections) and so, within a day or two, with a tremendous sense of revelation, we realized what the overlapping filament array structure was really like, and how it enabled so many of the previous observations to fall into place.

I realized that in my electron microscope cross-sections of muscle, the areas that did not show double-hexagonal arrays of thick and thin filaments, but only disordered distributions of thin filaments, were not examples of bad fixation, but were sections through I-band regions, and in a similar way I was able to recognize areas showing thick filaments alone as being sections through H-zones.

We quickly wrote up the work for *Nature* (11), sticking very close to the experiments and the immediate deductions from them because Frank Schmitt warned us against spoiling the paper with a lot of speculation about how the system might work! However, our minds were very full of ideas in this direction, and as I looked repeatedly through Jean's earlier light microscope photographs, I noticed that although sarcomere lengths varied somewhat between different fibrils in these glycerinated psoas muscle preparations (which had gone into rigor at different lengths during the glycerination procedure), the A-bands all seemed to be the same length. It was clear that we needed to make detailed observations of myofibrils as they shortened during ATP-induced contractions. This material would enable us to take advantage of the very clear and unambiguous images that the fibrils gave in phase contrast, as compared with normal images of single whole fibers, which were usually beset by optical artifacts arising from their much greater thickness and the resultant overlay of out-of-focus images of the repeating band pattern.

During the early summer of 1953 (20), I finally got around to writing a short paper about my electron microscope results confirming the presence of the double-hexagonal array expected from the X-ray diffraction studies. In the discussion, I pointed out that my earlier observation of a constant axial period during passive stretch would be compatible with a process in which the two sets of filaments slid past each other and that possibly a similar process might occur during contraction. Looking back on it now, it might have been fairer to have associated Jean somehow with this suggestion at that time because a vital part of its genesis was our discovery of the partially overlapping filament arrays. But at the time it seemed such an obvious possibility that I didn't think very much about this aspect, and neither did she, as far as I know, when she read the manuscript. Frank Schmitt sent the manuscript off to *Biophyica et Biochimica Acta* with his blessing, after some delay.

The main problem now was to get convincing evidence—good photographs—of what the A- and I-bands were doing during contraction. This was not easy because it all happened so quickly, even at cold-room temperature, and it took us some time to get together the necessary microcine-photography set-up, with high-intensity Xenon lamps. I used to go down to the Marine Biological Laboratory in Woods Hole quite frequently during summer weekends, staying with Andrew and Eve Szent-Györgyi. I also visited Andrew's older cousin, Professor Albert Szent-Györgyi, who was not at all enthusiastic about the finding that myosin filaments were confined to the A-band!

However, I did find a more receptive audience for our overlapping filament model and the X-ray and electron microscopy results in Andrew Huxley (no known relationship), who was visiting from England. I found that he was also working on band pattern changes in intact fibers, with Ralph Niedergerke, using a new type of interference light microscope that he (AFH) had built. He told me that they too had some preliminary indications of constant A-band length, and we agreed to communicate again when we had all got our experiments working properly and were nearing the publication stage.

During the latter part of that summer (1953), I also drove out to California via Yellowstone and back via New Mexico, Texas and New Orleans, camping out the whole way (part of the terms of my Fellowship was to see more of the USA!). I had the great fortune to be a participant in the remarkable Pasadena Conference, at which Perutz showed how protein structures could be solved by X-ray diffraction, and Crick and Watson described the DNA double helix and its implications, with Pauling and Delbruck and others to cheer them on.

Back at MIT in the fall, Jean and I were somewhat disappointed with the resolution of our ciné pictures, but found that we could supplement these with photographs taken with a still camera at various successive stages of contraction, by repetitive irrigations of the fibril preparation with small amounts of highly dilute ATP. We also found out how to make very clean myosin-extracted preparations after various degrees of shortening, in which we could see the I-segments very clearly and measure their lengths (admittedly in the absence of myosin, but the less clear-cut edges of the H-zone in intact fibrils gave consistent values) which, as we expected, remained constant, like the A-bands. However, we remained somewhat uncertain as to the situation at shorter lengths, when a dark line appeared in the center of the sarcomere, which we thought might represent the actin filaments coiling up in some way when interacting with myosin at greater degrees of shortening. It was not until several years later that I was able to obtain electron micrographs showing the double-overlap behavior convincingly, and it took very much longer (47) before micrographs of muscles rapidly frozen during contraction could rule out more conclusively the possibility of significant amounts of actin-folding or depolymerization during force development and shortening. Eventually, we were satisfied with our measurements, and as is well known, arranged that our paper and the corresponding one from Andrew Huxley and Ralph Niedergarke be published together in *Nature* (17, 30).

At that time, and for a while subsequently, we entertained two distinct possibilities for the mechanism that produced the sliding force. From energetic considerations and from the structural data, we estimated that under maximum load, the actin filaments needed to be pulled along a distance of about 100 Å each time about one third of the myosin molecules split one ATP (not too far from current values!). One possibility was that this represented the extent of movement of a crossbridge during its working stroke. This was a simple solution, but we were concerned about how such a large movement could be produced by changes in chemical bonding at the angstrom level. The other possibility we considered was some type of vernier mechanism, involving small sequential changes in periodicity in the actin filaments, perhaps brought about when myosin crossbridges attached to them, in a zipper-like manner. In this way, a change of one or two angstroms per monomer could be magnified into 50–100 Å of movement by the successive interaction of 50 crossbridges; analogous mechanisms could be devised involving similar small changes in myosin. Of course, both mechanisms were quite speculative at the time, and we mentioned them only very briefly in the 1954 *Nature* paper. However, we did write them up much more explicitly for a Society for Experimental Biology Symposium in the summer of 1954, when we had both returned to England. The Conference Proceedings volume was published the next year (12), but did not, I think, enjoy a very wide readership. We gradually discarded the vernier mechanism, largely because of the difficulty of getting it to work in stretched muscles at small degrees of overlap, and by the time of writing the 1957 paper (23), showing crossbridges very clearly in very thin longitudinal sections of rabbit muscle, I was almost entirely convinced that they must have, somehow, a working stroke of 50–100 Å.

## A Digression on Cell Motility

One of the first glimmerings of the idea that sliding filaments might be involved in movement in cells beside muscle cells arose very serendipitously early in the 1960s. After the success of seeing the double array of filaments and crossbridges in well-oriented thin sections of muscle in the electron microscope, I had spent almost two fruitless years trying to see significant internal structure in the filaments (1956–1958). For some sort of relief I had been making brief forays into virus structure, encouraged by Rosalind Franklin and Aaron Klug, who were doing X-ray work at Birkbeck College, just round the corner from my lab in Bernard Katz's Biophysics Department at University College. The first success I had was with tobacco mosaic virus (TMV) (in 1956) where, using the negative staining technique that I discovered by accident at this time (22), I could see the central channel in this long rod-shaped virus. After some unsuccessful attempts to get informative images of the nucleic acid component in TMV and in a number of small spherical viruses, using uranyl acetate as a positive stain, I went back to negative staining again, by which time Brenner & Horne had arrived at a simple procedure for carrying it out more reproducibly. In turn, I found that unbuffered uranyl acetate functioned as a superb negative stain, and Geoff Zubay and I had a lot of fun with ribosomes (33) and with turnip yellow mosaic virus (TYMV) (34), the first small spherical virus to be shown by electron microscopy to have fivefold symmetry (the protein subunits form a pentakis dodecahedron).

This success encouraged me to think of applying the same technique to muscle structure. First, one had to take the muscle apart in some way, which I found ridiculously easy to do by homogenizing relaxed muscle in a Waring blender. It was very gratifying to see so many thick filaments all the same expected length (1.5–1.6 µm), but a much more surprising and far-reaching result lay in store (24). Some years earlier I had discovered that heavy meromyosin would bind strongly to the I-segments left behind after myosin extraction from myofibrils, giving a large increase in density as seen in the phase-contrast light microscope. I therefore wondered what the effect would be on the appearance of isolated actin filaments in the electron microscope, expecting that the myosin heads would probably look just as disordered and degraded as they did on the thick filaments. But, of course, quite the contrary was the case. The myosin heads were obviously well preserved and well ordered in a beautiful double-helical structure, matching that of the actin filament structure underneath, which Jean Hanson and Jack Lowy had first observed (13). After looking at my pictures of these "decorated" actin filaments for about two days, the significance of what I was seeing suddenly dawned on me! They were structurally polarized, which meant that all the attached myosin heads and all the underlying actin sites must be oriented in the same direction. Clearly, such a polarity is what one would expect in a sliding filament system, but somehow the requirement had never occurred to me before—nor to anyone else, as far as I know!

After that, it did not take very long to show that actin filaments were indeed attached to the Z-line with the appropriate polarities and that each half of a myosin filament had a corresponding structural polarity, reversing at the M-line. So it all made a great deal of sense in terms of the crossbridge mechanism for muscle contraction. But it also showed that the direction of the force acting on an actin filament would be defined by the actin filament itself, which would only be able to interact with appropriately oriented myosin heads. So I argued (24) that an oriented gel of actin filaments whose polarization was predominantly in one direction might be able to propel itself along past myosin in the presence of ATP, and that this might have something to do with cytoplasmic streaming! At that time, actin was only thought to be present in muscle, but when it was discovered in many other cells, the idea became a lot more plausible, even if it was not exactly right. After Vivianne Nachmias and I (42) found that even slime mold actin could be decorated in just the same way with rabbit actin (a remarkable example of conservation), I became very intrigued with actin's possible movements and tried in many many ways—as did many others, no doubt—to construct an in vitro motility system in which bundles of actin filaments might be seen to move, in the light microscope, when interacting with myosin and ATP. We were all defeated for many years by actin's habit of forming bundles of mixed polarity (although Paul Matsudaira and I came close by using filaments grown from acrosomal bundles) and by the tricky problem of finding suitable surfaces for myosin to attach in a functioning state.

So I was absolutely delighted (though of course a little envious!) when Jim Spudich (a former colleague) and Mike Sheetz first did their famous experiment with Nitella (46), and even more so as the Spudich and Yanagida groups (40, 50) have continued to produce more and more elegant experiments on sliding actin filaments, culminating in those involving force and movements produced by single myosin molecules (9, 36). The corresponding experiments with kinesin and tubulin, a system first put on a clear basis by Vale and his colleagues (48), have been equally gratifying, and the whole subject area is discussed in several review articles in the present volume.

These in vitro sliding experiments were particularly helpful at that time because they provided renewed confirmation, by a novel, independent, and unexpectedly direct method, of the reality of actin filaments actively sliding along myosin heads whose tails were attached to a fixed support. This was important because by the mid-1980s, confidence in a straightforward sliding filament mechanism for muscle contraction had been significantly eroded by the failure of several types of spectroscopic experiments to show structural behavior of crossbridges of the kind expected (i.e. more than one attached configuration). An additional embarrassment was the virtual absence, from the X-ray pattern of isometrically contracting muscle, of low-order actin layer line reflections showing clear evidence of myosin head attachment in any defined configuration. There were also persistent claims by some people of A-band shortening. The in vitro studies re-established in everyone's mind, I believe, the conviction that the sliding force had to be generated by the myosin heads and that our task, as originally, was still to find out how they did it! So let me return to the muscle story itself.

## Why Has It Been So Difficult to Discover the Detailed Mechanism?

By the early 1970s, the time of the Cold Spring Harbor Symposium on muscle contraction (5), it was generally accepted that the sliding filament moving crossbridge model was correct. The much more detailed X-ray data (15, 27), including informative results from contracting muscle showing a major decrease in intensity of the myosin layer lines, confirmed and extended many aspects of such a model, and the Lymn/Taylor and Huxley/Simmons results gave important support from biochemistry and physiology (18, 41). In fact, several people asked me what I was going to work on next, now that the muscle problem was essentially solved, and were puzzled and disappointed when I said I would continue working on muscle because I did not think the evidence was really there yet.

What I had in mind was the fact that there was still very little direct evidence about what the crossbridges were actually doing during their force-producing interaction with actin. They were certainly moving from their more regular positions around the myosin filament backbone and moving towards actin (as shown by the X-ray data) (15, 27), but there was no direct evidence as to whether and when they actually attached to actin, although of course, it was entirely reasonable that they should do so. Similarly, there was no evidence as to what sort of structural changes in the myosin head, elsewhere in the molecule, or within the actin monomers, might be responsible for the generation of force and movement during the working stroke. It seemed to me that one could not just leave a problem when such crucial information was still lacking, particularly as new developments in X-ray diffraction (synchrotron radiation) (45) and electron microscopy (three-dimensional reconstruction) (6) offered excellent new ways to approach the question. If it were indeed a simple straightforward tilting mechanism, with most of the crossbridge population attached and generating force during isometric contraction and going steadily through repetitive cycles during shortening, then the evidence for this should be quite readily accessible when the new techniques were applied.

In practice, things were not so straightforward; it took another 10 years before synchrotron radiation began to fulfill its promise. In the meantime, we had to do the best we could with higher power rotating anode X-ray generators. One of the most obvious experiments was to apply a fairly quick release by about 2% of muscle length to an otherwise isometrically contracting whole muscle and look at the intensity changes in the equatorial reflections, which we could now do (with some difficulty) on a time-resolved basis using laboratory X-ray sources. Because there was such a large change upon activation and tension development (increase in intensity of [11], decrease of intensity [10]) (equatorial reflections), I expected that when all the crossbridges detached and went through one or two cycles of movement following the quick release (the tension fell to zero and then recovered again), there would be interesting intensity changes in the equatorial pattern. But there were none. This convinced me that there must be some very strange features of crossbridge behavior and that the problems were still certainly worthy of attention.

The powerful X-ray beam lines at the synchrotron radiation source at the European Molecular Biology Laboratory Outstation at DESY, Hamburg, developed in the early 1980s, enabled us to do many of the experiments that seemed an impossible dream in the 1950s, and we obtained many informative results (28, 29). The large and abrupt change in the intensity of the 143 Å meridional reflection, which Bob Simmons, Wasi Faruqi, and I found takes place almost simultaneously with a rapid quick release (32), remains the best and indeed almost the only experimental evidence we have that axial changes in crossbridge structure are very closely associated with the working stroke. [Importantly, it has now been shown by Irving and his colleagues (35) on single fibers that this change occurs during the tension redevelopment phase.] But my favorite experiment remains the one involving the actin second layer line and the evidence it provides that tropomyosin movement is responsible for switching on the actin filaments, as Haselgrove and I and Vibert, Lowy, and others had suggested earlier (14, 26, 49). To see that reflection flashing up immediately after electrical stimulation of the muscle, at a time significantly before any tension had developed, was a thrilling experience for Marcus Kress, Wasi Faruqi, and myself (39). We had feared that the changes might be too faint to see.

However, even with our best efforts and a lot of beam time, we were unable to see any reproducible changes in equatorial intensities produced by short quick releases, and this remains a big puzzle. There are a number of other related effects, for instance, delays in the onset of the 143 Å reflection spacing change at the beginning of fast shortening (31), which seem to show crossbridge interaction with thin filaments over longer distances than the tension generating part of the working stroke is likely to be (in any straightforward model of a lever arm). It seems as though very rapid completion of the working stroke leaves the crossbridge in a state where it can detach and re-attach again very quickly to a different actin monomer, closer to the Z-line. Whether this is merely a quirk of nucleotide-binding rates, or two head interactions, or whether it is telling us something very important about the basic mechanism of force development remains to be seen.

The high resolution structure of the myosin head (44) with its more globular catalytic, actin-binding domain and its elongated regulatory domain, projecting out sideways when the head is attached to actin, obviously provides a structural basis for the tilting crossbridge mechanisms that have long been postulated. The location of the normal binding sites for optical and spin labels in the catalytic domain, which might not have to change very much during a working stroke, could perhaps explain why changes in orientation of strongly attached heads have been so difficult to detect. However, there still seems to be a large amount of disorder in the attached heads during isometric contraction. I have made great efforts in recent years to obtain informative electron micrographs of thin sections of rapidly frozen, freeze-substituted contracting muscle, but although an ordered component is clearly present, it is quite sparse, as indeed one would expect from the low-angle X-ray diffraction patterns of contracting muscle. This may merely mean that only a very small fraction of crossbridges are in a tension-generating state at any one time (which is quite plausible), but it still remains true that a really decisive demonstration of an adequately large and specific change in the configuration of an attached crossbridge during the working stroke (or an equivalent change in structure of a myosin head produced by biochemical manipulation) has still to be produced. Thus the challenge to really understand the mechanism remains.

I consider myself very fortunate to have moved from physics to biology when I did. My motives for leaving physics were somewhat mixed. In part, as I have indicated, there was dismay and disillusion that the first practical consequences of all that beautiful work in atomic and nuclear physics had been the atom bomb, and my reluctant conclusion that I would never be able to enjoy working in that field without feelings of guilt. This was reinforced by the fact that my own contribution to society at that time had been to help improve target identification radar for Bomber Command. I was also influenced by another worry (which I think was exaggerated)—that the days when an individual experimenter could make a difference in the nuclear physics field were over, and that in the future just a few very good theoreticians, which I could never aspire to be, would tell great hoards of experimenters what to do and then interpret their results for them. In fact, there have been many important original contributions by individual experimenters since then (1947).

My reasons for going into biology were not clearly formulated, nor could they be at that time, especially given my ignorance of the subject. I had a vague notion that there must be many techniques in physics that could be applied to research in biology and medicine and that therefore a physicist, working with a "real" biologist, might be able to make a useful and interesting contribution. When I found that there was such a possibility, right there in the Cavendish Laboratory in Cambridge, it was an easy decision and an extraordinarily fortunate one for me. Not only was I "present at the Creation," so to speak, of the DNA double helix and the solution of protein structure by X-ray crystallography and much the founding of molecular biology, but I benefited enormously from the company of people with very clear minds and great (and justified) optimism about what could be accomplished. Moreover, since my own work prospered, I was able to enjoy a long and enthralling association with the MRC Laboratory of Molecular Biology in Cambridge, arguably the leader in the field, during one of the greatest periods of scientific development, certainly as great as the revolution in physics in the first part of this century, which had caught my imagination as a child. I sometimes regret that all the advanced physics I learned never had any application, but it encouraged in me the belief that everything in Nature could be explained rationally, eventually, and that after Part II Physics, understanding the basics of any other subject would be relatively easy!

A further piece of good fortune was that structure turned out to be so important for biological mechanisms and that my early faith that a combination of X-ray diffraction and electron microscopy would provide an extremely powerful tool for deciphering structure and function in numerous fields was fully confirmed. In the area of muscle and cell motility, the techniques for obtaining structural and mechanical information have been able to keep up very well with the questions arising from other techniques, over a long period of time. Just when it becomes possible to change individual amino acid residues in a myosin molecule, the high resolution three-dimensional structure of the myosin head is solved, so that interesting residues can be chosen. At the same time, it becomes feasible to measure forces and displacements on individual molecules, and perhaps even to follow the chemistry on single molecules too. There is still a great deal to learn from the X-ray diagrams of intact muscle, especially as brighter and brighter synchrotron sources become available; and a way still has to be found to obtain more detailed and reliable high resolution electron microscope images from rapidly frozen muscles during tension development and rapid length change. So there are plenty of interesting things still to do and good problems still to solve!

## Literature Cited

1. Astbury WT, Spark C. 1947. An electron microscope and X-ray study of actin: II. X-rays. *Biochim. Biophys. Acta* 1:388–92
2. Bear RS. 1944. X-ray diffraction studies on protein fibers. II. Feather rachis, porcupine quill tip and clam muscle. *J. Am. Chem. Soc.* 66:2043–50
3. Bear RS. 1945. Small angle X-ray diffraction studies of muscle. *J. Am. Chem. Soc.* 67:1625–26
4. Block SM, Goldstein LSB, Schnapp BJ. 1990. Bead movement by single kinesin molecules studied by optical tweezers. *Nature* 348:348–52
5. Cold Spring Harbor Symposium on

Quantitative Biology. 1972. *The Mechanism of Muscle Contraction.* Vol. 37

6. DeRosier DJ, Klug A. 1968. Reconstruction of the three-dimensional structures from electron micrographs. *Nature* 217:130–34

7. Ehrenberg W, Spear WE. 1951. An electrostatic focussing system and its application to a fine-focus X-ray tube. *Proc. Phys. Soc. B* 64:67–71

8. Elliott GF, Lowy J, Worthington CR. 1963. An X-ray and light diffraction study of the filament lattice of striated muscle in the living state and in rigor. *J. Mol. Biol.* 6:295–305

9. Finer JT, Simmons RM, Spudich JA. 1994. Single myosin mechanics: piconewton forces and nanometre steps. *Nature* 368:113–19

10. Hall CE, Jakus MA, Schmitt FO. 1945. The structure of certain muscle fibrils as revealed by the use of electron stains. *J. Appl. Phys.* 16:459–65

11. Hanson J, Huxley HE. 1953. The structural basis of the cross-striations in muscle. *Nature* 172:530–32

12. Hanson J, Huxley HE. 1955. The structural basis of contraction in striated muscle. In *Symp. Soc. Exp. Biol. Fibrous Proteins and their Biological Significance* 9:228–64

13. Hanson J, Lowy J. 1963. The structure of F-actin and of actin filaments isolated from muscle. *J. Mol. Biol.* 6:46–60

14. Haselgrove JC. 1972. X-ray evidence for a conformational change in the actin-containing filaments of vertebrate striated muscle. *Cold Spring Harbor Symp. Quant. Biol.* 37:341–52

15. Haselgrove JC, Huxley HE. 1973. X-ray evidence for radial crossbridge movement and for the sliding filament model in actively contracting skeletal muscle. *J. Mol. Biol.* 77:549–68

16. Holmes KC, Popp D, Gebhard W, Kabsch W. 1990. Atomic model of the actin filament. *Nature* 347:44–49

17. Huxley AF, Niedergerke R. 1954. Structural changes in muscle during contraction. Interference microscopy of living muscle fibers. *Nature* 173:971–73

18. Huxley AF, Simmons RM. 1971. Proposed mechanism of force generation in striated muscle. *Nature* 233:533–38

19. Huxley HE. 1951. Low-angle X-ray diffraction studies on muscle. *Disc. Faraday Soc.* 11:148

20. Huxley HE. 1953a. Electron microscope studies of the organization of the filaments in striated muscle. *Biochim. Biophys. Acta* 12:387–94

21. Huxley HE. 1953b. X-ray analysis and the problem of muscle. *Proc. R. Soc. London Ser. B* 141:59–62

22. Huxley HE. 1956. Some observations on the structure of tobacco mosaic virus. *Proc. 1st Eur. Reg. Conf. Elect. Microsc. Stockholm.* p. 260

23. Huxley HE. 1957. The double array of filaments in cross-striated muscle. *J. Biophys. Biochem. Cytol.* 3:631–48

24. Huxley HE. 1963. Electron microscope studies of the structure of natural and synthetic protein filaments from muscle. *J. Mol. Biol.* 7:281–308

25. Huxley HE. 1968. Structural differences between resting and rigor muscle: evidence from intensity changes in the low-angle equatorial X-ray diagram. *J. Mol. Biol.* 37:507–20

26. Huxley HE. 1972. Structural changes in the actin and myosin-containing filaments during contraction. *Cold Spring Harbor Symp. Quant. Biol.* 37:361–76

27. Huxley HE, Brown W. 1967. The low angle X-ray diagram of vertebrate striated muscle and its behavior during contraction and rigor. *J. Mol. Biol.* 30:383–434

28. Huxley HE, Faruqi AR. 1983. Time-resolved X-ray diffraction studies on vertebrate striated muscle. *Annu. Rev. Biophys. Bioeng.* 12:381–417

29. Huxley HE, Faruqi AR, Kress M, Bordas J, Koch MHJ. 1982. Time resolved X-ray diffraction studies of the myosin layerline reflections during muscle contraction. *J. Mol. Biol.* 158:637–84

30. Huxley HE, Hanson J. 1954. Changes in the cross-striations of muscle during contraction and stretch and their structural interpretation. *Nature* 173:973–76

31. Huxley HE, Simmons RM, Faruqi AR. 1989. Time-course of spacing change of 143 Å meridional crossbridge reflection during rapid shortening. *Biophys. J.* 55:12a

32. Huxley HE, Simmons RM, Faruqi AR, Kress M, Bordas J, Koch MHJ. 1983. Changes in the X-ray reflections from contracting muscle during rapid mechanical transients and their structural implications. *J. Mol. Biol.* 169:469–506

33. Huxley HE, Zubay G. 1960a. Electron microscope observations on the structure of microsomal particles from *E. coli. J. Mol. Biol.* 2:10–18

34. Huxley HE, Zubay G. 1960b. The structure of the protein shell of turnip yellow mosaic virus. *J. Mol. Biol.* 2:189–96

35. Irving M, Lombardi V, Piazzesi G, Ferenczi M. 1992. Myosin head movements are synchronous with the elementary force-generating process in muscle. *Nature* 357:156–58

36. Ishijima A, Harada Y, Kojima H, Funatsu T, Higuchi H, Yanagida T. 1994. Single-molecule analysis of the actomyosin motor using nano-manipulation. *Biochem. Biophys. Res. Comm.* 199: 1057–63

37. Kabsch W, Mannherz H-C, Such D, Pai E, Holmes KC. 1990. Atomic structure of the actin-DNAase I complex. *Nature* 347:37–44

38. Kishino A, Yanagida T. 1988. Force measurements by micromanipulation of a single actin filament by glass needles. *Nature* 334:74–76

39. Kress M, Huxley HE, Faruqi AR, Hendrix J. 1986. Structural changes during activation of frog muscle studied by time-resolved X-ray diffraction. *J. Mol. Biol.* 188:325–42

40. Kron SJ, Spudich JA. 1986. Fluorescent actin filaments move on myosin fixed to a glass surface. *Proc. Natl. Acad. Sci. USA* 83:6272–76

41. Lymn RW, Taylor EW. 1971. Mechanism of adenosine triphosphate hydrolysis by actomyosin. *Biochemistry* 10: 4617–24

42. Nachmias VT, Huxley HE, Kessler D. 1970. Electron microscope observations of actomyosin and actin preparations from *Physarum polycephalum*. *J. Mol. Biol.* 50:83–90

43. Rayment I, Holden HM, Whittaker M, Yohn CB, Lorenz M, et al. 1993a. Structure of the actin-myosin complex and its implications for muscle contraction. *Science* 261:58–65

44. Rayment I, Rypniewski WR, Schmidt-Base K, Smith R, Tomchick DR, et al. 1993b. Three-dimensional structure of myosin subfragment-1: a molecular motor. *Science* 261:50–57

45. Rosenbaum G, Holmes KC, Witz J. 1971. Synchrotron radiation as a source for X-ray diffraction. *Nature* 230:434–37

46. Sheetz MP, Spudich JA. 1983. Movement of myosin-coated fluorescent beads on actin cables in vitro. *Nature* 303:31–35

47. Sosa H, Popp D, Ouyang G, Huxley HE. 1994. Ultrastructure of skeletal muscle fibers studied by a plunge quick-freezing method: myofilament lengths. *Biophys. J.* 67:283–92

48. Vale RD, Reese TS, Sheetz MP. 1985. Identification of a novel force-generating protein, kinesin, involved in microtubule-based motility. *Cell* 42:39–50

49. Vibert PJ, Lowy J, Haselgrove JC, Poulson FR. 1972. Structural changes in the actin-containing filaments of muscle. *Nature New Biol.* 236:182

50. Yanagida T, Nakase M, Nishiyama K, Oosawa F. 1984. Direct observation of movement of single F-actin filaments in the presence of myosin. *Nature* 307:58–60

*Annu. Rev. Physiol. 1996. 58:21–50*

# DETERMINANTS OF MAXIMAL OXYGEN TRANSPORT AND UTILIZATION

*Peter D. Wagner*

Department of Medicine, 0623A, University of California San Diego, 9500 Gilman Drive, La Jolla, California 92093–0623

KEY WORDS: diffusion, convection, $\dot{V}O_2max$, muscle microcirculation, pulmonary gas exchange

---

## ABSTRACT

Maximal $\dot{V}O_2$ ($\dot{V}O_2max$) has mostly been the province of exercise physiologists wishing to provide a measure of athletic potential or to characterize subjects in exercise-related research. It is also used clinically to determine a patient's exercise capacity. More recently, it has been recognized that the study of $\dot{V}O_2max$ can provide fundamental insight into $O_2$ transport at all points between inspired air and muscle mitochondria. This review focuses on understanding how $\dot{V}O_2max$ is set and concludes that the more athletic one is, the more $\dot{V}O_2max$ is sensitive to $O_2$ transport conductances in the lungs, circulation, and skeletal muscle. These transport conductances form an integrated system, all components interacting to define $\dot{V}O_2max$. A particularly important component is diffusive conductance in muscle. This appears to be abnormal in chronic conditions such as obstructive pulmonary disease and heart and renal failure and may well explain why correction of central cardiovascular defects in $O_2$ transport in such patients fails to restore exercise capacity.

---

## INTRODUCTION

Oxidative phosphorylation within mitochondria of mammalian cells is the fundamental energy-producing biochemical process that uses oxygen ($O_2$) and makes life possible. The basic reaction involved is as follows:

$$3\ ADP + 3\ Pi + 1/2\ O_2 + NADH + H^+ \rightarrow 3\ ATP + NAD^+ + H_2O. \qquad 1.$$

In this reaction, ADP and ATP are adenosine di- and tri-phosphate, respectively (the latter containing the high energy bonds that are transduced into

21

0066–4278/96/0315–0021$08.00

energy when the reaction is reversed). Pi is inorganic phosphate, and NADH and $NAD^+$ are the reduced and oxidized forms of nicotinamide adenine dinucleotide. $H_2O$ is water, and $H^+$ is a hydrogen ion.

Understanding the determinants of maximal oxygen utilization, or $\dot{V}O_2max$, requires an understanding of the factors that limit the maximal forward rate of the above reaction. Basically they can be broken down into (a) those factors that determine the rate of $O_2$ transport from the environment to the mitochondrial sites of $O_2$ utilization and (b) those factors unrelated to $O_2$ transport that can influence the above reaction. These factors include a large number of biochemical phenomena related to substrate availability for, and enzyme acceleration of, the many reactions that feed oxidative phosphorylation such as the Krebs cycle and glycolysis. This subdivision may appear arbitrary, but it has a practical basis: On moving from rest to heavy exercise, acceleration of $O_2$ transport depends on physiological phenomena with a biophysical underpinning; enhancement of $O_2$ utilization through the second set of factors is, at least for short-term exercise, essentially dependent on intracellular biochemical processes. These different but interacting groups of factors thus require somewhat different approaches to facilitate their understanding. It is the thesis of this review that under most normal conditions, $O_2$ supply dictates $\dot{V}O_2max$ rather than substrate or enzyme availability. Accordingly, the focus will be mostly on $O_2$ transport, with evidence presented to support this underlying hypothesis.

Maximal $O_2$ utilization occurs during sustained extreme physical exertion. Termination of such exercise due to perceived inability by an individual to continue merges at least three separate sets of occurrences. First, the individual ceases exercise because of unpleasant symptoms such as undue shortness of breath, severe discomfort in the working muscles, or exhaustion. Second, exercise may be in part terminated because of fatigue, which should be distinguished from exhaustion and be reserved for a neuromuscular phenomenon in which muscle force cannot be maintained in the face of continued neurological stimulation. Finally, further effort may be unachievable due to limitation of $O_2$ supply to, and/or utilization of $O_2$ by, the mitochondria. It is this last occurrence that is the focus of our review. Confusion over determinants of exercise capacity has arisen because of failure to separate these three kinds of phenomena, which generally occur at the same time.

This review deals only with determinants of $\dot{V}O_2max$, not with symptoms or with fatigue.

## DEFINITION OF MAXIMAL $O_2$ UTILIZATION ($\dot{V}O_2max$)

Even limiting oneself to a discussion of $\dot{V}O_2max$ does not preclude confusion because $\dot{V}O_2max$ is a somewhat elusive variable both conceptually and experimentally. Thus applying the law of mass action to the above equation for oxidative phosphorylation suggests that as long as each reactant can be supplied and each product removed without limit, the rate of $O_2$ utilization should be able to increase without limit. However, to be a useful concept, given that in vivo there is finite availability of all substrates and enzymes, we should be content to discuss maximal $O_2$ utilization in the context of realistic metabolism. The fundamental point is that a maximal rate of $O_2$ utilization can in fact be shown experimentally to exist in normal skeletal muscle.

Thus, in intact mammals, at very high exercise levels, it can generally be shown that even if external power is increased, there is no significant further rise in $\dot{V}O_2$ (3, 36, 91, 98). The positive linear relationship between external power and $\dot{V}O_2$ characteristic of submaximal exercise flattens out (or asymptotes) to define $\dot{V}O_2max$ (Figure 1, *upper panel*). At the other end of the integrative spectrum, it is also known that $O_2$ availability determines $O_2$ utilization in simpler in vitro conditions such as in cell culture (111) (Figure 1, *lower panel*). In cell culture, below some $PO_2$, respiration falls linearly, showing that under such conditions, $O_2$ availability is limiting the rate of $O_2$ use through oxidative phosphorylation. Above that $PO_2$, $\dot{V}O_2$ is not dependent on $O_2$ availability but on enzyme or substrate levels. Has $\dot{V}O_2$ plateaued (Figure 1, *upper panel*) because of $O_2$ supply limitation or because of $O_2$-unrelated substrate/enzyme limitation as in Figure 1 (*lower panel*)?

The bulk of the evidence (reviewed below) points to $O_2$ supply limitation. A plethora of acute studies manipulating the $O_2$ transport pathway underlies this assertion, because it is reasonable to assume that acute studies (over a period of a few minutes) in intact humans or animals reflect constant structure and substrate/enzyme availability in the $O_2$ transport system components. Thus when $O_2$ availability is reduced acutely, $\dot{V}O_2max$ falls. This is true no matter whether the loss of $O_2$ transport occurs because of inspiratory hypoxia (73), reduced muscle blood flow (4, 10, 40), or reduced Hb concentration (39, 48, 116).

Although such studies provide convincing evidence that at subnormal rates of $O_2$ supply, $\dot{V}O_2max$ is indeed $O_2$ supply limited, the same conclusions are not reached concerning limits to $O_2$ utilization under normal baseline conditions. To evaluate this situation, which is probably the most important circumstance in which to understand how $\dot{V}O_2max$ is achieved, one must provide a mechanism of increasing $O_2$ availability and ask whether $\dot{V}O_2max$ is correspondingly higher. This is intrinsically difficult, particularly in intact animals or humans. Thus increasing $FIO_2$ all the way to 1.0 increases inspired $PO_2$ almost fivefold but increases the $O_2$ concentration of the arterial blood by only 8–10%, due to the flattening out of the $O_2$-Hb dissociation curve. Given that (*a*) the measurement of $\dot{V}O_2$ at the mouth is nearly impossible at $FIO_2 > 0.5$ for technical reasons, (*b*) measurement of $\dot{V}O_2$ during extreme exercise is

NORMAL TRAINED HUMAN SUBJECT

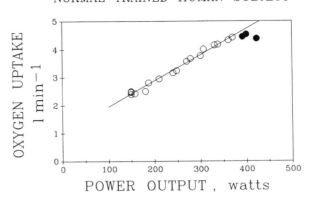

CULTURED BHK-21 KIDNEY CELLS

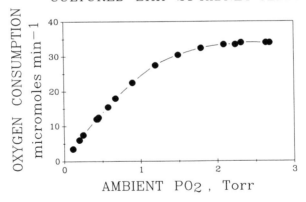

*Figure 1*   Upper panel shows 20 s-averaged data for a typical trained subject exercising at increasing intensity until exhaustion. Oxygen uptake ($\dot{V}O_2$) increases linearly (*open circles*) until just before exhaustion, when $\dot{V}O_2$ fails to further rise despite increasing effort (*closed circles*). Lower panel shows relationship between cultured kidney cell $\dot{V}O_2$ and $PO_2$ in the culture medium. Above about 2 torr, $\dot{V}O_2$ is $PO_2$ independent, but at lower values, $\dot{V}O_2$ is dependent on available $O_2$. Data from Wilson et al (111).

challenging at any $FIO_2$, and (*c*) only a small increase in $O_2$ transport is expected as noted above, it is not surprising that the anticipated effect of increasing $FIO_2$ on $\dot{V}O_2max$ has been difficult to verify (107, 108). However, acutely augmenting blood volume by transfusion has provided clear-cut and reproducible evidence of a higher $\dot{V}O_2max$ (11, 29, 81, 94) in intact humans, and increasing muscle blood flow in human or animal models has provided equally good evidence that when $O_2$ supply is increased by this method, so too is maximal $\dot{V}O_2$ (76, 86, 96).

The overall conclusion from such studies of intact systems in which $O_2$ supply has been augmented acutely, and thus prior to any structural or biochemical adaptation, is that $O_2$ supply does indeed limit the maximal rate of oxidative phosphorylation in normal circumstances. In vivo estimates of cytochrome $a,a_3$ redox state by near infrared spectroscopy (18) further support this conclusion. However, it should be noted that this technology is difficult and is contaminated by larger signals from myoglobin and hemoglobin; thus it is not surprising that others have failed to find such cytochrome reduction (95) during exercise.

If one reexamines the conclusion that $\dot{V}O_2max$ is generally limited by $O_2$ supply, it becomes necessary to refine one's definition of $\dot{V}O_2max$. This is because plateauing of $\dot{V}O_2$ will occur at different absolute values of $\dot{V}O_2$ as $O_2$ supply is acutely manipulated. Consequently, there is in practice no single, absolute $\dot{V}O_2max$ for intact biological systems but rather the following: For any given set of circumstances determining maximal $O_2$ supply, a plateau in $\dot{V}O_2$ (i.e. $\dot{V}O_2max$) can potentially be observed and defined. The word potential is used because due to discomfort, many individuals will quit exercise before a clear plateauing tendency is visible. Again, such plasticity of $\dot{V}O_2max$ is observed within the time it takes to manipulate $O_2$ supply, usually minutes. This must eliminate any structural or biochemical adaptation as the basis for the altered $\dot{V}O_2max$ under such conditions. Of course, $\dot{V}O_2max$ can be altered over a longer period by a combination of structural and biochemical changes induced by various stimuli, as is well known (reviewed in 7, 92).

The preceding presents a view that does not account for individual variability in maximal rates of $O_2$ transport and utilization. Such variability requires further modification of the above notions. Current evidence suggests that greater athletic ability for endurance activities is associated with greater vulnerability to limited $O_2$ supply. Thus augmenting $O_2$ supply improves $\dot{V}O_2max$ little if at all in untrained humans or nonathletic mammalian species, but such individuals are also less susceptible to reduced exercise capacity when $O_2$ supply is reduced than their more athletic counterparts (82). Also, acute hypoxia results in proportionately more reduction in maximal $\dot{V}O_2$ in athletes than in sedentary subjects (56). There are at least two possible reasons for this. First, if untrained individuals possess less metabolic machinery to use $O_2$ due to fewer mitochondria, they are less likely to be dependent on an $O_2$ supply that may be in excess for the respiratory potential. Second, maximal cardiac output is well known to be less than in trained subjects (7). A low cardiac output naturally favors diffusive loading of $O_2$ in the lungs and $O_2$ unloading in the tissues by providing potentially longer capillary transit times for the red cell. Consequently, natural or trained athletic ability must be taken into account in discussing the limits to exercise capacity to avoid needless confusion and pseudo-controversy over the importance of $O_2$ transport.

## DETERMINANTS OF MAXIMAL $O_2$ SUPPLY

The above introduction serves to focus attention on the $O_2$ transport pathway. To avoid confusion, this transport pathway must be clearly defined. Many workers, especially in clinical fields, consider $O_2$ transport to be the sum total of all $O_2$ transport components down to the arteriolar blood supply of the tissue in question. They call this total $O_2$ transport or $O_2$ delivery, which is the product of the blood flow rate to the tissue and the arterial concentration of $O_2$. Arterial $O_2$ concentration is itself a product essentially of arterial $O_2$ saturation ($SaO_2$) and Hb concentration ([Hb]), (ignoring the usually but not always minor contribution of physically dissolved $O_2$). The same investigators generally consider that arterial $O_2$ saturation represents lung function, but as will be shown below, this is an unjustified assumption if taken literally. Although lung function is certainly a major determinant of arterial saturation, so too is blood flow rate ($\dot{Q}T$) through the lungs, especially at maximal exercise, and this is largely determined by cardiac function. The above definition of $O_2$ delivery or transport is

$$\text{total } O_2 \text{ transport} = 1.39 \times \text{[Hb]} \times SaO_2 \times \dot{Q}T \qquad \qquad 2.$$

for the body as a whole. For any tissue, $\dot{Q}T$ (pulmonary blood flow or cardiac output) should be replaced by the corresponding tissue blood flow rate.

The above, however, ignores a critical component of the $O_2$ pathway—that between the tissue microcirculatory $O_2$ exchange vessels, which may include not only capillaries but also arterioles and venules (8, 20, 88) and the mitochondria. This is a physically short pathway and one in which $O_2$ is transported passively by diffusion (55). If all of the $O_2$ available as defined in Equation 2 were always completely transported to the mitochondria and consumed via Equation 1, Equation 2 would indeed suffice as a definition of $O_2$ transport. However, it is well known that blood flowing through exercising muscles is not depleted of $O_2$ even at $\dot{V}O_2max$ (68, 83). Consequently, the $O_2$ extraction process cannot be ignored. This is even more important in human disease states of compromised $O_2$ transport such as emphysema and bronchitis, lung fibrosis, chronic heart failure, and chronic renal failure with anemia, where recent evidence (see below) suggests that $O_2$ conductance from the tissue microcirculation to the mitochondria is particularly impaired.

Figures 2 and 3 lay out a standard conception of the $O_2$ transport pathway. Figure 2 shows all major steps, whereas Figure 3 magnifies the final component in the tissue of interest, generally, but not always, skeletal muscle.

# STRUCTURE

# FUNCTION

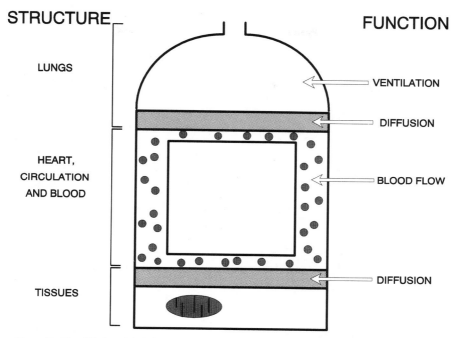

*Figure 2*  Simplified model of the $O_2$ transport pathway, showing the principal structures and their associated functions. $O_2$ transport requires the integrated interaction of the four principal functional components indicated, mixing convective and diffusive processes. Non-uniform distribution of ventilation, blood flow, and metabolic rate within the lungs or muscle tissues are neglected but will reduce transport if present.

If $O_2$ supply to mitochondria appears to be the normal determinant of $\dot{V}O_2$max, it is critical to develop a qualitative (and quantitative) construct accounting for the spectrum of experimental observations, each of which provides evidence for involvement of one or more, but usually not all, portions of the $O_2$ pathway in an integrative manner.

A simple construct for this simultaneously considers the two governing equations underlying $O_2$ transport: one that expresses the rate of $O_2$ transport by diffusion between the microcirculation and the mitochondria—Equation 3—and an expansion of Equation 2 that describes the rate of $O_2$ transport from the environment through the tissue microcirculation—Equation 4:

$$\dot{V}O_2 = DO_2 [PCAPO_2 - PMITOO_2].\qquad\qquad 3.$$

Here, $DO_2$ is a lumped $O_2$ conductance coefficient embodying all impediments to $O_2$ movement from the red cells to the mitochondria. $PCAPO_2$ and

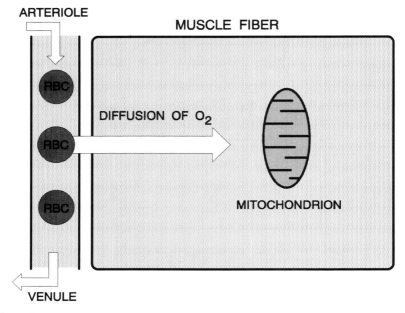

*Figure 3* Simplified model of $O_2$ transport in a skeletal muscle. $O_2$ is convected through the microcirculation from arteriole to venule, mostly in the red cell (RBC), and simultaneously diffuses out of the red cell through the capillary fluids, capillary wall, and interstitium to the cell membrane of the muscle fiber. $O_2$ then further diffuses to the mitochondria, a process probably enhanced by the presence of myoglobin in the cytoplasm.

PMITO$_2$ are average microvascular and mitochondrial PO$_2$ values, respectively, and $\dot{V}O_2$ is O$_2$ utilization.

The modification to Equation 2 acknowledges that not all O$_2$ is extracted from the arterial blood, such that

$$\dot{V}O_2 = 1.39 \; \dot{Q} \; [Hb] \; [SaO_2 - SvO_2], \qquad\qquad 4.$$

where SvO$_2$ is the O$_2$ saturation of venous blood from the tissue in question, whose blood flow is $\dot{Q}$. Dissolved O$_2$ in the blood is ignored for simplicity.

Considering the limiting case where at $\dot{V}O_2$max, PMITOO$_2$ is very close to zero (47), Equation 3 is simplified to

$$\dot{V}O_2\text{max} = DO_2\bullet \; PCAPO_2, \qquad\qquad 5.$$

where the variables on the right hand side of Equations 4 and 5 are those at $\dot{V}O_2$max.

If one now regards DO$_2$, $\dot{Q}$, [Hb], and SaO$_2$ as independent or input variables to the system, then Equations 4 and 5 form a system of two simultaneous equations in the two unknowns, $\dot{V}O_2$max and $SvO_2$, because it can be shown that $PCAPO_2$ is dependent on $SaO_2$ and $SvO_2$ and thus can be calculated from their values. It then remains to solve this pair of equations for $\dot{V}O_2$max and $SvO_2$, which is a problem well-suited to computer analysis (100).

The construct afforded by Equations 4 and 5, while clearly a simplification of reality, fits well into the observations about how $\dot{V}O_2$max varies with a number of different interventions that individually alter blood flow, [Hb], or arterial $O_2$ saturation. Thus it is evident that variation of any of the four input variables ($DO_2$, $\dot{Q}$, [Hb], and $SaO_2$) has the power to affect $\dot{V}O_2$max. These variables underlie changes in muscle $O_2$ transport ($DO_2$), blood flow ($\dot{Q}$), blood composition ([Hb]), and pulmonary function ($SaO_2$).

Numerous publications by Hogan and co-workers (38, 39, 41, 43, 45) and an analysis of these by Gainer (25) have explored how in a single animal model, these equations are borne out experimentally and explain the great majority of observations of effects of altering $O_2$ transport on $\dot{V}O_2$max. A related approach based on Ohm's law, different in detail but similar in concept, has been described by di Prampero & Ferretti (17) and is in general agreement with the above, although not mechanistic in construct.

Although the simplicity of such an analysis should be kept in mind, a major overall conclusion is inescapable: The concept of "the" limiting factor to $\dot{V}O_2$max is no longer an appropriate concept. All parts of the $O_2$ transport pathway are involved in determining $\dot{V}O_2$max. Thus a change in $O_2$ conductance of any one component will change $\dot{V}O_2$max in the same direction. The concept that must replace that of the limiting factor is reflected in the question: Quantitatively, what is the relative importance of each step of the $O_2$ transport pathway as a contributing determinant of $\dot{V}O_2$max?

## INFLUENCE OF INDIVIDUAL $O_2$ TRANSPORT PATHWAY STEPS ON $\dot{V}O_2$max

### Inspired $O_2$ Concentration

Whether studying intact individuals, isolated mitochondria, or preparations in between, altering the $O_2$ level to which muscle is exposed is both easy to do and of intrinsic interest. Consequently, much data exist on this topic, especially in intact animals and humans.

For instance, by changing barometric pressure (PB) (as in ascent to altitude or by diving) but not inspired $O_2$ concentration ($FIO_2$), inspired $PO_2$ ($PIO_2$) is altered; by changing $FIO_2$ at constant PB, similar changes in $PIO_2$ can be achieved (because $PIO_2$ is the product of PB and $FIO_2$). Comparison of these two strategies allows inferences on the role of PB to be made, and it appears

## ALTITUDE  AND  VO₂max

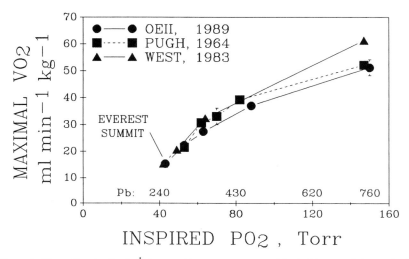

*Figure 4*  Dramatic reduction in V̇O₂max with ascent to extreme altitude. The curve is increasingly steep as PIO₂ falls (see text). Maximal V̇O₂ on the Everest summit is about 15 ml•kg⁻¹•min⁻¹, about equal to that of a patient with advanced cardiopulmonary disease at sea level.

that there is little evidence that PB itself acutely affects maximal O₂ transport and utilization. However, some workers feel that acute changes in PB can affect other transport processes such as that of water across capillary surfaces (57). For the present, it is reasonable to propose that most evidence suggests that altering inspiratory O₂ levels by either method is equivalent at the same PIO₂.

Classical studies of maximal exercise capacity in field and chamber ascents to extreme altitude (15, 73, 109) have shown how dramatically V̇O₂max is reduced as one climbs higher. Typical data are shown in Figure 4. The non-linearity of this relationship is explained by three factors. Firstly, the nonlinear shape of the O₂-Hb dissociation curve protects against desaturation of arterial blood at modest altitudes until arterial PO₂ begins to fall below about 60 torr, the knee of that curve. Secondly, and also because of the shape of the O₂-Hb curve, diffusion limitation of O₂ uptake in the lung is accentuated as PO₂ falls on to the steep portion of the dissociation curve (67). Thirdly, maximal cardiac output, and hence muscle blood flow, falls with adaptation to high altitude, the more so the higher the ascent (72, 75). Thus total O₂ transport (Equation 2) is reduced even further. There is a small counterbalancing factor that tends to oppose these negative effects—slightly increased extraction of O₂ from the muscle microcirculation, as the interaction between Equations 4 and 5 would require. This, however, is of little quantitative benefit.

Although such dramatic decreases in $\dot{V}O_2$max with hypoxia are easily shown and well understood, the converse is problematic. Increased $PIO_2$ in normal average subjects has produced small and thus equivocal results. Reviewed by Welch (108), a majority of studies show that $\dot{V}O_2$max is slightly increased by hyperoxia. Because of the flattening of the $O_2$-Hb curve at high $PIO_2$, one cannot expect more than about a 10% increase in $\dot{V}O_2$max from breathing pure $O_2$. This is because when room air is breathed, Hb is virtually fully saturated, even during heavy exercise, such that gains in arterial $O_2$ concentration reflect mostly added dissolved $O_2$. At the low solubility of $O_2$ (0.03 ml/liter•torr), a 500 torr increase in arterial $PO_2$ from 100 to 600 torr ($FIO_2$ from 0.21 to 1.0) produces only a 15-ml/liter increase in arterial $[O_2]$, which is about 10% or less of the total room air value of arterial $[O_2]$. Coupled to the difficulty in measuring $\dot{V}O_2$ using conventional expired gas analysis at high $FIO_2$ values and the fact that measured whole body $\dot{V}O_2$ reflects more than just muscle $O_2$ utilization, it is not surprising that studies often have been inconclusive. Although the $O_2$ loading limitation is hard to overcome in human subjects, studies adding a fluorocarbon to plasma to increase $O_2$ solubility have shown an increased $\dot{V}O_2$max in proportion to the increase in total $O_2$ transport (Equation 2) (45) in isolated dog muscle. In humans, the measurement problems and specificity of muscle $O_2$ use referred to above can be avoided if the arterial and venous circulations of the muscles are directly accessed. This can be done for the human quadriceps by means of arterial and femoral venous catheterization (1, 86). This also permits blood flow measurement and hence calculation of $\dot{V}O_2$ by Equation 4. When such studies are done, it is clear that $\dot{V}O_2$max is indeed increased by hyperoxia, at least in trained subjects (54). In sedentary individuals, the same methodology reveals no significant benefit of hyperoxia (82), and thus some of the confusion over effects of hyperoxia may reflect differences in the athletic capability of subjects (see above).

The influence of athletic state on sensitivity to hyperoxia (56) is perhaps best illustrated by elite athletes in whom exercise-induced arterial $O_2$ saturation is well known (16, 110). Powers and co-workers (71) found a predictably small but nonetheless significant increase in $\dot{V}O_2$max of elite athletes (70.1 to 74.7 ml•kg$^{-1}$•min$^{-1}$–1) as $FIO_2$ was increased from 0.21 to only 0.26, coincident with correction of modest exercise-induced arterial desaturation. The relative increase in saturation of 5.8% was similar to that of $\dot{V}O_2$max (6.6%). Even more clear-cut is the effect of hyperoxia in the thoroughbred racehorse (52). Here, due to a combination of pulmonary diffusion limitation causing hypoxemia and extreme rightward shift of the $O_2$-Hb curve due to hyperthermia, hypercapnia, and acidosis, arterial saturation at $\dot{V}O_2$max is about 80%. Breathing 35% $O_2$ restores saturation to about 98%, and both maximal speed and $\dot{V}O2$ are increased by the same relative amount, i.e. by almost 20% (P Wagner, unpublished observations).

Clearly, $VO_2$max varies acutely with $PIO_2$, and the more athletic the individual, the greater the effect.

## Pulmonary Function

Conceptually distinct from $PIO_2$ (which mathematically affects $PO_2$ at every point in the $O_2$ transport pathway independently of organ function) is the issue of how pulmonary function affects maximal $O_2$ transport. The potential exists for exceeding pulmonary $O_2$ and $CO_2$ exchange capacity in several ways. First, ventilatory limits may be reached such that further increases in exercise workload are not accompanied by corresponding increases in ventilation. The same could happen to pulmonary blood flow (see section on cardiovascular function). Second, the gas exchange process could be impaired by the demands of exercise. Thus rapid breathing rates could impair mixing of inhaled gas with that in the alveoli; high rates of blood and gas flow could result in their nonuniform distribution within the lungs. This would cause ventilation/perfusion ($\dot{V}A/\dot{Q}$) mismatch and reduce arterial $PO_2$ as a result. High blood flow rates reduce average red cell transit time in gas exchange vessels (despite vascular volume recruitment in the lung), and this could result in diffusion limitation of pulmonary $O_2$ uptake. The high pulmonary vascular pressures associated with high blood flow rates could lead to transient extravascular fluid accumulation or even microvascular rupture and these could negatively affect both $\dot{V}A/\dot{Q}$ matching and diffusion equilibration. Finally, because $\dot{V}O_2$ is known to rise relatively more than cardiac output, mixed venous $PO_2$ must fall (Equation 4). To the extent there are any intrapulmonary or postpulmonary (bronchial, Thebesian) shunts, arterial $PO_2$ will be reduced more during exercise than at rest due to the lower (venous) $PO_2$ of the blood that is carried.

Do any of these deleterious phenomena occur in normal subjects? Unequivocally, yes. The extent varies considerably among individuals, and not all of the above factors are important. However, relatively few normal human subjects perform maximal exercise without evidence of some degree of pulmonary dysfunction. Thus the common denominator of any of the above effects, the alveolar-arterial $PO_2$ difference (AaPO$_2$), is almost uniformly increased and progressively so, the more intense the exercise (106). At $\dot{V}O_2$max, values of AaPO$_2$ commonly reach 30 torr (corresponding values at rest are generally 5–10 torr).

Of the above potential factors, which appear to be important? In the average subject (neither sedentary nor elite), a combination of $\dot{V}A/\dot{Q}$ inequality and diffusion limitation of $O_2$ uptake accounts for a majority of the AaPO$_2$ (26,

30, 35, 103). Indirect evidence suggests that $\dot{V}A/\dot{Q}$ inequality is more likely due to transient pulmonary interstitial fluid accumulation than to the dynamic effects of high ventilation or blood flow per se (90). Pulmonary and postpulmonary shunts are trivial, generally not measurable factors. Gas mixing imperfection is similarly not considered to be of quantitative significance (37, 103). Ventilatory limits are not generally reached because arterial $PCO_2$ at $\dot{V}O_2max$ is classically 30–35 torr, well below resting levels, which implies that ventilation increases relatively even more than does $CO_2$ production (and thus $O_2$ utilization). On average, diffusion limitation accounts for more than half of the $AaPO_2$ at $\dot{V}O_2max$ with $\dot{V}A/\dot{Q}$ inequality contributing the remainder (26, 35, 103).

As with the effects of $PIO_2$ on $\dot{V}O_2max$, the effects of pulmonary dysfunction on $O_2$ exchange are systematically related to athletic capacity. Thus the most sedentary individuals (human and other) are least demonstrably affected by pulmonary dysfunction (14, 56, 82). There may be no evidence of diffusion limitation and certainly adequate ventilatory reserves exist to allow arterial $PCO_2$ to fall to between 30 and 35 torr. At the other extreme are elite athletes who usually show by several criteria quantitatively important effects of limited pulmonary function. Presumably due to their higher cardiac output (related to athletic prowess), there is a shorter red cell contact time in the lung, resulting in diffusion limitation and occasionally marked hypoxemia (71, 110). There can also be evidence of failure to maintain the typical hypocapnia of maximal exercise in elite athletes, with arterial $PCO_2$ increasing toward (normal resting) values of 40 torr (56). Coincident with this is evidence of expiratory flow limitation (51). This evidence is based on maximal flow-volume loop values (obtained at rest) being reached in mid-expiration during maximal exercise. Johnson et al (50) found, as might be expected, that expiratory flow limitation is more likely with advancing age because lung compliance increases, favoring dynamic compression of airways. However, it should be pointed out that expiratory flow limitation per se does not imply that a mechanical limit has been reached to total minute ventilation, even if arterial $PCO_2$ begins to rise. The control of breathing during exercise is complex and remains obscure. It may well be that the system accepts some compromise between the chemical drive to breathe (from $PCO_2$ and $H^+$) and the cost of breathing (mechanical and hence metabolic), which allows $PCO_2$ to rise even if there is still physical capacity to further ventilate (69). This is very difficult to resolve experimentally. Mechanical unloading studies replacing $N_2$ (of room air) with helium show an increase in ventilation (60, 70), but this does not resolve the question precisely because the mechanical situation has been changed. McParland's (62) studies interposing a deadspace volume between the subject and a valve box have shown no effect on $\dot{V}O_2max$ and a corresponding increase in minute ventilation to preserve alveolar ventilation. Although done only in moderately fit subjects ($\dot{V}O_2$max of 40–50 ml•min$^{-1}$•kg$^{-1}$), this certainly argues against a mechanical limit to breathing in this type of person.

The thoroughbred equine is an example of an elite athlete that demonstrates pulmonary functional limits to a greater extent than even Olympic-level human athletes. Marked arterial hypoxemia from diffusion limitation is the norm (104). This is not surprising because maximal cardiac output per kg body weight is about double that of a fit human (0.7 vs 0.4 L•min$^{-1}$•kg$^{-1}$), which would contribute to reduced transit time of red cells in the pulmonary circulation. In vivo arterial $PO_2$ (expressed at body temperature) is often in the 60–70 torr range; this is only occasionally seen in humans (16, 71, 110). In addition, arterial $PCO_2$ rises, often markedly, to between 50 and 60 torr at $\dot{V}O_2$max. Although this can be avoided with helium-$O_2$ breathing (22, 24), the issue of mechanical ventilatory limitation is still unresolved. There is more likelihood of resolving this in horses than in humans because of the stride-respiratory rate entrainment known to occur in this species (9).

Clearly, the lungs are problematic to $O_2$ transport, increasingly so with athletic capacity.

## Cardiovascular Function

Cardiac output rises linearly with exercise load in normal subjects and does not show evidence of reaching a plateau (2). In accord with the Frank-Starling relationship, higher ventricular filling pressures are observed (74); ventricular function studies and echocardiographic and electrocardiographic variables are all consistent with adequate myocardial $O_2$ supply for the cardiac workload imposed by the external power output (75). Evidence for ischemia in normal subjects does not exist clinically or physiologically, even at extreme altitudes equivalent to that of Mt. Everest (> 8,000 m, PB ~250 torr, $PIO_2$ ~43 torr, arterial $PO_2$ ~30 torr) (61, 75, 97).

Control of cardiac output and its distribution is complex and well described in classic texts (85) and is tied to exercise intensity through a variety of neuronal and hormonal factors mediated in large part by the autonomic nervous system, as well as by mechanical factors related to various muscle pumps that facilitate return of venous blood to the heart. This huge topic is not further addressed here.

Consequently, unlike the lungs, which show evidence of impaired function at $\dot{V}O_2$max, increasingly so with increasing athletic ability, there is little to suggest impaired cardiac function. It is well known that cardiac output is higher in athletes. This can be inferred simply from Equation 4, because (*a*) arterial saturation is if anything lower in athletes despite a higher $\dot{V}O_2$max, as discussed above, and (*b*) venous saturation is mostly low at all levels of athletic ability at $\dot{V}O_2$max. The only factor left to permit a higher $\dot{V}O_2$ in athletes is a high cardiac output. Therefore, it should come as no surprise that there is a close correlation between $\dot{V}O_2$max and maximal cardiac output over the range of athletic capacity (7). Elite athletes are marked by this attribute, perhaps above all others. Within an individual experimental preparation such as the isolated muscle, blood flow is similarly a key determinant of $\dot{V}O_2$max because of its dominant influence on total $O_2$ transport (Equation 2).

It is worth stressing that this close relationship does not exclude other factors from affecting maximal $O_2$ transport and $\dot{V}O_2$max.

An interesting question is the balance between the positive effects of a high cardiac output on convective $O_2$ transport to muscle (i.e. via Equation 2) and the coincident negative effects of the same high cardiac output on diffusive loading of $O_2$ in the lung and unloading in the tissues. This can be modeled cleanly; actual in vivo experiments altering flow are technically difficult and more importantly are muddied by unwanted potential secondary effects of change in microvascular flow distribution and blood volume in the lungs and muscle. Calculations suggest that in average subjects at sea level, humans are positioned delicately at a point such that decreases in cardiac output would greatly reduce $O_2$ transport, whereas increases would have only a modest beneficial effect due to increasing diffusion limitation (Figure 5). This is even more evident at extreme altitude where diffusion limitation is more apparent (105). Here the relatively low maximal cardiac output (of ~18 L•min$^{-1}$ at Mt. Everest compared to ≥25 L•min$^{-1}$ in the same subjects at sea level) (75) is not the limitation one might predict. Any gain in convective transport of $O_2$ that would result from a higher cardiac output is calculated to be completely offset by increased diffusion limitation in both the lungs and muscles (adapted from 101) (Figure 5).

The preceding discussion ties cardiac output to exercise load, implies no interference to cardiac function at $\dot{V}O_2$max, but suggests a counterbalancing effect on $O_2$ transport of a high cardiac output due to impaired $O_2$ diffusion equilibration in the lungs and muscles. Not addressed is whether cardiac output at $\dot{V}O_2$max has reached some mechanical limit that could be imagined simply by decreased ventricular filling time as the heart rate rises with exercise intensity. Abundant data, however, show that as heart rate increases generally linearly (with exercise load) all the way to $\dot{V}O_2$max, stroke volume asymptotes toward a plateau but does not fall (32). This would argue (but not prove) that a mechanical limit has not been reached. Moreover, it is possible to augment maximal cardiac output experimentally in normal subjects and animals. Horwitz & Lindenfeld (49) showed how maximal cardiac output could be increased 20-30% by blood volume augmentation using dextran. Of great interest, Stray-Gundersen et al (96) showed that pericardiectomy increased both cardiac output and $\dot{V}O_2$max by about 20% (compared to control sham-operated dogs). These data support the central theme of this review: $\dot{V}O_2$max is determined by $O_2$

# ELITE ATHLETE

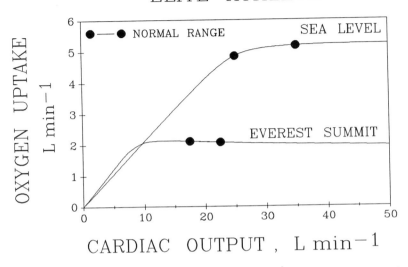

*Figure 5*   Modeling the effects of changes in cardiac output on $\dot{V}O_2$max. At sea level, maximal $\dot{V}O_2$ is sensitive to cardiac output but increases provide lessening benefit due to concurrent pulmonary and muscle diffusion limitation as capillary transit time falls. However, at altitude (Everest summit), due to even greater effects of diffusion limitation, cardiac output has essentially no influence on $\dot{V}O_2$max.

supply (and thus is altered predictably by changes in $O_2$ transport) rather than by mitochondrial oxidation capacity of muscle. Second, they suggest that at least in the untrained dog, ventricular function can be limited by pericardial constraints, probably by limiting diastolic filling. Thus, indirectly, there is a mechanical limit shown by these studies but one that can be modified by hypervolemia, for example.

The thoroughbred equine is an excellent example of the importance of blood volume and cardiac filling in the cardiac output response to exercise. This species is well known to use its large splenic reservoir of red cells to bolster both circulating blood volume and hematocrit during exercise (66). Splenectomy (with several weeks allowed for recovery and retraining) reduces cardiac output by about 20% at $\dot{V}O_2$max, and this is rapidly restored to normal by blood transfusion (102). Corresponding changes in $\dot{V}O_2$max accompany these changes in blood flow, as do reductions in right atrial pressure after splenectomy and restoration with transfusion.

In summary, unlike the lungs, cardiac function is well preserved during maximal exercise. However, it is quite dependent on ventricular filling as shown by pericardiectomy or volume loading or splenectomy. Increases in cardiac output are considerably offset by impaired diffusive $O_2$ transport both in the lungs and muscles such that in severe hypoxia, little or no increase in net $O_2$ transport is expected to result from increasing cardiac performance.

## $O_2$ Extraction from Blood

The close correlation of $\dot{V}O_2$max to cardiac output under normal circumstances, combined with the technical difficulties in studying $O_2$ extraction from blood in the muscles, has left this area relatively underinvestigated. However, the development of new approaches to measure $O_2$ transport and related phenomena by magnetic resonance, near infrared, and phosphorescence quenching-based techniques has rekindled interest. Moreover, there is a groundswell of opinion that in human chronic diseases such as heart failure, chronic obstructive lung disease, and chronic renal failure there may well be an independent defect of intramuscular $O_2$ transport that compounds the well-known convective $O_2$ transport defects (of reduced cardiac output, arterial $O_2$ saturation and [Hb], respectively).

The $O_2$ pathway from muscle microvascular red cells (RBC) to the mitochondria is complex, as shown in Figure 3. Sequential steps begin with chemical dissociation of $O_2$ from Hb. $O_2$ must then diffuse out of the red cell and through the plasma to the capillary wall. Further diffusion occurs through the capillary wall, interstitium, and sarcolemma to reach the interior of the myocyte. Potentially long diffusion distances may then exist for $O_2$ to reach distant mitochondria (although a commonly found sub-sarcolemmal juxtacapillary accumulation of mitochondria reduces the distance many $O_2$ molecules must traverse). The intracellular presence of myoglobin (Mb) is thought to facilitate the transport of $O_2$ within the cell (113, 115). This may be the result of the mobility of Mb itself, as well as the result of Mb-$O_2$ binding, which reduces intracellular free [$O_2$], and thus $PO_2$ and enhances the $PO_2$ gradient responsible for $O_2$ diffusion. Note that if the mitochondrial system is a syncytial network, as three-dimensional images suggest, rather than a collection of separate organelles, this network might influence $O_2$ pathways and may imply less of a role for Mb in intracellular $O_2$ transport than currently thought. Another potential perferential pathway for intracellular movement of $O_2$ independent of myoglobin is through lipid (59, 93).

Given the complexity of the $O_2$ transport pathway from Hb to the mitochondria, is there evidence that this pathway significantly impairs maximal $O_2$ transport, and if so, what can be said about the relative contributions of the various components to this impedance?

The answer is that there must be a significant impedance to this pathway, if for no other reason than muscle venous blood contains a fair amount of $O_2$ even at $\dot{V}O_2$max. Venous $PO_2$ is frequently 20 torr, with saturation of Hb in the 15% range for average normal subjects (83). What prevents 100% extraction of $O_2$? That it is not limited mitochondrial oxidative capacity in most subjects has already been documented (see above), based on immediate increases in $\dot{V}O_2$ as $O_2$ supply is enhanced. What processes could be responsible for incomplete extraction on the basis of impaired transport? This situation is analogous to that of dissecting the causes of the alveolar-arterial $PO_2$ difference in the process of pulmonary $O_2$ exchange. There are four possibilities:

1. A limited (finite) overall diffusional conductance for $O_2$ between Hb and the mitochondria (i.e. $DO_2$ of Equation 3);
2. Heterogeneity of perfusion with respect to local $O_2$ demand (not necessarily with respect to muscle mass per se);
3. Functional or structural shunts of arterial blood into the venous system;
4. Direct diffusion of $O_2$ from pre-exchange arteries to post-exchange veins through muscle tissue.

Evidence for items 3 and 4 in maximally exercising mammalian skeletal muscle is weak to nonexistent. Honig et al (46), using cryospectroscopy, have found no elevation of Hb-$O_2$ saturation in venules closely juxtaposed to arterioles in exercising dog muscle, and in any event, the importance of this phenomenon would decrease as muscle blood flow increases with exercise. In such muscles, there is no evidence of anatomical shunts. Heterogeneity, however, is another matter. Different fiber types have different $O_2$ requirements and thus probably different flow requirements, which would be disclosed by microsphere measures of regional muscle blood flow (13), but these can only be referenced to muscle mass, not metabolic rate ($\dot{V}O_2$). However, it is possible that blood flow and $\dot{V}O_2$ would be matched as a function of fiber type. More randomly based flow heterogeneity may occur, and it is clear from video microscopy of resting muscle that such uneven flow is seen (19, 21). Whether uneven flow functionally impacts $O_2$ transport depends on the size of the functional unit of muscle. Perhaps the presence of myoglobin facilitates the even distribution of $O_2$ even in the face of uneven blood flow. Perhaps local production of metabolites regulates local blood flow in tune with local $\dot{V}O_2$. The data of Gayeski et al (27, 28) show broadly similar intracellular $PO_2$ during exercise across a range of fibers, which suggests that this may be the case. Further evidence that the perfusion heterogeneity disclosed by microsphere measurements, with respect to mass, may not reflect perfusion/metabolism heterogeneity is in the studies of Hogan (38, 44). The same rate of $O_2$ supply into the muscle vasculature by perfusion of two bloods that differ only in Hb affinity produces a change in $\dot{V}O_2max$ exactly as predicted from a model of diffusion-limited $O_2$ transport. Heterogeneity does not lead to any effect of Hb-$O_2$ affinity on $\dot{V}O_2max$. However, the importance of heterogeneity during exercise is not fully resolved and must await undiscovered technologies for direct assessment of the distribution of flow and metabolic rate.

Returning to the $O_2$ pathway of Figure 3, can one tease out parts of that pathway likely to be more important in impeding $O_2$ transport than others? Classical work by Krogh (55) at the start of this century led to the simple idea that distance from the capillary integrated with position relative to arterial and venous ends of the microcirculation would dictate local $[O_2]$ within the cell on the basis of Fick's law of diffusion (Equation 3). This produced the concept of the "Krogh cylinder" and the "lethal corner" for $O_2$ insufficiency. More recent studies have considerably altered our view of this pathway due to the fact that the pathway is functionally and structurally very non-uniform. Basically, distance is thought to be unimportant. This is not because the laws of diffusion are wrong, but because intracellular $O_2$ conductance is evidently very high, negating the effects of distance. Evidence for this is Gayeski's (28) intracellular cryospectroscopic data showing intracellular $PO_2$ in working dog muscle of 1–3 torr when adjacent intravascular $PO_2$ lies between about 20 and 100 torr (with a mean value of ~40 torr). Thus most of the impedance is between the Hb molecule and the sarcolemma, a very short (2–3 μm) physical distance. Although Honig's technique has been questioned and has more limited spatial resolution than previously thought, the basic conclusion likely is correct. Theoretical calculations by Groebe & Thews (33) support this as well. Very recently, nuclear magnetic resonance measurements of intracellular myoglobin saturation in intact human quadriceps muscle at maximum $\dot{V}O_2$ further support this conclusion (77). Here, with Mb saturation averaging 60%, intracellular $PO_2$ averages only about 3 torr. Such agreement among three totally different approaches strengthens the general conclusions that $O_2$ transport is impeded mostly somewhere between the Hb molecule in the red cell and the muscle cell wall.

Slow chemical off-loading kinetics (34) and/or a large inter-red cell space reducing the effective red cell–capillary contact area for $O_2$ transport (23) could in theory be responsible for part of the impedance to $O_2$ transport. If relevant, both effects could change $O_2$ efflux rates in the same direction as changes in [Hb]. Hogan (39) found that [Hb] plays a large role in $O_2$ conductance in isolated canine muscle, and Schaffartzik (89) found similar effects in intact human as [Hb] was acutely varied. The original data of Cain (12) in dogs at rest, showing [Hb] dependance of $\dot{V}O_2$ at a given reduced level of $O_2$ delivery, can also be interpreted as evidence of this impedance. Augmenting the inter-red cell space with fluorocarbons to enhance plasma $O_2$ solubility (45) or with free Hb solution (42) has provided evidence that the normally carrier-free plasma space between microvascular red cells does not offer significant impedance to $O_2$ transport despite theoretical predictions to the contrary (23). Perhaps, mixing is rapid enough within the microvessels that the expected defect is not seen. Much more work needs to be done to resolve this issue. It is important to do so because the effect of [Hb] on $O_2$ conductance is substantial (39), because of interest in blood doping in sports medicine circles (29), and because of the development of manufactured soluble $O_2$ carriers (fluorocarbons, synthetic hemoglobins) in lieu of whole blood transfusion, carriers that will occupy the plasma space (6, 79, 112).

In most circumstances, [Hb] remains stable and within normal limits, yet there are very large differences in muscle $O_2$ conductance between different populations. Trained athletes have higher values than sedentary subjects (82, 83); training itself increases muscle $O_2$ conductance in the same person (82) by some 30%, without changes in [Hb]. However, in heart failure and chronic lung diseases, muscle $O_2$ conductance is very low, again in patients whose [Hb] is normal.

The remaining component to be addressed in the $O_2$ pathway in muscle, is the capillary wall itself. Intuitively, the richness of capillary supply is likely to be a key factor in determining $O_2$ conductance and in explaining the above differences between subject groups in $O_2$ transport within muscle. Bebout (5) compared genetically similar canine muscle that had undergone either endurance training or total immobilization and compared it to control, unexercised muscle. Maximal $\dot{V}O_2$ of the three groups related closely to the number of capillaries per fiber but not to diffusion distance or capillary density (a factor that depends on both capillary numbers and fiber area). Calculated muscle $O_2$ conductance related equally well to capillary number but not to distance-related parameters. These controlled studies support the well-established observations that endurance training in mammalian species increases the number of capillaries along with $\dot{V}O_2max$ (87). They also suggest that Oelz's (65) findings (that elite high-altitude climbers had pulmonary function no different from normal subjects but >20% capillary number per fiber in leg muscles) may account in part for ability to reach great altitudes without supplemental $O_2$. It is $O_2$ conductance in muscle that is predicted to be the most important factor capable of increasing $\dot{V}O_2max$ at great altitude (101).

In summary, it is clear that while much work remains to be done in muscle $O_2$ transport, the process of diffusion of $O_2$ between the red cell and the mitochondria encounters measurable impedance and explains in large part the way in which maximal $\dot{V}O_2$ is limited by $O_2$ supply.

## Relative Influence of Each Part of the $O_2$ Transport Pathway on Maximal $O_2$ Transport

To assess maximal $O_2$ transport conductance, experiments altering one pathway step at a time are necessary. Although this can be done, there are often one or more secondary effects in other parts of the $O_2$ transport pathway that

**Table 1**  Calculated responses to changes in key $O_2$ transport variables in the elite athlete

| 50% reduction | Transport variable | 50% increase |
|---|---|---|
| Sea level | | |
| −48.4 | Inspired $O_2$ concentration | +11.1 |
| −18.0 | Ventilation | +4.2 |
| −33.8 | Lung diffusing capacity | 7.2 |
| −38.5 | Cardiac output | +2.2 |
| −37.8 | Hemoglobin concentration | +4.3 |
| −33.7 | Muscle diffusing capacity | +5.5 |
| Extreme altitude (Everest summit) | | |
| −51.5 | Inspired $O_2$ concentration | +44.7 |
| −11.6 | Ventilation | +5.1 |
| −34.7 | Lung diffusing capacity | +19.7 |
| −1.2 | Cardiac output | −3.2 |
| −10.4 | Hemoglobin concentration | +2.2 |
| −33.6 | Muscle diffusing capacity | +14.9 |

Percent of change in $\dot{V}O_2$max for a 50% change (reduction or increase) in indicated variable

make it difficult to interpret the result as due only to the intended change of the primary variable. Theoretical calculations are useful in addressing such issues. Table 1 shows calculated sensitivity of $\dot{V}O_2$max to each of the primary $O_2$ transport conductances, at sea level and at extreme altitude (101), for a trained athlete (using a particular set of normal values). At sea level, $\dot{V}O_2$max is sensitive to all variables, at varying degrees. The effect of reducing $O_2$ conductance at any step is clearly much greater than that of increasing conductance by the same percent, consistent with the nonlinear behavior shown in Figure 5; but at altitude, pulmonary and intramuscular $O_2$ diffusional transport are relatively more important than blood flow. In most cases, the relative effect on $\dot{V}O_2$max is less than that of the altered conductance because for each, multiple opposing effects occur.

## Extrapolations to Disease

The majority of research discussed above comes from studies of normal human or animal skeletal muscle; however, the hope is to use these principles in the understanding and evaluation of disease. Although the fundamental physical basis of $O_2$ transport must be the same as in health, disease may affect the quantitative aspects of one or more components of the $O_2$ transport and utilization system. Caution is needed in interpreting data from patients with disease on a paradigm of normal physiology. On the other hand, attempting to make such interpretations would be an excellent way to create hypotheses. Perhaps the most instructive approach is to return to the two equations that describe $O_2$ transport in convective and diffusive terms (Equations 4 and 5, respectively). If one assumes that muscle venous $PO_2$ and mean capillary $PO_2$ rise and fall together (as conditions are altered) and proportionally, Equation 5 can be written as

$$\dot{V}O_2 = DO_2 \bullet k \bullet PvO_2. \hspace{3cm} 6.$$

On a diagram where $\dot{V}O_2$ is on the Y axis and $PvO_2$ is on the X axis, Equation 6 is a simple straight line through the origin; the slope is a function of the overall $O_2$ muscle conductance, $DO_2$ (Figure 6, *upper panel*). On the same diagram, Equation 4 can be plotted, given values for blood flow, arterial $O_2$ saturation, and [Hb]. Implicit is the ability to interconvert between $SvO_2$ and $PvO_2$, which requires knowledge of the $O_2$-Hb dissociation curve. This gives rise to the curved, negatively sloped line of Figure 6, which in fact represents an inverted $O_2$-Hb dissociation curve. The Y intercept of this curve, when $PvO_2 = 0$, equals total $O_2$ transport (Equation 2). The X intercept of this curve, hypothetically when $\dot{V}O_2 = 0$, must occur when $PvO_2 = $ arterial $PO_2$ and no $O_2$ is thus extracted from the blood. The key point is that the intersection of the two lines in Figure 6 gives the only point where the two transport processes yield the same $\dot{V}O_2$; this must be $\dot{V}O_2$max, and the corresponding $PvO_2$ is the obligatory venous $PO_2$, consistent with that $\dot{V}O_2$ and the given variables: $DO_2$, QT, [Hb], and $SaO_2$.

If any component of Equation 4 is perturbed, the shape and position of the curved line in Figure 6 (*upper panel*) must be changed. For example, reducing $SaO_2$ by breathing an hypoxic gas will produce the indicated shift in the curved line (Figure 6, *lower panel*) and a new lower point of intersection, with the straight line describing diffusive transport. Thus a given degree of hypoxemia is expected to produce a predictable new and lower $\dot{V}O_2$max that is not only proportional to the new, lower value of total $O_2$ transport (Equation 2) but also proportional to a new, lower venous $PO_2$ (Equation 6). Normal muscle has been shown to behave in this manner across several species [human (83), dog (43), rat (31), horse (102)] as arterial $PO_2$ is altered. Although this predictable behavior of $\dot{V}O_2$max does not distinguish between heterogeneity and diffusion limitation as causes of residual $O_2$ in venous blood, it permits an overall measurement of functional $O_2$ conductance as the slope of the straight line.

Clearly, to apply this concept to diseases, one must first demonstrate that $\dot{V}O_2$max is indeed dependent on $O_2$ supply. Thus proportional behavior among $\dot{V}O_2$max, total $O_2$ transport, and muscle venous $PO_2$ must be present as $O_2$ supply is manipulated. If so, the concept of Figure 6 is usefully applied. If not, one must conclude that $\dot{V}O_2$max is not limited by $O_2$ supply but rather by

CONVECTION AND DIFFUSION IN $O_2$ TRANSPORT

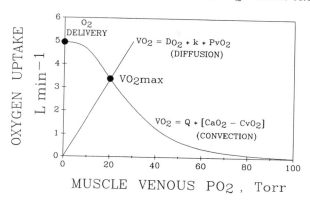

EFFECT OF HYPOXIA ON $VO_2max$

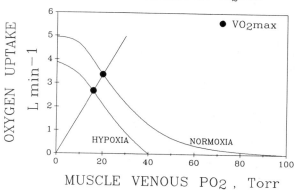

*Figure 6*  Upper panel: a conceptual approach to understanding the interaction between diffusion and convection in the lungs, circulation, and muscles, which sets $\dot{V}O_2max$. The line of positive slope is the graphical equivalent of Equation 6; the curved line of negative slope is the corresponding equivalent of Equation 4. Their intersection defines maximal $\dot{V}O_2$. Lower panel: effect of reduction in inspired $PO_2$ (from 100 to 40 torr) on $\dot{V}O_2max$ predicted from Equations 4 and 6. $\dot{V}O_2max$ and muscle venous $PO_2$ are proportional due to dependence of $O_2$ transport on intramuscular diffusion of $O_2$.

limits to muscle $O_2$ oxidative capacity, and thus the analysis of Figure 6 becomes inapplicable. However, data obtained to date, although preliminary, are concordant with $O_2$ supply limitation of $\dot{V}O_2max$ (78, 84).

Figure 7 shows mean data (99) of maximally exercising patients with chronic obstructive pulmonary disease (COPD) and similar data (82) from young healthy sedentary adults (about 35–40 ml•kg$^{-1}$•min$^{-1}$ $\dot{V}O_2max$). This is not a fair comparison, to be sure, because the COPD patients are considerably older: 50–70 years vs 20–30 years. Yet the comparisons are instructive. Convective $O_2$ transport is grossly reduced in COPD, which is shown by the curved line Y intercept (see above). However, the slope of the straight line is also much reduced from even normal sedentary subjects. This difference cannot be due to age alone: It is well known that $\dot{V}O_2max$ in the 50–70 age group is some 2–3 L•min$^{-1}$ for the average-sized person, not <1 L•min$^{-1}$ as shown for COPD. These data suggest a reduction in muscle $O_2$ conductance, and a good candidate mechanism would be a reduced muscle capillary bed. Although these data contain enough gaps to prevent a dogmatic conclusion, they suggest a testable hypothesis that COPD leads to an intrinsic myopathic interference to $O_2$ transport that reduces $\dot{V}O_2max$ below that which would otherwise be expected, given the degree of convective $O_2$ supply reduction from lung disease per se. This hypothesis definitely deserves follow-up, and if substantiated, would have potential therapeutic implications for improving exercise tolerance (by training to induce muscle capillary growth, for example). Conversely, a lung transplant that fully restored convective $O_2$ supply to normal, but left muscle $O_2$ conductance untouched, would provide little increase in $\dot{V}O_2max$ as Figure 7 implies.

Similar predictions might be made in other chronic diseases such as chronic heart failure and chronic renal failure. Indeed, renal failure patients have been shown to have a very disappointing exercise response to erythropoietin therapy despite returning [Hb] to near-normal values (63, 80). Thus the relative gain in $\dot{V}O_2max$ is much less than that of [Hb] itself. The analysis of Figure 6 lends itself to understanding this outcome. After first showing that $\dot{V}O_2max$ post-erythropoietin was $O_2$ supply dependent, Roca (84) found that the disappointingly small increase in $\dot{V}O_2max$ was due mostly to an $O_2$ conductance value 30% lower than that found in well-matched sedentary volunteers. Also contributing to the small improvement was a significant reduction in muscle blood flow accompanying and offsetting the $O_2$ transport benefit of the higher [Hb]. The basis for the low $O_2$ conductance is not known with certainty, but a low capillary number has been found by muscle biopsy in patients with chronic renal failure (64).

While much work needs to be done to better understand the physiological basis of impaired $O_2$ transport in muscle in chronic diseases. Disappointing degrees of exercise recovery following cardiac transplantation (53), lung transplantation (58), and erythropoietin therapy (63, 80) point to an intrinsic muscle

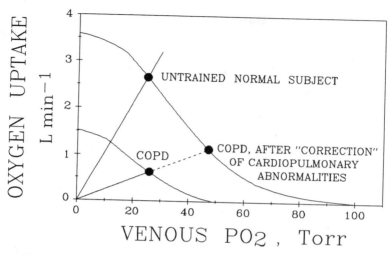

*Figure 7* Based on Figure 6, analysis of maximal exercise in a typical patient with chronic obstructive lung disease. Not only is convective $O_2$ supply into the muscle circulation greatly impaired (downward displacement of the curved line), but $O_2$ conductance from the circulation to the mitochondria is significantly reduced (reduced slope of the straight line). Note that even if heart and lung function could be restored to control levels, $VO_2$max would remain very low if muscle $O_2$ conductance were to remain the same.

defect in $O_2$ transport that may well be due to capillary rarefaction. This will be important to follow-up in parallel with continuing advances in the treatment of the underlying cardiac, pulmonary, or renal disease.

## SUMMARY

This review has focused on the hypothesis that maximal $O_2$ utilization during exercise ($\dot{V}O_2$max) is by and large the result of mitochondrial $O_2$ supply limitation rather than limited cellular oxidative capacity to use $O_2$, and much evidence has been presented to defend this position. On this basis, the major conclusions are

1. $\dot{V}O_2$max is not limited by just one component of the $O_2$ transport pathway. Rather $\dot{V}O_2$max is set by the quantitative interaction among all $O_2$ transport processes between the environment and the mitochondria.
2. Interference to conductance of any step in the pathway will predictably reduce $\dot{V}O_2$max; Figure 6 represents a useful paradigm for analyzing the

effects of one or more such changes on overall system performance. So too do corresponding if slightly different approaches (17).

3. What is the importance any one step in the pathway for $\dot{V}O_2$max? This can be deduced from the paradigm of Figure 6 under any given conditions, and calculated effects are shown in Table 1.

4. There is convincing evidence that the part of the $O_2$ transport pathway, from muscle microvascular red cells to the mitochondria, considerably hinders $O_2$ transport and thus contributes significantly to the setting of maximal $\dot{V}O_2$.

5. Some of this impedance occurs within the microvasculature related to the concentration of Hb, but the majority appears closely related the number of capillaries associated with each muscle fiber.

6. Preliminary evaluation of patients with chronic diseases such as heart failure, renal failure, and lung disease suggests that, in addition to obvious interference to convective $O_2$ transport to muscle (produced by low blood flow, [Hb], or arterial $O_2$ saturation, respectively), there is an intrinsic myopathic effect impeding $O_2$ transport within muscle. This may be due to capillary rarefaction, and if present, will require much work to elucidate. Success in this area could be of great clinical significance.

## Literature Cited

1. Andersen P, Saltin B. 1985. Maximal perfusion of skeletal muscle in man. *J. Physiol.* 366:233–49
2. Astrand PO, Cuddy TE, Saltin B, Stenberg J. 1964. Cardiac output during submaximal and maximal work. *J. Appl. Physiol.* 19:268
3. Astrand PO, Saltin B. 1961. Maximal oxygen uptake and heart rate in various types of muscular activity. *J. Appl. Physiol.* 16:977–81
4. Barclay JK, Stainsby WN. 1975. The role of blood flow in limiting maximal metabolic rate in muscle. *Med. Sci. Sports* 7(2):116–19
5. Bebout DE, Hogan MC, Hempleman SC, Wagner PD. 1993. Effects of training and immobilization on $\dot{V}O_2$ and $DO_2$ in dog gastrocnemius muscle in situ. *J. Appl. Physiol.* 74:1697–703
6. Biro GP. 1993. Perfluorocarbon-based red blood cell substitutes. *Transfusion Med.* 7(2):84–95
7. Blomqvist CG, Saltin B. 1983. Cardio-

vascular adaptations to physical training. *Annu. Rev. Physiol.* 45:169–89
8. Boeghold M, Johnson P. 1988. Periarteriolar and tissue $PO_2$ during sympathetic escape in skeletal muscle. *Am. J. Physiol.* 254:H929–36
9. Bramble DM, Carrier Dr. 1983. Running and breathing in mammals. *Science* 219:251–56
10. Brechue WF, Ameredes BT, Barclay JK, Stainsby WN. 1995. Blood flow and pressure relationships which determine $\dot{V}O_2$max. *Med. Sci. Sports Exerc.* 27(1):37–42
11. Buick FJ, Gledhill N, Froese AB, Spriet L, Meyers EC. 1980. Effect of induced erythrocythemia on aerobic work capacity. *J. Appl. Physiol.* 48:636–42
12. Cain SM. 1977. Oxygen delivery and uptake in dogs during anemic and hypoxic hypoxia. *J. Appl. Physiol.* 42:228–34
13. Cerretelli P, Marconi C, Pendergast D, Meyer M, Heisler N, Piiper J. 1984.

Blood flow in exercising muscles by xenon clearance and by microsphere trapping. *J. Appl. Physiol.* 56:24–30

14. Constantinopol M, Jones JH, Weibel ER, Taylor CR, Lindholm A, Karas RH. 1989. Oxygen transport during exercise in large mammals. II. Oxygen uptake by the pulmonary gas exchanger. *J. Appl. Physiol.* 67(2):871–78

15. Cymerman A, Reeves JT, Sutton JR, Rock PB, Groves BM, et al. 1989. Operation Everest II: maximal oxygen uptake at extreme altitude. *J. Appl. Physiol.* 66:2446–53

16. Dempsey JA, Hanson PG, Henderson KS. 1984. Exercise-induced arterial hypoxemia in healthy human subjects at sea level. *J. Physiol.* 355:161–75

17. di Prampero P, Ferretti G. 1990. Factors limiting maximal oxygen consumption in humans. *Respir. Physiol.* 80:113–28

18. Duhaylomgsod FG, Griebel JA, Bacon DS, Wolfe WG, Piantadosi CA. 1993. Effects of muscle contraction of cytochrome a,a₃ redox state. *J. Appl. Physiol.* 75:790–97

19. Duling BR, Damon DH. 1986. An examination of the measurement of flow heterogeneity in striated muscle. *Circ. Res.* 60:1–13

20. Ellis CG, Ellsworth ML, Pittman RN. 1990. Determination of red blood cell oxygenation in vivo by dual video densitometric image analysis. *Am. J. Physiol.* 258(4 Pt. 2):H1216–23

21. Ellis CG, Wrigley SM, Potter RF, Groom AC. 1990. Temporal distributions of red cell supply rate to individual capillaries of resting skeletal muscle, in frog and rat. *Int. J. Microcirc.: Clin. Exp.* 9(1):67–84

22. Erickson BK, Seaman J, Kubo K, Hiraga A, Kai M, et al. 1994. Mechanism of reduction in alveolar-arterial PO₂ difference by helium breathing in the exercising horse. *J. Appl. Physiol.* 76:2794–801

23. Federspiel WJ, Popel AS. 1986. A theoretical analysis of the effect of the particulate nature of blood on oxygen release in capillaries. *Microvasc. Res.* 32:164–89

24. Forster HV, Pan LG. 1988. Breathing during exercise: demands, regulation, limitations. *Adv. Exp. Med. Biol.* 227:257–76

25. Gainer JL. 1994. Evaluating the oxygen diffusing capacity of maximally stimulated canine muscle. *J. Appl. Physiol.* 76(4):1826–29

26. Gale GE, Torre-Bueno JR, Moon RE, Saltzman HA, Wagner PD. 1985. Ventilation/perfusion inequality in normal humans during exercise at sea level and simulated altitude. *J. Appl. Physiol.* 58(3):978–88

27. Gayeski TEJ, Honig CR. 1986. O₂ gradients from sarcolemma to cell interior in a red muscle at maximal V̇O₂. *Am. J. Physiol.* 251:789–99

28. Gayeski TEJ, Honig CR. 1988. Intracellular PO₂ in long axis of individual fibers in working dog gracilis muscle. *Am. J. Physiol.* 254:H1179–86

29. Gledhill N. 1982. Blood doping and related issues: a brief review. *Med. Sci. Sports Exerc.* 14:183–89

30. Gledhill N, Froese AB, Dempsey JA. 1977. Ventilation to perfusion distribution during exercise in health. In *Muscular Exercise and the Lung*, ed. JA Dempsey, CE Reed, pp. 325–44. Madison: Univ. Wisconsin Press

31. Gonzalez NC, Clancy RL, Wagner PD. 1993. Determinants of maximal oxygen uptake in rats acclimated to simulated altitude. *J. Appl. Physiol.* 75:1608–14

32. Grimby G, Nilsson NJ, Saltin B. 1966. Cardiac output during submaximal and maximal exercise in active middle-aged athletes. *J. Appl. Physiol.* 21(4):1150–56

33. Groebe K, Thews G. 1990. Calculated intra- and extracellular gradients in heavily working red muscle. *Am. J. Physiol.* 259:H84–92

34. Gutierrez G. 1986. The rate of oxygen release and its effect on capillary O₂ tension: a mathematical analysis. *Respir. Physiol.* 63:79–96

35. Hammond MD, Gale GE, Kapitan KS, Ries A, Wagner PD. 1986. Pulmonary gas exchange in humans during exercise at sea level. *J. Appl. Physiol.* 60(5):1590–98

36. Hill AV. 1926. *Muscular Activity,* Baltimore, MD: Williams & Wilkins

37. Hlastala MP, Scheid P, Piiper J. 1981. Interpretation of inert gas retention and excretion in the presence of stratified inhomogeneity. *Respir. Physiol.* 46:247–59

38. Hogan MC, Bebout DE, Wagner PD. 1991. Effect of increased Hb-O₂ affinity on V̇O₂max at constant O₂ delivery in dog muscle in situ. *J. Appl. Physiol.* 70(6):2656–62

39. Hogan MC, Bebout DE, Wagner PD. 1991. Effect of hemoglobin concentration on maximal O₂ uptake in canine gastrocnemius muscle in situ. *J. Appl. Physiol.* 70:1105–12

40. Hogan MC, Bebout DE, Wagner PD. 1993. Effect of blood flow reduction on maximal O₂ uptake in canine gastrocnemius muscle in situ. *J. Appl. Physiol.* 74:1742–47

41. Hogan MC, Bebout DE, Wagner PD, West JB. 1990. Maximal $O_2$ uptake of in situ dog muscle during acute hypoxemia with constant perfusion. *J. Appl. Physiol.* 69(2):570–76

42. Hogan MC, Kurdak SS, Richardson RS, Wagner PD. 1994. Partial substitution of red blood cells with free hemoglobin solution does not improve maximal $O_2$ uptake in working in situ muscle. In *Oxygen Transport to Tissue XVI*, ed. MC Hogan, O Mathieu-Costello, DC Poole, PD Wagner, 361:375–78. New York: Plenum

43. Hogan MC, Roca J, Wagner PD, West JB. 1988. Limitation of maximal oxygen uptake and performance by acute hypoxia in dog muscle in situ. *J. Appl. Physiol.* 65:815–21

44. Hogan MC, Roca J, West JB, Wagner PD. 1989. Dissociation of maximal $O_2$ uptake from $O_2$ delivery in canine gastrocnemius in situ. *J. Appl. Physiol.* 66(3):1219–26

45. Hogan MC, Willford DC, Keipert PE, Faithfull NS, Wagner PD. 1992. Increased plasma $O_2$ solubility improves $O_2$ uptake of in situ dog muscle working maximally. *J. Appl. Physiol.* 73(6):2470–75

46. Honig CR, Gayeski TEJ, Clark A Jr, Clark PAA. 1991. Arteriovenous oxygen diffusion shunt is negligible in resting and working gracilis muscles. *Am. J. Physiol.* 261:H2031–43

47. Honig CR, Gayeski TEJ, Federspiel WJ, Clark A Jr, Clark P. 1984. Muscle $O_2$ gradients from hemoglobin to cytochrome: new concepts, new complexities. *Adv. Exp. Med. Biol.* 169:23–38

48. Horstman DH, Gleser M, Wolfe D, Tyron T, Delehunt J. 1974, Effects of hemoglobin reduction on $VO_2$max and related hemodynamics in exercising dogs. *J. Appl. Physiol.* 37:97–102

49. Horwitz LD, Lindenfeld J. 1985. Effects of enhanced ventricular filling on cardiac pump performance in exercising dogs. *J. Appl. Physiol.* 59(6):1886–90

50. Johnson BD, Badr MS, Dempsey JA. 1994. Impact of the aging pulmonary system on the response to exercise. *Clin. Chest Med.* 15(2):229–46

51. Johnson BD, Saupe KW, Dempsey JA. 1992. Mechanical constraints on exercise hyperpnea in endurance athletes. *J. Appl. Physiol.* 73(3):874–86

52. Jones JH, Birks EK, Berry JD. 1989. Does oxygen transport limit $VO_2$max in horses? *FASEB J.* 3:A234 (Abstr.)

53. Kao AC, Van Trigt III P, Shaeffer-McCall GS, Shaw JP, et al. 1994. Central and peripheral limitations to upright exercise in untrained cardiac transplant recipients. *Circulation* 89(6):2605–15

54. Knight DR, Schaffartzik W, Poole DC, Hogan MC, Bebout DE, Wagner PD. 1993. Effects of hyperoxia on maximal leg $O_2$ supply and utilization in humans. *J. Appl. Physiol.* 75:2586–94

55. Krogh A. 1919. The number and distribution of capillaries in muscle with calculations of the pressure head necessary for supplying the tissue. *J. Physiol.* 52:409–15

56. Lawler J, Powers SK, Thompson D. 1988. Linear relationship between $VO_2$max and $VO_2$max decrement during exposure to acute hypoxia. *J. Appl. Physiol.* 64:1486–92

57. Levine BD, Kubo K, Kobayashi T, Fukushima M, Shibamoto T, Ueda G. 1988. Role of barometric pressure in pulmonary fluid balance and oxygen transport. *J. Appl. Physiol.* 64(1):419–28

58. Levy RD, Ernst P, Levine SM, Shennib H, Anzueto A, et al. 1993. Exercise performance after lung transplantation. *J. Heart Lung Transplant.* 12(1 Pt. 1):27–33

59. Londraville RL, Sidell BD. 1990. Ultrastructure of aerobic muscles in Antarctic fishes may contribute to maintenance of diffusive fluxes. *J. Exp. Biol.* 150:205–20

60. Maillard D, Delpuech C, Hatzfeld C. 1990. Ventilatory adjustments during sustained resistive unloading in exercising humans. *Eur. J. Appl. Physiol. Occupat. Physiol.* 60(2):120–26

61. Malconian M, Rock P, Hultgren HN, Donner H, Cymerman A, et al. 1990. Operation Everest II: the electrocardiogram during rest and exercise during a simulated ascent of Mt. Everest. *Am. J. Cardiol.* 65:1475–80

62. McParland C, Mink J, Gallagher CG. 1991. Respiratory adaptations to dead space loading during maximal incremental exercise. *J. Appl. Physiol.* 70(1):55–62

63. Metra M, Cannella G, LaCanna G, Guaini T, Sandrini M, et al. 1991. Improvement in exercise capacity after correction of anemia in patients with end stage renal failure. *Am. J. Cardiol.* 68:1060–66

64. Moore GE, Parsons B, Stray-Gundersen J, Painter PL, Brinker KR, Mitchell JH. 1993. Uremic myopathy limits aerobic capacity in hemodialysis patients. *Am. J. Kidney Dis.* 22(2):277–87

65. Oelz O, Howald H, di Prampero PE, Hoppeler H, Claassen H, et al. 1986. Physiological profile of world-class

high-altitude climbers. *J. Appl. Physiol.* 60:1734–42

66. Persson SGB. 1967. On blood volume and working capacity in horses. *Acta Vet. Scand. (Suppl.)* 19:1–189

67. Piiper J, Scheid P. 1981. Model for capillary-alveolar equilibration with special reference to $O_2$ uptake in hypoxia. *Respir. Physiol.* 46:193–208

68. Pirnay F, Lamy M, Dujardin J, Deroanne R, Petit M. 1972. Analysis of femoral venous blood during maximum exercise. *J. Appl. Physiol.* 33:289–92

69. Poon C-S. 1987. Ventilatory control in hypercapnia and exercise: optimization hypothesis. *J. Appl. Physiol.* 62(6): 2447–59

70. Powers SK, Jacques M, Richard R, Beadle RE. 1986. Effects of breathing a normoxic He-$O_2$ gas mixture on exercise tolerance and $\dot{V}O_2$max. *Int. J. Sports Med.* 7(4):217–21

71. Powers SK, Lawler J, Dempsey J, Dodd JA, Landry G. 1989. Effects of incomplete pulmonary gas exchange on $\dot{V}O_2$max. *J. Appl. Physiol.* 66:2491–95

72. Pugh LGCE. 1964. Cardiac output in muscular exercise at 5,800 m (19,000 ft). *J. Appl. Physiol.* 19:441–47

73. Pugh LGCE, Gill MB, Lahiri S, Milledge JS, Ward MP, West JB. 1964. Muscular exercise at great altitudes. *J. Appl. Physiol.* 19:431–40

74. Reeves JT, Bertron MG, Cymerman A, Sutton JR, Wagner PD, et al. 1990. Operation Everest II: cardiac filling pressures during cycle exercise at sea level. *Respir. Physiol.* 80:147–54

75. Reeves JT, Groves BM, Sutton JR, Wagner PD, Cymerman A, et al. 1987. Operation Everest II: preservation of cardiac function at extreme altitude. *J. Appl. Physiol.* 63:531–39

76. Richardson RS, Knight DR, Poole DC, Kurdak SS, Hogan MC, et al. 1995. Determinants of maximal exercise $\dot{V}O_2$ during single leg knee extensor exercise in man. *Am. J. Physiol.* 268(37):H1453–61

77. Richardson RS, Noyszewski EA, Kendrick KF, Leigh JS, Wagner PD. 1995. Myoglobin $O_2$ desaturation during exercise: evidence of limited $O_2$ transport. *J. Clin. Invest.* 96(4):1916–26

78. Richardson RS, Sheldon J, Poole DC, Hopkins SR, Ries AL, Wagner PD. 1995. 100% inspired $O_2$ increases quadriceps work capacity in patients with COPD. *Am. J. Respir. Crit. Care Med.* 151(4):A255 (Abstr.)

79. Riess JG. 1992. Overview of progress in the fluorocarbon approach to in vivo oxygen delivery. *Biomater. Artif.*

*Cells Immobil. Biotechnol.* 20(2–4): 183–202

80. Robertson HT, Haley NR, Guthrie M, Cardenas D, Eschbach JW, Adamson JW. 1990. Recombinant erythropoietin improves exercise capacity in anemic hemodialysis patients. *Am. J. Kidney Dis.* 15:325–32

81. Robertson R, Gilcher R, Metz K, et al. 1979. Central circulation and work capacity after red blood cell reinfusion under normoxia and hypoxia in women. *Med. Sci. Sports* 11:98

82. Roca J, Agustí AGN, Alonso A, Poole DC, Viegas C, et al. 1992. Effects of training on muscle $O_2$ transport at $\dot{V}O_2$max. *J. Appl. Physiol.* 73:1067–76

83. Roca J, Hogan MC, Story D, Bebout DE, Haab P, et al. 1989. Evidence for tissue diffusion limitation of $\dot{V}O_2$max in normal humans. *J. Appl. Physiol.* 67:291–99

84. Roca J, Marrades RM, Campistol J, Diaz O, Barberá JA, et al. 1995. Effects of erythropoietin (EPO) on leg $O_2$ transport at $\dot{V}O_2$max in patients with chronic renal failure (CRF). *Am. J. Respir. Crit. Care Med.* 151(4):A338 (Abstr.)

85. Rowell LB. 1993. *Human Cardiovascular Control,* New York: Oxford Univ. Press

86. Rowell LB, Saltin B, Kiens B, Christensen NJ. 1986. Is peak quadriceps blood flow in humans even higher during exercise with hypoxemia? *Am. J. Physiol.* 251:H1038–44

87. Saltin B, Gollnick PD. 1983. Skeletal muscle adaptability: significance for metabolism and performance. In *Handbook of Physiology. Skeletal Muscle,* ed. LD Peachy, RH Adrian, SR Geiger, pp. 555–631. Bethesda, MD: Am. Physiol. Soc.

88. Sarelius IH. 1993. Cell and oxygen flow in arterioles controlling capillary perfusion. *Am. J. Physiol.* 265(5 Pt. 2): H1682–87

89. Schaffartzik W, Barton ED, Poole DC, Tsukimoto K, Hogan MC, et al. 1993. Effect of reduced hemoglobin concentration on leg oxygen uptake during maximal exercise in humans. *J. Appl. Physiol.* 75:491–98

90. Schaffartzik W, Poole DC, Derion T, Tsukimoto K, Hogan MC, et al. 1992. VA/Q distribution during heavy exercise and recovery in humans: implications for pulmonary edema. *J. Appl. Physiol.* 72(5):1657–67

91. Seeherman HJ, Taylor CR, Maloiy GMD, Armstrong RB. 1981. Design of the mammalian respiratory system. II.

Measuring maximal aerobic capacity. *Respir. Physiol.* 44:11–23

92. Segal SS. 1992. Convective, diffusion, and mitochondrial utilization of oxygen during exercise. In *Energy Metabolism in Exercise and Sport,* ed. DR Lamb, CV Gisolfi, pp. 269–344. Dubuque, IA: Brown Commun. 5th ed.

93. Sidell BD. 1990. Physiologic roles of high lipid content in tissues of Antarctic fish species. In *Biology of Antarctic Fish,* ed. GB DiPrisco, B Maresca, B Tota, pp. 220–31. New York/Berlin: Springer-Verlag

94. Spriet LL, Gledhill N, Froese AB, Wilkes DL, Meyers EC. 1980. The effect of induced erythrocythemia on central circulation and oxygen transport during maximal exercise. *Med. Sci. Sports* 12:122

95. Stainsby WN, Brechue WF, O'Drobinak DM, Barclay JK, 1989. Oxidation/reduction state of cytochrome oxidase during repetitive contractions. *J. Appl. Physiol.* 67:2158–62

96. Stray-Gundersen J, Musch TI, Haidet GC, Swain DP, Ordway GA, Mitchell JH. 1986. The effect of pericardiectomy on maximal oxygen consumption and maximal cardiac output in untrained dogs. *Circ. Res.* 58(4):523–30

97. Suarez J, Alexander JK, Houston CS. 1987. Enhanced left ventricular systolic performance at high altitude during Operation Everest II. *Am. J. Cardiol.* 60:137–42

98. Taylor CR, Karas RH, Weibel ER, Hoppeler H. 1987. Adaptive variation in the mammalian respiratory system in relation to energetic demand: II. Reaching the limits to oxygen flow. *Respir. Physiol.* 69:7–26

99. Wagner PD. 1977. Ventilation-perfusion inequality and gas exchange during exercise in lung disease. See Ref. 30, pp. 345–56

100. Wagner PD. 1991. Central and peripheral aspects of oxygen transport and adaptations with exercise. *Sports Med.* 11(3):133–42

101. Wagner PD. 1993. Algebraic analysis of the determinants of $\dot{V}O_2$max. *Respir. Physiol.* 93:221–37

102. Wagner PD, Erickson BK, Kubo K, Hiraga A, Yamaya Y, et al. 1995. Maximum $O_2$ transport and utilization before and after splenectomy. *Equine Vet. J.* 18:82–89

103. Wagner PD, Gale GE, Moon RE, Torre-Bueno JR, et al. 1986. Pulmonary gas exchange in humans exercising at sea level and simulated altitude. *J. Appl. Physiol.* 61(1):260–70

104. Wagner PD, Gillespie JR, Landgren GL, Fedde MR, Jones BW, et al. 1989. Mechanism of exercise-induced hypoxemia in horses. *J. Appl. Physiol.* 66:1227–33

105. Wagner PD, Sutton JR, Reeves JT, Cymerman A, Groves BM, Malconian MK. 1987. Operation Everest II: pulmonary gas exchange during a simulated ascent of Mt. Everest. *J. Appl. Physiol.* 63(6):2348–59

106. Wasserman K, Whipp BJ. 1975. Exercise physiology in health and disease. *Am. Rev. Respir. Dis.* 112:219–49

107. Welch HG. 1982. Hyperoxia and human performance: a brief review. *Med. Sci. Sports Exerc.* 14:253–62

108. Welch HG. 1987. Effects of hypoxia and hyperoxia on human performance. *Exerc. Sports Sci. Rev.* 15:191–221

109. West JB, Boyer SJ, Graber DJ, Hackett PH, Maret KH, et al. 1983. Maximal exercise at extreme altitudes on Mt. Everest. *J. Appl. Physiol.* 55:688–98

110. Williams JH, Powers SK, Stuart MK. 1986. Hemoglobin desaturation in highly trained athletes during heavy exercise. *Med. Sci. Sports Exerc.* 18:168–73

111. Wilson DF, Erecinska M, Drown C, Silver IA. 1977. Effect of oxygen tension on cellular energetics. *Am. J. Physiol.* 233:C135–40

112. Winslow RM. 1992. Potential clinical applications for blood substitutes. *Biomater. Artif. Cells Immobil. Biotechnol.* 20(2–4):205–17

113. Wittenberg B, Wittenberg J, Caldwell P. 1975. Role of myoglobin in the oxygen supply to red skeletal muscle. *J. Biol. Chem.* 250:9038–43

114. Wittenberg BA, Wittenberg JB. 1987. Myoglobin-mediated oxygen delivery to mitochondria of isolated cardiac myocytes. *Proc. Natl. Acad. Sci. USA* 84:7503–7

115. Wittenberg BA, Wittenberg JB. 1989. Transport of oxygen in muscle. *Annu. Rev. Physiol.* 51:857–78

116. Woodson RD, Wills RE, Lenfant C. 1978. Effect of acute and established anemia on $O_2$ transport at rest, submaximal and maximal work. *J. Appl. Physiol.* 44:36–43

*Annu. Rev. Physiol.* 1996. 58:51–71

# MECHANISMS OF GENE EXPRESSION AND CELL FATE DETERMINATION IN THE DEVELOPING PULMONARY EPITHELIUM

## B. P. Hackett

Department of Pediatrics, Washington University School of Medicine, One Childrens Place, St. Louis, Missouri 63110

## C. D. Bingle

Department of Toxicology, Medical College of St. Bartholomew's Hospital, London, United Kingdom

## J. D. Gitlin

Department of Pediatrics, Washington University School of Medicine, One Childrens Place, St. Louis, Missouri 63110

KEY WORDS:    lung development, transcription factors, surfactant protein A, Clara cell secretory protein, forkhead proteins

---

### ABSTRACT

The pulmonary epithelium is a derivative of the foregut endoderm. Proliferation and differentiation of the primitive pulmonary epithelium result in an array of epithelial cell phenotypes that determine lung function and the response of the lung to injury, infection, or neoplastic transformation. The establishment of a cell phenotype requires the presence of transcription factors that activate or repress expression of specific genes. Members of the forkhead family of transcription factors, in particular HNF-3α, HNF-3β, HFH-4; the homeodomain protein TTF-1; and N-myc, are all expressed in the developing pulmonary epithelium and may play important regulatory roles during development. Two genes specific to the pulmonary epithelium, the surfactant protein A and Clara cell secretory protein genes, serve as useful paradigms for understanding the mechanisms regulating cell-specific gene expression in the pulmonary epithelium.

---

51

0066-4278/96/0315-0051$08.00

## INTRODUCTION

The pulmonary epithelium, extending from the trachea to the alveoli, is a complex tissue that performs a multitude of vital functions. In general, this epithelium is composed of two contiguous divisions: a proximal conducting region and a distal gas exchange region. This view, however, does not reflect the true variety of specialized activities necessary for normal pulmonary function. These functions include gas exchange between the respiratory and circulatory systems, synthesis and secretion of components of the extracellular lining of the lung, uptake and metabolism of secreted products and xenobiotics, fluid and electrolyte balance, and protection and repair of the epithelium following toxic or infectious injury (70). Accomplishing these various tasks requires an array of differentiated epithelial cells capable of sustaining these functions. Defining the mechanisms regulating cellular differentiation and gene expression in this epithelium is important to understanding the development of normal lung function.

Disorders of the pulmonary epithelium are important factors in lung pathophysiology. Inherited human diseases, such as cystic fibrosis, $\alpha_1$-anti-trypsin deficiency, and congenital alveolar proteinosis due to surfactant protein B deficiency, involve significant pulmonary epithelial dysfunction (9, 21, 64). In addition, the pulmonary epithelium is the most common site of neoplastic transformation in the lung (90). Because of its exposed location, the pulmonary epithelium is at risk of injury from infectious and toxic agents. Recovery from injury may result in a return to normal lung function or may result in chronic lung disease as in infants with bronchopulmonary dysplasia (26). Its accessibility also makes the pulmonary epithelium a suitable target for gene therapy. For cystic fibrosis, this treatment modality has reached the clinical trial stage (20). Other pulmonary diseases, including $\alpha_1$-anti-trypsin deficiency, surfactant protein B deficiency, and pulmonary neoplasia, may also be amenable to gene therapy. Thus understanding the regulation of cell-specific gene expression in the lung epithelium has importance not only in defining the mechanisms regulating the development of normal lung function but also in defining the pathophysiology of lung disease and targeting the expression of therapeutic genes to the epithelium.

This review focuses on the mechanisms regulating cell-specific gene expression in the pulmonary epithelium, as well as on the role of transcription factors during its development. As only a small fraction of the genes available to a cell are expressed in the differentiated state, mechanisms for regulating gene expression are needed to insure that the correct complement of genes is expressed in a given cell type. The specific array of genes expressed defines cell phenotype. Cell-specific gene expression implies the presence of regulatory molecules that activate or repress the expression of specific genes by either active or passive mechanisms. Passive control results in the permanent inactivation of a gene through epigenetic mechanisms. Active control involves conditional regulation of gene expression and, in general, entails the activity of transcription factors that can stimulate or inhibit gene expression (8). Although the general transcription factors, which include RNA polymerase II and the associated TFIIB, E, F, and H proteins, ultimately mediate the temporal and spatial regulation of gene expression, the presence or absence of additional proteins is required for cell-specific gene expression (60). Such proteins include transcription factors that recognize and bind to unique DNA sequences within specific genes, as well as co-activator proteins that guide protein-protein interactions between the specific and general transcription factors (29). Within any gene, multiple DNA sequence elements, both upstream and downstream from the transcription initiation site, are recognized by a variety of specific transcription factors. It is the interplay between these multiple regulatory proteins and their cognate DNA sequences that determines the temporal and spatial pattern of gene expression in the pulmonary epithelium.

## TRANSCRIPTION FACTORS AND PULMONARY EPITHELIAL DIFFERENTIATION

The pulmonary epithelium is derived from an outpocketing of the foregut endoderm into the mesenchyme of the fetal thorax. Proliferation of the primitive pulmonary epithelial cells results in a continuous epithelium from the trachea to the alveoli. In addition to this cellular proliferation, regional differentiation along the length of the developing epithelium results in the formation of at least 11 differentiated epithelial cell types that, to a large extent, determine lung function (66). Proliferation and differentiation of the pulmonary epithelium are largely completed during the perinatal period (66). This is in contrast to other organ systems, such as the gastrointestinal tract, in which cellular proliferation and differentiation occur throughout the lifetime of the organism. However, under certain circumstances in the lung, including mechanical or chemical injury, infection, or neoplastic transformation, these developmental programs may be reactivated, which can result in alterations in both lung structure and function (66).

The identification of specific transcription factors that mediate differentiation of the pulmonary epithelium is important in understanding the development of normal lung function and the response of the lung to injury. Transcription factors that may play a role in the developing pulmonary epithelium have been identified in several ways. First, recognition of known *cis*-acting elements in the regulatory regions of pulmonary genes has identified transcription factors involved in cell-specific pulmonary epithelial gene expression. Recognition of hepatocyte nuclear factor-3 (HNF-3) binding motifs in the

Clara cell secretory protein (CCSP) gene, for example, identified members of this family of transcription factors as regulators of CCSP gene expression (6, 7, 76). The known role of the HNF-3 proteins in cellular differentiation suggests that members of the family play a similar role in regulating differentiation of the pulmonary epithelium. The association between expression of a transcription factor in the pulmonary epithelium and developmental events has also identified potentially important regulatory molecules in the lung epithelium. The homeobox gene thyroid transcription factor-1 (*TTF-1*), for example, is expressed in the developing pulmonary epithelium at the time of initial branching of the lung bud from foregut endoderm (51). This temporal pattern of expression is consistent with a role for *TTF-1* in early differentiation of the pulmonary epithelium. Finally, a role for a known regulatory molecule in development of the pulmonary epithelium may be uncovered serendipitously. Targeted mutation of the N-*myc* gene by homologous recombination resulted in decreased pulmonary expression of N-*myc* and lung hypoplasia (61). Although this experiment was intended to study the effect of a null mutation on embryonic development, this partial knock-out reveals an important role for N-*myc* in lung epithelial development.

## Forkhead Domain Proteins (Winged-Helix)

HNF-3   HNF-3α and HNF-3β belong to the forkhead family of transcription factors named for the *Drosophila* mutation that results in an embryo with a duplicated anterior pole (85). Since isolation of the original family member, homologous proteins have been identified in a variety of metazoan organisms including *Caenorhabditis elegans*, *Xenopus*, zebrafish, chickens, rodents, and humans (49). These DNA-binding proteins are characterized by a conserved 100-amino acid DNA-binding domain termed the forkhead domain (49). X-ray crystallographic analysis of the HNF-3γ forkhead domain complexed to DNA reveals a three-dimensional structure that includes three α-helices, three β-pleated sheets, and two wing-like loops and has the appearance of a winged-helix (17). These DNA-binding proteins play important roles in cell fate determination and cell-specific gene expression (49).

During embryonic development, the patterns of expression of the *HNF-3* family members suggest that they play roles in regional differentiation of the gut endoderm and its derivatives including the lung (3, 62, 73). Both *HNF-3α* and *HNF-3β* are expressed in the anterior region of the primitive streak and in the node that arises from this region. As foregut invagination begins, *HNF-3α* and *HNF-3β* are detected in the differentiating endoderm. By embryonic day (E)9.0 of gestation in the mouse, distinct anterior boundaries of expression have been established: *HNF-3β* has the most anterior boundary in the stomatadeum, just anterior to the oral plate, and *HNF-3α* expression extends up

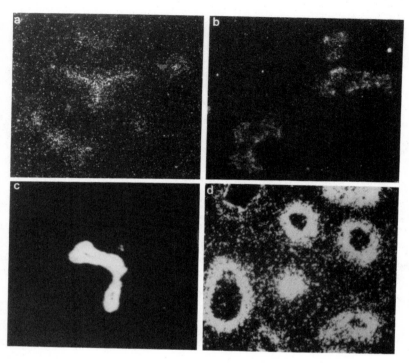

*Figure 1*  Expression of transcription factors in the developing pulmonary epithelium. (*a*) In situ hybridization of E13.5 murine lung for *HNF-3β* expression. Transcript is localized to the developing epithelium. (*b*) In situ hybridization of E14.5 murine lung for *HFH-4* expression. Transcript is localized to the developing proximal epithelium. (*c*) In situ hybridization of E11.5 rat lung for *TTF-1* expression. Transcript is localized to the epithelium of the dividing bronchi. (Reprinted from Reference 51, courtesy of the Company of Biologists Ltd.) (*d*) In situ hybridization of E14.5 murine lung for N-*myc* expression. Transcript is localized to the developing epithelium. (Reprinted from Reference 38, courtesy of Elsevier Science, Inc.)

to the oral plate. Expression of both genes extends posteriorly to the region of the hindgut (62). As organogenesis progresses along the foregut endoderm, *HNF-3α* and *HNF-3β* expression increases in the differentiating esophagus and laryngotracheal groove. Following lung budding, expression within the lung is restricted to the developing epithelium (Figure 1*a*) (3, 62). By E14.0 of murine gestation, *HNF-3β* expression is no longer detectable in the trachea or esophagus, whereas *HNF-3α* expression continues in these developing organs (62). Both *HNF-3α* and *HNF-3β* continue to be expressed in the bronchiolar epithelium throughout gestation and in the adult lung (7).

```
HNF-3β    H A K P P Y S Y I S L I T M A I Q Q S P N K M L T L S E I Y Q W I M D L F P F Y
fkh-3     P T - - - - - - - A - - A - - - - S - - G Q R A - - - G - - R Y - - G R - A - -
HFH-8     P E - - - - - - - A - - V - - - - S - - - - R - - - - - - - - F L O A R - - F
FREAC-2   P E - - - - - - - A - - V - - - - S - - S - R - - - - - - - - F L Q A R - - - F
FREAC-1   P E - - - - - - - A - - V - - - - S - - T - R - - - - - - - - F L Q R S - - - F
HFH-4     - V - - - - - - A T - - C - - M - A - K A T K I - - - A - - K - - T - N - C Y F


HNF3-β    R Q N Q Q R W Q N S I R H S L S F N D C F L K V P R A P D K P G K G S F W T L H
fkh-3     - H - R P G - - - - - - - - - - L - E - - V - - - - D D R - - - - - - Y - - - D
HFH-8     - G A Y - G - K - - V - - N - - L - E - - I - L - K G L G R - - - - H Y - - I D
FREAC-2   - G A Y - G - K - - V - - N - - L - E - - I - L - K G L G R - - - - H Y - - I D
FREAC-1   - G S Y - G - K - - V - - N - - L - E - - I - L - K G L G R - - - - H Y - - I D
HFH-4     - H A D P T - - - - - - - N - L - K - - I - - - - E K - E - - - - G - - R I D


HNF-3β    P D S G N M F E N G C Y L R R Q K R F K C
fkh-3     - - C H D - - Q H - S F - - - R R - - T K    62%
HFH-8     - A - E E - - - E - S F R - - P R G - R R    56%
FREAC-2   - A - E F - - - E - S F R - - P R G - R R    55%
FREAC-1   - A - E F - - - E - S F R - - P R G - R R    55%
HFH-4     - Q Y A E R L L S - A F K K - R L P P V H    48%
```

*Figure 2*  Comparison of DNA-binding domains of forkhead proteins expressed in the lung. Percent amino acid identity compared to HNF-3β is indicated at the end of each sequence. Overlined regions represent α-helical portions of the binding domains. (Reprinted from Reference 34a, courtesy of Marcel Dekker, Inc.)

Targeted disruption of the *HNF-3β* gene underscores the importance of this family member in embryogenesis (2, 86). The phenotype of homozygous mutants is an embryonic lethal due to failure of normal node and notochord development. Additionally, differentiation of the definitive endoderm is initiated, but foregut development is arrested at an early stage. Consequently, no development of foregut derivatives, such as the lung, is observed. That foregut development begins in the mutant mice suggests that other factors, perhaps *HNF-3α*, are capable of supporting the initial differentiation of the definitive endoderm, but that subsequent development requires the presence of *HNF-3β* (2, 86). Because this phenotype is lethal prior to lung budding, it has not been useful in determining the role of *HNF-3β* in subsequent lung development.

HFH-4    Subsequent to the isolation of the vertebrate *HNF-3* genes, genes with homologous DNA-binding domains have been identified (18, 19, 32, 40, 68). Some of these forkhead proteins are expressed in the lung, and their roles in cellular differentiation and cell-specific gene expression are worth exploring. Figure 2 compares the DNA-binding domains of forkhead proteins expressed in the lung. None of these family members, however, are exclusive to the lung, and several, including fkh-3, FREAC-1, and HFH-4, are expressed in both pulmonary and reproductive epithelium (32, 40, 68). Although these new family members show only 50 to 60% homology to the HNF-3β DNA-binding domain, α-helical regions of the domain required for DNA-protein interaction are highly conserved (Figure 2).

Among these recently identified forkhead genes, only *HFH-4* has been fully characterized with respect to its pattern of expression during lung development (32). *HFH-4* expression is first detected in the murine lung at E14.5 of gestation during the late pseudoglandular stage. At this time its expression is confined to the developing proximal respiratory epithelium and remains so throughout subsequent lung development (Figure 1*b*). No expression is detected in the more distal pulmonary epithelium or mesenchyme (32). Expression in the adult lung is also associated with the bronchiolar epithelium (18, 32). The timing of *HFH-4* expression during development coincides with the initial morphological distinction between proximal columnar and distal cuboidal pulmonary epithelial cells (84). Thus *HFH-4* expression precisely demarcates the differentiation of proximal and distal respiratory epithelium. This timing suggests a role for *HFH-4* in regulating the initial differentiation of these two distinct populations of pulmonary epithelial cells.

HFH-8/FREAC    The homology between the murine HFH-8 and human FREAC-2 and FREAC-1 DNA-binding domains is 92 and 91%. respectively, suggesting that these genes are the human homologues of the murine *HFH-8* gene (Figure 2). *FREAC-1* and *FREAC-2* are expressed in human fetal lung, although the precise timing and site of expression have not been described (68). *HFH-8* expression has been localized to the distal pulmonary epithelium in the adult murine lung, but its expression during lung development has not been characterized (18). In contrast to the proximal role of HFH-4, these data together suggest a role for this group of forkhead proteins in the developing distal pulmonary epithelium. Although recent data show that HFH-8 activates the surfactant protein B promoter, surfactant protein B is also expressed in more proximal Clara cells where *HFH-8* expression is not detectable (18, 88). This suggests that different arrays of transcription factors are regulating expression of the same gene in different cell types.

## Homeodomain Proteins (Helix-Turn-Helix)

Members of the homeodomain family of transcription factors were first identified as genes responsible for homeotic mutations in *Drosophila melanogaster* (59, 77). Since the original description of these genes over ten years ago, homologous family members have been identified in all metazoan organisms examined (43). Members of the homeodomain family of transcription factors are characterized by a conserved 60-amino acid DNA-binding domain termed the homeodomain. The 180 nucleotides encoding this domain are referred to as the homeobox (28). The homeodomain is characterized by four α-helical regions with helices II and III forming a characteristic helix-turn-helix motif (28). From the study of these genes in *Drosophila, C. elegans*, and vertebrates it has become clear that they are important determinants of body axis patterning and impart positional information to differentiating cells (46, 50).

Studies on the regulation of cell-specific gene expression in the thyroid gland have led to the isolation and characterization of a new homeodomain protein, named thyroid transcription factor-1 (TTF-1), expressed in both the thyroid gland and lung (22, 30, 31, 51). Both organs are derivatives of the foregut endoderm (51). The amino acid sequence of the TTF-1 homeodomain is about 40% homologous to the conserved DNA-binding domain of the primary *Drosophila* homeotic genes (31). DNA sequences that most efficiently bind TTF-1 have a core recognition motif of CAAG instead of the TAAT motif previously described for other homeodomain proteins (22).

During rat lung development, *TTF-1* expression is detected at E10.5 in the lung bud as the bud migrates ventrally from the foregut endoderm (Figure 1c) (51). As lung development progresses, *TTF-1* expression continues in the branching primordial pulmonary epithelium to at least E15.5. Expression is restricted to the epithelium at all stages of development with no transcript noted in the surrounding fetal mesenchyme or in the foregut prior to lung budding (51). By immunocytochemistry, TTF-1 protein is also present in the developing lung bud at E10.5 (51). The appearance of TTF-1 at the time of lung budding suggests that it plays an important role in the initial differentiation of the lung epithelium from the foregut endoderm.

## N-Myc (Helix-Loop-Helix/Leucine Zipper)

N-*myc* belongs to a family of proto-oncogenes that includes c-myc and L-*myc*. N-*myc* was first identified from human neuroblastoma cells as a sequence homologous to the previously isolated c-*myc* (56). A basic amino acid region in combination with a helix-loop-helix motif is located just upstream from a leucine zipper motif at the carboxyl-terminus of these proteins. The helix-loop-helix and leucine zipper motifs are thought to mediate homo- or heterodimerization of proteins with like motifs. The basic domain mediates binding to DNA target sequences. A domain required for transactivation is located in the amino-terminal region of these proteins (53). The Myc proteins appear to play important roles in regulating cell proliferation during normal development and neoplastic transformation. Evidence also suggests that decreased *myc* expression accompanies cellular differentiation (56)

During early embryonic development, N-*myc* expression is confined to the mesoderm. As mesodermal differentiation occurs, mesodermal N-*myc* expression decreases, and N-*myc* expression is detectable in developing organs including the lung (23). Expression in the murine lung is greatest at E12.5 and then declines (38, 63). By in situ hybridization, this expression has been localized to the bronchiolar epithelium from E12.5 to E16.5, with no expression detectable by E18.5 (Figure 1*d*). At these same stages of lung development, c-*myc* expression is restricted to the mesenchyme of the developing lung (38). The timing of N-*myc* expression in the lung is associated with the period of greatest pulmonary epithelial proliferation (38).

The importance of N-*myc* in proliferation of the pulmonary epithelium has been demonstrated by a targeted mutation in N-*myc* that results in reduced N-*myc* expression (61). Homologous recombination in this line of mice resulted in a "leaky" mutation that allows for reduced expression through alternative splicing. Homozygous mice die at birth of respiratory failure, and the only significant abnormality observed is pulmonary hypoplasia. This defect appears to be primarily a defect in distal lung development, with a reduced number of distal air spaces and apparently normal airway development. The defect in lung morphogenesis is readily apparent by E12.5. Total size of the lung is reduced (as opposed to the size of wild-type lung), and the number of peripheral epithelial branches is decreased. Measurement of N-*myc* mRNA levels in homozygous mutant animals reveals a 75% decrease in transcript abundance in the lung compared with wild-type animals (61).

Homologous recombination that creates a null mutation in the N-*myc* gene results in embryonic death at E10.5 to E12.5 of development (15, 74, 80). Normal embryonic development occurs up to day E10.5 in the mutant embryos, suggesting that N-*myc* expression is not essential for early embryogenesis. In homozygous mutant embryos after E10.5, development is disrupted in a number of organ systems including the lung. This disruption appears to occur after the onset of organogenesis (15, 74, 80). Lung budding occurs in the homozygous mutants at E9.5 with no detectable difference between the mutant and wild-type lungs at this stage. By E10.5, however, there is a clear defect in branching morphogenesis and the homozygous mutant lungs consist of only a trachea and mainstem bronchi with no distal branching (15, 80). Culturing explanted lungs from the homozygous mutant embryos in the presence of fetal calf serum stimulates branching to some degree, which suggests that serum components can at least in part overcome the lack of N-*myc* expression. Branching in these cultured lungs, however, is still reduced compared with explanted wild-type lungs cultured in the presence of serum (74).

## CELL-SPECIFIC PULMONARY EPITHELIAL GENE EXPRESSION

Within the pulmonary epithelium, the four surfactant protein genes and the Clara cell secretory protein (CCSP) gene exhibit distinct spatial and temporal patterns of gene expression. Regulation of this expression within the epithelium involves several components. First, because the onset of expression of each of these genes varies during lung development, what are the mechanisms regulating the temporal patterns of expression? Second, what are the determinants of the spatial pattern of expression of these genes in the lung? The pattern of expression of these genes in the epithelium is complex, with different cell types expressing different combinations of these genes. This complexity underscores the intricate regulatory mechanisms that are required for defining the spatial pattern of expression. Finally, what are the mechanisms involved in mediating the hormonal regulation of expression for each of these genes? Expression of all these genes is at least to some extent regulated by hormonal signals. These signals may be important in preparing the lung for ex utero life. The following sections review the current understanding of the regulation of the expression of two of these pulmonary epithelial genes, surfactant protein A (SP-A) and the CCSP gene, as paradigms for the regulation of pulmonary epithelial gene expression. We have chosen to focus on these two genes since much new information regarding regulation of their expression has become available in the last few years. Expression of the other surfactant proteins has been recently reviewed (37, 72).

## Surfactant Protein A (SP-A)

A single, approximately 5-kilobases SP-A gene encoded by six exons has been identified in the mouse, rat, and rabbit (44). In the human, two SP-A genes, SP-A1 and SP-A2, as well as a pseudogene, have been characterized (42, 45, 57). It was recently established that the SP-A1 gene is encoded by seven exons and SP-A2 by six exons (41). The processing of SP-A and its functions have been reviewed previously (47, 72). Expression of the SP-A gene is lung specific and in adult murine, rabbit, and human lung is localized to type II epithelial cells and Clara cells (4, 44). During murine lung development, expression of the SP-A gene is first detected by RNA blot analysis at E15.0 during the pseudoglandular stage of development (44). In the rat, rabbit, and human lung, SP-A transcript or protein has not been detected until the canalicular stage (4, 25, 78). In human fetal lung, transcript from the SP-A1 gene is detectable prior to SP-A2 transcript (58). This implies differences in the mechanisms regulating expression of the two genes.

Analysis of the 5'-flanking region of the SP-A gene has revealed potential sites of protein-DNA interaction. DNase I footprint analysis has revealed six regions of interaction in the rat SP-A promoter, three of which are specific for lung nuclear extract (48). Additionally, in the rabbit SP-A gene, two lung-specific DNase I hypersensitive sites have been identified (16). These hypersensitive sites were detectable with lung nuclear extract from E21.0 rabbit embryos prior to the expression of SP-A (16).

a. SP-A

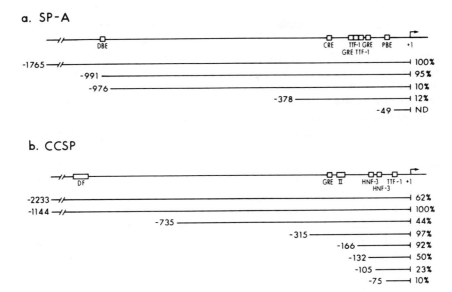

*Figure 3*  5′-Flanking regions of the (*a*) rabbit SP-A gene (27) and (*b*) rat CCSP gene (7). Regulatory elements are indicated by boxes; the transcription start site is indicated by an arrow. Lines below flanking region indicate promoter deletions with relative promoter activity compared to a 1765-base pair SP-A promoter in rat type II epithelial cells in the presence of Bt₂(cAMP) and to a 1144-base pair CCSP promoter in H441 cells. DBE, distal-binding element; CRE, cAMP response element; GRE, glucocorticoid response element; TTF-1, thyroid transcription factor-1 binding element; PBE, proximal-binding element; DF, distal footprinted region; II, region II; HNF-3, HNF-3 binding motifs; ND, not detectable.

Sequence analysis of the 5′-flanking region of the SP-A promoter reveals potential binding sites for a number of transcription factors (Figure 3*a*). A cAMP response element (CRE) has been identified in the rabbit SP-A promoter but has not been identified in the rat or murine genes (16, 44, 48). In the human SP-A1 and SP-A2 genes, a CRE is located within the second intron of the genes (57). Mutation of the CRE in the rabbit SP-A gene to a site with weaker cAMP-binding properties results in decreased basal activity of the rabbit SP-A promoter in transient transfection of rat type II epithelial cells (1). The relative induction by dibutyryl cAMP (Bt₂cAMP) is also reduced with the weaker binding site (1). Mutation of the CRE to a stronger binding motif results in increased basal activity compared to the wild-type promoter, but it has no significant effect on the relative induction by Bt₂cAMP (1). In cultured, human fetal lung tissue, induction of SP-A transcription by Bt₂cAMP is primarily a result of increased transcription from the SP-A2 gene (58). With respect to this differential regulation of the two human SP-A genes, it is interesting to note that the CRE sequence in SP-A2 (TGACCTCA) is identical to the rabbit CRE sequence and differs from the corresponding sequence in the less responsive SP-A1 gene (TGACCTGA) by a single nucleotide (58). Inhibition of the synthesis of endogenous cAMP in cultured, explanted fetal lung prevents the increase in SP-A expression seen in untreated lung explants (5). These data suggest that during lung development, changes in endogenous cAMP levels may mediate increases in SP-A gene expression.

Mendelson and co-workers have identified two E-box motifs in the rabbit SP-A promoter, a distal element (DBE) at −986 and a proximal element (PBE) at −87 (27) (Figure 3a). E-box motifs are binding sites for members of the helix-loop-helix family of DNA-binding proteins (24). Both of these sites bind proteins from lung nuclear extract. Binding activity is increased with nuclear extract from type II epithelial cells (27). Both in vivo and in vitro binding activity is greatest prior to the onset of SP-A gene expression (27). Deletion of the DBE results in decreased basal activity of the rabbit SP-A promoter and decreased induction by Bt$_2$cAMP (27) (Figure 3a). Deletion of the PBE results in nearly undetectable basal promoter activity and minimal induction by Bt$_2$-cAMP (27) (Figure 3a). These two E-box elements thus appear to act as important enhancers in the rabbit SP-A gene. Inspection of the rat, murine, and human SP-A genes reveals canonical E-box motifs (CANNTG) as well, but the importance of these motifs in regulating these genes has not been studied (42, 44, 48).

Recently, binding sites for the homeodomain transcription factor TTF-1 have been identified in the promoter region of the murine SP-A gene (14). Four of these sites are located in a region 168 to 231 bases upstream from the transcription start site (14). Regions with homologous sequences are also present in the 5'-flanking regions of the rat and rabbit SP-A genes (16, 48) (Figure 3a). Recombinant TTF-1 and nuclear proteins from the murine lung epithelial cell line MLE-15 bind to this region of the murine SP-A promoter (14). Antibody to TTF-1 recognizes the protein-DNA complexes formed with nuclear extract from MLE-15 cells (14). TTF-1 transactivates the SP-A promoter in HeLa cells, and deletion or mutation of the TTF-1 sites results in decreased basal activity of the SP-A promoter in MLE-15 cells and decreased transactivation of the SP-A promoter in HeLa cells (14). Although these data strongly support a role for TTF-1 in regulating SP-A expression, TTF-1 is present in the lung before SP-A is expressed, suggesting that additional proteins, either positive or negative regulators, are required for determining the timing of SP-A gene expression.

In all of the SP-A genes characterized thus far, including both human genes, a half-binding site for the glucocorticoid receptor (GRE) is located 140 to 150 bases upstream from the transcription initiation site (16, 42, 44, 48). In the rabbit gene, multiple half GREs have been identified (16) (Figure 3a). The effect of glucocorticoid treatment on SP-A gene expression is complex and appears to depend on the dose and timing of the steroid (10, 52, 87). The net effect is the result of increased SP-A gene transcription and decreased mRNA stability (10, 11, 39). The role of the half GREs in mediating these effects remains to be delineated.

## Clara Cell Secretory Protein (CCSP)

The CCSP gene is a single-copy gene comprised of three exons (36, 69, 81, 89). The rabbit uteroglobin gene appears to be a homologue of CCSP (36, 69, 89). Evidence suggests that CCSP may modulate inflammatory responses, but its biological role remains unknown (55). In the lung, expression of the CCSP gene is generally thought to be restricted to Clara cells (13, 35). In the adult rat lung, however, CCSP gene expression has been reported in type II epithelial cells in addition to Clara cells (83). During lung development, CCSP expression is first detected during the canalicular stage in murine and rat lung (34, 35, 83). CCSP protein is also detected in the human lung during the canalicular stage at 21 weeks of gestation (79).

Analysis of transgene expression regulated by the 5'-flanking region of the CCSP gene has revealed that 2.25 kilobases of 5'-flanking sequence are sufficient to direct cell-specific transgene expression (33, 82). Within this portion of the 5'-flanking sequence of the CCSP gene, several regions protected from DNase I digestion by lung cell nuclear extracts have been identified (6, 81, 82). Analysis of one of these regions from approximately 76 to 132 bases upstream from the transcription initiation site (referred to as region I) in the rat CCSP gene reveals binding motifs for several transcription factors, including HNF-3 (two sites) and Oct-1 (6, 76) (Figure 3b). Homologous regions are present in the murine and human CCSP genes, as well as in the rabbit uteroglobin gene (81, 89). Deletion of this region results in decreased rat CCSP promoter activity in transient transfection assays and in transgenic mice (7, 68a, 75) (Figure 3b). Elucidation of the proteins involved in interacting with this region by gel shift mobility assays and specific antibody reveals that HNF-3α, HNF-3β, Oct-1, JunB, and Fra 1 from lung epithelial cell nuclear extracts all interact with this region (6, 7, 76).

The role played by members of the HNF-3 family of transcription factors in transactivating the CCSP gene has been evaluated in some detail. Mutations in the HNF-3 sites in region I result in the specific loss of protein-DNA complexes in gel shifts and decreased promoter activity in H441 cells (6, 76). Mutation of a single HNF-3 site is sufficient to decrease promoter activity (75). Co-expression of HNF-3α or HNF-3β protein induces expression of a 1.17-kilobase CCSP promoter in H441 cells but not in Hep G2 cells (6, 7). With a

0.32-kilobase CCSP promoter, HNF-3β weakly inhibited CCSP promoter activity in H441 cells and showed much stronger inhibition of promoter activity in HeLa cells (75). With deletion of one of the two HNF-3 sites, HNF-3α still induces expression 2.5-fold (vs 2.8-fold with both sites), but basal activity of the promoter is reduced by 50% (7). Deletion of both HNF-3 sites completely inhibits HNF-3α induction and results in a further decrease in basal promoter activity in H441 cells (7) (Figure 3b). Expression of HNF-3α and HNF-3β in Clara cells has been demonstrated by RNA blot analysis and in situ hybridization (7). Interestingly, only HNF-3α is expressed in H441 cells, a lung cell line that morphologically is Clara cell-like but does not express the CCSP gene (7).

A second footprinted region (referred to as region II) has been identified in the rat and murine CCSP genes located about 200 bases upstream from the transcription initiation site (81, 82) (Figure 3b). It is interesting to note, however, that the rat and murine regions are not homologous (81). In the rat gene, this region is G/C rich, characteristic of the binding site for certain transcription factors (82). The human CCSP gene is also G/C rich in a homologous region (89). Deletion or mutation of this region in the rat promoter, but not the murine promoter, results in decreased CCSP promoter activity in H441 cells (75, 76, 82). In other studies, however, no significant change in promoter activity was noted in H441 cells when this region was deleted (7) (Figure 3b). Although deletion of region II in the murine gene did not decrease promoter activity in H441 cells, it did decrease promoter activity in transgenic mice; however, without a loss of cell-specific transgene expression (68a). Some of the differences observed in the activity of this region probably reflect differences between the non-homologous rat and murine regions and differences in the human H441 cell line and murine epithelial cells. Protein-DNA interactions have been described between rat region II and H441 and HeLa nuclear proteins although the proteins have not been identified (82). Region II also appears to affect the activity of region I (75). In the absence of region II, the presence of two HNF-3 sites in region I is additive as opposed to a promoter with a single HNF-3 site. With region II present, however, the two HNF-3 sites have a synergistic effect on promoter activity (75).

Co-transfection of H441 cells with a TTF-1 expression vector transactivates a 315-base pair CCSP promoter in transient transfection assays (Figure 4) (R Toonen, JD Gitlin, CD Bingle, unpublished observations). In Hep G2 cells, which do not support basal CCSP promoter activity, TTF-1 also transactivates the CCSP promoter (Figure 4). TTF-1 has the same effect on CCSP promoter activity in HeLa cells (12). With deletion of the CCSP promoter to 75 base pairs, TTF-1 induction is still observed in H441 cells (R Toonen, JD Gitlin, CD Bingle, manuscript in preparation). A region of the rat CCSP promoter from −51 to −42 binds recombinant TTF-1, and within this region, a degenerate

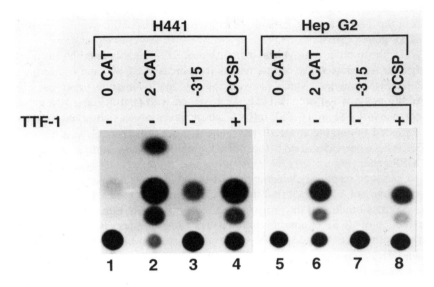

*Figure 4* Activation of CCSP by TTF-1. H441 cells or Hep G2 cells were transfected with the indicated chloramphenicol acetyl transferase (CAT) reporter plasmids in the presence (+) or absence (-) of a TTF-1 expression vector. CAT activity was determined by autoradiography of thin-layer chromatography plates used to separate acetylated from non-acetylated species. Lanes 1 and 5, promoterless CAT reporter; lanes 2 and 6, CAT reporter with SV40 promoter; lanes 3, 4, 7, and 8, CAT reporter with 315-base pair CCSP promoter.

TTF-1-binding motif has been identified (R Toonen, JD Gitlin, CD Bingle, manuscript in preparation).

More distal regions of the CCSP promoter also appear to be involved in regulating CCSP gene expression (Figure 3*b*). Deletion of the rat promoter from 2300 base pairs to 1350 or 1144 bases upstream from the transcription initiation site results in increased promoter activity in H441 cells, suggesting the presence of inhibitory sequences (6, 7, 82) (Figure 3*b*). Deletion of a footprinted region from −1020 to −1070 results in decreased promoter activity in H441 cells (7, 68a, 82) (Figure 3*b*). The specific proteins involved in these interactions have not been identified.

The minimal elements required to maintain cell-specific CCSP gene expression have not been precisely established. Deletion of the murine CCSP promoter to 166 base pairs still results in cell-specific expression in transgenic mice. Further deletion to 87 bases results in undetectable transgene expression (68a). In H441 cells, however, further deletion to a 75-base pair promoter with a CAT reporter gene still gives detectable expression (7). With the more sensitive luciferase reporter, a 29-base pair promoter gives activity in H441 cells and not in HeLa or A549 cells, which suggests that elements downstream from the TATA box are capable of supporting cell-specific expression of the CCSP gene (75).

Similar to other lung genes, expression of CCSP is regulated by hormonal signals. Adrenalectomy of rats results in decreased CCSP lung transcript by RNA blot analysis, which is reversible by hydrocortisone treatment (36). Additionally, when pregnant rats were treated with betamethasone, a greater increase in CCSP and CCSP mRNA during gestation was observed in fetuses of treated mothers compared with untreated controls (65). Several potential GREs have been identified in the promoter region of the rat, human, and murine CCSP genes (Figure 3b) (36, 69, 89). It is interesting to note that progesterone and estrogen response elements present in the homologous rabbit uteroglobin gene have not been identified in the CCSP gene (36, 89). There is, however, some cross-binding of the progesterone receptor to GREs that may explain the induction of CCSP expression in the uterus following progesterone and estrogen treatment or during specific stages of the estrus cycle in the human uterus (36, 67).

Finally, little is known regarding the developmental regulation of CCSP gene expression in the lung. Although 2.25 kilobases of the 5'-flanking region from the rat CCSP gene maintain the spatial pattern of endogenous CCSP gene expression in transgenic mice, this transgene exhibits a unique temporal pattern of expression (34). Transgene expression is detectable at least as early as E12.0, 4.5 to 5 days prior to endogenous CCSP gene expression. Because this observation was made in several different transgenic lines, it suggests that elements deleted in the construction of the transgene (either more distal regions of the promoter or within introns) mediate the developmental timing of CCSP gene expression in the lung (34).

## SUMMARY

The maturation of normal lung function depends on the ordered temporal and spatial patterning of lung development. In addition, the response of the lung to injury, infection, or neoplastic transformation may rely on the same developmental programs involved in early lung development. The correct completion of these developmental programs requires multiple regulatory molecules that mediate cellular proliferation and differentiation. The identification of these regulatory molecules in invertebrates such as *Drosophila* and *C. elegans* has greatly added to the understanding of how development is patterned in these organisms. The study of vertebrate development, and lung development in particular, is at the earliest stages of identifying the relevant regulators of cellular differentiation and cell-specific gene expression. Thus far, a single molecule that directs a cell to become a lung cell, or a specific type of lung cell, has not been identified. In the anterior pituitary, on the other hand, pit-1 appears to be the central protein in determining certain cell lineages (71). The lung, at least as we understand it at this point, appears to rely on multiple regulatory molecules to determine the correct temporal and spatial patterns of gene expression. In addition, the regulatory molecules that have been identified are not unique to the lung but also function in other organs. Some of these regulatory molecules, for example HNF-3α, HNF-3β, and TTF-1, appear to function in derivatives of the foregut endoderm. A clearer delineation of the relationships between these various regulatory molecules and an identification of their targets in the lung is required for a more complete understanding of the mechanisms regulating cellular differentiation and cell-specific gene expression in the pulmonary epithelium.

ACKNOWLEDGMENTS

The authors thank Steven L Brody for his helpful discussions and critical reading of the manuscript. The work described in this manuscript was supported in part by National Institutes of Health grants HL 41536 (JDG) and R29 HL 52581 (BPH).

## Literature Cited

1. Alcorn JL, Gao E, Chen Q, Smith ME, Gerard RD, Mendelson CR. 1993. Genomic elements involved in transcriptional regulation of the rabbit surfactant protein-A gene. *Mol. Endocrinol.* 7: 1072–85
2. Ang S-L, Rossant J. 1994. HNF-3β is essential for node and notochord formation in mouse development. *Cell* 78: 561–74
3. Ang S-L, Wierda A, Wong D, Stevens KA, Cascio S, et al. 1993. The formation and maintenance of the definitive endoderm lineage in the mouse: involvement of the HNF3/forkhead proteins. *Development* 119:1301–15
4. Auten RL, Watkins RH, Shapiro DL, Horowitz S. 1990. Surfactant apoprotein A (SP-A) is synthesized in airway cells. *Am. J. Respir. Cell Mol. Biol.* 3: 491–96
5. Ballard PL, Gonzales LW, Williams MC, Roberts JM, Jacobs MM. 1991. Differentiation of type II cells during explant culture of human fetal lung is accelerated by endogenous prostanoids and adenosine 3′,5′-monophosphate. *Endocrinology* 128:2916–24
6. Bingle CD, Gitlin JD. 1993. Identification of hepatocyte nuclear factor-3 binding sites in the Clara cell secretory protein gene. *Biochem. J.* 295:227–32
7. Bingle CD, Hackett BP, Moxley M, Longmore W, Gitlin JD. 1995. Role of HNF-3α and HNF-3β in Clara cell secretory protein gene expression in the bronchiolar epithelium. *Biochem. J.* 308: 197–202
8. Blau HM. 1992. Differentiation requires continuous active control. *Annu. Rev. Biochem.* 61:466–71
9. Boat TF, Welsh MJ, Beaudet AL. 1989. Cystic fibrosis. In *The Metabolic Basis of Inherited Disease*, ed. CR Scriver, AL Beaudet, WS Sly, D Valle, 108: 2649–80. New York: McGraw-Hill. 3006 pp.
10. Boggaram V, Smith ME, Mendelson CR. 1989. Regulation of expression of the gene encoding the major surfactant

protein (SP-A) in human fetal lung in vitro. *J. Biol. Chem.* 264:11421–27

11. Boggaram V, Smith ME, Mendelson CR. 1991. Posttranscriptional regulation of surfactant protein-A messenger RNA in human fetal lung in vitro by glucocorticoids. *Mol. Endocrinol.* 5:414–23

12. Bohinski RJ, DiLauro R, Whitsett JA. 1994. The lung-specific surfactant protein B gene promoter is a target for thyroid transcription factor 1 and hepatocyte nuclear factor 3, indicating common factors for organ-specific gene expression along the foregut axis. *Mol. Cell. Biol.* 14:5671–81

13. Broers JLV, Jensen SM, Travis WD, Pass H, Whitsett JA, et al. 1992. Expression of surfactant associated protein-A and Clara cell 10 kilodalton mRNA in neoplastic and non-neoplastic human lung tissue as detected by in situ hybridization. *Lab. Invest.* 66:337–46

14. Bruno MD, Bohinski RJ, Huelsman KM, Whitsett JA, Korfhagen TR. 1995. Lung cell-specific expression of the murine surfactant protein A (SP-A) gene is mediated by interactions between the SP-A promoter and thyroid transcription factor-1. *J. Biol. Chem.* 270:6531–36

15. Charron J, Malynn BA, Fisher P, Stewart V, Jeannotte L, et al. 1992. Embryonic lethality in mice homozygous for a targeted disruption of the N-*myc* gene. *Genes Dev.* 6:2248–57

16. Chen Q, Boggaram V, Mendelson CR. 1992. Rabbit lung surfactant protein A gene: identification of a lung-specific DNase I hypersensitive site. *Am. J. Physiol.* 262:L662–71

17. Clark KL, Halay ED, Lai E, Burley SK. 1993. Co-crystal structure of the HNF-3/fork head DNA-recognition motif resembles histone H5. *Nature* 364:412–20

18. Clevidence DE, Overdier DG, Peterson RS, Porcella A, Ye H, et al. 1994. Members of the HNF-3/forkhead family of transcription factors exhibit distinct cellular expression patterns in lung and regulate the surfactant protein B promoter. *Dev. Biol.* 166:195–209

19. Clevidence DE, Overdier DG, Tao W, Qian X, Pani L, et al. 1993. Identification of nine tissue-specific transcription factors of the hepatocyte nuclear factor 3/forkhead DNA-binding domain family. *Proc. Natl. Acad. Sci. USA* 90:3948–52

20. Colledge WH. 1994. Cystic fibrosis gene therapy. *Curr. Opin. Genet. Dev.* 4:466–71

21. Cox DW. 1989. $\alpha_1$-Antitrypsin deficiency. In *The Metabolic Basis of Inherited Disease*, ed. CR Scriver, AL Beaudet, WS Sly, D Valle, 96:2409–38. New York: McGraw-Hill. 3006 pp.

22. Damante G, Fabbro D, Pellizzari L, Civitareale D, Guazzi S, et al. 1994. Sequence-specific DNA recognition by the thyroid transcription factor-1 homeodomain. *Nucleic Acids Res.* 22:3075–83

23. Downs KM, Martin GR, Bishop JM. 1989. Contrasting patterns of *myc* and N-*myc* expression during gastrulation of the mouse embryo. *Genes Dev.* 3:860–69

24. Edmondson DG, Olson EN. 1993. Helix-loop-helix proteins as regulators of muscle-specific transcription. *J. Biol. Chem.* 268:755–58

25. Endo H, Oka T. 1991. An immunohistochemical study or bronchial cells producing surfactant protein A in the developing human fetal lung. *Early Hum. Dev.* 25:149–56

26. Finkelstein JN, Horowitz S, Sinkin RA, Ryan RM. 1992. Cellular and molecular responses to lung injury in relation to induction of tissue repair and fibrosis. *Clin. Perinat.* 19:603–20

27. Gao E. Alcorn JL, Mendelson CR. 1993. Identification of enhancers in the 5'-flanking region of the rabbit surfactant protein A (SP-A) gene and characterization of their binding proteins. *J. Biol. Chem.* 268:19697–709

28. Gehring WJ, Affolter M, Bürglin T. 1994. Homeodomain proteins. *Annu. Rev. Biochem.* 63:487–526

29. Gstaiger M, Knoepfel L, Georgiev O, Schaffer W, Hovens CM. 1995. A B-cell coactivator of octamer-binding transcription factors. *Nature* 373:360–62

30. Guazzi S, Lonigro R, Pintonello L, Boncinelli E, Di Lauro R, Mavilio F. 1994. The thyroid transcription factor-1 gene is a candidate for regulation by Hox proteins. *EMBO J.* 13:3339–47

31. Guazzi S, Price M, De Felice M, Damante G, Mattei M-G, Di Lauro R. 1990. Thyroid nuclear factor 1 (TTF-1) contains a homeodomain and displays novel DNA binding specificity. *EMBO J.* 11:3631–39

32. Hackett BP, Brody SL, Liang M, Zeitz ID, Bruns LA, Gitlin JD. 1995. Primary structure of hepatocyte nuclear factor/forkhead homologue 4 and characterization of gene expression in the developing respiratory and reproductive epithelium. *Proc. Natl. Acad. Sci. USA* 92:4249–53

33. Hackett BP, Gitlin JD. 1992. Cell-specific expression of a Clara cell secretory protein-human growth hormone in the bronchiolar epithelium of transgenic

mice. *Proc. Natl. Acad. Sci. USA* 89: 9079–83

34.  Hackett BP, Gitlin JD. 1994. 5'-Flanking region of the Clara cell secretory protein gene specifies a unique temporal and spatial pattern of gene expression in the developing pulmonary epithelium. *Am. J. Respir. Cell Mol. Biol.* 11:123–29

34a. Hackett BP, Gitlin JD. 1995. Role of transcription factors in the development of the pulmonary epithelium. In *Growth and Development of the Lung*, ed. JA McDonald. New York: Dekker. In press

35.  Hackett BP, Shimizu N, Gitlin JD. 1992. Clara cell secretory protein gene expression in bronchiolar epithelium. *Am. J. Physiol.* 262:L399–404

36.  Hagen G, Wolf M, Katyal SL, Singh G, Beato M, Suske G. 1990. Tissue-specific expression, hormonal regulation and 5'-flanking gene region of the rat Clara cell 10 kDa protein: comparison to rat uteroglobin. *Nucleic Acids Res.* 18:2939–46

37.  Hawgood S, Shiffer K. 1991. Structure and function of the surfactant-associated proteins. *Annu. Rev. Physiol.* 53:375–94

38.  Hirning U, Schmid P, Schulz WA, Rettenberger G, Hameister H. 1991. A comparative analysis of N-*myc* and c-*myc* expression and cellular proliferation in mouse organogenesis. *Mech. Dev.* 33: 119–26

39.  Iannuzzi DM, Ertsey R, Ballard PL. 1993. Biphasic glucocorticoid regulation of pulmonary SP-A: characterization of inhibitory process. *Am. J. Physiol.* 264:L236–44

40.  Kaestner KH, Lee K-H, Schlöndorff J, Hiemisch H, Monaghan AP, Schütz G. 1993. Six members of the mouse forkhead gene family are developmentally regulated. *Proc. Natl. Acad. Sci. USA* 90:7628–31

41.  Karinch AM, Floros J. 1995. 5' Splicing and alleic variants of the human pulmonary surfactant protein A genes. *Am. J. Respir. Cell Mol. Biol.* 12:77–88

42.  Katyal SL, Singh G, Locker J. 1992. Characterization of a second human pulmonary surfactant-associated protein SP-A gene. *Am. J. Respir. Cell Mol. Biol.* 6:446–52

43.  Kenyon C. 1994. If birds can fly, why can't we? Homeotic genes and evolution. *Cell* 78:175–80

44.  Korfhagen TR, Bruno MD, Glasser SW. Ciraolo PJ, Whitsett JA, et al. 1993. Murine pulmonary surfactant SP-A gene: cloning, sequence, and transcriptional activity. *Am. J. Physiol.* 263: L546–54

45.  Korfhagen TR, Glasser SW, Bruno MD, McMahan MJ, Whitsett JA. 1991. A portion of the human surfactant protein A (SP-A) gene locus consists of a pseudogene. *Am. J. Respir. Cell Mol. Biol.* 4:463–69

46.  Krumlauf R. 1994. Hox genes in vertebrate development. *Cell* 78:191–201

47.  Kuroki Y, Voelker DR. 1994. Pulmonary surfactant proteins. *J. Biol. Chem.* 269:25943–46

48.  Lacaze-Masmonteil T, Fraslon C, Bourbon J, Raymondjean M, Kahn A. 1992. Characterization of the rat pulmonary protein A promoter. *Eur. J. Biochem.* 206:613–23

49.  Lai E, Clark KL, Burley SK, Darnell Jr. JE. 1993. Hepatocyte nuclear factor 3/forkhead or "winged helix" proteins: a family of transcription factors of diverse biological function. *Proc. Natl. Acad. Sci. USA* 90:10421–23

50.  Lawrence PA, Morata G. 1994. Homeobox genes: their function in Drosophila segmentation and pattern formation. *Cell* 78:181–89

51.  Lazzaro D, Price M, De Felice H, Di Lauro R. 1991. The transcription factor TTF-1 is expressed at the onset of thyroid and lung morphogenesis and in restricted regions of the foetal brain. *Development* 113:1093–104

52.  Liley HG, White RT, Benson BJ, Ballard PL. 1988. Glucocorticoids both stimulate and inhibit production of pulmonary surfactant protein A in fetal human lung. *Proc. Natl. Acad. Sci. USA* 85:9096–100

53.  Lüscher B, Eisenman RN. 1990. New light on Myc and Myb. Part I. Myc. *Genes Dev.* 4:2025–35

54.  Deleted in proof

55.  Mantile G, Miele L, Cordella-Miele E, Singh G, Katyal SL, Mukherjee AB. 1993. Human Clara cell 10-kDa protein is the counterpart of rabbit uteroglobin. *J. Biol. Chem.* 268:20343–51

56.  Marcu KB, Bossone SA, Patel AJ. 1992. Myc function and regulation. *Annu. Rev. Biochem.* 61:809–60

57.  McCormick SM, Boggaram V, Mendelson CR. 1994. Characterization of mRNA transcripts and organization of human SP-A1 and SP-A2 genes. *Am. J. Physiol.* 266:L354–66

58.  McCormick SM, Mendelson CR. 1994. Human SP-A1 and SP-A2 genes are differentially regulated during development and by cAMP and glucocorticoids. *Am. J. Physiol.* 266:L367–74

59.  McGinnis W, Garber RL, Wirz J, Kuroiwa A, Gehring W. 1984. A homologous protein-coding sequence in Drosophila homeotic genes and is con-

servation in other metazoans. *Cell* 37: 403–8

60.   Mitchell PJ, Tijian R. 1989. Transcriptional regulation in mammalian cells by sequence-specific binding proteins. *Science* 245:371–78

61.   Moens CB, Auerbach AB, Conlon RA, Joyner AL, Rossant J. 1992. A targeted mutation reveals a role for N-*myc* in branching morphogenesis in the embryonic mouse lung. *Genes Dev.* 6:691–704

62.   Monaghan AP, Kaestner KH, Grau E, Schütz G. 1993. Postimplantation expression patterns indicate a role for the mouse forkhead/HNF-3 α, β, and γ genes in determination of the definitive endoderm, chordamesoderm and neuroectoderm. *Development* 119:567–78

63.   Mugrauer G, Alt FW, Ekblom P. 1988. N-*myc* proto-oncogene expression during organogenesis in the developing mouse as revealed by in situ hybridization. *J. Cell Biol.* 107:1325–35

64.   Nogee LM, Garnier G, Dietz HC, Singer L, Murphy AM, et al. 1994. A mutation in the surfactant protein B gene responsible for fatal neonatal respiratory disease in multiple kindreds. *J. Clin. Invest.* 93:1860–63

65.   Nord M, Andersson O, Brönnegaard M, Lund J. 1992. Rat lung polychlorinated biphenyl-binding protein: effect of glucocorticoids on the expression of the Clara cell-specific protein during fetal development. *Arch. Biochem. Biophys.* 296:302–7

66.   Penny DP. 1988. The ultrastructure of epithelial cells of the distal lung. *Int. Rev. Cytol.* 111:231–69

67.   Peri A, Cowan BD, Bhartiya D, Miele L, Nieman LK, et al. 1994. Expression of Clara cell 10-kD gene in the human endometrium and its relationship to ovarian menstrual cycle. *DNA Cell Biol.* 13:495–503

68.   Pierrou S, Hellqvist M, Samuelsson L, Enerbäck S, Carlsson P. 1994. Cloning and characterization of seven human forkhead proteins: binding site specificity and DNA bending. *EMBO J.* 13: 5002–12

68a.  Ray MK, Magdaleno SW, Finegold MJ, De Mayo FJ. 1995. *cis*-Acting elements involved in the regulation of mouse Clara cell-specific 10-kDa protein gene. *J. Biol. Chem.* 270:2689–94

69.   Ray MK, Magdaleno SW, O'Malley BW, De Mayo FJ. 1993. Cloning and characterization of the mouse Clara cell specific 10 kDa protein gene: comparison of the 5′-flanking region with the human, rat, and rabbit gene. *Biochem. Biophys. Res. Commun.* 197:163–71

70.   Rennard SI, Beckman JD, Robbins RA. 1991. Biology of airway epithelial cells. In *The Lung: Scientific Foundation*, ed. RG Crystal, JB West, PJ Barres, NS Cherniak, ER Weibel, 3:157–67. New York: Raven. 2224 pp.

71.   Rhodes SJ, DiMattia GE, Rosenfeld MG. 1994. Transcriptional mechanisms in anterior pituitary cell differentiation. *Curr. Opin. Gen. Dev.* 4:709–17

72.   Rooney SA, Young SL, Mendelson CR. 1994. Molecular and cellular processing of lung surfactant. *FASEB J.* 8:957–67

73.   Sasaki H, Hogan BLM. 1993. Differential expression of multiple forkhead related genes during gastrulation and axial pattern formation in the mouse embryo. *Development* 118:47–59

74.   Sawai S, Shimono A, Wakamatsu Y, Palmes C, Hanaoka K, Kondoh H. 1993. Defects of embryonic organogenesis resulting from targeted disruption of the N-*myc* gene in the mouse. *Development* 117:1445–55

75.   Sawaya PL, Luse DS. 1994. Two members of the HNF-3 family have opposite effects on a lung transcriptional element; HNF-3α stimulates and HNF-3β inhibits its activity of region I from the Clara cell secretory protein (CCSP) promoter. *J. Biol. Chem.* 269:22211–16

76.   Sawaya PL, Stripp BR, Whitsett JA, Luse DS. 1993. The lung-specific CC10 gene is regulated by transcription factors from the AP-1, octamer, and hepatocyte nuclear factor 3 families. *Mol. Cell. Biol.* 13:3860–71

77.   Scott MP, Weiner AJ. 1984. Structural relationship among genes that control development: sequence homology between the Antennapedia, Ultrabithorax and *fushi tarazu* loci of Drosophila. *Proc. Natl. Acad. Sci. USA* 81:4115–19

78.   Shimizu H, Miyamura K, Kuroki Y. 1991. Appearance of surfactant proteins, SP-A and SP-B, in developing rat lung and the effects of in vivo dexamethasone treatment. *Biochim. Biophys. Acta* 1081: 53–60

79.   Singh G, Singh J, Katyal SL, Brown WE, Kramps JA, et al. 1988. Identification, cellular localization, isolation, and characterization of human Clara cell-specific 10 kD protein. *J. Histochem. Cytochem.* 36:73–80

80.   Stanton BR, Perkins AS, Tessarollo L, Sassoon DA, Parada LF. 1992. Loss of N-*myc* function results in embryonic lethality and failure of the epithelial component of the embryo to develop. *Genes Dev.* 6:2235–47

81.   Stripp BR, Huffman JA, Bohinski RJ. 1994. Structure and regulation of the

murine Clara cell secretory protein gene. *Genomics* 20:27–35

82. Stripp BR, Sawaya PL, Luse DS, Wikenheiser KA, Wert SA, et al. 1992. *cis*-Acting elements that confer lung epithelial cell expression of the CC10 gene. *J. Biol. Chem.* 267:14703–12

83. Strum JM, Compton RS, Katyal SL, Singh G. 1992. The regulated expression of mRNA for Clara cell protein in the developing airways of the rat, as revealed by tissue in situ hybridization. *Tissue Cell* 24:467–71

84. Ten Have-Opbroek AAW. 1991. Lung development in the mouse embryo. *Exp. Lung Res.* 17:111–30

85. Weigel D, Jürgens G, Küttner F, Seifert E, Jäckle H. 1989. The homeotic gene forkhead encodes a nuclear protein and is expressed in the terminal regions of the Drosophila embryo. *Cell* 57:645–58

86. Weinstein DC, Ruiz i Altaba A, Chen WS, Hoodless P, Prezioso VR, et al. 1994. The winged-helix transcription factor HNF-3β is required for notochord development in the mouse embryo. *Cell* 78:575–88

87. Whitsett JA, Pilot T, Clark JC, Weaver TE. 1987. Induction of surfactant protein in fetal lung. Effects of cAMP and dexamethasone on SAP-35 RNA and synthesis. *J. Biol. Chem.* 262:5256–61

88. Wikenheiser KA, Wert SE, Wispé J, Stahlman M, D'Amore-Bruno M, et al. 1992. Distinct effects of oxygen on surfactant protein B expression in bronchiolar and alveolar epithelium. *Am. J. Physiol.* 262:L32–39

89. Wolf M, Klug J, Hackenberg R, Gessler M, Grzeschik KH, et al. 1992. Human CC10, the homologue of rabbit uteroglobin: genomic cloning, chromosomal localization and expression in endometrial cell lines. *Hum. Mol. Gen.* 1:371–78

90. Yesner R. 1993. Lung cancer. Pathogenesis and pathology. *Clin. Chest Med.* 14:17–30

*Annu. Rev. Physiol. 1996. 58:73–92*

# FORMATION OF PULMONARY ALVEOLI AND GAS-EXCHANGE SURFACE AREA: Quantitation and Regulation

*Gloria D. Massaro and Donald Massaro*

Lung Biology Laboratory, Departments of Pediatrics and Medicine, Georgetown University School of Medicine, Washington, DC 20007

KEY WORDS:    corticosteroid hormones, morphometry, fibroblasts, hyperoxia, hypoxia, glucocorticosteroid hormones, retinoic acid, oxygen consumption

## ABSTRACT

New morphometric procedures allow selection of alveoli for analysis in an unbiased manner and then to determine the volume of individual alveoli. The latter, together with the easily measured lung volume, allows the calculation of alveolar number. These new techniques have greatly increased the rigor of the study of the formation of alveoli and the manner in which this process is regulated. This review deals mainly with work based on these new morphometric methods that explore the regulation of the formation of alveoli and hence the size of the lung's gas-exchange surface area. We expect that continued application of these methods, buttressed with experiments at the cellular and molecular level, will result in a fundamental understanding of how the formation of alveoli and the size of the gas-exchange surface area is regulated. This new information holds the promise of translation into the induction of the formation of alveoli for therapeutic purposes.

## INTRODUCTION

Terminal bronchioles are the last nonalveolated airways. The lung's gas-exchange region is that part of the lung distal to terminal bronchioles. It is composed of the alveolar duct air space, the alveolar air space, and alveolar walls; the latter consist mainly of capillaries and capillary endothelium, alveolar epithelium, and extracellular matrix. The major lung cells in the gas-exchange region (47) are (*a*) alveolar type 1 cells, which form >90% of the

73

gas-exchange surface area (Sa) (2, 30); (*b*) alveolar type 2 cells, which synthesize, store, secrete, and take up pulmonary surfactant, (6, 26, 99), actively transport ions (41, 63), and may serve as progenitors for alveolar type 1 cells (38); (*c*) alveolar capillary endothelial cells, which in addition to forming the vascular component of the gas-exchange surface, alter the composition of the blood (80); and (*d*) interstitial cells, mainly fibroblasts (but of different phenotypes), that are responsible, at least in part, for forming the extracellular matrix of the gas-exchange region (31, 69). These alveolar wall cells, by largely undefined interactions among themselves and with the matrix they produce, and by equally undefined interactions with systemic agents, e.g. hormones and the environment, generate alveoli in sufficient number and size to efficiently and economically meet the gas-exchange requirements engendered by the organism's metabolic rate. This chapter reviews aspects of the regulation of the formation of alveoli and of the magnitude of the lung's gas-exchange surface area (Sa). We mainly, but not exclusively, review work in which alveoli were identified by analysis of serial lung sections and were chosen for analysis using unbiased methods. For excellent authoritative and more exhaustive reviews on lung development see References 15, 19, 92.

## METHODS TO MEASURE GAS-EXCHANGE SURFACE AREA AND THE VOLUME OF INDIVIDUAL ALVEOLI

The measurement of Sa by intersection and point counting, based on the method of Tomkeieff (23, 93), is not technically difficult and is free from restrictive assumptions (95). Such measurements have clearly shown Sa increases severalfold after birth and that this increase can be manipulated (19, 92). However, until recently, fundamental unanswered questions and important limitations addressing these questions have remained. For example, in spite of the substantial postseptation increase of Sa, there has been no clear indication that this is the result of the formation of new alveoli, enlargement of already formed alveoli, or both processes (see below). Many, including ourselves, have used the so-called mean chord length ($L_m$) obtained from single histological sections as an index of alveolar size and from alveolar size and lung volume have inferred alveolar number. However, use of this measurement to estimate alveolar size is flawed on several accounts. (*a*) Alveolar air spaces cannot be reliably distinguished from alveolar duct air spaces on single histological sections and, therefore, $L_m$ determined from single histological sections represents, to an unknown extent, the combination of alveolar air space and alveolar duct air space. (*b*) The inability to distinguish between these spaces, which can vary independently during normal development and can be differently affected by experimental conditions (9, 10), diminishes the sensitivity of this method as a measure of alveolar size. (*c*) Estimates of size made using single histological sections are influenced by alveolar size, shape, and distribution (95, 96). (*d*) Determinations of alveolar number from single histological sections entail assumptions about alveolar shape because shape enters into the calculations as a mean caliper diameter or as a shape factor (95, 96).

A recent approach to assessing alveolar dimensions entails an analysis of serially sectioned lung; this permits distinction of alveolar from alveolar duct air space (10, 70, 76). Having identified alveoli, the selector or disector methods (33, 89) can be used to chose alveoli for analysis in an unbiased manner, i.e. in a manner not influenced by their size, shape, or orientation. The volume of individual alveoli can be determined by the point-sampled intercepts method (46). Based on the average volume of individual alveoli, the total lung volume, easily measured by volume displacement (84), and the volume of alveolar air calculated from the fraction of lung that is alveolar air space (9, 10, 66), the number of alveoli can be calculated (9, 66). This approach is more time consuming than measurements of $L_m$, but it permits determination of alveolar size uninfluenced by the size of alveolar ducts and is therefore more sensitive and more accurate (GD Massaro & D Massaro, unpublished data). For excellent reviews of new stereological tools see References 11, 44, 45.

## ARCHITECTURAL MATURATION OF THE LUNG'S GAS-EXCHANGE REGION: FROM SACCULES TO ALVEOLI

The architecturally immature gas-exchange region of the lung is composed of large structures referred to as saccules to distinguish them from the smaller, more numerous structures of the mature gas-exchange region termed alveoli; the latter are formed at least in part by subdivision (septation) of the saccules. We shall maintain this nomenclature (18). However, if septation of the saccules has been experimentally prevented, or has not occurred for any reason, the resulting structures, although still large and unseptated (or incompletely septated), are nevertheless referred to as alveoli.

The architectural maturation of the lung's gas-exchange region is quite similar in all species studied in detail, including human (3, 13, 18, 28, 34–37, 57, 58, 100). The process entails the outgrowth of septa (septation) from the walls of the saccules that compose the gas-exchange region of the architecturally immature lung (18). Thinning, changes in cellular composition, and remodeling of the alveolar wall to form a single capillary network complete the process (termed alveolarization) that results in the architecturally mature but not yet full-sized lung, with its smaller, more numerous structures (alveoli) that have thinner and less cellular walls.

Although the anatomical changes that constitute alveolarization are very similar among species, the time of their occurrence varies in a manner that seems dictated, at least in part, by the activity life-style of the newborn. In so-called precocial species such as guinea pigs and range animals, the newborn have fur, sight, and within hours considerable locomotor activity. In these species, alveolarization occurs in utero, and at birth the lung is, except for its size, architecturally mature (2, 25, 28, 58, 97, 98). In altricial species such as rat, mouse, rabbit, and human, the newborn are rather helpless, have very poor locomotor ability, and alveolarization occurs in the early postnatal period or, in humans, in late gestation and in the first few postnatal years (3, 12, 18, 35–37, 57, 78, 100).

Three additional observations are worth mentioning regarding the time alveolarization occurs during an organism's development. (a) In species in which alveolarization and the serum glucocorticosteroid concentration have been measured, septation occurs when the organism's serum glucocorticosteroid concentration is low (2, 4, 10, 28, 48, 52, 65, 88). This observation has been exploited experimentally (see below, and References 10, 64, 65, 71). (b) Alve- olarization occurs mainly before (i.e. guinea pigs and range animals) or after (rat, mouse, rabbit) the late gestational maturation of the lung's surfactant system and rise of activity of some lung antioxidant enzymes (39, 55). The timing of alveolarization in relation to late gestational events seems pro- grammed to spread out the organism's energy requirements and yet, as noted above, meet its need for motor activity in the early postnatal period. (c) Alveolarization occurs under vastly different oxygen tensions in different species, and, as in humans, even within the same species. For example, alveo- larization in guinea pigs occurs in utero at a $P_{O_2}$ of ~25 torr; in rats it occurs postnatally at an alveolar $P_{O_2}$ of ~100 torr; and in humans, alveolarization occurs in utero at a $P_{O_2}$ of ~25 torr and continues after birth at an alveolar $P_{O_2}$ of ~100 torr. However, exposure of newborn rats to 13% $O_2$, which would provide an alveolar $P_{O_2}$ of 50 torr, well within the $P_{O_2}$ at which septation occurs in guinea pigs and in utero in humans, markedly impairs septation in a seemingly permanent manner (9, 68, and see above). Comparative interspe- cies studies on the molecular and cellular basis of alveolarization as it normally occurs in organisms under in utero conditions, in other organisms postnatally, and in humans under in utero and postnatal conditions would very likely provide important insights into the regulation of alveolarization and how its impairment by adverse environmental conditions might be prevented or re- versed.

## Quantitative Analysis of the Formation of Alveoli: Septation and Other Methods of Forming Alveoli

In two landmark papers, Burri et al in Weibel's laboratory (18, 20) provided morphological and morphometric evidence supporting earlier work in several species (18, 20) that the large saccules forming the gas-exchange region of the immature lung (either prenatal or postnatal) undergo septation to form alveoli. This work was extended in experiments in which serial lung sections were analyzed to identify alveoli (9, 67, 76), and by the use of techniques, partly developed in Bern (32, 33), that allow an unbiased selection of alveoli for analysis (32, 33, 46, 89).

Randell et al found a sixfold fall in volume as the gas-exchange saccules were septated to form alveoli (76). Of particular interest, their data indicate that in rats from birth to age 7 days, septation of saccules could account for only about one-third of the alveoli formed. This observation was confirmed and extended in rats studied at age 2 and 14 days (Table 1) (9). For example (Table 1), if all the alveoli present at age 14 days were generated by septation of the saccules present at age 2 days, we calculate from the identity

$$\frac{\bar{v} \text{ at age 2 days}}{\bar{v} \text{ at age 14 days}} \times N \text{ at age 2 } days$$

that there would be about $6 \times 10^6$ alveoli at age 14 days. However, at age 14 days there are $23 \times 10^6$ alveoli (Table 1). Therefore, only about 26% of the alveoli present at age 14 days were formed by septation of the gas-exchange saccules present at age 2 days; about three-quarters of the alveoli made during this time were formed by some other method(s). These reports (9, 76) confirm the notion that alveoli are formed during the period of septation by means in addition to septation (65).

The use of serial lung sections to identify alveoli and use of newer stereological techniques for their unbiased selection and quantitation provided an answer to the long-debated question of whether alveoli continue to be formed after septation of the original gas-exchange saccules is complete (see Reference 92 for a thorough review). It was found that although alveoli are formed most

**Table 1**  Changes in volume and number of gas-exchange structures during septation

| Age | Va, ml | $\bar{v} \ \mu m^3 \times 10^{-4}$ | $N \times 10^{-6}$ |
|---|---|---|---|
| 2 days | $0.19 \pm 0.02$ | $19.7 \pm 3.5$ | $1.03 \pm 0.17$ |
| 14 days | $0.77 \pm 0.03$ | $3.37 \pm 0.18$ | $23.0 \pm 1.4$ |

Va is the volume of the air space of alveolar saccules (age 2 days) or of alveoli air (age 14 days); $\bar{v}$ is the volume of an average saccule (age 2 days) or an average alveolus (age 14 days); $N$ is the number of saccules (age 2 days) or the number of alveoli (age 14 days) per rat. Mean $\pm$ SE are given. (From *Am. J. Physiol.* 1992. 263:L37–44, with permission.)

rapidly during the period of septation, they continue to be made after septation of the original gas-exchange saccules has ended (9).

Major remaining uncertainties about architectural aspects of the formation of alveoli include the following: By what method(s) other than septation of the original gas-exchange saccules are alveoli formed? Are alveoli formed by other methods generated among already formed alveoli? Are they formed only in the periphery (subpleural) region of the lung and, if so, by what method? Or are alveoli formed by other methods generated in central and peripheral regions of the lung? The average size of an individual alveolus increases with age (9). Is this because of enlargement of already formed alveoli, the formation of new large alveoli, or both processes? If already formed alveoli enlarge with age, is this the result of distention or elongation of septa and if the latter is true, what regulates the degree of elongation?

The report that the number of generations of conducting airways diminishes after birth in dogs suggests these airways may have been remodeled into gas-exchange airways, thereby increasing the number of alveoli (retrograde alveolarization) (12, 37). Because there are so few terminal bronchioles compared to the number of alveoli, it is unlikely that remodeling of a few generations of terminal bronchioles into gas-exchange structures would produce many alveoli. Furthermore, using rigorous sampling methods, three-dimensional reconstruction of the lung, and morphometric techniques, Randell et al (76) were unable to detect a change in the number of terminal bronchioles during the early postnatal period. Thus retrograde alveolarization is, at best, a minor means for forming alveoli.

Gas-exchange airways are branching extensions of conducting airways. It is therefore possible that continued branching of gas-exchange structures as the thorax enlarges may be an important other mechanism for the formation of alveoli. If branching morphogenesis is responsible for the formation of some alveoli, we think it is likely that the branching would occur from the most peripheral gas-exchange units as the thorax enlarges. This notion would be supported if lung growth was more rapid at its periphery than at its more central regions.

In an attempt to address the question of the site of lung growth, a marker was sought that would permanently mark already formed lung and thereby identify lung formed after the marking as having less or no marker. At the suggestion of S Sorokin (personal communication), silver, which had previously been used to mark the kidney for a similar purpose (56), was tried as a potential marker of the lung. Rats were provided with silver-containing drinking water from age 23 to 135 days (67). Fortunately, silver grains formed only in the interstitium. Tissue added after exposure to silver ended would not contain grains and hence would decrease the number of silver grains per volume of interstitial matrix; therefore, the fastest growing regions would have the lowest grain density. The location of silver grains at the end of exposure to silver-containing water, their numerical density at central and peripheral regions, and the rate of change and site of change of silver grain density during weeks after exposure to silver-containing water was stopped are consistent with a conclusion that central, as well as peripheral, gas-exchange matrix enlarged, but the enlargement was fastest in the subpleural region. However, the idea that new alveoli are formed among already present alveoli, i.e. in central areas, is not attractive because it would require extensive remodeling of already formed lung. By contrast, the formation of alveoli from a peripheral growth zone would not require extensive remodeling of formed lung and would therefore be more economical. These considerations suggest the fall in grain density in central regions of lung, which occurred after silver exposure was ended, represents enlargement of already formed alveoli. We suggest that the faster post-exposure fall in grain density that occurred in the subpleural region represents the formation of new alveoli, perhaps by branching morphogenesis, as the lung enlarges.

Formation of alveoli from the subpleural region is consistent with the report of a superficial mantle around developing acini in the fetal rat lung composed of primitive mesenchymal cells that constitute a growth zone (19, 21). Indeed, the subpleural region of the postnatal lung contains a mantle of fibroblasts (67), a cell type capable of producing mitogens and attractants for endothelial cells (29). We propose that subpleural fibroblasts, although morphologically similar to fi-broblasts elsewhere in the lung (67, 94), under appropriate stimuli give rise to matrix and to chemoattractants for other lung cells needed to form new alveoli. In addition, the data from the study marking lung with silver indicate it is important to include the subpleural region and its cells in studies on the mechanism and regulation of the formation of alveoli that use lung explants.

## OXYGEN, THE FORMATION OF ALVEOLI, AND THE LUNG'S GAS-EXCHANGE SURFACE AREA

"The organisms at present existing in a natural state on the surface of the earth are acclimated to the degree of oxygen tension in which they live: any decrease, any increase, seems to be harmful to them when they are in a state of health." This insight, now more or less taken for granted, is extraordinary for the time the words were published, ca 1878 (7). A substantial body of work since that time has verified Bert's conclusions.

### Hyperoxia

Exposure to a high $P_{O_2}$ during the life of eukaryotes is almost always due to medical therapy or biomedical research. Prematurely born infants often require supplemental oxygen, and because of this, there is great interest in the effect exposure to a high $P_{O_2}$ has on the developing lung. Early work had clearly shown that several days of exposure of animals to a high $P_{O_2}$ diminishes the developmental increase of the gas-exchange surface area (5, 22, 54, 85); in animals that septate postnatally, exposure to a high $P_{O_2}$ impairs septation and decreases the development of alveolar capillaries (16). Studies by Randell et al (76) have been especially useful. They compared rats at age 7 days that had been in air or in >95% $O_2$ from birth. They also examined identically exposed rats that were removed from hyperoxia at age 7 days and studied at age 40 days. Exposure to hyperoxia prevented both the decrease in alveolar size and the increase in alveolar number. Furthermore, estimates of the total number of alveoli formed and of the number of alveoli formed by septation indicate hyperoxia impaired the number of alveoli formed by septation and by other means.

Randell et al (77) also studied the more long-term effect on the lung of exposure to hyperoxia from birth to age 7 days. At age 40 days, 33 days after removal from hyperoxia, the size of the gas-exchange surface area, alveolar number, and the size of alveoli were equal in rats exposed only to air and in those initially exposed to $O_2$. However, the alveolar size distribution differed; at age 40 days rats previously exposed to $O_2$ had significantly more very small and very large alveoli than rats exposed to air. The very large alveoli could represent saccules that failed to septate. The basis for the presence of a large number of very small alveoli is unclear. They could reflect alveoli formed by septation after day 7 when the rats were removed from $O_2$; recall that septation continues normally in rats to age 14 days (76). They could also represent alveoli formed by other means or by septation and other means.

The presence of this unusual distribution of alveoli (i.e. very small and very large) in lungs of rats in whom septation was blunted by hyperoxia, but that nevertheless are equal in lung volume and gas-exchange surface area to alveoli in lungs of rats exposed only to air, may be a clue to the regulation of the formation of alveoli. We suggest that the presence of an increased number of very small alveoli and, therefore, of structures with a high surface-to-volume ratio reflects a regulatory mechanism that ensures the formation of sufficient surface area to meet the organism's metabolic needs ($O_2$ uptake and $CO_2$ elimination) within the constraints imposed by the volume (size) of the thorax. This suggestion is based on a consideration of the relationship between body mass, lung volume, surface area, and metabolism, as indicated by total oxygen consumption ($\dot{V}_{O_2}$), and body mass-specific $\dot{V}_{O_2}$, as discussed by Tenney & Remmers (91). In general, the larger the animal the greater its total $\dot{V}_{O_2}$ but the lower its body mass-specific $\dot{V}_{O_2}$. In their seminal paper, Tenney & Remmers, who were among the first to use the term quantitative morphology, found that across animal species lung volume is directly proportional to body mass;

put differently, lung volume makes up almost the same percentage of body volume in small and large animals (91). Because this is the case, the lungs of organisms with a high body mass-specific $\dot{V}_{O_2}$ must have evolved to meet this need, not by increasing lung volume out of proportion to body size, but rather by greater subdivision of the gas-exchange surface, i.e. by making smaller alveoli thereby providing more surface area per lung volume. Thus, because in the study by Randell et al (77) lung volume and gas-exchange surface area were equal in air-breathing rats and $O_2$-breathing rats (but the latter had more large alveoli, which provide less surface per volume than small alveoli), we suggest that those sites in the lung capable of forming alveoli were "instructed" to make small alveoli, thereby generating structures with a high surface-to-volume ratio. Another example of this proposed regulation is shown below in the discussion of the effect of retinoic acid on alveolar volume, number, and Sa (GD Massaro & D Massaro, unpublished observations). The signals and pathways by which metabolic need is translated into a particular lung architecture is a major unsolved problem and important challenge.

## Hypoxia

Biomedical interest in the effect of prolonged exposure to a low inspired $O_2$ pressure arises mainly because of the (currently) small number of the world's population who live at high altitudes and who are descended from individuals who have lived at high altitudes for generations; for ease of exposition we refer to these natives of high altitude who remain at high altitudes as highlanders; individuals of the same race who are born and live at sea level are referred to as lowlanders.

The pulmonary characteristics of highlanders have been extensively studied (50). The following aspects of their lung function are particularly relevant to this review. (a) Highlanders have a 38% higher residual lung volume than lowlanders (50). (b) Highlanders are reported to have larger and more alveoli than lowlanders (24, 83). (c) Compared with lowlanders, highlanders have a low maximum expiratory flow rate per lung volume and low upstream conductance (14). These last two observations have contributed to the notion that gestation and postnatal maturation at high altitude cause dysanaptic lung growth (disproportionate growth among different parts of an organ) (14). More specifically, it has been proposed that at high altitudes the lung's gas-exchange region, which in humans septates in substantial measure postnatally (57, 100) under the presumed stimulatory effect of a low $P_{O_2}$, becomes too large for the cross-sectional area of the conducting airways; the latter, achieving architectural maturity in utero, would not experience during development the presumed stimulation of the low $P_{O_2}$ of high altitude because of maternal adaptive responses, e.g. greater placental surface area. We believe, and discuss below, that aspects of this interpretation of the basis for the difference in lung function between lowlanders and highlanders are incorrect.

The importance of the time of occurrence of septation, prenatal or postnatal, on the effect of gestation and postnatal development at a low inspired $P_{O_2}$ is illustrated by several reports. Tenney & Remmers (90) compared the dimensions of terminal gas-exchange units and Sa in guinea pigs that were bred and raised for many generations at 4530 m and third-generation sheep resident at 4390 m with those in guinea pigs and sheep native to Hanover, New Hampshire (altitude 160 m). They did not find intraspecies differences in $L_m$ or Sa between highlander and lowlander animals. Thus gestation and postnatal development at high altitude did not influence the dimensions of terminal gas-exchange units in two species that septate in utero (28, 58).

More recently, studies were undertaken in which female rats, but not their prospective male consorts, were placed in 13% $O_2$ for 3 weeks before they were mated; they were maintained in 13% $O_2$ throughout gestation and, with their offspring, for various periods after the pups were born (9, 68). Table 2 shows that 2 days after birth, the only effect on the parameters measured, of being carried by acclimatized dams exposed to 13% $O_2$ during pregnancy, is a 30% larger volume of an average alveolus. The story is different at age 14 days; rats exposed to 13% $O_2$ after birth failed to septate as completely, and had two and one-half-fold fewer alveoli than air-breathing rats. The lower number of alveoli is not a reflection of a smaller thoracic volume because, in fact, lung volume is about 10% greater in 13% $O_2$-breathing rats than in air-breathing rats. At age 40 days, 13% $O_2$-breathing rats still had larger alveoli and a lower absolute gas-exchange surface area than air-breathing rats (Table 2).

We view the experiments with guinea pigs and sheep, which septate prenatally, and those with rats, which septate postnatally, as supporting the notion that the ambient $O_2$ tension has a greater impact on gas-exchange dimensions in organisms that septate postnatally than in those that septate in utero. Calculations described above and in Reference 9 indicate that 13% $O_2$-breathing rats had half as many alveoli formed by septation as air-breathing rats and only about one-third as many formed by other means. Thus the other method(s) of forming alveoli are more susceptible to hypoxia than is septation. In spite of a lower number of alveoli and a smaller absolute gas-exchange surface area, body mass-specific gas-exchange surface area is the same in both groups. This is of interest because by age 12–13 days, rat pups maintained in 10% $O_2$ from birth have a mass-specific $\dot{V}_{O_2}$ identical to that of air-breathing rats (72). Hence, in spite of impaired lung development in 13% $O_2$-breathing rats, their lung surface area is adequate for their $\dot{V}_{O_2}$.

Impaired septation in 13% $O_2$-breathing rats results in fewer alveolar attachments to small conducting airways and to small conducting blood vessels (68).

**Table 2** Lung parameters of rat pups, carried in utero by dams acclimatized to 13% $O_2$, that were born into and maintained in 13% $O_2$. Comparison to pups born from air-breathing dams, maintained in air after birth

| Parameter | Air | 13% $O_2$ | P |
|---|---|---|---|
| **Age 2 days** | | | |
| LV, ml | 0.45 ± 0.02 | 0.46 ± 0.02 | NS |
| LV/BW, ml/kg | 64.6 ± 1.3 | 64.7 ± 1.3 | NS |
| Sa, $cm^2$ | 146 ± 9.0 | 150 ± 5.0 | NS |
| Sa/BW, $cm^2$/g | 20.6 ± 0.6 | 21.7 ± 0.5 | NS |
| $\bar{v}$, $\mu m^3 \times 10^4$ | 9.7 ± 0.3 | 12.6 ± 0.8 | <0.05 |
| $N \times 10^6$ | 1.4 ± 0.2 | 1.4 ± 0.0 | NS |
| **Age 14 days** | | | |
| LV, ml | 1.57 ± 0.03 | 1.72 ± 0.06 | <0.05 |
| LV/BW, ml/kg | 61.3 ± 1.0 | 75.9 ± 1.2 | <0.01 |
| Sa, $cm^2$ | 770 ± 11 | 629 ± 44 | <0.01 |
| Sa/BW, $cm^2$/g | 29.0 ± 1.4 | 28.0 ± 0.9 | NS |
| $\bar{v}$, $\mu m^3 \times 10^4$ | 3.0 ± 0.1 | 7.4 ± 0.3 | <0.01 |
| $N \times 10^6$ | 24.2 ± 2.0 | 9.3 ± 0.8 | <0.01 |
| **Age 40 days** | | | |
| LV, ml | 5.6 ± 0.3 | 5.2 ± 0.4 | NS |
| LV/BW, ml/kg | 39.1 ± 0.8 | 48.9 ± 3.0 | <0.01 |
| Sa, $cm^2$ | 2,446 ± 90 | 1,829 ± 135 | <0.01 |
| Sa/BW, $cm^2$/g | 17.0 ± 0.7 | 17.3 ± 0.8 | NS |
| $\bar{v}$, $\mu m^3 \times 10^4$ | 6.1 ± 0.7 | 9.5 ± 0.8 | <0.01 |
| $N \times 10^6$ | 41.0 ± 2.1 | 25.5 ± 1.6 | <0.01 |

LV = lung volume; BW = body weight; Sa = gas-exchange surface area; $\bar{v}$ = average volume of an alveolus; $N$ = number of alveoli per rat; NS = p > 0.05. Values are mean ± SE. From *Am. J. Physiol.* 1991. 261:L370:77, with permission.)

We have proposed that, much as in emphysema where alveolar septa have been destroyed, resulting in premature closure of conducting airways (81), diminished septal attachments to conducting airways in 13% $O_2$-breathing rats might maintain their lung volume equal to that of the larger air-breathing rats by allowing premature closure of conducting airways and consequent air-trapping. If the large gas-exchange units reported to be present in highlanders (24, 83) represent impaired septation, the resulting fewer septal attachments to conducting airways could be responsible for the high residual volume, low maximum expiratory flow rate per lung volume, and low upstream conductance in highlanders compared with lowlanders (14, 50). We agree there is dysanaptic lung growth when organisms that septate postnatally develop in a low $P_{O_2}$ (50), but we propose that it is the fewer alveolar attachments to conducting airways resulting in less radial traction, rather than a too large gas-exchange region,

**Table 3**    Lung parameters: comparison of air-breathing rats to rats maintained in 13% $O_2$ from age 23 days to age 43 days

| Parameter | Air | | 13% $O_2$ | P |
|---|---|---|---|---|
| | Age 23 days | Age 44 days | Age 44 days | |
| LV, ml | 2.3 ± 0.1 | 6.7 ± 0.2 | 8.1 ± 0.3 | <0.01 |
| Sa, cm² | 1,199 ± 55 | 2952 ± 154 | 3,690 ± 167 | <0.01 |
| $\bar{v}$, $\mu m^3 \times 10^4$ | 3.9 ± 0.3 | 7.7 ± 0.5 | 9.8 ± 0.7 | <0.05 |
| $N \times 10^6$ | 30.5 ± 0.9 | 39.7 ± 1.4 | 42.9 ± 2.6 | <0.01 |

Rats were born from air-breathing dams and were maintained in air until age 23 days. They were then divided into two groups; rats in one group continued to remain in air and rats in the other group were placed in 13% $O_2$. Abbreviations and symbols as in Table 2; P values are for the difference between age 44 day old rats. (From *Am. J. Physiol.* 1991. 261:L370:77, with permission.)

that is responsible for the large residual volume and low upstream conductance found in highlanders.

The depressing effect 13% $O_2$ exposure from birth to age 44 days has on absolute Sa is quite different from the finding by several investigators that exposure to a low $P_{O_2}$ after the normal period of septation ends increases absolute Sa (5, 22, 68). This increase in Sa is brought about by a faster rate of alveolus formation and by the presence of larger alveoli (Table 3). It is not known if the larger alveoli reflect enlargement of alveoli present before exposure to a low $P_{O_2}$, the formation of larger alveoli during exposure to a low $P_{O_2}$, or both processes.

The different lung responses to a low $P_{O_2}$ between rats exposed during the period of septation and those exposed after the period of septation indicate that lung mechanisms for increasing Sa exhibit quite important developmentally regulated responses to environmental signals. Alternatively, these age-dependent responses to hypoxia could reflect different susceptibility to harmful effects of hypoxia, i.e. lung development in the early postnatal period could be more susceptible than lung development in older animals to the untoward effects of hypoxia.

Finally, it must be recalled that living at high altitude entails much more than simply exposure to a low $P_{O_2}$, as is usual in laboratory experiments. First, high altitude natives, human and animal, reflect the effects of generations of adaptation to, and selection for, the conditions at high altitude. Secondly, living at high altitude entails more than exposure to a low $P_{O_2}$; it may include a different climate, different food, and different activity life-style than lowlanders experience.

## CORTICOSTEROID HORMONES

The prescient suggestion by Buckingham et al (17) that corticosteroid hormones might be physiological modulators of fetal lung development led to great interest in their effect on such development, especially of the surfactant system. There was not a concomitant interest in the possibility that these hormones might play a role in postnatal lung development. However, the clear demonstration by Burri et al (18, 20) that in some species alveolarization is an early postnatal rather than a prenatal event raised the possibility that corticosteroid hormones, which strongly influence the postnatal development of the gastrointestinal system (49), the lung's anlage, might also influence the postnatal architectural development of the lung. Several considerations supported this possibility. The time-course of alveolarization in the rats (18, 20) and the time-course of changes in the serum concentration of corticosterone (the major glucocorticoid in the rat) (48) made it apparent that septation takes place during a trough in the serum concentration of corticosterone, whereas thinning of the alveolar walls is accelerated as the serum concentration of this hormone arises. The formation and elongation of structures like alveolar septa are brought about by folding epithelial sheets into ridges, a process that in part requires epithelial cell division, and glucocorticosteroids inhibit cell division in several tissues (61) including the lung (64, 65). In short, from the inhibitory effect glucocorticosteroids have on lung cell division (64, 65), and because of the timing of the process of septation in rats (18, 20) in relation to the pattern and timing of changes in the serum concentration of corticosterone in rats (48), it was reasoned that corticosterone might normally be involved in septation and thinning of the alveolar wall.

To test the possibility that corticosteroid hormones affect septation, dexamethasone, a synthetic glucocorticosteroid hormone, was administered to rats from age day 4 through age day 13. The intent was to maintain a high serum corticosteroid concentration during the period in which septation normally occurs instead of allowing that period to pass with, as is normal, a low serum concentration of glucocorticosteroids. The effect of this manipulation, assessed by measuring $L_m$ of the lung's gas-exchange units, indicated treatment with dexamethasone impaired septation; furthermore, and of great importance, the impairment persisted after dexamethasone was discontinued at age 14 days to age 60 days, i.e. 46 days after dexamethasone was discontinued (65). These finding were confirmed by others, and the time during which septation still had not occurred was extended to age 90 days, 76 days after the drug was discontinued (82). Because of the shortcomings of using $L_m$ to assess alveolar dimensions, these experiments were repeated, and the original findings and interpretations confirmed, in experiments in which alveoli were identified from serial lung sections and chosen for analysis using an unbiased selection method (10).

Blanco & Frank have reported that when dexamethasone is administered to rats for 10 days, beginning at age 18 days, it does not affect Sa, alveolar number, or alveolar volume (8). However, those authors do not provide information on the effect the dose of dexamethasone they used had on the rats' body weight. This information is important because between age 4 and 14 days there is a clear relation between the dose of dexamethasone and its effect on body weight and on the dimensions of terminal gas-exchange units (65). Furthermore, adrenalectomy in adult rats increases lung weight without a change in the lung's ratio of wet-to-dry weight (59), and adrenalectomy results in enlargement of the lung's gas-exchange surface area (1). Thus without information to show that the dose of dexamethasone used had some effect such as slowing the developmental increase in body weight, the conclusion by Blanco & Frank (8) that dexamethasone does not influence Sa or alveolar number after the early postnatal period is, in our opinion, not yet warranted and is at odds with the work of others (1).

Neither the cellular nor molecular mechanism by which dexamethasone impairs septation is apparent. However, there may be some useful clues. One of the hallmarks of the normal architectural maturation of the gas-exchange region during the period of septation is thinning and diminished cellular content of its wall (64). Within 48 h of the first of two treatments with dexamethasone, begun on postnatal day 4, virtually as much alveolar wall thinning occurred as normally takes place in diluent-treated rats between postnatal day 4 and 14 (the entire period of septation) (64). This rapid wall thinning was accompanied by an equally rapid development of a 30–40% lower volume of fibroblasts in the gas-exchange wall of rats treated with dexamethasone compared with rats treated with diluent; there was an associated fall in lipid-ladened fibroblasts of the volume fraction of lipid-inclusions they contained, which are the storage sites in the lung of vitamin A (73) (see below).

The molecular basis for dexamethasone's inhibition of septation is unknown, as is the cellular basis, but some observations that provide clues are worth mentioning. There are three proteins whose expression peaks in the rat lung during the time septation normally occurs and whose actions in other cell systems indicate that they influence developmental events; these are a 14-kDa β-galactoside-binding protein (27, 75), a cellular retinol-binding protein (74), and a cellular retinoic acid-binding protein (74). Dexamethasone treatment of neonatal rats blunts the expression in the lung of the β-galactoside-binding protein (27), and the expression in lung of cellular retinol-binding protein is diminished within hours of treating adult rats with dexamethasone (79). Retinoic acid, a metabolite of vitamin A, affects developmental events (43) and increases elastin synthesis by lipid-ladened fibroblasts (60), a process considered important for septation and one that markedly increases in rat lung during septation (75). Retinoids and glucocorticosteroids may exhibit mutually antagonistic actions (40, 42, 79), and retinoids are important regulatory signaling molecules for developmental events (43). Furthermore, infants with bronchopulmonary dysplasia (BPD) are commonly treated with glucocorticosteroid hormones (53); many infants with BPD have lower plasma concentration of retinol than premature infants without BPD (51, 86), and the lungs of infants with BPD fail to septate (62, 87).

## RETINOIC ACID AND THE POSTNATAL FORMATION OF ALVEOLI

The observations set forth in the preceding paragraph led to the hypothesis that treatment of newborn rats with retinoic acid would prevent the dexamethasone-induced inhibition of septation. To test this, newborn rats were divided into four groups and given one of the following treatments: diluent, dexamethasone, retinoic acid, or retinoic acid plus dexamethasone (GD Massaro & D Massaro, unpublished data). Dexamethasone treatment, as usual, almost completely prevented septation. Treatment with retinoic acid, begun at age 3 days, 1 day before starting the administration of dexamethasone and continuing during treatment with dexamethasone from age 4 through 13 days, largely prevented the inhibition of septation by dexamethasone; importantly, the body mass-specific gas-exchange surface area was identical to that in diluent-treated rats.

The most important potential clinical relevance of the inhibitory effect of dexamethasone on septation and its prevention by retinoic acid pertains to the use of glucocorticosteroid hormones as part of the treatment of BPD; this treatment (53) occurs during the period when human lungs normally septate (57, 100). Based on the ability of retinoic acid to prevent the inhibition of septation by dexamethasone, the possible inhibitory effect of corticosteroid treatment on septation in these infants may be heightened because prematurely born infants have a lower concentration of retinol in their umbilical vein blood than term infants do, and the blood concentration of retinol is lower at birth and at age 21 days in infants who develop BPD than in infants who do not develop BPD (51, 86).

Retinoic acid administered to otherwise untreated rats increased the number of alveoli formed but induced the formation of smaller alveoli than were formed in diluent-treated rats; however, in spite of their increased number, the induction of smaller alveoli prevented an increase in gas-exchange surface area compared to diluent-treated rats. This combination of findings—more alveoli, smaller alveoli, and no difference in gas-exchange surface area—suggests the operation of a control mechanism that inhibits the size of alveoli formed under the influence of a pharmacological agent that induces an increase in the number of alveoli formed in the absence of a metabolic need for a larger gas-exchange surface area. Put somewhat differently, we envisage two distinct processes: eruption of a septum and its elongation. We suggest eruption and elongation have different regulators; retinoic acid induces the eruption of a septum, but other agents or conditions regulate its length. In the face of excess eruptions, without a need for extra Sa, length is curtailed. Our interpretation also implies two stages of regulation in the formation of alveoli; one level of regulation is a yes or no decision to form a septum, the other regulation level is to determine the length of the septum.

## CODA

The lung's gas-exchange surface and its component parts, the pulmonary alveoli, must both be of a sufficient and appropriate size to meet the organism's requirements for the uptake of oxygen and elimination of carbon dioxide. The introduction, development, and use of quantitative morphology (morphometry), based on the theory of stereology by Weibel and his associates, have resulted in a marked increase in our understanding of the lung's contribution to the flow of oxygen from the inspired air to the molecules on the inner membrane of mitochondria. The more recent development of new methods by Cruz-Orive (32), Cruz-Orive & Weibel (33), and Gundersen et al (44–46) has allowed the applications of unbiased, accurate, and more sensitive methods to determine the size and, hence, number of alveoli. This approach has begun to increase our understanding of how alveoli are formed and how their formation is regulated. We think the continued application of these methods, buttressed with experiments at the cellular and molecular level, will result in a more fundamental understanding of how the formation of alveoli and the size of the gas-exchange surface area are regulated. This new information holds the promise of translation into the induction of the formation of alveoli for therapeutic purposes.

ACKNOWLEDGMENTS

This work is supported in part by grants from the National Heart, Lung, and Blood Institute HL37666 and HL20366 and by a bequest from the Wiggins Family.

## Literature Cited

1. Adkisson VT, Callas G. 1982. Morphometric changes in the lungs of rats following adrenalectomy supplemented by desiccated thyroid. *Anat. Rec.* 203: 147–56

2. Alcorn DG, Adamson TM, Maloney JE, Robinson PM. 1981. A morphologic and morphometric analysis of fetal lung development in the sheep. *Anat. Rec.* 201: 655–67

3. Amy RW, Bowes D, Burri PH, Haines J, Thurlbeck WM. 1977. Postnatal growth of the mouse lung. *J. Anat.* 124:131–51

4. Ballard PL, Klein AH, Fisher DA. 1983. Thyroid hormones and plasma corticosteroid binding globin capacity in fetal and newborn lambs. *Endocrinology* 113:1197–200

5. Bartlett D Jr. 1970. Postnatal growth of the mammalian lung: influence of low and high oxygen tensions. *Respir. Physiol.* 9:58–64

6. Batenburg JJ. 1992. Surfactant phospholipids: synthesis and storage. *Am. J. Physiol.* 262:L367–85

7. Bert P. 1878. *Barometric Pressure. Researches in Experimental Physiology.* Transl. MA Hitchock, FA Hitchcock, 1943. Columbus, Ohio: College Book Co. (From French)

8. Blanco LN, Frank L. 1993. The formation of alveoli in rat lung during the third and fourth postnatal weeks: effect of hyperoxia, dexamethasone, and deferoxamine. *Pediatr. Res.* 34:334–40

9. Blanco LN, Massaro D, Massaro GD. 1991. Alveolar size, number, and surface area: developmentally dependent response to 13% $O_2$. *Am. J. Physiol.* 261:L370–77

10. Blanco LN, Massaro GD, Massaro D. 1989. Alveolar dimensions and number: developmental and hormonal regulation. *Am. J. Physiol.* 257:L240–47

11. Bolender RP, Hyde DM, De Hoff RT. 1993. Lung morphometry: a new generation of tools and experiments for organ, tissue, cell, and molecular biology. *Am. J. Physiol.* 265: L521–48

12. Boyden EA, Tompsett DH. 1961. The postnatal growth of the lung in the dog. *Acta Anat.* 47:185–215

13. Boyden EA, Tompsett DH. 1965. The changing patterns of the developing lungs of infants. *Acta Anat.* 61:164–92

14. Brody JS, Lahiri S, Simpser M, Motoyama EK, Velasquez T. 1977. Lung elasticity and airways dyamics in Peruvian natives to high altitude. *J. Appl. Physiol.* 42:245–51

15. Brody JS, Thurlbeck WM. 1986. Development, growth, and aging of the lung. In *Handbook of Physiology. The Respiratory System*, ed. PT Macklem, J Mead, 3:355–86. Bethesda, MD: Am. Physiol. Soc. 386 pp.

16. Bucher JR, Roberts RJ. 1981. The development of the newborn rat lung in hyperoxia: a dose response study of lung growth, maturation, and changes in antioxidant enzyme activity. *Pediatr. Res.* 15:999–1008

17. Buckingham S, McNary WF, Sommers SC, Rothschild J. 1968. Is lung an analog of Moog's developing intestine? Phosphatases and pulmonary alveolar differentiation in fetal rabbits. *Fed. Proc.* 27:328

18. Burri PH. 1974. The postnatal growth of the rat lung. III. Morphology. *Anat. Rec.* 180:77–98

19. Burri PH. 1985. Development and growth of the human lung. In *Handbook of Physiology. The Respiratory System*, ed. AP Fishman, AB Fisher, 1:1–46. Bethesda, MD: Am. Physiol. Soc. 572 pp.

20. Burri PH, Dbaly J, Weibel ER. 1974. The postnatal growth of the rat lung. I. Morphometry. *Anat. Rec.* 178:711–30

21. Burri PH, Maschopulos M. 1992. Structural analysis of fetal rat lung development. *Anat. Rec.* 234:399–418

22. Burri PH, Weibel ER. 1971. Morphometric estimation of pulmonary diffusion capacity. II. Effect of $PO_2$ on the growing lung. Adaption of the growing rat lung to hypoxia and hyperoxia. *Respir. Physiol.* 11:247–64

23. Campbell H, Tomkeieff SI. 1952. Calculation of internal surface of a lung. *Nature* 170:117

24. Campos Rey De Castro J, Iglesias B. 1956. Mechanisms of natural acclimatization: preliminary report on anatomic studies at high altitudes. *US Air Force Sch. Aviation Med. Rep. 55–97*, San Antonio, TX

25. Castleman WL, Lay JC. 1990. Morphometric and ultrastructural study of postnatal lung growth and development in calves. *Am. J. Vet. Res.* 51: 789–95

26. Chander A, Fisher AB. 1990. Regulation of lung surfactant secretion. *Am. J. Physiol.* 258:L241–53

27. Clerch LB, Whitney P, Massaro D. 1989. Rat lung lectin gene expression is regulated developmentally and by dexamethasone. *Am. J. Physiol.* 256: C501–5

28. Collins MH, Kleinerman J, Moessinger AC, Collins AH, James LS, Blanc WA. 1986. Morphometric analysis of the growth of the normal fetal guinea pig lung. *Anat. Rec.* 216:381–91

29. Connolly DT, Stoddard BL, Harakas NK, Feder J. 1987. Human fibroblast-derived growth factor is a mitogen and chemoattractant for endothelial cells. *Biochem. Biophys. Res. Commun.* 144: 705–12

30. Crapo JD, Barry BE, Gehr P, Bachofen M, Weibel ER. 1982. Cell number and

cell characteristics of the normal human lung. *Am. Rev. Respir. Dis.* 125:740–45

31. Crouch, E. 1990. Pathobiology of pulmonary fibrosis. *Am. J. Physiol.* 259: L519–84

32. Cruz-Orive LM. 1987. Particle number can be estimated using a disector of unknown thickness: the selector. *J. Microsc. (Oxford)* 145:121–42

33. Cruz-Orive LM, Weibel ER. 1981. Sampling designs for stereology. *J. Microsc. (Oxford)* 122:235–57

34. Davies G, Reid L. 1970. Growth of the alveoli and pulmonary arteries in childhood. *Thorax* 25:669–81

35. Dingler EC. 1958. Wachstrum der Lung nach der Geburt. *Acta Anat. (Suppl. 30)* 32:1–86

36. Dubruil G, Lacoste A, Raymond R. 1936. Observations sur le development du poumon humain. *Bull. Histol. Appl. Physiol. Pathol. Tech. Microsc.* 13:135–45

37. Engle S. 1953. The structure of the respiratory tissue in the newly born. *Acta Anat.* 19:353–65

38. Evans MJ, Shami SG. 1989. Lung cell kinetics. In *Lung Cell Biology*, ed. D. Massaro, pp. 1–36. New York: Dekker

39. Frank L, Sosenko IRS. 1987. Prenatal development of lung antioxidant enzymes in four species. *J. Pediatr.* 110: 106–10

40. Franckhauser J, Antras-Ferry J, Robin P, Robin D, Forest C. 1994. Glucocorticoids antagonize retinoic acid stimulation of pepck gene transcription in 3T3-F442A adipocytes. *Cell. Mol. Biol.* 40:723–29

41. Goodman BE, Crandall ED. 1982. Dome formation in primary cultured monolayers of alveolar epithelial cells. *Am. J. Physiol.* 243:C96–100

42. Goradeski GI, Eckert RL, Utian WH, Sheean L, Rorke EA. 1989. Retinoids, sex steroids and glucocorticoids regulate ectocervical cell envelope formation but not the level of the envelope precursor, involucrin. *Differentiation* 42:75–80

43. Gudas LJ. 1994. Retinoids and vertebrate development. *J. Biol. Chem.* 269: 15399–402

44. Gundersen HJG, Bagger P, Bendtsen TF, Evans SM, Korbo L, et al. 1988. The new stereological tools: disector, fractionator, nucleator and point sampled intercepts and their use in pathological research and diagnosis. *Acta Pathol. Microbiol. Immunol. Scand.* 96: 857–81

45. Gundersen HJG, Bendtsen TF, Korbo L, Marcussen N, Moller A, et al. 1988. Some new, simple and efficient stereological methods and their use in pathological research and diagnosis. *APMIS* 96:379–94

46. Gundersen HJG, Jensen EB. 1985. Stereological estimation of the volume-weighted mean volume of arbitrary particles observed on random sections. *J. Microsc. (Oxford)* 138:127–42

47. Haies DM, Gil J, Weibel ER. 1981. Morphometric study of rat lung cells. *Am. Rev. Respir. Dis.* 123:533–41

48. Henning SJ. 1978. Plasma concentration of total and free corticosterone during development in the rat. *Am. J. Physiol.* 235:E451–56

49. Henning SJ. 1981. Postnatal development: coordination of feeding, digestion, and metabolism. *Am. J. Physiol.* 241: G199–14

50. Hurtado H. 1964. Animals in high altitudes: resident man. In *Handbook of Physiology. Adaptation to the Environment*, ed. DB Dill, EF Adolph, Sect. 4, 843–60. Washington, DC: Am. Physiol. Soc. 1056 pp.

51. Hustead VA, Gutcher GR, Anderson SA, Zachman RD. 1984. Relationship of vitamin A (retinol) status to lung disease in the preterm infant. *J. Pediatr.* 105:610–15

52. Jones CT. 1974. Corticosteroid concentrations in the plasma of fetal and maternal guinea pigs during gestation. *Endocrinology* 95:1129–33

53. Kari MA, Heinonen K, Ikonen RS, Koivisto M, Raivo KO. 1993. Dexamethasone treatment for preterm infants at risk for bronchopulmonary dysplasia. *Arch. Dis. Child.* 68:566–69

54. Kistler GS, Caldwell PRB, Weibel ER. 1966. Pulmonary pathology of oxygen toxicity. Part II: electron microscopic and morphometric study of rat lungs exposed to 97% $O_2$ at 258 torr (27,000 feet). *Aerospace Med. Res. Lab., AMRL, Annu. Summary Rep. No. 2*

55. Kitterman JA, Liggins GC, Campos GA, Clements JA, Forster CS, et al. 1981. Prepartum maturation of the lung: relation to cortisol. *J. Appl. Physiol.* 51:384–90

56. Kurtz SM, Feldman JD. 1962. Experimental studies on the formation of glomerular basement membrane. *J. Ultrastruct. Res.* 6:19–27

57. Langston C, Kida K, Reed M, Thurlbeck WM. 1984. Human lung growth in late gestation and in the neonate. *Am. Rev. Respir. Dis.* 129:607–13

58. Lechner AJ, Banchero N. 1982. Advanced pulmonary development in newborn guinea pigs (*Cavia porcellus*). *Am. J. Anat.* 163:235–46

59. Liebowitz D, Massaro GD, Massaro D. 1984. Adrenalectomy and surfactant in adult rats. *J. Appl. Physiol. Resp. Environ. Exercise Physiol.* 56:564–67

60. Liu R, Harvey CS, McGowan SE. 1993. Retinoic acid increases elastin in neonatal rat lung fibroblast cultures. *Am. J. Physiol.* 265:L430–37

61. Loeb JN. 1976. Corticosteroids and growth. *New Engl. J. Med.* 295:547–52

62. Margraf LR, Tomashefski JR Jr, Bruce MC, Dahms BB. 1991. Morphometric analysis of the lung in bronchopulmonary dysplasia. *Am. Rev. Respir. Dis.* 143:391–400

63. Mason RJ, Williams MC, Widdicombe JH, Sanders MJ, Misfeldt DS, Berry LC Jr. 1982. Transepithelial transport by pulmonary alveolar type II cells in culture. *Proc. Natl. Acad. Sci. USA* 79:6033–37

64. Massaro D, Massaro GD. 1986. Dexamethasone accelerates postnatal alveolar wall thinning and alters wall com- position. *Am. J. Physiol.* 251:R218–14

65. Massaro D, Teich N, Maxwell S, Massaro GD, Whitney J. 1985. Postnatal development of alveoli: regulation and evidence for a critical period in rats. *J. Clin. Invest.* 76:1297–305

66. Massaro GD, Massaro, D. 1992. Formation of alveoli in rats: postnatal effect of prenatal dexamethasone. *Am. J. Physiol.* 263:L37–41

67. Massaro GD, Massaro D. 1993. Postnatal lung growth: evidence that the gas-exchange region grows fastest at the periphery. *Am. J. Physiol.* 265:L319–22

68. Massaro GD, Olivier J, Dzikowski C, Massaro D. 1990. Postnatal development of lung alveoli: suppression by 13% $O_2$ and a critical period. *Am. J. Physiol.* 258:L321–27

69. McDonald JA. 1989. Receptors for extracellular matrix components. *Am. J. Physiol.* 257:L331–37

70. Mercer RR, Laco JM, Crapo JD. 1987. Three-dimensional reconstruction of alveoli in the rat lung for pressure-volume relationships. *J. Appl. Physiol.* 62:1480–87

71. Morishige WK, Joun NS. 1982. Influence of glucocorticoids on postnatal lung development in the rat: possible modulation by thyroid hormones. *Endocrinology* 111:1587–94

72. Mortola JP, Morgan CA, Virgona V. 1986. Respiratory adaptation to chronic hypoxia in newborn rats. *J. Appl. Physiol.* 61:1329–36

73. Okabe T, Yorifuji H, Yamada E. 1984. Isolation and characterization of vitamin A-storing lung cells. *Exp. Cell Res.* 154:125–35

74. Ong D, Chytil F. 1976. Changes in the levels of cellular retinol-and retinoic-acid-binding proteins of liver and lung during perinatal development of rat. *Proc. Natl. Acad. Sci. USA* 73:3976–78

75. Powell JT, Whitney PL. 1980. Postnatal development of rat lung: changes in lung lectin, elastin, acetylcholinesterase and other enzymes. *Biochem. J.* 188:1–8

76. Randell SH, Mercer RR, Young SL. 1989. Postnatal growth of pulmonary acini and alveoli in normal and oxygen-exposed rats studied by serial section reconstructions. *Am. J. Anat.* 186:55–68

77. Randell SH, Mercer RR, Young SL. 1990. Neonatal hyperoxia alters the pulmonary alveolar and capillary structure of 40-day old rats. *Am. J. Pathol.* 136:1259–66

78. Reid L. 1967. The embryology of the lung. In *Development of the Lung,* ed. AVS de Reuck, R Porter, pp. 109–30. Boston: Little, Brown & Co.

79. Rush MG, Riaz-Ul-Haq, Chytil F. 1991. Opposing effects of retinoic acid and dexamethasone on cellular retinol-binding protein ribonucleic acid levels in the rat. *Endocrinology* 129:705–9

80. Ryan JW. 1989. Peptidase enzymes of the pulmonary vascular surface. *Am. J. Physiol.* 257:L53–60

81. Saetta M, Ghezzo H, Kim WD, King M, Angus GE, et al. 1985. Loss of alveolar attachments in smokers. A morphometric correlate of lung function impairment. *Am. Rev. Respir. Dis.* 132:894–900

82. Sahebjami H, Domino M. 1989. Effects of postnatal dexamethasone treatment on development of alveoli in adult rats. *Exp. Lung Res.* 15:961–73

83. Saldana M, Garcia-Oyola E. 1970. Morphometry of the high altitude lung. *Lab. Invest.* 22:509

84. Scherle WA. 1970. A simple method for volumetry of organs in quantitative stereology. *Mikroskopie* 26:57–60

85. Schwinger G, Weibel ER, Kaplan HP. 1967. Pulmonary pathology of oxygen toxicity. Part III: electron microscopic and morphometric study of dog and monkey lungs exposed to 98% $O_2$ at 258 torr for 7 months and followed by 1 month recovery in room air. *Aerospace Med. Res. Lab., AMRL. Interim Sci. Rep. January*

86. Shenai JP, Chytil F, Stahlman MT. 1985. Vitamin A status of neonates with bronchopulmonary dysplasia. *Pediatr. Res.* 19:185–89

87. Sobonya RE, Logrinoff MM, Taussig

LM, Theriault A. 1982. Morphometric analysis of the lung in prolonged bronchopulmonary dysplasia. *Pediatr. Res.* 16:969–72

88. Sosenko IRS, Frank L. 1987. Guinea pig lung development: surfactant, morphology and premature viability. *Pediatr. Res.* 21:427–31

89. Sterio DC. 1984. The unbiased estimation of the number and sizes of arbitrary particles using the disector. *J. Microsc. (Oxford)* 134:7–136

90. Tenney SM, Remmers JE. 1963. Comparative quantitative morphology of the mammalian lung diffusing area. *Nature* 197:54–56

91. Tenney SM, Remmers JE. 1966. Alveolar dimensions in the lungs of animals raised at high altitude. *J. Appl. Physiol.* 21:1328

92. Thurlbeck WM. 1975. Postnatal growth and development of the lung. *Am. Rev. Respir. Dis.* 111:803–44

93. Tomkeiff SI. 1945. Linear intercepts, areas and volumes. *Nature* 155:24 (correction p.107)

94. Vaccaro C, Brody JS. 1978. Ultrastructure of developing alveoli. I. The role of the interstitial fibroblast. *Anat. Rec.* 192:467–80

95. Weibel ER. 1979. *Stereological Methods.* 1:9–196. New York: Academic

96. Weibel ER, Gomez DM. 1962. A principle for counting tissue structures on random sections. *J. Appl. Physiol.* 17: 343–48

97. Winkler GC, Cheville NF. 1984. The neonatal porcine lung: ultrastructural morphology and postnatal development of the terminal airways and alveolar region. *Anat. Rec.* 210:303–13

98. Winkler GC, Cheville NF. 1985. Morphometry of postnatal development in the porcine lung. *Anat. Rec.* 211:427–33

99. Wright JR. 1990. Clearance and recycling of pulmonary surfactant. *Am. J. Physiol.* 259:L1–12

100. Zeltner TB, Burri PH. 1987. The postnatal development and growth of the human lung. II. Morphology. *Respir. Physiol.* 67:269–82

Annu. Rev. Physiol. 1996. 58:93–113

# MORPHOGENESIS OF THE LUNG: Control of Embryonic and Fetal Branching

*S. Robert Hilfer*

Department of Biology, Temple University, Philadelphia, Pennsylvania 19122

KEY WORDS    cytoskeleton, extracellular matrix, growth factors, gene expression, saccule formation

### ABSTRACT

Lung development differs in the embryo and fetus with regard to branching pattern and organization of the epithelial cells. The surrounding mesodermal component, the capsule, has long been known to play a role in branching. As a result of recent analyses of distribution of components of the extracellular matrix coupled with interference with their expression, we are beginning to understand how branching is controlled. Insoluble macromolecules of the basal lamina and deeper extracellular matrix may act as physical barriers or traps to sequester soluble components. The soluble growth factors activate genes regulating cell proliferation.

## INTRODUCTION

Development of the mammalian lung can be divided into two processes: formation first of the airways and then of the saccular alveolar endings. The first process occurs by dichotomous branching of buds from the distal end of the trachea and proceeds by the formation of a series of branch points. Branching results in the establishment of tubules with decreasing diameter, which become the successive generations of bronchi (Figure 1). This process is called centrifugal because branching proceeds from the center in an outwardly radiating direction. The second process traditionally is described as beginning near the periphery of the late fetal lung and proceeding more or less centripetally (8) as alveolar sacs and then alveoli are formed along the distal-most branches of the bronchial tree (Figure 2). This process also may be centrifugal (9); therefore, it is more accurate to describe the two processes as dichotomous branching and saccule formation.

93

0066–4278/96/0315–0093$08.00

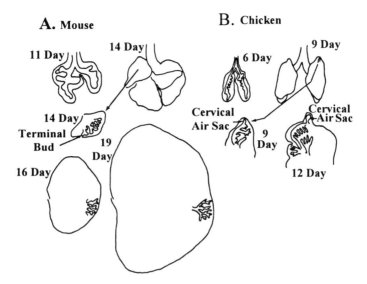

*Figure 1* Embryonic branching pattern in mouse and chicken. (*A*) The branches that form from primary bronchi in the day 11 mouse set the pattern of the lobes. These secondary bronchi branch many times so that a tree-like structure is formed by day 14. The branches at day 16 mark the end of the pseudoglandular phase; additional branching produces the endings that produce alveolar sacs by day 19. (*B*) By day 6 in the chicken, several secondary branches have formed from each elongated primary bronchus. Additional branching produces two types of terminal buds, those that will form part of the respiratory region and a few that will not branch again but will become air storage sacs. By day 9 the cervical air sac is established and by day 12 tertiary bronchi grow toward their neighbors to establish the loops that will be connected by the thin respiratory passages called air capillaries. (Modified with permission from Reference 21.)

Lung development also is described as occurring in four morphological phases or stages. The basic branching pattern is established during the embryonic or pseudoglandular stage. In the young fetus, lung development enters the second or canalicular stage in which the narrower bronchial passageways are formed by continued centrifugal branching. Close to birth, the third or saccular stage begins, with the expansion of the distal branches into alveolar sacs. The final or alveolar stage begins at various times in different mammals—from late fetal development in some species to after birth in mouse and rat. Additional alveolar sacs are formed along the distal branches and, finally, mature alveoli are formed by outpouching of the alveolar sacs.

These stages are characterized by distinctive morphological changes in both the epithelium of the endodermal lining and in the surrounding mesodermal covering. During the embryonic stage, the branching pattern establishes the number of lobes in the left and right lungs (Figure 1*A*). The branches are relatively large, with a clearly visible lumen surrounded by a pseudostratified epithelium of relatively tall cells. The mesoderm consists of a dense mesenchyme adhering to the basal surfaces of the epithelial cells, with oriented collagen fibrils along established branches (67). During the canalicular stage, the pseudostratified epithelium forms tubules so narrow that their lumina may not be visible by light microscopy. The terminal buds, however, are somewhat larger. The mesenchyme becomes divided into dense, cellular partitions or septa between the branches. The saccular stage is marked by the appearance of specialized epithelial cell types in the alveolar sacs (Figure 2B). Flattened type I pneumocytes form the lining of these expanded regions with nests of type II pneumocytes containing lamellar bodies. Expansion of the alveolar sacs is accompanied by thinning of the mesenchymal septa and an increase in the amount of extracellular matrix. This septal thinning continues in the alveolar stage to form the very thin and elastic connective tissue partitions surrounding alveoli, whereas denser connective tissue containing cartilage and smooth muscle surrounds the airways. These later stages of branching are accompanied by a concomitant development of a rich vascular supply surrounding the respiratory surfaces.

There is reason to believe that the processes of dichotomous branching and saccule formation are controlled differently based upon several lines of evidence (15a, 31a). The mesenchyme plays a role in branching, probably through changes in the composition of the extracellular matrix and macromolecules associated with epithelial cell surfaces. These macromolecules may act as structural elements in the processes of branching and cell differentiation. They undoubtedly also play a role in sequestering growth factors and other systemic factors through their binding sites. The goal of this review is to compare the evidence that has accumulated on the changes that occur during dichotomous branching and saccule formation in the lung, to relate the data to knowledge on the control of branching in similar organ primordia, and to recognize gaps in the data on lung branching that need to be filled to achieve an understanding of how the processes are controlled.

## CONTROL OF EMBRYONIC BRANCHING

The analysis of the initial branching pattern by experimental intervention has used primarily mouse and rat embryos, with some work in the chicken, which has a different branching pattern. In addition to the respiratory tree, the bird lung has a series of air sacs that store inspired air and pass it over the gas exchange surfaces during expiration. Gas exchange occurs during expiration as well as inspiration because the respiratory region consists of loops rather than blind sacs. These are formed as long branches from the primary bronchi, with secondary and tertiary branches forming cross connections (Figure 1B).

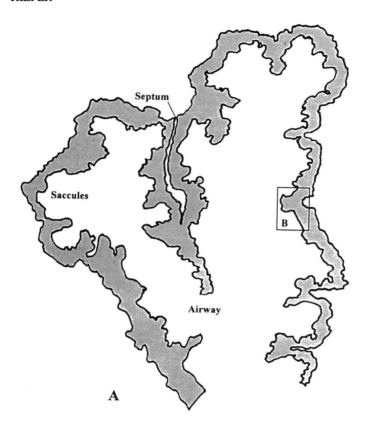

In spite of the different branching patterns, similar mechanisms appear to be involved in initiating and establishing branch points.

## Mesenchymal Involvement in Branching

The realization that the mesodermal component of the lung is required for development dates at least to the work of Rudnick (43). Chicken lung buds grafted to the extraembryonic membranes branch only if mesenchyme is included. As branching progresses, only the terminal buds are capable of forming new branches, whereas the proximal tubules become stabilized. Substitution of tracheal mesenchyme for that of the bronchial buds results in inhibition of further branching (4, 67). Furthermore, the amount of branching is directly proportional to the quantity of bronchial mesenchyme surrounding the buds (4, 31). Mesenchymes from gut-related primordia alter the branching pattern of chicken lung buds to resemble that of the donor organ (13), whereas ho-

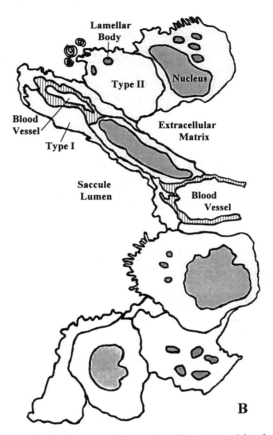

*Figure 2*  Saccule formation in the mouse and the major cell types comprising the epithelial wall. Diagrams are based upon tracings of transmission electron micrographs at low and high magnification. (A) Two branches near the periphery of a lung from a 19 day fetus. The epithelium is indented by thin partitions. The septum between the two main branches also is thin. (B) Enlargement of a region such as that boxed in *A*. The lumenal surface is bounded by flattened type I pneumocytes and cuboidal type II pneumocytes, which contain lamellar bodies. A thin septum between two saccules contains a narrow blood vessel.

mologous (bronchial) mesenchyme is necessary for branching of mouse bronchial buds (59, 61).

Although the proximal branches become stabilized once they are formed, even the trachea can be stimulated to resume branching and to form a supernumerary lung by replacement of its normal mesodermal covering with bronchial mesenchyme (4). Mesenchymes from some nonrespiratory sources such

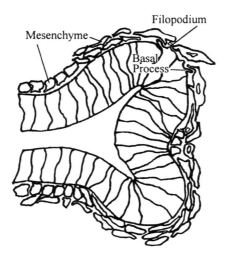

*Figure 3* Diagrammatic representation of terminal buds in a 16-day mouse lung, based upon tracings of light and transmission electron micrographs. Cuboidal mesenchymal cells are packed along established bronchi. Mesenchymal cells at the tips are flattened. Both mesenchymal and epithelial cells have cytoplasmic extensions that penetrate the discontinuous basal lamina (not drawn) at the buds.

as salivary and stomach primordia can stimulate the trachea to form a supernumerary bud; however, branching does not occur (67).

## Role of Extracellular Matrix

The apparent specificity of bronchial mesenchyme to cause branching of bronchial buds and to elicit formation of a supernumerary lung by the trachea points to the components of the extracellular matrix as the causative agents in branching. The matrix arises as a result of synthetic activity by the epithelium as well as by cells of the mesenchymal capsule. It is organized as a basal lamina close to the epithelial basal surface and forms an extended matrix that extends to and surrounds the mesenchymal cells of the capsule.

BASAL LAMINA    The basal lamina consists of a meshwork of type IV collagen combined with a lattice of the glycoprotein laminin (71). The layer also contains heparan sulfate proteoglycans such as perlecan and other glycoproteins that include entactin, tenascin, and fibronectin. The basal lamina of the developing lung forms a continuous layer in proximal regions but is discontinuous at sites of branching (7, 19). Direct contact between the epithelial buds and mesenchymal cells is established by filopodia of both cell types (24), which extend through the discontinuous basal lamina (Figure 3).


MESENCHYMAL MATRIX    Most mesenchymes are loose, fluid connective tissues; however, those surrounding epithelial primordia, including the lung buds, tend to be highly cellular with little intercellular space. The matrix surrounding organ primordia consists primarily of type I and III collagens, often decorated by the smaller type V, etc collagens. Interstices within the collagen mesh are occupied by chondroitin sulfate and other proteoglycans, hyaluronan, and glycoproteins such as fibronectin. Less is known about the organization of this matrix as compared with basal lamina. Assembly of the larger collagens into meshworks or bundles is thought to depend upon the type(s) of associated small collagens, as well as the binding of proteoglycans. During branching, the collagen surrounding the lung primordium becomes organized in distinct patterns (67). As the trachea and proximal bronchi are formed, they become surrounded progressively by thick collagen bundles that are oriented parallel to the direction of outgrowth. At the actively branching buds at the tips of the bronchi, where the basal lamina is discontinuous, collagen forms as a loose meshwork of fibrils or small fibers.


POSSIBLE ROLES OF MATRIX IN BRANCHING    There has been much speculation as to how the extracellular matrix might influence branching. (a) It could function as a physical barrier. For instance, the basal lamina might prevent epithelial-mesenchymal contact except at places where the layer has gaps at the bud tips. The extended matrix could prevent proximal branching by ensheathing the established airways and could establish branch points by acting as a barrier to growth at the site of a potential branch point or cleft. (b) It could act as a filter, permitting selected molecules to penetrate to the epithelial surface by regulation of the spaces within the mesh, charge density, or hydrophobicity. For instance, the type of proteoglycan or amount of hyaluronan could regulate the amount of bound water and relative charge density of the extracellular space. Glycoconjugate and collagen content could limit the size of molecules that could penetrate, especially if the molecules were bulky. (c) The matrix could sequester soluble molecules such as growth factors. Most of the components of the matrix have binding sites for each other and also for growth factors (43a, 63a, 71). These matrix receptors could either prevent their ligands from reaching the specific cell surface receptors except in restricted locations, or they could hold the ligands for release under certain conditions. (d) Finally, there is evidence that certain components of the matrix enhance binding of growth factors to their specific receptors.

## Experimental Analysis of the Role of Matrix in Branching

The most distinctive feature of a connective tissue is the composition of its extracellular matrix. Connective tissues within a single organ can contain quantitative and qualitative differences in the kinds of collagens, proteoglycans, and glycoproteins they possess as well as differences in their organization. Thus patterns of deposition or removal of these components are likely candidates for the way that mesenchyme could influence branching.

COLLAGEN    Because of the manner in which it is distributed in the lung primordia, collagen is thought to be involved in branching: Its organization into bundles surrounding established airways supports the conclusion that the collagen bundles prevent branching by proximal airways. Conversely, a loose meshwork, as well as discontinuities in the distal basal lamina, may be required for branching to continue. Type IV collagen is present in basal lamina along all epithelial surfaces, as well as in mesenchyme, from the initiation of lung outgrowth (11). Both the epithelium and mesenchyme appear capable of producing type IV collagen (62), based on their expression of mRNA for the $\alpha1(IV)$ chain. The interstitial collagens I and III show a different expression pattern; they are present within all parts of the lung primordium at early stages but become more concentrated in proximal regions as branching progresses (1, 20). Type V collagen also has been detected in embryonic lung in culture (28), but its distribution pattern has not been investigated.

Collagen was the first matrix component to be tested experimentally for a role in branching. Branching is inhibited when competitive inhibitors of collagen synthesis are added to culture medium (3, 57). The inhibitory response depends upon suppression of secretion by L-azetidine-3-carboxylic acid or $\alpha,\alpha'$ dipyridyl and does not occur when uncross-linked alpha chains are secreted in the presence of β-aminoproprionitrile. The effect on branching is not likely to be exerted through inhibition of type I collagen. Lungs branch normally in mice that are totally collagen I deficient as a result of the Mov13 insert (28). This is not surprising because collagen I is sparse in budding regions, and branching probably requires one of the reticulum-producing collagens, such as type III and V, which are both synthesized by the mutants.

The role of collagen in branching needs to be examined more thoroughly. The two studies indicate that the absence of an ordered collagen sheet is not simply permissive for branching. Because the inhibitors should affect all collagen types except perhaps type IV deposition, collagen may have a more direct role in establishing a branch point. Examination of salivary branching has shown that the amount of collagen secreted affects the number of branches that are formed (15). The first step in the establishment of a branch point is the deposition of a strand of type III collagen in a cleft (35). It would be instructive to use the same approaches to examine a possible similar role for type III collagen in lung branching.

PROTEOGLYCAN    Another class of widely distributed components of matrix are the proteoglycans and the glycosaminoglycan (GAG), hyaluronan. These molecules bind to collagen, often masking antigenic sites (64). Histochemical staining for GAGs shows intense staining in clefts and along cell bases of established bronchi (20). Heparan sulfate proteoglycan (perlecan) immunolocalizes to lung basal lamina from the earliest stages of branching and to the surfaces of adjacent mesenchymal cells (24). There are few treatments that interfere with proteoglycan synthesis or deposition. Incubation with heparitinase has been used to study the effects of heparan sulfate proteoglycan deprivation during salivary branching (36), and specific β-xylosides competitively inhibit chondroitin sulfate proteoglycan synthesis by acting as a carrier for free GAG synthesis. Salivary branching is inhibited by β-xyloside, with concomitant 50% depression of proteoglycan synthesis and approximately a sevenfold increase in free GAG, whereas the α-anomer affects neither branching nor chondroitin sulfate synthesis (58). Treatment of lung primordia with concentrations of β-xyloside, which depress proteoglycan synthesis, inhibits branching, but similar concentrations of α-xyloside also inhibit branching without affecting GAG synthesis (56). Proteoglycans may play different roles according to their location within the developing lung basal lamina or extended matrix, as well as depending on the type of GAGs they carry. It therefore seems likely that the role of proteoglycans/GAGs in lung branching will not be assessed until syntheses of specific ligands are manipulated by incorporation of specific oligonucleotide sequences or DNA constructs. By examination of epithelial/mesenchymal recombinants in which one component has been transfected, it may be possible to discover if deposition or removal of a particular component plays a role in branching.

GLYCOPROTEINS    If the fenestrated basal lamina at branch points is important for budding, its structure must be controlled by differential assembly of the glycoproteins, which are an integral part of that layer. The assembly of a laminin sheet, with its bound entactin, is essential for formation of the basal lamina (71). Laminin, a heterotrimer, localizes to basal lamina of all epithelia and to the compact mesenchyme surrounding the buds (24, 12). At early developmental stages, discontinuous labeling of the β and γ chains is seen for bud tips (46). Expression of α chains occurs with a continuous distribution at bud tips, as well as in regions between buds and along proximal bronchi (62). Both epithelial and mesenchymal cells produce mRNA for α, β, and γ chains from the beginning of lung development (46, 62). The β and γ chains are produced by both cell types; however, the mesenchyme expresses the α chain in the bronchial regions, whereas the epithelium expresses the $\alpha$ chain in the buds (62). There may be higher expression of the $\gamma$ chain at bud tips than more proximally. Entactin (nidogen) is found uniformly distributed in basal laminae throughout the developing lung (14), but mRNA is expressed only by mesenchymal cells (14, 62).

Experimental intervention has been used to test the role of laminin in lung branching. Fewer branches are formed and end buds become dilated in the presence of polyclonal antibody to laminin (44). Several parts of the laminin trimer potentially are involved. Inhibition occurs when the terminal knob of the $\alpha$ chain or the cell receptor at the cross is inactivated by monoclonal antibodies against different regions of laminin (45). Branching also is inhibited by monoclonal antibody against the nidogen-binding domain (14). Incubation of lung primordia with an antibody against the RGD receptor also inhibits branching (41). This integrin receptor binds both laminin and fibronectin, so the basis for the inhibition is not clear. Integrin receptors and fibronectin are localized along bronchial surfaces and mesenchyme cells in a pattern that does not suggest a relationship with branch points (12).

Tenascin is another major component of the cell surface environment; it occurs as alternate splice variants of its fibronectin-like repeats. Tenascin localizes to the basal lamina of lung buds and in groups of mesoderm cells adjacent to bud tips (1). Proximal regions stain less intensely than budding regions. In situ hybridization shows that tenascin mRNA is present only in the epithelial cells of the buds and not in proximal epithelium or mesenchyme cells (27). Branching of the lung is inhibited by incubation with a polyclonal antibody to tenascin-C (70). Branching does not occur normally when bacterial expression proteins containing the fibronectin-like domains are added to the medium, whereas expression protein containing the terminal fibrinogen domain is not inhibitory. Antibodies against the bacterial proteins containing the fibronectin-like domains also do not stop branching. An interpretation of this result is lacking. The relationship between tenascin and other glycoproteins and surface receptors in the lung has not been investigated.

## Epithelial Responses

Branching begins with the initial response of a bud to form a cleft. Once a cleft is established, formation of the newest airways depends upon an increase in cell number. Formation of a cleft requires changes in cell shape, presumably through deformations in the cytoskeleton. Increase in cell number results from cell proliferation controlled by soluble factors.

CELL SHAPE CHANGES    Virtually no attention has been paid to changes in the cytoskeleton during lung branching. The cell apices have circumferential bundles of actin filaments, but their putative role in cleft formation has not been tested as in the salivary primordium (60). Although cytochalasin inhibits branching (16), its effect on actin organization has not been studied. Thus it is not known if the initial generation of a branch point depends solely upon formation of a barrier by extracellular matrix or if the location of the branch is controlled by the epithelium. It seems likely that signaling does occur because branching is inhibited by incubation with monoclonal antibody against the cell adhesion molecule E-cadherin (22). The cadherins are linked to the cytoskeleton through association of catenins with the cytoplasmic domain and could participate in cellular shape changes. This is an area ripe for investigation because it could provide clues to the stimulatory and inhibitory effects of the matrix components described above.

CELL PROLIFERATION AND BRANCHING    Cell proliferation is a critical part of branching, with estimates of up to a 40-fold increase in size during embryonic growth. The matrix could act as a filter for growth factors that promote cell proliferation by preventing binding or penetration in proximal regions and by promoting activation at the periphery. In the lung, growth of bronchial buds seems to occur by maintenance rather than by stimulation of a high division rate (18). At the time that the primary bronchi are formed, more than 90% of the epithelial cells incorporate $^3$H-thymidine into DNA. Later, the percent of labeled cells drops to 30% in trachea and established bronchi, while it remains at 95% in the buds. Branching is inhibited when DNA synthesis is inhibited with aphidicolin (16).

The inability of foreign mesenchymes to promote normal branching of bronchial buds or to initiate tracheal branching could be an inability to stimulate mitosis rather than some deficiency in matrix deposition or removal. For instance, branching stops when lung buds are combined with salivary mesenchyme from young embryos but continues with serial transplantation of the salivary mesenchyme (29). Ability of the trachea to form a bud also may depend upon maintenance of a high rate of cell proliferation; substitution of bronchial for tracheal mesenchyme results in the retention of the higher percent of labeled cells in the tracheal epithelium (18). These results are consistent with failure of mesenchymes, which do not support branching, to produce the appropriate types or quantities of growth factor(s).

GROWTH FACTORS AND BRANCHING    Cell proliferation is controlled by growth factors that act as positive or negative regulators. Epidermal growth factor (EGF) is a prime example of a stimulatory factor. EGF immunolocalizes to all lung cells but stains the bronchial endings more intensely; the EGF receptor is expressed in the same pattern (65). Thymidine incorporation increases in the epithelium of chicken lung primordia when EGF is added to the culture medium and a supernumerary lung bud forms when a pellet of EGF is placed next to the trachea (17). DNA synthesis and branching also are stimulated by addition of EGF to cultures of mouse lung primordia (49). Inhibition of the EGF receptor by tryphostin, which blocks its receptor tyrosine kinase activity, has the reverse effect, suppressing branching and thymidine incorporation. Incorporation of antisense EGF oligodeoxynucleotide into lung cultures inhibits translation of EGF mRNA, resulting in decreased amounts of EGF, depression of DNA synthesis, and inhibition of branching (65). EGF receptors are up-regulated when lung primordia are treated with retinoic acid, which results in increased branching activity (47). These results are consistent with the interpretation that branching requires cell proliferation that is stimulated by EGF, which is produced locally. However, the cell type that synthesizes EGF needs to be investigated.

Other polypeptide growth factors that stimulate epithelial DNA synthesis do not have as clear an effect on lung development. For instance, platelet-derived growth factor (PDGF) localizes to both epithelium and mesenchyme. Treatment of lung primordia with antisense oligodeoxynucleotide against PDGF-B reduces the size of the lung primordium relative to control cultures, but does not affect the number of buds that are formed (55). Tumor necrosis factor-$\alpha$ (TNF-$\alpha$), a product of the histocompatibility complex, is not known to stimulate mitosis. It is expressed in lung mesenchyme cells close to the surface of epithelial branches (23). TNF receptor is found ubiquitously throughout the mesenchyme and at apical surfaces of the respiratory epithelium. Addition of TNF-$\alpha$ to culture medium accelerates branching. This growth factor is of interest because its expression is stimulated by cortisone. The effect of TNF-$\alpha$, however, appears to be principally on later stages of development (see below).

In contrast, transforming growth factor-$\beta$ (TGF-$\beta$) inhibits epithelial proliferation while stimulating mesenchymal proliferation (34). TGF-$\beta$1 is synthesized by epithelial cells based upon localization of antibody against the pro region of the protein. Mesenchymal cells close to the epithelium also express TGF-$\beta$1, whereas those farther away do not. The secreted protein is found in higher concentrations at branch points and proximal airways than at bud tips (20). Addition of TGF-$\beta$1 to culture medium inhibits branching (48).

MODE OF ACTION OF GROWTH FACTORS    The peptide growth factors bind to components of the extracellular matrix, particularly those containing heparan sulfate chains. There is evidence that binding to heparan may facilitate binding to more specific receptors, but the matrix also may act to increase effective levels of a growth factor. Activation of the receptor results in activation of proto-oncogenes, which produce transcription factors. By controlling expression of other genes, these genes can control entry into or withdrawal from the mitotic cycle.

Virtually nothing is known about the relationship between soluble growth factors and deposition or turnover of extracellular matrix during embryonic lung development. The same is true for gene activation by EGF or PDGF. TGF-β1 influences the expression of N-*myc*. N-*myc* expression is required for lung branching because embryos with mutations of the gene form only the first bronchial branches (32). Addition of TGF-β1 to lung cultures at concentrations that inhibit branching also reduce N-*myc* expression (48). Expression of N-*myc* is reduced before branching is inhibited, and N-*myc* is expressed again if TGF-β1 is removed from the medium. Because branching normally does not occur where TGF-β1 expression is high along established bronchi, it seems likely that inhibition of N-*myc* expression may cause loss of branching activity in the proximal airways as they are formed. Then, N-*myc* expression should be high at bud tips and under other conditions where branching is stimulated, such as with increased levels of EGF (17, 65).

Several other transcription factors are differentially expressed during early stages of branching. For instance, c-*fos* is expressed in epithelial cells at bud tips during the pseudoglandular phase (33). Similarly thyroid transcription factor (TTF-1) is expressed in the distal-most epithelium from the time that bronchial buds begin to grow out from the trachea (30). The factors initiating their synthesis have not been investigated in the lung, nor is it clear what role they may play in branching.

## BRANCHING TO FORM ALVEOLAR ENDINGS

A major distinguishing feature of saccule formation is the differentiation of specialized respiratory cell types, principally type I and type II pneumocytes (Figure 2B). Type II pneumocytes are recognized by their synthesis of several surfactant proteins and disaturated phosphatidylcholine. These products are visible by electron microscopy as lamellar bodies. Type I pneumocytes are identified principally by their flattened shape, although some progress is being made in identifying unique synthetic characteristics (25). Formation of type I pneumocytes from the low columnar embryonic epithelium results in increased surface area and wider lumina in saccules (Figure 2). One question to be addressed is whether this change in surface area drives the fetal branching rather than cleft formation and cell proliferation.

Formation of alveolar sacs and alveoli also is coincident with a major change in the character of the intraepithelial mesenchymal partitions (9, 52, 53). The highly cellular and thick septa become thinner and contain a higher proportion of extracellular matrix. The composition of the matrix also changes. Although fetal mesenchyme may play a role similar to that of embryonic mesenchyme, it also could be responding to changes in the epithelium, rather than causing them.

## Mesenchyme and Saccule Formation

Manipulation of mesenchyme during fetal development alters branching and saccule formation just as it does during embryonic branching. Mouse tracheal mesenchyme or chicken nonrespiratory air sac mesenchyme suppresses branching of mouse respiratory endings from the canalicular phase (21). Reciprocal combinations of mouse and chicken respiratory epithelium and mesenchyme cause the mouse to form parabronchi and the chicken to form blind sacs. Chick air sacs, which normally do not branch, form buds in combination with mouse respiratory mesenchyme, but the air sac epithelial cells do not form pneumocytes. Thus mesenchyme influences the branching pattern even during fetal development, but only respiratory epithelium can form pneumocytes.

Mesenchyme could exert an effect on the respiratory epithelium in much the same way as during embryonic branching. It could control deposition or removal of specific structural units during remodeling of septa or it could sequester or exclude soluble factors, or both.

## Experimental Manipulation of Extracellular Matrix

PROTEOGLYCAN    The respiratory region develops abnormally when proteoglycan synthesis is inhibited with β-xyloside. Alveolar sacs do not form, lumina remain narrow, and septa are embryonic in appearance (52). The epithelium has a higher proportion of embryonic (columnar) cells at the expense of type II pneumocytes, but the percent of type I cells is within the normal range as compared with cultures in the presence of the inactive α-anomer or in control medium. This reduced representation of type II cells coincides with a 74% reduction in surfactant lipid in comparison with control lungs, i.e. tissue not inhibited by β-xyloside. Chondroitin sulfate in proteoglycan is decreased by 70% upon treatment with β-xyloside without affecting heparan sulfate and heparin (53).

The lung contains chondroitin sulfate proteoglycans that are major components of extracellular matrix, including versican (69), biglycan, and decorin (42). Synthesis of these proteoglycans should be inhibited equally by β-xyloside. Therefore, it is not known which specific proteoglycan plays a role in the formation of alveoli. The regional distribution of specific proteoglycans has not been studied within the fetal lung. However, lung fibroblasts can be separated into two classes with different synthetic activities depending upon their proximity to the epithelium (10). In monolayer culture, fibroblasts harvested from the epithelial surfaces at the pseudoglandular stage primarily secrete hyaluronan. More peripheral fibroblasts of early fetuses synthesize chondroitin and heparan sulfates. By the canalicular stage, peripheral fibro-blasts also synthesize hyaluronan, coincident with thinning of the septa. The potential role of hyaluronan in septal thinning is worth investigating.

GLYCOPROTEINS    In contrast to inhibition of proteoglycan synthesis, interfer-ence with glycoprotein synthesis inhibits differentiation of type I pneumocytes. Respiratory regions at the canalicular stage develop abnormally when cultured with tunicamycin, an inhibitor of N-glycosylation (66). In addition to reducing the proportion of type I cells coincident with a higher proportion of embryonic epithelial cells, tunicamycin inhibits thinning of the septa and retention of narrow epithelial lumina, much like the action of β-xyloside. Transmission electron microscopy shows that these cultures contain a normal number of type II pneumocytes but fewer type I pneumocytes than normal control lungs. Tunicamycin inhibits the synthesis of all N-linked glycoproteins, including the same complement described above for embryonic lungs. In order to understand the basis for the inhibitory effects of tunicamycin, the role of individual glyco-proteins needs to be studied with blocking antibodies and DNA probes, as has been done for embryonic branching.

COLLAGEN    Inhibitors of collagen synthesis interfere with growth of fetal lungs and type II cell differentiation (2). Type I collagen is not likely to be involved because mutant mice lacking collagen I have essentially normal lungs (28). The mutant lungs contain elevated levels of types III and V collagen, with an increase in the type V to type III ratio. The lungs also contain type III collagen at the epithelial/mesenchymal interface, and fibrils are visible by electron microscopy. Rapid collagen synthesis occurs during fetal develop-ment, but a large proportion of the preexisting collagen is degraded (5).

Expansion of epithelial surface area during formation of alveolar sacs and alveoli should be accompanied by changes in basal laminae. Type IV collagen invests the terminal sacs as well as more proximal regions of the fetal lung (11). Degradation of collagen is accomplished by specific collagenases. Turn-over of type IV collagen predominates during this time, with the tissue ex-pressing a high level of type IV collagenase activity but little type I collagenase activity (5). These results are consistent with the suggestion that changes in the basal lamina in general, and its type IV collagen in particular, are necessary for saccule formation. Thus the effects of all the studies on inhibition of matrix synthesis may be related to interference with assembly of the basal lamina, a possibility that should be tested.

## Soluble Factors and Formation of Alveolar Endings

Growth promoting activities have been investigated more in terms of physi-ological maturation than saccule formation. Hormonal involvement in matu-

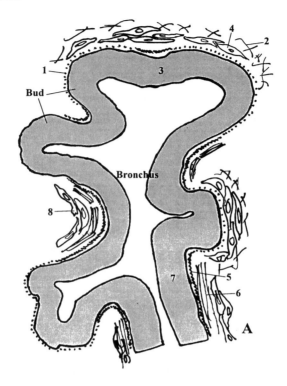

ration is well documented. Corticosteroids and thyroxine accelerate the formation of alveoli and differentiation of respiratory cell types in organ culture and
in utero (6, 39). Epithelial cells flatten in the alveolar endings and septa become
thinner.

In addition, several peptide growth factors influence maturation, particularly the differentiation of type II pneumocytes. The effects of corticosteroids
may be to stimulate mesenchyme cells to produce fibroblast pneumocyte
factor (FPF), a protein of 5–15 kDa synthesized on an mRNA of about 400
bases (50, 51). FPF is not produced until the saccular stage and, in culture,
is synthesized in response to corticosteroids in the medium. The concomitant
differentiation of type II cells may result from this stimulation (40), but there
is no known effect on branching. Because the gene has not been cloned and
sequenced, it is not known if FPF is a member of one of the recognized
families of growth factors. EGF may play a role in maturation of lung
fibroblasts and thus make them receptive to stimulation by corticosteroids.
EGF mRNA and receptors localize only to fibroblasts and not epithelium
(26, 38, 54).

Another possible mode of action of corticosteroids is through activation of

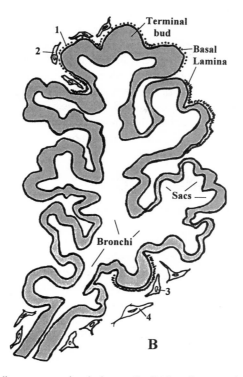

*Figure 4* Summary diagram comparing the known distribution of macromolecules in mouse lung primordia at (A) 16 days and (B) 19 days of gestation. Basal lamina is represented by short slashes, where continuous, and dots, where discontinuous. Numbers refer to the locations listed below. 4A (1) bud basal lamina: discontinuous, collagen IV, perlecan, LM β and γ discontinuous, LM α and entactin, TN high, EGFr and EFG high; (2) bud matrix: collagen I and II low, TGF-β1 low; (3) bud epithelium: α, β, and γ LM mRNA; TN mRNA, TNFr, TGF-β1, N-myc low; (4) bud mesenchyme: TNFr and TNFα mRNA, β and γ LM mRNA, near-HA, far-CSPG, TGF-β1 mRNA; (5) stalk basal lamina: collagen IV, perlecan, LM α, β, and γ continuous; entactin; (6) stalk matrix: collagen I and III high, TGF-β1 high, TN low, EGF; (7) stalk epithelium: EGFr, TNFr, Collagen IV mRNA, β and γ LM mRNA, N-myc high; (8) stalk mesenchyme: collagen IV mRNA, α, β, and γ LM mRNA; entactin mRNA, TNFr, TGF-β mRNA. 4B (1) matrix: collagen I, III, IV; high collagenase IV; TGF-β; (2) mesenchyme: TNF-α, TGF-β mRNA, FPF, EGFr, EGF? (3) near mesenchyme: hyaluronan, CSPG; (4) far mesenchyme: hyaluronan, CSPG.

TNF-α in the mesodermal cells adjacent to alveolar endings. Addition of TNF-α to cultures markedly increases surfactant synthesis, similar to elevated cortisone levels (23), although there appears to be little stimulation of type II pneumocyte formation in these cultures.

TGF-β inhibits surfactant synthesis by human lung in culture (68). TGF-β can overcome the effects of FPF when lungs are treated with both (37). TGF-β mRNA is expressed in the fibroblasts and not in the epithelium during the early saccular period but is reduced in the rat fetus before birth (63). TGF-β inhibits the growth of isolated lung fibroblasts in culture and increases the synthesis of the small chondroitin/dermatan sulfate proteoglycan, biglycan, whereas decorin synthesis is unchanged (42). Because the distribution of these proteoglycans has not been described in intact developing lungs, it is not clear what role TGF-β may play in saccule formation.

## CONCLUSIONS AND PROSPECTUS

In recent years, much information has accumulated on the distribution of matrix macromolecules and growth factors during embryonic branching of the lung. Similar but not as complete information exists for the fetal period when respiratory endings begin to differentiate. The role of these molecules in branching has been tested by the use of metabolic inhibitors, antibodies against specific components, and probes against transcription. The current status is diagrammatically represented in Figure 4.

Based on the use of inhibitors and stimulators, it is clear that a number of these components must play important roles both in embryonic branching and saccule formation. Of particular interest during embryonic branching are types III and V collagen, chondroitin sulfate proteoglycan, laminin, tenascin, TGF-β, and their receptors. Saccule formation appears to be influenced by chondroitin sulfate proteoglycan, hyaluronan, unspecified glycoprotein(s), types III and V collagen, EGF, TNF-α, TGF-β, and their receptors. Much work remains to be done on the relationships among these molecules, which fall into broad categories of structural and soluble classes. Critical tests also need to be devised to test causality; it is often difficult to separate an effect that is epiphenomenal from one that acts to produce a morphological change. This is especially important in evaluating the events that produce the first alveolar saccules because the data do not yield a conclusion on whether the driving force comes from changes in the shape of epithelial cells or from modulation of the connective tissue septa. Finally, data are just beginning to appear on gene activation as a result of signaling by changes in structural macromolecules and soluble factors. There is great potential for elucidation of control mechanisms by continued efforts involving genetic analyses.

## Literature Cited

1. Abbott LA, Lester SM, Erickson CA. 1991. Changes in mesenchymal cell-shape, matrix collagen and tenascin accompany bud formation in the early chick lung. *Anat. Embryol.* 183:299–311

2. Adamson IY, King GM. 1987. L-azetidine-2-carboxylic acid retards lung growth and surfactant synthesis in fetal rats. *Lab. Invest.* 57:439–45

3. Alescio T. 1973. Effect of a proline analogue, azetidine-2-carboxylic acid, on the morphogenesis of mouse embryonic lung. *J. Embryol. Exp. Morphol.* 29:439–51

4. Alescio T, Cassini A. 1962. Induction in vitro of tracheal buds by pulmonary mesenchyme grafted on tracheal epithelium. *J. Exp. Zool.* 150:83–94

5. Arden MG, Spearman MA, Adamson IY. 1993. Degradation of type IV collagen during the development of fetal rat lung. *Am. J. Resp. Cell Mol. Biol.* 9:99–105

6. Ballard PL. 1982. Hormonal aspects of fetal lung development. In *Lung Development: Biological and Clinical Perspectives,* ed. PM Farrell, 2:205–53. New York: Academic. 307 pp.

7. Bluemink JG, Maurik PV, Lawson KA. 1976. Intimate cell contacts at the epithelial/mesenchymal interface in embryonic mouse lung. *J. Ultrastruc. Res.* 55:257–70

8. Boyden EA. 1972. Development of the human lung. In *Practice of Pediatrics,* ed. VC Kelley, 4:1–17. New York: Harper & Row

9. Burri PH, Moschopulos M. 1992. Structural analysis of fetal rat lung development. *Anat. Rec.* 234:399–418

10. Caniggia I, Tanswell K, Post M. 1992. Temporal and spatial differences in glycosaminoglycan synthesis by fetal lung fibroblasts. *Exp. Cell Res.* 202:252–58

11. Chen JM, Little CD. 1987. Cellular events associated with lung branching morphogenesis including the deposition of collagen type IV. *Dev. Biol.* 120:311–21

12. Chen W-T, Chen J-M, Mueller SC. 1986. Coupled expression and colocalization of 140K cell adhesion molecules, fibronectin, and laminin during morphogenesis and cytodifferentiation of chick lung cells. *J. Cell Biol.* 103:1073–90

13. Dameron F. 1961. L'influence de divers mésenchymes sur la differenciation de l' épithélium pulmonaire de l'embryon de poulet en culture in vitro. *J. Embryol. Exp. Morphol.* 9:628–33

14. Ekblom P, Ekblom M, Fecker L, Klein G, Zhang H-Y, et al. 1994. Role of mesenchymal nidogen for epithelial morphogenesis in vitro. *Development* 120:2003–14

15. Fukuda Y, Masuda Y, Kishi J-I, Hasimoto Y, Hayakawa T, et al. 1988. The role of interstitial collagens in cleft formation of mouse embryonic submandibular gland during initial branching. *Development* 103:259–67

15a. Goldin GV. 1980. Towards a mechanism for morphogenesis in epithelio-mesenchymal organs. *Q. Rev. Biol.* 55:251–65

16. Goldin GV, Hindman HM, Wessells NK. 1984. The role of cell proliferation and cellular shape change in branching morphogenesis of the embryonic mouse lung: analysis using aphidicolin and cytochalasins. *J. Exp. Zool.* 232:287–96

17. Goldin GV, Opperman LA. 1980. Induction of supernumerary tracheal buds and the stimulation of DNA synthesis in the embryonic chick lung and trachea by epidermal growth factor. *J. Embryol. Exp. Morphol.* 60:235–43

18. Goldin GV, Wessells NK. 1979. Mammalian lung development: the possible role of cell proliferation in the formation of supernumerary tracheal buds and in branching morphogenesis. *J. Exp. Zool.* 208:337–46

19. Grant MM, Cutts NR, Brody JS. 1983. Alterations in lung basement membrane during fetal growth and type 2 cell development. *Dev. Biol.* 97:173–83

20. Heine UI, Munoz EF, Flanders KC, Roberts AB, Sporn MB. 1990. Colocalization of TGF-beta 1 and collagen I and III, fibronectin and glycosaminoglycans during lung branching morphogenesis. *Development* 109:29–36

21. Hilfer SR, Rayner R, Brown JW. 1985. Mesenchymal control of branching pattern in the fetal mouse lung. *Tissue Cell* 17:523–38

22. Hirai Y, Nose A, Kobayashi S, Takeichi M. 1989. Expression and role of E- and P-cadherin adhesion molecules in embryonic histogenesis I. Lung epithelial morphogenesis. *Development* 105:263–70

23. Jaskoll TF, Boyer PD, Melnick M. 1994. Tumor necrosis factor-α and embryonic mouse lung morphogenesis. *Dev. Dyn.* 201:137–50

24. Jaskoll TF, Slavkin HC. 1984. Ultrastructural and immunofluorescence studies of basal-lamina alterations during mouse-lung morphogenesis. *Differentiation* 28:36–48

25. Joyce-Brady MF, Brody JS. 1990. Ontogeny of pulmonary alveolar epithelial markers of differentiation. *Dev. Biol.* 137:331–48

26. Keller GH, Ladda RL. 1981. Correlation between phosphatidylcholine labeling and hormone receptor levels in alveolar type II epithelial cells: effects of dexamethasone and epidermal growth factor. *Arch. Biochem. Biophys.* 211: 321–26

27. Koch M, Wehrle-Haller B, Baumgartner S, Spring J, Brubacher D, Chiquet M. 1991. Epithelial synthesis of tenascin at tips of growing bronchi and graded accumulation in basement membrane and mesenchyme. *Exp. Cell Res.* 194:297–300

28. Kratochwil K, Dziadek M, Lohler J, Harbers K, Jaenisch R. 1986. Normal epithelial branching morphogenesis in the absence of collagen I. *Dev. Biol.* 117:596–606

29. Lawson KA. 1983. Stage specificity in the mesenchyme requirement of rodent lung epithelium in vitro: a matter of growth control? *J. Embryol. Exp. Morphol.* 74:183–206

30. Lazzaro D, Price M, De Felice M, Di Lauro R. 1991. The transcription factor TTF-1 is expressed at the onset of thyroid and lung morphogenesis and in restricted regions of the foetal brain. *Development* 113:1093–104

31. Masters JRW. 1976. Epithelial-mesenchymal interaction during lung development: the effect of mesenchymal mass. *Dev. Biol.* 51:98–108

31a. Minoo P, King RJ. 1994. Epithelial-mesenchymal interactions in lung development. *Annu. Rev. Physiol.* 56:13–45

32. Moens CB, Stanton BR, Parada LF, Rossant J. 1993. Defects in heart and lung development in compound heterozygotes for two different targeted mutations at the N-myc locus. *Development* 119:485–99

33. Molinar-Rode R, Smeyne RJ, Curran T, Morgan JJ. 1993. Regulation of protooncogene expression in adult and developing lungs. *Mol. Cell. Biol.* 13:3213–20

34. Moses HL, Yang EY, Pietenpol JA. 1990. TGF-β stimulation and inhibition of cell proliferation: new mechanistic insights. *Cell* 63:245–47

35. Nakanishi Y, Nogawa H, Hashimoto Y, Kishi J-I, Hayakawa T. 1988. Accumulation of collagen III at the cleft points of developing mouse submandibular epithelium. *Development* 104:51–59

36. Nakanishi Y, Uetmatsu J, Takamatsu H, Fukuda Y, Yoshida K. 1993. Removal of heparan sulfate chains halted epithelial branching morphogenesis of the developing mouse submandibular gland in vitro. *Dev. Growth Diff.* 35:371–84

37. Nielsen HC, Kellogg CK, Doyle CA. 1992. Development of fibroblast-type-II cell communications in fetal rabbit lung organ culture. *Biochim. Biophys. Acta* 1175:95–99

38. Partanen A-M, Thesleff I. 1987. Localization and quantitation of $^{125}$I epidermal growth factor binding in mouse embryonic tooth and other embryonic tissues at different developmental stages. *Dev. Biol.* 120:186–97

39. Post M, Barsoumian A, Smith BT. 1986. The cellular mechanisms of glucocorticoid acceleration of fetal lung maturation. *J. Biol. Chem.* 261:2179–84

40. Post M, Floros J, Smith BT. 1984. Inhibition of lung maturation by monoclonal antibodies against fibroblast-pneumocyte factor. *Nature* 308:284–86

41. Roman J, Little CW, McDonald JA. 1991. Potential role of RGD-binding integrins in mammalian lung branching morphogenesis. *Development* 112:551–58

42. Romaris M, Heredia A, Molist A, Bassols A. 1991. Differential effect of transforming growth factor β on proteoglycan synthesis in human embryonic lung fibroblasts. *Biochim. Biophys. Acta* 1093: 229–33

43. Rudnick D. 1933. Developmental capacities of the chick lung in chorioallantoic grafts. *J. Exp. Zool.* 66:125–54

43a. Sakaguchi K, Yanagashita M, Takeuchi Y, Aurbach GD. 1991. Identification of heparan sulfate proteoglycan as a high affinity receptor for acidic fibroblast growth factor (aFGF) in a parathyroid cell line. *J. Biol. Chem.* 266:7270–78

44. Schuger L, O'Shea S, Rheinheimer J, Varani J. 1990. Laminin in lung development: effects of anti-laminin antibody in murine lung morphogenesis. *Dev. Biol.* 137:26–32

45. Schuger L, Skubitz APN, O'Shea KS, Chang JF, Varani J. 1991. Identification of laminin domains involved in branching morphogenesis: effects of anti-laminin monoclonal antibodies on mouse embryonic lung development. *Dev. Biol.* 146:531–41

46. Schuger L, Varani J, Killen PD, Skubitz APN, Gilbride K. 1992. Laminin expression in the mouse lung increases with development and stimulates spontaneous organotypic rearrangement of mixed lung cells. *Dev. Dyn.* 195:43–54

47. Schuger L, Varani J, Mitra R Jr, Gilbride K. 1993. Retinoic acid stimulates mouse lung development by a mechanism involving epithelial-mesenchymal interac-

tion and regulation of epidermal growth factor receptors. *Dev. Biol.* 159:462–73

48. Serra R, Pelton RW, Moses HL. 1994. TGFβ1 inhibits branching morphogenesis and N-*myc* expression in lung bud organ cultures. *Development* 120:2153–61

49. Seth R, Shum L, Wu F, Wuenschell C, Hall FL, et al. 1993. Role of epidermal growth factor expression in early mouse embryo lung branching morphogenesis in culture: antisense oligodeoxynucleotide inhibitory strategy. *Dev. Biol.* 158:555–59

50. Smith BT. 1979. Lung maturation in the fetal rat: acceleration by the injection of fibroblast pneumocyte factor. *Science* 20:1094–95

51. Smith T, Post M. 1989. Fibroblast-pneumocyte factor. *Am. J. Physiol.* 257:L174–78

52. Smith CI, Hilfer SR, Searls RL, Nathanson MA, Allodoli MD. 1990. Effects of β-D-xyloside on differentiation of the respiratory epithelium in the fetal mouse lung. *Dev. Biol.* 138:42–52

53. Smith CI, Webster EH, Nathanson MA, Searls RL, Hilfer SR. 1990. Altered patterns of proteoglycan deposition during maturation of the fetal mouse lung. *Cell Diff. Dev.* 32:83–96

54. Snead ML, Luo W, Oliver P, Nakamura M, Don-Wheeler G, et al. 1989. Localization of epidermal growth factor precursor in tooth and lung during embryonic mouse development. *Dev. Biol.* 134:420–29

55. Souza P, Sedlackova L, Kuliszewski M, Wang J, Liu J, et al. 1994. Antisense oligodeoxynucleotides targeting PDGF-B mRNA inhibit cell proliferation during embryonic rat lung development. *Development* 120:2163–73

56. Spooner B, Basset K, Spooner B Jr. 1988. Sulfated GAG and lung development. *J. Cell Biol.* 107:159a (Abstr.)

57. Spooner BS, Faubion JM. 1980. Collagen involvement in branching morphogenesis of embryonic lung and salivary gland. *Dev. Biol.* 77:84–102

58. Spooner BS, Thompson-Pletscher HA. 1986. Matrix accumulation and the development of form: proteoglycans and branching morphogenesis. In *Regulation of Matrix Accumulation*, ed. RP Meacham, pp. 399–444. New York: Academic

59. Spooner BS, Wessells NK. 1970. Mammalian lung development: interactions in primordium formation and bronchial morphogenesis. *J. Exp. Zool.* 175:445–54

60. Spooner BS, Wessells NK. 1972. An analysis of salivary gland morphogenesis: role of cytoplasmic microfilaments and microtubules. *Dev. Biol.* 27:38–54

61. Taderera JV. 1967. Control of lung differentiation in vitro. *Dev. Biol.* 16:489–512

62. Thomas T, Dziadek M. 1994. Expression of collagen α1(IV), laminin and nidogen genes in the embryonic mouse lung: implications for branching morphogenesis. *Mech. Dev.* 45:193–201

63. Torday JS, Kourembanas S. 1990. Fetal rat lung fibroblasts produce a TGF-β homolog that blocks alveolar type II cell maturation. *Dev. Biol.* 139:35–41

63a. Vogel KG. 1994. Glycosaminoglycans and proteoglycans. In *Extracellular Matrix Assembly and Structure*, ed. PD Yurchenco, DE Birk, RP Meacham, pp. 243–79. San Diego: Academic

64. von der Mark K, von der Mark H, Gay S. 1976. Study of differential collagen synthesis during development of the chick embryo by immunofluorescence. II Localization of type I and type II collagen during long bone development. *Dev. Biol.* 53:153–70

65. Warburton D, Seth R, Shum L, Horcher PG, Hall FL, et al. 1992. Epigenetic role of epidermal growth factor expression and signalling in embryonic mouse lung morphogenesis. *Dev. Biol.* 149:123–33

66. Webster EH, Hilfer SR, Searls RL. 1993. Effect of tunicamycin on maturation of fetal mouse lung. *Am. J. Physiol.* I 265:L250–59

67. Wessells NK. 1970. Mammalian lung development: interactions in formation and morphogenesis of tracheal buds. *J. Exp. Zool.* 175:455–66

68. Whitsett JA, Weaver TE, Lieberman MA, Clark JC, Daugherty C. 1987. Differential effects of epidermal growth factor and transforming growth factor-β on synthesis of $M_r$=35,000 surfactant-associated protein in fetal lung. *J. Biol. Chem.* 262:7908–13

69. Yamagata M, Shinomura T, Kimata K. 1993. Tissue variation of two large chondroitin sulfate proteoglycans (PG-M/versican and PG-H/aggrecan) in chick embryos. *Anat. Embryol.* 187:433–44

70. Young SL, Chang L-Y, Erickson H P. 1994. Tenascin-C in rat lung: distribution, ontogeny and role in branching morphogenesis. *Dev. Biol.* 161:615–25

71. Yurchenko PD, O'Rear JJ. 1994. Basal lamina assembly. *Curr. Opin. Cell Biol.* 6:674–81

Annu. Rev. Physiol. 1996. 58:115–41

# MOLECULAR MECHANISMS OF β-ADRENERGIC RELAXATION OF AIRWAY SMOOTH MUSCLE

*Michael I. Kotlikoff*

Department of Animal Biology, School of Veterinary Medicine, University of Pennsylvania, Philadelphia, Pennsylvania 19104-6046

*Kristine E. Kamm*

Department of Physiology, Southwestern Medical Center, University of Texas, Dallas, Texas 75235

KEY WORDS:    calcium-activated potassium channel, myosin light chain kinase, G proteins, phosphorylation, phosphatase

## ABSTRACT

This review summarizes recent data on the two specific mechanisms of β-adrenergic relaxation of airway smooth muscle. $\beta_2$-adrenergic receptor stimulation results in the opening of large-conductance, calcium-activated potassium channels, and an attendant hyperpolarization of the myocyte. Coupling between receptor and channel occurs by phosphorylation-dependent and phosphorylation-independent mechanisms. Inhibition of channel opening by specific peptidyl toxins results in a shift in the dose-dependent relaxation of this tissue by β-adrenergic hormones. There is also evidence that β-adrenergic hormones can decrease the calcium sensitivity of contractile elements. This desensitization does not result from the phosphorylation of myosin light chain kinase but may be associated with the activation of a myosin light chain phosphatase.

## INTRODUCTION

$\beta_2$-Adrenergic receptor stimulation results in the relaxation of vascular and nonvascular smooth muscle and is an important mode of therapeutic bronchodilation. The differential actions of adrenergic hormones on the heart and the airways formed the basis of observations that led to the subdivision of β-adrenergic actions nearly three decades ago (86). However, the substantial

115

diversity in excitability and electrical behavior that exists between different smooth muscle tissues (reviewed in 21) and the cascade of cellular events associated with cyclase-linked hormone stimulation of smooth muscle (reviewed in 105) present difficulties for the generalization of functionally important, specific molecular mechanisms associated with the relaxation of smooth muscle. Despite these difficulties, recent data have provided important information about β-adrenergic modulation of specific proteins involved in excitation-contraction coupling and the physiological relevance of several of these regulatory mechanisms. This review summarizes data on the mechanisms of β-adrenergic relaxation of airway smooth muscle, with concentration on information about the effects of β-adrenergic receptor stimulation on the activity of effector proteins whose actions at the molecular level have recently been characterized. Two of these effectors have generated considerable interest as important functional targets during hormone-mediated relaxation of smooth muscle: large conductance, calcium-activated potassium ($K_{Ca}$ or maxi-K) channel and myosin light chain kinase. Considerable information is now available with respect to the structure, function, and hormone coupling of these proteins.

# β-ADRENERGIC REGULATION OF POTASSIUM CHANNELS

## Hyperpolarization of Smooth Muscle

Some of the earliest experiments examining the mechanisms of adrenergic hormone action indicated that β-adrenergic stimulation hyperpolarized smooth muscle (20, 36, 37, 67, 140). These studies showed that isoproterenol increased the resting membrane potential of smooth muscle cells and decreased electrical activity in spontaneously active preparations and that these actions were mimicked by cyclic nucleotides. Although hyperpolarization is not invariably observed in smooth muscles (21), and the functional importance of this hyperpolarization is a matter of considerable debate (see below), these and many subsequent studies clearly established the existence of molecular coupling mechanisms linking β-adrenergic receptor stimulation to membrane hyperpolarization in a variety of smooth muscles.

A second feature of these early studies was the demonstration of the involvement of potassium channels in hormone-stimulated hyperpolarization. It was quickly established that the ability of β-adrenergic agents or cyclic AMP (cAMP) to hyperpolarize smooth muscle was abolished at higher extracellular potassium concentrations (67, 140), which suggested that the hyperpolarizing actions resulted from an augmentation of potassium conductance. In airway smooth muscle, in which β-adrenergic therapy has been a major therapeutic modality, studies by several groups established the hyperpolarizing action of β-adrenergic hormones (23, 44, 45, 56, 63, 75, 137, 146). Using classical electrophysiological methods, it was demonstrated that during hormone stimulation electrotonic potentials evoked by hyperpolarizing or depolarizing current injections were diminished, thus indicating an increase in membrane conductance (5, 23, 63, 146); maximal hormone stimulation resulted in a hyperpolarization that approached the potassium equilibrium potential (5). These studies established an essential link between β-adrenergic receptor stimulation and modulation of membrane potassium channel function; the elaboration of the specific target channel proteins, as well as the mechanisms of receptor/channel linkage, were to await fundamental advances in the fields of ion channels and G proteins.

## Potassium Channels in Smooth Muscle

The importance of membrane potassium conductances for the maintenance of normal electrical behavior in smooth muscle has long been known. In the presence of potassium ($K^+$) channel blockers, poorly excitable smooth muscles such as tracheal and bronchial smooth muscle develop spontaneous electrical activity and tone (62, 65, 73, 74, 78, 103). Conversely, agents that augment potassium conductance and hyperpolarize smooth muscle have a marked relaxant effect (6, 16, 120). Thus potassium channels seem to be important for the maintenance of normal electrical and contractile stability and underlie the passive electrical behavior of airway smooth muscle. It is now clear that the activity of numerous specific gene products contributes to the aggregate potassium conductance in smooth muscle. These include large conductance, calcium- and voltage-activated potassium ($K_{Ca}$) channels, also termed maxi-K or calcium-activated K channels; a number of low conductance, voltage-dependent potassium channels (11, 19, 51) belonging to a large and diverse gene family and functionally resembling classical delayed rectifier ($K_{dr}$) channels found in nerve and heart (64, 125); ATP-sensitive potassium ($K_{ATP}$) (12, 33, 106, 142) channels, whose activity is increased when the concentration of ATP falls at the cytosolic channel surface; and inwardly rectifying potassium channels ($K_{IR}$) (14, 38, 119). The diversity of potassium channel expression clearly contributes to the substantial differences in resting and stimulated electrical and mechanical activity among different smooth muscles. To date, $K_{Ca}$ (7, 8, 25, 81, 84) and $K_{ATP}$ (163) channels have been implicated in adenylyl cyclase-linked hormonal regulation in smooth muscle. However, several delayed rectifier channels expressed in smooth muscle have consensus phosphorylation sites or are regulated by phosphorylation (18, 58, 122, 159), and their involvement in β-adrenergic hyperpolarization cannot be excluded. For airway smooth muscle, there is now a substantial amount of information indicating that β-adrenergic stimulation results in the activation of $K_{Ca}$ channels and that modulation of the activity of these channels may be a functionally significant component of hormonal bronchodilation.

## Calcium-Activated Potassium Channels

The earliest patch-clamp studies in airway myocytes identified a prominent, large-conductance calcium-activated potassium channel (94) similar to that reported in skeletal muscle (87) and other smooth muscle cells (15, 135, 136). These and subsequent whole-cell studies demonstrated the enormous potential $K_{Ca}$ conductance in the sarcolemmal membrane of smooth muscle cells. Given the large single-channel conductance (over 220 pS) and the invariant finding of numerous channels in every patch of smooth muscle membrane, it could be calculated that even modest changes in the mean open-state probability ($P_o$) of $K_{Ca}$ channels would markedly alter the membrane potential of smooth muscle cells, which have an input resistance on the order of 1 G$\Omega$. It is likely, however, that the $P_o$ of a single $K_{Ca}$ channel is quite low under physiological conditions in unstimulated cells. Most studies report an open-state probability of approximately 0.01 at 0 mV and 100 nM calcium (49, 81, 129, 156). Considering that this value reflects the combined activity of between 5 and 15 channels (26), the open-probability of a single channel is on the order of 0.001 and probably substantially lower at more physiological membrane potentials, consistent with the fact that on-cell recordings generally require substantial depolarizations to show significant channel activity (94). Because dialyzed whole-cell recordings necessitate a predetermined cytosolic calcium concentration and buffering capacity and because these conditions affect $K_{Ca}$ channel activity, measurements under such conditions may provide a poor indication of current availability under physiological conditions. Permeabilized whole-cell recordings in which the cytosol is not buffered have indicated that little $K_{Ca}$ current is available in ferret and human airway myocytes in the absence of hormone stimulation (40, 42). Consistent with this result, charybdotoxin, a peptidyl inhibitor of $K_{Ca}$ channels, did not contract tissues that were treated with tetrodotoxin and atropine to prevent effects of neural release of neurotransmitters. These findings have led to the suggestion that $K_{Ca}$ channel activity is not an important determinant of resting smooth muscle tone. However, this may not be the case for all smooth muscles, which vary substantially in resting excitability. One important determinant of channel activity may be the generation of spontaneous transient outward currents (STOCs). These currents are often observed in whole-cell recordings and could reflect channel activity associated with localized intracellular calcium release (13, 128); such currents would be expected to markedly affect myocyte membrane potential, particularly since evidence of their activity has been observed in recordings from isolated airway segments (3).

Substantial progress has been made in terms of the molecular identification of $K_{Ca}$ channel proteins. *mSLO*, the mammalian homologue of the *Drosophila slowpoke* gene (9), has recently been cloned and expressed (22, 115). The gene encodes a protein that is highly homologous with the pore-forming $\alpha$ subunit of other voltage-gated potassium channels but contains an extended C-terminal region. The six transmembrane segments characteristic of all voltage-dependent cation channels are present, and the putative H5 pore region is highly homologous with other potassium channels. Alternative splice sites are present in the extended C-terminal region, which encodes segments S7 to S10, and multiple splice variants have been detected (22). Expression of the $\alpha$ subunit produces a functional channel with the appropriate conductance (272 pS in 156 mM K; 22). Channel activity is augmented by increasing calcium concentration at the cytoplasmic membrane surface, although the expressed channel appears to have low calcium sensitivity and is blocked by the peptidyl scorpion toxins that bind to the external surface of the channel pore. The calcium-binding site on the protein is believed to be contained within the extended C-terminal segment (158), because replacing this region with that of the *Drosophila* protein confers the calcium sensitivity of the latter protein. A second subunit has been purified (48) and cloned (76) from smooth muscle, and coexpression of this smaller subunit markedly increases calcium sensitivity (96). Both the $\alpha$ and $\beta$ subunits contain several consensus protein kinase A (PKA) phosphorylation sites, although the site(s) associated with physiological regulation have not been determined.

## Molecular Mechanisms of Receptor/Channel Coupling

SIGNALING REACTIONS    The now classical pathway by which hormone receptors activate adenylyl cyclase and initiate downstream signaling has been well established. Binding of a hormone to its receptor results in a structural change in the receptor and the activation of the associated G protein, such that the affinity of the $\alpha$ subunit of the heterotrimeric Gs protein complex for GDP is reduced. GTP, present in stoichiometric excess within the cell, binds to the $\alpha$ subunit, which results in the dissociation of $\alpha$ (GTP) and the $\beta\gamma$ subunits. The activated (GTP bound) $\alpha$ subunit binds to and activates adenylyl cyclase, i.e. integral membrane proteins in the plasma membrane; the activated enzyme catalyzes the synthesis of cAMP from ATP. cAMP in turn activates cAMP-dependent protein kinases, which transfer a phosphate group from ATP to specific serine or threonine residues on target proteins, thus modifying their function. In addition to the activation of PKA, however, evidence from several laboratories indicates that cGMP-dependent protein kinases (PKGs) may be activated by physiological increases in cAMP (66, 85, 90, 151). As described below, evidence exists for the activation of potassium conductances by both protein kinases, which indicates the potential relevance of kinase cross activation.

PHOSPHORYLATION-DEPENDENT COUPLING   Phosphorylation of potassium channels by cyclase-linked receptors appears to be a fundamental mechanism by which cellular excitability is regulated by hormones (70, 89). Numerous electrophysiological demonstrations of this modulation have been reported (10, 17, 39, 88, 157), including the modulation of cloned channels in expression systems (18, 58, 159). Given the previously established link between β-adrenergic relaxation and cellular hyperpolarization in smooth muscle, the demonstration of the specific potassium conductance involved in this process was an important advance in the understanding of hormonal regulation of smooth muscle excitability. Experiments first in cultured aortic myocytes (127) and then in tracheal myocytes (84) established $K_{Ca}$ channels as a major target of β-adrenergic regulation. As shown in Figure 1, experiments by Kume et al in the laboratory of Tomita demonstrated that application of a physiological concentration of β-adrenergic hormone to isolated airway myocytes increased $K_{Ca}$ channel activity in on-cell recordings. They further demonstrated that this coupling was augmented by the phosphatase inhibitor okadaic acid, that inhibition of phosphatase activity augmented channel activity in on-cell patches, and that application of purified cAMP-dependent protein kinase mimicked the action in inside-out patches. These experiments indicated that a traditional phosphorylation-dependent coupling exists between β-receptor stimulation and $K_{Ca}$ channels in smooth muscle. Hormone stimulation resulted in an increase in the open-state probability, without a change in the single-channel conductance. Such coupling was not entirely unexpected because an identical regulatory mechanism had previously been demonstrated for calcium-activated potassium channels in the brain (39). In the experiments of Kume et al, stimulation of channel activity by purified PKA in isolated inside-out patches required ATP and was augmented by phosphatase inhibition. Thus the stimulation of β₂ receptors by physiologically relevant concentrations of hormone (0.2 μM isoproterenol) presumably resulted in the generation of cAMP, the dissociation of the regulatory subunit from the PKA holoenzyme, and phosphorylation of the channel or associated regulatory protein.

This phosphorylation-dependent stimulatory coupling mechanism is further supported by the demonstration of the ATP-dependent stimulation of channel activity by the catalytic subunit of PKA, as shown in Figure 2 (81). Stimulation by the kinase was dose dependent, requiring 0.12 U/ml kinase for half-maximal stimulation. Similar results were obtained previously by Savaria et al from channels reconstituted in planar lipid bilayers (130) and by Carl et al (25), who demonstrated the effect of the catalytic subunit of PKA on $K_{Ca}$ channel activity in inside-out patches from colonic myocytes and the augmentation of these

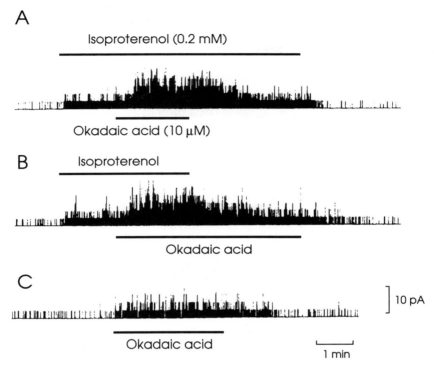

*Figure 1* Isoproterenol activates $K_{Ca}$ channels in tracheal myocytes. (*A*) Application of 0.2 μM isoproterenol to the external surface of the myocytes markedly increased $K_{Ca}$ channel activity recorded from a cell-attached patch. Channel activity was further increased by the application of the phosphatase inhibitor okadaic acid (10 μM) during application of the β-adrenergic hormone. (*B, C*) Okadaic acid also affects the time-course of channel activity following hormone removal and the basal activity of the channel. In the presence of okadaic acid, channel activity was prolonged following washout of the hormone (compare with panel *A*). These data are consistent with a stimulatory mechanism whereby exposure to the β-adrenergic hormone results in phosphorylation of the channel protein or a regulatory protein augmenting channel open-probability. A return to basal activity channel would presumably require dephosphorylation by protein phosphatase 1 or 2A (high-affinity inhibition by okadaic acid). (Reproduced with permission from Kume et al, Reference 86.)

actions by phosphatase inhibition. The latter data suggest an active regulation of channel activity by endogenous kinase and phosphatase activity that is preserved in purified channel preparations and present in isolated membrane patches. That is, the augmentation of kinase action by phosphatase inhibitors in excised patches suggests that phosphatase molecules are intimately associated with channels in the membrane. Previous studies using brain $K_{Ca}$ channels

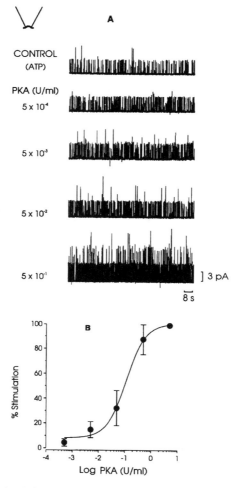

*Figure 2*   $K_{Ca}$ channel activity is enhanced by the catalytic subunit of cAMP-dependent protein kinase (PKA) in a concentration-dependent manner. (*A*) Cumulative addition of PKA to an excised inside-out patch from a ferret tracheal myocyte in the presence of ATP (500 μM). PKA progressively stimulated $K_{Ca}$ channel activity. (*B*) Dose-response relationship from five experiments similar to that shown in *A*. Circles represent the percent stimulation of total open-state probability ($nP_o$), plotted as a function of the concentration of the catalytic subunit of PKA. The solid line represents a best fit of the data to a saturation isotherm (r = .998); the parameters for the curve are basal activity 8.2%, $EC_{50}$ 0.12 U/ml; and Hill slope 1.2. (Reproduced with permission from Kume et al, Reference 81.)

reconstituted into planar lipid bilayers also indicated that endogenous kinase activity was closely associated with the purified channel (28).

In addition to the cAMP-dependent protein kinase augmentation of channel activity, cGMP-dependent protein kinase has been shown to activate $K_{Ca}$ channels in smooth muscle cells (123). Activation by the purified kinase requires ATP and cGMP and results in an approximately 8.9-fold increase in $nP_o$, a stimulation that is similar in magnitude to that observed for PKA (maximal stimulation 7.4-fold; 81). Taken together with evidence indicating that β-adrenergic stimulation may result in the activation of cGMP-dependent protein kinase in smooth muscle (see above), it is possible that coupling between β-adrenoreceptors and $K_{Ca}$ channels may occur at least partly through the stimulation of PKG by cAMP.

PHOSPHORYLATION-INDEPENDENT COUPLING    Whereas the stimulation of $K_{Ca}$ channel activity by kinase-mediated phosphorylation of the channel protein or associated regulatory proteins is well established, evidence also suggests that this is not the only mechanism by which hormone-mediated channel stimulation occurs. Recent studies have demonstrated a membrane-delimited, phosphorylation-independent coupling between $β_2$-receptors and $K_{Ca}$ channels in smooth muscle (80, 81, 132), similar to the $G_S$-mediated coupling between $β_1$ receptors and L-type calcium channels in cardiac muscle (124, 162). As shown in Figure 3, $K_{Ca}$ channels are activated by isoproterenol in outside-out patches under conditions that are extremely unlikely to support kinase-mediated phosphorylation (81). That is, hormone-stimulated coupling was demonstrated in outside-out patches in the presence of the ATP analogue AMP-PNP to competitively inhibit ATP availability for cAMP synthesis or phosphate transfer. Hormone coupling required GTP and was blocked by GDPβS, which suggests that the signaling pathway involves the binding of GTP to a G protein and the subsequent dissociation of the heterotrimer. As predicted for such a process, channel stimulation was achieved by the addition of GTP to the cytosolic surface of patches pre-exposed to isoproterenol. Moreover, the GTP-activated α subunit of the stimulatory G protein, $G_S$, directly activated $K_{Ca}$ channels in inside-out patches (Figure 4), and this activation was not affected by the presence of a competitive inhibitor of ATP or by an inhibitor of cAMP-dependent protein kinase. An identical stimulatory coupling scheme has been identified in membranes from coronary myocytes (132); reconstituted channels were activated by isoproterenol (extracellular) in the presence of GTP (intracellular), by GTPγS (intracellular), and by $G_{Sα}$ in the presence of the inhibitory peptide of PKA (intracellular). Thus stimulation of $K_{Ca}$ channels by $G_S$-linked receptors can occur independently of phosphorylation in smooth muscle cells. This stimulation bears substantial similarity to the membrane-delimited regulatory actions of G proteins described in other systems (29, 55).

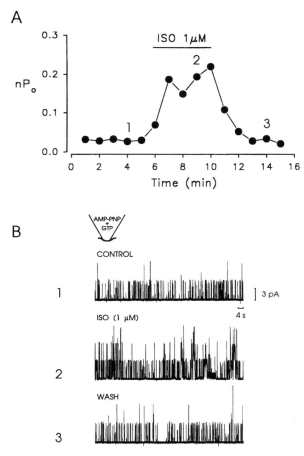

*Figure 3*  Isoproterenol stimulates $K_{Ca}$ channels independently of phosphorylation. Outside-out patches from a ferret tracheal myocyte were exposed to GTP (100 µM) and AMP-PNP (1 mM) at the cytosolic (pipette) surface. (*A*) Plot of $nP_o$ (calculated over 1 min intervals) vs time for the duration of an experiment in which the extracellular surface of the membrane was perfused with isoproterenol (ISO, 1 µM) and then washed out. Numbers show the temporal relationship of the traces shown in *B*. (*B*) Unitary $K_{Ca}$ channel currents recording before, during, and after exposure to isoproterenol. Traces show approximately 1 min of channel activity from each experimental condition at the points indicated in *A*. (Reproduced with permission from Kume et al, Reference 81.) 1994.

The degree to which phosphorylation-dependent and -independent coupling mechanisms contribute to the overall hyperpolarizing effect is not yet certain. It should be noted, however, that numerous studies have documented a substantial dissociation between hormone-mediated responses and hormone-me-

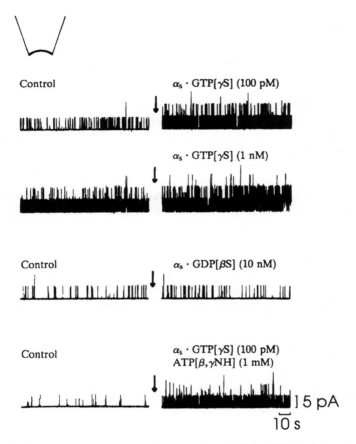

*Figure 4* Recombinant α$_S$ proteins activate K$_{Ca}$ channels independently of phosphorylation. Addition of α$_S$ GTPγS to the cytosolic (bath) surface of an inside-out patch from a porcine tracheal myocyte. In the absence of ATP, addition of 100 pM protein rapidly stimulated K$_{Ca}$ channel activity, which was further augmented by addition of 1 nM protein. Stimulatory activity was not observed with proteins reacted with GDPβS (*third panel*), and was equivalent in the presence of a nonmetabolizable ATP analogue (*bottom panel*). (Reproduced with permission from Kume et al, Reference 80.)

diated increases in cellular cAMP concentration (54, 81, 155, 164). Equivalent functional responses following adrenoreceptor stimulation occur at substantially lower concentration of cAMP than those produced by forskolin or cAMP analogues. Moreover, cAMP analogues (43) and phosphodiesterase inhibitors are relatively weak relaxants of airway smooth muscle (118, 152). Although cAMP-independent coupling between β$_2$ receptors and K$_{Ca}$ channels does not necessarily underlie these phenomena, the data are suggestive of additional mechanisms of adrenergic hormone signaling.

## Importance of Hyperpolarization in Muscle Relaxation

$\beta$-Adrenergic stimulation of smooth muscle cells appears to activate a signaling cascade that modifies the function of numerous proteins involved in excitation-contraction coupling (50, 90, 92, 101, 105, 131). However, the functional importance of activation of potassium channels and cellular hyperpolarization in $\beta$-adrenergic bronchial relaxation is somewhat controversial. Certainly, cellular hyperpolarization does not completely underlie bronchial relaxation because $\beta$-adrenergic relaxation occurs in the absence of hyperpolarization (5, 79). However, recent experiments have demonstrated that the relaxant ability of isoproterenol and other $\beta_2$-selective agents is markedly decreased when $K_{Ca}$ channel opening is prevented by the selective inhibition of $K_{Ca}$ using charybdotoxin or iberiotoxin (68, 69, 100). As shown in Figure 5, following precontraction with a cholinergic agonist, the dose-dependent relaxation of guinea pig tracheal rings is markedly blunted in the presence of iberiotoxin. The selectivity of this toxin in inhibiting $K_{Ca}$ channels would seem to indicate that under the conditions employed, the ability of the hormone agonist to open $K_{Ca}$ channels comprises a surprisingly important component of the relaxant ability of the hormone. However, inhibitory interactions between $K_{Ca}$ channel blockers and $\beta$-adrenergic hormones may also stem from a functional antagonism. Because channel antagonists increase basal tone in guinea pig tissue (69), and because nifedipine blocks this effect of charybdotoxin (57), the actions of the $K_{Ca}$ channel inhibitors in blocking $\beta$-adrenergic relaxation are likely owing to a depolarization of the tissue and opening of voltage-dependent calcium channels (138). Such actions could produce an increase in $[Ca^{2+}]_i$ that would antagonize $\beta$-adrenergic relaxation whether or not $K_{Ca}$ channels are modulated by the hormone. In human airways, however, charybdotoxin does not increase resting tone (40, 100), thus making functional antagonism less likely. Moreover, charybdotoxin does not markedly alter the relaxation caused by hyperpolarizing agents such as lemakalim (68, 100), which might be expected if the actions of the $K_{Ca}$ channel inhibitor were due merely to a depolarizing action and a functional antagonism at the level of membrane potential. Although these experiments are not considered definitive, and it is possible that the degree of involvement of $K_{Ca}$ channels in $\beta$-adrenergic relaxation depends substantially on the conditions chosen, the data indicate that coupling between $\beta$-adrenergic receptors and $K_{Ca}$ channels can underlie a significant component of the relaxant action of these hormones. One reason why the opening of $K_{Ca}$ channels may be particularly important during cholinergic excitation-contraction coupling is that the closing of $K_{Ca}$ channels by a pertussis-sensitive signaling pathway

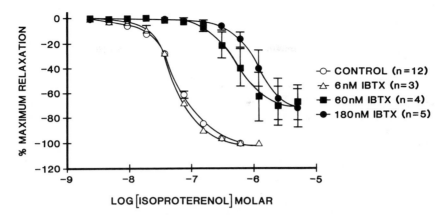

*Figure 5* Effect of iberiotoxin (IBTX) on β-adrenergic relaxation of carbachol contracted airway smooth muscle. Guinea pig tracheal rings were precontracted with 0.34 µM carbachol (1.4 µM indomethacin present), and then relaxed by cumulative addition of isoproterenol. Exposure to 60 and 180 nM iberiotoxin, a selective inhibitor of $K_{Ca}$ channels, shifted the dose-dependent relaxation significantly. Symbols show mean responses expressed as a percent of maximal isoproterenol relaxations. Vertical lines show standard errors. (Reproduced with permission from Jones et al, Reference 69.)

occurs during cholinergic contraction (30, 82), and this inhibitory coupling is necessary for full-force generation (83). Thus under conditions in which channel opening is strongly suppressed, β-adrenergic agonists would be expected to directly compete with this inhibition and open $K_{Ca}$ channels (80). It is likely that the resulting hyperpolarization critically affects the steady-state activation characteristics of voltage-dependent calcium channels (41, 71, 107, 150). One would therefore predict that isoproterenol would have a greater effect on $[Ca^{2+}]_i$ during cholinergic contraction than during KCl-induced contraction because cholinergic contractions would rely on a decrease in $K_{Ca}$ channel activity and because hyperpolarization associated with increases in potassium conductance would be self-limiting in KCl-induced contractions. Numerous studies have indicated that β-adrenergic hormones preferentially antagonize agonist-induced contractions. Moreover, measurements of $[Ca^{2+}]_i$ in smooth muscle segments during excitation-contraction coupling indicate that β-adrenergic hormones reduce $[Ca^{2+}]_i$ during agonist-induced, but not KCl-induced, contractions (1, 27, 34, 95, 114, 148, 161). At discussed below, however, adrenergic hormones modulate several processes of calcium homeostasis in smooth muscle and a precise estimation of the functional importance of hyperpolarization, and thus molecular pathways linking β-adrenergic receptor stimulation to $K_{Ca}$

channel opening, may depend substantially on experimental conditions and may vary greatly between smooth muscles.

## REGULATION OF INTRACELLULAR CALCIUM

In smooth muscle, tension is regulated by the calcium/calmodulin-dependent phosphorylation of myosin regulatory light chains, as described below. Much evidence indicates that β-adrenergic hormones decrease $[Ca^{2+}]_i$ in smooth muscle and that this reduction ($[Ca^{2+}]_i$) is the major factor in relaxation, although little consensus exists with respect to the physiologically relevant regulatory mechanisms. As discussed above, hormone-induced hyperpolarization of the myocyte is only one such mechanism by which $[Ca^{2+}]_i$ is reduced. Although a full discussion of these data is beyond the scope of this review, other mechanisms by which cyclase-linked hormones may alter calcium homeostasis include the augmentation of sarcolemmal $Ca^{2+}$ATPase (46), inhibition of phospholipase C (90, 101), augmentation of $Na^+$-$Ca^{2+}$ exchange (92, 131), and stimulation of sarcoplasmic reticulum $Ca^{2+}$ATPase through phosphorylation of phospholamban (24, 32, 99, 105, 121), resulting in an enhanced uptake of calcium into intracellular stores (77, 102, 153). In addition, as discussed below, the relationship between $[Ca^{2+}]_i$ and myosin light chain phosphorylation may be altered by hormone stimulation.

## DESENSITIZATION OF CONTRACTILE ELEMENTS TO CALCIUM

In addition to effecting airway smooth muscle relaxation by diminishing $[Ca^{2+}]_i$ via hyperpolarization and/or other mechanisms, there is evidence that β-adrenergic agents may diminish $Ca^{2+}$ sensitivity of the contractile elements. A cAMP-dependent pathway has been shown to reduce isometric force independently of alterations in $[Ca^{2+}]_i$ in both permeabilized and intact airway smooth muscle; however, the contribution of this effect to β-adrenergic action varies greatly depending upon conditions of activation. Evidence suggests that desensitization of contraction does not result from phosphorylation-mediated desensitization of myosin light chain kinase to activation by $Ca^{2+}$/calmodulin but possibly from activation of myosin light chain phosphatase. The background and evidence leading to these conclusions are reviewed below.

### $Ca^{2+}$ Sensitivity of Smooth Muscle Contraction

Smooth muscle contraction is brought about by the MgATP-dependent cyclic binding of myosin in thick filaments with actin in thin filaments. The actin-activated MgATPase activity of smooth muscle myosin is inhibited by its

20-kDa regulatory light chain (RLC) subunit; inhibition is removed following phosphorylation of the RLC at serine 19 by $Ca^{2+}$- and calmodulin-dependent myosin light chain kinase (MLCK) (52). Inhibition is restored following dephosphorylation of myosin RLC by a myosin-bound type-1 protein phosphatase, PP1M (4). The relative activities of MLCK and PP1M determine the steady-state value of RLC phosphorylation, which in turn is an important determinant of isometric force. The $Ca^{2+}$-dependence of steady-state force in smooth muscle results predominantly, if not wholly, from the $Ca^{2+}$-dependence of myosin RLC phosphorylation by MLCK (104); however, the precise dependence of force on $[Ca^{2+}]_i$ (the $Ca^{2+}$ sensitivity of force) can vary depending upon second messenger pathways utilized by specific stimuli (91, 139). Mechanisms involved in altering the $Ca^{2+}$ sensitivity of force are evaluated by establishing two relations: (a) the $Ca^{2+}$ dependence of RLC phosphorylation and (b) the RLC phosphorylation dependence of force. A change in slope of the former suggests that second messengers can modify MLCK or PP1M activities at fixed $[Ca^{2+}]_i$, whereas a change in slope of the latter suggests that regulatory elements in addition to RLC phosphorylation are enlisted. Additional or collateral regulation of smooth muscle contraction may arise from the action of one or both of two actin-binding proteins, caldesmon and calponin. Both inhibit actin-activated myosin MgATPase in vitro, and inhibition is reversed by the binding of $Ca^{2+}$/calmodulin or by phosphorylation (93, 160). While the importance of regulation by myosin phosphorylation in vivo is well accepted, the necessity and relative contribution of thin filament regulation is debated.

cAMP-dependent protein kinase phosphorylates purified MLCK resulting in a tenfold decrease in the sensitivity of MLCK to activation by $Ca^{2+}$/calmodulin (2, 31). It was hypothesized that cAMP promotes relaxation of smooth muscle by inhibiting RLC phosphorylation via phosphorylation of MLCK by PKA. To date, this is the only biochemical mechanism described by which cAMP would lead to desensitization of the contractile response to $[Ca^{2+}]_i$; other biochemical effects remain to be explored.

Smooth and nonmuscle cells express a common form of myosin light chain kinase (47). The arrangement of the catalytic and regulatory domains of smooth muscle MLCK is shown in Figure 6. The catalytic core, in the central region, is highly homologous to other protein kinases and contains determinants for ATP and RLC binding. Located C-terminal of the catalytic core is a short segment that binds calmodulin with high affinity. Calmodulin binding results in activation of the phosphotransferase reaction by removing autoinhibition, which is conferred by a region linking the catalytic core and calmodulin-binding domain (144). C-terminal of the calmodulin-binding domain, as illustrated in Figure 6, are sites of phosphorylation (including site A) that have been shown in vitro as substrates for several protein kinases, including PKA, PKC, and the $Ca^{2+}$/calmodulin-dependent multifunctional protein kinase II (CaMK

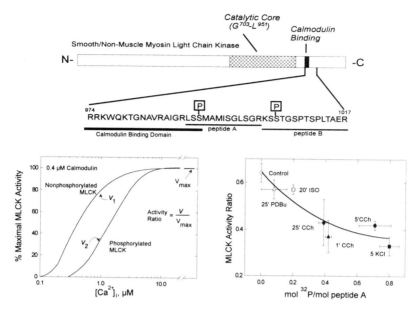

*Figure 6*   Phosphorylation of smooth muscle myosin light chain kinase at site A results in diminished sensitivity to activation by $Ca^{2+}$/calmodulin in vitro and in vivo. *Upper panel*: Domain organization and sites of phosphorylation of MLCK by PKA (145). MLCK has a catalytic core in the center that is similar in sequence to other protein kinases. On the C-terminal side of the catalytic core is an autoinhibitory domain adjacent to or overlapping with the calmodulin-binding domain. Expanded below is the continuous sequence of a portion of the rabbit smooth muscle MLCK (47). Serine residues phosphorylated by PKA are identified, and phosphopeptides derived from tryptic digestion are labeled A and B. (Reproduced with permission from Stull et al, Reference 145.) *Lower left panel*: Illustration of activity ratio assay to assess changes in $Ca^{2+}$ activation properties resulting from phosphorylation of MLCK (98). In dilute homogenates with 0.4 μM calmodulin added, the calcium concentrations required for half-maximal activation of enzyme activity are less when MLCK is not phosphorylated than when phosphorylated, whereas $V_{max}$ is unchanged. Alterations in the $Ca^{2+}$ activation properties of MLCK in tissue homogenates can be assessed by comparison of the ratio of activities measured at 1 and 100 μM $Ca^{2+}$ ($v/V_{max}$), where a value of 0.8 ($v1/V_{max}$) indicates maximal sensitivity to $Ca^{2+}$, and a value of 0.3 ($v2/V_{max}$) indicates maximal desensitization resulting from phosphorylation. (Reproduced with permission from Miller et al, Reference 98.) *Lower right panel*: Correlation of activity ratio assay with phosphorylation of site A in MLCK isolated from treated tissues. [32]P-labeled strips of bovine trachealis were treated with 0.1 μM carbachol (CCh) (1, 5, 25 min); 65 mM KCl plus 0.1 μM atropine (5 min); 3 μM isoproterenol (ISO) (20 min); or 1 μM phorbol dibutyrate (PDBu) (25 min); and quick frozen (143). MLCK phosphorylation was analyzed for stoichiometry of phosphate incorporation in site A as described. In parallel experiments, homogenates of tissues treated identically in the absence of [32]P were assayed for MLCK activity ratio. (Reproduced with permission from Stull et al, Reference 143.)

II) (31, 53, 60, 61, 109). In the absence of $Ca^{2+}$/calmodulin, these kinases phosphorylate both site A and a second site, which leads to a tenfold increase in the concentration of $Ca^{2+}$/calmodulin required for half-maximal activation ($K_{CaM}$). In the presence of $Ca^{2+}$/calmodulin, phosphate is incorporated into the second site with no effect on MLCK activation properties. MLCK is also phosphorylated by cGMP-dependent protein kinase but not in site A; moreover, phosphorylation has no effect on the $Ca^{2+}$/calmodulin activation properties of MLCK (108). Sequence analysis of MLCK sites phosphorylated by PKA revealed that the serine phosphorylated in site A is immediately adjacent to the calmodulin-binding domain (91), whereas the serine phosphorylated in site B is more toward the C-terminus (91, 117); thus site A is situated to affect $Ca^{2+}$/calmodulin binding and activation of MLCK. MLCK is dephosphorylated by both protein phosphatases 1 and 2A (111, 116), and in vivo evidence suggests that MLCK is dephosphorylated by the same phosphatase that dephosphorylates myosin RLC (147, 148).

Phosphorylation of site A exerts its effect on $Ca^{2+}$/calmodulin activation properties of MLCK independently of phosphorylation of site B or other sites. This conclusion is supported by the following observations. (*a*) Phosphorylation of site B has no effect on the $Ca^{2+}$/calmodulin activation properties of MLCK, as described above. (*b*) Mutation of sites A (Ser-992) and B (Ser-1005) to neutral (alanine) or acidic (aspartate) residues is expected either to have little effect on kinase activation (neutral) or to increase $K_{CaM}$ by introduction of negative charge that would mimic that introduced by phosphate incorporation (acidic). Substitution of either neutral or acidic amino acids in site B had no effect on calmodulin activation properties, whereas the introduction of aspartate for the phosphoacceptor at site A resulted in a significant increase in $K_{CaM}$ (72). (*c*) Importantly, the $Ca^{2+}$/calmodulin activation properties of MLCK correlate with the stoichiometry of $^{32}$P incorporation in site A of MLCK isolated from intact smooth muscle, which is independent of phosphate content in other sites (143) (*lower panels,* Figure 1). The $Ca^{2+}$/calmodulin activation properties of MLCK can be assessed in dilute homogenates of tissues that are frozen following various treatments. Alterations in the ratio of activities at 1:100 $\mu$M $Ca^{2+}$ ($v/V_{max}$) may be used to calculate fold changes in $K_{CaM}$ based upon a quantitative relationship (98). The relationship between MLCK activity ratio and extent of phosphorylation of phosphopeptide A was determined for MLCK isolated from $^{32}$P-labeled trachealis tissues treated with activators of PKA, PKC, and CaMK II (143). As seen in Figure 1, there is a direct relationship between the extent of phosphorylation of site A and the MLCK activity ratio, with the solid line representing the relation predicted from the quantitative relationship between site A phosphorylation and the activity ratio. Treatment conditions resulted in widely varying stoichiometry of $^{32}$P incorporation into other sites that did not correlate in any way with the enzyme activation properties (143). Interestingly, the extent of site A phosphorylation in MLCK was greatest under conditions resulting in elevated $[Ca^{2+}]_i$. Subsequent studies in permeabilized tracheal cells and tissues showed that MLCK site A is phosphorylated in a $Ca^{2+}$/calmodulin-dependent manner by CaMK II (147, 149).

## Alterations in $Ca^{2+}$ Sensitivity in Response to Elements of the β-Adrenergic Pathway

As discussed above, the predominant component in the relaxation response to β-adrenergic agents is a reduction in $[Ca^{2+}]_i$. However, conditions have been documented under which addition of the catalytic subunit of cAMP-dependent protein kinase results in diminished force at fixed $[Ca^{2+}]_i$ in permeabilized trachealis (141), as well as in other smooth muscles (97, 110, 112, 126). Isoproterenol or forskolin inhibit the contraction of intact depolarized trachealis without changing $[Ca^{2+}]_i$ (113, 148). Is myosin light chain kinase phosphorylation responsible for $Ca^{2+}$ desensitization in response to β-adrenergic agents or cAMP?

With the discovery that site A phosphorylation in MLCK caused desensitization to activation by $Ca^{2+}$/calmodulin, experiments with skinned fibers provided circumstantial support for such an effect. In addition, it was demonstrated that MLCK phosphorylation increased from 1.0 to 1.7 mol phosphate/mol MLCK in $^{32}$P-labeled tracheal smooth muscle in response to forskolin (35). Forskolin treatment was also accompanied by diminished RLC phosphorylation and force, consistent with a role for MLCK phosphorylation in smooth muscle relaxation. However, the sites of phosphorylation were not identified by peptide mapping, nor were the $Ca^{2+}$/calmodulin activation properties measured. Miller et al (98) demonstrated that β-adrenergic stimulation of trachealis resulted in activation of the cAMP system and relaxation, but no change occurred in the $Ca^{2+}$/calmodulin activation properties of MLCK; thus no evidence arose for decreased enzyme activity resulting from phosphorylation.

The development and use of $Ca^{2+}$ indicators in smooth muscle has resulted in improved precision in interpretation of the mechanisms of action of β-adrenergic agonists. Figure 7 illustrates the effect of isoproterenol on the $Ca^{2+}$ dependence of both RLC phosphorylation and MLCK activation properties in bovine trachealis (148). Under all conditions, the dependence of isometric force on RLC phosphorylation was unaltered, thus force was inhibited in proportion to RLC phosphorylation following treatment with isoproterenol. For contractions elicited by the muscarinic agonist carbachol (*left panel*, Figure 7), the application of isoproterenol resulted in decreased $[Ca^{2+}]_i$, with no change in the $Ca^{2+}$ dependence of RLC phosphorylation. In intact muscle, as in permeabilized preparations (described above), the MLCK activity ratio decreased as $[Ca^{2+}]_i$ increased, consistent with $Ca^{2+}$-dependent phosphorylation of MLCK.

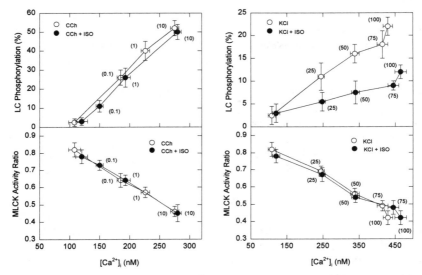

*Figure 7* Effect of isoproterenol (ISO) on [Ca$^{2+}$]$_i$, myosin light chain phosphorylation, and MLCK activity ratio in bovine trachealis stimulated with carbachol (CCh) or KCl. Tracheal smooth muscle strips were loaded with Fura-2, and [Ca$^{2+}$]$_i$ was estimated following 2 min stimulation alone (*open circles*) or after preincubation with 5 μM isoproterenol for 5 min (*closed circles*) (148). *Left panels*: Responses to CCh or CCh plus ISO, numbers in parentheses represent the concentrations of CCh in μM. Although the relationship between [Ca$^{2+}$]$_i$ and RLC phosphorylation did not change, the responsiveness to carbachol decreased in tissues pretreated with isoproterenol. *Right panels*: Responses to KCl or KCl plus ISO, numbers in parentheses represent concentrations of KCl in mM. Note differences in scales for [Ca$^{2+}$]$_i$ and LC phosphorylation between carbachol- and KCl-treated tissues. (Reproduced with permission from Tang et al, Reference 148.)

Treatment with isoproterenol actually led to a reduction in MLCK phosphorylation as a result of its action in reducing [Ca$^{2+}$]$_i$. The effect of isoproterenol on the Ca$^{2+}$ dependence of RLC phosphorylation in KCl-depolarized trachealis (*right panel*, Figure 7) was strikingly different from that obtained with carbachol. RLC phosphorylation was depressed without a decrease in [Ca$^{2+}$]$_i$. The desensitization of RLC phosphorylation to [Ca$^{2+}$]$_i$ did not result from alterations in the activation properties of MLCK, however. MLCK phosphorylation remained Ca$^{2+}$ dependent during depolarization, and because isoproterenol had no effect on [Ca$^{2+}$]$_i$, there was no effect of isoproterenol on MLCK activation properties. Similar to results obtained using trachealis, the hog carotid artery stimulated with histamine was relaxed by forskolin in a [Ca$^{2+}$]$_i$ and RLC phosphorylation-dependent manner, whereas KCl-depolarized strips showed RLC dephosphorylation and relaxation in response to forskolin without diminished $[Ca^{2+}]_i$ (154). Also similar to results with trachealis, forskolin affected MLCK activation properties only secondarily to changes brought about in $[Ca^{2+}]_i$. Thus activation of the cAMP-dependent pathway does not result in enhanced phosphorylation of MLCK at site A.

How do isoproterenol or other activators of the cAMP pathway desensitize the contractile elements to $[Ca^{2+}]_i$? Current evidence suggests that desensitization of force to $[Ca^{2+}]_i$ is brought about by desensitization of RLC phosphorylation. Whereas alterations in MLCK activation properties cannot account for desensitization, we postulate that the cAMP pathway results in stimulation of myosin phosphatase (148). The activities of type 1 protein phosphatase catalytic subunit isoforms are regulated by association with targeting subunits and by binding to cytosolic inhibitors (59). Smooth muscle PP1M is bound to myosin by a pair of myosin-binding subunits (130 and 20 kDa) that increase the activity of the catalytic subunit, PP1Cβ (37 kDa), toward smooth muscle myosin (4, 27a, 133, 134). Myosin phosphatase is inhibited by a receptor-coupled and G protein-dependent pathway in smooth muscle (reviewed in 139). Although the mechanisms involved are not completely understood, it was recently shown that thiophosphorylation of the 130-kDa regulatory subunit of PP1M is associated with a significant decrease in enzyme activity as well as a decrease in the $Ca^{2+}$ sensitivity of force and RLC phosphorylation (152a). There are several potential phosphorylation sites on the smooth muscle 130-kDa targeting subunit, including four for PKA; the effects of PKA phosphorylation on PP1M activity have not yet been defined (133). Whether myosin phosphatase activity is stimulated directly or indirectly by the β-adrenergic pathway remains to be investigated. Future studies will undoubtedly reveal additional mechanisms whereby PP1M activity is regulated by second messenger pathways.

## Literature Cited

1. Abe A, Karaki H. 1992. Mechanisms underlying the inhibitory effect of dibutyryl cyclic AMP in vascular smooth muscle. *Eur. J. Pharmacol.* 211: 305–11
2. Adelstein RS, Conti MA, Hathaway DR, Klee CB. 1978. Phosphorylation of smooth muscle myosin light chain kinase by the catalytic subunit of adenosine 3′: 5′-monophosphate-dependent protein kinase. *J. Biol. Chem.* 253:8347–50
3. Ahmed F, Foster RW, Small RC, Weston AH. 1984. Some features of the spasmogenic actions of acetyl-choline and histamine in guinea-pig isolated trachealis. *Br. J. Pharmacol.* 83: 227–33
4. Alessi D, MacDougall LK, Sola MM, Ikebe M, Cohen P. 1992. The control of protein phosphatase-1 by targetting subunits. The major myosin phosphatase in avian smooth muscle is a novel form of protein phosphatase-1. *Eur. J. Biochem.* 210:1023–35
5. Allen SL, Beech DJ, Foster RW, Morgan GP, Small RC. 1985. Electrophysiological and other aspects of the relaxant action of isoprenaline in guinea-pig iso-

lated trachealis. *Br. J. Pharmacol.* 86: 843–54

6. Allen SL, Boyle JP, Cortijo J, Foster RW, Morgan GP, Small RC. 1986. Electrical and mechanical effects of BRL34915 in guinea-pig isolated trachealis. *Br. J. Pharmacol.* 89:395–405

7. Anwer K, Oberti C, Perez GJ, Perez-Reyes N, McDougall JK, et al. 1993. Calcium-activated K+ channels as modulators of human myometrial contractile activity. *Am. J. Physiol.* 265: C976–85

8. Anwer K, Toro L, Oberti C, Stefani E, Sanborn BM. 1992. $Ca^{2+}$-activated $K^+$ channels in pregnant rat myometrium: modulation by a β-adrenergic agent. *Am. J. Physiol.* 263:C1049–56

9. Atkinson NS, Robertson GA, Ganetzky B. 1991. A component of calcium-activated potassium channels encoded by the *Drosophilia slo* locus. *Science* 253: 551–53

10. Augustine CK, Bezanilla F. 1990. Phosphorylation modulates potassium conductance and gating current of perfused giant axons of squid. *J. Gen. Physiol.* 95:245–71

11. Beech DJ, Bolton TB. 1989. Two components of potassium current activated by depolarization of single smooth muscle cells from the rabbit portal vein. *J. Physiol.* 418:293–309

12. Beech DJ, Bolton TB. 1989. Properties of the cromakalim-induced potassium conductance in smooth muscle cells isolated from the rabbit portal vein. *Br. J. Pharmacol.* 98:851–64

13. Benham CD, Bolton TB. 1986. Spontaneous transient outward currents in single visceral and vascular smooth muscle cells of the rabbit. *J. Physiol.* 381:385–406

14. Benham CD, Bolton TB, Denbigh JS, Lang RJ. 1987. Inward rectification in freshly isolated single smooth muscle cells of the rabbit jejunum. *J. Physiol.* 383:461–76

15. Benham CD, Bolton TB, Lang RJ, Takewaki T. 1986. Calcium-activated potassium channels in single smooth muscle cells of rabbit jejunum and guinea-pig mesenteric artery. *J. Physiol.* 371:45–67

16. Black JL, Armour CL, Johnson PRA, Alouan LA, Barnes PJ. 1990. The action of potassium channel activator, BRL 38227 (lemakalim), on human airway smooth muscle. *Am. Rev. Respir. Dis.* 142:1384–89

17. Blumenthal EM, Kaczmarek LK. 1992. Modulation by cAMP of a slowly activating potassium channel expressed in *Xenopus* oocytes. *J. Neurosci.* 12:290–96

18. Bosma MM, Allen ML, Martin TM, Tempel BL. 1993. PKA-dependent regulation of mKv1.1, a mouse *shaker*-like potassium channel gene, when stable expressed CHO cells. *J. Neurosci.* 13: 5242–50

19. Boyle JP, Tomasic M, Kotlikoff MI. 1992. Delayed rectifier potassium channels in canine and porcine airway smooth muscle cells. *J. Physiol.* 447: 329–50

20. Bülbring E, Tomita T. 1969. Increase of membrane conductance by adrenaline in the smooth muscle of guinea-pig taenia coli. *Proc. R. Soc. London Ser. B.* 172:89–102

21. Bülbring E, Tomita T. 1987. Catecholamine action on smooth muscle. *Pharmacol. Rev.* 39:49–96

22. Butler A, Tsunoda S, McCobb DP, Wei A, Salkoff L. 1993. *mSLO*, a complex mouse gene encoding "maxi" calcium-activated potassium channels. *Science* 261:221–24

23. Cameron AR, Johnston CF, Kirkpatrick CT, Kirkpatrick MCA. 1983. The quest for the inhibitory neurotransmitter in bovine tracheal smooth muscle. *J. Exp. Physiol.* 68:413–26

24. Carafoli E. 1994. Biogenesis: plasma membrane calcium ATPase: 15 years of work on the purified enzyme. *FASEB J.* 8:993–1002

25. Carl A, Kenyon JL, Uemura D, Fusetani N, Sanders KM. 1991. Regulation of $Ca^{2+}$-activated $K^+$ channels by protein kinase A and phosphatase inhibitors. *J. Physiol.* 261:C387–92

26. Carl A, Sanders KM. 1990. Measurement of single channel open probability with voltage ramps. *J. Neurosci. Meth.* 33:157–63

27. Chen XL, Rembold CM. 1992. Cyclic nucleotide-dependent regulation of $Mn^{2+}$ influx, $[Ca^{2+}]_i$, and arterial smooth muscle relaxation. *Am. J. Physiol.* 263: C468–73

27a. Chen YH, Chen MX, Alessi DR, Campbell DG, Shanahan C, et al. 1994. Molecular cloning of cDNA encoding the 110 kDA and 21 kDa regulatory subunits of smooth muscle protein phosphatase 1M. *FEBS Lett.* 35:51–55

28. Chung S, Reinhart PH, Martin BL, Brautigan D, Levitan IB. 1991. Protein kinase activity closely associated with a reconstituted calcium-activated potassium channel. *Science* 253:560–62

29. Clapham DE. 1994. Direct G protein activation of ion channels? *Annu. Rev. Neurosci.* 17:441–64

30. Cole WC, Carl A, Sanders KM. 1989. Muscarinic suppression of $Ca^{2+}$-depend-

ent K current in colonic smooth muscle. *Am. J. Physiol.* 257:C481–87

31. Conti MA, Adelstein RS. 1981. The relationship between calmodulin binding and phosphorylation of smooth muscle myosin kinase by the catalytic subunit of 3′:5′ cAMP-dependent protein kinase. *J. Biol. Chem.* 256:3178–81

32. Cornwell TL, Pryzwansky KB, Wyatt TA, Lincoln TM. 1991. Regulation of sarcoplasmic reticulum protein phosphorylation by localized cyclic GMP-dependent protein kinase in vascular smooth muscle cells. *Mol. Pharmacol.* 40:923–31

33. Daut J, Maier-Rudolph W, von Beckerath N, Mehrke G, Gunther K, Goedel-Meinen L. 1990. Hypoxic dilation of coronary arteries is mediated by ATP-sensitive potassium channels. *Nature* 247:1341–44

34. DeFeo TT, Morgan KG. 1989. Calcium-force coupling mechanisms during vasodilator-induced relaxation of ferret aorta. *J. Physiol.* 412:123–33

35. de Lanerolle P, Nishikawa M, Yost DA, Adelstein RS. 1984. Increased phosphorylation of myosin light chain kinase after an increase in cyclic cAMP in intact smooth muscle. *Science* 223:1415–17

36. Diamond J, Marshall JM. 1969. A comparision of the effects of various smooth muscle relaxants of the electrical and mechanical activity of rat uterus. *J. Pharmacol. Exp. Ther.* 168:21–30

37. Diamond J, Marshall JM. 1969. Smooth muscle relaxants: dissociation between resting membrane potential and resting tension in rat myometrium. *J. Pharmacol. Exp. Ther.* 168:13–20

38. Edwards FR, Hirst GD. 1988. Inward rectification in submucosal arterioles of guinea-pig ileum. *J. Physiol.* 404:437–54

39. Ewald DA, Williams A, Levitan IB. 1985. Modulation of single $Ca^{2+}$-dependent $K^+$-channel activity by protein phosphorylation. *Nature* 315:503–6

40. Fleischmann BK, Hay DWP, Kotlikoff MI. 1994. Control of basal tone by delayed rectifier potassium channels in human airways. *Am. Rev. Respir. Dis.* 149:A1080

41. Fleischmann BK, Murray RK, Kotlikoff MI. 1994. A voltage window for sustained elevation of cytosolic calcium in smooth muscle cells. *Proc. Natl. Acad. Sci. USA* 91:11914–18

42. Fleischmann BK, Washabau RJ, Kotlikoff MI. 1993. Control of resting membrane potential by delayed rectifier potassium currents in ferret airway smooth muscle cells. *J. Physiol.* 468:625–38

43. Francis SH, Noblett BD, Todd BW, Wells JN, Corbin JD. 1988. Relaxation of vascular and tracheal smooth muscle by cyclic nucleotide analogs that preferentially activate purified cGMP-dependent protein kinase. *Mol. Pharmacol.* 34:506–17

44. Fujiwara T, Sumimoto K, Itoh T, Kuriyama H. 1988. Relaxing effects of procaterol, a $\beta_2$-adrenergic stimulant on smooth muscle cell of the dog trachea. *Br. J. Pharmacol.* 93:199–209

45. Fuller RW, Dixon CM, Cuss FM, Barnes PJ. 1987. Bradykinin-induced bronchoconstriction in humans. Mode of action. *Am. Rev. Respir. Dis.* 135:176–80

46. Furukawa K-I, Tawada Y, Shigekawa M. 1988. Regulation of the plasma membrane $Ca^{2+}$ pump by cyclic nucleotides in cultured vascular smooth muscle cells. *J. Biol. Chem.* 263:8058–65

47. Gallagher PJ, Herring BP, Griffin SA, Stull JT. 1991. Molecular characterization of a mammalian smooth muscle myosin light chain kinase. *J. Biol. Chem.* 266:23936–44

48. Garcia-Calvo M, Knaus H-G, McManus OB, Giangiacomo KM, Kaczorowski GJ, Garcia ML. 1994. Purification and reconstitution of the high-conductance, calcium-activated potassium channel from tracheal smooth muscle. *J. Biol. Chem.* 269:676–82

49. Green KA, Foster RW, Small RC. 1991. A patch-clamp study of K+-channel activity in bovine isolated tracheal smooth muscle cells. *Br. J. Pharmacol.* 102:871–78

50. Hall IP, Hill SJ. 1988. Beta-adrenoceptor stimulation inhibits histamine-stimulated inositol phospholipid hydrolysis in bovine tracheal smooth muscle. *Br. J. Pharmacol.* 95:1204–12

51. Hart PJ, Overturf KE, Russell SN, Carl A, Hume JR, et al. 1993. Cloning and expression of Kv1.2 class delayed rectifier K+ channel from canine colonic smooth muscle. *Proc. Natl. Acad. Sci. USA* 90:9659–63

52. Hartshorne DJ. 1987. Biochemistry of the contractile process in smooth muscle. In *Physiology of the Gastrointestinal Tract,* ed. LR Johnson, pp. 423–82. New York: Raven

53. Hashimoto Y, Soderling TR. 1990. Phosphorylation of smooth muscle myosin light chain kinase by $Ca^{2+}$/calmodulin-dependent protein kinase-II. Comparative study of the phosphoryla-

tion sites. *Arch. Biochem. Biophys.* 278: 41–45

54. Hei Y, MacDonell KL, McNeill JH, Diamond J. 1991. Lack of correlation between activation of cyclic AMP-dependent protein kinase and inhibition of contraction of rat vas deferens by cyclic AMP analogs. *Mol. Pharmacol.* 39:233–38

55. Hepler JR, Gilman AG. 1992. G proteins. *Trends Biochem. Sci.* 17:383–87

56. Honda K, Satake T, Takagi K, Tomita T. 1986. Effects of relaxants on electrical and mechanical activities in the guinea-pig tracheal muscle. *Br. J. Pharmacol.* 87:665–71

57. Huang J-C, Garcia ML, Reuben JP, Kaczorowski GJ. 1993. Inhibition of $\beta$-adrenoceptor agonist relaxation of airway smooth muscle by $Ca^{2+}$-activated $K^+$ channel blockers. *Eur. J. Pharmacol.* 235:37–43

58. Huang X-Y, Morielli AD, Peralta EG. 1994. Molecular basis of cardiac potassium channel stimulation by protein kinase A. *Proc. Natl. Acad. Sci. USA* 91:624–28

59. Hubbard MJ, Cohen P. 1993. On target with a new mechanism for the regulation of protein phosphorylation. *Trends Biochem. Sci.* 18:172–77

60. Ikebe M, Inagaki M, Kanamaru K, Hidaka H. 1985. Phosphorylation of smooth muscle myosin light chain kinase by $Ca^{2+}$-activated, phospholipid-dependent protein kinase. *J. Biol. Chem.* 260:4547–50

61. Ikebe M, Reardon S. 1990. Phosphorylation of smooth myosin light chain kinase by smooth muscle $Ca^{2+}$/calmodulin-dependent multifunctional protein kinase. *J. Biol. Chem.* 265:8975–78

62. Imaizumi Y, Watanabe M. 1981. The effect of tetraethylammonium chloride on potassium permeability in the smooth muscle cell membrane of canine trachea. *J. Physiol.* 316:33–46

63. Ito Y, Tajima K. 1982. Dual effects of catecholamines on pre- and post-junctional membranes in the dog trachea. *Br. J. Pharmacol.* 75:433–40

64. Jan LY, Jan YN. 1992. Structural elements involved in specific $K^+$ channel functions. *Annu. Rev. Physiol.* 54:537–55

65. Janssen LJ, Daniel EE. 1991. Depolarizing agents induce oscillations in canine bronchial smooth muscle membrane potential: possible mechanisms. *J. Pharmacol. Exp. Ther.* 259:110–17

66. Jiang H, Colbran JL, Francis SH, Corbin JD. 1992. Direct evidence for cross-activation of cGMP-dependent protein kinase by cGMP in pig coronary arteries. *J. Biol. Chem.* 267:1015–19

67. Johansson B, Johnsson O, Axelsson J, Wahlstrom B. 1967. Electrical and mechanical characteristics of vascular smooth muscle response to norepinephrine and isoproterenol. *Circ. Res.* 21:619–33

68. Jones TR, Charette L, Garcia ML, Kaczorowski GJ. 1990. Selective inhibition of relaxation of guinea-pig trachea by charybdotoxin, a potent $Ca^{2+}$-activated $K^+$ channel inhibitor. *J. Pharmacol. Exp. Ther.* 255:697–706

69. Jones TR, Charette L, Garcia ML, Kaczorowski GJ. 1993. Interaction of iberiotoxin with $\beta$-adrenoreceptor agonists and sodium nitroprusside on guinea pig trachea. *J. Appl. Phsyiol.* 74:1879–84

70. Kaczmarek LK. 1988. The regulation of neuronal calcium and potassium channels by protein phosphorylation. *Adv. Second Messenger Phosphorylation Res.* 22:113–38

71. Kamishima T, Nelson MT, Patlak JB. 1992. Carbachol modulates voltage sensitivity of calcium channels in bronchial smooth muscle in rats. *Am. J. Physiol.* 32:C69–77

72. Kamm KE, Luby-Phelps K, Tansey MG, Gallagher PJ, Stull JT. 1995. Regulation of myosin light chain kinase activity in smooth muscle. In *Regulation of the Contractile Cycle in Smooth Muscle*, ed. M Ito, pp. 139–58. Tokyo: Springer-Verlag

73. Kannan MS, Jager LP, Daniel EE, Garfield RE. 1983. Effects of 4-aminopyridine and tetraethylammonium chloride on the electrical activity and cable properties of canine tracheal smooth muscle. *J. Pharmacol. Exp. Ther.* 227:706–16

74. Kirkpatrick CT. 1975. Excitation and contraction in bovine tracheal smooth muscle. *J. Physiol.* 244:263–81

75. Kirkpatrick CT. 1981. Tracheobronchial smooth muscle. In *Smooth Muscle: An Assessment of Current Knowledge,* ed. E Bülbring, AF Brading, AW Jones, T Tomita, pp.385–95 London: Edward Arnold

76. Knaus HG, Garcia-Calvo M, Kaczorowski GJ, Garcia ML. 1994. Subunit composition of the high conductance calcium-activated potassium channel from smooth muscle, a representative of the *mSlo* and *slowpoke* family of potassium channels. *J. Biol. Chem.* 369:3921–24

77. Komori S, Bolton TB. 1989. Actions of guanine nucleotides and cyclic nucleotides on calcium stores in single patch-

clamped smooth muscle cells from rabbit portal vein. *Br. J. Pharmacol.* 97: 973–82

78. Kroeger EA, Stephens NL. 1975. Effect of tetraethylammonium on tonic airway smooth muscle: initiation of phasic electrical activity. *Am. J. Physiol.* 228:633–36

79. Kumar MA. 1978. The basis of β-adrenergic bronchodilation. *J. Pharmacol. Exp. Ther.* 206:528–34

80. Kume H, Graziano MP, Kotlikoff MI. 1992. Stimulatory and inhibitory regulation of calcium-activated potassium channels by guanine nucleotide-binding proteins. *Proc. Natl. Acad. Sci. USA* 89:11051–55

81. Kume H, Hall I, Washabau RJ, Takagi K, Kotlikoff MI. 1994. β-adrenergic agonists regulate $K_{Ca}$ channels in airway smooth muscle by cAMP dependent and independent mechanisms. *J. Clin. Invest.* 93:371–79

82. Kume H, Kotlikoff MI. 1991. Muscarinic inhibition of single $K_{Ca}$ channels in smooth muscle cells by a pertussis-sensitive G protein. *Am. J. Physiol.* 261:C1204–9

83. Kume H, Mikawa K, Takagi K, Kotlikoff MI. 1995. Role of G proteins and $K_{Ca}$ channels in the muscarinic and β-adrenergic regulation of tracheal smooth muscle. *Am. J. Physiol.* 12:L221–29

84. Kume H, Takai A, Tokuno H, Tomita T. 1989. Regulation of $Ca^{2+}$-dependent $K^+$-channel activity in tracheal myocytes by phosphorylation. *Nature* 341:152–54

85. Landgraf W, Hullin R, Gobel C, Hofmann F. 1986. Phosphorylation of cGMP-dependent protein kinase increases the affinity for cyclic AMP. *Eur. J. Biochem.* 154:113–17

86. Lands AM, Arnold A, McAuliff JP, Luduena FP, Brown TG. 1967. Differentiation of receptor systems activated by sympathomimetic amines. *Nature* 214:597–98

87. Latorre R, Vergara C, Hidalgo C. 1982. Reconstitution in planar lipid bilayers of a $Ca^{2+}$-dependent $K^+$ channel from transverse tubule membranes isolated from rabbit skeletal muscle. *Proc. Natl. Acad. Sci. USA* 79:805–9

88. Lemos JR, Novak-Hofer I, Levitan IB. 1985. Phosphoproteins associated with the regulation of a specific potassium channel in the identified *Aplysia* neuron R15. *J. Biol. Chem.* 260:3207–14

89. Levitan IB. 1988. Modulation of ion channels in neurons and other cells. *Annu. Rev. Neurosci.* 11:119–36

90. Lincoln TM, Cornwell TL, Taylor AE. 1990. cGMP-dependent protein kinase mediates the reduction of $Ca^{2+}$ by cAMP in vascular smooth muscle cells. *Am. J. Physiol.* 258:C399–407

91. Lukas TJ, Burgess WH, Prendergast FG, Lau W, Watterson DM. 1986. Calmodulin binding domains: characterization of a phosphorylation and calmodulin binding site from myosin light chain kinase. *Biochemistry* 25:1458–64

92. Madison JM, Brown JK. 1988. Differential inhibitory effects of forskolin, isoproterenol, and dibutyryl cyclic adenosine monophosphate on phosphoinositide hydrolysis in canine tracheal smooth muscle. *J. Clin. Invest.* 82:1462–65

93. Marston SB, Redwood CS. 1991. The molecular anatomy of caldesmon. *Biochem. J.* 279:1–16

94. McCann JD, Welsh MJ. 1986. Calcium-activated potassium channels in canine airway smooth muscle. *J. Physiol.* 372:113–27

95. McDaniel NL, Rembold CM, Richard HM, Murphy RA. 1991. Cyclic AMP relaxes swine arterial smooth muscle predominantly by decreasing cell $Ca^{2+}$ concentration. *J. Physiol.* 439:147–60

96. McManus OW, Helms LMH, Pallanck L, Ganetzky B, Swanson R, Leonard RJ. 1995. Functional role of the β subunit of high-conductance calcium-activated potassium channels. *Cell* 14:1–20

97. Meisheri KD, Rüegg JC. 1983. Dependence of cyclic-AMP induced relaxation on $Ca^{2+}$ and calmodulin in skinned smooth muscle of guinea pig Taenia coli. *Pflügers Arch.* 399:315–20

98. Miller JR, Silver PJ, Stull JT. 1983. The role of myosin light chain kinase phosphorylation in β-adrenergic relaxation of tracheal smooth muscle. *Mol. Pharmacol.* 24:235–42

99. Missiaen L, Wuytack F, Raeymaekers L, DeSmedt H, Droogmans G, et al. 1991. $Ca^{2+}$ extrusion across plasma membrane and $Ca^{2+}$ uptake by intracellular stores. *Pharmacol. Ther.* 50:191–232

100. Miura M, Belvisi MG, Stretton D, Yacoub MH, Barnes PJ. 1992. Role of potassium channels in bronchodilator response in human airways. *Am. Rev. Respir. Dis.* 146:132–36

101. Moore EDW, Fay FS. 1993. Isoproterenol stimulates rapid extrusion of sodium from isolated smooth muscle cells. *Proc. Natl. Acad. Sci. USA* 90:8058–62

102. Mueller E, van Breeman C. 1979. Role of intracellular $Ca^{2+}$ sequestration in beta adrenergic relaxation of airway smooth muscle. *Nature* 281:682–83

103. Muraki K, Imaizumi Y, Kawai T, Watanabe M. 1990. Effects of tetraethylammonium and 4-aminopyridine on outward currents and excitability in canine tracheal smooth muscle cells. *Br. J. Pharmacol.* 100:507–15

104. Murphy RA. 1994. What is special about smooth muscle? The significance of covalent crossbridge regulation. *FASEB J.* 8:311–18

105. Murray KJ. 1990. Cyclic AMP and mechanisms of vasodilation. In *Pharmacology and Therapeutics*, ed. MJ Lewis, pp. 329–45. Oxford: Pergamon

106. Nelson MT, Huang Y, Brayden JE, Hescheler J, Standen NB. 1990. Arterial dilations in response to calcitonin gene-related peptide involve activation of $K^+$ channels. *Nature* 344:770–73

107. Nelson MT, Patlak JB, Worley JF, Standen NB. 1990. Calcium channels, potassium channels, and voltage dependence of arterial smooth muscle tone. *Am. J. Physiol.* 259:C3–18

108. Nishikawa M, de Lanerolle P, Lincoln TM, Adelstein RS. 1984. Phosphorylation of mammalian myosin light chain kinases by the catalytic subunit of cyclic AMP-dependent protein kinase and by cyclic GMP-dependent protein kinase. *J. Biol. Chem.* 259:8429–36

109. Nishikawa M, Shirakawa S, Adelstein RS. 1985. Phosphorylation of smooth muscle myosin light chain kinase by protein kinase C. Comparative study of the phosphorylated sites. *J. Biol. Chem.* 260:8978–83

110. Nishimura J, van Breemen C. 1989. Direct regulation of smooth muscle contractile elements by second messengers. *Biochem. Biophys. Res. Commun.* 163:929–35

111. Nomura M, Stull JT, Kamm KE, Mumby MC. 1992. Site-specific dephosphorylation of smooth muscle myosin light chain kinase by protein phosphatases 1 and 2A. *Biochemistry* 31:11915–20

112. Ozaki H, Blondfield DP, Hori M, Sanders KM, Publicover NG. 1992. Cyclic AMP-mediated regulation of excitation-contraction coupling in canine gastric smooth muscle. *J. Physiol.* 447:351–72

113. Ozaki H, Kwon S-C, Tajimi M, Karaki H. 1990. Changes in cytosolic $Ca^{2+}$ and contraction induced by various stimulants and relaxants in canine tracheal smooth muscle. *Pflügers Arch.* 416:351–59

114. Deleted in proof

115. Pallanck L, Ganetzky B. 1994. Cloning and characterization of human and mouse homologues of the *Drosophila*

calcium-activated potassium channel gene, *slowpoke. Hum. Mol. Genet.* 3:1239–43

116. Pato MD, Adelstein RS. 1983. Purification and characterization of a multisubunit phosphatase from turkey gizzard smooth muscle. The effect of calmodulin binding to myosin light chain kinase on dephosphorylation. *J. Biol. Chem.* 258:7047–54

117. Payne ME, Elzinga M, Adelstein RS. 1986. Smooth muscle myosin light chain kinase. Amino acid sequence at the site phosphorylated by adenosine cyclic 3′,5′-phosphate-dependent protein kinase whether or not calmodulin is bound. *J. Biol. Chem.* 261:16346–50

118. Qian Y, Naline E, Karlsson JA, Raeburn D, Advenier C. 1993. Effects of rolipram and siguazodan on the human isolated bronchus and their interaction with isoprenaline and sodium nitroprusside. *Br. J. Pharmacol.* 109:774–78

119. Quayle JM, McCarron JG, Brayden JE, Nelson MT. 1993. Inward rectifier $K^+$ currents in smooth muscle cells from rat resistance-sized cerebral arteries. *Am. J. Physiol.* 265:C1363–70

120. Raeburn D, Brown TJ. 1991. RP 49356 and cromakalim relax airway smooth muscle in vitro by opening a sulphonylurea-sensitive $K^+$ channel: a comparison with nifedipine. *J. Pharmacol. Exp. Ther.* 256:480–85

121. Raeymaekers L, Hofmann F, Casteels R. 1988. Cyclic GMP-dependent protein kinase phosphorylates phospholamban in isolated sarcoplasmic reticulum from cardiac and smooth muscle. *Biochem. J.* 252:269–73

122. Roberds SL, Tamkun MM. 1991. Cloning and tissue-specific expression of five voltage-gated potassium channel cDNAs expressed in rat heart. *Proc. Natl. Acad. Sci. USA* 88:1798–802

123. Robertson BE, Schubert R, Hescheler J, Nelson MT. 1993. cGMP-dependent protein kinase activates Ca-activated K channels in cerebral artery smooth muscle cells. *Am. J. Physiol.* 265:C299–303

124. Rosenthal W, Hescheler J, Trautwein W, Schultz G. 1988. Control of voltage-dependent $Ca^{2+}$ channels by G protein-coupled receptors. *FASEB J.* 2:2784–90

125. Rudy B. 1988. Diversity and ubiquity of K channels. *Neuroscience* 25:729–49

126. Rüegg UT, Doyle VM, Zuber JF, Hof RP. 1985. A smooth muscle cell line suitable for the study of voltage sensitive calcium channels. *Biochem. Biophys. Res. Commun.* 130:447–53

127. Sadoshima J, Akaike N, Kanaide H,

Nakamura M. 1988. Cyclic AMP modulates Ca-activated K channel in cultured smooth muscle cells of rat aortas. *Am. J. Physiol.* 255:H754–59

128. Saunders H-M, Farley JM. 1991. Spontaneous transient outward currents and $Ca^{2+}$-activated $K^+$ channels in swine tracheal smooth muscle cells. *J. Pharmacol. Exp. Ther.* 257:1114–20

129. Saunders H-M, Farley JM. 1992. Pharmacological properties of potassium currents in swine tracheal smooth muscle. *J. Pharmacol. Exp. Ther.* 260:1038–44

130. Savaria D, Lanoue C, Cadieux A, Rousseau E. 1992. Large conducting potassium channel reconstituted from airway smooth muscle. *Am. J. Physiol.* 262:L327–36

131. Scheid CR, Fay FS. 1984. Beta-adrenergic effects on transmembrane $^{45}Ca$ fluxes in isolated smooth muscle cells. *Am. J. Physiol.* 246:C431–38

132. Scornik FS, Codina J, Birnbaumer L, Toro L. 1993. Modulation of coronary smooth muscle $K_{Ca}$ channels by Gs alpha independent of phosphorylation by protein kinase A. *Am. J. Physiol.* 265:H1460–65

133. Shimizu H, Ito M, Miyahara M, Ichikawa K, Okubo S, et al. 1994. Characterization of the myosin-binding subunit of smooth muscle myosin phosphatase. *J. Biol. Chem.* 269:30407–11

134. Shirazi A, Iizuka K, Fadden P, Mosse C, Somlyo AP, et al. 1994. Purification and characterization of the mammalian myosin light chain phosphatase holoenzyme. *J. Biol. Chem.* 269:31598–606

135. Singer JJ, Walsh JV. 1984. Large conductance $Ca^{2+}$-activated $K^+$ channels in smooth muscle cell membrane. *Biophys. J.* 45:68–70

136. Singer JJ, Walsh JVJ. 1986. Large-conductance $Ca^{2+}$-activated $K^+$ channels in freshly dissociated smooth muscle cells. *Membr. Biochem.* 6:83–110

137. Small RC. 1982. Electrical slow waves and tone of guinea-pig isolated trachealis muscle: effects of drugs and temperature changes. *Br. J. Pharmacol.* 77:45–54

138. Small RC, Chiu P, Cook SJ, Foster RW, Isaac L. 1993. β-adrenoreceptor agonists in bronchial asthma: role of $K^+$-channel opening in mediating their bronchodilator effects. *Clin. Exp. Allergy* 23:802–11

139. Somlyo AP, Somlyo AV. 1994. Signal transduction and regulation in smooth muscle. *Nature* 372:231–36

140. Somlyo AV, Haeusler G, Somlyo AP. 1970. Cyclic adenosine monophosphate: potassium-dependent action on vascular smooth muscle membrane potential. *Science* 169:490–91

141. Sparrow MP, Pfitzer G, Gagelmann M, Rüegg JC. 1984. Effect of calmodulin, $Ca^{2+}$, and cAMP protein kinase on skinned tracheal smooth muscle. *Am. J. Physiol.* 246:C308–14

142. Standen NB, Quayle JM, Davies NW, Brayden JE, Huang Y, Nelson MT. 1989. Hyperpolarizing vasodilators activate ATP-sensitive $K^+$ channels in arterial smooth muscle. *Science* 245:177–80

143. Stull JT, Hsu L-C, Tansey MG, Kamm KE. 1990. Myosin light chain kinase phosphorylation in tracheal smooth muscle. *J. Biol. Chem.* 265:16683–90

144. Stull JT, Krueger JK, Kamm KE, Gao Z-H, Zhi G, Padre R. 1995. Myosin light chain kinase. In *Biochemistry of Smooth Muscle,* ed. M Barany, pp. 119–30. Orlando, FL: Academic

145. Stull JT, Tansey MG, Tang D-C, Word RA, Kamm KE. 1993. Phosphorylation of myosin light chain kinase: a cellular mechanism for $Ca^{2+}$ desensitization. *Mol. Cell. Biochem.* 127/128:229–37

146. Suzuki H, Morita K, Kuriyama H. 1976. Innervation and properties of the smooth muscle of the dog trachea. *Jpn. J. Physiol.* 26:303–20

147. Tang D-C, Kubota Y, Kamm KE, Stull JT. 1993. GTPγS-induced phosphorylation of myosin light chain kinase in smooth muscle. *FEBS Lett.* 331:272–75

148. Tang D-C, Stull JT, Kubota Y, Kamm KE. 1992. Regulation of the $Ca^{2+}$ dependence of smooth muscle contraction. *J. Biol. Chem.* 267:11839–45

149. Tansey MG, Word RA, Hidaka H, Singer HA, Schworer CM, et al. 1992. Phosphorylation of myosin light chain kinase by the multifunctional calmodulin-dependent protein kinase II in smooth muscle cells. *J. Biol. Chem.* 267:12511–16

150. Tomasic M, Boyle JP, Worley JI, Kotlikoff MI. 1992. Contractile agonists activate voltage-dependent channels in airway smooth muscle cells. *Am. J. Physiol.* 263:C106–13

151. Torphy TJ, Freese WB, Rinard GA, Brunton LL, Mayer SE. 1982. Cyclic nucleotide-dependent protein kinases in airway smooth muscle. *J. Biol. Chem.* 257:11609–16

152. Torphy TJ, Undem BJ, Cieslinski LB, Luttmann MA, Reeves ML, Hay DW. 1993. Identification, characterization and functional role of phosphodiesterase isozymes in human airway smooth mus-

cle. *J. Pharmacol. Exp. Ther.* 265:1213–23

152a. Trinkle-Mulcahy L, Ichikawa K, Hartshorne DJ, Siegman MJ, Butler TM. 1995. Thiophosphorylation of the 130-kDa subunit is associated with a decreased activity of myosin light chain phosphatase in $\alpha$-toxin-permeabilized smooth muscle. *J. Biol. Chem.* 270: 18191–94

153. Twort CHC, van Breemen C. 1988. Cyclic guanosine monophosphate-enhanced sequestration of $Ca^{2+}$ by sarcoplasmic reticulum in vascular smooth muscle. *Circ. Res.* 62:961–64

154. Van Riper DA, Weaver BA, Stull JT, Rembold CM. 1995. Myosin light chain kinase phosphorylation in swine carotid artery contraction and relaxation. *Am. J. Physiol.* 268:42466–75

155. Vegesna RVK, Diamond J. 1984. Effects of isoproterenol and forskolin on tension, cyclic AMP levels, and cyclic AMP dependent protein kinase activity in bovine coronary artery. *Can. J. Physiol. Pharmacol.* 62:1116–23

156. Wade GR, Sims SM. 1993. Muscarinic stimulation of tracheal smooth muscle cells activates large-conductance $Ca^{2+}$-dependent $K^+$ channel. *Am. J. Physiol.* 265:C658–65

157. Walsh KB, Kass RS. 1988. Regulation of a heart potassium channel by protein kinase A and C. *Science* 242:67–69

158. Wei A, Solaro C, Lingle C, Salkoff L. 1994. Calcium sensitivity of BK-type $K_{Ca}$ channels determined by a separable domain. *Neuron* 13:671–81

159. Wilson GG, O'Neill CA, Sivaprasadarao A, Findlay JB, Wray D. 1994. Modulation by protein kinase A of a cloned rat brain potassium channel expressed in *Xenopus* oocytes. *Pflügers Arch.* 428:186–93

160. Winder SJ, Walsh MP. 1993. Calponin: thin filament-linked regulation of smooth muscle contraction. *Cell. Signaling* 5:677–86

161. Xuan YT, Watkins WD, Whorton AR. 1991. Regulation of endothelin-mediated calcium mobilization in vascular smooth muscle cells by isoproterenol. *Am. J. Physiol.* 260:C492–502

162. Yatani A, Codina J, Imoto Y, Reeves JP, Birnbaumer L, Brown AM. 1987. A G protein directly regulates mammalian cardiac calcium channels. *Science* 238:1288–92

163. Zhang L, Bonev AD, Mawe GM, Nelson MT. 1994. Protein kinase A mediates activation of ATP-sensitive $K^+$ currents by CGRP in gallbladder smooth muscle. *Am. J. Physiol.* 267:G494–99

164. Zhou H-L, Newsholme SJ, Torphy TJ. 1992. Agonist-related differences in the relationship between cAMP content and protein kinase activity in canine trachealis. *J. Pharmacol. Exp. Ther.* 261: 1260–67

*Annu. Rev. Physiol. 1995. 58:143–70*

# DEFECTS IN G PROTEIN-COUPLED SIGNAL TRANSDUCTION IN HUMAN DISEASE[1]

## A. M. Spiegel

Metabolic Diseases Branch, National Institute of Diabetes and Digestive and Kidney Diseases, National Institutes of Health, Bethesda, Maryland 20892

KEY WORDS: receptor, mutations, hormone resistance, GTPase, endocrine hyperfunction

## ABSTRACT

G proteins couple receptors for many hormones and neurotransmitters to effectors that regulate second messenger metabolism. G protein-coupled receptors comprise a superfamily with the common structural feature of a single polypeptide with seven membrane-spanning domains. G proteins themselves are heterotrimers with an $\alpha$ subunit that binds guanine nucleotides. In the basal state, G proteins tightly bind GDP; receptor activation allows exchange of bound GDP for GTP that activates the G protein and causes it to modulate effector activity. An intrinsic GTPase activity hydrolyzes bound GTP to GDP thereby deactivating the G protein. The effects (cholera, whooping cough) of bacterial toxins that target G proteins for covalent modification signal the potential importance of G protein dysfunction as a cause of human disease. Conceptually, G protein dysfunction could involve gain or loss of function. For $G_s$, examples of both types have already been defined. Mutations in G protein-coupled receptors have also been identified in several human diseases. Germline loss of function mutations in rhodopsin, cone opsins, the V2 vasopressin receptor, ACTH receptor, and calcium-sensing receptor are responsible for retinitis pigmentosa, color blindness, nephrogenic diabetes insipidus, familial ACTH resistance, and familial hypocalciuric hypercalcemia, respectively. Missense mutations that cause constitutive receptor activation have been identified in the TSH and LH receptors.

# OVERVIEW OF G PROTEIN-COUPLED SIGNAL TRANSDUCTION

In the two to three decades since their initial discovery and purification (punctuated by the award of the 1994 Nobel Prize in Physiology or Medicine to Martin Rodbell and Alfred G Gilman), there has been a virtual avalanche of information on G proteins. These proteins convey information carried by diverse extracellular first messengers from the outside to the inside of the cell by coupling a distinct class of receptors, G protein-coupled receptors (GPCRs), to diverse effectors (Figure 1). We now possess a wealth of structural and functional data on each of the components involved in G protein-mediated signal transduction that has permitted the identification of specific defects in these transduction signals as the cause of a wide array of human diseases. The actions of cholera and pertussis toxins provided the first evidence that G protein

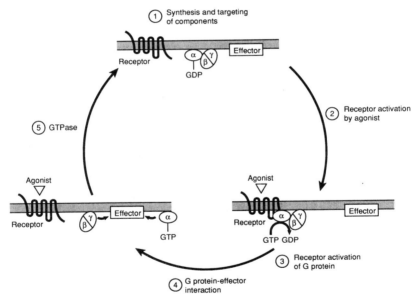

*Figure 1* The G protein GTPase cycle. Potential sites for disease-causing abnormalities are numbered. In each panel, the shaded region denotes the plasma membrane, with extracellular above and intracellular below. In the basal state, the G protein is a heterotrimer with GDP tightly bound to the α subunit. The agonist-activated receptor catalyzes release of tightly bound GDP, which permits GTP to bind. The GTP-bound α subunit dissociates from the βγ dimer. Arrows between the GTP-bound α subunit and effector and between the βγ dimer and effector indicate regulation of effector activity by the respective subunits. Under physiologic conditions, effector regulation by G protein subunits is transient and is terminated by the GTPase activity of the α subunit. The latter converts bound GTP to GDP, thus returning the α subunit to its inactivated state with high affinity for the βγ dimer, which reassociates to again form the heterotrimer.

dysfunction (in both instances due to bacterial toxin-catalyzed covalent modification of G protein α subunits) could cause human disease. Subsequently, many mutations have been identified in both GPCRs and G proteins in numerous different disorders.

First we give a necessarily brief overview of GPCR and G protein structure and function. For details, the interested reader is referred to several recent and comprehensive reviews (2, 18, 39, 63, 68, 71). Then our current information on mutations in GPCRs and G protein α subunits in disorders of humans (and, in a few instances, mice) is reviewed. Although defects in many other components of the G protein-mediated signal transduction system that include βγ subunits and effectors, desensitization components such as receptor kinases and β-arrestins, and more distal components such as second messenger-activated kinases and their substrates may likely prove to be important as causes of human disease, there are presently far fewer examples of these and they are not covered in this review.

## G Protein-Coupled Receptor Structure and Function

The sole known function of GPCRs is to catalyze release of tightly bound GDP from G protein α subunits (Figure 1). Agonist binding promotes the conformation of the GPCR that favors G protein coupling and facilitates guanine nucleotide exchange. Key structure-function questions include: What are the structural determinants of agonist binding; what changes in structure occur upon agonist binding; and what are the structural determinants of G protein coupling? Key cell biologic questions are: How does the receptor become correctly folded and oriented topographically within the membrane; and how is it correctly targeted to the plasma membrane?

Although there are still no definitive answers to any of these questions, a large amount of data support certain broad generalizations. Hydrophobicity analysis of the predicted amino acid sequence of all GPCRs studied to date suggests the topography depicted in Figure 2. A low-resolution electron diffraction structure for rhodopsin supports the occurrence of seven membrane-spanning α helices and suggests their possible orientation within the bilayer (2). Glycosylation and formation of the disulfide between e1 and e2 may be important for proper folding and membrane targeting. Superimposed on the basic theme depicted in Figure 2 are numerous variations that correspond to the diversity of ligands (retinal, monoamines, divalent cations, odorants, peptides, proteases, and glycoprotein hormones) that bind to GPCRs, as well as the selectivity of GPCRs for the G protein to which they couple. The N term (Figure 2) varies dramatically in length with only the longer ones having signal sequences. The relative size of the C term and i3 also show substantial variation. The number and precise sites of glycosylation are variable.

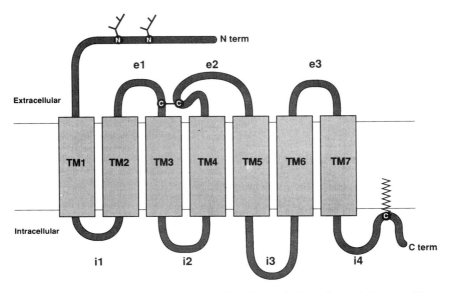

*Figure 2* Schematic two-dimensional representation of a generic G protein-coupled receptor. The amino-terminus (N term) is located extracellularly and is shown with two N-linked glycosylation sites. The seven putative membrane-spanning α helices are shown as vertical rectangles and are numbered TM1–TM7. The three extracellular and the three intracellular loops are labeled e1–e3 and i1–i3, respectively. A disulfide linkage of cysteines in e1 and e2 is shown, as is a palmitoylated cysteine in the intracellular carboxy-terminus (C term) predicted to create a fourth intracellular loop (i4).

Agonist-binding sites and G protein-coupling sites cannot be definitively determined without a high-resolution three-dimensional structure. Nonetheless, extensive studies employing affinity labeling, peptide mimetics of receptor intracellular loops, site-directed mutagenesis, and receptor chimeras permit some inferences. Agonist binding for the opsins and for GPCRs that bind monoamines occurs within a pocket created by the transmembrane helices. This may also be true for GPCRs that bind peptides, but for the latter there is evidence for involvement of the N term and/or extracellular loops. The intracellular loops and C term are critical for G protein interaction, but the relative importance of particular regions such as i3 in determining the specificity of G protein-coupling varies among GPCRs. These regions are illustrated in Figure 2.

## G Protein Structure and Function

G proteins consist of three distinct polypeptide gene products. The α subunit binds guanine nucleotides with high affinity and specificity. The β and γ polypeptides are tightly but noncovalently associated in a functional dimer subunit. The heterotrimer is associated with the inner surface of the plasma membrane (Figure 1), at least in part, as a result of post-translational lipid modifications: prenylation of the γ polypeptide carboxy-terminus and palmitoylation and, in some cases, myristoylation of the α subunit amino-terminus (68). The heterotrimer is required for high-affinity coupling to GPCR. Upon α subunit binding of GTP and dissociation from the βγ dimer, each subunit can independently modulate the activity of one or more effectors such as adenylyl cyclase (the enzyme that generates the second messenger cAMP), other second messenger-generating enzymes, or ion channels (39).

There are 16 mammalian α subunit genes. They vary in range of expression and in specificity of receptor-effector coupling. Their predicted amino acid sequences show at least 40% identity corresponding to conserved regions involved in guanine nucleotide binding (68). Similar three-dimensional structures have been reported for two α subunits (8, 41), which suggest that all α subunits may share a common overall structure comprised of two major domains: a guanine nucleotide-binding domain itself similar to that previously determined for the *ras* proto-oncogene, and an α helical domain that may serve to keep guanine nucleotide tightly bound as well as to enhance α subunit GTPase activity (34). Structures of guanine nucleoside di- and triphosphate-bound α subunits pinpoint regions involved in a conformational shift upon GTP binding that promotes effector interaction and also highlight two residues critical for normal GTPase activity: glutamine 227 (equivalent to 61 in *ras*) and arginine 201 (the site of cholera toxin catalyzed ADP-ribosylation) in $G_s$-α, the G protein mediating stimulation of cAMP formation. Mutagenesis and other studies suggest that the α subunit amino-terminus is important for βγ dimer interaction, the carboxy-terminus for receptor coupling, and regions near the carboxy-terminus for effector interaction (39, 68). At present definitive data on the sites of these interactions are unavailable, but crystallization of α subunits as heterotrimers and with portions of receptors or effectors should shortly provide three-dimensional structural information.

## G PROTEIN-COUPLED RECEPTOR AND G PROTEIN DEFECTS: GENERAL CONSIDERATIONS

Defective signal transduction could result from quantitative and/or qualitative alterations in GPCRs and G proteins, including changes in expression level, post-translational modifications, and mutations. Mutations may occur as somatic (postzygotic) events or may be inherited (germline). Phenotypic manifestations of mutations will depend on whether they are somatic or germline and on the range of expression of the involved gene. Germline mutations of ubiquitously expressed genes will often cause generalized manifestations (although germline mutations of some ubiquitously expressed tumor suppressor genes predispose to a restricted number of tumors). Germline mutations of genes with a restricted range of expression and somatic mutations of ubiquitously expressed genes will generally cause more focal manifestations. Certain germline mutations may be incompatible with normal embryonic development and therefore cannot be the cause of diseases manifesting primarily postnatally. This may be relevant for certain GPCR and G protein mutations (see below).

## Loss-of-Function Mutations

This category includes mutations that preclude normal formation of stable mRNA and/or protein, as well as mutations that permit protein synthesis but block normal membrane targeting (step 1 in Figure 1). For GPCRs there is evidence that a large number of naturally occurring mutations may cause protein misfolding and abnormal trafficking, e.g. retention in the endoplasmic reticulum. Similar, naturally occurring mutations of mammalian $\alpha$ subunits have not been identified, although a loss-of-function mutation predicted to prevent myristoylation and hence membrane targeting of a *C. elegans* $\alpha$ subunit was recently reported (62). GPCR mutations that do not prevent normal protein synthesis and membrane targeting may nonetheless cause loss-of-function by impairing high-affinity agonist binding or receptor activation by agonist (step 2 in Figure 1) or by preventing normal receptor coupling to and activation of G protein (step 3 in Figure 1). For G proteins, mutations that block receptor coupling or activation by GTP (step 3 in Figure 1) and mutations that impair effector interaction (step 4 in Figure 1) will likewise cause loss-of-function.

## Gain-of-Function Mutations

The mechanism of and structural basis for GPCR activation by agonists have not been defined. One model suggests that GPCR may fluctuate between conformations that either promote or preclude G protein coupling. In this model, unoccupied receptors may rarely spontaneously assume the activated conformation that favors G protein coupling, and agonists increase the proportion of receptor in the activated conformation by stabilizing the receptor in this conformation. Dramatic overexpression of the normal $\beta$-adrenergic receptor in the hearts of transgenic mice led to maximal activation of cardiac cAMP formation that is completely independent of agonist, presumably because with this degree of receptor expression, the rare spontaneously activated conformation occurs frequently enough to activate fully the available G protein (36). Mutations of critical residues that may normally be involved in keeping the receptor in the inactive conformation may mimic the effect of agonist by promoting receptor activation (step 2 in Figure 1) (63). G proteins may be activated independently of receptor by $\alpha$ subunit mutations that either permit more rapid spontaneous release of GDP (step 3 in Figure 1) or block the GTPase reaction (step 5 in Figure 1) that terminates G protein-effector interaction.

## MUTATIONS IN G PROTEIN-COUPLED RECEPTORS

Table 1 lists sporadic and inherited disorders in which loss- or gain-of-function mutations have been identified in GPCR genes. The sections that follow discuss these disorders and are organized by GPCR subfamily.

### Opsins

The four visual pigments in the human eye—rhodopsin (the rod photoreceptor pigment) and the blue, green, and red cone opsins—are related in structure, but not sequence, to bacteriorhodopsin, a light-driven proton pump rather than a GPCR (2). Like bacteriorhodopsin, the human opsins have a core structure consisting of seven membrane-spanning helices with a retinal covalently bound to a lysine (296 in rhodopsin) in TM7. Glutamate 113 in rhodopsin TM3 serves as the counterion to the lysine-bound retinal. Photon capture in rhodopsin converts a bound antagonist to an agonist by causing isomerization of 11-*cis* retinal to all-*trans*. This leads to a shift in protonation to glutamate 134 at the cytoplasmic base of TM3 and a likely conformational change in the cytoplasmic loops that promotes G protein activation.

**Table 1**  Diseases caused by GPCR mutations

| Receptor | Disease | Mutation type |
|----------|---------|---------------|
| Cone opsins | Color blindness | Loss |
| Rhodopsin | Retinitis pigmentosa | Loss/gain |
| Rhodopsin | Congenital night blindness | Gain |
| V2 vasopressin | Nephrogenic diabetes insipidus | Loss |
| ACTH | Familial ACTH resistance | Loss |
| LH | Familial male precocious puberty | Gain |
| LH | Male-pseudohermaphroditism | Loss |
| TSH | Sporadic hyperfunctional thyroid nodules | Gain |
| TSH | Familial hypothyrodism | Loss |
| CaR | Hypercalcemia/neonatal severe primary hyperparathyrodism | Loss |
| CaR | Familial hypoparathyroidism | Gain |
| Thromboxane $A_2$ | Congenital bleeding | Loss |
| Endothelin B | Hirschsprung disease | Loss |
| PTH/PTHrP | Jansen metaphyseal chondrodysplasia | Gain |
| MSH | Mouse hypo- or hyperpigmentation | Loss or gain |
| GRF | *little* mouse | Loss |

Mutations in each of the visual pigments lead to a number of disorders in humans. These are only briefly discussed here; the interested reader is referred to several recent extensive reviews for specific mutations and other details (18, 33, 37, 74). Common forms of color blindness are due to loss-of-function mutations in either the red or green cone opsin genes (38). The red and green pigment genes are arranged in tandem on the X chromosome and are relatively frequently subject to unequal recombination events resulting in gain or loss of entire genes or formation of red-green hydrid genes with altered absorption properties. Total color blindness results from loss-of-function mutations involving both red and green pigment genes (38). This can follow from a recombination event that eliminates all but a defective gene harboring a cysteine203arginine mutation in loop e2. This change disrupts an essential disulfide between loops e2 and e1. A number of heterozygous point mutations in the blue pigment gene on chromosome 7 cause autosomal dominant forms of deficient blue spectral sensitivity. A common polymorphism, serine or alanine at position 180, in the red pigment gene accounts for genetic variation in sensitivity to long wavelength light (38).

Retinitis pigmentosa (RP) is characterized by progressive photoreceptor degeneration and blindness. The disorder shows extensive phenotypic and genetic heterogeneity, with X-linked, autosomal-recessive and -dominant forms. About 30% of the dominant form is due to >60 different mutations in the rhodopsin gene on chromosome 3 (18, 33, 37, 38, 74). These are not simple loss-of-function mutations but rather act dominantly, in ways not completely clarified, to cause photoreceptor degeneration. The majority are thought to cause abnormal protein folding with retention in the endoplasmic reticulum and eventual cell destruction. Missense mutations in the amino-terminus, transmembrane domains, and loops e1 and e2 are most often involved. Missense mutations changing lysine 296, site of retinal attachment, to glutamate or methionine have been identified in subjects with a form of autosomal-dominant RP thought to be caused by constitutive rhodopsin activation (73). Loss of retinal binding is believed to relieve inhibitory constraints between the transmembrane helices and cause light-independent activation. In autosomal-recessive forms of RP, loss-of-function mutations of both alleles of the rhodopsin gene have been found (26, 56). Congenital stationary night blindness is an autosomal-dominant disorder considered distinct from RP. Affected individuals do not show progressive photoreceptor degeneration but show night blindness from earliest childhood. Heterozygous rhodopsin mutations identified in this disorder include glycine90aspartate (TM2) and alanine292glutamate (TM7) (38). Either mutant adds negative charge to the retinal binding pocket that may weaken the normal salt bridge between lysine 296 and glutamate 113. Although the mutants still bind retinal and are thus not always constitutively activated (unlike lysine 296 mutants discussed above), a small percent of unliganded opsins postulated to occur at steady state would, if mutant, be activated. The resultant background noise would diminish low-light sensitivity yielding the night blindness phenotype. Lack of photoreceptor degeneration may reflect the milder degree of rhodopsin activation.

## Monoamine Receptors

Receptors in this subfamily, including adrenergic, dopaminergic, serotoninergic, histaminergic, muscarinic, and cholinergic, are similar topographically and show significant sequence identity in the transmembrane domains to the opsin subfamily. Although the agonist is not covalently bound as for opsins, there is considerable evidence that the agonist binds within a pocket formed from the transmembrane helices (71). An aspartate in TM3 is characteristic of this receptor subfamily and is likely a counterion to the amine of the bound agonist. Cloning has revealed many more receptor subtypes for each ligand than suspected based on classic pharmacology. Whereas some of these subtypes are fairly widely expressed, others show distinct, often fairly restricted, ranges of expression. This has important implications for predictions concerning phenotypic manifestations of receptor defects.

As yet, no mutants in this receptor subfamily have been definitively linked to disease. Polymorphisms in several receptor genes (e.g. D2 and D4 dopamine) have been identified, but no clear functional significance has been demonstrated (18). Although several monoamine receptors are attractive candidate genes for such neuropsychiatric diseases as schizophrenia, bipolar affective disorders, and Gilles de la Tourette syndrome, neither linkage analysis nor direct mutation screening has provided evidence for an association (18). Dopamine inhibits prolactin secretion and lactotroph growth through D2 receptors. Loss-of-function mutations in this receptor could thus occur in prolactinomas, but none were found in a study of a large number of pituitary tumors (11). Putative association of alcoholism with the D2 dopamine receptor gene based on linkage analysis using a polymorphism remains controversial (18). Several polymorphisms have been identified in the β2-adrenergic receptor (53). Most are silent; the few that alter amino acids were not found more commonly in asthmatics than in normal individuals, except for residue 16 where substitution of glycine for arginine was found more frequently in nocturnal asthmatics (78). The glycine 16 variant was shown in vitro to be more easily down-regulated, which suggests that this receptor variant may predispose to some forms of asthma, but further studies are needed to confirm this finding. The β3-adrenergic receptor is expressed only in certain types of adipocytes (brown fat in rodents). A polymorphism in loop i1 (tryptophan or arginine at residue 64) has been identified in this receptor. The functional significance of this polymorphism has not been defined, but an increased frequency of the arginine 64 form of the receptor has been found in subjects with obesity, decreased resting metabolic rate, and earlier occurrence of non-insulin-dependent diabetes mellitus (79). Loss-of-function of the β3-adrenergic receptor could predispose to obesity by reducing adipocyte sensitivity to lipolysis, but the significance of the tryptophan64arginine variation will require further study.

## V2 Vasopressin Receptor

The V2 vasopressin receptor belongs to a subfamily of neurohypophyseal peptide hormone receptors that includes the V1a and V1b vasopressin and oxytocin receptors. The subfamily shows overall similarity to the opsin and monoamine receptors with a generally short amino-terminus lacking a signal sequence, putative disulfide linking loops e1 and e2, and tandem cysteines 341 and 342 that are presumed to be palmitoylated. Affinity labeling suggests that loop e1 is involved in agonist binding (21). The V2 vasopressin receptor gene is strongly expressed in the renal medulla and was localized to chromosome Xq28, immediately making it likely that mutations in this gene would be the cause of nephrogenic diabetes insipidus (NDI). Most cases of NDI are linked to the same locus; a minority of NDI families show autosomal-recessive inheritance and mutations distal to the receptor, e.g. mutations in the cAMP-regulated water channel may be causal (9).

Normally, dehydration increases serum osmolarity, which triggers release of vasopressin from the posterior pituitary. Vasopressin acts on renal V2-type receptors coupled to $G_s$ to enhance water reabsorption and increase urine concentration. In NDI, affected males fail to concentrate their urine in response to endogenous and exogenous vasopressin. Resistance is limited to V2 vasopressin response; the pressor effect of vasopressin, a $V_1$ response, is unimpaired. Obligate carrier females generally show no overt clinical manifestations, but vasopressin resistance is demonstrable by water deprivation testing (35). Rarely will females be severely affected, presumably owing to unfavorable random X-inactivation. A family with partial resistance due to an apparent right-shift in vasopressin response has been reported (55). The localized manifestations in this inherited disorder are perfectly compatible with mutations in a gene localized in expression, the V2 vasopressin receptor. Because males are hemizygous for this gene, a single loss-of-function mutation suffices to cause disease. An approximate 50% reduction in normal receptors, the statistically likely situation in most carrier females, is evidently insufficient to cause clinical disease.

Although the disease can be lethal or cause severe brain damage due to dehydration if unrecognized in the neonatal period, the clinical course is generally benign provided subjects have access to and drink sufficient fluid. As with retinitis pigmentosa, the combination of nonlethality and an obvious phenotype has provided numerous subjects for molecular genetic studies. A very large number of distinct mutations in the V2 vasopressin receptor have already been identified in affected subjects (Table 2) (3, 20, 35, 42, 43, 57, 77, 84, 85, 90) that involve virtually every region of the receptor. Most families have "private" mutations, although there appear to be a few mutational hot spots with the same mutation found in several apparently unrelated families (3). Nonsense mutations and those causing frameshifts leading to premature stop codons presumably abolish function by causing synthesis of a truncated (and possibly unstable) protein. Truncation of other GPCRs, e.g. β-adrenergic and muscarinic, anywhere proximal to TM6 abolishes function. The arginine 337 nonsense mutant, however, would truncate the receptor just proximal to

**Table 2** Loss-of-function V2 vasopressin receptor mutations in nephrogenic diabetes insipidus

| Mutation[a] | Location | Mutation[a] | Location |
|---|---|---|---|
| S8fshift[b] | Nterm | W164S | TM4 |
| L16fshift[b] | Nterm | S167T or S167L | TM4 |
| S21fshift[b] | Nterm | **R181C** | e2 |
| L44P or L44F | TM1 | R202C | e2 |
| L53R | TM1 | T204N | e2 |
| L62P | TM1 | Y205C | e2 |
| L62fshift[b] | TM1 | Y205fshift[b] | e2 |
| L62/A63/R64[c] | TM1/i1 | V206D | e2 |
| H70fshift[b] | i1 | Q225stop | TM5 |
| W71stop | i1 | I228fshift[b] | i3 |
| H80R | TM2 | **R230fshift[b]** | i3 |
| L83P | TM2 | E242stop | i3 |
| D85N | TM2 | R247fshift[b] | i3 |
| V88M | TM2 | G254fshift[b] | i3 |
| P95L | TM2 | **H261fshift[b]** | i3 |
| R106C | e1 | V277A | TM6 |
| L111fshift[b] | e1 | V278 or V279[c] | TM6 |
| C112R | e1 | Y280C | TM6 |
| **R113W** | e1 | W284stop | TM6 |
| **Q119stop** | TM3 | A285P | TM6 |
| Y124stop | TM3 | **P286R** | TM6 |
| S126F | TM3 | L292P | TM6 |
| **Y128S** | TM3 | W293stop | TM6 |
| A132D | TM3 | L312stop | TM7 |
| **R137H** | i2 | W323R | TM7 |
| R143P | i2 | R337stop | Cterm |
| G153fshift[b] | i2 | | |

[a] Bold type indicates that the functional effect of the mutation has been defined by expression studies.
[b] Frameshift follows listed amino acid and causes subsequent stop codon and premature truncation of protein product.
[c] Deletion.

the putatively palmitoylated cysteines in the carboxy-terminus (84). Expression studies indicate that this mutation in fact causes loss-of-function (D Wenkert & AM Spiegel, unpublished observations).

Of the many missense mutations, comparatively few have actually been expressed to demonstrate their functional effect. The arginine113tryptophan mutant appears to cause decreased transport to the plasma membrane, perhaps by interfering with disulfide formation involving the adjacent cysteine 112 (4). Several other missense mutations in loops e1 and e2 that either replace a cysteine or create an additional cysteine may act similarly. In one study, however, normal cell surface-staining of an epitope-tagged arginine181cysteine (loop e2) mutant was observed, although neither agonist binding nor cAMP stimulation was evident (43). A tyrosine128serine mutant and a proline286arginine mutant gave the same results (43). Tyrosine 128 is conserved in all members of the vasopressin receptor subfamily, and proline 286 is conserved at the equivalent position in TM6 in most GPCRs. Likewise, an arginine equivalent to arginine 137 at the junction of TM3 and i2 is conserved [as part of the asparate-arginine-tyrosine (DRY) motif] in most GPCRs. When the arginine137histidine mutant is expressed, it fails to couple normally to $G_s$ thus abolishing cAMP stimulation (57). Many other missense mutants have not yet been expressed but are predicted to cause loss-of-function as they are nonconservative substitutions, e.g. creation of $\alpha$ helix-disrupting prolines in the transmembrane domains, or involving residues generally conserved among GPCRs or within the vasopressin subfamily. A disproportionately high number of the missense mutations involve the transmembrane domains, which underlines the critical role of these regions in normal receptor assembly and function. Study of NDI families has also revealed several silent polymorphisms, as well as sequence variants including threonine7serine, glycine12glutamate, alanine61valine, alanine147valine, and deletion of four residues in i3 (arginine 247 to glycine 250) shown (43) or predicted (3) not to affect function.

## Glycoprotein Hormone Receptors

The glycoprotein hormone receptors, including those for luteinizing hormone/ human chorionic gondatotropin (LH/hCG), follicle-stimulating hormone (FSH) and thyroid-stimulating hormone (TSH), comprise a distinct subset of the GPCR superfamily. A distinctive feature is their long (almost 400 residue) amino-terminus with a signal sequence and multiple glycosylation sites. The amino-terminus is involved in high-affinity agonist binding. Glycoprotein hormone receptors are expressed primarily in the target cells in the gonads and thyroid for their respective pituitary hormone agonists. A number of sporadic and inherited disorders have been found to be caused by loss- and gain-of-function mutations in the TSH and LH receptors (Table 3).

**Table 3**  Left Side: Loss-of-function LH-R mutations in male pseudohermaphroditism and familial Leydig cell hypoplasia and gain-of-function mutations in familial or sporadic male precocious puberty. Right Side: Loss-of-function TSH-R mutations in familial hypothyroidism and gain of function mutations in sporadic thyroid adenomas and familial nonautoimmune hyperthyroidism

| Mutation[a] | Location | Mutation[a] | Location |
|---|---|---|---|
| LH-R | | TSH-R | |
| Loss | | Loss | |
| **C545stop** | TM5 | **P162A** | Nterm |
| **A593P** | TM6 | **I167N** | Nterm |
| Gain | | Gain | |
| **I542L** | TM5 | I486F or M | e 1 |
| **D564G** | i3 | **S505R** | TM3 |
| **M571I** | TM6 | **V509A** | TM3 |
| **A572V** | TM6 | **D619G** | i3 |
| **T577I** | TM6 | **A623I** or **V** | TM6 |
| **D578Y** | TM6 | **F631C** or **L** | TM6 |
| **D578G** | TM6 | **T632I** | TM6 |
| D578V | TM6 | **D633Y** or **E** | TM6 |
| **C581R** | TM6 | **C672Y** | TM7 |

[a] Bold type indicates that the functional effect of the mutation has been defined by expression studies.

MALE PSEUDOHERMAPHRODITISM/LEYDIG CELL HYPOPLASIA    This is a rare autosomal-recessive condition that interferes with normal male external genital development in affected 46,XY subjects. The phenotype ranges from forms presenting as 46,XY females to milder forms in males with hypergonadotropic hypogonadism and micropenis. The phenotype in affected 46,XX females is not clear but could conceivably be primary amenorrhea with LH resistance. Studies of two separate kindreds have revealed loss-of-function mutations of the LH receptor in affected 46,XY subjects (24, 30). One is a nonsense mutation, cysteine545stop in TM5, that truncates the receptor; the other is a missense mutation, alanine593proline, at the junction of TM6 and loop e3. Both abolish LH stimulation of cAMP; the missense mutation caused no change in binding affinity but a decrease in maximal binding (24). It seems more likely that the receptor is poorly expressed at the cell surface perhaps because of the effect of the proline on folding. Direct assays for surface expression of the mutant receptor need to be done. The alanine593proline mutation was found on both alleles of two affected siblings, products of a consanguineous marriage. The nonsense mutation was found in only one allele of two affected siblings; it is unclear if this mutation exerts a dominant-negative effect or if the subjects are compound heterozygotes with another mutation as yet to be identified. The phenotype caused by these LH receptor loss-of-function mutations points to important effects of LH receptor stimulation on Leydig cell development and formation of the male genitalia.

FAMILIAL TSH RESISTANCE    This is an autosomal-recessive form of congenital hypothyroidism with TSH resistance not due to thyroid autoantibodies. In three affected sisters born to unrelated parents, two distinct mutations of the TSH receptor gene were identified in each allele: proline162alanine and asparagine167isoleucine (75). Each heterozygous parent had one of the mutant alleles. Expression studies indicated that the paternal mutant allele, isoleucine 167, showed virtually no TSH stimulation, whereas the maternal mutant allele, alanine 162, was partially active. A polymorphism at position 52, leucine or proline, had no functional effect. Loss-of-function mutations in both alleles of the TSH receptor gene readily explain the isolated TSH resistance observed. The functional effect of these mutations points to the importance of the involved residues of the large extracellular amino-terminus in agonist binding. Three-dimensional structural data, however, will be needed to define precisely the sites of receptor-ligand binding. An autosomal-recessive, TSH-resistant form of hypothyroidism in mice (*hyt/hyt*) is due to a homozygous loss-of-function mutation, proline556leucine, in TM4 of the TSH receptor (70). The involved proline is highly conserved in most GPCRs.

FAMILIAL MALE PRECOCIOUS PUBERTY (FMPP)/TESTOTOXICOSIS    This is generally an autosomal dominantly inherited disorder although it may also occur sporadically. Affected males show signs of virilization, often by age four, with premature epiphyseal closure leading to eventual short stature. Low serum gonadotropins implicate autonomous gonadal hyperfunction. The localized manifestations, Leydig cell hyperfunction, in a dominantly inherited disorder prompted a search for gain-of-function mutations in the LH receptor, which led to initial identification of a heterozygous missense mutation in TM6, aspartate578glycine, in affected members of several kindreds (64). Expression of the mutant receptor indicates that unlike the wild-type, it causes agonist-independent stimulation of cAMP formation but not of inositol phosphate formation (23). Subsequently, a number of other activating mutations have been identified in affected subjects with FMPP as well as sporadic forms of the disease (23, 25, 29, 87, 88). An aspartate578tyrosine mutant causing greater cAMP stimulation than the other activating mutations was identified in a subject with precocious puberty by age one year (29). This suggests a correlation between severity of phenotype and degree of activation of the mutant receptor. However, the basis for timing of onset of manifestations, given that this is a germline mutation, is not well understood. Also, lack of clinical manifestations in females with the mutant receptor argues that LH stimulation alone is inadequate to trigger puberty; presumably FSH action is also required for ovarian steroidogenesis, whereas LH-receptor-stimulated cAMP in Leydig cells is alone sufficient to stimulate testosterone formation. With one exception, mutations in FMPP are missense mutations in TM6 or the adjoining part of loop i3 (Table 3). This has prompted speculation that the involved residues are required to keep the receptor in an inhibited (non-G protein interacting) conformation, perhaps by interaction with specific residues in neighboring TM domains. Missense mutants incapable of such specific interactions would relieve inhibitory constraints and lead to agonist-independent activation (63, 64).

HYPERFUNCTIONING THYROID ADENOMAS AND NON-AUTOIMMUNE AUTOSOMAL DOMINANT HYPERTHYROIDISM  Hyperfunctioning thyroid adenomas, so-called hot nodules, are benign, sporadic tumors that produce and secrete thyroid hormone independently of TSH. Because cAMP stimulates both proliferation and differentiated function of thyroid cells, activating somatic mutations of the $G_s$-coupled TSH receptor could cause such tumors, and indeed, some were found (44). Germline mutations also causing activation of the TSH receptor have been identified in affected members of kindreds with autosomal-dominant non-autoimmune hyperthyroidism, and a new germline-activating mutation of the receptor gene was found in a case of congenital hyperthyroidism (10, 22). The mutations identified to date (10, 22, 44, 45, 51) involve not only TM6 residues but also residues in other regions of the receptor (Table 3), suggesting that the TSH receptor may be more generally susceptible to activation than is the LH receptor. As for the LH receptor mutations, those of the TSH receptor selectively cause agonist-independent activation of cAMP but not inositol phosphate formation.

GRAVES' DISEASE  In this disorder, TSH-independent hyperthyroidism is caused by immunoglobulins that bind to and stimulate the extracellular part of the TSH receptor. Although it was suggested that a rare polymorphism in the receptor gene (threonine for proline at residue 52) might predispose to Graves' disease, a study of 156 normal subjects and 88 with Graves' disease failed to demonstrate an association with the disease (81).

## $Ca^{2+}$-Sensing Receptor

A cDNA encoding a bovine parathyroid $Ca^{2+}$-sensing receptor (CaR) was initially obtained by expression cloning using the *Xenopus* oocyte system (5). The predicted amino acid sequence suggests that this receptor and the metabotropic glutamate receptors comprise a distinct subset of the GPCR superfamily that is characterized by a very long (about 600 amino acids) extracellular amino-terminus, the signature seven membrane-spanning domain, and a long (about 200 amino acids) intracellular carboxy-terminus. The CaR contains

**Table 4**  Loss-of-function CaR mutations in familial hypocalciuric hypercalcemia and neonatal severe hyperparathyroidism and gain-of-function mutations in autosomal-dominant hypoparathyroidism

| Mutation[a] | Location | Mutation[a] | Location |
|---|---|---|---|
| Loss | | Loss | |
| R63M | Nterm | S608stop | Nterm |
| R67C | Nterm | S658Y | TM2 |
| T139M | Nterm | G670R | TM2 |
| G144E | Nterm | P749R | e2 |
| R186Q | Nterm | **R796W** | i3 |
| D216E | Nterm | V818I | TM6 |
| Y219S | Nterm | T877 frameshift | Cterm |
| R228Q | Nterm | Gain | |
| | | **E128A** | Nterm |
| E298K | Nterm | Q246R | Nterm |

[a] Bold type indicates that the functional effect of the mutation has been defined by expression studies.

multiple acidic residues in the amino-terminus that may be involved in binding extracellular $Ca^{2+}$ with low affinity. Functional and genetic (see below) evidence suggests that $Ca^{2+}$ binding to the receptor activates it and promotes coupling to one or more members of the $G_q$-family. This causes PLC-$\beta$ stimulation and resultant increased intracellular $Ca^{2+}$. The receptor is expressed predominantly in parathyroid but also in kidney, brain, and several other tissues. Through as yet undefined mechanisms, receptor activation in parathyroid cells inhibits parathyroid hormone (PTH) secretion, and in renal distal tubules, receptor activation may inhibit calcium reabsorption.

FAMILIAL HYPOCALCIURIC HYPERCALCEMIA (FHH) AND NEONATAL SEVERE PRIMARY HYPERPARATHYROIDISM (NSPHPT)    FHH is an autosomal-dominant disorder characterized by general insensitivity to extracellular ionized calcium concentration. The clinical manifestations are generally benign and include hypercalcemia with circulating PTH that is either normal (inappropriately so in view of the raised serum calcium) or frankly elevated, and hypocalciuria relative to the filtered load. Linkage to chromosome 3q2 in most families (a few families show no linkage to 3q suggesting genetic heterogeneity) directed attention to CaR as a candidate gene because of its localization to 3q2. Screening of multiple families for CaR mutations has revealed a number of distinct missense mutations (Table 4) (6, 46, 49); they are unlikely to represent common polymorphisms because they were not found in a large number of normal individuals. One mutant receptor, R796W, was expressed and shown to have a markedly attenuated response to extracellular $Ca^{2+}$.

NSPHPT is characterized by severe hypercalcemia, relative hypocalciuria, and often bony demineralization. The disease can be lethal if parathyroidectomy is not performed. Linkage analysis using markers on 3q2 in families with parental consanguinity and offspring with NSPHPT provided evidence that the disease may be caused by a homozygous dose of the affected gene (50). Homozygosity for the E296K mutation of the CaR was identified in one case of NSPHPT (49). Thus far the majority of the mutations in the CaR identified in these disorders have been missense mutations in the large extracellular amino-terminus. Precisely how these mutations impair function has not been clarified. Defects in protein folding, membrane targeting, calcium binding, and G protein-coupling are all possible. One mutation, S608stop, is predicted to truncate the receptor before TM1 and might even cause secretion of the extracellular domain. Another mutation involves insertion of an Alu sequence in exon 7 at threonine 877 causing a frameshift and loss of the normal sequence of 878 to 1085. This mutant was identified in FHH kindreds from Nova Scotia and was found in homozygous form in members with NSPHPT (19).

Whatever the mechanism of the loss-of-function, the presumption is that a heterozygous mutation that impairs calcium sensitivity underlies the hypercalcemia and hypocalciuria that typify FHH. Not only is the set point for calcium inhibition of PTH secretion increased, but the loss of renal sensitivity to extracellular calcium could explain the relative hypocalciuria. In NSPHPT, homozygous loss-of-function mutations (or potentially compound heterozygotes) cause greater calcium insensitivity and hence a more severe phenotype. Indeed, it is possible that homozygosity for truly null mutations might be incompatible with life.

AUTOSOMAL-DOMINANT HYPOPARATHYROIDISM (ADH)    At least two kindreds have been described with mild hypocalcemia and relatively low PTH in which affected individuals were found to have missense mutations (see Table 4) in the CaR (47, 48). In one case, the E128A mutant was expressed in *Xenopus* oocytes and shown to be hypersensitive to $Ca^{2+}$, i.e. it showed increased activation compared to wild-type for any level of $Ca^{2+}$ (48). The data are consistent with a gain-of-function mutation that constitutively activates the CaR causing it to inhibit PTH secretion at subnormal extracellular $Ca^{2+}$ concentrations. Both mutations are in the extracellular amino-terminus, and both cause a net increase in positive charge, but how this could lead to receptor activation is unclear.

## PTH/CT Receptor Family

This is a distinct GPCR subfamily with strong homology among its members but relatively low homology to other subsets of the GPCR superfamily. The amino-terminus is intermediate in length between that of short GPCRs such as the opsins and long ones such as the glycoprotein hormone receptors. The amino-terminus contains a signal sequence, a number of cysteines conserved in all members of the subfamily, and divergent residues that may contribute to ligand-binding specificity. In addition to PTH and calcitonin (CT), members include secretin, VIP, PACAP, glucagon, GRF, GLP-1, and CRF. The D/E-R-Y/W motif at the end of TM3 in most GPCRs is not present in this subfamily. These receptors all couple primarily to $G_s$, but can also activate $G_q$ at generally higher agonist concentrations.

Mice homozygous for the *little* mutation show growth hormone-deficient dwarfism and are resistant to growth hormone-releasing factor. The disorder is due to a loss-of-function missense mutation (aspartate60glycine) in the GRF receptor gene (12). The involved residue is highly conserved in members of this subfamily and may be critical for normal folding of the extracellular domain and/or normal agonist binding.

Jansen-type metaphyseal chondrodysplasia is a rare form of human dwarfism caused by abnormal endochondral bone formation and associated with PTH-independent hypercalcemia and hypophosphatemia. A new activating heterozygous mutation (histidine223arginine) was identified in the PTH receptor gene of an affected subject (59). The mutated receptor caused ligand-independent stimulation of cAMP but not inositol phosphate formation in transfected cells. The involved histidine residue in loop i1 is conserved in all members of this subfamily and may be important in normal G protein activation. Constitutive activation of the PTH receptor by mimicking the effects of PTH or PTHrP hypersecretion can readily explain the hypercalcemia and hypophosphatemia. Abnormal endochondral bone formation in this disease is also consistent with a critical role for this receptor in normal proliferation and differentiation of growth-plate chondrocytes; knock-out of this receptor gene in mice causes a lethal phenotype characterized by severe chondrodysplasia (59).

Pseudohypoparathyroidism type Ib (PHP Ib) is a disease characterized by isolated resistance to PTH (hypocalcemia and hyperphosphatemia despite hypersecretion of PTH). The localized manifestations and the failure of PTH to elicit a normal increase in urinary cAMP excretion in affected individuals led to the hypothesis that the disease could be caused by loss-of-function mutations in the PTH receptor. This has not been supported by a study of the receptor gene in 18 subjects with the disorder. In these persons, no mutations of functional consequence were identified (60). Indeed, the aforementioned lethal phenotype of homozygous disruption of the receptor gene in mice makes it unlikely that the human disease could be due to null mutations involving both alleles. A study of the PTH receptor in skin fibroblasts from subjects with PHP Ib, however, showed reduction in both PTH-stimulated cAMP formation and in receptor mRNA in a subset of patients (72). It is thus likely that the molecular defect in PHP Ib is heterogeneous, and it is possible that in some subjects a reduction in receptor number may be causal.

A polymorphism at position 40 (glycine or serine) of the glucagon receptor gene was identified that resulted in a threefold lower affinity (for the serine variant) for agonist binding (15). The serine variant of the receptor was significantly more common in French subjects with non-insulin-dependent diabetes mellitus (NIDDM) than in controls. The suggestion that this variant receptor predisposes to NIDDM will require further study.

## Melanocortin Receptors

This subfamily includes receptors for ACTH, various forms of melanocyte-stimulating hormone (MSH), and cannabinoids and is characterized by being relatively small (297 residues for ACTH receptor) and lacking the putative disulfide between loops e1 and e2, as well as conserved prolines in TM4 and 5. The ACTH receptor is predominantly expressed in adrenal cortex. Loss-of-function mutations in both alleles of this receptor gene cause familial gluco-corticoid deficiency, an autosomal-recessive disorder characterized by ACTH resistance, hyperpigmentation (due to stimulation of skin MSH receptors by excessive ACTH), and a spectrum of manifestations of relative glucocorticoid deficiency including hypoglycemia, failure to thrive, and frequent infections (76, 82). Among the mutations so far described are isoleucine44methionine (TM1), serine74isoleucine (TM2), serine120arginine (TM3), arginine128cysteine and arginine146histidine (loop i2), leucine192frameshift (TM5), and arginine201stop (loopi3). Affected individuals may be compound heterozygotes or homozygous for particular mutations. As with other hereditary diseases caused by receptor loss-of-function mutations (cf nephrogenic diabetes insipidus), a relatively large number of mutations in many regions of the receptor can occur. By analogy with activating TSH receptor mutations in sporadic hyperfunctioning thyroid adenomas (see above), adrenocortical neoplasms could in theory be caused by ACTH receptor-activating mutations, but none were found in a study of 17 benign and 8 malignant adrenal cortical tumors (28). In contrast, both activating and loss-of-function mutations in the MSH receptor of mice with genetic forms of hyper- and hypopigmentation, respectively, have been identified (54).

## Other Receptors

Hirschsprung's disease is a multigenic disorder characterized by failure of innervation of the gastrointestinal tract. One form of the disease appears to be due to a loss-of-function mutation (cysteine is substituted for trytophan276, a highly conserved residue in TM5) in the endothelin-B receptor (52). Homozygotes for the mutation have a substantially greater risk of developing the disease than do heterozygotes. How this mutation leads to the phenotype is unclear, but targeted disruption of the receptor gene in mice and a mutant mouse (*piebald-lethal*) with a deletion of the receptor gene have a similar phenotype, which suggests an essential role for this receptor in development of certain neural crest-derived cells.

An arginine60leucine mutation in loop i1 of the thromboxane $A_2$ receptor has been identified in platelets from affected members of two unrelated families with a dominantly inherited bleeding disorder (16). The mutation does not affect binding but impairs second messenger production specifically in response to thromboxane $A_2$ receptor agonists but not other platelet agonists such as thrombin. Even subjects with the mutation in heterozygous form showed impaired platelet response, suggesting that the mutation could act as a dominant-negative perhaps by binding agonist and then failing to activate G protein.

# MUTATIONS IN G PROTEINS

## Albright Hereditary Osteodystrophy

Pseudohypoparathyroidism (PHP) is defined as resistance to PTH. Unlike PHP Ib (discussed above) in which resistance is limited to PTH, a subset of patients with PHP, termed type Ia, show more generalized hormone resistance, for example, to thyrotropin and gonadotropins, and phenotypic features such as obesity, short stature, mild mental retardation and bony anomalies, collectively termed Albright hereditary osteodystrophy (AHO). In families with AHO, individuals with the phenotypic features, but without hormone resistance are said to have pseudoPHP (PPHP). Because hormone resistance in PHP Ia is proximal to cAMP generation and is not limited to PTH alone, a germline mutation in a ubiquitously expressed gene such as $G_s$-$\alpha$, which couples multiple hormone receptors to stimulation of cAMP formation, seems plausible. Indeed, biochemical and immunochemical measurements of $G_s$-$\alpha$ in membranes from multiple cell types of subjects with AHO reveal an approximate 50% reduction (69). Analysis of the $G_s$-$\alpha$ gene on the distal long arm of chromosome 20 shows distinct heterozygous loss-of-function mutations in multiple AHO kindreds (see 68 and references therein for detailed mutation listing). Most mutations impair mRNA and/or protein formation; a minority appear to be missense mutations, e.g. arginine385histidine, which uncouples $G_s$ from receptors (61). An alanine366serine mutation was found in two unrelated males with the features of PHP Ia but with the unique additional feature of gonadotropin-independent precocious puberty (17). The latter condition can be due to signal transduction defects that cause LH-independent stimulation of Leydig cell cAMP formation (e.g. constitutive activation of LH receptor in

FMPP discussed above or of $G_s$-$\alpha$ in McCune-Albright syndrome discussed below). The paradoxical combination of hormone resistance and autonomous gonadal hyperfunction is likely due to the unique properties of this missense mutant. Alanine 366 is highly conserved in all G-$\alpha$ subunits and is likely involved in tight binding of GDP. GDP dissociates more readily from the serine mutant allowing GTP to bind independently of receptor catalysis (step 3 in Figure 1). In vitro expression studies show that this leads to protein instability at normal body temperature accounting for the loss-of-function, but at 32°C, the lower temperature prevailing in the testes, the mutant protein is stable and constitutively activated.

Although deficiency in functional $G_s$-$\alpha$ offers a partial explanation for PHP Ia, several questions remain to be answered. (*a*) Why is there such variability in hormone resistance? Essentially all subjects show PTH and TSH resistance, but vasopressin and ACTH resistance are not apparent even though the latter receptors are also coupled to $G_s$. (*b*) How does $G_s$-$\alpha$ deficiency relate to the AHO phenotype? (*c*) Subjects with PPHP show the identical $G_s$-$\alpha$ mutations as their family members with PHP yet are not hormone resistant. What accounts for this difference? Further studies on the stoichiometry of receptors, G proteins, and effectors in various tissues and on the modulatory effects of other gene products may provide answers. Creation of a mouse $G_s$-$\alpha$ gene knock-out should offer a useful model for such studies.

## Acromegaly and Hyperfunctional Thyroid Nodules

In vitro studies of somatotroph tumors from patients with acromegaly showed that there was constitutive activation of cAMP formation in about 40% (67). Studies of the $G_s$-$\alpha$ gene from such tumors (27) showed heterozygous missense mutations involving arginine 201 (the residue covalently modified by cholera toxin) or glutamine 227 (corresponding to glutamine 61, an oncogenic hot spot in *ras*). Both residues are highly conserved in all G-$\alpha$ subunits, and are seen in the three-dimensional structure to be intimately involved in binding the $\gamma$ phosphate of GTP (8). These somatic mutations cause constitutive $G_s$-$\alpha$ activation by inhibiting the GTPase turn-off reaction (step 5 in Figure 1). Thus cAMP is stimulated independently of GRF, and hyperfunction and benign cell proliferation result. Similar mutations have been found in sporadic hyperfunctional thyroid nodules (32). In the latter case, somatic mutations in either the TSH receptor (see above) or in $G_s$-$\alpha$ can give the same result.

## McCune-Albright Syndrome (MAS)

MAS is characterized by a classic triad of polyostotic fibrous dysplasia, *cafe-au-lait* skin hyperpigmentation, and precocious puberty, but many variations on this triad occur. Endocrine manifestations may include autonomous hyperfunction of somatotrophs, thyroid, and adrenal cortex in addition to or instead of gonadotropin-independent precocious puberty. The cause of such pleiotropic manifestations in a sporadic disorder was obscure until it was recognized that although a germline-activating mutation in the $G_s$-$\alpha$ gene might be lethal, a somatic mutation occurring early in embryogenesis could lead to constitutively increased cAMP formation in many tissues. Given the ability of cAMP to stimulate both proliferation and differentiated function of certain cell types, notably endocrine cells and melanocytes, an activating $G_s$-$\alpha$ mutation could explain many features of MAS. Analysis of multiple tissues from a number of affected subjects revealed arginine201cysteine or histidine mutations in a mosaic pattern consistent with an early postzygotic somatic event (83). Arginine 201 missense mutations were also identified in pathologic but not normal bone from subjects with MAS and in the focal bone lesion in subjects with monostotic fibrous dysplasia (66). This suggests a spectrum of diseases due to somatic activating $G_s$-$\alpha$ gene mutations ranging from those occurring early in embryogenesis and leading to a wide distribution with pleiotropic, potentially severe manifestations (65) to those occurring later as more focal events and leading to localized manifestations such as somatotroph tumors in acromegaly.

## Other G Protein Defects

G protein defects have been implicated in a number of neuropsychiatric disorders, in alcoholism (80), diabetes mellitus, and hypertension (7), but with evidence that is at best indirect (68, 69). Thus far, molecular genetic studies have failed to identify specific G protein defects in such disorders. For example, the sequence of $G_s$-$\alpha$ cloned from spontaneously hypertensive rats reported to show defective cAMP stimulation was the same as that of the nonhypertensive strain (14), and linkage of the $G_s$-$\alpha$ gene was excluded in nine kindreds with bipolar disorder (31). Any defects in G proteins in such disorders may be more subtle than mutations or may be secondary to other changes. Because $G_s$ has been most intensively studied, it is not surprising that thus far most examples of G protein defects in human diseases involve this G protein. As other, more recently characterized G proteins are studied, additional defects are likely to be identified. Indeed, $G_{i2}$-$\alpha$ arginine 179 mutations (equivalent to position 201 in $G_s$-$\alpha$) have been found in a small number of ovarian and adrenalcortical tumors (32). Since such activating mutations of $G_{i2}$-$\alpha$ are mildly transforming in transfected fibroblasts, it has been presumed that the mutations identified in tumors are causal, but this remains to be proven. A role, if any, for activating mutations of $G_{12}$-$\alpha$, which is highly transforming in fibroblasts (86), in naturally occurring tumors remains speculative. Likewise, a postulated connection between $G_o$ and Alzheimer's disease, based on the observation that the amyloid precursor protein can activate $G_o$, requires further study (40).

## CONCLUSIONS

The cloning of genes encoding GPCRs and G proteins has permitted direct testing of hypotheses concerning the role of these genes in a variety of human diseases. The subsequent identification of numerous mutations in GPCR and G protein genes as the cause of these diseases has had a number of important implications: (*a*) Such mutations provide valuable structure-function information not readily obtained by more random artificial mutagenesis studies. Activating mutations in particular have provided novel insights into critical structural domains, and underscore the fact that the information needed to signal to the next component in a cascade (e.g. receptor activation of G protein or G protein activation of effector) is an inherent property of each component. (*b*) GPCR and G protein mutations offer unique clues to pathophysiologic mechanisms. For example, the megacolon phenotype of endothelin-B receptor mutations reveals an unexpected role for this receptor in intestinal ganglion cell development, and the lack of a phenotypic effect of activating mutations of the LH receptor in females emphasizes the importance of FSH action in pubertal development in females. (*c*) Identification of mutations in GPCRs and G proteins already has diagnostic implications. For example, immediate postnatal diagnosis of a V2 vasopressin receptor mutation in an at-risk male from a kindred with NDI permitted rapid treatment and prevention of potentially brain-damaging dehydration (3). Eventually, information gained from elucidation of GPCR and G protein mutations should lead to more specific and more effective treatment. For example, in RP due to a constitutively activating rhodopsin mutation, certain retinal derivatives may prove effective in blocking receptor activation and hence photoreceptor degeneration (13). It may be possible to develop such antagonists for other diseases caused by activated receptors. Blocking constitutive $G_s$ protein activation, for example with dominant-negative subunits of cAMP-dependent protein kinase, would represent a novel approach to treatment of the crippling bone lesions in MAS. (*d*) Finally, success to date will prompt further search for mutations and other lesions in GPCRs and G proteins as the cause of additional diseases. Artificially created activated mutants of the $\alpha_{1B}$-adrenergic receptor are oncogenic (1), and the human *mas* oncogene has the structure of a GPCR (89). This suggests a broader role for GPCRs in neoplasia than the limited one identified for the TSH receptor in thyroid nodules.

As powerful gene-targeting methods are applied to GPCRs and G proteins, novel targets for mutation screening should emerge. For example, knock-out of the $G_{i2}$-$\alpha$ gene in mice surprisingly causes ulcerative colitis (58). Also, polymorphisms in many GPCR and G protein genes have already been identified and there are likely many more. There is already an indication that some of these may not cause disease by themselves but may predispose to disease;

for instance, polymorphisms in the glucagon and β3-adrenergic receptors may predispose to NIDDM (see above). Future studies are likely to reveal additional examples of mutations and polymorphisms in GPCR and G protein genes relevant to human disease.

ACKNOWLEDGMENT

I am grateful to Andrew Shenker for helpful discussions.

*Literature Cited*

1. Allen LF, Lefkowitz RJ, Caron MG, Cotecchia S. 1991. G-protein-coupled receptor genes as protooncogenes: constitutively activating mutation of the $\alpha_{1B}$-adrenergic receptor enhances mitogenesis and tumorigenicity. *Proc. Natl. Acad. Sci. USA* 88:11354–58

2. Baldwin JM. 1994. Structure and function of receptors coupled to G proteins. *Curr. Opin. Cell Biol.* 6:180–90

3. Bichet DG, Birnbaumer M, Lonergan M, Arthus MF, Rosenthal W, et al. 1994. Nature and recurrence of AVPR2 mutations in X-linked nephrogenic diabetes insipidus. *Am. J. Hum. Genet.* 55:278–86

4. Birnbaumer M, Gilbert S, Rosenthal W. 1994. An extracellular congenital nephrogenic diabetes insipidus mutation of the vasopressin receptor reduces cell surface expression, affinity for ligand, and coupling to the $G_s$/adenylyl cyclase system. *Mol. Endocrinol.* 8:886–94

5. Brown EM, Gamba G, Riccardi D, Lombardi M, Butters R, et al. 1993. Cloning and characterization of an extracellular $Ca^{2+}$-sensing receptor from bovine parathyroid. *Nature* 366:575–80

6. Brown EM, Pollak M, Hebert SC. 1995. Sensing of extracellular $Ca^{2+}$ by parathyroid and kidney cells: cloning and characterization of an extracellular $Ca^{2+}$-sensing receptor. *Am. J. Kidney Dis.* 25:506–13

7. Chatziantoniou C, Ruan X, Arendshorst WJ. 1995. Defective G protein activation of the cAMP pathway in rat kidney during genetic hypertension. *Proc. Natl. Acad. Sci. USA* 92:2924–28

8. Coleman DE, Berghuis AM, Lee E, Linder ME, Gilman AG, Sprang SR. 1994. Structures of active conformations of $G_{i\alpha1}$ and the mechanism of GTP hydrolysis. *Science* 265:1405–12

9. Deen PM, Verdijk MA, Knoers NV, Wieringa B, Monnens LA, et al. 1994. Requirement of human renal water channel aquaporin-2 for vasopressin-dependent concentration of urine. *Science* 264:92–95

10. Duprez L, Parma J, Van Sande J, Allgeier A, Leclère J, et al. 1994. Germline mutations in the thyrotropin receptor gene cause non-autoimmune autosomal dominant hyperthyroidism. *Nat. Genet.* 7:396–401

11. Friedman E, Adams EF, Hoog A, Gejman PV, Carson E, et al. 1994. Normal structural dopamine type 2 receptor gene in prolactin-secreting and other pituitary tumors. *J. Clin. Endocrinol. Metab.* 78:568–74

12. Godfrey P, Rahal JO, Beamer WG, Copeland NG, Jenkins NA, Mayo KE. 1993. GHRH receptor of little mice contains a missense mutation in the extracellular domain that disrupts receptor function. *Nat. Genet.* 4:227–32

13. Govardhan CP, Oprian DD. 1994. Active site-directed inactivation of constitutively active mutants of rhodopsin. *J. Biol. Chem.* 269:6524–27

14. Gurich RW, Beach RE, Caflisch CR. 1994. Cloning of the α-subunit of $G_s$ protein from spontaneously hypertensive rats. *Hypertension* 24:595–99

15. Hager J, Hansen L, Vaisse C, Vionnet N, Philippi A, et al. 1995. A missense mutation in the glucagon receptor gene is associated with non-insulin-dependent diabetes mellitus. *Nat. Genet.* 9:299–304

16. Hirata T, Kakizuka A, Ushikubi F, Fuse

I, Okuma M, Narumiya S. 1994. Arg[60] to Leu mutation of the human thromboxane $A_2$ receptor in a dominantly inherited bleeding disorder. *J. Clin. Invest.* 94:1662–67

17. Iiri T, Herzmark P, Nakamoto JM, van Dop C, Bourne HR. 1994. Rapid GDP release from $G_{s\alpha}$ in patients with gain and loss of endocrine function. *Nature* 371:164–68

18. Iismaa TP, Biden TJ, Shine J. 1995. *G Protein-Coupled Receptors,* Austin, TX: Landes. 181 pp.

19. Janicic N, Pausova Z, Cole DC, Hendy GN. 1995. Insertion of an Alu sequence in the calcium-sensing receptor gene in familial hypocalciuric hypercalcemia and neonatal severe hyperparathyroidism. *Am. J. Hum. Genet.* 56:880–86

20. Knoers NV, van den Ouweland AM, Verdijk M, Monnens LA, van Oost BA. 1994. Inheritance of mutations in the $V_2$ receptor gene in thirteen families with nephrogenic diabetes insipidus. *Kidney. Int.* 46:170–76

21. Kojro E, Eich P, Gimpl G, Fahrenholz F. 1993. Direct identification of an extracellular agonist binding site in the renal $V_2$ vasopressin receptor. *Biochemistry* 32:13537–44

22. Kopp P, Van Sande J, Parma J, Duprez L, Gerber H, et al. 1995. Brief report: congenital hyperthyroidism caused by a mutation in the thyrotropin-receptor gene. *New Engl. J. Med.* 332:150–54

23. Kosugi S, Van Dop C, Geffner ME, Rabl W, Carel J-C, et al. 1995. Characterization of heterozygous mutations causing constitutive activation of the luteinizing hormone receptor in familial male precocious puberty. *Hum. Mol. Genet.* 4:183–88

24. Kremer H, Kraaij R, Toledo SPA, Post M, Fridman JB, et al. 1995. Male pseudohermaphroditism due to a homozygous missense mutation of the luteinizing hormone receptor gene. *Nat. Genet.* 9:160–64

25. Kremer H, Mariman E, Otten BJ, Moll GWJ, Stoelinga GBA, et al. 1993. Cosegregation of missense mutations of the luteinizing hormone receptor gene with familial male-limited precocious puberty. *Hum. Mol. Genet.* 2:1779–83

26. Kumaramanickavel G, Maw M, Denton MJ, John S, Srikumari CRS, et al. 1994. Missense rhodopsin mutation in a family with recessive RP. *Nat. Genet.* 8:10–11

27. Landis CA, Masters SB, Spada A, Pace AM, Bourne HR, Vallar L. 1989. GTPase inhibiting mutations activate the alpha chain of $G_s$ and stimulate adenylyl cyclase in human pituitary tumours. *Nature* 340:692–96

28. Latronico AC, Reincke M, Mendonca BB, Arai K, Mora P, et al. 1995. No evidence for oncogenic mutations in the adrenocorticotropin receptor gene in human adrenocortical neoplasm. *J. Clin. Endocrinol. Metab.* 80:875–77

29. Laue L, Chan WY, Hsueh AJW, Kudo M, Hsu SY, et al. 1995. Genetic heterogeneity of constitutively activating mutations of the human luteinizing hormone receptor in familial male-limited precocious puberty. *Proc. Natl. Acad. Sci. USA* 92:1906–10

30. Laue L, Wu SM, Kudo M, Hsueh AJW, Griffin JE, et al. 1994. An inactivating mutation of the human luteinizing hormone receptor gene in familial Leydig cell hypoplasia. *Mol. Biol. Cell* 5:68a (Abstr. 391)

31. Le F, Mitchell P, Vivero C, Waters B, Donald J, et al. 1994. Exclusion of close linkage of bipolar disorder to the $G_s$-$\alpha$ subunit gene in nine Australian pedigrees. *J. Affect. Disord.* 32:187–95

32. Lyons J, Landis CA, Harsh G, Vallar L, Grünewald K, et al. 1990. Two G protein oncogenes in human endocrine tumors. *Science* 249:655–59

33. Macke JP, Davenport CM, Jacobson SG, Hennessey JC, Gonzalez-Fernandez F, et al. 1993. Identification of novel rhodopsin mutations responsible for retinitis pigmentosa: implications for the structure and function of rhodopsin. *Am. J. Hum. Genet.* 53:80–89

34. Markby DW, Onrust R, Bourne HR. 1993. Separate GTP binding and GTPase activating domains of a $G\alpha$ subunit. *Science* 262:1895–901

35. Merendino JJ Jr, Spiegel AM, Crawford JD, O'Carroll AM, Brownstein MJ, Lolait SJ. 1993. Brief report: a mutation in the vasopressin $V_2$-receptor gene in a kindred with X-linked nephrogenic diabetes insipidus. *New Engl. J Med.* 328:1538–41

36. Milano CA, Allen LF, Rockman HA, Dolber PC, McMinn TR, et al. 1994. Enhanced myocardial function in transgenic mice overexpressing the $\beta_2$-adrenergic receptor. *Science* 264:582–86

37. Min KC, Zvygaga TA, Cypress AM, Sakmar TP. 1993. Characterization of mutant rhodopsins responsible for autosomal dominant retinitis pigmentosa: mutations on the cytoplasmic surface affect transducin activation. *J. Biol. Chem.* 268:9400–4

38. Nathans J. 1994. In the eye of the beholder: visual pigments and inherited

variation in human vision. *Cell* 78:357–60

39. Neer EJ. 1995. Heterotrimeric G proteins: organizers of transmembrane signals. *Cell* 80:249–57

40. Nishimoto I, Okamoto T, Matsuura Y, Takahashi S, Murayama Y, Ogata E. 1993. Alzheimer amyloid protein precursor complexes with brain GTP-binding protein Go. *Nature* 362:75–79

41. Noel JP, Hamm HE, Sigler PB. 1993. The 2.2 Å crystal structure of transducin-alpha complexed with GTP gamma S. *Nature* 366:654–63

42. Oksche A, Dickson J, Schulein R, Seyberth HW, Muller M, et al. 1994. Two novel mutations in the vasopressin V₂ receptor gene in patients with congenital nephrogenic diabetes insipidus. *Biochem. Biophys. Res. Commun.* 205:552–57

43. Pan Y, Wilson P, Gitschier J. 1994. The effect of eight V₂ vasopressin receptor mutations on stimulation of adenylyl cyclase and binding to vasopressin. *J. Biol. Chem.* 269:31933–37

44. Parma J, Duprez L, Van Sande J, Cochaux P, Gervy C, et al. 1993. Somatic mutations in the thyrotropin receptor gene cause hyperfunctioning thyroid adenomas. *Nature* 365:649–51

45. Paschke R, Tonacchera M, Van Sande J, Parma J, Vassart G. 1994. Identification and functional characterization of two new somatic mutations causing constitutive activation of the thyrotropin receptor in hyperfunctioning autonomous adenomas of the thyroid. *J. Clin. Endocrinol. Metab.* 79:1785–89

46. Pearce SHS, Trump D, Wooding C, Besser GM, Chew SL, et al. 1994. Four novel mutations in the calcium-sensing receptor gene associated with familial benign (hypocalciuric) hypercalcemia. *J. Bone Miner. Res.* 9:S145 (Abstr.)

47. Perry YM, Finegold DN, Armitage MM, Ferrell RE. 1994. A missense mutation in the Ca-sensing receptor causes familial autosomal dominant hypoparathyroidism. *Am. J. Hum. Genet.* 55:A17 (Abstr.)

48. Pollak MR, Brown EM, Estep HL, McLaine PN, Kifor O, et al. 1994. Autosomal dominant hypocalcemia caused by a calcium-sensing receptor gene mutation. *Nat. Genet.* 8:303–7

49. Pollak MR, Brown EM, Wu Chou Y-H, Hebert SC, Marx SJ, et al. 1993. Mutations in the human Ca²⁺-sensing receptor gene cause familial hypocalciuric hypercalcemia and neonatal severe hyperparathyroidism. *Cell* 75:1297–303

50. Pollak MR, Wu Chou Y-H, Marx SJ,

Steinmann B, Cole DEC, et al. 1994. Familial hypocalciuric hypercalcemia and neonatal severe hyperparathyroidism: effects of mutant gene dosage on phenotype. *J. Clin. Invest.* 93:1108–12

51. Porcellini A, Ciullo I, Laviola L, Amabile G, Fenzi G, Avvedimento VE. 1994. Novel mutations of thyrotropin receptor gene in thyroid hyperfunctioning adenomas. Rapid identification by fine needle aspiration biopsy. *J. Clin. Endocrinol. Metab.* 79:657–61

52. Puffenberger EG, Hosoda K, Washington SS, Nakao K, DeWit D, et al. 1994. A missense mutation of the endothelin-B receptor gene in multigenic Hirschsprung's disease. *Cell* 79:1257–66

53. Reihsaus E, Innis M, MacIntyre N, Liggett SB. 1993. Mutations in the gene encoding for the β₂-adrenergic receptor in normal and asthmatic subjects. *Am. J. Respir. Cell. Mol. Biol.* 8:334–39

54. Robbins LS, Nadeau JH, Johnson KR, Kelly MA, Roselli-Rehfuss L, et al. 1993. Pigmentation phenotypes of variant extension locus alleles result from point mutations which alter MSH receptor function. *Cell* 72:827–34

55. Robertson GL, Scheidler JA. 1981. A newly recognized variant of familial nephrogenic diabetes insipidus distinguished by partial resistance to vasopressin (type 2). *Clin. Res.* 29:555A (Abstr.)

56. Rosenfeld PJ, Cowley GS, McGee TL, Sandberg MA, Berson EL, Dryja TP. 1992. A *Null* mutation in the rhodopsin gene causes rod photoreceptor dysfunction and autosomal recessive retinitis pigmentosa. *Nat. Genet.* 1:209–13

57. Rosenthal W, Antaramian A, Gilbert S, Birnbaumer M. 1993. Nephrogenic diabetes insipidus: a V₂ vasopressin receptor unable to stimulate adenylyl cyclase. *J. Biol. Chem.* 268:13030–33

58. Rudolph U, Finegold MJ, Rich SS, Harriman GR, Srinavasan Y, et al. 1995. Ulcerative colitis and adenocarcinoma of the colon in $G_{\alpha\text{-}i2}$-deficient mice. *Nature Genet.* 10:141–48

59. Schipani E, Kruse K, Juppner H. 1995. A constitutively active mutant PTH-PTHrP receptor in Jansen-type metaphyseal chondrodysplasia. *Science* 268:98–100

60. Schipani E, Weinstein LS, Bergwitz C, Lida-Klein A, Kong XF, et al. 1995. Pseudohypoparathyroidism type Ib is not caused by mutations in the coding exons of the human PTH/PTHrP receptor gene. *J. Clin. Endocrinol. Metab.* 80:1611–21

61. Schwindinger WF, Miric A, Zimmer-

man D, Levine MA. 1994. A novel $G_{s\alpha}$ mutant in a patient with Albright hereditary osteodystrophy uncouples cell surface receptors from adenylyl cyclase. *J. Biol. Chem.* 269:25387–91

62. Segalat L, Elkes DA, Kaplan JM. 1995. Modulation of serotonin-controlled behaviors by $G_o$ in *Caenorhabditis elegans. Science* 267:1648–51

63. Shenker A. 1995. G protein-coupled receptor structure and function: the impact of disease-causing mutations. *Baillière's Clin. Endocrinol. Metab.* In press

64. Shenker A, Laue L, Kosugi S, Merendino JJ Jr, Minegishi T, Cutler GB Jr. 1993. A constitutively activating mutation of the luteinizing hormone receptor in familial male precocious puberty. *Nature* 365:652–54

65. Shenker A, Weinstein LS, Moran A, Pescovitz OH, Charest NJ, et al. 1993. Severe endocrine and non-endocrine manifestations of the McCune-Albright syndrome associated with activating mutations of the stimulatory G protein, $G_s$. *J. Pediatr.* 123:509–18

66. Shenker A, Weinstein LS, Sweet DE, Spiegel AM. 1994. An activating $G_{s\alpha}$ mutation is present in fibrous dysplasia of bone in the McCune-Albright syndrome. *J. Clin. Endocrinol. Metab.* 79: 750–55

67. Spada A, Vallar L, Faglia G. 1992. G protein oncogenes in pituitary tumors. *Trends Endocrinol. Metab.* 3:355–60

68. Spiegel AM, Jones TLZ, Simonds WF, Weinstein LS. 1994. *G Proteins,* Austin, TX: Landes. 144 pp.

69. Spiegel AM, Weinstein LS, Shenker A. 1993. Abnormalities in G protein-coupled signal transduction pathways in human disease. *J. Clin. Invest.* 92:1119–25

70. Stein SA, Oates EL, Hall CR, Grumbles RM, Fernandez LM, et al. 1994. Identification of a point mutation in the thyrotropin receptor of the *hyt/hyt* hypothyroid mouse. *Mol. Endocrinol.* 8: 129–38

71. Strader CD, Fong TM, Tota MR, Underwood D. 1994. Structure and function of G protein-coupled receptors. *Annu. Rev. Biochem.* 63:101–32

72. Suarez F, Lebrun JJ, Lecossier D, Escoubet B, Coureau C, Silve C. 1995. Expression and modulation of the parathyroid hormone (PTH)/PTH-related peptide receptor messenger ribonucleic acid in skin fibroblasts from patients with type Ib pseudohypoparathyroidism. *J. Clin. Endocrinol. Metab.* 80:965–70

73. Sullivan JM, Scott KM, Falls HF, Richards JE, Sieving PA. 1994. A novel rhodopsin mutation at the retinal binding site (Lys-296-Met) in ADRP. *Invest. Ophthalmol. Visual Sci.* 34:1149

74. Sung C-H, Davenport CM, Nathans J. 1993. Rhodopsin mutations responsible for autosomal dominant retinitis pigmentosa: clustering of functional classes along the polypeptide chain. *J. Biol. Chem.* 268:26645–49

75. Sunthornthepvarakul T, Gottschalk ME, Hayashi Y, Refetoff S. 1995. Resistance to thyrotropin caused by mutations in the thyrotropin-receptor gene. *New Engl. J. Med.* 332:155–60

76. Tsigos C, Arai K, Hung W, Chrousos GP. 1993. Hereditary isolated glucocorticoid deficiency is associated with abnormalities of the adrenocorticotropin receptor gene. *J. Clin. Invest.* 92:2458–61

77. Tsukaguchi H, Matsubara H, Aritaki S, Kimura T, Abe S, Inada M. 1993. Two novel mutations in the vasopressin $V_2$ receptor gene in unrelated Japanese kindreds with nephrogenic diabetes insipidus. *Biochem. Biophys. Res. Commun.* 197:1000–10

78. Turki J, Pak J, Green SA, Martin RJ, Liggett SB. 1995. Genetic polymorphisms of the $\beta_2$-adrenergic receptor in nocturnal and nonnocturnal asthma. *J. Clin. Invest.* 95:1635–41

79. Walston J, Silver K, Bogardus C, Knowler WC, Celi FS, et al. 1995. Time of onset of non-insulin-dependent diabetes mellitus and genetic variation in the $\beta_3$-adrenergic-receptor gene. *New Engl. J. Med.* 333:343–47

80. Wand GS, Waltman C, Martin CS, McCaul ME, Levine MA, Wolfgang D. 1994. Differential expression of guanosine triphosphate binding proteins in men at high and low risk for the future development of alcoholism. *J. Clin. Invest.* 94:1004–11

81. Watson PF, French A, Pickerill AP, McIntosh RS, Weetman AP. 1995. Lack of an association between a polymorphism in the coding region of the thyrotropin receptor gene and Graves' disease. *J. Clin. Endocrinol. Metab.* 80: 1032–35

82. Weber A, Toppari J, Harvey RD, Klann RC, Shaw NJ, et al. 1995. Adrenocorticotropin receptor gene mutations in familial glucocorticoid deficiency: relationships with clinical features in four families. *J. Clin. Endocrinol. Metab.* 80:65–71

83. Weinstein LS, Shenker A, Gejman PV, Merino MJ, Friedman E, Spiegel AM. 1991. Activating mutations of the stimulatory G protein in the McCune-Albright

syndrome. *New Engl. J. Med.* 325:1688–95

84. Wenkert D, Merendino JJ Jr, Shenker A, Thambi N, Robertson GL, et al. 1994. Novel mutations in the $V_2$ vasopressin receptor gene of patients with X-linked nephrogenic diabetes insipidus. *Hum. Mol. Genet.* 3:1429–30

85. Wildin RS, Antush MJ, Bennett RL, Schoof JM, Scott CR. 1994. Heterogeneous AVPR2 gene mutations in congenital nephrogenic diabetes insipidus. *Am. J. Hum. Genet.* 55:266–77

86. Xu N, Bradley L, Ambdukar I, Gutkind JS. 1993. A mutant α subunit of $G_{12}$ potentiates the eicosanoid pathway and is highly oncogenic in NIH 3T3 cells. *Proc. Natl. Acad. Sci. USA* 90:6741–45

87. Yano K, Hidaka A, Saji M, Polymeropoulos MH, Okuno A, et al. 1994. A sporadic case of male-limited precocious puberty has the same constitu-tively activating point mutation in luteinizing hormone/choriogonadotropin receptor gene as familial cases. *J. Clin. Endocrinol. Metab.* 79:1818–23

88. Yano K, Saji M, Hidaka A, Moriya N, Okuno A, et al. 1995. A new constitutively activating point mutation in the luteinizing hormone/choriogonadotropin receptor gene in cases of male-limited precocious puberty. *J. Clin. Endocrinol. Metab.* In press

89. Young D, Waitches G, Birchmeier C, Fasano O, Wigler M. 1986. Isolation and characterization of a new cellular oncogene encoding a protein with multiple potential transmembrane domains. *Cell* 45:711–19

90. Yuasa H, Ito M, Oiso Y, Kurokawa M, Watanabe T, et al. 1994. Novel mutations in the $V_2$ vasopressin receptor gene in two pedigrees with congenital nephrogenic diabetes insipidus. *J. Clin. Endocrinol. Metab.* 79:361–65

*Annu. Rev. Physiol. 1996. 58:171–86*

# GLUCOKINASE MUTATIONS, INSULIN SECRETION, AND DIABETES MELLITUS

*Graeme I. Bell,*[1,2] *Simon J. Pilkis,*[3] *Irene T. Weber,*[4] *and Kenneth S. Polonsky*[2]

[1]Howard Hughes Medical Institute and Departments of Biochemistry and Molecular Biology and [2]Medicine, The University of Chicago, Chicago, Illinois 60637; [3]Department of Biochemistry, University of Minnesota, Minneapolis, Minnesota 55455; and [4]Department of Pharmacology, Jefferson Cancer Institute, Thomas Jefferson University, Philadelphia, Pennsylvania 19107

KEY WORDS:   glycolysis, genetics, glucose homeostasis, insulin, diabetes mellitus

### ABSTRACT

The glycolytic enzyme glucokinase plays a key role in glucose sensing by the insulin-secreting pancreatic β-cells, and mutations in the gene encoding this enzyme are a common cause of maturity-onset diabetes of the young (MODY), a form of non-insulin-dependent diabetes mellitus characterized by autosomal-dominant inheritance and onset before 25 years of age. Twenty-eight different mutations in this gene have been identified in subjects with MODY. Clinical studies have shown that subjects with MODY due to mutations in glucokinase have elevated fasting and postprandial glucose levels with normal first-phase insulin secretory responses to intravenous glucose injection and normal insulin secretion rates over a 24-h period. However, the dose-response curve relating glucose and insulin secretion rate obtained during graded intravenous glucose infusions was shifted to the right in subjects with glucokinase mutations, indicating decreased sensitivity to glucose. In normal subjects, the β-cell was most sensitive to an increase in glucose concentration between 5.5 and 6.0 mM, whereas in patients with glucokinase mutations, the maximum responsiveness was increased to 6.5 to 7.5 mM glucose. These studies indicate that glucokinase is an important component of the glucose-sensing mechanism of the β-cell.

## Introduction

Glucose is an essential energy source for mammalian cells. Nonetheless, despite its importance as a metabolic fuel and a building block for other biological macromolecules, high plasma glucose levels such as those that characterize subjects with diabetes mellitus are pathogenic and can lead to serious micro-

171

and macrovascular complications, with resulting cardiovascular disease, blindness, renal failure, nerve damage, and increased mortality (61). The levels of glucose in the circulation are maintained within a relatively narrow range through the combined action of insulin and glucagon. In normal healthy subjects, fasting and postprandial glucose concentrations range from 65 to 105 mg/dl (3.6 to 5.8 mM) and following a meal usually do not exceed 140 to 150 mg/dl (7.8 to 8.3 mM). Central to this tight regulation of plasma glucose levels is the ability of the β-cell to secrete insulin in response to small incremental increases in glucose. The molecular mechanisms by which this is accomplished have been the subject of intensive investigation. Two contrasting theories have been proposed to explain the effect of glucose on insulin secretion (31). The glucoreceptor theory postulates that D-glucose interacts with a stereospecific receptor, possibly located in the plasma membrane, and the binding of glucose initiates a cascade of events leading to insulin release; there is little direct support for this theory. The second, the fuel hypothesis for nutrient-stimulated insulin release, proposes that the metabolism of glucose is responsible for generating the signal for insulin secretion and that the glycolytic enzyme glucokinase is the β-cell glucose sensor. The results of physiological, biochemical, and molecular biological studies of insulin secretion have shown that glucokinase and glucose metabolism play a central role in regulating glucose-stimulated insulin secretion, consistent with the fuel hypothesis for insulin secretion (19, 32, 33). In addition, a recent demonstration that mutations in glucokinase can result in diabetes mellitus have confirmed the prominent role of this enzyme in regulating insulin secretion (3, 14).

In pancreatic β-cells, the metabolism of glucose is initiated with its phosphorylation by glucokinase, a member of a family of evolutionary and structurally related hexokinases (ATP:hexose 6-phosphotransferases, EC 2.7.1.1) present in all eukaryotic cells from yeast to mammals (37, 55, 58). The reaction catalyzed by glucokinase and other hexokinases, D-glucose + ATP→D-glucose-6-phosphate + ADP, is the first reaction in glycolysis, as well as the first rate-limiting reaction in the metabolism of glucose. Mammalian tissues contain four different hexokinases, which in rat are termed hexokinases I–IV in order of increasing net charge (16, 41, 43, 55). Hexokinase type IV, or glucokinase, is expressed in insulin-secreting pancreatic β-cells (32, 33). It is also the principal glucose-phosphorylating activity in the liver (32, 37) and is expressed in rare neuroendocrine cells of the brain and gastrointestinal tract (23). The enzymatic properties of glucokinase distinguish it from other mammalian hexokinases (Table 1), including a lower affinity for glucose and other hexoses, and the absence of significant feedback inhibition by physiological levels of glucose-6-phosphate. Glucokinase also has a smaller size (50 kDa) than the other hexokinases (100 kDa). Glucokinase (1) and hexokinases I (35, 44), II (54), and III (45) have been cloned, and these studies have shown that hexokinases are essentially dimers of glucokinase, consistent with a long-standing hypothesis that a primordial glucokinase-like gene gave rise to the hexokinases by gene duplication. The similarity in exon-intron organization of glucokinase (30) and hexokinase genes (25, 40) supports this hypothesis.

We review the role of glucokinase in the development of a form of non-insulin-dependent (type 2) diabetes mellitus (NIDDM), termed maturity onset diabetes of the young (MODY), and the effect of mutations in the glucokinase gene on glucose-stimulated insulin secretion. The structure of the glucokinase gene and its regulation by insulin, glucagon, and other hormones, and during development have been recently reviewed by Printz et al (41) and Iynedjian (22).

## *Mutations in Glucokinase are Associated with MODY*

NIDDM is a clinically and genetically heterogeneous disorder characterized by impaired insulin secretion and diminished insulin action in peripheral tissues (39, 61). It is unlikely to be due to a single etiological mechanism, but rather results from complex interactions between hereditary and environmental factors. NIDDM usually develops in individuals of middle age, often in association with obesity, and family studies suggest that this form of NIDDM has a complex, i.e. non-Mendelian, mode of inheritance, with interactions between several different susceptibility genes being necessary for its development. Although NIDDM is more common in older middle-aged individuals, it may occur at any age. MODY is a form of NIDDM characterized by onset before 25 years of age and autosomal-dominant inheritance (12). These features have facilitated genetic-linkage studies of MODY and have led to the identification of genes on chromosomes 20 (MODY1) (4), 7 (MODY2) (13, 18), and 12 (MODY3) (57) whose mutations can cause this form of diabetes. In addition, there are likely to be other MODY genes because there are families with MODY that show no evidence of linkage to MODY1, MODY2, or MODY3. Although MODY is generally considered to be a rather rare form of NIDDM, recent studies suggest that its prevalence may be much higher than commonly believed (27), especially as younger individuals are often asymptomatic with normal fasting blood glucose levels even though they may have a diabetic oral glucose tolerance test (12).

The MODY1 and MODY3 loci have not been cloned, and the nature of the proteins encoded by these genes is unknown. The MODY2 locus encodes glucokinase (14). The human glucokinase gene is composed of 12 exons that span a region of >50,000 base pairs of chromosome band 7p13 (Figure 1) (48, 53). It has two tissue-specific promoters (22, 41), one of which is active in pancreatic β-cells and the other in hepatocytes, a feature that allows glucokinase expression to be independently regulated in these two cell types. Human β-cell glucokinase mRNA is the product of exons 1a and 2–10 (Figure 1) (26). The major liver glucokinase mRNA is derived from exons 1b and 2–10, and a minor

**Table 1**  Properties of mammalian hexokinases

| | Hexokinase I | Hexokinase II | Hexokinase III | Hexokinase IV/ glucokinase | Yeast hexokinase |
|---|---|---|---|---|---|
| $K_m$ glucose (mM) | 0.04 | 0.13 | 0.02 | 5 | 0.1 |
| Hill coefficient | 1.0 | 1.0 | 1.0 | 1.6 | 1.0 |
| $K_m$ ATP (mM) | 0.42 | 0.70 | 1.29 | 0.2 | 0.2 |
| $K_i$ Glu-6-P (mM) | | | | | |
| vs glucose | 0.021 | 0.16 | 0.92 | 60 | — |
| vs ATP | 0.026 | 0.021 | 0.074 | 15 | 9.1 |
| Size (kDa) | 100 | 100 | 100 | 50 | 50 |
| Tissue distribution | Many tissues with high levels in brain | Many tissues with high levels in muscle and adipose tissue | Liver and kidney | Liver and pancreatic $\beta$-cells | |

Glu-6-P, glucose-6-phosphate. Adapted from References 16, 55, 58, 62.

transcript is encoded by exons 1b, 1c, and 2–10 (52). Protein synthesis is initiated within exons 1a, 1b, and 1c, which results in the synthesis of glucokinase molecules with different NH$_2$-terminal sequences for the first 14–16 amino acids, depending on the specific isoform; the human β-cell and major and minor liver forms are 465, 466, and 464 amino acids in size, respectively.

To date, 28 different mutations have been identified in the glucokinase gene in subjects with diabetes mellitus (Figure 1). These mutations include 19 missense mutations that change the sequence of glucokinase, 4 nonsense mutations that result in the synthesis of a truncated glucokinase molecule, and 5 mutations (deletions and mRNA splicing mutations) that result in the synthesis of a mRNA molecule that cannot encode a normal functional protein. The majority of the mutations shown in Figure 1 have been identified in patients with MODY (14). They have also been found in women with gestational-onset diabetes mellitus (47, 63) and in subjects who were believed to have late-onset NIDDM (24, 46, 49) but probably had unrecognized MODY. Although glucokinase mutations are a major cause of MODY, at least in French families (14), linkage studies (8, 63) and direct screening for mutations (7, 11, 34, 63) indicate that they are very rare in subjects with the common late-onset form of NIDDM and thus not a significant contributory factor in the development of this form of diabetes mellitus.

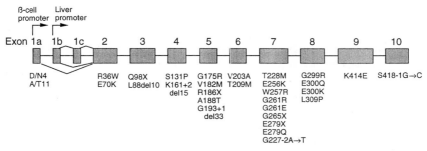

*Figure 1*  Schematic structure of human glucokinase gene and locations of mutations identified in subjects with MODY. Exons are shown as numbered boxes and are joined by lines indicating introns. The β-cell and liver-specific promoters are noted. The β-cell form of glucokinase mRNA is a product of exons 1a, and 2–10, and the major and minor liver forms are from exons 1b and 2–10, and exons 1b, 1c, and 2-10, respectively. In this report, amino acids are designated relative to β-cell glucokinase. Single-letter abbreviations for the amino acids are used: A, alanine; D, aspartic acid; E, glutamic acid; G, glycine; K, lysine; L, leucine; M, methionine; P, proline; N, asparagine; Q, glutamine; R, arginine; S, serine; T, threonine; V, valine; W, tryptophan; and X, stop codon. The mutations read as follows: E70K means glutamic acid 70 has been mutated to lysine. The mutation L88del10 involves deletion of a 10-base pair segment that includes the last base of codon 88 and the following 9 base pairs—this results in the deletion of three amino acids, and a change in reading frame. The other two deletions, K161+2del15 and G193+1del33, result in mutation of the splice donor sites: K161+2del15 results in deletion of the T of the GT in the splice donor site of intron 4 and the following 14 base pairs; G193+1del33 results in deletion of the GT at the beginning of the splice donor site of intron 5 and the following 31 base pairs. Two substitutions of conserved residues of the splice donor and acceptor sites were also identified: G227-2A→T is a mutation of the splice acceptor site in intron 6 from AG→TG; and S418G→C is a mutation of the splice donor site in intron 9 from AG→AC. Adapted from References 4 and 15.

Glucokinase mutations have been found in French (14, 17, 63), British (49), Swedish (59), Japanese (11, 24, 46), African-American (15), Hispanic-American (Puerto Rican) (47), and African (Congo) (17) subjects, which suggests that they occur in individuals of all racial and ethnic groups. Two amino acid polymorphisms have also been identified in the β-cell-specific $NH_2$-terminal region of glucokinase (exon 1a; Figure 1) (7, 14): Asp/Asn (D/N) and Ala/Thr (A/T) at residues 4 and 11, respectively. A number of nucleotide polymorphisms have also been reported, none of which are associated with diabetes mellitus (7, 11, 14, 48).

Glucokinase mutations have been identified in exons 2–10, with the majority being clustered in exon 5, which encodes a region that undergoes glucose-induced conformational change associated with closure of the active-site cleft, and exons 6–8, which encode residues in the active site and active site cleft (15, 38, 48, 51). The effects of the missense mutations on the enzymatic properties of glucokinase have been studied by expressing normal and mutant forms of human β-cell glucokinase in *Escherichia coli* and measuring the activity of the purified recombinant enzyme (15, 38, 51). All of the mutations associated with MODY have reduced enzymatic activity including decreased $V_{max}$ and/or increased $K_m$ for glucose.

A molecular model of human β-cell glucokinase based on the crystal structure of the closely related yeast hexokinase (31% amino acid identity) has been constructed (Figure 2) (42). In the open, unliganded configuration, i.e. in the absence of glucose, glucokinase is predicted to fold into two domains separated by a large cleft leading to the active site (Figure 2a). Upon binding of glucose, there is a large conformational change with rotation of the smaller lobe (the upper lobe in the model shown in Figure 2) relative to the larger lobe, which results in closure of the active site and brings ATP into close proximity to the C6-hydroxyl group of glucose (Figure 2b). This substrate-induced conformational change is essential for catalysis and is probably also responsible for the enzyme's substrate specificity. The missense mutations in glucokinase that cause MODY can be thought of as preventing the normal conformationally driven catalysis by several different mechanisms. For example, Val-182 (Figure 2c), which has been mutated to Met in a patient with MODY, is located in the smaller upper lobe of the enzyme whose rotation leads to cleft closure, which suggests that this relatively conservative amino acid replacement interferes with the glucose-induced rotation of this region of the enzyme. Other mutations involve residues such as Glu-256 (Figure 2c) that are located in the active site and are involved in binding glucose (15, 38, 42), and such glucose-binding site mutations also have been shown to prevent the glucose-induced conformational change (62). Finally, some mutations such as Leu-309→Pro (Figure 2c) distort the structure of glucokinase and thereby impair the substrate-induced conformational change. The study of patients with glucokinase mutations has led to the identification of amino acids that play a critical role in catalysis and provided a better understanding of the complex structural changes that occur when glucokinase binds glucose.

## Glucokinase Mutations and Insulin Secretion

The autosomal-dominant pattern of inheritance of MODY implies that the β-cell and hepatocyte, the two major sites of expression of this enzyme, express both normal and mutant glucokinase molecules. Because glucokinase is a monomer (38), it seems unlikely that the mutant protein binds to the normal functional enzyme and inhibits its activity. Moreover, the spectrum of mutations observed (nonsense, missense, deletions, splicing) is inconsistent with these being gain-of-function mutations generating a glucokinase molecule with new properties. Rather, the data are most consistent with a gene-dosage mechanism (48), with normal levels of glucokinase activity being required for normal cellular function. Meglasson & Matschinsky (33) have suggested that a 15% decrease in cellular levels of glucokinase activity in the β-cell could shift the threshold for glucose-stimulated insulin secretion from 5 to 6 mM glucose.

Subjects with MODY due to mutations in the glucokinase gene are predicted to have glucokinase levels that are 50--100% of normal, depending upon the effect of the specific mutation on enzyme activity. Individuals with mutations resulting in the synthesis of an abnormal mRNA or truncated form of glucokinase are predicted to have levels of glucokinase activity that are 50% of normal, whereas subjects expressing a mutant glucokinase molecule with reduced but measurable enzymatic activity are predicted to have cellular levels of glucokinase activity that are 50–100% of normal depending upon the activity of mutant enzyme. The diverse spectra of glucokinase mutations associated with MODY suggest that any reduction in normal levels of glucokinase activity in β-cells, and presumably also hepatocytes, impairs glucose metabolism by these tissues. Although we believe that the data are most consistent with a gene-dosage mechanism as the cause of MODY, we cannot exclude the possibility that some mutations may affect glucokinase activity by other mechanisms, perhaps by disrupting its interaction with other cellular proteins such as the glucokinase regulatory protein (56).

Because glucokinase has the central role of the β-cell glucose sensor, decreased levels of glucokinase activity in β-cells are predicted to lead to a defect in glucose-stimulated insulin secretion. The effects of glucokinase deficiency on insulin secretion have been studied directly in human subjects with glucokinase mutations (5, 18, 36) and in transgenic mice (9). MODY patients with glucokinase mutations have a very mild form of NIDDM, with fasting plasma glucose levels of 110 (6.1 mM) to 140 mg/dl (7.8 mM) (5, 14, 18, 39). The elevation in plasma glucose observed in subjects with glucokinase mutations

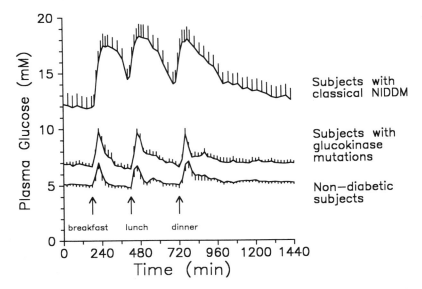

*Figure 3* Twenty-four hour plasma glucose profiles of subjects with glucokinase mutations, classical late-onset NIDDM, and normal healthy controls. Subjects were maintained on a weight-maintenance diet. Time 0 corresponds to the time when sampling was begun, and time 0900, 1300, and 1800 when breakfast, lunch, and dinner were presented, respectively. Adapted from References 5 and 39.

is more modest than is seen in classical NIDDM and is evident in both the fasted state and following a meal (Figure 3). The peak postprandial glucose levels do not exceed 10 mM and return to fasting levels after each meal. This mild hyperglycemic syndrome is generally stable over time and can usually be treated with dietary therapy alone or diet and oral hypoglycemic agents.

The average basal insulin secretion rate does not differ between subjects with glucokinase mutations and controls (77±15 vs 79±13 pmol/min, P >0.8) nor does the total amount of insulin secreted over the 24-h period (185±21 vs 216±21 nmol, P >0.26) differ (5). Following large intravenous bolus injections of glucose or ingestion of a mixed meal, subjects with glucokinase mutations had insulin secretory responses that were inappropriately low considering the prevailing hyperglycemia observed in these subjects. However, the severe abnormalities of insulin secretion, which are characteristic of subjects with classical NIDDM, namely absent first-phase insulin secretion following intra-venous glucose injection and markedly delayed and blunted response to mixed meals, were not observed. Subjects with glucokinase mutations did show a reduced insulin secretory response to a graded stepwise infusion of glucose, a

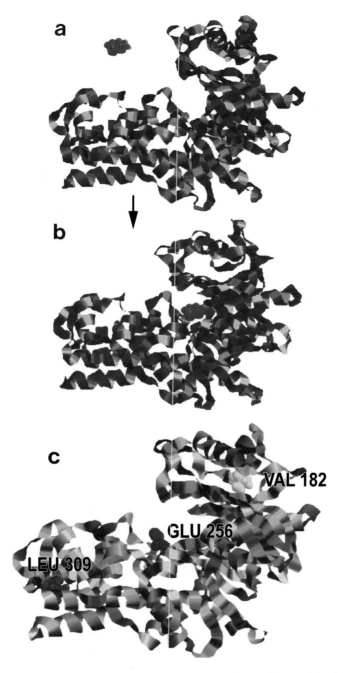

*Figure 2* Model for the structure of human glucokinase. (*a*) A ribbon diagram of the alpha-carbon backbone of human glucokinase in the open, unliganded conformation. In this projection, the active-site cleft is formed by the smaller upper lobe and the larger lower lobe. (*b*) The closed conformation of glucokinase with glucose (green) bound in the active site. (*c*) Locations of three residues Val-182 (yellow), Glu-256 (green), and Leu-309 (red) that, when mutated, can cause MODY. Mutations of these residues prevent the glucose-induced conformation and lock the enzyme in a more open conformation. (Adapted from Reference 42 and R St Charles et al, unpublished data.)

test of the ability of the β-cell's ability to sense glucose. After an overnight fast, sequential 40-min infusions of progressively increasing doses of glucose between 1 and 8 mg/kg/min were administered. In control subjects, the relationship between insulin secretion rate and glucose concentration was linear over the range of glucose concentrations encountered under normal physiological circumstances, i.e. between 5 and 9 mM, and insulin secretion increased dramatically in response to a modest increase in plasma glucose above the basal level (Figure 4). For example, a 0.7 mM increase in plasma glucose from 4.8 to 5.5 mM elicited an approximate twofold increase in the insulin secretion rate. In contrast, the β-cells of subjects with glucokinase mutations were poorly responsive to glucose within the normal fasting range, and insulin secretion rates were reduced 61%. In addition, the glucose-insulin secretion dose-response curve was shifted to the right and was not linear, being particularly flat in the range representing normal basal glucose concentrations of 5.5–6.0 mM (Figure 4). In normal control subjects, the β-cell was most sensitive to an increase in glucose concentrations between 5.5 and 6.0 mM, whereas in subjects with glucokinase mutations, the point of maximum responsiveness was

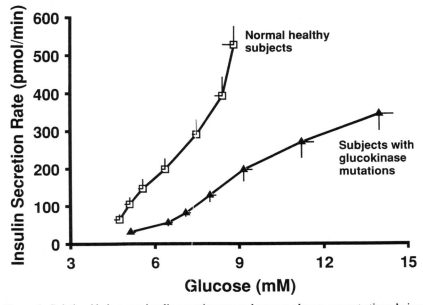

*Figure 4*  Relationship between insulin secretion rate and average glucose concentrations during graded intravenous glucose infusion studies. The lowest insulin secretion rates and glucose levels were measured under basal conditions, and subsequent values were obtained during glucose infusion rates of 1, 2, 3, 4, 6, and 8 mg/kg/min, respectively. Insulin secretion rates were derived by deconvolution of peripheral C-peptide levels using individual C-peptide kinetic parameters. Adapted from Reference 5.

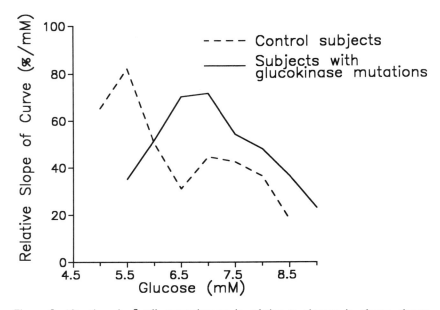

*Figure 5* Alterations in β-cell responsiveness in relation to changes in plasma glucose concentration. The relative slope of the insulin secretion rate for 0.5 mM increments in glucose concentration is shown relative to the corresponding glucose concentrations. Adapted from Reference 5.

increased to between 6.5 and 7.5 mM glucose (Figure 5). Thus β-cell responsiveness to glucose was greatest at and slightly above the fasting glucose levels in each group (Figure 5).

Even mutations such as E300Q that were associated with a mild impairment of in vitro enzymatic activity (this mutation had no effect on $V_{max}$ and increased the $K_m$ for glucose threefold; 15) were associated with a >50% reduction in insulin secretion rate, implying that the levels of glucokinase activity are an important determinant of the β-cell response to glucose. There also appeared to be a direct relationship between the predicted effect of a mutation on glucokinase levels and the degree of impairment of insulin secretion (5). For example, subjects with nonsense or splicing mutations or missense mutations that had little or no activity, i.e. mutations predicted to result in glucokinase levels that are 50% of normal, had lower insulin secretion rates than those subjects expressing a mutant form of glucokinase that still had significant activity.

Although glucokinase mutations in their heterozygous form are associated with a >50% reduction in insulin secretion rate (5), this decrease is less than predicted (50), which suggests that mechanisms may exist in the β-cell, especially in subjects with severe mutations, to compensate for the reduction in glucokinase activity and cause a relative improvement in insulin secretory response. To examine the nature of this compensatory mechanism, a clinical protocol was developed to determine whether mild hyperglycemia induced by infusion of glucose could improve the insulin secretory response because enhanced β-cell sensitivity to glucose has been observed in vivo (60) and in vitro (29) following exposure to high glucose levels. Figure 6 shows the dose-response relationship between glucose and insulin secretion rate defined before and after subjects received an intravenous infusion of glucose for 42 h at a rate of 4–6 mg/kg per min. In the control subjects, glucose administration increased the insulin secretory response by 24%. The increase in insulin secretion in response to glucose infusion was even greater in subjects with glucokinase mutations, with a 45% increase in the insulin secretory response. These results indicate that the severely reduced insulin secretion rates found in subjects with glucokinase mutations can be improved by physiological stimuli such as glucose. Moreover, it may be possible to exploit this observation and develop new agents with a similar priming effect on insulin secretion that could be used to improve insulin secretion in diabetic patients. The molecular basis of this priming effect of glucose on insulin secretion is unknown, but possibilities include increased glucokinase expression or altered interactions between glucokinase and other cellular proteins.

The effects of a reduction in glucokinase activity in β-cells on glucose-stimulated insulin secretion have also been studied in transgenic mice expressing a glucokinase ribozyme to attenuate glucokinase mRNA levels in the β-cells of these animals (9). Glucokinase activity in these mice was decreased by 70%, and there was a marked reduction in glucose-stimulated insulin secretion and decreased sensitivity to glucose with rightward shift in the glucose-insulin dose-response curve. However, these mice had normal fasting plasma glucose levels and glucose tolerance, suggesting that the mild hyperglycemia seen in human subjects with glucokinase mutations may be due to abnormal hepatic glucose metabolism, a hypothesis that needs to be tested directly in these subjects.

The effect on insulin secretion of increasing the flux of glucose through glycolysis by overexpression of a low $K_m$ hexokinase has also been studied in transgenic mice (10) and in vitro in isolated islets (2) and insulin-secreting cell lines (21). These studies showed increased insulin secretion at low glucose concentrations and enhanced β-cell sensitivity to glucose in contrast to the impaired glucose-stimulated insulin secretory response associated with a reduction in glucose metabolism due to decreased levels of glucokinase activity. These findings indicate that the rate of flux of glucose through glycolysis plays a central role in regulating insulin secretion.

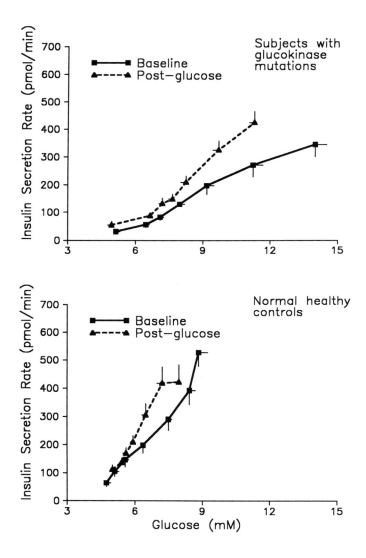

*Figure 6* Priming effects of glucose on insulin secretion. Insulin secretion rate was determined following an overnight fast (baseline) and after a 42-h continuous infusion of glucose (4–6 mg/kg/min) (post-glucose) in subjects with glucokinase mutations and in normal healthy controls. Adapted from Reference 5.

## Concluding Remarks

The demonstration that mutations in glucokinase are associated with MODY confirms the key role played by this enzyme in glucose sensing and the regulation of insulin secretion. Moreover, the studies of glucokinase mutations in MODY patients show how a multidisciplinary approach can lead to a better understanding of the molecular biology and physiology of insulin secretion. They also indicate that MODY resulting from glucokinase mutations represents a primary β-cell defect and that insulin resistance is not a major contributing factor to the development of diabetes mellitus in these individuals. The MODY1 and MODY3 mutations also appear to affect β-cell function (6, 20, 57), suggesting that the MODY form of NIDDM is primarily a disorder of the β-cell and insulin secretion. Because there are no obvious candidate genes involved in insulin biosynthesis or secretion in the regions of the MODY1 and MODY3 loci, the isolation and characterization of these genes may lead to the identification of possibly novel proteins involved in the regulation of β-cell function. Finally, glucokinase mutations are associated with a very mild form of diabetes mellitus with little evidence of diabetic complications (14). Thus identification of a glucokinase mutation in a patient with MODY suggests a relatively good prognosis compared with other forms of this disorder.

ACKNOWLEDGMENTS

The studies from our laboratories cited in this review are supported by the Howard Hughes Medical Institute; National Institutes of Health grants DK-20595 (Diabetes Research and Training Center), DK-26678 (Clinical Nutrition Research Unit), DK-31842, DK-38354, DK-44840, and DK-46562; Jack and Dollie Galter Center of Excellence of the Juvenile Diabetes Foundation International; and an unrestricted grant for cardiovascular research from Bristol-Myers Squibb.

## Literature Cited

1. Andreone TL, Printz RL, Pilkis SJ, Magnuson MA, Granner DK. 1989. The amino acid sequence of rat liver glucokinase deduced from cloned cDNA. *J. Biol. Chem.* 264:363–69

2. Becker TC, BeltrandelRio H, Noel RJ, Johnston JH, Newgard CB. 1994. Overexpression of hexokinase I in isolated islets of Langerhans via recombinant adenovirus: enhancement of glucose metabolism and insulin secretion at basal but not stimulatory glucose levels. *J. Biol. Chem.* 269:21234–38

3. Bell GI, Froguel P, Nishi S, Pilkis SJ, Stoffel M, et al. 1993. Mutations of the human glucokinase gene and diabetes mellitus. *Trends Endocrinol. Metabol.* 4:86–90

4. Bell GI, Xiang K-S, Newman MV, Wu S-W, Wright LG, et al. 1991. Gene for

non-insulin-dependent diabetes mellitus (maturity-onset diabetes of the young subtype) is linked to DNA polymorphism on human chromosome 20q. *Proc. Natl. Acad. Sci. USA* 88:1484–88

5. Byrne MM, Sturis J, Clément K, Vionnet N, Pueyo ME, et al. 1994. Insulin secretory abnormalities in subjects with hyperglycemia due to glucokinase mutations. *J. Clin. Invest.* 93:1120–30

6. Byrne MM, Sturis J, Fajans SS, Ortiz FJ, Stoltz A, et al. 1995. Altered insulin secretory responses to glucose in subjects with a mutation in the *MODY1* gene on chromosome 20. Diabetes 44: 699–704

7. Chiu KC, Tanizawa Y, Permutt MA. 1993. Glucose gene variants in the common form of NIDDM. *Diabetes* 42:579–82

8. Cook JTE, Hattersley AT, Christopher P, Bown E, Barrow B, et al. 1992. Linkage analysis of glucokinase gene with NIDDM in Caucasian pedigrees. *Diabetes* 41:1496–500

9. Efrat S, Leiser M, Wu Y-J, Fusco-DeMane D, Emran OA, et al. 1994. Ribozyme-mediated attenuation of pancreatic β-cell glucokinase expression in transgenic mice results in impaired glucose-induced insulin secretion. *Proc. Natl. Acad. Sci. USA* 91:2051–55

10. Epstein PN, Boschero AC, Atwater I, Cai X, Oberbeek PA. 1992. Expression of yeast hexokinase in pancreatic β cells of transgenic mice reduces blood glucose, enhances insulin secretion, and decreases diabetes. *Proc. Natl. Acad. Sci. USA* 89:12038–42

11. Eto K, Sakura H, Shimokawa K, Kadowaki H, Hagura R, et al. 1993. Sequence variations of the glucokinase gene in Japanese subjects with NIDDM. *Diabetes* 42:1133–37

12. Fajans SS. 1989. Maturity-onset diabetes of the young (MODY). *Diabetes Metabol. Rev.* 5:579–606

13. Froguel P, Vaxillaire M, Sun F, Velho G, Zouali H, et al. 1992. Close linkage of glucokinase locus on chromosome 7 to early-onset non-insulin-dependent diabetes mellitus. *Nature* 356:162–64

14. Froguel P, Zouali H, Vionnet N, Velho G, Vaxillaire M, et al. 1993. Familial hyperglycemia due to mutations in glucokinase: definition of a subtype of diabetes mellitus. *New Engl. J. Med.* 328: 697–702

15. Gidh-Jain M, Takeda J, Xu LZ, Lange AJ, Vionnet N, et al. 1993. Glucokinase mutations associated with non-insulin-dependent (type 2) diabetes mellitus have decreased enzymatic activity: im-

plications for structure/function relationships. *Proc. Natl. Acad. Sci. USA* 90: 1932–36

16. Grossbard L, Schimke RT. 1966. Multiple hexokinases of rat tissues. Purification and comparison of soluble forms. *J. Biol. Chem.* 241:3546–60

17. Hager J, Blanché H, Sun F, Vionnet N, Vaxillaire M, et al. 1994. Six mutations in the glucokinase gene identified in MODY by using a nonradioactive sensitive screening technique. *Diabetes* 43: 730–33

18. Hattersley AT, Turner RC, Permutt MA, Patel P, Tanizawa Y, et al. 1992. Linkage of type 2 diabetes to the glucokinase gene. *Lancet* 339:1307–10

19. Henquin J-C. 1994. Cell biology of insulin secretion. In *Joslin's Diabetes Mellitus*, ed. CR Kahn, GC Weir, pp. 56–80. Philadelphia: Lea & Febiger. 1068 pp. 13th ed.

20. Herman WH, Fajans SS, Ortiz FJ, Smith MJ, Sturis J, et al. 1994. Abnormal insulin secretion, not insulin resistance, is the genetic or primary defect of MODY in the RW pedigree. *Diabetes* 43:40–46

21. Ishihara H, Asano T, Tsukuda K, Katagiri H, Inukai K, et al. 1994. Overexpression of hexokinase I but not GLUT1 glucose transporter alters concentration dependence of glucose-stimulated insulin secretion in pancreatic β-cell line MIN6. *J. Biol. Chem.* 269: 3081–87

22. Iynedjian PB. 1993. Mammalian glucokinase and its gene. *Biochem. J.* 293:1–13

23. Jetton TL, Liang Y, Pettepher CC, Zimmerman EC, Cox FG, et al. 1994. Analysis of upstream glucokinase promoter activity in transgenic mice and identification of glucokinase in rare neuroendocrine cells in the brain and gut. *J. Biol. Chem.* 269:3641–54

24. Katagiri H, Asano T, Ishihara H, Inukai K, Anai M, et al. 1992. Nonsense mutation of glucokinase gene in late-onset non-insulin-dependent diabetes mellitus. *Lancet* 340:1316–17

25. Kogure H, Shinohara Y, Terada H. 1993. Evolution of the type II hexokinase gene by duplication and fusion of the glucokinase gene with conservation of its organization. *J. Biol. Chem.* 268: 8422–24

26. Koranyi LI, Tanizawa Y, Welling CM, Rabin DU, Permutt MA. 1992. Human islet glucokinase gene: isolation and sequence analysis of full-length cDNA. *Diabetes* 41:807–11

27. Ledermann HM. 1995. Is maturity onset

diabetes at young age (MODY) more common in Europe than previously assumed? *Lancet* 345:648

28. Deleted in proof

29. Liang Y, Najafi H, Smith RH, Zimmerman EC, Magnuson MA, et al. 1992. Concordant glucose induction of glucokinase gene usage, and glucose-stimulated insulin release in pancreatic islets maintained in organ culture. *Diabetes* 41:792–806

30. Magnuson MA, Andreone TL, Printz RL, Koch S, Granner DK. 1989. Rat glucokinase gene: structure and regulation by insulin. *Proc. Natl. Acad. Sci. USA* 86:4838–42

31. Malaisse WJ. 1995. Insulin secretion and beta cell metabolism. In *Endocrinology*, ed. LJ DeGroot, pp. 1329–36. Philadelphia: Saunders. 3024 pp. 3rd ed.

32. Matschinsky FM. 1990. Glucokinase as glucose sensor and metabolic signal generator in pancreatic beta-cells and hepatocytes. *Diabetes* 39:647–52

33. Meglasson MD, Matschinsky FM. 1984. New perspectives on pancreatic islet glucokinase. *Am. J. Physiol.* 246:E1–13

34. Nishi S, Hinata S, Matsukage T, Takeda J, Ichiyama A, et al. 1994. Mutations in the glucokinase gene are not a major cause of late-onset type 2 (non-insulin-dependent) diabetes mellitus in Japanese subjects. *Diabetic Med.* 11:193–97

35. Nishi S, Seino S, Bell GI. 1988. Human hexokinase: sequences of amino- and carboxyl-terminal halves are homologous. *Biochem. Biophys. Res. Commun.* 157:937–43

36. Page RCL, Hattersley AT, Levy JC, Barrow B, Patel P, et al. 1994. Clinical characteristics of subjects with a missense mutation in glucokinase. *Diabetic Med.* 12:209–17

37. Pilkis SJ, Granner DK. 1992. Molecular physiology of the regulation of hepatic gluconeogenesis and glycolysis. *Annu. Rev. Physiol.* 54:885–909

38. Pilkis SJ, Weber IT, Harrison RW, Bell GI. 1994. Glucokinase: structural analysis of a protein involved in susceptibility to diabetes. *J. Biol. Chem.* 269:21925–28

39. Polonksy KS. 1995. The β-cell in diabetes: from molecular genetics to clinical research. *Diabetes* 44:707–17

40. Printz RL, Koch S, Potter LR, O'Doherty RM, Tresinga J-J, Granner DK. 1993. Hexokinase II mRNA and gene structure, regulation by insulin, and evolution. *J. Biol. Chem.* 268:5209–19

41. Printz RL, Magnuson MA, Granner DK. 1993. Mammalian glucokinase. *Annu. Rev. Nutr.* 13:463–96

42. St. Charles R, Harrison RW, Bell GI, Pilkis SJ, Weber IT. 1994. Molecular model of human β-cell glucokinase built by analogy to the crystal structure of yeast hexokinase B. *Diabetes* 43:784–91

43. Schimke RT, Grossbard L. 1968. Studies on isozymes of hexokinase in animal tissues. *Ann. NY Acad. Sci.* 151:332–50

44. Schwab DA, Wilson JE. 1989. Complete amino acid sequence of rat brain hexokinase, deduced from the cloned cDNA, and proposed structure of a mammalian hexokinase. *Proc. Natl. Acad. Sci. USA* 86:2563–67

45. Schwab DA, Wilson JE. 1991. Complete amino acid sequence of the type III isozyme of rat hexokinase, deduced from the cloned cDNA. *Arch. Biochem. Biophys.* 285:365–70

46. Shimada F, Makino H, Hashimoto N, Taira M, Seino S, et al. 1993. Type 2 (non-insulin-dependent) diabetes mellitus associated with a mutation of the glucokinase gene in a Japanese family. *Diabetologia* 36:433–37

47. Stoffel M, Bell KL, Blackburn CL, Powell KL, Seo TS, et al. 1993. Identification of glucokinase mutations in subjects with gestational diabetes mellitus. *Diabetes* 42:937–40

48. Stoffel M, Froguel P, Takeda J, Zouali H, Vionnet N, et al. 1992. Human glucokinase gene: isolation, characterization, and identification of two missense mutations linked to early-onset non-insulin-dependent (type 2) diabetes mellitus. *Proc. Natl. Acad. Sci. USA* 89:7698–702

49. Stoffel M, Patel P, Lo Y-MD, Hattersley AT, Lucassen AM, et al. 1992. Missense glucokinase mutation in maturity-onset diabetes of the young and mutation screening in late-onset diabetes. *Nature Genet.* 2:153–56

50. Sturis J, Kurland IJ, Byrne MM, Mosekilde E, Froguel P, et al. 1994. Compensation in pancreatic β-cell function in subjects with glucokinase mutations. *Diabetes* 43:718–23

51. Takeda J, Gidh-Jain M, Xu LZ, Froguel P, Velho G, et al. 1993. Structure/function studies of human β-cell glucokinase: enzymatic properties of a sequence polymorphism, mutations associated with diabetes, and other site-directed mutants. *J. Biol. Chem.* 268:15200–4

52. Tanizawa Y, Koranyi LI, Welling CM, Permutt MA. 1991. Human liver glucokinase gene: cloning and sequence determination of two alternatively spliced cDNAs. *Proc. Natl. Acad. Sci. USA* 88:7294–97

53. Tanizawa Y, Matsutani A, Chiu KC, Permutt MA. 1992. Human glucokinase gene: isolation, structural characterization, and identification of a microsatellite repeat polymorphism. *Mol. Endocrinol.* 6:1070–81

54. Thelen AP, Wilson JE. 1991. Complete amino acid sequence of the type II isozyme of rat hexokinase, deduced from the cloned cDNA: comparison with a hexokinase from novikoff ascites tumor. *Arch. Biochem. Biophys.* 286: 645–51

55. Ureta T. 1982. The comparative enzymology of vertebrate hexokinases. *Comp. Biochem. Physiol.* 71B:549–55

56. van Shaftingen E, Detheux M, Veiga de Cunha M. 1994. Short-term control of glucokinase activity: role of a regulatory protein. *FASEB J.* 8:414–19

57. Vaxillaire M, Boccio V, Philippi A, Vigouroux C, Terwilliger J, et al. 1995. A gene for maturity onset diabetes of the young (MODY) maps to chromosome 12q. *Nature Genet.* 9:418–23

58. Viola RE, Raushel FM, Rendina AR, Cleland WW. 1982. Substrate synergism and the kinetic mechanism of yeast hexokinase. *Biochemistry* 21:1295–302

59. Wajngot A, Alvarsson M, Glaser A, Efendic S, Luthman H, Grill V. 1994. Glucose potentiation of arginine-induced insulin secretion is impaired in subjects with a glucokinase Glu256Lys mutation. *Diabetes* 43:1402–6

60. Ward WK, Halter JB, Beard JC, Porte D. 1984. Adaptation of B and A cell function during prolonged glucose infusion in human subjects. *Am. J. Physiol.* 246:E405–11

61. Weir GC, Leahy JL. 1994. Pathogenesis of non-insulin-dependent (type II) diabetes mellitus. In *Joslin's Diabetes Mellitus*, ed. CR Kahn, GC Weir, pp. 240–81. Philadelphia: Lea & Febiger. 1068 pp. 13th ed.

62. Xu LZ, Zhang W, Weber IT, Harrison RW, Pilkis SJ. 1994. Site-directed mutagenesis studies on the determinants of sugar specificity and cooperative behavior of human β-cell glucokinase. *J. Biol. Chem.* 269:27458–65

63. Zouali H, Vaxillaire M, Lesage S, Sun F, Velho G, et al. 1993. Linkage analysis and molecular scanning of glucokinase gene in NIDDM families. *Diabetes* 42: 1238–45

*Annu. Rev. Physiol. 1996. 58:187–207*

# MOLECULAR MECHANISM OF GROWTH HORMONE ACTION

## Christin Carter-Su, Jessica Schwartz, and Lisa S. Smit

Department of Physiology, University of Michigan Medical School, Ann Arbor, Michigan 48109-0622

KEY WORDS:    JAK kinases, GH receptor, MAP kinases, insulin receptor substrates, Stats

### ABSTRACT

Although the ability of growth hormone (GH) to stimulate body growth and regulate metabolism has been recognized for many years, only recently has insight been gained into the molecular mechanisms by which binding of GH to its receptor (GHR) elicits its diverse effects. This review provides an overview of what is currently known about the molecular mechanisms of GH action. The model presented is one in which GH binding to two GHRs causes dimerization of GHR, activation of the GHR-associated JAK2 tyrosine kinase, and tyrosyl phosphorylation of both JAK2 and GHR. These events recruit and/or activate a variety of signaling molecules, including MAP kinases, insulin receptor substrates, phosphatidylinositol 3′ phosphate kinase, diacylglycerol, protein kinase C, intracellular calcium, and Stat transcription factors. These signaling molecules contribute to the GH-induced changes in enzymatic activity, transport function, and gene expression that ultimately culminate in changes in growth and metabolism.

## INTRODUCTION

For understanding regulation of normal growth and metabolism, it is essential to understand the molecular basis of growth hormone (GH) action. Until recently, insight into the molecular mechanisms by which binding of GH to its receptor (GHR) elicits changes in cellular activities has been limited. Our understanding of GH signaling has been greatly aided by cloning of the cDNA encoding GHR (72); by classification of GHR as a member of the cytokine/hematopoietin receptor superfamily (9); by recognition that one GH molecule binds to two GHRs (26, 32); and by the recent identification of JAK2 as a GHR-associated tyrosine kinase activated in response to GH (4). As a result of these important findings, a number of signaling molecules with

187

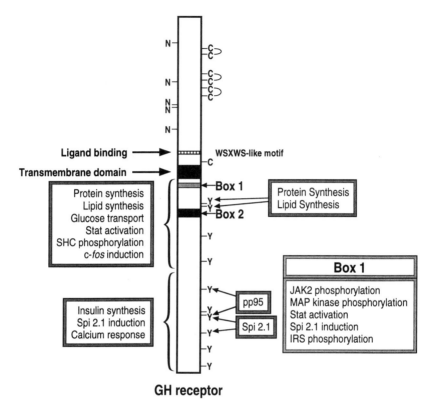

**GH receptor**

*Figure 1* Growth hormone receptor. The transmembrane domain is shown in black. The extracellular asparagines (N) that are potential N-linked glycosylation sites are shown on the left. The 10 cytoplasmic tyrosines present in rat GHR (Y) and 7 extracellular cysteines (C) are shown on the right, with the 3 pairs of linked cysteines indicated. The position of the WSXWS-like motif is indicated by the striped box. Intracellular Box 1 (proline-rich domain) and Box 2 are shown as gray boxes. Regions of GHR shown to be required for various functions are indicated.

known function have now been identified that interact with GHR, JAK2, and/or an associated protein. Signaling pathways utilizing these and other signaling molecules, as well as their cellular endpoints, have also begun to be identified. While the details of all of these GH/GHR signaling pathways are not yet known and other pathways remain to be determined, the studies summarized in this review have advanced our knowledge of the signaling cascades initiated by GH binding to its receptor, thereby providing important insight into how GH elicits its diverse effects on growth and metabolism.

# STRUCTURE OF THE GH RECEPTOR

GHR was first cloned from rabbit and human liver cDNA libraries (72) and has now been cloned from liver cDNA libraries of rat, mouse, cow, pig, sheep, and chicken (reviewed in 68). The cDNAs encode a ~70-kDa protein containing a single membrane-spanning domain (Figure 1), which migrates as a ~120–130-kDa protein in SDS-polyacrylamide gels when expressed in mammalian cells (4, 72, 115, 131). Glycosylation and possibly ubiquitination contribute to the larger size of the expressed protein (57, 72). Deletions and point mutations in the GHR gene in individuals with Laron dwarfism (1, 2, 47) provide evidence that the cloned GHR is important for human growth. The cloned GHR has also been shown to increase insulin biosynthesis when expressed in RIN5-AH cells (15) and cellular proliferation in Ba/F3 and FDC-P1 cells (23, 132). In CHO cells, expressed GHR stimulates tyrosine phosphorylation of cellular proteins, microtubule-associated protein (MAP) kinase activity, intracellular $Ca^{2+}$ concentrations, Stat protein activation, c-*fos* expression, protein synthesis, and glucose transport (14, 38, 49, 80; LS Smit, DJ Meyer, N Billestrup, G Norstedt, J Schwartz & C Carter-Su, submitted).

Based upon sequence analysis, GHR is classified as a member of the cytokine/hematopoietin receptor superfamily (9). This superfamily also includes receptor subunits for prolactin (PRL) and a variety of cytokines and growth factors, including erythropoietin (EPO), interleukins (ILs) 2–7, 9, 11, and 12, thrombopoietin, leukemia-inhibitory factor (LIF) (60, 86, 129). Receptors for IFN $\alpha/\beta$, IFN$\gamma$, and IL-10 are more distantly related and are considered class II receptors in this family (9, 61). Members of this family have a single membrane-spanning domain and limited homology in the extracellular domain, including a stretch of about 210 amino acids conserved at a relatively low level (15–35%), four cysteines, a tryptophan, and a membrane-proximal WSXWS motif (69). The WXSWX motif in GHR contains conservative substitutions and has been postulated to play a critical role in ligand binding (32).

In its cytoplasmic domain, GHR shares two motifs with other members of the cytokine receptor superfamily. One is a membrane-proximal, proline-rich motif referred to as Box 1. It is present in all members and consists of eight amino acids ($\psi$-X-X-X-Al-P-X-P, where $\psi$ represents hydrophobic residues and Al represents aliphatic residues) (8, 24, 82, 84). This motif in mammalian GHR contains ILPPVPVP. The second cytoplasmic motif (Box 2), present in many cytokine receptors, begins with a cluster of hydrophobic amino acids and ends with one or two positively charged amino acids (82). In GHR, Box 2 is located approximately 30 amino acids carboxy terminal to Box 1 and spans about 15 amino acids (28). Mutation or deletion of Box 1 and/or Box 2 in

GHR and other cytokine receptor family members results in defective ligand-mediated cellular growth in IL-3-dependent cell lines expressing the appropriate receptor, suggesting that these regions play critical roles in receptor-mediated signal transduction (7, 28, 45, 48, 59, 82, 132).

## GHR SIGNAL TRANSDUCTION

### GH Binding and Receptor Dimerization

Based on crystallography, size exclusion chromatography, calorimetry, and fluorescence quenching experiments using solubilized extracellular domain of the GHR (denoted GHBP), one GH is hypothesized to complex with two GHRs (26, 32). The binding of GH to GHBP appears to be sequential, leading to the hypothesis that GH binding causes GHR dimerization (Figure 2). Studies in which $^{125}$I-hGH is covalently cross-linked to full-length or truncated GHR indicate that like GHBP, GHR also forms dimers (L Rui, LS Argetsinger, D Virgo & C Carter-Su, unpublished data), although whether dimer formation is GH dependent is not yet known. The finding that a mutated GH (G120R) that fails to induce GHBP dimerization is biologically inactive when added to cells expressing GHR (44, 102, 138) suggests that GH-induced dimerization of GHR is required for GH action. Additional changes in GHR conformation resulting from the binding of GH to two GHRs are also likely to be important for GH signaling.

### Activation of JAK2 Tyrosine Kinase by GH

Among the most rapid cellular responses to GH are the binding of the tyrosine kinase JAK2 to GHR and the activation of JAK2 (4, 128). JAK2 is a member of the Janus family of cytoplasmic tyrosine kinases that currently include JAK1, JAK2, JAK3, and tyk2 (40, 58, 105, 133, 136). Although initially GH was not observed to activate JAK1 in 3T3-F442A fibroblasts or IM-9 cells (4, 102), additional studies using a higher affinity JAK1 antibody demonstrated that GH induces low-level tyrosyl phosphorylation of JAK1 in 3T3-F442A fibroblasts and COS cells transfected with cDNAs for both murine GHR and JAK1 (LS Smit, DJ Meyer, N Billestrup, G Norstedt, J Schwartz & C Carter-Su, submitted; W-H Huo & C Carter-Su, unpublished data). GH also stimulates the tyrosyl phosphorylation of JAK3 in a transformed T-cell line, although to a significantly lesser extent than the potent activator of JAK3, IL-2 (67). Thus, whereas JAK2 appears to be the primary JAK family member activated by GH, JAK1 and JAK3 may also be activated by GH and thereby mediate at least some effects of GH. Whether GH activates Tyk2 is unclear. Although GH-dependent phosphorylation of Tyk2 was not detected in IM-9 cells (4),

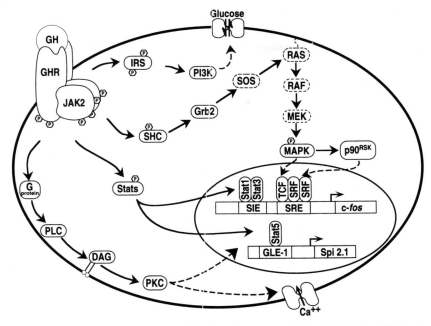

*Figure 2*   GHR Signaling pathways. Possible signaling pathways initiated by binding of GH to its receptor are shown. The dotted lines indicate molecules or pathways that have not yet been shown to be involved in GH-dependent signal transduction but are likely to be employed by GH because they are utilized by other growth factors that activate the indicated downstream signaling molecules.

experimental conditions were such that a low level of activation might have been missed.

Activation of JAK kinases is a characteristic shared among members of the cytokine receptor family, with different ligands showing preferences for different JAK family members (4, 40, 67, 113, 135, 136). The origin of specificity in response to GH rather than to other ligands that activate JAK kinases is an issue of obvious importance. The source is likely found in cell-specific receptor expression, activation of different combinations of JAK family members, different magnitudes and time course of activation for each JAK, interaction of JAK signaling pathways with other signaling pathways, as well the binding of different downstream signaling molecules to phosphorylated tyrosine-containing motifs specific to each receptor. It is interesting to note that in 3T3-F442A fibroblasts, GH stimulates tyrosyl phosphorylation of JAK2 more than 15 times more effectively than IFNγ or LIF. In contrast, the three ligands stimulate tyrosyl phosphorylation of JAK1 to similar extents (5; LS Smit, DJ Meyer, N Billestrup, G Norstedt, J Schwartz & C Carter-Su, submitted).

Studies using truncated and mutated GHR have implicated the Box 1 motif as a necessary component for GH-dependent JAK2 association with GHR and for tyrosyl phosphorylation and activation of JAK2 (42, 109, 128, 132). Specific deletion of Box 1 destroys GHR-JAK2 association and GH-dependent JAK2 phosphorylation. Interestingly, mutation to alanine of a single proline in this region of human GHR also abolishes GH-induced JAK2 tyrosyl phosphorylation (132). Although the Box 1 motif appears to play a primary role in GHR-JAK2 association, more distal regions appear to augment the interaction (42, 109, 119). Similarly, membrane-proximal regions containing Box 1 and/or 2 of the cytoplasmic domains of EPO-R, PRL-R, and gp130 have been implicated in JAK2-receptor association and/or JAK2 activation (28, 119, 135). The mechanism by which GH or other cytokines activate JAK kinases is not known. However, one hypothesis consistent with what is known about GHR structure and tyrosine kinase activation in general is that binding of GH to two GHR molecules increases the affinity of JAK2 for each GHR and allows two JAK2 molecules to come into sufficiently close proximity to transphosphorylate one or more tyrosines in the kinase domain of the paired JAK2, thereby activating JAK2.

Consistent with the activation of JAK2 as an initial signaling event for GHR, GHR mutants that lack the JAK2 binding site fail to elicit GH-dependent increased tyrosyl phosphorylation of SHC proteins, IRS 1 and 2, and extracellular signal-regulated kinases (ERKs) 1 and 2 in CHO cells, increased insulin synthesis, induction of the *spi* 2.1 gene, and GH-dependent mitogenesis in FDC-P1 cells and Ba/F3 cells (13, 23, 51, 79, 132). Thus it is possible that a primary role of GH binding to GHR is to facilitate recruitment and activation of JAK2. Subsequent signaling events may require JAK2 and not necessarily GHR itself. Consistent with this hypothesis, a rat GHR/JAK2 chimera directly linking the C-terminal one-third of JAK2 to the external and transmembrane domains of GHR conveys GH-dependent transcriptional activation via the c-*fos* promoter (43).

## GH-Dependent Tyrosyl Phosphorylation of GHR and JAK2

Tyrosine kinase signaling is often mediated by the binding of Src-homology 2 (SH2) domain-containing signaling proteins to phosphorylated tyrosines in the kinase itself or in other kinase substrates (87). In response to GH, both JAK2 and GHR become phosphorylated on tyrosines (4, 41, 101), presumably as a result of JAK2 activation. The presence of 48 tyrosines in murine JAK2 suggests that multiple signaling molecules may interact with JAK2 (105). Which tyrosines are phosphorylated in response to GH or other activating ligands is not presently known. The cytoplasmic domain of rat GHR contains a more limited number (10) of potential tyrosyl phosphorylation sites. Of these, six (Y333, Y487, Y534, Y566, Y595, and Y626) are conserved in all cloned species of GHR. Experiments using truncated and mutated rat GHR indicate that GHR is phosphorylated on tyrosines in both the C- and N-terminal halves of the cytoplasmic domain (127a). Y534 is reported to be the strongest phosphorylation site in the cytoplasmic domain of pig GHR (X Wang, CJ Darus, N Billestrup & JJ Kopchick, submitted). In the N-terminal half of rat GHR, Y333 and/or Y338 appear to be the predominant phosphorylation sites (127a). Consistent with the importance of phosphorylated tyrosines for GH signaling, mutational analysis indicates that Y534 and Y566 in pig GHR are required for GH-dependent activation of *spi* 2.1/CAT constructs and that Y487 and Y534 are required for GH-promoted tyrosyl phosphorylation of pp95 (X Wang, CJ Darus, N Billestrup & JJ Kopchick, submitted). Y333 and/or Y338 have been reported to be required for GH-stimulated lipid and protein synthesis (74).

## *Activation of MAP Kinases by GH*

In addition to GHR and JAK2, a large number of other proteins become tyrosyl phosphorylated in response to GH (16, 54, 103). This suggests that JAK2 phosphorylates proteins in addition to JAK2 and GHR and/or that proteins that bind to activated JAK2 and/or GHR initiate signaling pathways involving other tyrosine kinases or phosphatases. The first two GH-dependent tyrosyl phosphorylated proteins identified were the MAP kinases designated ERKs 1 and 2 (3, 18, 134). MAP kinases, activated by a number of receptor and nonreceptor tyrosine kinases, including GH (3, 18, 134), are believed to play a critical role in the regulation of growth and differentiation (22).

One pathway leading from membrane receptor tyrosine kinases to MAP kinases involves SHC, Grb2, son-of-sevenless (Sos), ras, raf, and MAP/ERK kinase (MEK) (25). GH has been demonstrated to promote rapid tyrosyl phosphorylation of the 66-, 52-, and 46-kDa SHC proteins in 3T3-F442A fibroblasts (127). GH also induces the binding of a GHR-JAK2 complex to the SH2 domain of the SHC proteins fused to glutathione S-transferase (GST) and the association of Grb2 with SHC. These results suggest that GH stimulates the association of SHC proteins with JAK2-GHR complexes via the SH2 domain of SHC proteins. SHC is then tyrosyl phosphorylated by JAK2, which permits the binding of Grb2 to SHC. Although GH has not been shown to activate the remaining molecules in this signaling cascade (Sos, ras, raf and MEK), it seems likely that the recruitment of SHC and Grb2 are early events in GH activation of ERKs 1 and 2 via this pathway. GH activation of MAP kinases requires the proline-rich Box 1 of GHR, the same region implicated in JAK activation, providing further evidence for a role of JAK2 in the activation of MAP kinases (128). MAP kinase substrates include other protein kinases (e.g. c-Raf-1, the S6 kinases designated $p70^{rsk}$ and $p90^{rsk}$), phospholipase $A_2$, cytoskeletal proteins, and transcription factors (e.g. c-*Jun* and ternary complex factors (TCFs), including p62$^{TCF}$/Elk-1) (reviewed in 31). Of these, GH has been shown to activate the S6 kinase, p90$^{rsk}$, in 3T3-F442A fibroblasts (3). Presumably some of the other substrates are phosphorylated by MAP kinases in response to GH and are responsible for other actions of GH.

## Utilization of IRS-1, IRS-2, and PI 3′ Kinase by GH

Under certain circumstances, GH is known to have rapid, insulin-like effects, including increased glucose transport as a consequence of the recruitment of Glut1 and Glut 4 transporters to the plasma membrane (30, 50, 120; H Feng & C Carter-Su, unpublished data; T-W Gong & J Schwartz, unpublished data), which suggests that GH and insulin may share some signaling molecules. A principal substrate of the insulin receptor, IRS-1, has been shown to be tyrosyl phosphorylated in response to GH in primary cultures of rat adipocytes, 3T3-F442A fibroblasts, and CHO cells expressing recombinant GHR (5, 90, 110). Recent studies indicate that GH also stimulates tyrosyl phosphorylation of IRS-2 (LS Argetsinger, MG Myers Jr, N Billestrup, G Norstedt, MF White & C Carter-Su, submitted), an IRS-1 related protein (117a).

In studies using truncated and mutated GHRs expressed in CHO cells, the region of GHR required for GH-induced tyrosyl phosphorylation of IRS-1 and IRS-2 corresponded to that required for JAK2 association and activation. Specific tyrosines in GHR were not required for IRS phosphorylation (5; LS Argetsinger, MG Myers Jr, N Billestrup, G Norstedt, MF White & C Carter-Su, submitted), consistent with the absence of a putative IRS-1 binding site in GHR (85). These findings suggest that the role of GHR in GH-dependent tyrosyl phosphorylation of IRS-1 and -2 is to activate JAK2. Upon autophosphorylation, JAK2 then binds to and phosphorylates IRS-1 and -2 directly or via an intermediary protein.

Tyrosines in IRS-1 and -2 that are phosphorylated in response to insulin or IGF-1 provide binding sites for multiple SH2 domain-containing proteins, including the 85-kDa regulatory subunit of PI 3′ kinase (116, 117). GH also stimulates binding of IRS-1 and -2 to the 85-kDa regulatory subunit of PI 3′ kinase (5, 90; LS Argetsinger, MG Myers, Jr, N Billestrup, G Norstedt, MF White & C Carter-Su, submitted). PI 3′ kinase has been implicated in the stimulatory actions of insulin on glucose transport, DNA synthesis, and activity of p70$^{rsk}$, an enzyme implicated in cell cycle regulation (20). Consistent with a role for PI 3′ kinase in the insulin-like metabolic effects of GH, the PI 3′ kinase inhibitor wortmannin blocks the ability of GH to stimulate lipid synthesis (and presumably its rate-limiting step, glucose transport) and to inhibit noradrenaline-induced lipolysis in rat adipocytes (91). Like GH stimulation of phosphorylation of IRS-1 and IRS-2, stimulation by GH of lipid synthesis and glucose transport requires the N-terminal, but not the C-terminal, half of GHR (49, 80).

## The Role of Protein Kinase C in Signaling by GH

Several lines of evidence suggest that protein kinase C (PKC) plays a role in GH-initiated signal transduction. Rapid, transient induction by GH of relatively small increases in DAG, a known activator of PKC, have been reported (36, 66, 93, 125). In Ob1771 preadipocytes, the change in DAG is accompanied by increased levels of phosphocholine and is blocked by pertussis toxin (19), suggesting that GH mediates DAG production by means of phosphatidyl-choline breakdown involving a phospholipase C coupled to the GHR via a pertussis toxin-sensitive G protein. In contrast, in kidney proximal tubule membranes, the change in DAG is accompanied by rapid, transient increases in levels of inositol triphosphate ($IP_3$) (93). Whether GH-dependent PKC activation lies downstream of JAK2 or is a JAK-independent pathway remains to be determined. PtdIns-3,4-P2 and PtdIns-3,4,5-P3, byproducts of PI 3′ kinase, have recently been shown to activate the $Ca^{2+}$-independent PKC iso-forms, $\gamma$, $\epsilon$, and $\eta$ (123). This raises the possibility that GH may also activate PKC via a pathway involving IRS proteins and PI 3′ kinase.

Chronic treatment of cells with phorbol ester 12-myristate 13-acetate (PMA) to deplete PKC, and/or addition of inhibitors of PKC, markedly reduce the ability of GH to stimulate lipogenesis (108), induce c-fos expression (56, 107, 125), stimulate binding of nuclear protein to C/EBP oligonucleotide (21), and increase $[Ca^{2+}]_i$ (S Gaur, H Yamaguchi & HM Goodman, submitted), suggesting that these actions of GH may require activation of PKC or be modulated by PKC. Although some studies (3) also suggest a role for PKC in the GH-dependent activation of MAP kinases and p90[rsk], others argue against such a role (18, 134).

## Regulation of Intracellular Calcium by GH

GH has been reported to cause an increase in intracellular free calcium concentrations in freshly isolated rat adipocytes (96, 98), IM-9 lymphocytes (62), and in CHO cells expressing rat GHR (14). This increase is dependent upon the presence of extracellular $Ca^{2+}$ and is blocked by verapamil and nimodipine (14; S Gaur, H Yamaguchi & HM Goodman, submitted), which suggests that GH activates voltage-sensitive L-type calcium channels. The GH-induced increase in $[Ca^{2+}]_i$ in rat adipocytes is mimicked by DAG and blocked by the PKC inhibitor calphostin C and a specific inhibitor of phospholipase C (S Gaur, H Yamaguchi & HM Goodman, submitted), which leads to the hypothesis that GH activates L-type calcium channels by a mechanism that involves phospholipid hydrolysis and activation of PKC. GH-induced expression of a *spi* 2.1 promoter/CAT construct and the refractory effects of GH on metabolism in adipocytes (50) are blocked by verapamil (14, 96), indicating that the actions of GH may be dependent upon the GH-induced increase in $[Ca^{2+}]_i$. Further evidence that refractoriness to the insulin-like effect of GH requires increased $[Ca^{2+}]_i$ and calmodulin is provided by the findings that (*a*) inhibition of cal-modulin with calmidozolium or trifluoropirazine, or depletion of cellular cal-cium by incubation in calcium-free medium, reverses refractoriness to the insulin-like effects of GH in rat adipocytes; (*b*) incubation of GH-responsive cells with the calcium ionophore A23187 in the presence of normal extracel-lular calcium concentrations causes the cells to become refractory; and (*c*) $[Ca^{2+}]_i$ is twice as high in refractory cells as in sensitive cells (97). Mutagenesis studies in CHO cells suggest that GH-dependent increases in $[Ca^{2+}]_i$ require the C-terminal half of GHR but may not require the prolines in Box 1 (14), thus raising the possibility that calcium signaling may be independent of JAK2 activation.

## GH-REGULATED EVENTS IN THE NUCLEUS

Many of the signaling events and phosphorylation cascades described above culminate in GH-regulated changes in the expression of genes in target cells. Recent evidence indicates that GH regulates activity of transcription factors as well as tissue-specific genes likely to mediate its long-term physiological actions.

### Activation of Stat Family Proteins by GH

A recently described family of transcription factors that serve as signal transducers and activators of transcription (Stat) participates in GH signaling between the receptor and the nucleus. Originally identified in IFN-signaling pathways (27), Stat proteins are latent cytoplasmic factors containing SH2 and SH3 domains. Upon tyrosyl phosphorylation, often via a JAK kinase–initiated cascade, cytoplasmic Stat proteins complex with other Stat and/or non-Stat proteins, translocate to the nucleus, bind to DNA, and activate transcription of target genes. GH has been shown to induce tyrosyl phosphorylation of several Stat (or Stat-related) proteins. Stat1/p91 originally identified in IFN signaling; Stat3/APRF (acute-phase response factor) involved in IL-6 and LIF signaling; and/or Stat5/MGF (mammary gland factor) involved in Prl signaling are tyrosyl phosphorylated in GH-treated 3T3-F442A fibroblasts, in liver hy-pophysectomized rats treated with GH and in GH-treated CHO cells expressing recombinant GHR (17, 54, 55, 77; Y Han, DW Leaman, F Gouilleux, B Bronner IM Kerr, WI Wood, GR Stark, submitted; LS Smit, DJ Meyer, N Billestrup, G Norstedt, J Schwartz, C Carter-Su, submitted; GS Campbell &

C Carter-Su, unpublished observations). Consistent with their role as transcription factors, Stat proteins are present in GH-induced DNA-binding complexes for several genes. In the c-*fos* promoter, GH induces the binding of three complexes to the Sis-inducible element (SIE) (17, 55, 77). Because Stat1 can form homodimers through SH2-phosphotyrosine interactions (100), the three GH-induced SIE-binding complexes are thought to contain Stat1 and Stat3 homodimers and Stat1 and Stat3 heterodimers, respectively. In Ba/F3 cells transfected with GHR, GH induces binding of Stat1-containing complexes to the SIE and the IFNγ-response region (GRR) (132). GH also stimulates the binding of Stat5 to the IFNγ-activated sequence (GAS)-like response element (GLE-1) in the *spi* 2.1 gene (137) and of binding an unknown Stat-related protein to GRR in IM-9 cells (39). Stat4 may be a minor component in SIE-binding complexes in liver (55). Activation of Stats by GH appears to be cell-type dependent because GH was not observed to activate Stat1 in IM-9 cells (39, 102). GH-stimulated Stat3 activation occurs in the absence of Stat1 activation, indicating that Stats can be activated by GH independently of each other (LS Smit, DJ Meyer, N Billestrup, G Norstedt, J Schwartz & C Carter-Su, submitted; Y Han, DW Leaman, F Gouilleux, B Groner, IM Kerr, WI Wood & GR Stark, submitted). DNA binding of Stat-containing complexes may represent an important contribution to induction of gene expression by GH and suggests a direct pathway (GHR→JAK→Stats→target gene) by which GH can elicit nuclear events. Activation of Stat proteins is also observed upon ligand binding to many members of the cytokine receptor superfamily (27), suggesting that activation of Stat proteins is a common mechanism by which cytokines and growth factors regulate transcription.

Analysis of GH signaling in a JAK2-deficient cell line and truncated and mutated GHRs indicates that Stat activation requires JAK2 activation (132; LS Smit, DJ Meyer, N Billestrup, G Norstedt, J Schwartz & C Carter-Su, submitted; Y Han, DW Leaman, F Gouilleux, B Groner, IM Kerr, WI Wood & GR Stark, submitted). However, no specific phosphorylated tyrosines in GHR appear to be required for activation of Stats 1 or 3 by GH (131a; LS Smit, DJ Meyer, N Billestrup, G Norstedt, J Schwartz & C Carter-Su, submitted), and GHR does not contain the Stat3- (YXXQ) or Stat1-association motifs found in gp130 and IFNγ-containing receptors, respectively (53, 114). In contrast, JAK2 contains motifs identical or similar to these Stat-association motifs. These findings suggest that in the case of GH, where JAK2 phosphorylation is substantial and no regions of GHR are directly implicated in Stat activation, Stats 1 and 3 may bind primarily to JAK2 or to proteins that bind JAK2. For other cytokines that activate JAK kinases to a lesser extent than GH but activate Stat proteins to a similar or greater extent, Stat1 and/or Stat3 activation may be augmented by high-affinity Stat-binding sites in the receptors themselves. Alternatively, a region of GHR not involving a phosphorylated tyrosine may be involved in Stat activation, or GH may utilize an intermediary protein in this activation. Other cytokines may employ the same accessory protein, a different protein, or no additional proteins to activate Stat proteins.

## Induction of Early-Response Genes by GH

GH rapidly induces the expression of early-response genes, including c-*fos* and c-*jun* (36, 56, 107), that encode transcription factors implicated in cell growth and differentiation and that may regulate genes involved in long-term responses to GH. For example, in 3T3-F442A adipocytes, binding of Fos-containing DNA-binding complexes is required for expression of the adipocyte-specific gene aP2 (111), which suggests that Fos contributes to GH-dependent cell differentiation by regulating the expression of tissue-specific genes. The binding of CAAT/enhancer binding proteins (C/EBP) β and γ, transcription factors implicated in adipocyte differentiation, is also stimulated by GH in 3T3-F442A cells, each isoform apparently stimulated by a different mechanism (21). GH also rapidly induces the expression of c-*myc* (83), which encodes a transcription factor involved in cell proliferation.

Analysis of the regulation by GH of early-response genes has provided insight into signaling between GHR and the nucleus. In the c-*fos* gene, upstream regulatory sequences include the serum response element (SRE), which binds serum response factor (SRF) and TCFs (126). The SRE has been found to mediate induction of c-*fos* by GH (78). A rapid and transient induction by GH of binding of SRF-containing complexes to the SRE (73) may be related to such mediation. MAP kinases, activated by GH and a number of other growth factors (3, 18, 81, 134), are reported to phosphorylate SRF via p90$^{rsk}$ (92) and TCFs, in the latter case stimulating transcriptional activity (46, 65, 75). These observations suggest a pathway involving GHR→MAP kinase→ SRE-associated proteins→Fos by which GH stimulation is likely to result in nuclear events contributing to the ability of GH to promote cell growth and differentiation. The relationship(s), if any, between the pathways from the GHR to the SRE and the Stat-mediated pathway to the SIE remain to be determined.

## Genes Related to Long-Term Actions of GH

Many physiological actions of GH require long-term exposure to the hormone (hours to days), presumably reflecting effects of GH on expression of genes that are mediated by the rapid signaling events and regulation of transcription factors discussed above. Among its targets, GH regulates adipocyte differentiation and an array of metabolic responses in adipocytes (30, 52). Adipocyte differentiation appears to reflect regulation by GH of several genes known to be expressed as adipocytes differentiate (10, 112), including those encoding glycerol phosphate dehydrogenase (GPD), a lipogenic enzyme; aP2/422, a lipid-binding protein; and lipoprotein lipase (LPL) (35, 89). Fos is reported to participate in regulation of aP2 and LPL (6, 33), which suggests the sequence GH→Fos→adipocyte-specific genes→adipocyte differentiation. Some long-term metabolic events regulated by GH also reflect regulation of expression of genes. For example, chronic inhibition by GH of glucose transport in adipocytes (95) is due, at least in part, to decreased expression of the Glut 1 glucose transporter (118).

GH-regulated genes in the liver include the gene encoding insulin-like growth factor 1 (IGF-1), a serum mediator of some actions of GH (29, 63). IGF-1 gene expression is stimulated by GH in liver by predominantly transcriptional mechanisms (11, 76), although the mechanisms have proven difficult to delineate. The kinetics of induction by GH of a DNase hypersensitive site in the second intron of the IGF-1 gene parallels the pattern of stimulation of IGF-1 transcription by GH (11), suggesting that the hypersensitive site is involved in induction of IGF-1 by GH. Protein-binding sites have been identified in the IGF-1 promoter, but none appear to be affected by GH treatment (121, 122). More recent work indicates that other tissues including adipocytes and chondrocytes increase IGF-1 mRNA expression in response to GH (34, 64, 88, 130), suggesting that local IGF-1 contributes to some GH responses. IGF-1 has a high affinity for a family of IGF-binding proteins (IGF-BPs) (94), which can modulate its biological actions. Regulation by GH of genes encoding IGF-BPs (37, 99) adds another level of complexity to the relationship between GH and IGF-1.

Several other GH-regulated genes in the liver have provided important insights into GH signaling. The *spi* 2.1 gene, encoding a liver-specific serine protease inhibitor, is stimulated by GH in vivo and in vitro (70, 139). The stimulation by GH is mediated via a 45-bp GH-response sequence (139) containing GAS-like elements, which binds proteins induced by GH (106, 122). The complex has recently been found to contain the transcription factor Stat5 (137). Similar sequences are also present in the GH-regulated somatostatin gene (12). The proline-rich region of GHR was shown to be important for GH-dependent activation of *spi* 2.1 (51), implying that JAK2 is required for GH-induced *spi* 2.1 expression. Interestingly, tyrosines 534 and 566 in the C-terminal half of the cytoplasmic domain of GHR are required for stimulation via the *spi* 2.1 promoter (X Wang, CJ Darus, N Billestrup & JJ Kopchick, submitted), whereas stimulation of c-*fos* requires only the N-terminal half of GHR (49). These observations suggest that there are multiple mechanisms for regulation of gene expression via GHR.

Hepatic expression of genes encoding cytochrome P450 enzymes involved in steroid metabolism, which are either male or female specific, is strongly influenced by sex differences in the pattern of GH secretion (71). Regulation in vitro of expression of several P450 2C genes by a complex interplay of GH, IGF-1, and thyroid hormones and involving a permissive effect of protein kinase C led to the suggestion that more than one signal transduction mechanism mediates regulation of hepatic genes by GH (124, 125). Taken together, it is clear that regulation of a variety of genes by multiple mechanisms underlies multiple responses to GH in various target tissues.

## CONCLUDING REMARKS

Work carried out largely since 1991 has given us significant insight into the molecular mechanisms by which binding of GH to its receptor elicits the diverse effects of GH. GH has been shown to bind sequentially to two GHBPs, leading to the hypothesis that GH binding causes both dimerization of GHR and conformational changes important for GH function. These changes result in increased binding to GHR of JAK2, a nonreceptor tyrosine kinase, and promote activation of JAK2. Other JAK kinases may also be activated, although probably to a lesser extent. In turn, both GHR and JAK2 are phosphorylated on tyrosines, presumably by the activated JAK2. These phosphorylated tyrosines serve as docking sites for SH2 domain-containing signaling molecules. Subsequent signaling events include activation of MAP kinases, presumably via a SHC→Grb2→Sos→ras→raf→MEK pathway; tyrosyl phosphorylation of IRS-1 and IRS-2; association of IRS-1 with PI 3′ kinase; activation of PI 3′ kinase; activation of a phospholipase with subsequent formation of DAG and activation of PKC; increases in intracellular calcium concentration, most likely as a result of increased L-type Ca channels; and activation of the latent transcription factors Stats 1, 3, and 5. The activation of MAP kinases, which are known to phosphorylate transcription factors, and Stats is likely to play a role in the GH-dependent induction of transcription of c-*fos*, an event thought to be important for GH-induced cellular differentiation. GH stimulates transcription of a number of other genes, including *spi* 2.1 and somatostatin. Analysis of the regions of GHR required for activation of these signaling molecules indicates that JAK2 is required for activation of SHC, Grb2, MAP kinases, IRS-1 and -2, and PI-3 kinase, and Stats 1 and 3. Direct interactions of SHC, IRS-1 and -2, and Stats 1 and 3 with GHR have not been demonstrated, which suggests that these signaling molecules might bind to phosphorylated tyrosyl residues in JAK2 itself or to as yet unidentified accessory molecules. In contrast, regions of GHR other than those required for GH-dependent activation of JAK2 are required for GH-induced increases in intracellular calcium concentrations and GH-stimulated expression of the *spi* 2.1 and somatostatin genes. Thus the findings described here suggest that signaling mechanisms initiated by binding of GH to GHR are complex. Identification of which pathways elicit which responses, how the different signaling cascades intersect, further characterization of the role of GHR in initiating these pathways, and the identification of new pathways promise to be fascinating challenges that should provide a greater understanding of how GH elicits its diverse effects on body growth and metabolism.

## Literature Cited

1. Amselem S, Duquesnoy P, Attree O, Novelli G, Bousnina S, et al. 1989. Laron dwarfism and mutations of the growth hormone-receptor gene. *N. Engl. J. Med.* 321:989–95

2. Amselem S, Sobrier ML, Duquesnoy P, Rappaport R, Postel-Vinay M-C, et al. 1991. Recurrent nonsense mutations in the growth hormone receptor from patients with Laron dwarfism. *J. Clin. Invest.* 87:1098–102

3. Anderson NG. 1992. Growth hormone activates mitogen-activated protein kinase and S6 kinase and promotes intracellular tyrosine phosphorylation in 3T3-F442A preadipocytes. *Biochem. J.* 284:649–52

4. Argetsinger LS, Campbell GS, Yang X, Witthuhn BA, Silvennoinen O, et al. 1993. Identification of JAK2 as a growth hormone receptor-associated tyrosine kinase. *Cell* 74:237–44

5. Argetsinger LS, Hsu GW, Myers MG Jr, Billestrup N, Norstedt G, et al. 1995. Growth hormone, interferon-gamma, and leukemia inhibitory factor promoted tyrosyl phosphorylation of insulin receptor substrate-1. *J. Biol. Chem.* 270: 14685–92

6. Barcellini-Couget S, Pradines-Figueres A, Roux P, Dani C, Ailhaud G. 1993. The regulation of growth hormone of lipoprotein lipase gene expression is mediated by c-*fos* protooncogene. *Endocrinology* 132:53–60

7. Baumann H, Symes AJ, Comeau MR, Morella KK, Wang YFD, et al. 1994. Multiple regions within the cytoplasmic domains of the leukemia inhibitory factor receptor and gp130 cooperate in signal transduction in hepatic and neuronal cells. *Mol. Cell. Biol.* 14:138–46

8. Bazan JF. 1989. A novel family of growth factor receptors: a common binding domain in the growth hormone, prolactin, erythropoietin and IL-6 receptors, and the p75 IL-2 receptor beta-chain. *Biochem. Biophys. Res. Commun.* 164:788–95

9. Bazan JF. 1990. Haemopoietic receptors and helical cytokines. *Immunol. Today* 11:350–54

10. Bernlohr DA, Bolanowski MA, Kelly TJ Jr, Lane MD. 1985. Evidence for an increase in transcription of specific mRNAs during differentiation of 3T3-L1 preadipoctyes. *J. Biol. Chem.* 260: 5563–67

11. Bichell DP, Kikuchi K, Rotwein P. 1992. Growth hormone rapidly activates insulin-like growth factor I gene transcription in vivo. *Mol. Endocrinol.* 6: 1899–908

12. Billestrup N. 1993. Signal transduction by the growth hormone receptor. *Program, 75th Annu. Meet. Endocrine Soc.* p. 27

13. Billestrup N, Allevato G, Norstedt G, Moldrup A, Nielsen JH, et al. 1994. Identification of intracellular domains in the growth hormone receptor involved in signal transduction. *Proc. Soc. Exp. Biol. Med.* 206:205–9

14. Billestrup N, Bouchelouche P, Allevato G, Ilondo M, Nielsen JH. 1995. Growth hormone receptor C-terminal domains required for growth hormone-induced intracellular free Ca$^{2+}$ oscillations and gene transcription. *Proc. Natl. Acad. Sci. USA* 92:In press

15. Billestrup N, Moledrup A, Serup P, Mathews LS, Norstedt G, et al. 1990. Introduction of exogenous growth hormone receptors augments growth hormone-responsive insulin biosynthesis in rat insulinoma cells. *Proc. Natl. Acad. Sci. USA* 87:7210–14

16. Campbell GS, Christian LJ, Carter-Su C. 1993. Evidence for involvement of the growth hormone receptor-associated tyrosine kinase in actions of growth hormone. *J. Biol. Chem.* 268:7427–34

17. Campbell GS, Meyer DJ, Raz R, Levy DE, Schwartz J, et al. 1995. Activation of acute phase response factor (APRF)/ Stat3 transcription factor by growth hormone. *J. Biol. Chem.* 270:3974–79

18. Campbell GS, Miyaska T, Pang L, Saltiel AR, Carter-Su C. 1992. Stimulation by growth hormone of MAP kinase activity in 3T3-F442A fibroblasts. *J. Biol. Chem.* 267:6074–80

19. Catalioto RM, Ailhaud G, Negrel R. 1990. Diacylglycerol production induced by growth hormone in Ob1771 preadipocytes arises from phosphatidylcholine breakdown. *Biochem. Biophys. Res. Commun.* 173:840–48

20. Cheatham B, Vlahos CJ, Cheatham L, Wang L, Blenis J, et al. 1994. Phosphatidylinositol 3-kinase activation is required for insulin stimulation of pp70 S6 kinase, DNA synthesis, and glucose transporter translocation. *Mol. Cell. Biol.* 14:4902–11

21. Clarkson RW, Chen CM, Harrison S, Wells C, Muscat GEO, et al. 1995. Early responses of *trans*-activating factors to growth hormone in preadipcoytes: differential regulation of CCAAT enhancer-binding protein-beta (C/EBPβ) and C/EBPγ. *Mol. Endocrinol.* 9:108–20

22. Cobb MH, Robbins DJ, Boulton TG. 1991. ERKs, extracellular signal-regulated MAP-2 kinases. *Curr. Opin. Cell Biol.* 3:1025–32

23. Colosi P, Wong K, Leong S. R, Wood WI. 1993. Mutational analysis of the intracellular domain of the human growth hormone receptor. *J. Biol. Chem.* 268:12617–23

24. Cosman D, Lyman SD, Idzerda RL, Beckmann MP, Park LS, et al. 1990. A new cytokine receptor superfamily. *Trends Biochem. Sci.* 15:265–70

25. Crews CM, Erikson RL. 1993. Extracellular signals and reversible protein phosphorylation: what to MEK of it all. *Cell* 74:215–17

26. Cunningham BC, Ultsch M, De Vos AM, Mulkerrin MG, Clauser KR, et al. 1991. Dimerization of the extracellular domain of the human growth hormone receptor by a single hormone molecule. *Science* 254:821–25

27. Darnell JE Jr, Kerr IM, Stark GR. 1994. Jak-STAT pathways and transcriptional activation in response to IFNs and other extracellular signaling proteins. *Science* 264:1415–21

28. DaSilva L, Howard OMZ, Rui H, Kirken RA, Farrar WL. 1994. Growth signaling and JAK2 association mediated by membrane-proximal cytoplas-

mic regions of prolactin receptors. *J. Biol. Chem.* 269:18267–70

29. Daughaday WH, Rotwein P. 1989. Insulin-like growth factors I and II. Peptide, messenger ribonucliec acid and gene structures, serum, and tissue concentrations. *Endocr. Rev.* 10:68–91

30. Davidson MB. 1987. Effect of growth hormone on carbohydrate and lipid metabolism. *Endocr. Rev.* 8:115–31

31. Davis RJ. 1993. The mitogen-activated protein kinase signal transduction pathway. *J. Biol. Chem.* 268:14553–56

32. deVos AM, Ultsch M, Kossiakoff AA. 1992. Human growth hormone and extracellular domain of its receptor: crystal structure of the complex. *Science* 255: 306–12

33. Distel R, Ro HS, Rosen BS, Groves D, Spiegelman BM. 1987. Nucleoprotein complexes that regulate gene expression in adipocyte differentiation: direct participation of c-*fos*. *Cell* 49:835–44

34. Doglio A, Dani C, Fredrikson G, Grimaldi P, Ailhaud G. 1987. Acute regulation of insulin-like growth factor-I gene expression by growth hormone during adipose cell differentiation. *EMBO J.* 6:4011–16

35. Doglio A, Dani C, Grimaldi P, Ailhaud G. 1986. Growth hormone regulation of the expression of differentiation-dependent genes in preadipocyte Ob1771 cells. *Biochem. J.* 238:123–29

36. Doglio A, Dani C, Grimaldi P, Ailhaud G. 1989. Growth hormone stimulates c-*fos* gene expression by means of protein kinase C without increasing inositol lipid turnover. *Proc. Natl. Acad. Sci. USA* 86:1148–52

37. Domene H, Krishnamurthi K, Eshet R, Gilad I, Laron Z, et al. 1993. Growth hormone (GH) stimulates insulin-like growth factor-I (IGF-I) and IGF-I-binding protein-3, but not GH receptor gene expression in livers of juvenile rats. *Endocrinology* 133:675–82

38. Emtner M, Mathews LS, Norstedt G. 1990. Growth hormone (GH) stimulates protein synthesis in cells transfected with GH receptor complementary DNA. *Mol. Endocrinol.* 4:2014–20

39. Finbloom DS, Petricoin EF III, Hackett RH, David M, Feldman GM, et al. 1994. Growth hormone and erythropoietin differentially activate DNA-binding proteins by tyrosine phosphorylation. *Mol. Cell Biol.* 14:2113–18

40. Firmbach-Kraft I, Byers M, Shows T, Dalla-Favera R, Krolewski JJ. 1990. Tyk2, prototype of a novel class of non-receptor tyrosine kinase genes. *Oncogene* 5:1329–36

41. Foster CM, Shafer JA, Rozsa FW, Wang X, Lewis SD, et al. 1988. Growth hormone promoted tyrosyl phosphorylation of growth hormone receptors in murine 3T3-F442A fibroblasts and adipocytes. *Biochemistry* 27:326–34

42. Frank SJ, Gilliland G, Kraft AS, Arnold CS. 1994. Interaction of the growth hormone receptor cytoplasmic domain with the JAK2 tyrosine kinase. *Endocrinology* 135:2228–39

43. Frank SJ, Woelsung Y, Zhao Y, Goldsmith JF, Gilliland G, et al. 1995. Regions of the JAK2 tyrosine kinase required for coupling to the growth hormone receptor. *J. Biol. Chem.* 270: 14776–85

44. Fuh G, Cunningham BC, Fukunaga R, Nagata S, Goeddel DV, et al. 1992. Rational design of potent antagonists to the human growth hormone receptor. *Science* 256:1677–80

45. Fukunaga R, Ishizaka-Ikeda E, Nagata S. 1993. Growth and differentiation signals mediated by different regions in the cytoplasmic domain of granulocyte colony-stimulating factor receptor. *Cell* 74:1079–87

46. Gille H, Sharrocks AK, Shaw PE. 1992. Phosphorylation of transcription factor p62TCF by MAP kinase stimulates ternary complex formation at c-fos promoter. *Nature* 358:414–17

47. Godowski PJ, Leung DW, Meacham LR, Galgani JP, Hellmiss R, et al. 1989. Characterization of the human growth hormone receptor gene and demonstration of a partial gene deletion in two patients with Laron-type dwarfism. *Proc. Natl. Acad. Sci. USA* 86:8083–87

48. Goldsmith MA, Xu W, Amaral MC, Kuczek ES, Greene WC. 1994. The cytoplasmic domain of the interleukin-2 receptor beta chain contains both unique and functionally redundant signal transduction elements. *J. Biol. Chem.* 269: 14698–747

49. Gong T-WL, Meyer D, Wang X, Billestrup N, Norstedt G, et al. 1994. Regulation of c-fos expression and glucose transport by a truncated growth hormone receptor. *Program, 76th Annu. Meet. Endocrine Soc.* p. 465

50. Goodman HM. 1968. Growth hormone and the metabolism of carbohydrate and lipid in adipose tissue. *Ann. NY Acad. Sci.* 148:419–40

51. Goujon L, Allevato G, Simonin G, Paquereau L, Le Cam A, et al. 1994. Cytoplasmic sequences of the growth hormone receptor necessary for signal transduction. *Proc. Natl. Acad. Sci. USA* 91:957–61

52. Green H, Morikawa M, Nixon T. 1985. A dual effector theory of growth-hormone action. *Differentiation* 29:195–98

53. Greenlund AC, Farrar MA, Viviano B, Schreiber RD. 1994. Ligand-induced IFN-gamma receptor tyrosine phosphorylation couples the receptor to its signal transduction system (p91). *EMBO J.* 13:1591–600

54. Gronowski AM, Rotwein P. 1994. Rapid changes in nuclear protein tyrosine phosphorylation after growth hormone treatment in vivo. Identification of phosphorylated mitogen-activated protein kinase and stat91. *J. Biol. Chem.* 269:7874–78

55. Gronowski AM, Zhong Z, Wen Z, Thomas MJ, Darnell JE Jr, et al. 1995. Nuclear actions of growth hormone: rapid tyrosine phosphorylation and activation of Stat1 and Stat3 after in vivo growth hormone treatment. *Mol. Endocrinol.* 9:171–77

56. Gurland G, Ashcom G, Cochran BH, Schwartz J. 1990. Rapid events in growth hormone action. Induction of c-fos and c-jun transcription in 3T3-F442A preadipocytes. *Endocrinology* 127:3187–95

57. Harding PA, Wang XZ, Kelder B, Souza S, Okada S, et al. 1994. In vitro mutagenesis of growth hormone receptor Asn-linked glycosylation sites. *Mol. Cell. Endocrinol.* 106:171–80

58. Harpur AG, Andres A-C, Ziemiecki A, Aston RR, Wilks AF. 1992. JAK2, a third member of the JAK family of protein tyrosine kinases. *Oncogene* 7: 1347–53

59. He, T-C, Jiang N, Zhuang H, Quelle D, Wojchowski D. 1994. The extended box 2 subdomain of erythropoietin receptor is nonessential for Jak2 activation yet critical for efficient mitogenesis in FDC-ER cells. *J. Biol. Chem.* 269:18291–94

60. Hilton DJ, Hilton AA, Raicevic A, Rakar S, Harrison-Smith M, et al. 1994. Cloning of a murine IL-11 receptor alpha-chain; requirement for gp130 for high affinity binding and signal transduction. *EMBO J.* 13:4765–75

61. Ho ASY, Liu Y, Khan T, Hsu D-H, Bazan JF, et al. 1993. A receptor for interleukin 10 is related to interferon receptors. *Proc. Natl. Acad. Sci. USA* 90:11267–71

62. Ilondo MM, De Meyts P, Bouchelouche P. 1994. Human growth hormone increases cytosolic free calcium in cultured human IM-9 lymphocytes: a novel mechanism of growth hormone transmembrane signalling. *Biochem. Biophys. Res. Commun.* 202:391–97

63. Isaksson OGP, Eden S, Jansson J-O. 1985. Mode of action of pituitary growth hormone on target cells. *Annu. Rev. Physiol.* 47:483–99

64. Isgaard J, Moller C, Isaksson O. GP, Nilsson A, Mathews LS, et al. 1988. Regulation of insulin-like growth factor messenger ribonucleic acid in rat growth plate by growth hormone. *Endocrinology* 122:1515–20

65. Janknecht R, Ernst WH, Pingoud V, Nordheim A. 1993. Activation of ternary complex factor Elk-1 by MAP kinases. *EMBO J.* 12:5097–104

66. Johnson RM, Napier MA, Cronin MJ, King KL. 1990. Growth hormone stimulates the formation of sn-1,2-diacylglycerol in rat hepatocytes. *Endocrinology* 127:2099–103

67. Johnston JA, Kawamura M, Kirken RA, Chen Y-Q, Blake TB, et al. 1994. Phosphorylation and activation of the Jak-3 Janus kinase in response to interleukin-2. *Nature* 370:151–53

68. Kelly PA, Ali S, Rozakis M, Goujon L, Nagano M, et al. 1993. The growth hormone/prolactin receptor family. *Rec. Prog. Horm. Res.* 48:123–64

69. Kelly PA, Djiane J, Postel-Vinay M-C, Edery M. 1991. The prolactin/growth hormone receptor family. *Endocrinol. Rev.* 12:235–51

70. LeCam A, Pages G, Auberger P, LeCam G, Leopold P, et al. 1987. Study of a growth hormone-regulated protein secreted by rat hepatocytes: cDNA cloning, anti-protease activity and regulation of its synthesis by various hormones. *EMBO J.* 6:1225–32

71. Legraverend C, Mode A, Wells T, Robinson I, Gustafsson J-A. 1992. Hepatic steroid hydroxylating enzymes are controlled by the sexually dimorphic pattern of growth hormone secretion in normal and dwarf rats. *FASEB J.* 6:711–18

72. Leung DW, Spencer SA, Cachianes G, Hammonds RG, Collins C, et al. 1987. Growth hormone receptor and serum binding protein: purification, cloning and expression. *Nature* 330:537–43

73. Liao J, Rosenspire K, Schwartz J. 1995. Regulation by growth hormone of proteins associated with the c-fos serum response element. *Program, 77th Annu. Meet. Endocrine Soc.* p. 348

74. Lobie PE, Allevato G, Nielsen JH, Norstedt G, Billestrup N. 1995. Requirement of tyrosine residues 333 and 338 of the growth hormone (GH) receptor for selected GH stimulated function. *J. Biol. Chem.* In press

75. Marais R, Wynne J, Treisman R. 1993. The SRF accessory protein Elk-1 contains a growth factor-regulated transcriptional activation domain. *Cell* 73: 381–93

76. Mathews LS, Norstedt G, Palmiter RD. 1986. Regulation of insulin-like growth factor I gene expression by growth hormone. *Proc. Natl. Acad. Sci. USA* 83: 9343–47

77. Meyer DJ, Campbell GS, Cochran BH, Argetsinger LS, Larner AC, et al. 1994. Growth hormone induces a DNA binding factor related to the interferon-stimulated 91 kD transcription factor. *J. Biol. Chem.* 269:4701–4

78. Meyer DJ, Stephenson EW, Johnson L, Cochran BH, Schwartz J. 1993. The serum response element can mediate the induction of c-fos by growth hormone. *Proc. Natl. Acad. Sci. USA* 90:6721–25

79. Moldrup A, Billestrup N, Dryberg T, Nielsen JH. 1991. Growth hormone action in rat insulinoma cells expressing truncated growth hormone receptors. *J. Biol. Chem.* 266:17441–45

80. Moller C, Emtner M, Arner P, Norstedt G. 1994. Growth hormone regulation of lipid metabolism in cells transfected with growth hormone receptor cDNA. *Mol. Cell. Endocrinol.* 99:111–17

81. Moller C, Hansson A, Enberg B, Lobie PE, Norstedt G. 1992. Growth hormone induction of tyrosine phosphorylation and activation of mitogen activated protein kinases in cells transfected with rat GH receptor cDNA. *J. Biol. Chem.* 267:23403–8

82. Murakami M, Narazaki M, Hibi M, Yawata H, Yasukawa K, et al. 1991. Critical cytoplasmic region of the interleukin 6 signal transducer gp130 is conserved in the cytokine receptor family. *Proc. Natl. Acad. Sci. USA* 88:11349–53

83. Murphy LJ, Bell GI, Friesen HG. 1987. Growth hormone stimulates sequential induction of c-myc and insulin-like growth factor I expression in vivo. *Endocrinology* 120:1806–12

84. O'Neal KD, Yu-Lee L-Y. 1993. The proline-rich motif (PRM): a novel feature of the cytokine receptor superfamily. *Lymphokine Cytokine Res.* 12: 309–12

85. O'Neill TJ, Craparo A, Gustafson TA. 1994. Characterization of an interaction between insulin receptor substrate 1 and the insulin receptor by using the two-hybrid system. *Mol. Cell. Biol.* 14:6433–42

86. Paul WE, Seder RA. 1994. Lymphocyte respones and cytokines. *Cell* 76:241–51

87. Pawson T, Schlessinger J. 1993. SH2 and SH3 domains. *Curr. Biol.* 3:434–42

88. Peter MA, Winterhalter KH, Peter MA,

Boni-Schnetzler M, Froesch ER, et al. 1993. Regulation of insulin-like growth factor-I (IGF-I) and IGF-binding proteins by growth hormone in rat white adipose tissue. *Endocrinology* 133: 2624–31

89. Pradines-Figueres A, Barcellini-Couget S, Dani C, Vannier C, Ailhaud G. 1990. Transcriptional control of the expression of lipoprotein lipase gene by growth hormone in preadipoctye OB1771 cells. *J. Lipid Res.* 31:1283–91

90. Ridderstrale M, Degerman E, Tornqvist H. 1995. Growth hormone stimulates the tyrosine phosphorylation of the insulin receptor substrate-1 and its association with phosphatidylinositol 3-kinase in primary adipocytes. *J. Biol. Chem.* 270:3471–74

91. Ridderstrale M, Tornqvist H. 1994. PI-3-kinase inhibitor wortmannin blocks the insulin-like effects of growth hormone in isolated rat adipocytes. *Biochem. Biophys. Res. Commun.* 203: 306–10

92. Rivera VM, Miranti CK, Misra RP, Ginty DD, Chen R-H, et al. 1993. A growth factor-induced kinase phosphorylates the serum response factor at a site that regulates its DNA-binding activity. *Mol. Cell. Biol.* 13:6260–73

93. Rogers SA, Hammerman MR. 1989. Growth hormone activates phospholipase C in proximal tubular basolateral membranes from canine kidney. *Proc. Natl. Acad. Sci. USA* 86:6363–66

94. Rosenfeld RG, Lamson G, Pham H, Oh Y, Conover C, et al. 1990. Insulinlike growth factor-binding proteins. *Rec. Prog. Horm. Res.* 46:99–163

95. Schwartz J, Carter-Su C. 1988. Effects of growth hormone on glucose metabolism and glucose transport in 3T3-F442A cells. Dependence on cell differentiation. *Endocrinology* 122: 2247–56

96. Schwartz Y, Goodman HM. 1990. Refractoriness to the insulin-like effects of growth hormone depends upon calcium. *Endocrinology* 126:170–76

97. Schwartz Y, Goodman HM, Yamaguchi H. 1991. Refractoriness to growth hormone is associated with increased intracellular calcium in rat adipocytes. *Proc. Natl. Acad. Sci. USA* 88:6790–94

98. Schwartz Y, Yamaguchi H, Goodman HM. 1992. Growth hormone increases intracellular free calcium in rat adipocytes: correlation with actions on carbohydrate metabolism. *Endocrinology* 131:772–78

99. Seneviratne C, Luo J, Murphy LJ. 1990.

Transcriptional regulation of rat insulin-like growth factor-binding protein-1 expression by growth hormone. *Mol. Endocrinol.* 4:1199–204

100. Shuai K, Horvath CM, Huang LHT, Qureshi SA, Cowburn D, et al. 1994. Interferon activation of the transcription factor Stat91 involves dimerization through SH2-phosphotyrosyl peptide interactions. *Cell* 76:821–28

101. Silva CM, Day RN, Weber MJ, Thorner MO. 1993. Human growth hormone (GH) receptor is characterized as the 134-kilodalton tyrosine-phosphorylated protein activated by GH treatment in IM-9 cells. *Endocrinology* 133:2307–12

102. Silva CM, Lu H, Weber MJ, Thorner MO. 1994. Differential tyrosine phosphorylation of JAK1, JAK2, and STAT1 by growth hormone and interferon-gamma in IM-9 cells. *J. Biol. Chem.* 269:27532–39

103. Silva CM, Weber MJ, Thorner MO. 1993. Stimulation of tyrosine phosphorylation in human cells by activation of the growth hormone receptor. *Endocrinology* 132:101–8

104. Silvennoinen O, Schindler C, Schlessinger J, Levy DE. 1993. Ras-independent growth factor signaling by transcription factor tyrosine phosphorylation. *Science* 261:1736–39

105. Silvennoinen O, Witthuhn B, Quelle FW, Cleveland JL, Yi T, et al. 1993. Structure of the JAK2 protein tyrosine kinase and its role in IL-3 signal transduction. *Proc. Natl. Acad. Sci. USA* 90:8429–33

106. Sliva D, Wood TJJ, Schindler C, Lobie PE, Norstedt G. 1994. Growth hormone specifically regulates serine protease inhibitor gene transcription via gamma-activated sequence-like DNA elements. *J. Biol. Chem.* 42:26208–14

107. Slootweg MC, deGroot RP, Herrmann-Erlee MP, Koornneef I, Kruijer W, et al. 1991. Growth hormone induces expression of c-*jun* and *jun* B oncogenes and employs a protein kinase C signal transduction pathway for the induction of c-*fos* oncogene expression. *J. Mol. Endocrinol.* 6:179–88

108. Smal J, De Meyts P. 1987. Role of kinase C in the insulin-like effects of human growth hormone in rat adipocytes. *Biochem. Biophys. Res. Commun.* 147:1232–40

109. Sotiropoulos A, Perrot-Applanat M, Dinerstein H, Pallier A, Postel-Vinay M-C, et al. 1994. Distinct cytoplasmic regions of the growth hormone receptor are required for activation of JAK2, mitogen-activated protein kinase, and

transcription. *Endocrinology* 135:1292–98

110. Souza SC, Frick GP, Yip R, Lobo RB, Tai L-R, et al. 1994. Growth hormone stimulates tyrosine phosphorylation of insulin receptor substrate-1. *J. Biol. Chem.* 269:30085–88

111. Spiegelman BM, Distel RJ, Ro H-S, Rosen BS, Satterberg B. 1988. Fos protooncogene and the regulation of gene expression in adipocytes differentiation. *J. Cell Biol.* 107:829–32

112. Spiegelman BM, Frank M, Green H. 1983. Molecular cloning of mRNA from 3T3 adipocytes. Regulation of mRNA content for glycerophosphate dehydrogenase and other differentiation-dependent proteins during adipocyte development. *J. Biol. Chem.* 258:10083–89

113. Stahl N, Boulton TG, Farruggella T, Ip NY, Davis S, et al. 1994. Association and activation of Jak-Tyk kinases by CNTF-LIF-OSM-IL-6 beta receptor components. *Science* 263:92–95

114. Stahl N, Farruggella TJ, Boulton TG, Zhong Z, Darnell JE Jr, et al. 1995. Modular tyrosine-based motifs in cytokine receptors specify choice of STATs and other substrates. *Science* 267:1349–53

115. Stubbart JR, Barton DF, Tai P-KK, Stred E, Gorin E, et al. 1991. Antibodies to cytoplasmic sequences of cloned liver growth hormone (GH) receptors recognize GH receptors associated with tyrosine kinase activity. *Endocrinology* 129:1659–70

116. Sun XJ, Crimmins DL, Myers MG Jr, Miralpeix M, White MF. 1993. Pleiotropic insulin signals are engaged by multisite phosphorylation of IRS-1. *Mol. Cell. Biol.* 13:7418–28

117. Sun XJ, Rothenberg P, Kahn CR, Backer JM, Araki E, et al. 1991. Structure of the insulin receptor substrate IRS-1 defines a unique signal transduction protein. *Nature* 352:73–77

117a. Sun XJ, Wang L-M, Zhang Y, Yenish L, Myers MG Jr, et al. 1995. Role of IRS-2 in insulin and cytokine signaling. *Nature.* In press

118. Tai P-KK, Liao J-F, Chen EH, Dietz JJ, Schwartz J, et al. 1990. Differential regulation of two glucose transporters by chronic growth hormone treatment of cultured 3T3-F442A adipose cells. *J. Biol. Chem.* 265:21828–34

119. Tanner JW, Chen W, Young RL, Longmore GD, Shaw AS. 1995. The conserved box 1 motif of cytokine receptors is required for association with JAK kinases. *J. Biol. Chem.* 270:6523–30

120. Tanner JW, Leingang KA, Mueckler

MM, Glenn KD. 1992. Cellular mechanism of the insulin-like effect of growth hormone in adipocytes. *Biochem. J.* 282:99–106

121. Thomas MJ, Kikuchi K, Bichell DP, Rotwein P. 1994. Rapid activation of rat insulin-like growth factor-I gene transcription by growth hormone reveals no alterations in deoxyribonucleic acid-protein interactions within the major promoter. *Endocrinology* 135:1584–92

122. Thomas MJ, Kikuchi K, Bichell DP, Rotwein P. 1995. Characterization of deoxyribonucleic acid-protein interactions at a growth hormone-inducible nuclease hypersensitive site in the rat insulin-like growth factor-I gene. *Endocrinology* 136:562–69

123. Toker A, Meyer M, Reddy KK, Falck JR, Aneja R, et al. 1994. Activation of protein kinase C family members by the novel polyphosphoinositides PtdIns-3,4-P2 and PtdIns-3,4,5-P3. *J. Biol. Chem.* 269:32358–67

124. Tollet P, Enberg B, Mode A. 1990. Growth hormone (GH) regulation of cytochrome P-450IIC12, insulin-like growth factor-1 (IGF-1), and GH receptor messenger RNA expression in primary rat hepatocytes: a hormonal interplay with insulin, IGF-1, and thyroid hormone. *Mol. Endocrinol.* 4:1934–42

125. Tollet P, Legraverend C, Gustafsson J-A, Mode A. 1991. A role for protein kinases in the growth hormone regulation of cytochrome P4502C12 and insulin-like growth factor-I messenger RNA expression in primary adult rat hepatocytes. *Mol. Endocrinol.* 5:1351–58

126. Treisman R. 1992. The serum response element. *Trends Biol. Sci.* 17:423–26

127. VanderKuur J, Allevato G, Billestrup N, Norstedt G, Carter-Su C. 1995. Growth hormone-promoted tyrosyl phosphorylation of Shc proteins and Shc association with Grb2. *J. Biol. Chem.* 270:7587–93

127a. VanderKuur JA, Wang X, Zhang L, Allevato G, Billestrup N, et al. 1995. GH-dependent phosphorylation of tyrosine 333 and/or 338 of the growth hormone receptor. *J. Biol. Chem.* In press

128. VanderKuur JA, Wang X, Zhang L, Campbell GS, Allevato G, et al. 1994. Domains of the growth hormone receptor required for association and activation of JAK2 tyrosine kinase. *J. Biol. Chem.* 269:21709–17

129. Vigon I, Mornon J-P, Cocault L, Mitjavila M-T, Tambourin P, et al. 1992.

Molecular cloning and characterization of MPL, the human homolog of the v-mpl oncogene: identification of a member of the hematopoietic growth factor receptor superfamily. *Proc. Natl. Acad. Sci. USA* 89:5640–44

130. Vikman K, Carlsson B, Billig H, Eden S. 1991. Expression and regulation of growth hormone (GH) receptor messenger ribonucleic acid (mRNA) in rat adipose tissue, adipocytes, and adipocyte precursor cells: GH regulation of GH receptor mRNA. *Endocrinology* 129: 1155–61

131. Wang X, Uhler M, Billestrup N, Norstedt G, Talamantes F, et al. 1992. Evidence for association of the cloned liver growth hormone receptor with a tyrosine kinase. *J. Biol. Chem.* 267:17390–96

131a. Wang Y-D, Wong K, Wood WI. 1995. Intracellular tyrosine residues of the human growth hormone receptor are not required for the signaling of proliferation or Jak-STAT activation. *J. Biol. Chem.* 270:7021–24

132. Wang Y-D, Wood WI. 1995. Amino acids of the human growth hormone receptor that are required for proliferation and Jak-Stat signaling. *Mol. Endocrinol.* 9:303–11

133. Wilks AF, Harpur AG, Kurban RR, Ralph SJ, Zurcher G, et al. 1991. Two novel protein-tyrosine kinases, each with a second phosphotransferase-related catalytic domain, define a new class of protein kinase. *Mol. Cell. Biol.* 11:2057–65

134. Winston LA, Bertics PJ. 1992. Growth hormone stimulates the tyrosyl phosphorylation of 42- and 45-kDa ERK-related proteins. *J. Biol. Chem.* 267:4747–51

135. Witthuhn BA, Quelle FW, Silvennoinen O, Yi T, Tang B, et al. 1993. JAK2 associates with the erythropoietin receptor and is tyrosine phosphorylated and activated following stimulation with erythropoietin. *Cell* 74:227–36

136. Witthuhn BA, Silvennoinen O, Miura O, Lai KS, Cwik C, et al. 1994. Involvement of the Jak-3 Janus kinase in signalling by interleukins 2 and 4 in lymphoid and myeloid cells. *Nature* 370:153–57

137. Wood TJJ, Sliva D, Lobie PE, Pircher T, Gouilleux F, et al. 1995. Mediation of growth hormone-dependent transcriptional activation of mammary gland factor Stat 5. *J. Biol. Chem.* 270:9448–53

138. Xu BC, Chen WY, Gu T, Ridgway D, Wiehl P, et al. 1995. Effects of growth hormone (GH) antagonists on 3T3-F442A preadipocyte differentiation. *J. Endocrinol.* In press

139. Yoon JB, Berry SA, Seelig S, Towle HC. 1990. An inducible nuclear factor binds to a growth hormone-regulated gene. *J. Biol. Chem.* 265 (32):19947–54

Annu. Rev. Physiol. 1996. 58:209–29

# TRANSGENIC APPROACHES TO SALIVARY GLAND RESEARCH

*Linda C. Samuelson*

Department of Physiology, University of Michigan, Ann Arbor, Michigan 48109–0622

KEY WORDS:  transgenic mice, gene transfer, salivary gland gene expression, neoplasia, recombinant adenovirus

### ABSTRACT

This review discusses the use of transgenic technology for the study of salivary gland function and development. Methods for gene transfer in the salivary gland of experimental mammals are described, including use of conventional and embryonic stem cell-derived transgenic mice and direct gene transfer techniques employing recombinant adenovirus vectors. Tissue-specific expression studies in transgenic mice have defined a number of salivary gland-specific promoter/enhancers that can be used to direct transcription into different salivary cell types. The consequences of expression of various oncogenes in the salivary glands of transgenic mice for the induction of neoplasia and hyperplasia are described. Recently, the use of adenoviral vectors has been demonstrated to be a powerful new approach to transfer genes into the salivary gland. This technology should have a major impact on the study of salivary gland gene expression, as well as provide a means to express therapeutic proteins in the salivary gland.

## GENE TRANSFER TECHNOLOGIES

### Introduction

Transgenic approaches have been used to selectively alter the normal development and physiology of experimental mammals. These studies have had a profound influence on our understanding of the processes of mammalian development, tissue-specific gene expression, neoplasia, and animal physiology, and have been useful for the development of animal models of human disease. The expression of recombinant DNA constructs in animals can be accomplished in different ways, some that involve the permanent remodeling of the genome, as in transgenic mice and rats, and others that involve transient

209

transfer into somatic tissues, as is the case with recombinant adenovirus vectors. Transgenic techniques have become essential to an understanding of salivary gland function and gene expression because of the paucity of salivary gland cell lines that maintain a differentiated phenotype. The expression of recombinant DNA constructs can be used to alter normal salivary gland physiology and thus expand our understanding of salivary function at a molecular level in an integrative setting. However, before proteins of interest can be directed to the correct salivary cell type, transcriptional control sequences capable of driving gene expression in the salivary glands of animals must be identified. Initial transgenic mouse experiments have now identified several promoter/enhancer regions of salivary genes that direct gene expression to various salivary cell types. Applications have been primarily directed toward the characterization of these sequences to identify tissue-specific transcription factors and the mechanism of salivary-specific gene expression, as well as the expression of various oncogenes, to test the sensitivities of different salivary cell types to neoplastic transformation. This review first briefly describes techniques for gene transfer into experimental mammals and then discusses the application of transgenic technology for salivary gland research.

## Transgenic Mice

CONVENTIONAL TRANSGENIC MICE    The most widely used transgenic approach involves the stable transfer of recombinant DNA molecules into the germline of mice. The generation of transgenic mice was independently reported by several laboratories in 1980 and 1981 (7, 11, 26, 99, 100). To produce transgenic mice, a linear DNA construct, or transgene, is microinjected into the pronuclei of fertilized mouse eggs, and the eggs are implanted into pseudopregnant females. Typically 20% of the mice that are born from the injected embryos have incorporated the transgene into their genomes. Integration is random, usually occurs at a single site, and can include from one to hundreds of copies of the transgene (Table 1). Integration normally occurs before the first zygotic cleavage event; consequently, all the tissues of the mouse, including the germ cells, contain the same transgene insert. The transgene phenotype can be studied in detail over a number of generations by breeding the founder mice. The transgene array is generally stable, but expansion or contraction can occur in homozygotes, presumably by unequal crossing over within the repetitive transgene insert. For this reason, it is common practice to propagate a transgenic line by breeding wild-type mice to hemizygotes, which carry one copy of the transgene array. This cross necessitates screening progeny by Southern blot hybridization or polymerase chain reaction (PCR) to identify the half that are transgenic. Transgene expression is overlaid upon the normal complement of gene expression, thus only dominant phenotypes can be evalu-

**Table 1**  Comparison of the features of conventional transgenic and ES cell derived transgenic mice

|  | Conventional transgenic | ES-transgenic[a] |
|---|---|---|
| Transgene phenotype | Dominant | Recessive or dominant |
| Insertion site | Random | Targeted |
| Transgene copy number | Variable (1–100) | Single copy |
| Reporter expression | Influenced by the site of integration | Parallels endogenous gene expression[b] |
| Other events | Insertional mutation (5–10%) | None |

[a] ES-transgenic mice are produced from ES cell lines preselected to have defined genetic modifications.

[b] For targeted alleles with reporter genes inserted downstream of the endogenous gene promoter.

ated. Occasionally (5–10%) the insertion causes a secondary gene mutation unrelated to the transgene. In these strains, the transgene can be used as a molecular tag for the gene causing the mutant phenotype and thus facilitate cloning the gene (54). Several excellent reviews have been written on the use of transgenic mice in research (9, 10, 22, 32, 40, 65), and detailed technical manuals are available that describe the procedures used to produce and analyze transgenic mice (16, 24, 25, 36, 45, 46, 70).

ES-CELL TRANSGENIC MICE    More recently, another technique for producing transgenic mice has been developed utilizing pluripotent mouse embryonic stem (ES) cells. This technique exploits the unique ability of these cultured cells to contribute to the germline of a developing mouse, together with homologous recombination techniques, to generate mice with defined genetic modifications. Isolation of ES cell lines from the inner cell mass (ICM) of preimplantation blastocysts was reported by Evans & Kaufman (21) and Martin (48) in 1981. These cells can be grown continuously in culture in an undifferentiated, pluripotent state and genetically manipulated using somatic cell genetic techniques. Specific gene mutations are introduced into an endogenous gene copy by homologous recombination with a DNA construct containing an engineered mutation. Homologous recombination in cultured ES cells, also known as gene targeting, is an infrequent event; random insertion is the most common pathway for integration of DNA introduced into these cells. Experimental strategies have been developed to increase the efficiency of homologous recombination (35, 91), enhance selection techniques (47), and efficiently screen hundreds of colonies (73), to facilitate the recovery of targeted ES clones. Because the targeting frequency is improved with isogenic DNA (91), mouse gene sequences used in the targeting vector should be cloned from the strain of origin for the ES cells, 129/Sv. Investigators cloning new genes in the mouse should consider screening a 129/Sv genomic library to facilitate possible targeting experiments in the future.

Once a targeted ES cell line has been identified and characterized, the cells are microinjected into a preimplantation embryo where the ES cells mix with the host ICM and contribute to all the tissues of the developing chimera, including the germ cells. Breeding chimeras allows the transmission of the engineered gene mutation and the establishment of a mutant mouse line. ES transgenics can be generated with a variety of different mutations ranging from large gene deletions (106) to changes as subtle as a single nucleotide substitution (34, 75, 98). Several excellent reviews have been written on the topic of ES-transgenics that include an overview of the technique (5, 12), research applications (10, 23), the design of targeting vectors (33), and procedures to make and analyze ES cell-transgenic mice (66, 86, 103). Key differences in the features of conventional and ES transgenic mice are summarized in Table 1. These differences stem primarily from the ability to manipulate ES cell clones in culture and thereby create transgenics from cells that have undergone rare targeting events. In contrast to conventional transgenics, ES-transgenics replace the endogenous gene, which allows the evaluation of recessive as well as dominant transgene phenotypes.

## Transgenic Rats and Other Mammals

With the development of enhanced embryo manipulation techniques in other species, some of the technology developed for transgenic mice has been adapted for the generation of transgenic rats, pigs, and other mammals. Rats, for example, may hold certain advantages over mice in that they may be better models of physiological processes because of their larger size and their past use in model systems. However, the methods for transforming the germline of other mammals are not widely available and are substantially more expensive than transgenic mice. In addition, at this time ES cell transgenic technology is available only in the mouse. Efforts are under way to develop rat ES cell lines, thus the capacity to generate ES-transgenic rats with specific gene disruptions may be available in the near future. Physiologists should also continue to develop more mouse models of physiological processes to take full advantage of the current transgenic capabilities in the mouse.

## Direct Gene Transfer with Adenovirus Vectors

Advances in gene therapy research have developed a number of viral vectors that are capable of infecting somatic cells and transfering recombinant DNA constructs for expression in a wide range of adult tissues. Perhaps the most promising general viral vector for the transfer of episomal DNAs into somatic cells is provided by adenovirus. Adenovirus causes respiratory disease in humans. Its genome is composed of a linear double-stranded DNA approximately 36 kilobases (kb) in length, of which 7.5 kb can be substituted with foreign DNA (3). After infection, the adenovirus particle enters the host cell by endocytosis and its DNA moves to the nucleus, where it is maintained as an episomal molecule. The duration of transgene expression after adenoviral delivery is limited because the virus cannot replicate, and it does not normally integrate into the host genome. Excellent reviews have been written on the use of recombinant adenovirus for gene transfer (3, 8, 41).

The important advantage of adenovirus is its capability to efficiently deliver recombinant DNA molecules into the nucleus of a wide variety of cells, both in vitro and in vivo. However, limitations in the size of the foreign DNA accommodated by the viral genome and the difficulty in preparing the recombinant virus reduce its general usefulness. Thus alternative methods have been developed that take advantage of the efficient cellular uptake mechanisms of adenovirus without the limitations inherent in preparing the recombinant virus. Adenovirus has specialized mechanisms that function to reduce degradation and transfer its genome into the nucleus of the host cell. This feature has been used to augment the cellular uptake of plasmid DNA constructs into cells. The plasmid DNA is either covalently linked to the surface of the adenovirus particle before infection (14) or simply co-applied with adenovirus (76, 104). Adenovirus methods have recently been demonstrated to be effective for gene transfer into the salivary gland (49, 63), and this technology holds great promise for the analysis of salivary gene expression.

## Factors Affecting Transgene Expression

After transfer into an experimental mammal, the expression of a transgene is dependent on a number of factors. Transcription is controlled by complex interactions between DNA sequences and nuclear proteins to regulate the cell specificity, developmental timing, and hormonal modulation of transgene expression. The promoter is located just upstream of the transcription start site and contains binding sites for proteins important for building the transcriptional machinery needed to synthesize RNA. Enhancer regions contain binding sites for protein factors that interact with the transcriptional machinery to control RNA synthesis. Each gene has a unique assortment of enhancers that can be distributed in the promoter region, as well as at variable distances both upstream and downstream of the transcription start site. Strong promoter/enhancers from simian virus 40 (SV40), Rous sarcoma virus (RSV), and cytomegalovirus (CMV) are active in the majority of cell types, including the salivary gland (49, 63), because they contain a number of binding sites for ubiquitous transcription factors. Tissue-specific promoter/enhancers can be used to restrict transgene expression to one or more tissues (see Reference 39 for a review). Because gene expression is complex and the elements regulating transcription can, in some instances, be quite distant from the promoter, gene segments critical for proper expression patterns must be empirically determined, often by testing a number of different transgene constructs. In general, it is desirable to initiate transgenic mouse studies with very large gene segments to improve the likelihood of including essential regulatory elements in the transgene constructs. Comparison of the expression of different transgene constructs provides information about the positions of general or salivary-specific enhancer elements.

Another factor influencing the expression of an integrated transgene is the insertion site. For this reason, it is usually recommended that conventional transgenic mouse studies include several independently generated lines for each transgene construct to control for line-specific expression patterns owing to the integration site. In some cases, DNA sequences have been identified for genes or gene clusters that appear to operate as global chromatin regulators and buffer the transgene sequences from surrounding sequences. This has been best studied in the globin gene cluster where a region several kb upstream from the β-globin gene cluster, termed the locus activator region (LAR), operates to give correct developmental gene expression in a position-independent and copy number-dependent manner (18, 27). Another sequence shown to improve the efficacy of a mammary-specific construct in transgenic mice is the chicken lysozyme matrix attachment region (MAR) (51); however, this MAR does not appear to act uniformly to buffer transgene expression from the surrounding sequences (39).

## TRANSGENE EXPRESSION IN THE SALIVARY GLAND OF TRANSGENIC MICE

### Tissue-Specific Gene Expression

A number of genes that code for abundant salivary proteins have been cloned, including genes that are predominantly expressed in a single salivary gland, such as α-amylase and parotid secretory protein (*Psp*), as well as genes expressed in both salivary and extra-salivary tissues, such as renin and kallekrein. To determine the mechanisms for transcriptional regulation in the salivary gland, salivary transgene constructs have been introduced into the genomes of transgenic mice. Evaluation of the expression patterns has defined gene fragments sufficient to drive expression in various salivary glands, including the serous acinar cells of the parotid gland (17, 42, 92, 96), submandibular gland (SMG) (79, 85), and sublingual gland (SLG) (17, 42, 56), and the granular convoluted tubules of the SMG (60, 94) (Table 2). In most examples, the exact positions and nature of the salivary-specific regulatory sequences have not been fully characterized. Further transgenic expression studies are needed to

**Table 2** Transgene promoter/enhancers expressed in the salivary gland of transgenic mice

| Promoter/enhancer | Minimal gene region[a] | Predominant transgene expression | | Reference |
|---|---|---|---|---|
| | | Salivary gland[b] | Other tissues[c] | |
| Human salivary amylase *AMYIC* | −1.0 to −0.3 | Parotid | Very low | 92 |
| Mouse parotid secretory protein *Psp*[b] | 25-kb gene fragment | Parotid (high) SLG, SMG | None | 42 |
| *Lama* | Minigene with 4.6-kb 5' flank | SLG and parotid (low) | None | 56 |
| Rat proline-rich protein *R15* | −6.0 to −1.7 | Parotid[d] | Very low | 97 |
| Mouse major urinary protein *Mup-1.5b* | −3.5 to −1.9 | SMG | None | 79 |
| Rat tissue kallekrein *rKlkl* | −1.7 to +2 | SLG (low)[e] | Several | 83 |
| Mouse renin *Ren-2* | 16-kb gene fragment | SMG | Kidney | 60, 94 |
| *Ren-1*[D] | 19-kb gene fragment | SMG (low) | Kidney | 57 |
| Human cystatin *CST1* | 22-kb gene fragment | Parotid, SMG | Lacrimal | 17 |
| Mouse mammary tumor virus *MMTV-LTR* | −1.2 to + 0.1 | Salivary gland | Mammary and other secretory epithelium | 15, 50, 58, 68, 87, 88 |

[a] The minimal gene region, in kilobase pairs, sufficient to drive expression in the salivary gland is indicated. Gene numbering is relative to the start of transcription, defined as +1.
[b] The specific salivary gland and salivary cell type in which the transgene promoter/enhancer are active are indicated when known. SMG, submandibular gland; SLG, sublingual gland.
[c] Tissues with a relatively high level of consistent transgene expression are noted. The reader is referred to the primary publications to obtain information regarding consistent low levels of extra salivary expression.
[d] Transgene expression was observed only when animals are treated with isoproterenol or dietary tannins.
[e] Extremely low expression in the parotid and SMG was detected by Southern blot analysis of RT-PCR products.

describe the sequences, as well as to define easily manipulated promoter/enhancer fragments for transgenic experiments designed to alter the physiology of the salivary glands through the expression of specific transgenes.

α-AMYLASE    Amylase is an abundant product of the serous acinar cells of the pancreas and salivary gland. Salivary and pancreatic amylases are encoded by distinct but closely related genes (30, 62) that are arranged in a single cluster in the mouse (71, 101) and human (28, 29). The amylase gene clusters arose from a series of gene duplications, and the human and mouse gene families appear to have expanded independently during mammalian evolution (74). One indication of the independent evolution of the human and mouse salivary amylase genes is provided by the observation that their promoter sequences are unrelated. The mouse promoter is associated with a nontranslated exon 50 base pairs (bp) in length that is located 7 kb upstream of the first protein coding exon (105). In contrast, the human salivary amylase promoter is associated with a nontranslated exon 170 bp in length that is located 0.5 kb upstream of the first protein coding exon (29).

Expression of both the mouse and human salivary amylase genes has been examined in transgenic mice, with marked differences in their ability to be transcribed in the salivary gland, relating to the differences in their promoter structures. A cosmid clone containing the complete mouse salivary amylase gene *Amy1.1* was microinjected into oocytes to generate two independent transgenic lines (38). This gene contains two distinct promoters with differing patterns of expression: a salivary promoter, active only in the parotid acinar cells, and a weaker, nonspecific promoter, active at a low level in a number of tissues. Jones et al (38) demonstrated that the nonspecific promoter was active in transgenic mice, whereas the parotid promoter did not function. The lack of expression of the parotid promoter was presumably due to the absence of the salivary-specific enhancer elements from this 44-kb transgene construct and predicts that these sequences lie more that 5 kb upstream or 12 kb downstream of the gene. This result stands in contrast to the pattern of expression of the human salivary amylase promoter in transgenic mice as reported in Ting et al (92). In this study, a cosmid clone containing the human *AMY1C* gene was appropriately expressed in the parotid gland of transgenic mice. Further analysis of transgenic lines carrying transgenes with different amounts of 5'-flanking DNA identified a 0.7-kb *AMY1C* fragment (−1.0 to −0.3 kb) that was sufficient to drive expression in the parotid gland when coupled to a heterologous promoter and reporter gene (92). Thus parotid-specific enhancers are located within 1 kb of the human salivary amylase promoter, yet appear to lie some distance from the mouse salivary amylase promoter.

It is interesting to note that in spite of the striking differences between the human and mouse salivary amylase promoters, human salivary amylase constructs were expressed in transgenic mouse salivary gland, indicating conservation of salivary transcriptional regulatory mechanisms between mouse and human. Surprisingly, the human salivary enhancer region is contained within an endogenous retrovirus associated with the human amylase promoter (74, 92). DNA-binding studies with mouse parotid nuclear extracts have demonstrated tissue-specific binding to the amylase-associated virus (92). Identification of this binding activity should provide information regarding the transcription factors regulating amylase gene expression in the salivary gland.

PAROTID SECRETORY PROTEIN    Although PSP is the most abundant protein secreted from the mouse parotid gland, its function in the oral cavity remains obscure (44, 78). PSP is encoded by a single-copy gene that is predominantly expressed in the serous acinar cells of the parotid gland and at lower levels in the SMG and SLG (72). Correct salivary-specific expression of *Psp* constructs in transgenic mice has been reported from Hjorth's laboratory (42, 56). Transgenic mice prepared from a mouse $Psp^b$ cosmid clone, which included 11.4 kb of 5'-flanking sequences and 2.5 kb of 3'-flanking sequences, expressed the transgene at high levels in the parotid gland and at lower levels in the SMG and SLG (42), the expected pattern of expression for this gene. Remarkably, steady-state levels of the $Psp^b$ transcript equaled or exceeded mRNA levels of the endogenous gene. The high level of expression of this transgene indicates that all the elements necessary for proper tissue-specific and high-level expression were included in the 25-kb cosmid clone. Smaller *Psp* transgenes containing varying amounts of 5'-flanking sequence fused to a *Psp* minigene were also expressed in the salivary glands; however, the level of expression in the parotid gland was only 1% of the endogenous gene levels (56). The minigene constructs maintained the high level of expression in the SLG observed with the cosmid transgene. The selective reduction of parotid expression indicates that an enhancer(s) necessary for high level transcription in the parotid is missing from the minigene constructs. Analysis of various 5' deletion constructs of the *Psp* minigene localized the position of critical transcriptional control sequences for basal expression in both parotid and SLG to a region between −4.6 kb and −3.1 kb. These results indicate that the minimal salivary-specific enhancer(s) are within 5 kb of the gene and that enhancer(s) for high level expression in the parotid are located elsewhere within the 25-kb cosmid clone.

INDUCIBLE EXPRESSION OF A PROLINE-RICH PROTEIN PROMOTER    The proline-rich proteins (PRPs) are thought to function by forming a protective coat on the hard and soft tissues of the mouth. PRP gene expression is dramatically induced by β-adrenergic stimulation or by ingesting dietary tannins (2, 52, 53). This response may function to protect organisms from the toxic effects of tannins, common in the human diet (52). Correct inducible and tissue-specific expression of the rat PRP gene *R15* in transgenic mice has been recently demonstrated (97). *R15* transgenes containing 10 kb and 6 kb of 5'-flanking sequences fused to the chloramphenicol acetyl transferase (CAT) gene were expressed in both the parotid and SMG only after β-adrenergic stimulation with isoproterenol, or after tannin feeding. In contrast, a construct containing 1.7 kb of 5'-flanking DNA was observed to have significant extra-salivary expression and to have lost inducible gene expression. Confirmation that sequences between −6.1 kb and 1.7 kb were capable of directing correct salivary-specific and inducible gene expression was obtained by coupling this region to a heterologous promoter and reporter gene (97; D Ann, personal communication). The *R15* promoter/enhancer defined in this study should be useful for conditional expression of proteins into the parotid acinar cells. Transgene expression would be silent until the animals were fed tannins or treated with $\beta_1$-adrenergic stimulants, which would allow for the analysis of transgenes that are toxic to the mice or for evaluation of the acute affects of the expression of a particular protein in the salivary gland.

MOUSE MAJOR URINARY PROTEIN   Mouse major urinary proteins (MUPs) are major protein constituents of the urine of adult mice. They are encoded by a large multigene family with differing tissue specificity in the salivary glands, lachrymal glands, and liver. Transgenic mouse studies have been performed on one subfamily of MUP genes (79, 85), which is normally expressed in the SMG and at a much lower level in the SLG (77). A 9.4-kb genomic fragment containing the *Mup-1.5b* gene was expressed at greater levels than the endogenous gene in the SMG of transgenic mice (79). Further analysis of deletion constructs identified a 1.6-kb 5'-flanking segment that was required for high-level expression in the SMG (85). Of particular interest is the observation that the endogenous *Mup-1.5b* gene is not normally expressed, which suggests that long-range inhibitory position effects may silence this gene (79). This control region is currently the best characterized for high-level constitutive expression in the SMG of transgenic mice (Table 2).

KALLEKREIN   In the examples described above, the transfer of a large genomic clone containing the complete gene was usually sufficient for expression in the salivary gland of transgenic mice. In general this was not true for kallekrein transgenes, where salivary expression was not observed in spite of the transfer of substantial amounts of genomic sequence. Kallikrein is a serine protease encoded by a tightly linked multigene family. A number of transgenic lines have been generated from the rat kallikrein genes; however, they were either not expressed or expressed at very low levels in the salivary glands (83). This result was unexpected because one feature unifying the various kallikrein family members is their high-level expression in the ductal cells of the SMG (6, 90, 102). For example, an intact tissue kallikrein gene (*rKlk1*), including 4.5 kb of 5'-flanking sequence and 4.7 kb of 3'-flanking sequence, was expressed in the SLG and SMG, but at very low levels, and tonin gene (*rKlk2*; another member of the kallikrein gene family) and prostate kallikrein (*rKlk8*) transgene constructs were not expressed in the salivary gland (83). In many cases, the expected transgene expression in extra-salivary tissues was observed. The block to salivary expression was probably not due to a species barrier because, at least in the case of a *rKlk8* construct, expression in transgenic rat salivary gland was also not observed (83). The uniform lack of expression of a large number of different kallekrein transgenes in the salivary gland led to the speculation that a dominant control region may impose salivary gland expression on the extended kallikrein family locus (83).

RENIN    Renin is expressed at high levels in the granular convoluted tubules of the SMG in mice. Salivary renin does not participate in the regulation of blood pressure and appears in this tissue as a consequence of the divergent regulation of a duplicated renin gene copy in the mouse (80). Renin expression in the salivary gland is induced by androgen, and levels in the granular convoluted tubules of the adult male SMG are quite high (94, 95). The analysis of various renin transgenes in transgenic mice has been reviewed by Sigmund & Gross (80). A 16-kb fragment containing the complete *Ren-2* gene was expressed in the SMG and kidney of transgenic mice at levels comparable to those of the endogenous renin gene (94). Moreover, transgene expression in the salivary gland tissue responded to androgens and thyroxine (95). To further define the regulatory regions of the *Ren-2* gene, Sola et al (84) and Sigmund et al (81) coupled promoter/enhancer fragments to SV40 large T antigen (Tag). A construct containing 4.6 kb of 5'-flanking DNA was expressed with the proper tissue specificity (80, 81), whereas a smaller construct containing 2.5 kb of 5'-flanking DNA was not expressed in SMG or kidney (84). This result suggests that the critical salivary control sequences are located between −4.6 and −2.5 kb upstream of this gene.

MOUSE MAMMARY TUMOR VIRUS    The mouse mammary tumor virus–long terminal repeat (MMTV-LTR) has been used extensively in transgenic mouse experiments to promote the expression of various genes into the mammary gland for the analysis of development and neoplasia in this tissue. Transgenes containing the MMTV-LTR are also expressed in the secretory epithelium of a number of tissues, including the salivary gland, which suggests that these secretory cells may contain common transcription factors. Stewart et al (88) observed consistent high-level expression of an MMTV-*myc* fusion gene in the salivary gland of transgenic mice. The consequences of expression of the *myc* oncogene, as well as other oncogenes, for the development of neoplasia in the salivary gland are discussed below. For salivary-specific gene expression, a 1.1-kb fragment of the MMTV promoter/enhancer was sufficient to drive expression in salivary, mammary, and other tissues (88). The occurrence of acinar and ductal cell neoplasia in parotid and SMG with MMTV-promoted oncogenes indicates that this promoter/enhancer is broadly expressed in the salivary epithelium (Table 3).

**Table 3**   Salivary gland neoplasia in transgenic mice expressing various oncogenes

| Oncogene | Promoter/enhancer | Salivary gland pathology | Reference |
|---|---|---|---|
| c-myc | MMTV-LTR | None | 43, 88 |
| v-Ha-ras | MMTV-LTR | Sporadic parotid acinar cell carcinomas | 15, 82, 93 |
| v-Ha-ras | Wap | Sporadic SMG adenosquamous carcinomas | 1, 61 |
| int-1 | MMTV-LTR | Sporadic adenocarcinomas | 96 |
| int-3 | MMTV-LTR | Bilateral polyclonal ductal cell hyperplasia of the major and minor glands and sporadic adinocarcinomas | 37 |
| c-neu | MMTV-LTR | Parotid bilateral polyclonal serous cell hyperplasia and mucus cell hypertrophy | 5, 59 |
| c-erbB-2 | MMTV-LTR | Focal epithelial cell hypertrophy or hyperplasia | 89 |
| SV40-Tag | Salivary amylase AMYlC | Parotid acinar cell hyperplasia | LC Samuelson, unpublished data |
| SV40-Tag | EGF | SMG ductal cell hyperplasia | 67 |

## Salivary Gland Neoplasia and Hyperplasia

Carcinogenesis is a multistep process involving the activation, mutation, or loss of a set of genes collectively referred to as oncogenes or tumor suppressers. These oncogenes include cellular genes such as ras and myc, which are normally activated during cell proliferation. When deregulated, these genes can lead to unchecked growth and, through secondary stochastic events, tumor formation. Tumor suppressers such as p53 function to sequester or deactivate growth-stimulating signals and thus, when lost, can also lead to unchecked growth and the propensity for tumor formation. Transgenic mice provide an excellent approach to test the action of a particular oncogene in a complex developmental system and decipher its function in the pathway to tumor formation. This approach has been useful for understanding the variable sensitivities of each tissue or cell type to the transforming potential of a particular oncogene under study. The function of dominant-acting oncogenes can be tested in conventional transgenic mice, and excellent reviews of this process have been published (13, 31). The ability to disrupt particular genes in a mouse using homologous recombination in ES cells can be used to test the function of tumor suppresser genes, which exhibit a phenotype when they are absent. Mice deficient in p53 were observed to have a high incidence of tumor formation in a variety of tissues (19), indicating that p53 probably plays a role in the regulation of growth control in a number of different cell types. However, p53 does not appear to have an essential function in the organism because these mice develop normally and reproduce. Cancer occurs in p53-deficient animals at a high frequency such that by 6 months of age, 74% develop neoplasms (19).

A study of tumor formation in the salivary gland has benefited from the extensive analysis of the mechanisms of tumor formation in the mammary gland. The most widely used promoter for targeting expression of oncogenes in the mammary epithelium, MMTV-LTR, is also active in the salivary gland. Thus the investigation of the action of specific oncogenes for proliferation and tumor formation of the mammary gland has yielded insights into the sensitivity of the salivary glands to these genes. The salivary gland pathology induced by a variety of oncogenes in transgenic mice is summarized in Table 3. Expression of the *myc* oncogene, although capable of inducing mammary adenocarcinomas, did not have an apparent effect on the salivary gland in spite of its relatively abundant expression (43, 88). In contrast, expression of the activated oncogene encoded by the viral Harvey ras gene (v-Ha-*ras*) with either the mouse whey acidic protein (*Wap*) promoter/enhancer or MMTV-LTR led to the sporadic development of salivary gland adenocarcinomas in transgenic mice (1, 15, 61, 82, 93). Interestingly, the MMTV-*ras* construct induced parotid gland tumors (15), and the *Wap-ras* transgene induced SMG tumors (61). The molecular basis for this difference has not been described but is presumably due to differences in the levels of v-Ha-*ras* in these two tissues in the various transgenic lines. Sporadic salivary gland adenocarcinomas were also observed in transgenic mice expressing *int-1* and *int-3* under the regulation of the MMTV-LTR (37, 96).

In general, the development of salivary gland adenocarcinomas in the transgenic mice was a sporadic event that resulted in the formation of presumably clonal tumor nodules. Thus the expression of these particular oncogenes was not in itself sufficient to cause the malignant transformation of the salivary epithelium. Tumor formation appeared to require secondary mutations in other cellular oncogenes. The requirement for multiple hits has been a general observation for tumor formation in different tissue types in transgenic mice (13, 31). Intercrossing MMTV-*myc* and MMTV-*ras* transgenic mice to obtain animals that express both oncogenes in the salivary gland did not appear to accelerate the rate or incidence of tumors (four salivary tumors/21 mice) above that already observed for the MMTV-*ras* oncogene (six salivary tumors/35 mice) (82). This is in contrast to the development of tumors in the mammary gland, in which a synergistic effect of these two oncogenes was observed. Thus expression of the *myc* oncogene did not have a discernible effect on the growth or differentiation of the salivary gland, even when paired with another transforming oncogene, which suggests that the targets for *myc* activation of onco-genesis are not available or that additional secondary events are required for *myc*-promoted oncogenesis in the salivary epithelial cells (82).

In contrast to the appearance of salivary gland adenocarcinomas, several oncogenes were described that produce bilateral polyclonal hyperplasia (Table 3). This phenotype was apparent in MMTV-*int-3* transgenics, which exhibited severe ductal cell hyperplasia and incomplete differentiation of the major and minor salivary glands (37). Transgenic mice harboring the MMTV-*c-neu* trans-gene exhibited bilateral enlargement of the parotid glands, characterized by serous cell hyperplasia and mucus cell hypertrophy (4, 59). In contrast to *int-3* transgenics, this hyperplasia was not accompanied by neoplastic transforma-tion, perhaps because of the shortened life span of these mice due to their early development of mammary tumors. The *c-erbB-2* oncogene was observed to induce focal epithelial cell hypertrophy or hyperplasia (89). SV40-Tag was also observed to induce salivary gland hyperplasia. Expression in parotid acinar cells using the human salivary amylase promoter *AMY1C* resulted in bilateral parotid acinar cell hyperplasia (LC Samuelson, unpublished data), and expres-sion in the granular convoluted tubules of the SMG using the epidermal growth factor (EGF) promoter resulted in hyperproliferation and immaturity of these cells in the transgenic mice (67).

Because these studies were primarily focused on the effects of oncogene expression in the mammary gland, information regarding salivary gland pa-thology was often limited. Before firm conclusions regarding the phenotype can be drawn, detailed analysis of the salivary gland needs to be performed, as has been the case for MMTV-*ras* transgenics (15) and Wap-*ras* transgenics (61). Because the mammary phenotype is so severe, in some instances, for example with the *neu* oncogene, it may be necessary to generate transgenics with a salivary-specific promoter to enable the mice to live longer and study the long-term consequences of oncogene expression in the salivary gland. Intercrossing the various transgenic lines may reveal the interactions between specific oncogenes and can be used to test if they function in a synergistic manner to accelerate the incidence or rate of salivary tumors. Finally, these transgenic mice provide a useful source of transformed salivary cells for the establishment of new cell lines. The field of salivary gland research has been hampered by a paucity of cultured cell lines that maintain the features of differentiated salivary epithelium. Targeted oncogenesis in transgenic mice offers an abundant source of proliferating salivary cells of various cell types for optimization of culture conditions and ultimately the formation of new cell lines. This approach has proven useful for the generation of a number of new cell lines from a variety of tissues, including pancreatic endocrine and exocrine cell lines (20, 64), liver cell lines (69), and neuroendocrine cell lines (55).

# ADENOVIRUS-MEDIATED GENE TRANSFER INTO THE SALIVARY GLAND

The accessibility of the major salivary gland ducts entering the mouth makes direct gene transfer techniques an attractive option for the salivary glands. Efficient transfer of gene constructs into the salivary glands of the rat using recombinant adenovirus has been recently reported from the laboratories of Baum & Crystal (49). Direct in vivo gene transfer to the parotid, SMG, and SLG was accomplished by retrograde ductal injection of replication-deficient recombinant adenovirus. Microscopic analysis 24–48 h after administration of an RSV-$\beta$-galactosidase recombinant adenovirus (Ad.RSV$\beta$gal) demonstrated transgene expression in acinar and ductal epithelial cells in all three salivary glands. Infection of salivary gland cells with a recombinant adenovirus vector encoding $\alpha_1$-antitrypsin (Ad$\alpha_1$AT) resulted in secretion of the protein into the saliva, thus indicating the potential application of this technique for the oral delivery of therapeutic substances (49). Recently, this study has been extended to show that recombinant adenovirus was not necessary for efficient gene transfer; cotransfer of plasmid DNA constructs with nonrecombinant adenovirus resulted in efficient plasmid transgene delivery into the salivary glands (63). The adenovirus-facilitated transfer of a SV40-luciferase plasmid construct showed peak expression approximately 18–24 h after delivery, followed by a steady decrease to background levels by 5 days. The demonstration of efficient expression of plasmids after adenovirus-facilitated transfer greatly enhances the usefulness of adenovirus for analysis of salivary gland gene expression because a large number of transgene constructs can be tested without the difficulty and expense of preparing recombinant virus. The study by O'Connell and co-workers (63) used this approach to characterize the expression of plasmid constructs consisting of the glutamine/glutamic acid-rich protein (GRP) promoter/enhancer driving the CAT reporter gene. CAT expression was observed specifically in the acinar cells of the SMG, similar to the expression pattern of the endogeneous GRP gene. Adenovirus-assisted gene transfer has many advantages over conventional transgenic techniques for studies of gene expression: (*a*) Expression can be evaluated within 24 h after gene transfer. In contrast, the production and analysis of transgenic mice takes several months to a year. This feature greatly reduces the cost and accelerates the pace of gene expression studies. (*b*) Adenoviral gene transfer techniques should be applicable to many different species, which will permit analysis in mammals other than the mouse. (*c*) Because the virus does not integrate, transgene expression will not be susceptible to variable gene expression from the insertion site. However, adenovirus gene transfer is transient and thus cannot be used to evaluate the consequences of long-term expression of transgenes, for example, for testing oncogene action, or for the analysis of genes affecting salivary gland development.

## FUTURE DIRECTIONS

Transgenic technology bridges the fields of molecular physiology and integrative whole-animal physiology. The identification of genetic control regions capable of reproducibly directing the expression of a transgene into a particular cell type allows the molecular transformation of salivary cells to alter their physiology in defined ways. ES-transgenic approaches can be used to evaluate the consequences of specific deficiencies, and conventional transgenics or adenovirus gene transfer can be used to evaluate dominant transgenes. Although significant advances have been made in the characterization of salivary-specific promoters, further definition of these sequences in transgenic animals is required to define easily manipulated promoter/enhancers for efficient expression in the salivary gland. Adenovirus gene transfer technology should greatly accelerate the pace of promoter characterization studies in the near future. A better understanding of the molecular basis of salivary gene expression should lead to the identification of key transcription factors for salivary gland organogenesis.

The development of transgenic technology for the salivary glands has the potential to be clinically relevant. Gene transfer into the salivary glands may be one route for delivery of therapeutic substances to an individual. Mastrangeli et al (49) have demonstrated that adenovirus can be used for gene transfer into human salivary glands and that proteins encoded by recombinant virus can be synthesized and secreted into the mouth. Furthermore, Mikkelsen et al (56) have shown that a conventional transgenic mouse expressing Factor VIII light chain in the salivary glands with a *Psp* minigene construct resulted in the secretion of the human protein into saliva. The salivary glands hold several advantages for gene therapy: (*a*) The tissue is easily reached through the ducts entering the mouth. (*b*) Salivary cells are designed to synthesize and secrete abundant quantities of proteins. (*c*) The synthesis and secretion of substances into saliva allows continual delivery into the body through the gastrointestinal system. However, before adenovirus-mediated gene transfer can be a routine delivery system, safety issues and immune reactions to the infection must be addressed.

ACKNOWLEDGMENTS

Thanks to Drs. Ann, Baum, O'Connell, and Tabak for communicating preprints of manuscripts, to Sally Camper for helpful comments on the manuscript, and to Max Fawley for assisting with library research. Research in the author's laboratory is supported by the National Institutes of Health.

## Literature Cited

1. Andres A-C, Schonenberger C-A, Groner B, Hennighausen L, LeMeur M, Gerlinger P. 1987. Ha-*ras* oncogene expression directed by a milk protein gene promoter: tissue specificity, hormonal regulation, and tumor induction in transgenic mice. *Proc. Natl. Acad. Sci. USA* 84:1299–1303

2. Ann DK, Clements S, Johnstone EM, Carlson DM. 1987. Induction of tissue-specific proline-rich protein multigene families in rat and mouse parotid glands by isoproterenol. *J. Biol. Chem.* 262:899–904

3. Berkner KL. 1988. Development of adenovirus vectors for the expression of heterologous genes. *BioTechniques* 6:616–29

4. Bouchard L, Lamarre L, Trembly PJ, Jolicoeur P. 1989. Stochastic appearance of mammary tumors in transgenic mice carrying MMTV *c-neu* oncogene. *Cell* 57:931–36

5. Bradley A, Hasty P, Davis A, Ramirez-Solis R. 1992. Modifying the mouse: design and desire. *Biotechnology* 10:534–39

6. Brady JM, MacDonald RJ. 1990. The expression of two kallikrein gene family members in rat kidney. *Arch. Biochem. Biophys.* 278:342–49

7. Brinster RL, Chen HY, Trumbauer ME, Senear AW, Warren R, Palmiter, RD. 1981. Somatic expression of herpes thymidine kinase in mice following injection of a fusion gene into eggs. *Cell* 27:223–31

8. Brody SL, Crystal RG. 1994. Adenovirus-mediated in vivo gene transfer. *Ann. NY Acad. Sci.* 716:90–101

9. Camper SA. 1987. Research applications of transgenic mice. *BioTechniques* 5:638–50

10. Camper SA, Saunders TL, Kendall SK, Keri RA, Seasholtz AF, et al. 1995. Implementing transgenic and embryonic stem cell technology to study gene expression, cell-cell interactions, and gene function. *Biol. Reprod.* 52:246–57

11. Constantini F, Lacy E. 1981. Introduction of a rabbit β-globin gene into the mouse germline. *Nature* 294:92–94

12. Capecchi M. 1994. Targeted gene replacement. *Sci. Am.* 270:52–59

13. Cory S, Adams JM. 1988. Transgenic mice and oncogenesis. *Annu. Rev. Immunol.* 6:25–48

14. Curiel DT. 1994. High-efficiency gene transfer mediated by adenovirus-poly-lysine-DNA complexes. *Ann. NY Acad. Sci.* 716:36–56

15. Dardick I, Burford-Mason AP, Garlick DS, Carney WP. 1992. Morphological evaluation of acinic cell carcinomas in the parotid gland of male transgenic (MMTV/v-Ha-*ras*) mice as a model for human tumors. *Vir. Arch. Path. Anat.* 421:105–13

16. DePamphilis ML, Herman SA, Martinez-Salas E, Chalifour LE, Wirak DO, et al. 1988. Microinjecting DNA into mouse ova to study DNA replication and gene expression and to produce transgenic animals. *BioTechniques* 6:662–80

17. Dickinson DP, Thiesse M. 1995. Tissue-specific expression of human cystatin genes in transgenic mice. *J. Dent. Res.* 74:85A

18. Dillon N, Grosveld F. 1993. Transcriptional regulation of multigene loci: multilevel control. *Trends Genet.* 9:134–37

19. Donehower LA, Harvey M, Slagle BL, McAuthur MJ, Montgomery CA, et al. 1992. Mice deficient for p53 are developmentally normal but susceptible to spontaneous tumours. *Nature* 356:215–21

20. Efrat S, Linde S, Kofod H, Spector D, Delannoy M, et al. 1988. Beta-cell lines derived from transgenic mice expressing a hybrid insulin-gene-oncogene. *Proc. Natl. Acad. Sci. USA* 85:9037–41

21. Evans MJ, Kaufman MH. 1981. Establishment in culture of pluripotential cells from mouse embryos. *Nature* 292:154–56

22. Field LJ. 1993. Transgenic mice in cardiovascular research. *Annu. Rev. Physiol.* 55:97–114

23. Fung-Leung W-P, Mak TW. 1992. Embryonic stem cells and homologous recombination. *Curr. Opin. Immunol.* 4:189–94

24. Gendron-Maguire M, Gridley T. 1993. Identification of transgenic mice. *Methods Enzymol.* 225:794–99

25. Gordon JW. 1993. Production of trans-

genic mice. *Methods Enzymol.* 225:747–71

26. Gordon JW, Scangos GA, Plotkin DJ, Barbosa JA, Ruddle FH. 1980. Genetic transformation of mouse embryos by microinjection of purified DNA. *Proc. Natl. Acad. Sci. USA* 77:7380–84

27. Grosveld F, van Assendelft GB, Greaves DR, Kollias G. 1987. Position-independent, high-level expression of the human β-globin gene in transgenic mice. *Cell* 51:975–85

28. Groot PC, Bleeker MJ, Pronk JC, Arwert F, Mager WH, et al. 1989. The human α-amylase multigene family consists of haplotypes with variable numbers of genes. *Genomics* 5:29–42

29. Gumucio DL, Wiebauer K, Caldwell RM, Samuelson LC, Meisler MH. 1988. Concerted evolution of human amylase genes. *Mol. Cell. Biol.* 8:1197–205

30. Hagenbüchle O, Bovey R, Young RA. 1980. Tissue-specific expression of mouse α-amylase genes: nucleotide sequence of isoenzyme mRNAs from pancreas and salivary gland. *Cell* 21:179–87

31. Hanahan D. 1988. Dissecting multistep tumorigenesis in transgenic mice. *Annu. Rev. Genet.* 22:479–519

32. Hanahan, D. 1989. Transgenic mice as probes into complex systems. *Science* 246:1265–75

33. Hasty P, Bradley A. 1993. Gene targeting vectors for mammalian cells. In *Gene Targeting: A Practical Approach*, ed. AL Joyner, pp 1–31. Oxford: Oxford Univ. Press

34. Hasty P, Ramirez-Solis R, Krumlauf R, Bradley A. 1991. Introduction of a subtle mutation into the *Hox-2.6* locus in embryonic stem cells. *Nature* 350:243–46

35. Hasty P, Rivera-Perez J, Chand C, Bradley A. 1991. Target frequency and integration pattern of insertion and replacement vectors in embryonic stem cells. *Mol. Cell. Biol.* 11:4509–17

36. Hogan B, Constantini F, Lacy E. 1986. *Manipulating the Mouse Embryo.* Cold Spring Harbor, NY: Cold Spring Harbor Lab.

37. Jhappan C, Gallahan D, Stahle C, Chu E, Smith GH, et al. 1992. Expression of an activated *Notch*-related *int-3* transgene interferes with cell differentiation and induces neoplastic transformation in mammary and salivary glands. *Genes Dev.* 6:345–55

38. Jones JA, Keller SA, Samuelson LC, Osborn L, Rosenberg MP, Meisler MH. 1989. A salivary amylase transgene is efficiently expressed in liver but not

parotid gland of transgenic mice. *Nucleic Acids. Res.* 17:6613–23

39. Keegan CE, Karolyi, IJ, Burrows HL, Camper SA, Seasholtz AF. 1994. Homologous recombination in fertilized mouse eggs and assessment of heterologous locus control region function. *Transgenics* 1:439–49

40. Koretsky AP. 1992. Investigation of cell physiology in the animal using transgenic technology. *Am. J. Physiol.* 262: C261–75

41. Kozarsky KF, Wilson JM. 1993. Gene therapy: adenovirus vectors. *Curr. Opin. Genet. Dev.* 3:499–503

42. Larsen HJ, Brodersen CH, Hjorth JP. 1994. High-level salivary gland expression in transgenic mice. *Transgenic Res.* 3:311–16

43. Leder A, Pattengale PK, Kuo A, Stewart TA, Leder P. 1986. Consequences of widespread deregulation of the *c-myc* gene in transgenic mice: multiple neoplasms and normal development. *Cell* 45:485–95

44. Madsen HO, Hjorth JP. 1985. Molecular cloning of the PSP mRNA. *Nucleic Acids Res.* 20:2249–55

45. Mann JR. 1993. Surgical techniques in production of transgenic mice. *Methods Enzymol.* 225:782–93

46. Mann JR, McMahon AP. 1993. Factors influencing frequency production of transgenic mice. *Methods Enzymol.* 225: 771–81

47. Mansour SL, Thomas KR, Capecchi MR. 1988. Disruption of the proto-oncogene *int-2* in mouse embryo-derived stem cells: a general strategy for targeting mutations to non-selectable genes. *Nature* 336:348–52

48. Martin GR. 1981. Isolation of a pluripotential cell line from early mouse cultured in medium conditioned with teratocarcinoma cells. *Proc. Natl. Acad. Sci. USA* 78:7634–39

49. Mastrangeli A, O'Connell B, Aladib W, Fox PC, Baum BJ, Crystal RG. 1994. Direct in vivo adenovirus-mediated gene transfer to salivary glands. *Am. J. Physiol.* 266:G1146–55

50. Matsui Y, Halter SA, Holt JT, Hogan BLM, Coffey RJ. 1990. Development of mammary hyperplasia and neoplasia in MMTV-TGFα transgenic mice. *Cell* 61:1147–55

51. McKnight RA, Shamay A, Sankaran L, Wall RJ, Hennighauser L. 1992. Matrix-attachment regions can impart position-independent regulation of a tissue-specific gene in transgenic mice. *Proc. Natl. Acad. Sci. USA* 89:6943–47

52. Mehansho H, Ann DK, Butler LG, Ro-

gler J, Carlson DM. 1987. Induction of proline-rich proteins in hamster salivary glands by isoproterenol treatment and an unusual growth inhibition by tannins. *J. Biol. Chem.* 262:12344–50

53. Mehansho H, Hagerman A, Clements S, Butler L, Rogler J, Carlson DM. 1987. Modulation of proline-rich biosynthesis in rat parotid glands by sorghums with high tannin levels. *Proc. Natl. Acad. Sci. USA* 80:3948

54. Meisler MH. 1992. Insertional mutation of "classical" and novel genes in transgenic mice. *Trends Genet.* 8:341–44

55. Mellon PL, Windle JJ, Weiner RI. 1991. Immortalization of neuroendocrine cells by targeted oncogenesis. *Rec. Prog. Horm. Res.* 47:69–96

56. Mikkelsen TR, Brandt J, Larsen HJ, Larsen BB, Poulsen K, et al. 1992. Tissue-specific expression in the salivary glands of transgenic mice. *Nucleic Acids. Res.* 20:2249–55

57. Miller CCJ, Carter AT, Brooks JI, Lovell-Badge RH, Brammar WJ. 1989. Differential extra-renal expression of the mouse renin genes. *Nucleic Acids. Res.* 17:3117–28

58. Mok E, Golovkina TV, Ross SR. 1992. A mouse mammary tumor virus mammary gland enhancer confers tissue-specific but not lactation-dependent expression in transgenic mice. *J. Virol.* 66:7529–32

59. Muller WJ, Sinn E, Pattengale PK, Wallace R, Leder P. 1988. Single-step induction of mammary adenocarcinomas in transgenic mice bearing the activated *c-neu* oncogene. *Cell* 54:105–15

60. Mullins JJ, Sigmund CD, Kane-Haas C, McGowan RA, Gross KW. 1989. Expression of the DBA/2J *Ren-2* gene in the adrenal gland of transgenic mice. *EMBO J.* 8:4065–72

61. Neilson LL, Discafini CM, Gurani M, Tyler RD. 1991. Histopathology of salivary and mammary gland tumors in transgenic mice expressing a human Ha-*ras* oncogene. *Cancer Res.* 51: 3762–67

62. Nishide T, Emi M, Nakamura Y, Matsubara K. 1986. Corrected sequences of cDNAs for human salivary and pancreatic α-amylases. *Gene* 50:371–72

63. O'Connell BC, Hagen KGT, Lazowski KW, Tabak LA, Baum BJ. 1995. Facilitated DNA transfer to rat submandibular gland in vivo and GRP-Ca gene regulation. *Am. J. Physiol.* 368: G1074–78

64. Ornitz DM, Hammer RE, Messing A, Palmiter RD, Brinster RL. 1987. Pancreatic neoplasia induced by SV40 T-antigen expression in acinar cells of transgenic mice. *Science* 238:188–94

65. Palmiter RD, Brinster RL. 1986. Germline transformation of mice. *Annu. Rev. Genet.* 20:465–99

66. Papaioannou V, Johnson R. 1993. Production of chimeras and genetically defined offspring from targeted ES cells. In *Gene Targeting: A Practical Approach*, ed. AL Joyner, pp 107–46. Oxford: Oxford Univ. Press

67. Pascall JC, Surani MA, Barton SC, Vaughan TJ, Brown KD. 1994. Directed expression of simian virus 40 T-antigen in transgenic mice using the epidermal growth factor gene promoter. *J. Mol. Endocrinol.* 12:313–25

68. Pattengale PK, Stewart TA, Leder A, Sinn E, Muller W, et al. 1989. Animal models of human disease: pathobiology and molecular biology of spontaneous neoplasms occurring in transgenic mice carrying and expressing activated cellular oncogenes. *Am. J. Pathol.* 135:39–61

69. Paul D, Höhne M, Pinkert C, Piasecki A, Ummelmann E, Brinster RL. 1988. Immortalized differentiated hepatocyte lines derived from transgenic mice harboring SV40 T-antigen genes. *Exp. Cell. Res.* 175:354–62

70. Pinkert CA. 1994. *Transgenic Animal Technology.* San Diego: Academic

71. Pittet A-C, Schibler U. 1985. Mouse alpha-amylase loci, Amy-1$^a$ and Amy-2$^a$, are closely linked. *J. Mol. Biol.* 182:359–65

72. Poulsen K, Jakobsen BK, Mikkelsen BM, Harmark K, Nielsen JT, Hjorth JP. 1986. Coordination of murine parotid secretory protein and salivary amylase expression. *EMBO J.* 5:1891–96

73. Ramirez-Solis R, Rivera-Perez J, Wallace JD, Wims M, Zheng H, Bradley A. 1992. Genomic DNA microextraction: a method to screen numerous samples. *Anal. Biochem.* 201:331–35

74. Samuelson LC, Wiebauer K, Snow CM, Meisler MH. 1990. Retroviral and pseudogene insertion sites reveal the lineage of human salivary and pancreatic amylase genes from a single gene during primate evolution. *Mol. Cell. Biol.* 10:2513–20

75. Sauer B. 1993. Manipulation of transgenes by site-specific recombination: use of cre recombinase. *Methods Enzymol.* 225:890–900

76. Seth P, Rosenfeld M, Higginbothan J, Crystal RG. 1994. Mechanism of enhancement of DNA expression consequent to cointernalization of a replication-deficient adenovirus and un-

modified plasmid DNA. *J. Virol.* 68: 933–40

77. Shahan K, Denaro M, Gilmartin M, Shi Y, Derman E. 1987. Nucleotide sequences of liver, lachrymal, and submaxillary gland mouse major urinary protein mRNAs: mosaic structure and constuction of panels of gene-specific synthetic oligonucleotide probes. *Mol. Cell. Biol.* 7:1947–54

78. Shaw P, Schibler U. 1986. Structure and expression of the parotid secretory protein of mouse. *J. Mol. Biol.* 192:567–76

79. Shi Y, Son HJ, Shahan K, Rodriguez M, Constantini F, Derman E. 1989. Silent genes in the mouse major urinary protein gene family. *Proc. Natl. Acad. Sci. USA* 86:4584–88

80. Sigmund CD, Gross KW. 1991. Structure, expression, and regulation of the murine renin genes. *Hypertension* 18: 446–57

81. Sigmund CD, Jones CA, Fabian JR, Mullins JJ, Gross KW. 1990. Tissue- and cell-specific expression of a renin promoter-T antigen reporter gene construct in transgenic mice. *Biochem. Biophys. Res. Commun.* 170:344–50

82. Sinn E, Muller W, Pattengale P, Tepler I, Wallace R, Leder P. 1987. Coexpression of MMTV/v-Ha-*ras* and MMTV/c-*myc* genes in transgenic mice: synergistic action of oncogenes in vivo. *Cell* 49:465–75

83. Smith MS, Lechago J, Wines DR, MacDonald RJ, Hammer RE. 1992. Tissue-specific expression of kallikrein family transgenes in mice and rats. *DNA Cell Biol.* 11:345–58

84. Sola C, Tronik D, Dreyfus M, Babinet C, Rougeon F. 1989. Renin-promoter SV40 large T antigen transgenes induce tumors irrespective of normal cellular expression of renin genes. *Oncogene Res.* 5:149–53

85. Son HJ, Shahan K, Rodriguez M, Derman E, Constantini F. 1991. Identification of an enhancer required for the expression of a mouse major urinary protein gene in the submaxillary gland. *Mol. Cell. Biol.* 11:4244–52

86. Stewart C. 1993. Production of chimeras between embryonic stem cells and embryos. *Methods Enzymol.* 225:823–55

87. Stewart TA, Hollingshead PG, Pitts SL. 1988. Multiple regulatory domains in the mouse mammary tumor virus long terminal repeat revealed by analysis of fusion genes in transgenic mice. *Mol. Cell. Biol.* 8:473–79

88. Stewart TA, Pattengale PK, Leder P. 1984. Spontaneous mammary adenocarcinomas in transgenic mice the carry

and express MTV/myc fusion genes. *Cell* 38:627–37

89. Stoocklin E, Botteri F, Groner B. 1993. An activated allele of the c-*erbB-2* oncogene impairs kidney and lung function and causes early death in transgenic mice. *J. Cell Biol.* 122:199–208

90. Swift GH, Dagorn JC, Ashley PL, Cummings SW, MacDonald RJ. 1982. Rat pancreatic kallikrein mRNA: nucleotide sequence and amino acid sequence of the encoded preproenzyme. *Proc. Natl. Acad. Sci. USA* 79:7263–67

91. te Riele H, Maandag ER, Berns A. 1992. Highly efficient gene targeting in embryonic stem cells through homologous recombination with isogenic DNA constructs. *Proc. Natl. Acad. Sci. USA* 89: 5128–32

92. Ting C-N, Rosenberg MP, Snow CM, Samuelson LC, Meisler MH. 1992. Endogenous retroviral sequences are required for tissue-specific expression of a human salivary amylase gene. *Genes Dev.* 6:1457–65

93. Tremblay PJ, Pothier R, Hoang T, Tremblay G, Browstein S, et al. 1989. Transgenic mice carrying the mouse mammary tumor virus *ras* fusion gene: distinct effects in various tissues. *Mol. Cell. Biol.* 9:854–59

94. Tronik D, Dreyfus M, Babinet C, Rougeon F. 1987. Regulated expression of the *Ren-2* gene in transgenic mice derived from parental strains carrying only the *Ren-1* gene. *EMBO J.* 6:983–87

95. Tronik D, Rougeon F. 1988. Thyroxine and testosterone transcriptionally regulate renin gene expression in the submaxillary gland of normal and transgenic mice carrying extra copies of the *Ren-2* gene. *FEBS Lett.* 234:336–40

96. Tsukamoto AS, Grosschedl R, Guzman RC, Parslow T, Varmus HE. 1988. Expression of the *int-1* gene in transgenic mice is associated with mammary gland hyperplasia and adenocarcinomas in male and female mice. *Cell* 55:619–25

97. Tu Z-J, Lazowski KW, Ehlenfeldt RC, Wu G, Lin HH, Kousvelari E, Ann DK. 1993. Isoproterenol/tannin-dependent *R15* expression in transgenic mice is mediated by an upstream parotid control region. *Gene Exp.* 3:289–305

98. Valancius V, Smithies O. 1991. Testing an "in-out" targeting procedure for making subtle genomic modifications in mouse embryonic stem cells. *Mol. Cell. Biol.* 11:1402–8

99. Wagner EF, Hoppe PC, Jollick JD, Scholl DR, Hodinda RL, Gault JB. 1981. Microinjection of a rabbit β-globin gene in zygotes and its subsequent expression

in adult mice and their offspring. *Proc. Natl. Acad. Sci. USA* 78:6376–80

100. Wagner EF, Stewart TA, Mintz B. 1981. The human β-globin gene and a functional thymidine kinase gene in developing mice. *Proc. Natl. Acad. Sci. USA* 78:5016–20

101. Wiebauer K, Gumucio DL, Jones JM, Caldwell RM, Hartle HT, Meisler MH. 1985. A 78-kilobase region of mouse chromosome 3 contains salivary and pancreatic amylase genes and a pseudogene. *Proc. Natl. Acad. Sci. USA* 82:5446–49

102. Wines DR, Brady JM, Pritchett DB, Roberts JL, MacDonald RJ. 1989. Organization and expression of the rat kallikrein gene family. *J. Biol. Chem.* 264:7653–62

103. Wurst W, Joyner AL. 1993. Production of targeted embryonic stem cell clones. In *Gene Targeting: A Practical Approach*, ed. AL Joyner, pp 33–61. Oxford: Oxford Univ. Press

104. Yoshimura K, Rosenfeld MA, Seth P, Crystal RG. 1993. Adenovirus-mediated augmentation of cell transfection with unmodified plasmid vectors. *J. Biol. Chem.* 268:2300–3

105. Young RA, Hagenbüchle O, Schibler U. 1981. A single mouse α-amylase gene specifies two different tissue-specific mRNAs. *Cell* 23:451–58

106. Zhang H, Hasty P, Bradley A. 1994. Targeting frequency for deletion vectors in embryonic stem cells. *Mol. Cell. Biol.* 14:2404–10

*Annu. Rev. Physiol. 1996. 58:231–51*

# MOLECULAR GENETICS OF EARLY LIVER DEVELOPMENT

*Kenneth S. Zaret*

Department of Molecular Biology, Cell Biology and Biochemistry, Box G, Brown University, Providence, Rhode Island 02912

KEY WORDS: liver, development, transcription factor, gene regulation, transgenics

---

## ABSTRACT

The control of liver development was originally defined by classical histology and tissue transplantation studies twenty to thirty years ago. In the past ten years, molecular biology studies have revealed numerous transcription factors important for adult liver differentiation. Recent work in which genes encoding regulatory proteins are inactivated in transgenic mice is evaluated in order to assess the consequences on liver development. The transgenic studies emphasize the roles of growth factors and signal transducers and the conservation of the basic components of signaling pathways in evolution.

---

## INTRODUCTION AND PERSPECTIVES

The study of liver development is currently in a state of flux. The cell lineages giving rise to the organ and accompanying changes in tissue morphology were initially defined by classical histology and tissue explant studies nearly thirty years ago (60). Over the past ten years, the application of molecular biology techniques has revealed a host of transcription factors important for adult liver differentiation, as assessed by the factors' enrichment in liver and ability to activate genes in differentiated hepatocytes (129). The classical and molecular approaches are now being joined by reverse genetics, whereby genes encoding regulatory proteins are inactivated in transgenic mice to assess the consequences on liver development. The results have been quite surprising; mutations of proteins identified by their roles in adult hepatocyte differentiation are found to affect the development of various non-hepatic tissues, whereas mutations of proteins expressed in many different adult cell types are found to perturb liver development selectively. Taken together, the latest transgenic studies emphasize the roles of growth factors and signal transducers and the need to re-evaluate the roles of transcription factors causing liver-specific expression. This review critically examines these issues and attempts to syn-

231

0066-4278/96/0315-0231$08.00

thesize what is known from classical and molecular studies. In addition, comparisons are made with different organisms to highlight mechanisms that appear conserved in evolution.

Before we consider hepatic development in detail, it is worth pointing out why the liver has attracted so much attention as a model system, particularly from molecular biologists. In addition to its being an essential organ, the liver is, in several ways, similar to the most tractable systems for experimental molecular biology, i.e. *E. coli* and the yeast *S. cerevisiae*. The liver is composed predominantly of one cell type, the hepatocyte, which to a large extent exhibits phenotypic homogeneity similar to a clone of microbes. Like the single-celled organisms, hepatocytes express a wide array of functions in response to changing metabolic demands, implicating a need for diversity in genetic control. It is relatively easy to obtain large amounts of hepatocytes, thereby facilitating biochemical analysis, and as is true for microbial paradigms, there exists a rich history of classical genetic and physiological studies of the liver and liver-derived cell lines, providing a foundation for a mechanistic analysis of development.

A limitation of the study of hepatic development has been the lack of a precursor cell line that differentiates into hepatocytes in culture. By contrast, it is possible to induce certain fibroblast cell lines to differentiate into either adipocytes or muscle cells in vitro (37, 111). Despite cell heterogeneity in the differentiating cultures and the difficulty of studying non-dividing fat and muscle cells, the elucidation of relevant regulatory factors and signaling networks has refined our understanding of genetic control in these systems (115, 123). The ability of the adult liver to regenerate has led to an intensive search for a stem cell compartment in the organ. Recent cell marking and transplantation studies, however, provide strong evidence that after partial hepatectomy, hepatocytes themselves have considerable capacity to proliferate (30, 84). Nevertheless, during prolonged states of liver damage, such as during carcinogenesis or exposure to dietary toxins, small cells with ovoid nuclei, or "oval cells," can differentiate into hepatocytes (29, 96, 99, 100, 114). The lack of cloned oval cell lines has complicated lineage analysis, and a potential early developmental role for oval cells has not been addressed.

While the definitive hepatocyte precursor cell has remained elusive, much has been learned from studying well-differentiated hepatoma cell lines, their de-differentiated variants, and hepatoma-fibroblast cell hybrids (11, 35, 51). Indeed, understanding the signaling molecules and regulatory factors that cause the loss and restoration of the differentiated state in cell culture has been the significant driving force in the molecular genetic approach to liver development. The present-day ability to alter gene function at will, using transgenic mice (14), is allowing theories derived from cells in culture to be tested in vivo and brings the liver system one step closer to the most refined experimental models. The application of such genetic technology is still in its infancy, so we can anticipate that the future will bring advances in experimental approach as well as new biological insight into liver organogenesis.

## FORMATION OF THE DEFINITIVE ENDODERM

### Morphology

Examination of serial sections of embryos at different stages first revealed that hepatocytes in most vertebrates emanate from the definitive endoderm lining the developing gut (e.g. see 26).  Understanding early hepatic specification therefore requires understanding how the definitive endoderm is formed and how a particular region of the endoderm is programmed to give rise to hepatocytes. Considering that the endoderm also gives rise to components of the lung, pancreas, thyroid, and alimentary canal, the mechanism of hepatocyte formation is likely to involve the specification of hepatic characteristics as well as restrictive mechanisms that prevent the formation of other endodermal-derived structures. This positive and negative control is evident at the levels of cell signaling and gene regulation, as discussed below.

The definitive endoderm should not be confused with primitive endoderm of the early embryo, the latter giving rise to visceral endoderm of the yolk sac. Visceral endoderm is a secretory and digestive tissue (48) and produces many proteins in common with hepatocytes (113), but it remains extraembryonic and does not give rise to definitive gut endoderm or hepatocytes. However, it is interesting to note that several transcription factors enriched in liver, such as HNF1β and HNF4, are also enriched in the yolk sac (17, 24, 110), consistent with the expression of some of the same secretory and digestive proteins in both tissues (113).

During gastrulation of the embryo, the definitive endoderm germ layer is created, and the mesoderm and ectoderm germ layers are also established. Gastrulation occurs as the primitive streak forms along the midline from the posterior to the center of the epiblast, where Hensen's node arises, and is displaced anteriorly toward the presumptive head region. As these structures develop posterior to anterior, the flanking primitive ectoderm migrates into and then away from the midline, which results in the conversion of primitive ectoderm (or epiblast) into definitive ectoderm, mesoderm, and endoderm. Careful cell marking studies have established that these processes take place between 6.5 and 7.5 days' gestation in the mouse embryo (56, 79). Similar events occur in avian gastrulation (86, 94), whereas germ layer formation in amphibian development occurs as cells move through a blastopore (101).

### Molecular Control

Considering the complex tissue movements and coincident differentiation of the three germ layers, it is not surprising that a large number of regulatory proteins and growth factors are being discovered in the primitive streak and node in birds and mammals and around the blastopore in amphibia. Gene disruption studies have confirmed a role in germ layer development for secreted proteins, such as the TGFβ homologue nodal (132), and for factors such as goosecoid (9) and brachyury (39, 125), which act by unknown mechanisms. Unfortunately, no gene has been shown to be required for the formation of the definitive endoderm.

One explanation for the lack of discovery of genes that control endoderm formation is that such genes may also be involved in the earlier or simultaneous development of other germ layers; thus mutation of the genes may not yield a prominent endoderm-deficient phenotype. For example, consider the gene for transcription factor *HNF3β*, which is expressed in the primitive streak and node in the mouse (3, 68, 89, 91); and the HNF3 homologues XFKH1 and *pintallavis* in *Xenopus* (22, 90), and *axial* in zebrafish (106), which are expressed in the blastopore lip and in the midline of the gastrula, respectively. After gastrulation in the mouse, *HNF3β* expression persists in the notochord, neural tube floor plate, and endoderm; i.e. in portions of all three germ layers (3, 68, 89, 91). In the adult, HNF3 is expressed in the liver, lung, and other endoderm-derived tissues, where the factor activates particular target genes (53, 54). Homozygous deletion of the *HNF3β* gene is embryonically lethal, apparently due to defects in the node and the absence of a neural tube (2, 122). Some endoderm cells do form in *HNF3β* mutants; however, they remain on the outside of the head region and fail to proliferate or invaginate to form a gut. Thus, whereas *HNF3β* is not necessary for the initial specification of endoderm cells, it may be necessary for their further development. To prove this hypothesis it will be necessary to create mice in which *HNF3β* function is selectively deleted in the endoderm germ layer.

Genetic studies in *Drosophila melanogaster* provide clear evidence for the ability of proteins related to HNF3 to control gut development. *Drosophila* embryos express a protein called fork head, which is similar in size and structure to HNF3 (120). HNF3 and fork head are 90% identical in amino acid sequence over their DNA-binding domains, and fork head is expressed in the anterior and posterior gut of the fly (121), similar to HNF3 expression in mammalian gut endoderm. Mutations of fork head block the formation of the foregut and hindgut (121), which is more extreme in phenotype than the failure of the foregut to invaginate in *HNF3β* homozygous mutants. Furthermore, as described above, in the mammalian case the gut defect could be a secondary consequence of perturbations of the mesodermal and ectodermal components, whereas in the fly, the *fork head* mutant phenotype appears selective for the gut. However, additional complexity in mammals is indicated by the existence of two other HNF3 family members, HNF3α and HNF3γ (53, 54). HNF3α is first expressed slightly later than HNF3β in gastrulation (3, 68, 89, 91) but in similar tissues, whereas HNF3γ is first expressed in the early liver and more posterior endoderm, after the gut has formed (68). Recent genetic studies have shown that homozygous disruption of the *HNF3γ* gene has no discernible effect on mouse development, whereas *HNF3α* gene disruption is perinatal lethal, apparently due to defects in induction of metabolic genes in the liver (K Kaestner & G Schütz, personal communication). The more severe phenotype of the *HNF3β* mutation shows that the proteins have critical non-overlapping functions. However, the ability of at least HNF3α and HNFβ to bind and *trans*-activate identical target genes (54) means that in some contexts their functions may be redundant. Thus experimental inactivation of both *HNF3α* and *HNF3β* genes selectively in the early endoderm may be necessary to definitively establish a role for this class of proteins in mammalian gut development. For example, homozygous inactivation of either the *MyoD* or *Myf-5* genes in mice has modest effects on skeletal muscle development, but simultaneous inactivation of both genes blocks skeletal muscle formation (87).

Even if *HNF3α* and *HNF3β* together turn out to be nonessential for endoderm development, understanding the extracellular signals and responsive factors causing early HNF3 expression should provide insight into the establishment of the endoderm. Transcription factors activating the HNF3β promoter in adult liver include a newly discovered protein, about which little is known, and HNF3β itself (74). Thus it appears that once the *HNF3β* gene is activated, the gene product helps maintain its own synthesis. Secretion of the protein sonic hedgehog (shh) by the notochord can induce *HNF3β* expression in the adjacent neural tube floor plate (25). Although *shh* is expressed in the definitive endoderm (25), its function there has not been investigated. As discussed below, *shh* may be important for endodermal-mesenchymal interactions occurring later in development.

Another approach to understanding regulators of HNF3 expression in the endoderm is the identification of mammalian counterparts to genes that control *fork head* in *Drosophila*. The powerful genetics of the fly system has unveiled several regulators of *fork head* expression, including *tailless* (78), an orphan nuclear receptor, and the zinc-finger transcription factors *trithorax* (52) and *huckebein* (12), the latter of which is in the Spl/egr family. A mouse homologue of *tailless* was recently cloned but unfortunately found not to be expressed in the endoderm lineage (67), a result that illustrates the lack of strong predictability of the approach. However, considering the fundamental nature of gut development among all metazoans, it would be surprising if there were not some correspondence between the early regulators across different phyla.

It is important to note that most experimental studies of early germ layer development have focused on mesoderm induction and early neural patterning. Consequently, little is known about molecules that control the formation of early endoderm. Therefore, endoderm development is a rich field waiting to be investigated.

## DEVELOPMENT OF HEPATIC PRIMORDIA

### Tissue Movements and Early Gene Expression

The dearth of experimental studies on endoderm germ layer formation is to some extent compensated for by the considerable amount of work done on endoderm cell differentiation. Indeed, early liver development was one of the original experimental systems for studying vertebrate organogenesis. The major conclusion to be drawn from the pioneering work of Le Douarin and colleagues twenty to thirty years ago is that there is a series of inductive interactions between the endoderm and flanking mesoderm, or mesenchyme, that sequentially restrict and specify developmental fates of both tissues, thus forming the liver parenchyma and its associated vasculature. Virtually all of the definitive work in this area was performed on chick embryos (57–60), and recent studies on the mouse seem to confirm the basic principles (41).

Hepatocytes develop from endoderm of the ventral foregut. The foregut itself is formed by an invagination of the ventral surface of the head fold region, after the head process extends anterior to the node in germ layer formation (88, 112). The resulting cavity within the head fold forms the foregut pocket and is lined with a single cell layer of endoderm. Simultaneously, at about 7.5 to 8 days' gestation in the mouse, an invagination of the posterior region of the embryo forms the hindgut. The developing heart then appears as a protrusion from the ventral wall of the foregut, at about 8.5 days' gestation, forming what appears to be a lobe of tissue beneath the head folds. Between 8.5 and 9 days' gestation, a region of the foregut endoderm adjacent to the cardiac mesenchyme begins to proliferate; these cells will ultimately give rise to the liver. Endoderm defining both the foregut and hindgut moves toward the midsection of the embryo, at 9 to 9.5 days. By 9.5 days, movement of the foregut toward the midsection brings the presumptive hepatic endoderm away from direct contact with the cardiac mesenchyme. Cells of the hepatic endoderm then begin to migrate in a cord-like fashion into the surrounding mesenchyme of the septum transversum. There the cords intermingle with the vitelline veins, which themselves begin to anastomose into a venous bed where the liver begins to form.

The initial differentiation of hepatocytes clearly occurs during the aforementioned stages, prior to the formation of the liver organ. Indirect immunofluorescence and in situ hybridization studies of α-fetoprotein (AFP), a fetal liver marker, have shown that AFP is first expressed in the presumptive hepatic endoderm as the cells proliferate, at about 9 days' gestation in the mouse (98,

99). Albumin mRNA, another liver marker, becomes detectable when the cells begin to migrate into the septum transversum (16, 92, 99). Also, when the hepatic endoderm region is removed from the embryo at such stages and cultured in the presence of the appropriate hormones, urea cycle enzymes specific to hepatocytes are induced (124). Thus we can conclude that hepatic differentiation begins at this early phase of liver development, well before the structure of the organ is defined.

## Endodermal-Mesenchymal Interactions

What are the tissue interactions and inductive events that commit a particular region of endoderm to become hepatocytes? What additional inductive processes occur as the hepatic endoderm migrates into the septum transversum? Answers to these questions come from experiments in which chick embryo tissues were excised and either transplanted to other regions of the embryo or cultured in vitro under different conditions. The ability to perform transplantations on living embryos has made the chick the experimental system of choice for studies of early organogenesis.

## Determination of Hepatic Endoderm

Discovering the stage at which endoderm gains the potential to become hepatocytes, or is determined, required the creation of a transplantation system for assaying developmental potency. Le Douarin showed that if an obstacle was placed between anterior hepatic endoderm and the more posterior, lateral plate mesenchyme of a 12 somite chick embryo, the posterior mesenchyme would develop into a lobe of liver-like tissue containing endothelial cells but devoid of hepatic parenchyma (58, 60). The same would occur if a patch of tissue was removed between anterior endoderm and posterior mesenchyme (60). When presumptive hepatic endoderm from slightly earlier stage embryos was transplanted to the "empty" mesenchyme lobe of chick embryos at 12 somites, the endoderm would invade the mesenchyme and grow to form a chimeric lobe of liver. However, anterior endoderm from the much earlier head process stage failed to develop upon transplantation; thus the endoderm was not yet determined. Similar negative results were obtained with endoderm from the head fold to 4 somite stages. Endoderm from the foregut pocket at 5–6 somite stages (corresponding to about day 8 to 8.5 of mouse gestation), which had been in contact with cardiac mesenchyme, successfully developed into hepatic parenchyma after transplantation. Le Douarin therefore concluded that hepatic determination takes place at about the 5 somite stage in the chick. Similar results were obtained by Fukuda with quail embryos (33).

One of the potential difficulties in interpreting all such transplantation experiments requiring tissue outgrowth is that the transplanted cells may have particular growth requirements not supplied by their new environment. There-fore, the failure to observe development may be due to insufficient growth signals that may be secondary to cell type determination. As described in further detail below, liver development may require different growth factors at different stages.

In addition, early assays for hepatic development were primarily morpho-logical, e.g. by observing the formation of a lobe of liver tissue or a differen-tiated histological appearance such as the accumulation of glycogen granules. Thus the assays depended on relatively advanced cell type differentiation with requirements that could be far more complex than those required solely for determination or the early steps of differentiation. Consequently, negative results from tissue interactions in the early transplantation studies should be viewed with caution because they may have missed potential inductive capaci-ties. It would be interesting to see the transplantation studies repeated today using sensitive detection systems, such as RT-PCR, to study early markers of hepatic cell commitment, such as AFP and albumin, and with culture systems that do not require outgrowth of transplanted (or explanted) tissue.

With the aforementioned caveats in mind, the transplantation studies of Le Douarin (60) and Fukuda-Taira (34) suggest that different areas of mesoderm have different inductive capacities. For example, while anterior endoderm from the head process and head fold stages failed to develop upon transplantation, it would develop into a liver lobe if transplanted along with the associated "pre-cardiac" mesenchymes (34, 59, 60). By contrast, transplantation of pos-terior mesenchyme from early-stage embryos failed to support hepatogenesis (34, 60). This situation is reminiscent of the control of endoderm differentiation in *Drosophila*, where genetic studies have shown that the expression of par-ticular homeobox-containing regulatory proteins in different regions of the mesoderm, under the influence of *Ubx*, confers the ability to induce endoderm to develop into different gut tissues (19). Some of the downstream targets of the homeobox proteins in mesoderm have been identified, and as expected, they encode secreted signaling molecules. Examples include decapentaplegic (*dpp*), a TGFβ-like factor (72); and wingless (wg), a homologue of the secreted *int-1* proto-oncogene (85). Dpp and wg are expressed in the middle and pos-terior constrictions, respectively of the fly midgut mesoderm (73, 85), with dpp inducing the homeobox protein labial (lab) in the adjacent endoderm of the middle constriction (42, 73, 83). Lab is hypothesized to induce genes encoding digestive enzymes specific to that portion of the gut. Thus the fly system provides genetic evidence for regional specification of mesoderm and reveals how a regulatory cascade endows a segment of mesoderm with distinct inductive capacities.

In the chick there may also be specialization of the endoderm with regard to its potential to respond to cardiac mesenchyme. At the head process stage, the responsive endoderm maps to a relatively broad region anterior to the node, but not posterior (34, 60). Interestingly, HNF3$\alpha$ and HNF3$\beta$ are expressed in the same anterior region in the mouse embryo (3, 68, 89, 91); thus one or both of these proteins might induce genes in endoderm that cause responsiveness to the mesenchyme. According to transplantation studies, as development proceeds the zone of responsive endoderm shrinks from a wide lateral area at the head fold stage to the narrow medial region of the foregut pocket, by the early somite stages (60). Clearly, the broad zone of responsive endoderm at early stages must have the potential to differentiate into a wide variety of tissue types, not just liver, and the fraction of cells in the transplants giving rise to hepatocytes is not known. Thus it is unclear whether heterogeneity exists in the endodermal cell population or if all cells in the responsive endodermal region are similarly pluripotent.

## Molecular Signaling Mechanisms and Genetic Control

One explanation for the reduction in the relative amount of endoderm responsive to cardiac mesenchyme, as development proceeds, is that lateral endodermal cells capable of giving rise to liver either migrate to or are selectively taken up into the foregut region as the embryo grows. Another possibility is that hepatic determination may involve restriction in developmental potential. That is, initially pluripotent endoderm may be subject to inhibitory signals that successively restrict developmental fates. By this theory, exposure to the inappropriate mesenchyme in the transplantation experiments might actively inhibit hepatocyte formation rather than fail to induce it. Although this is an extreme view of the role of restriction, it seems likely that both restriction and induction contribute to cell type determination. An example of a restrictive mechanism is DNA methylation, which can be inhibitory to gene activation (7). Indeed, recent studies have shown that at the blastocyst stage apparently the entire mammalian genome becomes demethylated and then specific DNA sequences become methylated (50). Thus one model to explain the reduction in responsive endoderm is that DNA methylase activity is either stimulated in lateral endoderm or inhibited in medial endoderm.

How are signals sent and received between the endoderm and cardiac mesenchyme? Interposition of filter barriers between the two tissues failed to inhibit hepatic induction in tissue explants (58), which suggests the presence of a diffusible signal, but later studies using electron microscopy showed that cell processes extended through the filter (60). Presently it appears that hepatic induction requires either direct cell contact between the endoderm and mesenchyme cells or exposure to a product secreted by the cardiac mesenchyme that has limited potential for diffusion. Excellent candidates for the latter would be extracellular matrix proteins or growth factors that are sequestered locally by the extracellular matrix. For example, it is well known that collagens (6, 21, 27, 65) and other extracellular matrix proteins (8, 15) strongly stimulate adult hepatocyte differentiation. Acidic fibroblast growth factor (aFGF), which is secreted into the extracellular matrix and retained there (20), appears to be important for organogenesis in a variety of systems. In fact, aFGF is expressed at high levels early in cardiac development (66), and an aFGF receptor is expressed throughout the definitive endoderm (75, 104). Therefore it seems feasible that FGF signaling from cardiac mesoderm to the endoderm plays a role in early hepatic specification. The definitive endoderm also expresses sonic hedgehog (shh) mRNA (25), which encodes a secreted protein important for the development of limb buds and the central nervous system (76). Shh secretion by the endoderm could influence the flanking mesenchyme during organogenesis; the mesenchyme ultimately gives rise to endothelial cells in the liver. Indeed, an interplay between shh and FGF secretion defines a signaling network that is thought to control limb bud development (55, 71).

In sum, the serendipitous discoveries of well-known signaling molecules and receptors in and around the definitive endoderm may provide clues about the mechanism of hepatic determination. The selective inactivation of these proteins in the relevant cell lineages will be required to test function. As a successful example of this approach, transgenic mice expressing a dominant-negative FGF receptor in early lung epithelium were severely impaired for branching morphogenesis and differentiation of that tissue, thereby establishing a role for FGF signaling in lung development (77).

A host of growth factors has been shown to play a role in normal liver growth and regeneration (30), and it seems likely that at least some of the factors will play a role in early hepatic specification. The hypothesis that growth factors are important for specification is attractive because, as described above, the first morphological differentiation of hepatic endoderm is an increase in proliferation. The expression of AFP and albumin in this rapidly expanding cell population suggests that proliferation and differentiation are not incompatible at this stage of development. Therefore, it seems feasible that the growth factor requirements of hepatic primordia may be intrinsic to the process of cell type specification. Mechanistically, this could occur by activating intracellular signaling cascades that induce new groups of regulatory proteins or by increasing the frequency of DNA replication and hence chromatin remodeling, during which time existing regulatory proteins could gain access to DNA.

Regardless of the particular signaling molecules involved, their binding must lead to changes in transcriptional potential. In this regard, note that the levels of HNF3α and HNF3β mRNA are particularly high in the presumptive hepatic endoderm of 8.5 day mouse embryos (3). Thus elevated HNF3 concentration and increased binding to target genes could help potentiate gene activation as other developmental signals come into play. The strong similarity between the structure of the HNF3 DNA-binding domain and the structure of linker histone molecules (18) and the ability of HNF3-like proteins to help organize nucleosome position (64) suggest that potentiation of gene activity by HNF3 could occur at the level of chromatin organization. By this model, hepatic determination could involve the reorganization or disruption of nucleosomes at specific target genes. Such nucleosomal changes could readily affect the ability of other transcription factors to bind DNA, as has recently been demonstrated with in vitro studies of mononucleosome particles (1). Other chromatin-based mechanisms for regulating gene access include DNA methylation, as mentioned above, and the activities of locus control regions and nuclear matrix attachment sites (31). Thus the developmental sequence of induction of transcription factors could reflect their hierarchical function in a chromatin context, and hepatic determination at the level of the gene could involve a reorganization of chromatin components that permit or deny other factors access to the DNA.

Another transcription factor induced in the hepatic endoderm and enriched in adult liver tissue is HNF4 (24, 102, 110). HNF4 binds and activates numerous liver-specific genes but is also expressed in intestine and kidney of the adult (102). Thus the adult pattern of expression of HNF4 is not restricted to endoderm-derived tissues, in contrast to the case for HNF3 proteins. HNF4 is also expressed in the visceral endoderm of the yolk sac (24, 110), a non-embryonic tissue, where it is likely to induce secreted proteins that nourish the growing embryo. The importance of HNF4 in the visceral endoderm is underscored by the phenotype of embryos containing a homozygous, targeted disruption of the HNF4 gene: Gastrulation is severely impaired, and the primitive embryonic ectoderm, which gives rise to the other germ layers, dies out. Because HNF4 is not expressed in the epiblast (primitive ectoderm) at this stage, the embryonic-lethal defect is apparently due to lack of proper function of the yolk sac. In any event, as with the early lethality of the HNF3β gene disruption (2, 122), the HNF4 mutant phenotype prevents a direct assessment of the role of the factor when it is induced in early liver development. Understanding HNF4 function in hepatogenesis will require making transgenic mice that selectively inactivate the protein in the definitive endoderm.

Perhaps the most provocative aspect of HNF4 expression in the hepatic endoderm relates to the structure of the protein itself. HNF4 is a member of the nuclear receptor superfamily of transcription factors (102) and contains an extended carboxy-terminal domain that is clearly homologous to amino acid sequences in receptors for steroids, retinoic acid, and other signaling molecules (28). However, because HNF4 is active when transfected into a variety of cells in the absence of added or known ligand, it is designated an orphan receptor and may function without a ligand (102). Of course, the transformed cell lines in which HNF4 has been tested may fortuitously express a relevant ligand. It is interesting to speculate that during development HNF4 may be activated by either a paracrine factor secreted by cardiac mesenchymal cells or by an autocrine factor produced by the replicating hepatic endoderm. With this model, identifying a ligand for HNF4 protein may shed light on signaling that controls early hepatic specification. Similarly, understanding how the HNF4 gene is turned on, as well as genes for early hepatic differentiation markers, such as AFP and albumin, is certain to provide essential clues.

Like the *fork head* homologue of HNF3, the existence of a recently discovered HNF4 homologue, HNF4(D), expressed in *Drosophila*, illustrates the high degree of evolutionary conservation of developmental control proteins (131). HNF4(D) is expressed in the fat body, midgut, and Malpighian tubules of the fly embryo, analogous to the expression of HNF4 in the mammalian liver, intestine, and kidney, and a deletion spanning the HNF4(D) locus causes developmental defects in the larval tissues (131). The creation of cells and tissues specialized for digestion and metabolism are the defining feature of metazoans; thus we can expect to find additional examples of factors involved in hepatic specification that are fundamentally conserved across the animal kingdom. Perhaps variations in such mechanisms give rise to other tissues derived from gut endoderm.

Gene disruption studies have shown that transcription factors can function in different tissue types and at different developmental stages. Although this may reflect the need to induce the same target genes in the different contexts, it more likely illustrates the combinatorial principle of gene control; i.e. it is more efficient to regulate many genes with a relatively small number of transcription factors used in different combinations than it is with the many more factors required if each factor separately regulated or defined each genetic context (127). Both the diverse embryonic expression patterns and the genetic inactivation studies confirm the combinatorial model for the known transcription factors enriched in adult liver. There does not appear to be a single regulatory factor that specifies the hepatocyte; a combination of factors, perhaps including some to be discovered, seem to define the cell type.

## MORPHOGENESIS OF THE LIVER

### Secondary Inductive Events During Organ Formation

As cords of hepatic primordia migrate from the gut endoderm into the septum transversum, they come in contact with collagenous strands of the mesenchyme and into the proximity of the sparse cells of the new environment (16). Thus the early hepatocytes are exposed to a new extracellular matrix and, potentially, new diffusible signaling proteins from the mesenchymal cells. Cell explant and transplant studies showed that outgrowth and differentiation of hepatic endoderm requires a supporting mesenchymal environment, constituting a second step of hepatic induction (41, 58, 60). All derivatives of lateral plate mesoderm were able to support hepatic outgrowth, whereas head and dorsal trunk mesenchyme were not. As described above, these kinds of studies failed to distinguish between effects on growth and differentiation. Regardless of the complexity of the relevant signals and their integration with one another, the tissue transfer studies made clear the importance of secondary interactions with mesenchyme.

Shortly after the hepatic primordia invade the septum transversum, the endothelial layer around the vitelline veins thickens and begins to develop vascular spaces (44). It has been hypothesized that at this stage the early hepatocytes counter-induce the surrounding mesenchyme, stimulating it to develop into the supporting framework of the liver (57). Although this concept is attactive, it is noteworthy that in manipulated embryos the presumptive hepatic (lateral plate) mesenchyme can develop into a liver lobe-like structure in the absence of hepatic parenchyma (60; and see discussion above). The early hepatocytes have also been postulated to have an inductive effect on endothelial cells because at this stage, the nearby vitelline veins branch extensively and form a capillary bed (23, 97). Continued anastomosis of the hepatic cords and blood vessels eventually leads to the formation of the liver sinusoids. The connection of cells between the developing liver and the gut tube then decreases, while the adjacent posterior endoderm develops into the bile duct and gall bladder. The early morphogenesis of the liver occurs very rapidly; by 10.5 days' gestation in the mouse, one day after the hepatic cords invade the mesenchyme, the liver is a discernable structure. Another day later the liver vasculature has matured sufficiently so that hematopoietic cells begin to migrate there, apparently from the yolk sac (45). During this time, the size of the liver multiplies several-fold, and the hepatocytes begin to express many new enzymes and secretory proteins required for its function.

## Control of Organogenesis

Despite the number of liver transcription factors shown by gene targeting studies to be important for non-liver tissues, a growing number of investigators are finding highly specific liver developmental defects when genes for non-hepatic regulatory proteins are inactivated. Also, expression of the unusually diverse array of liver metabolic enzymes and secreted products may require an unusually large number of both liver-enriched and ubiquitous regulatory factors. In any event, as described below, we are gaining considerable insight into the signaling pathways required for liver organogenesis from fortuitous discoveries in other areas; what goes around, comes around.

For example, the c-*jun* proto-oncogene is a component of the transcription factor AP-1 and is expressed in a variety of cell types (82). C-jun protein heterodimerizes with c-fos or fos-related proteins to form the AP-1 complex, and AP-1 activates genes in many cells in direct response to protein kinase C (4, 61). Homozygous inactivation of the c-*jun* gene results in severe hypoplasia of hepatic parenchyma, causing embryonic mortality (40). Hepatocytes do form in c-*jun* homozygotes, but they fail to proliferate sufficiently. The growth defect is intrinsic to hepatocytes because in chimeric mice, c-*jun* homozygous mutant cells failed to populate the liver (40). Inactivation of the c-*fos* gene has no effect on liver development (47, 119); so the critical c-*jun* partner in liver development must be a different *fos* family member. These studies show that a form of AP-1 is essential for expansion of the hepatic parenchyma and thus may implicate the protein kinase C signal pathway in liver growth.

Hepatocyte growth factor (HGF), also known as scatter factor, stimulates growth and migration of a variety of cell types and may be important for various mesenchymal-epithelial interactions in development (38, 130). While the growth stimulatory properties of HGF on hepatocytes have been known for some time (130), morphogenic effects have been observed with in vitro developmental systems for studying kidney tubule epithelia, the nervous system, and angiogenesis (13, 36, 69, 105, 107). Homozygous inactivation of the HGF gene has recently been found to affect none of the latter processes, but like the c-*jun* mutation, it causes hypoplasia of the hepatic parenchyma (93). In addition, the development of trophoblast cells of the placenta is impaired (93, 117). The liver defect of the HGF mutants is manifest several days later than is seen with the c-*jun* mutants, which is consistent with the time of maximal expression of HGF in hepatic sinusoidal cells derived from the mesenchyme (103). The HGF receptor c-met is expressed by hepatocytes, and upon HGF binding it activates an intracellular signaling pathway (10, 70). In sum, hepatic proliferation may be sustained first by a signal involving the protein kinase C pathway and c-jun, followed by HGF triggering of c-met. Of course, the involvement of other signals is not excluded.

Several other genes expressed in many different cell types have now been shown to affect liver development, albeit less dramatically than c-*jun* and HGF. Inactivation of the RXRα gene, which encodes a nuclear receptor that binds 9-*cis* retinoic acid, retards liver development but without visible morphological abnormalities (108). Inactivation of the retinoblastoma (RB) tumor suppressor gene leads to impaired erythropoiesis in the embryo (43), apparently due to a defect in the hepatocyte environment (K MacLeod & T Jacks, personal communication). In addition, RB$^-$ hepatocytes have unusually large nuclei (126). Inactivation of the gene encoding the p65/relA subunit of the transcription factor NF-κB is embryonically lethal, apparently due to apoptosis of hepatocytes at days 15–16 of mouse gestation (5). Thus the normal function of p65 in this context may be to either promote hepatocyte growth or block competing apoptotic signals.

## Gene Controlling Liver Maturation at Birth

Just prior to birth and shortly thereafter a large number of liver metabolic enzymes are induced. This dramatic change allows the neonate to properly manage nutrients taken up from the diet. Not unexpectedly, numerous transcription factors are induced perinatally. One example is C/EBPα, the first leucine zipper protein to be discovered. It is highly enriched in adult liver and adipose tissue and binds and activates numerous liver- and fat-specific genes involved in carbohydrate and lipid metabolism (32, 46, 62, 128). Inactivation of the C/EBPα gene causes postnatal lethality, apparently due to impaired induction of enzymes that control energy homeostasis in liver and brown fat (118). A related protein, C/EBPβ, binds and regulates liver-specific genes during the acute phase response to infection (80). Inactivation of the C/EBPβ gene does not affect liver development but does cause increased sensitivity to pathogens, possibly due in part to the failure to maintain acute-phase gene expression (95, 109). Although C/EBPα and C/EBPβ recognize virtually identical DNA sequences (46), the different effects of their mutation indicate that the genetic context of their binding sites dictates where they will function.

The transcription factor HNF1α, a member of the homeobox family, is enriched in adult liver and kidney and induced in the mouse liver at day 10 of gestation (116a). Transient transfection assays showed a critical role for HNF1α in binding and activating many liver-specific genes (116). Also, the presence of HNF1α, but not the closely related protein HNF1β (vHNF1), was associated with the differentiated phenotype in cultured hepatoma cells (116). Thus it was quite surprising to discover that inactivation of the HNF1α gene has no early developmental effect on the liver. Rather, the HNF1α- mice are born apparently normal but then fail to grow properly, and most animals die within the first month or two of life (M Pontiglio et al, personal communication). The primary defect appears to be insufficient glucose resorption in the kidney, causing a wasting syndrome. Compensation by HNF1β could explain the lack of an embryo liver phenotype; HNFβ binds HNF1α sites and is expressed in early development (17). Inactivation of both genes will be required to resolve the issue of redundancy.

# FUTURE STUDIES

The direct study of liver-enriched regulatory factors and fortuitous discoveries of more generally expressed proteins is providing clues about cell signaling and genetic control in liver development. It seems clear that we are obtaining only an initial glimpse of the complexity involved, as the relevant molecules discovered so far fall in quite different regulatory pathways. Three approaches to the identification of additional proteins that control early liver development can be envisaged. The first, as was done with HGF, would be to analyze the developmental role of additional proteins implicated in hepatic regeneration, because the mechanism of regeneration may recapitulate part of what occurs during development. Second, as was done with fork head and HNF4(D), would be to examine the activities of additional homologues of endoderm developmental factors found in other experimentally tractable systems such as *Drosophila* and *Xenopus*. Third, a differential screen to isolate cDNAs expressed specifically in the hepatic primordia might provide an unbiased approach toward identifying relevant regulators and signaling pathways.

Understanding the molecular mechanisms involved in early liver development will provide insight into growth control, gene activation, organ morphogenesis, and hepatic regeneration. Discovering such mechanisms will eventually lead to the ability to manipulate hepatogenesis in disease states and understand how to prevent liver damage in the healthy. It is likely that some of the regulatory proteins described here will be among the first targets for developing therapies and preventatives. In addition, the conservation of the proteins' functions in different organisms suggests that they will provide clues to understanding more about the development of the liver and of other tissues emanating from the gut endoderm.

ACKNOWLEDGMENTS

The author wishes to thank John Coleman, Angela Grant, Rossana Gualdi, and José Lora for comments on the manuscript and Susan Sage for help in its preparation. Support has been provided by the National Institutes of Health.

## Literature Cited

1.  Adams CC, Workman JL. 1995. Binding of disparate transcriptional activators to nucleosomal DNA is inherently cooperative. *Mol. Cell. Biol.* 15:1405–21
2.  Ang S-L, Rossant J. 1994. *HNF-3β* is essential for node and notochord formation in mouse development. *Cell* 78: 561–74
3.  Ang S-L, Wierda A, Wong D, Stevens KA, Cascio S, et al. 1993. The formation and maintenance of the definitive endoderm lineage in the mouse: involvement of HNF3/*fork head* proteins. *Development* 119:1301–15
4.  Angel P, Imagawa M, Chiu R, Stein B, Imbra RJ, et al. 1987. Phorbol ester-inducible genes contain a common

*cis* element recognized by a TPA-modulated *trans*-acting factor. *Cell* 49:729–39

4a. Arias IM, Boyer RL, Fausto N, Jakoby WB, Schachter DA, Shafritz DA, eds. 1994. *The Liver: Biology and Pathobiology.* New York: Raven. 1628 pp.

5. Beg AA, Sha WC, Bronson RT, Ghosh S, Baltimore D. 1995. Embryonic lethality and liver degeneration in mice lacking the RelA component of NF-κB. *Nature* 376:167–70

6. Ben-Ze'ev A, Robinson GS, Bucher NLR, Farmer SR. 1988. Cell-cell and cell-matrix interactions differentially regulate the expression of hepatic and cytoskeletal genes in primary cultures of rat hepatocytes. *Proc. Natl. Acad. Sci. USA* 85:2161–65

7. Bird A. 1992. The essentials of DNA methylation. *Cell* 70:5–8

8. Bissell DM, Caron JM, Babiss LE, Friedman JM. 1990. Transcriptional regulation of the albumin gene in cultured rat hepatocytes: role of basement membrane matrix. *Mol. Biol. Med.* 7: 187–97

9. Blum M, Gaunt SJ, Cho KWY, Steinbeisser H, Blumberg B, et al. 1992. Gastrulation in the mouse: the role of the homeobox gene goosecoid. *Cell* 69: 1097–106

10. Bottaro DP, Rubin JS, Faletto DL, Chan AM-L, Kmiecik TE, et al. 1991. Identification of the hepatocyte growth factor receptor as the *c-met* proto-oncogene product. *Science* 251:802

11. Brown JE, Weiss MC. 1975. Activation of production of mouse liver enzymes in rat hepatoma-mouse lymphoid cell hybrids. *Cell* 6:481–94

12. Brönner G, Chu-LaGraff Q, Doe CQ, Cohen B, Weigel D, et al. 1994. Sp1/egr-like zinc-finger protein required for endoderm specification and germ-layer formation in *Drosophila. Nature* 369: 664–68

13. Bussolino F, Di Renzo MF, Ziche M, Bocchietto E, Olivero M, et al. 1992. Hepatocyte growth factor is a potent angiogenic factor which stimulates endothelial cell motility and growth. *J. Cell Biol.* 119:629–41

14. Capecchi MR. 1989. Altering the genome by homologous recombination. *Science* 244:1288–92

15. Caron JM. 1990. Induction of albumin gene transcription in hepatocytes by extracellular matrix proteins. *Mol. Cell. Biol.* 10:1239–43

16. Cascio S, Zaret KS. 1991. Hepatocyte differentiation initiates during endodermal-mesenchymal interactions prior to

liver formation. *Development* 113:217–25

17. Cereghini S, Ott M, Power S, Maury M. 1992. Expression patterns of vHNF1 and HNF1 homeoproteins in early postimplantation embryos suggest distinct and sequential developmental roles. *Development* 116:783–97

18. Clark KL, Halay ED, Lao E, Burley SK. 1993. Co-crystal structure of the HNF3/*fork head* DNA recognition motif resembles histone H5. *Nature* 364:412–20

19. Crabtree GR, Schibler U, Scott MP. 1992. Transcriptional regulatory mechanisms in liver and midgut morphogenesis of vertebrates and invertebrates. In *Transcriptional Regulation,* 40:1063–75. Cold Spring Harbor, NY: Cold Spring Harbor Lab. Press

20. Delli-Bovi P, Curatola AM, Newman KM, Sato Y, Moscatelli D, et al. 1988. Processing, secretion, and biological properties of a novel growth factor of the fibroblast growth factor family with oncogenic potential. *Mol. Cell. Biol.* 8: 2933–41

21. DiPersio CM, Jackson DA, Zaret KS. 1991. The extracellular matrix coordinately modulates liver transcription factors and hepatocyte morphology. *Mol. Cell. Biol.* 11:4405–14

22. Dirksen ML, Jamrich M. 1992. A novel, activin-inducible, blastopore lip-specific gene of *Xenopus laevis* contains a *fork head* DNA-binding domain. *Genes Dev.* 6:599–608

23. Du Bois AM. 1963. The embryonic liver. In *The Liver,* ed. CH Rouiller, 1:1–39. New York: Academic

24. Duncan SA, Manova K, Chen WS, Hoodless P, Weinstein DC, et al. 1994. Expression of transcription factor HNF-4 in the extraembryonic endoderm, gut, and nephrogenic tissue of the developing mouse embryo: HNF-4 is a marker for primary endoderm in the implanting blastocyst. *Proc. Natl. Acad. Sci. USA* 91:7598–602

25. Echelard Y, Epstein DJ, St-Jacques B, Shen L, Mohler J, et al. 1993. Sonic hedgehog, a member of a family of putative signaling molecules, is implicated in the regulation of CNS polarity. *Cell* 75:1417–30

26. Elias H. 1955. Origin and early development of the liver in various vertebrates. *Acta Hepatol.* 3:1–57

27. Enat R, Jefferson DM, Ruiz-Opazo N, Gatmaitan Z, Leinwand LA, Reid LM. 1984. Hepatocyte proliferation in vitro: its dependence on the use of serum-free, hormonally defined medium and sub-

strata of extracellular matrix. *Proc. Natl. Acad. Sci USA.* 81:1411–15

28. Evans RM. 1988. The steriod and thyroid hormone receptor superfamily. *Science* 240:889–95

29. Farber E. 1956. Similarities in the sequence of early histological changes induced in the liver of the rat by ethionine, 2-acetylaminofluorence, and 3'-methyl-4-dimethylaminoazobenzene. *Cancer Res.* 16:142–48

30. Fausto N, Webber EM. 1994. Liver regeneration. See Ref. 4a, pp. 1059–74

31. Felsenfeld G. 1992. Chromatin as an essential part of the transcriptional mechanism. *Nature* 355:219

32. Freytag SO, Paielli DL, Gilbert JD. 1994. Ectopic expression of the CCAAT/enhancer-binding protein α promotes the adipogenic program in a variety of mouse fibroblastic cells. *Genes Dev.* 8:1654–63

33. Fukuda S. 1979. The development of hepatogenic potency in the endoderm of quail embryos. *J. Embryol. Exp. Morphol.* 52:49–62

34. Fukuda-Taira S. 1981. Hepatic induction in the avian embryo: specificity of reactive endoderm and inductive mesoderm. *J. Embryol. Exp. Morphol.* 63:111–25

35. Gourdeau H, Fournier REK. 1990. Genetic analysis of mammalian cell differentiation. *Annu. Rev. Cell Biol.* 6:69–94

36. Grant DS, Kleinman HK, Goldberg ID, Bhargava MM, Nickoloff BJ, et al. 1993. Scatter factor induces blood vessel formation in vivo. *Proc. Natl. Acad. Sci. USA* 90:1937–41

37. Green H, Kehinde O. 1974. Sublines of mouse 3T3 cells that accumulate lipid. *Cell* 1:113–16

38. Gumbiner BM. 1992. Epithelial morphogenesis. *Cell* 69:385–87

39. Herrmann BG, Labeit S, Poustka A, King TR, Lebrach H. 1990. Cloning of the T gene required in mesoderm formation in the mouse. *Nature* 343:617

40. Hilberg F, Aguzzi A, Howells N, Wagner EF. 1993. c-Jun is essential for normal mouse development and hepatogenesis. *Nature* 365:179–81

41. Houssaint E. 1980. Differentiation of the mouse hepatic primordium. I. An analysis of tissue interactions in hepatocyte differentiation. *Cell Diff.* 9:269–79

42. Immerglöck K, Lawrence PA, Bienz M. 1990. Induction across germ layers in Drosophila mediated by a genetic cascade. *Cell* 62:261–68

43. Jacks T, Fazeli A, Schmitt EM, Bronson RT, Goodell MA, Weinberg RA. 1992.

Effects of an *Rb* mutation in the mouse. *Nature* 359:295–300

44. Johnson GR, Jones RO. 1975. Differentiation of the mammalian hepatic primordium in vitro. *J. Embryol. Exp. Morphol.* 30:83–96

45. Johnson GR, Moore MA. 1975. Role of stem cell migration in initiation of mouse foetal liver haemopoiesis. *Nature* 258:726–28

46. Johnson PF, Williams SC. 1994. CCAAT/enhancer binding (C/EBP) proteins. See Ref. 116a, Chpt. 12:

47. Johnson RS, Spiegelman BM, Papaioannou V. 1992. Pleiotropic effects of a null mutation in the c-*fos* proto-oncogene. *Cell* 71:577–86

48. Jollie WP. 1990. Development, morphology, and function of the yolk sac placenta of laboratory rodents. *Teratology* 41:361–81

49. Deleted in proof

50. Kafri T, Ariel M, Brandeis M, Shemer R, Urven L, et al. 1992. Developmental pattern of gene-specific DNA methylation in the mouse embryo and germ line. *Genes Dev.* 6:705–14

51. Kelsey G. 1994. Genetic analysis of liver-specific gene expression. See Ref. 116a, Chpt. 14

52. Kuzin B, Tillib S, Sedkov Y, Mizrokhi L, Mazo A. 1994. The *Drosophila trithorax* gene encodes a chromosomal protein and directly regulates the region-specific homeotic gene *fork head. Genes Dev.* 8:2478–90

53. Lai E, Prezioso VR, Smith E, Litvin O, Costa RH, Darnell JE Jr. 1990. HNF-3A, a hepatocyte-enriched transcription factor of novel structure is regulated transcriptionally. *Genes Dev.* 4:1427–36

54. Lai E, Prezioso VR, Tao W, Chen WS, Darnell JE Jr. 1991. Hepatocyte nuclear factor 3A belongs to a gene family in mammals that is homologous to the *Drosophila* homeotic gene *fork head. Genes Dev.* 5:416–27

55. Laufer E, Nelson CE, Johnson RL, Morgan BA, Tabin C. 1994. *Sonic hedgehog* and *Fgf-4* act through a signaling cascade and feedback loop to integrate growth and patterning of the developing limb bud. *Cell* 79:993–1003

56. Lawson KA, Meneses JJ, Pedersen RA. 1991. Clonal analysis of epiblast fate during germ layer formation in the mouse embryo. *Development* 113:891–911

57. Le Douarin L. 1970. Induction of determination and induction of differentiation during development of the liver and certain organs of endomesodermal origin. In *Tissue Interactions During*

*Organogenesis,* ed. E Wolff, pp. 37–70. New York: Gordon & Breach

58. Le Douarin N. 1964. Etude expacrimentale de l'organogengrse du tube digestif et du foie chez l'embryon de poulet. *Bull. Biol. Fr. Belg.* 98:543–676
59. Le Douarin N. 1968. Synthese du glycogene dans les hepatocytes en voie de differentiation: role des mesenchymes homologue et heterologues. *Dev. Biol.* 17:101–14
60. Le Douarin NM. 1975. An experimental analysis of liver development. *Med. Biol.* 53:427–55
61. Lee W, Mitchell P, Tijan R. 1987. Purified transcription factor AP-1 interacts with TPA-inducible enhancer elements. *Cell* 49:741–52
62. Lin F-T, Lane MD. 1994. CCAAT/enhancer binding protein α is sufficient to initiate the 3T3-L1 adipocyte differentiation program. *Proc. Natl. Acad. Sci. USA* 91:8757–61
63. Deleted in proof
64. McPherson CE, Shim E-Y, Friedman DS, Zaret KS. 1993. An active tissue-specific enhancer and bound transcription factors existing in a precisely postioned nucleosomal array. *Cell* 75:387–98
65. Michalopoulos G, Pitot HC. 1975. Primary culture of parenchymal liver cells on collagen membranes. *Exp. Cell Res.* 94:70–78
66. Mima T, Ueno H, Fischman DA, Williams LT. 1995. Fibroblast growth factor receptor is required for in vivo cardiac myocyte proliferation at early embryonic stages of heart development. *Proc. Natl. Acad. Sci. USA* 92:467–71
67. Monaghan AP, Grau E, Bock D, Schütz G. 1995. The mouse homolog of the orphan nuclear receptor *tailless* is expressed in the developing forebrain. *Development* 121:839–53
68. Monaghan AP, Kaestner KH, Grau E, Schütz G. 1993. Postimplantation expression patterns indicate a role for the mouse *fork head*/HNF-3α, β, and γ genes in determination of the definitive endoderm, chordamesoderm and neuroectoderm. *Development* 119:567–78
69. Montesano R, Matsumoto K, Nakamura T, Orci L. 1991. Identification of a fibroblast-derived epithelial morphogen as hepatocyte growth factor. *Cell* 67:901–8
70. Naldini L, Weidner KM, Vigna E, Gaudino G, Bardelli A, et al. 1991. Scatter factor and hepatocyte growth factor are indistinguishable ligands for the *MET* receptor. *EMBO J.* 10:2867–78
71. Niswander L, Martin GR. 1993. FGF-4

and BMP-2 have opposite effects on limb growth. *Nature* 361:68
72. Padgett RW, St Johnson RD, Gelbart WM. 1987. A transcript from a *Drosophila* pattern gene predicts a protein homologous to the transforming growth factor-β family. *Nature* 325:81–84
73. Panganiban GEF, Reuter R, Scott MP, Hoffman FM. 1990. A *Drosophila* growth factor homolog, decapentaplegic, regulates homeotic gene expression within and across germ layers during midgut morphogenesis. *Development* 110:1041–50
74. Pani L, Qian X, Clevidence D, Costa RH. 1992. The restricted promoter activity of the liver transcription factor hepatocyte nuclear factor 3β involves a cell-specific factor and positive autoactivation. *Mol. Cell. Biol.* 12:552–62
75. Partanen J, Mäkelä TP, Eerola E, Korhonen J, Hirvonen H, et al. 1991. FGFR-4, a novel acidic fibroblast growth factor receptor with a distinct expression pattern. *EMBO J.* 10:1347–55
76. Perrimon N. 1995. Hedgehog and beyond. *Cell* 80:517–20
77. Peters K, Werner S, Liao X, Wert S, Whitsett J, Williams L. 1994. Targeted expression of a dominant negative FGF receptor blocks branching morphogenesis and epithelial differentiation of the mouse lung. *EMBO J.* 14:3296–301
78. Pignoni F, Baldarelli RM, Steingrimsson E, Diaz RJ, Patapoutian A, et al. 1990. The Drosophila gene *tailless* is expressed at the embryonic termini and is a member of the steroid receptor superfamily. *Cell* 62:151–63
79. Poelmann RE. 1981. The head-process and the formation of the definitive endoderm in the mouse embryo. *Anat. Rec.* 162:41–49
80. Poli V, Ciliberto G. 1994. Transcriptional regulation of acute phase genes by IL-6 and related cytokines. See Ref. 116a, Chpt. 8
81. Deleted in proof
82. Ransone LJ, Verma IM. 1990. Nuclear proto-oncogenes *fos* and *jun. Annu. Rev. Cell Biol.* 6:539–57
83. Reuter R, Panganiban GEF, Hoffman FM, Scott MP. 1990. Homeotic genes regulate the spatial expression of putative growth factors in the visceral mesoderm of *Drosophila* embryos. *Development* 110:1031–40
84. Rhim JA, Sandgren EP, Degen JL, Palmiter RD, Brinster RL. 1994. Replacement of diseased mouse liver by hepatic cell transplatation. *Science* 263:1149–52
85. Rijeswijk F, Schuermann M, Wagenaar

E, Parren P, Weigel D, Nusse R. 1987. The Drosophila homolog of the mouse mammary oncogene *int-1* is identical to the segment polarity gene *wingless*. *Cell* 50:649–57

86. Rosenquist GC. 1971. The location of the pregut endoderm in the chick embryo at the primitive streak stage as determined by radioautographic mapping. *Dev. Biol.* 26:323–35

87. Rudnicki MA, Schnegelsberg PNJ, Stead RH, Braun T, Arnold H-H, Jaenisch R. 1993. MyoD or Myf-5 is required for the formation of skeletal muscle. *Cell* 75:1351–59

88. Rugh R. 1968. *The Mouse: Its Reproduction and Development*. Minneapolis, MN: Burgess. 430 pp.

89. Ruiz i Altaba A, Jessell TM. 1993. Sequential expression of HNF-3α and HNF-3β by embryonic organizing centers: the dorsal lip/node, notochord, and floor plate. *Mech. Dev.* 44:91–108

90. Ruiz i Altaba A, Jessell TM. 1992. *Pintallavis*, a gene expressed in the organizer and midline cells of frog embryos: involvement in the development of the neural axis. *Development* 116:81–93

91. Sasaki H, Hogan BLM. 1993. Differential expression of multiple fork head related genes during gastrulation and pattern formation in the mouse embryo. *Development* 118:47–59

92. Schmid P, Schulz WA. 1990. Coexpression of the C-MYC protooncogene with α-fetoprotein and albumin in fetal mouse liver. *Differentiation* 45:96–102

93. Schmidt C, Bladt F, Goedecke S, Brinkmann V, Zschiesche W, et al. 1995. Scatter factor/hepatocyte growth factor is essential for liver development. *Nature* 373:699–702

94. Schoenwolf GC, Garcia-Martinez V, Dias MS. 1992. Mesoderm movement and fate during avian gastrulation and neurulation. *Dev. Dynamics* 193:235–48

95. Screpanti I, Romani L, Musiani P, Modesti A, Fattori E, et al. 1995. Lymphoproliferative disorder and imbalanced T-helper response in C/EBPβ-deficient mice. *EMBO J.* 14:1932–41

96. Sell S. 1993. The role of determined stem-cells in the cellular lineage of hepatocellular carcinoma. *Int. J. Dev. Biol.* 37:189–201

97. Severn CB. 1968. A morphological study of the development of the human liver. *Am. J. Anat.* 133:85–108

98. Shiojiri N. 1981. Enzymo- and immunocytochemical analyses of the differentiation of liver cells in the prenatal mouse. *J. Embryol. Exp. Morphol.* 62:139–52

99. Shiojiri N, Lemire JM, Fausto N. 1991. Cell lineages and oval cell progenitors in rat liver development. *Cancer Res.* 51:2611–20

100. Sigal SH, Brill S, Fiorino AS, Reid LM. 1992. The rat as stem cell and lineage system. *Am. J. Physiol.* 263:G139–48

101. Sive HL. 1993. The frog prince-ss: A molecular formula for dorsoventral patterning in *Xenopus*. *Genes Dev.* 7:1–12

102. Sladek FM, Zhong W, Lai E, Darnell JE Jr. 1990. Liver enriched transcription factor HNF-4 is a novel member of the steroid hormone receptor superfamily. *Genes Dev.* 4:2353–64

103. Sonnenberg E, Meyer D, Weidner KM, Birchmeier C. 1993. Scatter factor/hepatocyte growth factor and its receptor, the c-met tyrosine kinase, can mediate a signal exchange between mesenchyme and epithelia during mouse development. *J. Cell Biol.* 123:223–35

104. Stark KL, McMahon JA, McMahon AP. 1991. FGFR-4, a new member of the fibroblast growth factor receptor family, expressed in the definitive endoderm and skeletal muscle lineages of the mouse. *Development* 113:641–51

105. Stern CD, Ireland GW, Herrick SE, Gherardi E, Gray J, et al. 1990. Epithelial scatter factor and development of the chick embryonic axis. *Development* 110:1271–84

106. Strähle U, Blader P, Henrique D, Ingham PW. 1993. Axial, a zebrafish gene expressed along the developing body axis, show altered expression in *cyclops* mutant embryos. *Genes Dev.* 7:1436–46

107. Streit A, Stern CD, Théry C, Ireland GW, Aparicio S, et al. 1995. A role for HGF/SF in neural induction and its expression in Hensen's node during gastrulation. *Development* 121:813–24

108. Sucov HM, Dyson E, Gumeringer CL, Price J, Chien KR, Evans RM. 1994. RXRα mutant mice establish a genetic basis for vitamin A signaling in heart morphogenesis. *Genes Dev.* 8:1007–18

109. Tanaka T, Akira S, Yoshida K, Umemoto M, Yonneda Y, et al. 1995. Targeted disruption of the NF-IL6 gene discloses its essential role in bacteria killing and tumor cytotoxity by macrophages. *Cell* 80:353–61

110. Taraviras S, Monaghan AP, Schütz G, Kelsey G. 1994. Characterization of the mouse HNF-4 gene and its expression during mouse embryogenesis. *Mech. Dev.* 48:67–79

111. Taylor SM, Jones PA. 1979. Multiple new phenotypes induced in 10T1/2 and

3T3 cells treated with 5-azacytidine. *Cell* 17:771–79

112. Theiler K. 1989. *The House Mouse.* New York: Springer-Verlag. 178 pp.

113. Thomas T, Southwell BR, Schreiber G, Jaworowski A. 1990. Plasma protein synthesis and secretion in the visceral yolk sac of the fetal rat: gene expression, protein synthesis and secretion. *Placenta* 11:413–30

114. Thorgeirsson SS, Evarts RP. 1990. Hepatic stem cell compartment in the rat. In *Hepatic Metabolism and Disposition of Endo- and Xenobiotics,* ed. KW Bock, S Matern, W Gerok, R Schmid, 19–26. Dordrech/Boston/London: Kluwer Academic, Falk Symp.

115. Tontonoz P, Hu E, Spiegelman BM. 1994. Stimulation of adipogenesis in fibroblasts by PPARγ2, a lipid-activated transcription factor. *Cell* 79:1147–56

116. Tronche F, Rollier A, Bach I, Weiss MC, Yaniv M. 1989. The rat albumin promoter: cooperation with upstream elements is required when binding of APF/HNF1 to the proximal element is partially impaired by mutation or bacterial methylation. *Mol. Cell. Biol.* 9: 4759–66

116a. Tronche F, Yaniv M, eds. 1994. *Liver Gene Expression.* Austin, TX: Landes. 350 pp.

117. Uehara Y, Minowa O, Mori C, Shiota K, Kuno J, et al. 1995. Placental defect and embryonic lethality in mice lacking hepatocyte growth factor/scatter factor. *Nature* 373:702

118. Wang ND, Finegold MJ, Bradley A, Ou CN, Abdelsayed SV, et al. 1995. Impaired energy homeostasis in C/EBPα knockout mice. *Science* 269:1108–12

119. Wang Z-Q, Ovitt C, Grigoriadis AE, Möhle-Steinlein U, Rüther U, Wagner EF. 1992. Bone and haematopoietic defects in mice lacking c-*fos. Nature* 360: 741–44

120. Weigel D, Jäckle H. 1990. The *fork head* domain: a novel DNA binding motif of eukaryotic transcription factors. *Cell* 63:455–56

121. Weigel D, Jürgens G, Küttner F, Seifert E, Jäckle H. 1989. The homeotic gene *fork head* encodes a nuclear protein and

is expressed in the terminal regions of the Drosophila embryo. *Cell* 57:645–58

122. Weinstein DC, Ruiz i Altaba A, Chen WS, Hoodless P, Prezioso VR, et al. 1994. The winged-helix transcription factor *HNF-3β* is required for notochord development in the mouse embryo. *Cell* 78:575–88

123. Weintraub H. 1993. The MyoD family and myogenesis: redundancy, networks, and thresholds. *Cell* 75:1241–44

124. Westenend PJ, Dahmen R, Charles R, Lamers WH. 1986. Hormonal inducibility of liver-specific enzymes in cultured rat embryos. *Acta Morphol. Neerl. Scand.* 24:165–80

125. Wilkinson DG, Bhatt S, Herrmann BG. 1990. Expression pattern of the mouse T gene and its role in mesoderm formation. *Nature* 343:657–59

126. Williams BO, Schmitt EM, Remington L, Bronson RT, Albert DM, et al. 1994. Extensive contribution of *Rb*-deficient cells to adult chimeric mice with limited histopathological consequences. *EMBO J.* 13:4251–59

127. Yamamoto KR. 1985. Steroid receptor regulated transcription of specific genes and gene networks. *Annu. Rev. Genet.* 19:209–52

128. Yeh W-C, Cao Z, Classon M, McKnight SL. 1995. Cascade regulation of terminal adipocyte differentiation by three members of the C/EBP family of leucine zipper proteins. *Genes Dev.* 9: 168–81

129. Zaret KS. 1994. Genetic control of hepatocyte differentiation. See Ref. 4a, pp. 53–67

130. Zarnegar R, Defrances MC, Michalopoulos GK. 1994. Hepatocyte growth factor. See Ref. 4a, p. 1047

131. Zhong W, Sladek FM, Darnell JE Jr. 1993. The expression pattern of a *Drosophila* homolog to the mouse transcription factor HNF-4 suggests a determinative role in gut formation. *EMBO J.* 12:537–44

132. Zhou X, Sasaki H, Lowe L, Hogan BL, Kuehn MR. 1993. Nodal is a novel TGF-beta-like gene expressed in the mouse node during gastrulation. *Nature* 361:543

Annu. Rev. Physiol. 1996. 58:253–73

# THE TREFOIL PEPTIDE FAMILY

## B. E. Sands and D. K. Podolsky

Gastrointestinal Unit and the Center for the Study of Inflammatory Bowel Disease, Massachusetts General Hospital and Harvard Medical School, Boston, Massachusetts 02114

KEY WORDS: ITF, pS2, spasmolytic polypeptide, mucin glycoprotein, wound healing

## ABSTRACT

The unique three-loop structure of the trefoil motif, formed by intrachain disulfide bonds in a 1-5, 2-4, 3-6 configuration between six conserved cysteine residues, is the defining feature of a recently recognized family of peptides. Expression of trefoil peptides is closely related to that of mucin glycoproteins in diverse biological sources. Three distinct members of the family (pS2, intestinal trefoil factor, and spasmolytic polypeptide) are produced in the mammalian gastrointestinal tract by mucus-secreting cells and targeted primarily for luminal secretion. The compact structure of the trefoil motif may be responsible for marked resistance of trefoil peptides to proteolytic digestion, enabling them to function in the harsh environment of the gastrointestinal lumen. Trefoil peptides are ectopically expressed adjacent to areas of inflammation within the gastrointestinal tract and may play an important role in both maintaining the barrier function of mucosal surfaces and facilitating healing after injury.

## INTRODUCTION

The trefoil peptide family is comprised of several small proteins, identified over the past ten years, that appear to share common structural features distinguishing them from other recognized peptide families and superfamilies. Recent evidence, both direct and indirect, supports the impression that the trefoil peptides may share key functional properties that result, at least in part, from their common structural features. The unique structural motif that defines the trefoil peptide family was first noted in 1984 by Thim who recognized the presence of an identical array of six cysteines in pancreatic spasmolytic polypeptide (pSP) and pS2 (73, 74). pSP was first isolated by Thim and colleagues from the porcine pancreas, and pS2 was subsequently identified through molecular cloning from an estrogen-responsive human breast cancer-

253

derived cell line and found to be expressed in the normal gastric mucosa. In addition to these two factors, a protein isolated from the skin of *Xenopus laevis* was also noted to contain six cysteine residues in nearly identical positions (74). These proteins were predicted to assume a clover-leaf or "trefoil" configuration on the basis of intrachain disulfide bonding (Figure 1).

Over the past several years, additional members of the trefoil peptide family have been identified, leading to the appreciation that at least one member is expressed in tissue-specific fashion in each region of the mammalian gastrointestinal tract. Insights into the function of these highly conserved peptides have lagged until recently. Superficial similarity to the epidermal growth factor (EGF) family of growth factors initially suggested a possible role in the modulation of growth (74). As new members of the trefoil peptide family have

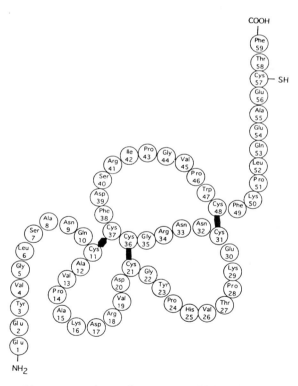

*Figure 1*   Amino acid sequence and secondary structure of hITF (4, 20). The 1-5, 2-4, 3-6 configuration of disulfide bonds between conserved cysteine residues is characteristic of the trefoil motif found in all members of the trefoil peptide family (74). A seventh cysteine residue (Cys 57) does not participate in intrachain disulfide bonding but permits homodimer formation in solution under non-reducing conditions (7, 79).

been recognized and made available through techniques of molecular biology and protein chemistry, it has been possible to clarify the role of trefoil peptides in epithelial biology. Trefoil peptides appear to contribute both to maintenance of the normal mucosal barrier and repair of mucosal integrity after injury. In addition to the recognition of an important functional role in mucosal biology, study of the trefoil peptides has provided an opportunity to elucidate the mechanisms of transcriptional regulation of developmental and tissue-specific gene expression within the mammalian gastrointestinal tract.

## DEFINITION OF THE TREFOIL MOTIF

The trefoil motif (also called the P-domain) (34) is comprised of six conserved cysteine residues that permit the formation of three intrachain disulfide bonds. The characteristic cysteine bridge configuration of 1-5, 2-4, and 3-6 (56, 74) distinguishes the trefoil peptides from other biologically important molecules with intrachain disulfide bonding (e.g. EGF/TGF-α family cysteine bonding configuration of 1-3, 2-4, and 5-6) (74). The characteristically bridged cysteine residues are contained within roughly 50 amino acid residues with similar spacing, as well as with additional conservation of arginine, glycine, and tryptophan residues to yield a defined trefoil motif: CX9CX9CX4CCX9WCF (34) (Table 1).

## MEMBERS OF THE TREFOIL PEPTIDE FAMILY

### Spasmolytic Polypeptide (SP)

Pancreatic spasmolytic polypeptide (pSP) was first isolated by Jørgensen et al (40) in 1982 from a side-fraction obtained in the purification of insulin from porcine pancreas. pSP was found to be abundant in porcine pancreas, 100 mg/kg, or roughly half the insulin content of this organ (76). Initial characterization revealed a molecule containing 106 amino acid residues in a single chain, with seven disulfide bridges (40). The protein was found to be resistant to digestion with trypsin and chymotrypsin, a property compatible with its stability within pancreatic secretions, which contain high concentrations of proteases (40). It was surmised that resistance to proteolytic digestion resulted from the extensive intrachain cross-linking. When the sequences of amino acids 14–49 and 63–98 were aligned, identical amino acid residues were found in 18 out of 36 positions, later recognized to represent tandem trefoil motifs contained within this single molecule (78).

### pS2

In the same year that SP was sequenced, Masiakowski et al cloned an estrogen-inducible cDNA designated pS2 from a library of the breast cancer cell

**Table 1**  Alignment of the amino acid sequences of mature mammalian trefoil peptides[a]

```
mITF     IAADYVGLSPSQC-----MVPANV-----RVDCGYPSVTSEQCNNRGCCFDSSIPNVPWCFKPL-----Q------ETECT-F
rITF     KAQEFVGLSPSQC-----MVPTNV-----RVDCGYPTVTSEQCNNRGCCFDSSIPNVPWCFKPL-----Q------ETECT-F
hITF     -AEEYVGLSANQC-----AVPAKD-----RVDCGYPHVTPKECNNRGCCFDSRIPNMPWCFKPL-----K------ETECTLH
m pS2    QA---QAQEETC-----IMAPRE-----RINCGFPGVTAQQCTERGCCFDDSVRGFPWCFHPMAIENTQ------EEECP-F
h pS2    EA-----QTETC-----TVAPRE-----RQNCGFPGVTPSQCANKGCCFDDTVRGVPWCFYPN-----TIDVP P EEECE-F
mSP (A)  -----EKPSPP-----C RCSRLTPHN RKNCGFPGITSEQC-FDLCCFDSSVAGVPWCFHPL-----P------NQESE-Q
mSP (B)  -------C-----VMEVSA-----RKNCGYPGISPEDCASR N CCFSNLIFEVPWCFFPQ-----S------VEDCH-Y
rSP (A)  -----EKPSPCRC SRMTPS N-----RKNCGFPGITSNQCFNLGCCFDSSVAGVPWCFH P L-----P------NQASE-Q
rSP (B)  -------C-----VMEVSA-----RENCGYPGISPEDCASRHCCFSNLIFEVPWCFFPQ-----S------VDDCH-Y
pSP (A)  QKPAACRCS-------RQDPKN-----RVNCGFPGITSDQCFTSGCCFDSQVPGVPWCFKPL-----P------AQESE-E
pSP (B)  -------C-----VMEVSA-----RKNCGYPGISPEDCARRNCCFSDTIPEVPWCFFPM-----S------VEDCH-Y
hSP (A)  ---EKPSPCQC-----SFLSPHN-----RTNCGFPGITSDQCFDNGCCFDSSVTGVPWCFHPL-----P------KQESD-Q
hSP (B)  -------C-----VMEVSD-----RRNCGYPGISPEECASRKCCFSNFIFEVPWCFFPN-----S------VEDCH-Y
Zpx      LCSD-------VPVQD-----RLPCATAPISQEDCEELGCCHSSEEVN------------ACY - Y
```

[a] Vertical dotted lines join conserved residues; horizontal dashes represent spaces inserted to maximize alignment. For mSP (80), rSP (37), pSP (78), and hSP (80), the sequences designated (A) and (B) represent the first and second of the tandem trefoil motifs borne by all SP homologues. Zpx denotes rabbit zona pellucida protein (3). Other sequences include h pS2 (53); m pS2 (44); hITF (56); rITF (63); and mITF (46). The ALIGN PLUS program (Scientific and Educational Software, State Line, PA) was employed to determine alignment according to the method of Needleman & Wunsch (1970. *Mol. Biol.* 48:443–53).

line MCF-7 (47). The pS2 cDNA contained an open reading frame encoding a predicted 84-residue protein presumed to represent a propeptide (36), which after cleavage of signal peptide yields a 58 amino acid secretory protein (53). The deduced amino acid sequence of pS2, later confirmed by microsequencing, demonstrates a single trefoil motif (53).

Although derived from a breast cancer cell line and expressed in roughly 50% of human breast carcinomas (61), pS2 is not a major constituent of normal breast tissue (59). In contrast to the insignificant amounts of pS2 mRNA and protein that can be detected in normal breast, pS2 is normally expressed in high levels in the human stomach (58).

## *Intestinal Trefoil Factor*

In 1987, Suemori et al cloned a cDNA from a rat jejunal library that had a predicted amino acid sequence containing a single trefoil motif (68). Northern blot analysis demonstrated a single transcript of 430 bases present in small and large intestine. The open reading frame of the cDNA clone was found to encode an 81 amino acid protein with a predicted 21 amino acid signal peptide. Antiserum raised against a synthetic peptide of the predicted C-terminal sequence further demonstrated that expression of the protein is confined to goblet cells, with abundant staining of the mucus layer overlying the intestinal epithelium. This trefoil peptide was designated intestinal trefoil factor (ITF) (68).

While ITF is most abundantly expressed by the intestinal goblet cells, physiologic expression in small amounts has also been reported in the cardiac glands of the rat stomach (9) and within the uterus, although mRNA was not observed in this tissue at the time of its initial identification (30). Of note, the goblet cells of the cardia, like the intestinal goblet cells, secrete neutral mucin. It has been suggested that ITF may be coexpressed with the gene products of the *MUC2* or *MUC3* genes, also found in intestine, whereas pS2 and SP, found largely in cells that stain for acidic mucin, might be coexpressed with the gene products of the *MUC1* gene (83). ITF mRNA is also found in the kidney in the rat (68), with immunohistochemistry apparently localizing the protein to the principal cells of the collecting ducts (J Stow, K Lynch-Devaney, D Podolsky, preliminary observations), although no ITF was detected in the normal mouse kidney (46). ITF is also produced by the goblet cells of the conjunctiva in the eye and is a constituent of the secretions overlying the external surface of the eye (I Gipson & D Podolsky, personal observation). Homologues of the rat ITF (rITF) have been demonstrated in human (hITF) (30, 56) and mouse (mITF) (10, 46).

Both human and rat ITF are expressed almost exclusively by goblet cells in the small and large intestine (56). In situ hybridization of small intestine confirmed the presence of hITF message in goblet cells, with immunogold

**Table 2**    Amino acid identity among trefoil peptide homologues[a]

| Trefoil peptides | | | Amino acid identity (%) |
|---|---|---|---|
| hITF | X | rITF | 70 |
| hITF | X | mITF | 73 |
| mITF | X | rITF | 90 |
| hSP | X | rSP | 89 |
| hSP | X | pSP | 80 |
| mSP | X | rSP | 93 |
| rSP | X | rITF | 45 |
| mSP | X | mITF | 36 |
| m pS2 | X | mITF | 35 |
| hITF | X | h pS2 | 36 |
| hITF | X | hSP | 28 |
| hITF | X | xSL | 43 |

[a] Comparison of the percentage of amino acid identity among trefoil peptide homologues (ITF, pS2, SP) from different animal species (m, mouse; r, rat; p, porcine; h, human) demonstrates relatively high levels of identity (from 70 to 93%). In contrast, different trefoil peptides compared within the same species display a lower percent of amino acid identity (28 to 45%), equivalent to the similarity between mammalian trefoil peptide hITF and the amphibian trefoil-bearing protein spasmolysin derived from *Xenopus laevis* (xSL) (33), at 43% (56).

localization of ITF within goblet cell theca and along the mucin layer covering the microvillus surface (56). Although the ITF peptide contains a single trefoil motif, the molecule may exist in solution as a homodimer (79). Antibody raised to the C-terminal unique 21 residues of both native and recombinant rITF consistently recognize a 7-kDa band on western blot, along with a 14-kDa band under non-reducing conditions (H Kindon & D Podolsky, unpublished observations). These observations are consistent with the notion that ITF may form dimers through disulfide bonding via a seventh cysteine present in this peptide that does not participate in the trefoil domain (7, 79).

## Mammalian Homologues of pSP, pS2, and rITF

The discovery of homologues of pSP, pS2, and ITF in other mammalian species has confirmed that these peptides reflect distinct evolutionary consensus peptides rather than counterparts that are expressed with a different tissue distribution among various mammalian species. As noted in Table 2, highest levels of sequence homology are found between corresponding trefoil peptides from different species (generally 70–80% identity; e.g. hITF vs rITF = 78%) compared to different trefoil peptides within a single species (generally 30–45%

identity; e.g. hITF vs hSP-28% identity, and hITF vs pS2-36% identity) (56). The patterns of regional and cell selective trefoil peptide expression have been conserved throughout mammalian evolution.

Despite the general conservation of patterns of expression of different trefoil peptides, some variations in the sites of expression of SP among species have been observed. The prototype of the species, pSP, was isolated from porcine pancreas; however, the human (80) and rodent (rat and mouse) homologues are found predominantly in gastric antrum (25, 37, 44). mSP has been found in pancreas (80). Smaller amounts of rSP and hSP have been found within the Brunner's glands of the duodenum (25, 37). Because of this discrepancy in tissue specificity, the initial p in pSP originally connoted pancreas but now stands for porcine, consistent with the evolving nomenclature of the trefoil family and avoiding the implication that all members of the SP family localize to the pancreas (75).

This discrepancy notwithstanding, the notion that trefoil expression is site-specific within the gastrointestinal tract generally holds true even for the SP proteins. The expression of hSP within the stomach is limited to the deep foveolar pits of the gastric antrum. In contrast, pS2 is located in more superficial cells and is found distributed more broadly throughout the body and fundus of the stomach, as well as the antrum (80). The distribution of rat SP is similar to that in humans (25, 37). In a manner similar to ITF in the intestine, both pS2 and hSP are abundantly secreted into the gastric lumen and are present in relatively high concentrations within the overlying mucus layer (37).

The demonstration within a single animal species of a distinct gene encoding each of these proteins directly confirms the inference that these peptides are the products of several conserved genes, e.g. in humans hITF, pS2, and hSP (80); in mouse mITF (46), m pS2, and mSP (44). Interestingly, the genes for hSP and pS2 have been localized to chromosome 21 (72) within 213 kilobases of each other (81). Although the developmental and physiologic expression of mSP and the mouse homologue of pS2 are distinct, this finding raises the possibility of coordinate gene expression for these mammalian trefoil peptides, with some common promoter elements, as well as divergent control of transcription by elements unique to each gene. In contrast, the mouse homologue of ITF has been mapped to mouse chromosome 15, in a region syntenic with human chromosome 8 (10), perhaps consistent with its divergent pattern of expression.

The tissue-specific and cellular patterns of expression of the three known major mammalian trefoil peptides are distinct but complementary. Collectively, pS2, SP, and ITF are expressed along virtually the entire length of the gastrointestinal tract. Whether this distinct pattern of expression signifies differences in peptide function is not known, although some insights are provided by the observation of specific patterns of ectopic expression of trefoil peptides in disease states (see below).

## Amphibian Trefoil Proteins

An amphibian trefoil protein was first cloned from the skin of the African clawed frog *Xenopus laevis* and was originally called spasmolysin (33). This relatively large (~130 kDa) protein was initially presumed to undergo post-translational processing to yield two single-trefoil motif-containing peptides, and another peptide bearing two trefoil motifs, as well as a region of extensive glycosylation (33). Subsequently, this protein, called frog integumentary mucin-A.1 (FIM-A.1), was found not to be cleaved (27). Thus FIM-A.1 exists in *Xenopus* skin as a peptide containing four trefoil domains, as well as extensively glycosylated domains containing mucin type *O*-glycosidally-linked oligosaccharide side chains (27), which have not been found in association with any mammalian trefoil peptides. Subsequently, amphibian dermal glands have been found to express additional trefoil motif-containing proteins secreted onto the frog's skin. These included a second FIM containing six trefoil domains (FIM-C.1) (29) and a smaller, single-trefoil domain protein (22). In contrast, xP2, a 17-kDa protein with two trefoil domains, although present in *Xenopus* skin, does not appear to be secreted onto the mucus coating of the skin (31).

After the identification of FIM-A.1 and recognition of the homology to peptides present within the mammalian gastrointestinal tract, efforts were directed to identify family members within the amphibian stomach. These efforts have led to demonstration of two proteins designated xP1 and xP4, containing one and four trefoil motifs, respectively, within the frog stomach (28). Both are expressed by the surface mucous cells of *Xenopus* gastric mucosa (28). xP4 is believed to be *N*-glycosylated (28).

The evolutionary conservation of the trefoil motif from the amphibian *Xenopus* to human implies the functional importance of this structure. The unusual structures of FIM-A.1 and FIM-C.1 offer a potentially important insight into a functional relationship of trefoil peptides and mucin glycoprotein. The trefoil-containing members of the FIM family are comprised of a glycosylated mucin backbone in association with the trefoil domains. In this context, it is interesting to note that within the mammalian gastrointestinal tract, the trefoil peptides are produced primarily by mucus-secreting cells: SP by mucous neck cells (25, 37), ITF by goblet cells (56), and pS2 by superficial gastric foveolar cells (58). This circumstantial evidence suggests that trefoil peptides and mucin glycoproteins are functionally interactive, a concept supported more directly by recent studies (see below).

## Other Mammalian Proteins Containing Trefoil Domains

The intestinal brush border protein sucrase-isomaltase appears to contain a trefoil motif (80), whereas a newly isolated protein of the rabbit zona pellucida contains a partial trefoil domain (3). Although these proteins can be distinguished from the archetypal trefoil peptides that are secreted into the gastrointestinal lumen, these non-classic trefoil-bearing proteins may share two features with the trefoil peptides. First, resistance to proteolytic digestion resulting from the compact secondary structure of the trefoil motif may permit sucrase-isomaltase present on the enterocyte apical surface to remain biologically active despite exposure to luminal and cell surface proteases (80). Second, the trefoil motif might participate in the binding of carbohydrate moieties (54) such as the sugar substrates of sucrase-isomaltase or the carbohydrate sidechains of mucin glycoproteins in the mucus layer of the gastrointestinal tract of the zona pellucida.

## CHARACTERIZATION OF TREFOIL PROTEIN GENES AND REGULATORY ELEMENTS

Insights into the regulation of trefoil peptide expression have been obtained through molecular cloning of the human pS2 and rat ITF genes. The *pS2* gene was cloned from DNA derived from both placenta and the human breast cancer cell line MCF-7, with a finding of identical gene structures and 5'-flanking region and exonic sequences (38). The *pS2* gene is composed of three exons of 125, 153, and 212 bp, with two intervening introns of 3.1 and 0.77 Kb (38). A number of potential transcriptionally active elements were identified: a TATA box 29 bp upstream of the transcriptional start site, as well as two CAAT elements at −72 and −639 and a potential Sp1-binding site at −12 (38). Functional analysis of the promoter initially localized an estrogen-responsive region in the promoter between −428 to −332 (52). This same region contains enhancer elements for 12-*O*-tetra-decanoylphorbol-13-acetate (TPA), epidermal growth factor, and c-Ha-*ras* and c-*jun* proteins (52). Further analysis by site-directed mutagenesis pinpointed the estrogen-responsive element (ERE) to 13 bp from −405 to −393, consisting of an imperfect palindrome, similar to previously characterized EREs (2).

In our laboratory, the rat ITF gene expressed within the intestinal goblet cell was cloned as a model to identify elements responsible for specifying gene expression within this tissue and cell type (63). The gene is comprised of three exons spanning 4.8 kb and has a single transcriptional start site. Using transient transfection of constructs containing varying length of the 5'-flanking region linked to a reporter gene in intestinal epithelial cell lines, high levels of expression were found in cell lines with a goblet cell-like phenotype, compared with very low levels of expression observed in non-goblet cell-like intestinal cell lines. Furthermore, this specificity was present even with constructs containing only the proximal-most 153 bp of the 5'-flanking region. Using laser confocal microscopy, it was also possible to localize expression of 5'-flanking region constructs to cells that simultaneously stain for mucin, which indicates that promoter directed expression in association with goblet cell-like phenotypic differentiation (63).

## STRUCTURAL BIOCHEMISTRY OF THE TREFOIL MOTIF

### Resolution of the Trefoil Structure

The physical structure of pSP has been elucidated by both NMR spectroscopy (5, 6) and X-ray crystallography (16, 21), which demonstrate that the trefoil domain confers distinctive tertiary structure. The relatively short loops result in an especially compact peptide (21). Each trefoil domain of pSP contains an antiparallel β-sheet with a short helix above and below (21); a cleft 8–10 Å wide between loops 2 and 3 is present within each trefoil domain (21). The most highly conserved residues of the trefoil motif are situated around this groove formed by the peptide backbone (21). Residues with side chains projecting into the groove are completely conserved between the two domains of pSP (Ile24, Phe36, Pro44, and Trp45) (6). This groove may be capable of binding an oligosaccharide, or a portion of a polysaccharide chain (21). The two trefoil domains of pSP are spatially related with twofold symmetry in the crystalline form contributing to the peptide's compactness (6). In the crystalline form, homodimer formation not present in solution contributes further to compactness (54). The terminal ends of pSP are not easily accessible as a result of the Cys6-Cys104 disulfide bridge (21). Collectively, these structural features may facilitate the marked resistance of pSP to proteolytic degradation and lend further support to a possible role in the stabilization of mucin (21).

### Physical Interactions Between Trefoils and Mucin Glycoproteins

The coexpression of trefoil peptides and mucin glycoproteins within goblet cells (or their equivalent in other regions of the gastrointestinal tract) and secretion onto the mucosal surface has prompted evaluation of potential interaction between these two secretory products. A relationship between these products is also suggested by the combination of trefoil and mucin glycoprotein-like domains within single molecules in amphibian skin (27, 29). Using light scattering and falling ball viscometry techniques, an increase in the viscosity of pure mucin glycoproteins has been observed following the addition of trefoil peptides (H Kindon et al, manuscript in preparation). Of note, essentially equivalent complex formation was observed when human or rat colonic mucin glycoprotein was mixed with rat or human ITF. Similarly, hSP also promoted aggregation with colonic mucin glycoproteins and, conversely, rITF complexed with rat gastric mucin glycoprotein. In contrast, monomeric (reduced) rITF could not form complexes and actively competed with hSP, inhibiting aggregation. Collectively, these observations suggest that divalent trefoil peptides generallly serve to bridge mucin glycoprotein through structural features common to each class of protein. These findings further suggest that one possible mechanism of cytoprotection conferred by the trefoils is stabilization of the physical properties of the mucoviscous layer that overlies all gastrointestinal epithelium.

## TREFOIL PROTEIN FUNCTION

Functional characterization of a trefoil peptide was first carried out with native purified pSP (39). With recent production of recombinant trefoil proteins by expression cloning in yeast (39) and other eukaryotic expression systems, more extensive characterization of trefoil peptides has been possible.

### Motility and Gastric Acid Secretion

An initial pharmacologic screen of pSP resulted in the demonstration of the ability to decrease the contraction of electrically induced smooth muscle contraction in vitro, leading to the designation spasmolytic polypeptide (39). Intestinal propulsion was also inhibited in intact animals (39). pSP reduced intestinal propulsion when administered subcutaneously, with a potency roughly six times greater than atropine (39). pSP retained spasmolytic activity, despite exposure to trypsin, chymotrypsin, and hydrochloric acid (39). Resistance to hydrolysis is consistent with the observation that orally administered pSP suppresses intestinal contraction in rabbits. Pentagastrin-induced gastric acid secretion was also suppressed after oral administration in rats and cats. Although the relevance of these pharmacologic effects to the physiologic function of pSP could not be determined by these studies, they suggest that this protein could mediate important biologic effects on the gastrointestinal tract from within the lumen, the natural site of secretion.

### Modulation of Growth

Soon after designation of the trefoil peptides, these factors were hypothesized to function as growth modulating factors (74). Whereas three intrachain disulfide bonds are also characteristic of the EGF family, as well as insulin-like growth factors I and II, the primary and secondary structures of the trefoil proteins are distinct from these structurally unrelated growth factors (21, 74). Although pSP has been reported to produce modest increases in proliferation of the breast and colon cancer cell lines MCF-7 and HCT 116 (35), it is unclear whether this in vitro observation reflects a physiologic function. In recent studies, neither hSP, hITF, nor rITF were found to cause significant alteration in proliferation of the human colon cancer cell lines HT-29, CaC02, T84, or the non-transformed rat intestinal epithelial cell lines IEC-6 and IEC-17 (17).

Increased expression of trefoil proteins has been observed in a variety of tumors in humans. Within the gastrointestinal tract, both pS2 and hSP have been found to be expressed in carcinomas of the biliary tract (63), pancreas (32, 45), stomach (32, 69), colon, and esophagus (32, 45). In addition, the pS2 protein is found expressed in a variety of epithelial cancers outside the gastrointestinal tract, including some lung cancers (32, 45), ovarian mucinous and serous cystadenocarcinomas (32, 45), and cervical, endometrial, prostate, and bladder cancers (32).

pS2 was originally cloned as the product of an estrogen-responsive gene expressed in breast cancer (36, 47–49, 51, 53, 57, 61, 66). The presence of pS2 expression correlates with estrogen-responsiveness of the tumor (43, 60, 64) and appears to correlate with improved survival more reliably than presence of estrogen or progesterone receptors (19). The *pS2* gene contains an estrogen-responsive element (ERE) (2, 52), and *pS2* gene transcription has been shown to be a primary response to estrogen in the breast cancer cell line MCF-7 (4). Increased trefoil peptide expression has also been found in benign and pre-malignant neoplastic lesions, as well as in frankly malignant tumors. Thus pS2 is highly expressed in hyperplastic polyps of the colon (26), as well as in islands of gastric metaplasia in both Barrett's esophagus (23) and the proximal duodenum (24).

Whether increased trefoil peptide expression is an epiphenomenon of the dysplasia-neoplasia sequence or a factor contributing to the malignant phenotype has yet to be established. If trefoil proteins regulate growth, it appears that they exert their effects through mechanisms distinct from those of conventional peptide growth factors. Although pS2 is found to be expressed in about half of all human breast cancers (61), overexpression of pS2 in mammary tissue in transgenic mice does not result in either hyperplasia or dysplasia (82). In addition, no growth advantage is observed in suckling pups who ingest high concentrations of pS2 in milk (82). Indeed, improved disease-free survival associated with the presence of pS2 in breast cancer (19) suggests that pS2 does not have significant growth stimulating effects, and studies of breast cancer cell lines have not demonstrated an autocrine growth stimulatory effect for pS2 (15, 41). It is interesting to note that although gastric mucosa is not an estrogen-responsive tissue, an EGF-responsive element in the pS2 promoter may contribute to physiologic expression (52).

Trefoil peptides, though predominantly expressed by mucin-secreting epithelial cells and targeted for lumenal secretion, have also been found in some neuroendocrine cells of the gastrointestinal tract (85). pS2, but not hSP, has been observed to be copackaged with chromogranin A in neurosecretory granules in proximity to sites of mucosal ulceration within the intestine and is apparently secreted along the basolateral surface of the cell (85). Whether this alternate mode of secretion might play a role in local cell growth is not known, but this observation may at least partially account for the increased serum and urine levels of pS2 observed in patients with Crohn's disease, a chronic ulcerative condition of the human intestine (62). At least one trefoil peptide has been localized to the brain in *Xenopus* (31), but trefoils have not been observed in the neuronal tissue of mammals.

## Specific Ligand-Receptor Interactions

Specific binding to receptors on isolated rat intestinal cell membranes was observed in early studies of pSP (20). The binding sites appeared to be heterogeneous, with a dissociation constant ($K_d$) of 130 nM (20). Although inhibition of adenylate cyclase activity was also demonstrated upon binding (20), the observed dissociation constant is 10- to 100-fold higher than a classical peptide hormone-receptor interaction (75). Furthermore, the dissociation constant did not significantly change when porcine intestinal cell preparations were employed, which suggests that the putative ligand-receptor interaction was not weakened by differences in protein sequence specific to species (75).

An *E. coli* fusion protein of rITF and β-galactosidase also appeared to bind to specific sites within colonic crypts, the foveolar and surface epithelium of stomach, and the collecting ducts of the kidney (8). The physiologic relevance of these binding sites has yet to be determined, but preliminary observations suggest that tyrosine phosphorylation of the surface adhesion molecule E-cadherin may occur after exposure of a human colon cancer cell line to rITF (N Wright, personal communication). Intestinal epithelial ion transport has been reported to be enhanced by ITF, but not by SP, further suggesting a specific ligand-receptor interaction (14).

## TREFOIL PEPTIDES AND GASTROINTESTINAL TRACT MUCOSAL FUNCTION

Increased expression of trefoil peptides has been observed in a variety of ulcerating conditions of the gastrointestinal tract (86). In areas of pseudopyloric metaplasia surrounding ulcers due to Crohn's disease, an ectopic recapitulation of the pattern of trefoil expression in the stomach has been found (62). Ductules that appear to open onto the mid-villus through a communicating pore adjacent to Crohn's ulcerations in the intestine have been described (84). Cells that stain for pS2 are found in the deepest acinar portion of these ductules, whereas more superficial cells contain SP as assessed by immunohistochemical staining (62). Cells producing trefoil peptides not normally present in the intestine have been proposed to promote wound healing (68, 86). In addition, cells that appear to stain for EGF by immunohistochemistry have been described within the deepest part of the acinar portion of the new ductule (84). Because the physiologically important EGF receptors are believed to be distributed along the basolateral surface of enterocytes, rather than the apical surface (50), trefoil peptides may be a key link through which EGF promotes mucosal healing. As noted above, an EGF response element is present in the pS2 promoter, which might in part account for expression of this protein in stomach (52). However, despite the demonstration of EGF immunoreactivity in the acinar portion of pseudopyloric metaplasia of the intestine (24, 62), mRNA encoding EGF has not been reported in these sites.

Ectopic expression of trefoil peptides adjacent to areas of ulceration provides circumstantial evidence of a role in wound healing. However, protein expression in metaplastic tissue may be a consequence of phenotype without truly reflecting a physiologic function, e.g. sucrase-isomaltase expressed in intestinal metaplasia of the esophagus (87) is unlikely to play a direct role in protecting the esophageal mucosa against injury from acid reflux. Nonetheless, it should be noted that expression of trefoil peptides is highly induced in animal models of gastrointestinal ulceration. In a rat model of gastric ulceration induced by glacial acetic acid, a thousandfold increase in immunoreactive ITF in the surrounding tissue was observed, compared to fourfold induction of rSP by day 40 when healing was nearly complete (70). As assessed by immunohistochemistry, highest levels of expression of these trefoil peptides were present closest to the ulcer, with diminishing levels at greater distances from the lesion (70). In contrast, a similar model of ulceration induced by application of acetic acid to rat intestinal serosa demonstrated greater increases in rSP expression than that observed for ITF (12). Other groups have reported that alterations in trefoil peptides may occur immediately (67) or in a substantially delayed fashion (13), which would seem to preclude a primary role in healing.

Recent experimental observations support the impression that trefoil peptides play an important role in mucosal healing. Topical (lumenal) recombinant hSP or recombinant rITF (administered by gavage) given prior to gastric injury with ethanol or indomethacin effected virtually complete protection against ulceration (1). Both human and rat ITF appeared to have equivalent protective ability. These observations suggest that mucosal protection may be a generic property of the trefoil peptide family. The mechanisms conferring mucosal protection are not yet understood, although in these studies, protective effects were observed only when trefoil peptides were administered orally but not after parenteral administration (1). Furthermore, as noted above, preliminary studies using dynamic light scattering have demonstrated that trefoil peptides interact directly with mucin glycoproteins to form complexes. In contrast, another group has observed protective effects of hSP administered by parenteral infusion to rats treated with indomethacin (55).

Trefoil peptides and mucin glycoproteins acting cooperatively may have an important effect on restitution, the process responsible for the immediate repair of defects in the epithelium. In the process of restitution, cell migration with flattening and spreading into the wound of epithelial cells surrounding the defect enables re-establishment of the continuity of the epithelium and reconstitution of the mucosal barrier much more rapidly than a proliferative response can achieve permanent healing.

A simple cell culture model of restitution utilizing monolayers of IEC-6 cells (a nontransformed crypt cell-like rat intestinal epithelial cell line) wounded in a standardized fashion by razor edge has facilitated insight into the contribution of trefoil peptides to this process (11, 18). Utilizing this model, several cytokines and growth factors have been demonstrated to increase the rate of restitution through a TGF-$\beta$-dependent pathway, which may be blocked by neutralizing anti-TFG-$\beta$ antisera (18). Transcription of TGF-$\beta$ increases significantly in wounded monolayers and is further stimulated by those cytokines, which enhance migration (18). Thus TGF-$\beta$ appears to be a pivotal cytokine in promoting restitution, serving as a fluid common pathway through which factors acting at the basolateral surface of the epithelium promote restitution.

The addition of trefoil peptides also enhances restitution in wounded epithelial monolayers (17). However, in contrast to cytokines, the effect of trefoil peptides is independent of TGF-$\beta$. Thus the addition of neutralizing anti-TGF-$\beta$ antibodies did not abrogate the enhancement of wound healing, and the effects of exogenous trefoil peptides and TGF-$\beta$ appear to be additive (17). Most importantly, trefoil peptide and mucin glycoproteins acted in a cooperative fashion to enhance restitution. This cooperative effect was observed when recombinant hSP was combined with mucin glycoproteins from both small or large intestine isolated from either rat or human. Non-mucin glycoproteins did not enhance trefoil peptide-induced restitution (17). These experiments suggest that trefoil peptides and mucin glycoproteins, both products of the mucin-producing cells of the gastrointestinal tract, enhance mucosal wound healing in a cooperative fashion through a TGF-$\beta$-independent mechanism, which complements TGF-$\beta$-dependent mechanisms operating at the basolateral pole of the epithelium. Most importantly, these effects appear to be generic to trefoil peptides and mucin glycoproteins and are not specific to individual trefoil peptides or mucin glycoprotein from various sites in the gastrointestinal tract or from different animal species.

In addition to promoting healing of epithelial monolayers after injury, recent studies demonstrate that trefoil peptides and mucin glycoproteins act in a cooperative fashion to protect monolayers of intestinal epithelial cells against a variety of injurious agents. Intestinal epithelial cell lines form a relatively impermeable barrier to the inert marker mannitol when grown on a permeable supporting membrane. Injurious agents, including *C. difficile* toxin A, and bile salts (taurocholic acid and oleic acid), damage the integrity of the monolayer barrier, with penetration of the marker mannitol. Both native and recombinant rITF or hITF, or hSP in combination with gastrointestinal tract-derived mucin glycoproteins, when applied to the monolayer prior to adding the agent, markedly diminished the injury. Although the addition of either a trefoil peptide or a mucin glycoprotein individually conferred protection, combinations of a trefoil peptide and a mucin glycoprotein provided increased protection in an additive and occasionally synergistic fashion. These effects also appear to be generic to trefoil peptides and gastrointestinal tract mucin glycoproteins (42). Thus protection conferred by combinations of gastric mucin glycoproteins with either native or recombinant ITF, or colonic mucin glycoprotein with recombinant hSP, was similar to that observed with combinations of colonic mucin glycoproteins and ITF, or gastric mucin glycoprotein with hSP. Similarly, the source species (human or rat) did not appear to alter the additive nature of the effect, with combinations of rat and human proteins conferring protection similar to that of combinations of trefoil peptides and mucin glycoprotein from the same species. Non-mucin glycoproteins alone or in combination with trefoil peptides were ineffective in protecting against injury (42). These studies provide further evidence of a generalized interaction between trefoil peptides and mucin glycoproteins within the gastrointestinal tract and for a role in the prevention of injury to the mucosal epithelium. Further studies are needed to define whether the protective effects of trefoil peptide and mucin glycoprotein combinations result from stabilization of the physical structure of mucin, or a more direct effect on the epithelium via specific receptors, or both.

## CONCLUSIONS

Although much has been learned about the trefoil peptides in the relatively brief period of time since their identification, many questions about the function of trefoil peptides and the relationship of function to the unique structure of the trefoil motif remain unanswered. Trefoil peptides appear to play a role in maintaining the normal mammalian gastrointestinal mucosa, but the precise mechanisms through which they promote mucosal integrity remain to be elucidated. The presence of specific trefoil-ligand interactions, as well as the subsequent steps in mucosal healing and protection, must be clarified. Functional analysis of trefoil gene promoters may yield improved understanding of the interplay of *cis*- and *trans*-regulatory transcriptional factors that result in the highly specific pattern of trefoil peptide expression in the physiologic state, as well as the elements contributing to ectopic expression after injury. More detailed study of the structure-function relationships of the trefoil peptides themselves are needed to determine the basis of trefoil peptide-mucin glyco-protein interactions and the mechanisms through which trefoil peptides and mucin glycoproteins promote epithelial continuity and mucosal response to injury.

## Literature Cited

1. Babyatsky MW, Thim L, Podolsky DK. 1994. Trefoil peptides protect against ethanol and indomethacin induced gastric injury in rats. *Gastroenterology* 106: A43 (Abstr.)

2. Berry M, Nunez A-M, Chambon P. 1989. Estrogen-responsive element of the human *pS2* gene is an imperfectly palindromic sequence. *Proc. Natl. Acad. Sci. USA* 86:1218–22

3. Bork P. 1993. A trefoil domain in the major rabbit zona pellucida protein. *Protein Sci.* 2:669–70

4. Brown AMC, Jeltsch J-M, Roberts M, Chambon P. 1984. Activation of *pS2* gene transcription is a primary response to estrogen in the human breast cancer cell line MCF-7. *Proc. Natl. Acad. Sci. USA* 81:6344–48

5. Carr MD. 1992. $^1$H NMR-based determination of the secondary structure of procine pancreatic spasmolytic polypeptide: one of a new family of "Trefoil" motif containing cell growth factors. *Biochemistry* 31:1998–2004

6. Carr MD, Bauer CJ, Gradwell MJ, Feeney J. 1994. Solution structure of a trefoil-motif-containing cell growth factor, porcine spasmolytic protein. *Proc. Natl. Acad. Sci. USA* 91:2206–10

7. Chinery R, Bates PA, De A, Freemont PS. 1995. Characterisation of the single copy trefoil peptides intestinal trefoil factor and pS2 and their ability to form covalent dimers. *FEBS Lett.* 357: 50–54

8. Chinery R, Poulsom R, Elia G, Hanby AM, Wright NA. 1993. Expression and purification of a trefoil peptide motif in

a β-galactosidase fusion protein and its use to search for trefoil-binding sites. *Eur. J. Biochem.* 212:557–63

9. Chinery R, Poulsom R, Robert LA, Jeffery RE, Longcroft JM, et al. 1992. Localization of intestinal trefoil-factor mRNA in rat stomach and intestine by hybridization in situ. *Biochem. J.* 285:5–8

10. Chinery R, Poulsom R, Wright NA. 1995. mITF, a mouse trefoil peptide homologous with rat intestinal trefoil factor, is located on murine chromosome 15. *Gastroenterology* 108(4):A456 (Abstr.)

11. Ciacci C, Lind SE, Podolsky DK. 1993. Transforming growth factor β regulation of migration in wounded rat intestinal epithelial monolayers. *Gastroenterology* 105:93–101

12. Cook GA, Skultety KJ, Yeomans ND, Giraud AS. 1994. Increased trefoil peptide expression in a rat model of intestinal repair. *Gastroenterology* 106:A195 (Abstr.)

13. Cook GA, Yeomans ND, Giraud AS. 1995. Trefoil peptide expression falls following gastric mucosal injury but is induced in a TGFα-dependent manner late in repair. *Gastroenterology* 108: A75 (Abstr.)

14. Cox HM, Chinery R, Wright NA. 1993. An epithelial ion transport role of intestinal trefoil factor but not for pancreatic spasmolytic polypeptide. *Regul. Pept.* 47:90

15. Davidson NE, Bronzert DA, Chambon P, Gelmann EP, Lippman ME. 1986. Use of two MCF-7 cell variants to evaluate the growth regulatory potential of

estrogen-induced products. *Cancer Res.* 46:1904–8

16. De A, Brown DG, Gorman MA, Carr M, Sanderson MR, Freemont PS. 1994. Crystal structure of a disulfide-linked "trefoil" motif found in a large family of putative growth factors. *Proc. Natl. Acad. Sci. USA* 91:1084–88

17. Dignass A, Lynch-Devaney K, Kindon H, Thim L, Podolsky DK. 1994. Trefoil peptides promote epithelial migration through a transforming growth factor β-independent pathway. *J. Clin. Invest.* 94:376–83

18. Dignass A, Podolsky DK. 1993. Cytokine modulation of intestinal epithelial cell restitution: central role of transforming growth factor β. *Gastroenterology* 105:1323–32

19. Foekens JA, Rio M-C, Seguin P, van Putten WLJ, Fauque J, et al. 1990. Prediction of relapse and survival in breast cancer patients by pS2 protein status. *Cancer Res.* 50:3832–37

20. Frandsen EK, Jørgensen KH, Thim L. 1986. Receptor binding of pancreatic spasmolytic polypeptide (PSP) in rat intestinal mucosal cell membranes inhibits the adenylate cyclase activity. *Regul. Pept.* 16:291–97

21. Gajhede M, Petersen TN, Henriksen A, Petersen JFW, Dauter Z, et al. 1993. Pancreatic spasmolytic polypeptide: first three-dimensional structure of a member of the mammalian trefoil family of peptides. *Structure* 1(4):253–62

22. Gmach M, Berger H, Thalhammer J, Kreil G. 1990. Dermal glands of *Xenopus laevis* contain a polypeptide with a highly repetitive amino acid sequence. *FEBS Lett.* 260:145–48

23. Hanby AM, Jankowski J, Poulsom R, Singh S, Elia G, Wright NA. 1992. Expression of pS2 and hSP in Barrett's mucosa and oesophageal carcinoma. *Gut* 33:S32 (Abstr.)

24. Hanby AM, Poulsom R, Elia G, Singh S, Longcroft JM, Wright MA. 1993. The expression of the trefoil peptides pS2 and human spasmolytic polypeptide (hSP) in "gastric metaplasia" of the proximal duodenum: implications for the nature of "gastric metaplasia." *J. Pathol.* 169:355–60

25. Hanby AM, Poulsom R, Singh S, Elia G, Jeffery RE, Wright NA. 1993. Spasmolytic polypeptide is a major antral peptide: distribution of the trefoil peptides human spasmolytic polypeptide and pS2 in the stomach. *Gastroenterology* 105:1110–16

26. Hanby AM, Poulsom R, Singh S, Jankowski J, Hopwood D, et al. 1993. Hyperplastic polyps: a cell lineage which both synthesizes and secretes trefoil-peptides and has phenotypic similarity with the ulcer-associated cell lineage. *Am. J. Pathol.* 142(3):663–68

27. Hauser F, Gertzen E-M, Hoffmann W. 1990. Expression of spasmolysin (FIM-A.1): an integumentary mucin from *Xenopus laevis. Exp. Cell Res.* 189:157–62

28. Hauser F, Hoffmann W. 1991. xPI and xP4. P-domain peptides expressed in *Xenopus laevis* stomach mucosa. *J. Biol. Chem.* 266(31):21306–9

29. Hauser F, Hoffmann W. 1992. P-domains as shuffled cysteine-rich modules in integumentary mucin C.1 (FIM-C.1) from *Xenopus laevis.* Polydispersity and genetic polymorphism. *J. Biol. Chem.* 267(34):24620–24

30. Hauser F, Poulsom R, Chinery R, Rogers LA, Hanby AM, et al. 1993. hP1.B, a human P-domain peptide homologous with rat intestinal trefoil factor, is expressed also in the ulcer-associated cell lineage and the uterus. *Proc. Natl. Acad. Sci. USA* 90:6961–65

31. Hauser F, Roeben C, Hoffmann W. 1992. xP2, a new member of the P-domain peptide family of potential growth factors, is synthesized in *Xenopus laevis* skin. *J. Biol. Chem.* 267(20):14451–55

32. Henry JA, Bennett MK, Piggott NH, Levett DL, May FEB, Westley BR. 1991. Expression of the pNR-2/pS2 protein in diverse human epithelial tumours. *Br. J. Cancer* 64:677–82

33. Hoffmann W. 1988. A new repetitive protein from *Xenopus laevis* skin highly homologous to pancreatic spasmolytic polypeptide. *J. Biol. Chem.* 263(16):7686–90

34. Hoffmann W, Hauser F. 1993. The P-domain or trefoil motif: a role in renewal and pathology of mucous eithelia? *Trends Biochem. Sci.* 18:239–43

35. Hoosein NM, Thim L, Jørgensen KH, Brattain MG. 1989. Growth stimulatory effect of pancreatic spasmolytic polypeptide on cultured colon and breast tumor cells. *FEBS Lett.* 247(2):303–6

36. Jakowlew SB, Breathnach R, Jeltsch J-M, Masiakowski P, Chambon P. 1984. Sequence of the pS2 mRNA induced by estrogen in the human breast cancer cell line MCF-7. *Nucleic Acids Res.* 12(6):2861–77

37. Jeffrey GP, Oates PS, Wang TC, Babyatsky MW, Brand SJ. 1994. Spasmolytic polypeptide: a trefoil peptide secreted by rat gastric mucous cells. *Gastroenterology* 106:336–45

38. Jeltsch J-M, Roberts M, Schatz C,

Garnier JM, Brown AMC, Chambon P. 1987. Structure of the human oestrogen-responsive gene pS2. *Nucleic Acids Res.* 15(4):1401–14

39. Jørgensen KD, Diamant B, Jørgensen KH, Thim L. 1982. Pancreatic spasmolytic polypeptide (PSP): III. Pharmacology of a new porcine pancreatic polypeptide with spasmolytic and gastric acid secretion inhibitory effects. *Regul. Pept.* 3:231–43

40. Jørgensen KH, Thim L, Jacobsen HE. 1982. Pancreatic spasmolytic polypeptide (PSP): 1. Preparation and initial chemical characterization of a new polypeptide from porcine pancreas. *Regul. Pept.* 3:207–19

41. Kida N, Yoshimura T, Mori K, Havasm K. 1989. Hormonal regulation of synthesis and secretion of pS2 protein relevant to growth of human breast cancer cells (MCF-7). *Cancer Res.* 49:3494–98

42. Kindon H, Pothoulakis C, Thim L, Lynch-Devaney K, Podolsky DK. 1995. Trefoil peptides protect intestinal epithelial monolayer/barrier function: cooperative interaction with mucin glycoprotein. *Gastroenterology.* In press

43. Koerner FC, Goldberg DE, Edgerton SM, Schwartz LH. 1992. pS2 protein and steroid hormone receptors in invasive breast carcinomas. *Int. J. Cancer* 52:183–88

44. Lefebvre O, Wolf C, Kédinger M, Chenard M-P, Tomasetto C, et al. 1993. The mouse one P-domain (pS2) and two P-domain (mSP) genes exhibit distinct patterns of extression. *J. Cell Biol.* 122 (1):191–98

45. Luqmani YA, Ryall G, Shousha S, Coombes RC. 1992. An immunohisto-chemical survey of pS2 expression in human epithelial cancers. *Int. J. Cancer* 50:302–4

46. Mashimo H, Podolsky DK, Fishman MC. 1995. Structure and expression of murine intestinal trefoil factor: high evolutionary conservation and post-natal expression. *Biochem. Biophys. Res. Commun.* 210:31–37

47. Masiakowski P, Breathnach R, Bloch J, Gannon F, Krust A, Chambon P. 1982. Cloning of cDNA sequences of hormone-regulated genes from the MCF-7 human breast cancer cell line. *Nucleic Acids Res.* 10(24):7895–903

48. May FEB, Westley BR. 1986. Cloning of estrogen-regulated messenger RNA sequences from human breast cancer cells. *Cancer Res.* 46:6034–40

49. May FEB, Westley BR. 1988. Identification and characterization of estrogen-regulated RNAs in human breast cells. *J. Biol. Chem.* 263:12901–8

50. Ménard D, Pothier P. 1991. Radiographic localization of epidermal growth factor receptors in human fetal gut. *Gastroenterology* 101:640–64

51. Mori K, Fujii R, Kida N, Ohta M, Hayaski K. 1988. Identification of a polypeptide secreted by human breast cancer cells (MCF-7) as the human estrogen-responsive gene (pS2) product. *Biochem. Biophys. Res. Commun.* 155:366–72

52. Nunez A-M, Berry M, Imler J-L, Chambon P. 1989. The 5' flanking region of the *pS2* gene contains a complex enhancer region responsive to oestrogens, epidermal growth factor, a tumour promoter (TPA), the c-Ha-ras oncoprotein and the *c-jun* protein. *EMBO J.* 8(3):823–29

53. Nunez A-M, Jakowlev S, Briand J-P, Gaire M, Krust A, et al. 1987. Characterization of the estrogen-induced pS2 protein secreted by the human breast cancer cell line MCF-7. *Endocrinology* 121(5):1759–65

54. Otto B, Wright N. 1994. Trefoil peptides: coming up clover. *Curr. Biol.* 4(9):835–38

55. Playford RJ, Marchbank T, Chinery R, Evison R, Pignatelli M, et al. 1995. Human spasmolytic polypeptide is a cytoprotective agent that stimulates cell migration. *Gastroenterology* 108:108–16

56. Podolsky DK, Lynch-Devaney K, Stow JL, Oates P, Murgue B, et al. 1993. Identification of human intestinal trefoil factor: goblet cell-specific expression of a peptide targeted for apical secretion. *J. Biol. Chem.* 268(9):6694–702

57. Prud'Homme J-F, Fridlansky F, Le Cunff M, Atger M, Mercier-Bodard C, et al. 1985. Cloning of a gene expressed in human breast cancer and regulated by estrogen in MCF-7 cells. *DNA* 4:11–21

58. Rio M-C, Bellocq JP, Daniel JY, Tomasetto C, Lathe R, et al. 1988. Breast cancer-associated pS2 protein: synthesis and secretion by normal stomach mucosa. *Science* 241:705–8

59. Rio M-C, Bellocq JP, Gairard B, Koehl C, Renaud R, Chambon P. 1988. Specific expression of human *pS2* gene in breast cancer. *Biochimie* 70:961–68

60. Rio M-C, Bellocq JP, Gairard B, Rasmussen UB, Krust A, et al. 1987. Specific expression of th *pS2* gene in subclasses of breast cancers in comparison with expression of the estrogen and progesterone receptors and the oncogene

*ERBB2. Proc. Natl. Acad. Sci. USA* 84:9243–47

61. Rio M-C, Chambon P. 1990. The *pS2* gene, mRNA, and protein: a potential marker for human breast cancer. *Cancer Cells* 2(8-9):269–74

62. Rio M-C, Chenard M-P, Wolf C, Marcellin L, Tomasetto C, et al. 1991. Induction of *pS2* and hSP genes as markers of mucosal ulceration of the digestive tract. *Gastroenterology* 100:375–79

63. Sands BE, Ogata H, Lynch-Devaney K, deBeaumont M, Ezzell RM, Podolsky DK. 1995. Molecular cloning of the rat intestinal trefoil factor gene: characterization of an intestinal goblet cell-associated promoter. *J. Biol. Chem.* 270 (16):9353–61

64. Schwartz LH, Koerner FC, Edgerton SM, Sawicka JM, Rio M-C, et al. 1991. *pS2* expression and response to hormonal therapy in patients with advanced breast cancer. *Cancer Res.* 51:624–28

65. Seitz G, Thelsinger B, Tomasetto G, Rio M-C, Chambon P, et al. 1991. Breast cancer-associated protein pS2 expression in tumors of the binary tract. *Am. J. Gastroenterol.* 86(10):1491–94

66. Skilton RA, Luqmani YA, McLelland RA, Coombes RC. 1989. Characterization of a messenger RNA selectively expressed in human breast cancer. *Br. J. Cancer* 60:168–75

67. Stettler Ch, Schmassmann A, Poulsom R, Hirschi C, Flogerzi B, et al. 1995. Effect of hepatocyte growth factor on expression of trefoil peptides in injured gastric mucosa. *Gastroenterology* 108: A226 (Abstr.)

68. Suemori S, Lynch-Devaney K, Podolsky DK. 1991. Identification and characterization of rat intestinal trefoil factor: tissue- and cell-specific member of the trefoil protein family. *Proc. Natl. Acad. Sci. USA* 88:11017–21

69. Takahasi H, Kida N, Fujii R, Tanaka K, Ohta M, et al. 1990. Expression of the *pS2* gene in human gastric cancer cells derived from poorly differentiated adenocarcinoma. *FEBS Lett.* 261(2): 283–86

70. Taupin DR, Cook GA, Yeomans ND, Giraud AS. 1994. Increased trefoil peptide expression occurs late in the healing phase in a model of gastric ulceration in the rat. *Gastroenterology* 106:A195 (Abstr.)

71. Taupin DR, Ooi K, Shulkes A, Giraud AS. 1994. Identification of human intestinal trefoil factor in the colonic adenoma-carcinoma sequence. *Gastroenterology* 106:A635 (Abstr.)

72. Theisinger B, Welter C, Grzeschik K-H, Blin N. 1992. Assignment of the gene for human spasmolytic protein (hSP/S ML1) to chromosome 21. *Hum. Genet.* 89:681–82

73. Thim L. 1988. A surprising sequence homology. *Biochem. J.* 253:309

74. Thim L. 1989. A new family of growth factor-like peptides: "trefoil" disulphide loop structures as a common feature in breast cancer associated peptide (pS2), pancreatic spasmolytic polypeptide (PSP), and frog skin peptides (spasmolysins). *FEBS Lett.* 250(1):85–90

75. Thim L. 1994. Trefoil peptides: a new family of gastrointestinal molecules. *Digestion* 55:353–60

76. Thim L, Jørgensen KH, Jørgensen KD. 1982. Pancreatic spasmolytic polypeptide (PSP): II. radioimmunological determination of PSP in porcine tissues, plasma and pancreatic juice. *Regul. Pept.* 3:221–30

77. Thim L, Norris K, Norris F, Nielsen PF, Bjorn SE, et al. 1993. Purification and characterization of the trefoil peptide human spasmolytic polypeptide (hSP) produced in yeast. *FEBS Lett.* 318(3):345–52

78. Thim L, Thomsen J, Christensen M, Jørgensen KH. 1985. The amino acid sequence of pancreatic spasmolytic polypeptide. *Biochim. Biophys. Acta* 827:410–18

79. Thim L, Wöldike HF, Nielsen PF, Christensen M, Lynch-Devaney K, Podolsky DK. 1995. Characterization of human and rat intestinal trefoil factor produced in yeast. *Biochemistry* 34(14):4757–64

80. Tomasetto C, Rio M-C, Gautier C, Wolf C, Hareuveni M, et al. 1990. hSP, the domain-duplicated homolog of pS2, is co-expressed with pS2 in stomach but not in breast carcinoma. *EMBO J.* 9(2):407–14

81. Tomasetto C, Rockel N, Mattei MG, Fujita R, Rio M-C. 1992. The gene encoding the human spasmolytic protein (SML1/hSP) is in 2lq22.3, physically linked to the homologous breast cancer marker gene BCEI/pS2. *Genomics* 13: 1328–33

82. Tomasetto C, Wolf C, Rio M-C, Mehtali M, LeMeur M, et al. 1989. Breast cancer protein pS2 synthesis in mammary gland of transgenic mice and secretion into milk. *Mol. Endocrinol.* 3(10):1579–84

83. Wright NA. 1993. Trefoil peptides and the gut. *Gut* 34:577–79

84. Wright NA, Pike C, Elia G. 1990. Induction of a novel epidermal growth factor-secreting cell lineage by mucosal ulceration in human gastrointestinal stem cells. *Nature* 343:82–85

85. Wright NA, Poulsom R, Stamp G, Van Norden S, Sarraf C, et al. 1992. Trefoil peptide gene expression in gastrointestinal epithelial cells in inflammatory bowel disease. *Scand. J. Gastroenterol.* 27(Suppl. 193):76–82

86. Wright NA, Poulsom R, Stamp GWH, Hall PA, Jeffery RE, et al. 1990. Epidermal growth factor (EGF/URO) induces expression of regulatory peptides in damaged human gastrointestinal tissues. *J. Pathol.* 162:279–84

87. Wu GD, Beer DG, Moore JH, Orringer MB, Appelman HD, Traber PG. 1993. Sucrase-isomaltase gene expression in Barrett's esophagus and adenocarcinoma. *Gastroenterology* 105:837–44

*Annu. Rev. Physiol. 1996. 58:275–97*

# INTESTINE-SPECIFIC GENE TRANSCRIPTION

## Peter G. Traber and Debra G. Silberg

Departments of Medicine and Genetics, University of Pennsylvania, Philadelphia, Pennsylvania 19104-6144

KEY WORDS:    epithelium, transgene, homeobox, development, mouse, GATA, HNF-1

### ABSTRACT

The diverse cellular lineages that populate the intestinal epithelium are derived from committed stem cells located in intestinal crypts. The complex architecture of the intestinal epithelium results from well-orchestrated processes of cell-lineage allocation, proliferation of immature cells in the crypt compartment, differentiation of various cell lineages, migration of cells in defined patterns, and cell-specific programmed senescence. The patterns of intestinal gene transcription in the context of this complex architecture are regulated by the combinatorial effect of multiple positive and negative regulatory elements. Although the DNA regulatory elements required to recapitulate the pattern of endogenous gene expression appear to be spread over relatively large genomic distances, short promoters of several intestinal genes are sufficient to direct intestine-specific transcription. The sucrase-isomaltase gene promoter has multiple regulatory elements that bind tissue-restricted transcription factors. A critical factor in regulating the sucrase-isomaltase promoter is *Cdx2*, an intestine-specific homeobox gene related to *caudal*, that may also have a broader role in intestinal development and morphogenesis. As additional regulatory elements and their cognate DNA-binding proteins are identified, the challenge will be to define their integrated role in the regulation of intestine-specific genes and in the development and maintenance of the intestinal epithelium.

## INTRODUCTION

The function of the mammalian intestinal mucosa is defined by the sets of genes expressed in differentiated epithelial cell phenotypes. The expression of individual proteins in the intestine may be regulated at multiple control points, including synthesis and degradation of mRNA, translation of mRNA into protein, and processing or modification of synthesized proteins. Control of RNA synthesis (gene transcription) is one critical regulatory control point, particularly for tissue-specific, differentiation-dependent, and developmental

275

0066-4278/96/0315-0275$08.00

expression. This review examines the transcriptional control of genes that are expressed predominantly in intestinal epithelial cells. Presently, our understanding of intestinal gene transcription in the context of the integrated organ architecture is rudimentary. However, recent studies have begun to unravel the combinatorial network of transcriptional proteins that direct transcription of genes to intestinal epithelial cells.

## ORGANIZATION AND DEVELOPMENT OF THE INTESTINAL EPITHELIUM AND GENE EXPRESSION

An understanding of intestinal gene transcription must be placed in the context of the architecture of the intestinal epithelium, a structure with an exquisitely regulated spatial organization. Moreover, the developmental history of gene transcription may provide critical insight into the combined effect of temporally regulated transcriptional elements. The history of transcriptional events for a particular gene during developmental transitions also may aid in understanding the mechanisms that maintain adult patterns of gene transcription, as well as adaptation to disease. Given the primacy of the mouse as a mammalian developmental model, we describe the relationship of gene expression to the development and structure of the mouse intestinal epithelium. Many aspects of human intestinal development, as well as the architecture of the adult epithelium, closely parallel that of mouse, although there are important timing differences related to the duration of gestation (93).

The epithelium of the adult intestine is continually replaced from committed stem cells that are fixed approximately four cell positions above the base of the crypt (8, 28, 29). The crypts in mouse are monoclonal, but it is unclear how many stem cells there are in a single crypt or whether there is a hierarchical organization of stem cells that are in different stages of commitment to cell lineages (67). Stem cells give rise to four highly specialized epithelial phenotypes including absorptive enterocytes, mucous-secreting goblet cells, a variety of enteroendocrine cells that secrete specific hormones, and Paneth cells that synthesize antibacterial peptides and enzymes (9). The mechanisms of lineage allocation from stem cells have not been elucidated, but an understanding of this process may result from studies of the mechanisms that specify cell-specific gene transcription.

Crypt cells undergo several rounds of cell division while they reside in the crypt compartment. Enterocytes, oligomucous cells, and enteroendocrine cells migrate towards the villus tip, whereas Paneth cells reside in the base of the crypt. Because ultrastructural features of specific phenotypes are identifiable in crypts, it appears that the commitment to a particular lineage occurs early after the initial stem cell division. The preponderance of absorptive enterocytes on villi suggests that immature enterocytes in crypts are the most abundant proliferating cells. Proliferation ceases in the upper third of the crypt, and cell division does not occur once the cells migrate onto the villus. This is not an irreversible state, however, because enterocytes are capable of re-entering S phase (DNA syntheses) when forced to express the large T antigen of SV40 virus (31).

The complete process of differentiation occurs within the confined architecture of the crypt-villus unit. Differentiation can be viewed as the expression of gene products that endows the cell with functions associated with the terminal cellular phenotype. However, in any cell lineage there may be multiple differentiated states defining a continuum extending from the committed cell that arises from the stem cell pool to the villus tip cell undergoing a degenerative process. Because of their abundance, enterocytes have been most intensively analyzed with respect to the spatial expression of differentiated gene products. Although differentiation occurs along the crypt-villus axis for other epithelial cell types, the expression of specific gene products has not been as well defined as for enterocytes. Thus the timing and spatial localization of differentiation processes may vary for different cell lineages.

Most gene products that are characteristic of the differentiated enterocyte are first expressed in the upper crypt region near the crypt-villus junction. Many mRNAs, proteins, and enzymatic activities that define important enterocyte functions have been shown to be expressed first at this critical junction. For example, intestine-specific mRNAs that are expressed in this pattern include sucrase-isomaltase (SI) (51, 91, 95), lactase-phlorizin hydrolase (LPH) (70), and the sodium-glucose cotransporter 1 (35). Other intestinal gene products with a tissue-restricted pattern of expression, including aminopeptidase N (60), liver fatty acid-binding protein (36), GLUT 5, the fructose transporter (68), the $Na^+/H^+$ exchanger-3 (5), and cytochromes P450 IIA and IIB (92), are also first expressed at the crypt-villus junction. This listing of genes is not intended to be inclusive because genes expressed in this pattern continue to be described. Although direct measurement of transcription is not feasible in the intestinal epithelium, the abrupt increase in mRNA levels at the crypt-villus junction and evidence from transgenic mouse studies (outlined below) suggest that transcriptional induction of differentiated genes is intimately associated with the cessation of proliferation of cells in the upper third of the crypt. We suggest that this rapid induction of transcription of multiple genes is likely to involve the activation of preformed transcription factors rather than the de novo synthesis of all transcriptional proteins necessary for gene transcription.

The migration along the villus and the sloughing of epithelial cells at villus tip is a well organized process. In the adult mouse intestine, each villus is populated by the cells generated from 6 to 12 crypts. The cells that migrate out of a single crypt move in a cohesive band up the side of the villus to the point at the villus tip where they exfoliate into the lumen (66, 79). Several patterns of mRNA expression in enterocytes have been noted as they move from the base of the villus to the tip. One of the more commonly identified patterns is maximal expression of the mRNA at the crypt-villus junction through the mid-villus region, followed by a marked decrease in levels at the villus tip, as with the SI gene (51, 91, 95). In addition to a decrease in specific mRNA levels, fragmentation of DNA occurs in villus tip cells, which is suggestive of apoptosis or programmed cell death (25). Although the process of cell sloughing is not well characterized, the underlying mechanism is most likely loss of attachment to the underlying matrix rather than an active extrusion by advancing cells. These observations suggest that epithelial cells undergo an ordered process of cell senescence that includes cessation of transcription of certain intestine-specific genes and loss of attachment to matrix. However, it should be noted that some mRNAs such as SGLT-1 persist at high levels in villus tip cells (35). The mechanisms underlying decreased expression of mRNAs in villus tip cells and the relationship to a program of cellular senescence will require additional investigation.

Non-enterocyte epithelial cells also have specific patterns of cellular migration in the crypt-villus unit. Paneth cells move to the base of the crypt and have a total life span of between three and four weeks, after which they are presumably removed by a process of apoptosis (6). Goblet cells migrate in a similar pattern and at a similar rate to enterocytes, but no clear change in gene expression at the crypt-villus junction has been found. In fact, the few goblet cell gene products that have been described appear to be expressed throughout the length of the crypt-villus axis (10, 17). The enteroendocrine cell compartment is very complex, with over a dozen specific cell types (72, 107). Although these cells generally migrate in a pattern similar to that of enterocytes, there is evidence that some types of enteroendocrine cells have a longer residence time in the epithelium (90). The process of enteroendocrine cell differentiation may proceed along several hierarchical lineages with early cells in the lineages expressing several hormones and later cells expressing only one predominant form (73). Therefore, the process of differentiation in the intestinal epithelium varies depending on the lineage compartment.

The intricate structure of the adult epithelium arises as a result of multiple developmental transitions beginning in the mouse embryo and culminating after weaning, which occurs during the third week of life. The primitive gut tube, comprised of endoderm surrounded by mesenchyme, is established at approximately embryonic day 9 (E9). At E15 the pseudostratified endoderm undergoes a cranial to caudal transition into a simple columnar epithelium with nascent villi. Simultaneous with this important morphological change, the expression of certain intestine-specific genes is first detected (70, 76). From immediately before birth (at E19) to the second week of life, crypts develop from the intervillus epithelium and villi lengthen. Near the end of the third week of life, the suckling-weaning transition occurs, another major change in the developing mouse intestine (32, 33). This transition is marked by a cranial to caudal wave of cytodifferentiation and induction of gene expression. Although this transition occurs at the time of weaning and may occur precociously by forced weaning or administration of corticosteroids or thyroid hormones, the occurrence of this transition appears to be genetically predetermined. Thus by the mid-fourth postnatal week, the mouse small intestine has attained its adult form.

## REGULATION OF INTESTINAL PATTERNS OF GENE TRANSCRIPTION

An emerging theme in biology is that transitions in cell phenotypes are directed by the combinatorial effects of transcription factors expressed in (*a*) all cell types, (*b*) a few cell types (tissue-restricted), and (*c*) a single cell type (tissue-specific). Although the regulation of developmental transitions occurs through multiple mechanisms, including cell-matrix and cell-cell interactions and growth factors, it is the regulation of transcription that ultimately controls major phenotypic changes in cells. Similar to other tissues, the intricate coordination of gene expression during development of the mouse small intestine appears to be regulated predominantly by transcription of individual genes. The use of transgenic mice to examine patterns of intestinal gene transcription, pioneered by Gordon and colleagues (88, 89), has provided multiple insights into transcriptional mechanisms. Regulation of gene transcription in transgenic mice has been studied for several enterocyte genes, including members of the fatty acid-binding protein gene family and disaccharidases, as well as a few genes expressed in non-enterocytic cell lineages. The regulation of the fatty acid-binding protein gene family has included studies on intestinal fatty acid-binding protein (fabpi) (89), liver fatty acid-binding protein (fabpl) (88), and ileal lipid-binding protein (ilbp) (14). The most extensively investigated disaccharidase is sucrase-isomaltase (SI) (50, 51), although investigations have been initiated with lactase-phlorizin hydrolase (LPH) (97). Other genes that will lend insight into regulation of cell-specific transcription include the cryptdin gene family in Paneth cells (6), secretin in enteroendocrine cells (46), and intestinal trefoil protein in goblet cells (77). These transgenic studies have been very useful for deriving insights into the biology of intestinal epithelial cells, as reviewed previously (27–29, 34). This discussion concentrates on the implications of these studies for regulation of gene transcription, and a synthesis of the combined findings of these studies is used to highlight a number of concepts that appear to be recurring themes for the regulation of intestinal genes.

## Regulatory Elements in the Immediate 5' Upstream Region of Intestinal Genes Are Able to Direct Transcription to Intestinal Epithelial Cells

Full recapitulation of the patterns of intestinal gene transcription requires multiple regulatory elements acting in concert. For example, it has been estimated that there are seven functional elements in the region from nucleotides $-4000$ to $+21$ of the fabpl gene (71). In contrast, the elements sufficient to simply direct intestine-specific transcription for several genes appear to be embedded in relatively short stretches of DNA immediately upstream of the start of transcription. For example, nucleotides $-103$ to $+28$ of the rat fabpi gene are able to limit transcription to small intestinal enterocytes (12), although elements outside this region act to modulate expression (11, 12, 75, 89). A short region of the fabpl gene ($-132$ to $+21$) directs transcription of reporter genes to both hepatocytes and enterocytes (84), consistent with the pattern of expression of the endogenous gene (11, 30, 74, 84, 88). As details of the tissue-specific transcriptional mechanisms for these two related genes are characterized, comparison of the expression in liver and intestine should prove useful for understanding molecular differences between these two endodermally derived epithelial organs. The regulation of ilbp, another member of the fatty acid-binding protein family, was recently examined in transgenic animals. Similar to fabpi, a short promoter region containing nucleotides $-145$ to $+48$ was capable, in some transgenic lines, of directing transcription specifically to the distal portions of the small intestine (14).

The regulation of both the human and mouse SI genes has been investigated in transgenic mice (50, 51). Initially, long segments of both the human ($-3524$ to $+54$; 51) and mouse ($-8500$ to $+54$; 50) genes were shown to direct transcription specifically to intestinal epithelial cells. More recently, however, a short evolutionarily conserved promoter region ($-201$ to $+54$ in the mouse gene) has been shown to be sufficient to direct transcription specifically to the intestinal epithelium in most transgenic lines (J Tung & PG Traber, unpublished observations). Discrete DNA regulatory elements in this promoter and their cognate DNA-binding proteins are discussed below.

A number of other intestinal genes have been studied in transgenic mice, but mapping of regulatory elements has not progressed to the point of sufficiently narrowing the important region for cell-specific expression. Paneth cells express multiple defensin genes, termed cryptdins, that are lumenally secreted antibacterial peptides (63). Recently, nucleotides $-6500$ to $+34$ of the cryptdin-2 gene was found to direct expression of a reporter construct to Paneth cells (6). The 5'-flanking region of the secretin gene ($-1600$ to $+32$) has been shown to direct expression to intestinal enteroendocrine cells in the same distribution as the endogenous gene, although there was some ectopic expression in other tissues, including spleen, liver, testis, and thymus (46). A fascinating and unexpected finding resulted from an experiment designed to examine the expression of a chimeric construct linking the promoter for the mouse ornithine transcarbamylase gene (OTC) to the human cDNA for OTC for the purpose of correcting deficiency of this enzyme in the sparse fur mouse (40). OTC is normally expressed in both the liver and intestinal epithelium. However, the expression of the transgene was found only in the intestine and not in the liver, indicating that OTC represents another gene where there is complex interaction between liver and intestinal regulation.

In summary, those enterocyte-specific genes that have been examined in transgenic mice have short promoter regions capable of directing expression specifically to intestinal epithelial cells. Although it is clear that a number of DNA regulatory elements located outside of these short promoters are required for complete recapitulation of the epithelial cell lineage and temporal and spatial patterns of expression, careful examination of these promoters will likely lead to insights into intestinal gene transcription.

## Differential Gene Expression in Intestinal Epithelial Cell Lineages Appears to be Regulated by Both Positive and Negative Regulatory Elements

The expression of transgenes in different intestinal cell phenotypes has provided insight into the mechanisms that limit gene expression to a specific lineage. Recent data on the regulation of the SI gene demonstrates several aspects of cell-lineage-specific transcriptional regulation (50). Transgenic mice containing a construct linking bases −8500 to +54 of the mouse SI gene to the human growth hormone gene demonstrated intestine-specific expression, but high levels of GH were detected in each of the four phenotypes, including enterocytes, enteroendocrine cells, goblet cells, and Paneth cells (50). In contrast, it is well known that SI mRNA and protein are expressed only in enterocytes (51). These data suggest, therefore, that all intestinal epithelial cells contain the cellular machinery to direct transcription of the SI gene in the adult mouse epithelium. Furthermore, the developmental expression of the transgene in these animals suggests that there is a sequential activation of the transgene in different cell lineages with full expression in all epithelial cells attained by 33 days after birth (50). The several explanations for this developmental sequence of events include multiple elements within −8500 to +54 that are temporally activated in different cells, a threshold effect of transcription factors on the same element, or differential expression of other cofactors that mediate protein-protein interactions with DNA-binding proteins. What does the pattern of expression of the transgene in all adult epithelial cells imply for the regulation of the endogenous SI gene? One possibility is that the SI gene is transcribed in all epithelial cells but that differential regulation of SI mRNA stability results in stable expression of SI mRNA only in enterocytes. A second possibility is that transcription of the SI gene may be normally repressed in nonenterocytic cells via DNA elements that are not contained in the −8500 to +54 construct. Data obtained from enterocytic and enteroendo-crine cell lines are consistent with a transcriptional silencer hypothesis (50).

Findings in *fabpl* transgenic mice suggest that repression of transcription in certain cell lineages may be a common mechanism for restricting expression in the intestinal epithelium. Initial observations made in *fabpl* transgenic mice, using a construct linking bases −4000 to +21 of the *fabpl* promoter to the human growth hormone gene, showed that the transgene was aberrantly ex-pressed in certain enteroendocrine cells (88). Later experiments using immu-noelectron microscopy further showed that the transgene in these animals was expressed in each of the four intestinal epithelial phenotypes (96). Thus similar to the conclusions for the SI promoter, these investigators proposed that a transcriptional silencer outside of the limits of the construct was responsible for limiting expression of the endogenous gene to enterocytes. Therefore, we hypothesize that transcriptional repressors or silencers play a major role in the regulation of cell lineage gene transcription and, by extension, in the process of lineage allocation. Recent evidence from other tissues for repressors having this function (78), in combination with the data on SI and fabpl regulation, provides strong support for this hypothesis. Identification of the repressor/si-lencer elements in intestinal genes and their cognate DNA-binding proteins is expected to provide important insight into lineage allocation.

## Regulation of Spatial and Temporal Intestinal Gene Expression Requires Both Positive and Negative Regulatory Elements

The spatial assignment of gene expression in the intestine is remarkably complex. Although the spatial localization of biological functions has been recognized for decades, Gordon and his colleagues were the first to empha-size the importance of spatial addresses for gene regulation along the vertical (crypt-villus) and horizontal (cranial-caudal) axes of the gut. Moreover, they emphasized how these spatial addresses for gene transcription are temporally regulated during intestinal development and aging. Their findings have been summarized in a number of insightful reviews (27, 29, 34).

The onset of expression of enterocytic genes at the crypt-villus junction appears to be regulated by a combination of positive and negative elements. All fabpl transgenic constructs examined thus far demonstrate precocious expression of the transgene in crypt enterocytes (88, 96), indicating the like-lihood that a repressor element outside of the studied genomic DNA (−4000 to +21) is responsible for silencing expression of the endogenous gene. The importance of repressors for expression along the crypt-villus axis has been most clearly shown for the fabpi gene. Nucleotides −277 to +28 of the fabpi gene are capable of recapitulating the normal pattern of fabpi expression, with transcription initiated in the upper third of the crypt near the crypt-villus junction (12). However, the use of nucleotides −103 to +28 in transgenic mice resulted in precocious expression of the transgene in mid-crypt cells, although enterocyte-specific expression was maintained. There is a similar situation for the SI gene, although the elements have been less precisely defined. Bases −3424 to +54 of the human SI gene directed expression of the transgene to both enterocytes and enteroendocrine cells, but the vertical pattern of expression in enterocytes was similar to the endogenous gene (51). As described above, when bases −8500 to +54 of the mouse SI gene were used in transgenic mice, all intestinal epithelial cells expressed the transgene. In enterocytes, expression of the transgene was readily detectable in crypts, but expression was markedly increased at the crypt-villus junction. Therefore, for a number of genes examined, the transcriptional machinery necessary for expression is present in crypt enterocytes, but transcription of the endogenous gene is normally repressed. One caveat that should be considered in the analysis of these transgenic studies is that the level of expression of the transgene and/or the sensitivity of the detection method may give a false impression regarding the difference in expression between crypt and villus cells.

One of the most fascinating concepts emerging from transgenic studies is the fact that multiple elements are required for regulation along the horizontal axis of the intestine. Every gene that has been studied, including fabpl, fabpi, ilbp, and SI, has been found to have different DNA regulatory elements that are required for modulating transcription in different bowel segments.

The final concept that has been underscored by transgenic experiments is that all regulatory elements must be considered in the context of a temporal pattern of activation during intestinal development and aging. Description of the developmental expression of transgenes can be found in numerous publications and reviews by Gordon and colleagues (27, 29, 34, 74, 76). One study showed that transcriptional elements may continue to be regulated well into adulthood (11), thereby expanding the intestinal developmental time frame.

## INTESTINE-SPECIFIC PROMOTERS

Transgenic mouse experiments show that the fidelity of transcriptional activation and repression within cell lineages and along the spatial axes of the intestine is regulated for each gene by a combination of multiple transcriptional elements. This complexity will require careful analysis of each regulatory element, and its interaction with other elements, to formulate a molecular

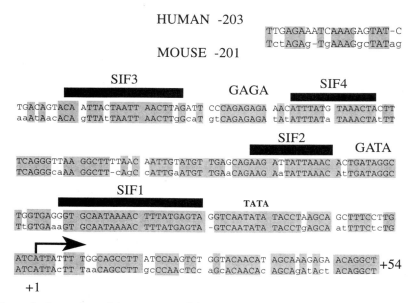

*Figure 1* Comparison of the sequences of the mouse and human promoters of the sucrase-isomaltase gene. The arrow indicates the start of transcription, which was determined in human and mouse genes by primer extension analysis. TATA indicates the putative binding site of TBP. Black bars over the sequence indicate regions that have been shown to have DNase I footprints using nuclear extracts from various cell types (described further in text). SIF is an abbreviation for sucrase isomaltase footprint. GATA and GAGA indicate sites that may bind a particular class of transcription factor and, therefore, are potential functional elements in the promoter (see text).

model for regulation of intestinal gene transcription. Because short promoter regions of several genes are capable of restricting expression to intestinal epithelial cells, an understanding of the molecular mechanisms of this restricted gene transcription is an important first step in unraveling the complexity of the overall process. Short promoter regions for several intestinal genes, including SI, fabpi, and ilbp, have been shown in transgenic mice to direct transcription to enterocytes. This discussion concentrates on SI with a briefer treatment of fabpi and ilbp.

The evolutionarily conserved portion of the mouse SI gene (−201 to +54) has recently been shown to direct intestine-specific gene transcription in transgenic mice (J Tung & PG Traber, unpublished data). Expression of the transgene was found predominantly in enterocytes, although there was expression in some enteroendocrine cells. This region of the SI gene has been mapped in cell lines for nuclear protein-binding sites and transcriptionally functional elements (86, 94, 104, 105) and thus serves as a good model for understanding the molecular mechanisms for intestine-specific transcriptional regulation. A summary of the confirmed and possible regulatory sites is shown in Figure 1. Most analyses of these regulatory elements have been performed in cell lines, although some of the DNA-protein interactions have been evaluated using intestinal epithelial cell nuclear extracts. The primary cell line used in these studies was Caco-2, which was derived from a colonic adenocarcinoma and, in some respects, models a differentiated enterocyte in cell culture, particularly in the postconfluent state (65). For analysis of the SI promoter, it is important to note that Caco-2 cells express significant amounts of SI mRNA and protein.

## SIF1-Binding Proteins and the Caudal-Related Family of Transcription Factors

Sequence analysis of the SI promoter revealed a 22-base region immediately upstream of the putative TATA box that is identical between mouse (94) and human (105) genes. Studies on the interaction of nuclear proteins with the promoter region confirmed that this evolutionarily conserved DNA sequence may be important for SI gene transcription. DNase I footprint analysis showed that nuclear proteins from Caco-2 cells protected this 22-base region, whereas nuclear extracts from HepG2 cells, a liver cancer cell line, or HeLa cells, a cervical cancer cell line, did not contain nuclear proteins that interacted with this site. (The site was named SIF1 for sucrase isomaltase footprint 1.) Additional analysis showed that this site interacted with nuclear proteins in some intestinal cell lines and intestinal epithelial cells but not with nuclear extracts from multiple other cell types (94). Transfection of chimeric SI promoter-luciferase plasmids into Caco-2, HepG2, and HeLa cells demonstrated that the human SI promoter (−183 to +54) directed transcription specifically in Caco-2 cells and that this activity was in large part dependent on the SIF1 sequence (94). Thus the SIF1 element was found to be a functional activator of SI promoter transcription, which binds nuclear proteins found only in intestinal cell lines.

SIF1-interacting proteins were cloned by screening a mouse small intestinal λ gt11 expression library utilizing the molecular interaction between the SIF1 DNA sequence and fusion proteins expressed by the phage vector (86). One cDNA isolated in this fashion encoded a protein in the caudal family of homeodomain containing proteins. *Caudal* is a homeobox gene (*cad*) involved in early axial pattern formation in *Drosophila melanogaster* (49, 57–59). Using the sequence of the *cad* gene, other *caudal* family members have been cloned from multiple animal species (4, 7, 22, 23, 26, 38, 39, 81). In mouse, there have been three independent *caudal*-related genes cloned—*Cdx1* (18), *Cdx2* (37, 38, 86), and *Cdx4* (24). The cloned cDNA that interacted with the SIF1 element was found to contain the full coding sequence of *Cdx2* (86). Studies have confirmed that Cdx2 protein interacts specifically with the SIF1 element and that it serves to activate transcription of the SI promoter (86). Antibodies generated to Cdx2 protein were used to show that the predominant, if not the exclusive, SIF1-binding protein in intestinal cell lines is the Cdx2 protein (86). Therefore, Cdx2 is an excellent candidate as a critical transcriptional protein for regulation of the SI gene in the intestine.

The current information regarding the function of the SIF1 element and Cdx2 does not definitively confirm their importance for SI gene transcription in vivo. Function of the SIF1 element has been demonstrated in cell lines, which must be confirmed by site-directed mutants of the promoter expressed in transgenic mice. The most direct assessment of the importance of Cdx2 on expression of SI would be to eliminate expression of the Cdx2 protein in Caco-2 cells and determine whether SI expression is affected. This approach is feasible because Cdx2 seems to be the only SIF1-binding protein expressed in Caco-2 cells. Despite these caveats, the evidence is strong that the Cdx2 protein is involved in transactivation of the SI promoter.

## SIF2 and SIF3 Elements and Hepatocyte Nuclear Factor 1 (HNF-1)

Both the SIF2 and 3 elements in the SI promoter were shown to act as positive regulatory elements in transfection studies (86). Moreover, DNA-binding studies indicated that the same nuclear-binding protein binds to both elements with different affinities. Because of marked similarity of SIF3 to the consensus sequence for HNF-1, we examined HNF-1 proteins to determine if they were involved in regulation of the SI promoter. HNF-1 is a member of a class of transcription proteins containing a DNA-binding domain that is distantly related to the homeodomain and binds to DNA as dimers [for review see (52)]. The two members of this family that have been described are HNF-1$\alpha$ (3, 21, 41, 44, 53), expressed in liver, kidney, stomach, and small and large intestine (3, 19, 45); and HNF-1$\beta$ (2, 15, 53, 69), which is expressed in liver, stomach, large and small intestine, kidney, ovary, and lung (53).

We found that the SIF2 and SIF3 DNA elements bind HNF-1$\alpha$ and HNF-1$\beta$ with different affinities (104). This analysis was performed using nuclear extracts from a cell line that does not express HNF-1 protein after transfection with an expression vector for either HNF-1$\alpha$ or HNF-1$\beta$. The HNF-1$\alpha$ and HNF-1$\beta$ proteins bound to the SIF2 DNA element with nearly identical affinities, whereas HNF-1$\alpha$ bound to the SIF3 element with approximately a sixfold greater affinity than HNF-1$\beta$ (104). An interesting functional difference was found between HNF-1$\alpha$ and HNF-1$\beta$ in transfection experiments. Cotransfection of an HNF-1$\alpha$ expression vector activated transcription of SI promoter constructs containing either a SIF2 or SIF3 element. In contrast, HNF-1$\beta$ was unable to activate transcription from either construct.

Because of the wide tissue distribution of HNF-1α and HNF-1β, it is clear that these proteins are not sufficient for intestinal transcription of the SI gene. However, they may interact with other proteins such as Cdx2, resulting in augmentation of transcription. There are a number of mechanisms by which HNF-1 proteins might modify expression of the SI gene during development and in the adult intestine. The different effects of HNF-1α and HNF-1β on the SI promoter suggest that different ratios of these two proteins may have different effects on SI promoter activation. HNF-1α and HNF-1β have been shown to be expressed in all epithelial cells along the entire length of the small intestine and colon, with a higher ratio of HNF-1β to HNF-1α in the colon than the small intestine (80). HNF-1α is expressed at high levels in crypt cells and expression gradually tapers off until there are low levels in the villus tip (80); the protein persists in tip cells (56). HNF-1β is also expressed at high levels in crypt cells, but there was a more precipitous decline in levels resulting in low levels of expression in all villus cells (80); protein expression has not been examined. Thus different levels of the two proteins along the horizontal and vertical axes of the intestine may potentially modulate transcription. The ability of HNF-1α and HNF-1β to heterodimerize with each other adds another level of complexity to potential regulatory effects on the SI promoter (16, 53, 69). Another potential level for regulation is via a dimerization cofactor-(DCoH), which regulates formation of tetrameric complexes of HNF-1 proteins (54).

## GATA-Binding Proteins

The first GATA-binding transcription protein (GATA-1) was cloned by virtue of its interaction with an important regulatory element [(A/T)GATA(A/G)], which is present in promoters and enhancers of genes expressed in hematopoietic cells (99). GATA-1 was found to activate transcription of hematopoietic promoters and enhancers by binding to DNA via a protein domain containing two similar zinc fingers. Additional GATA proteins have been cloned by virtue of their homology to GATA-1 in the zinc finger DNA-binding domain. Of great potential interest for regulation of intestinal genes, GATA-4, -5, and -6 are expressed in the developing and adult stomach and intestine, as well as the heart (1, 42). GATA-4 is expressed in a restricted pattern in the adult mouse with abundant mRNA found in heart, ovary, and testes and lower amounts in lung, liver, and small intestine (1). GATA-4 mRNA is expressed in primitive endoderm in day 5 embryos, in intestinal endoderm in day 14 embryos, and in both crypt and villus epithelium in the adult mouse intestine (1). Mouse GATA-5 and -6 have not yet been cloned, but the chicken genes have interesting differential patterns of expression in the developing chicken gut (42). Therefore, it is likely that GATA factors are important for gene regulation in intestinal tissue.

The interaction of GATA-binding proteins with the SI promoter and their influence on regulation of gene transcription is an interesting possibility. A consensus GATA site in the SI promoter (TGATAG) has not been investigated as extensively as SIF1, 2, and 3, but there is preliminary evidence that intestinal cell lines express GATA-binding proteins, that known GATA-binding proteins interact with the SI promoter GATA site, and that mutation of the GATA site significantly impairs SI promoter transcription (S Long, L Chen & PG Traber, unpublished data). Additional work will be required to characterize regulation of the SI promoter via this element and to determine which GATA factors may be involved in this regulation. In addition, careful analysis of GATA protein expression in the developing mouse intestine may provide insight into their role in intestinal gene expression.

## Other Potential Regulatory Elements and Binding Proteins

One element in the SI promoter that is evolutionarily conserved contains an inverted repeat of TTTA separated by two bases (SIF4 in Figure 1). Although a weak footprint is found in this region, using Caco-2 nuclear extracts (94), a strong footprint is found using liver nuclear extract (106). Screening a liver cDNA expression library with a double-stranded oligonucleotide probe for SIF4 resulted in identification of the mouse orthologue of human E4BP4 (106), a transcription factor of the basic-leucine zipper class that has been shown to be a transcriptional repressor protein (13). The mRNA for this protein seems to be ubiquitously expressed in the mouse, and it is unclear what function it may play in the regulation of the SI gene (PG Traber, unpublished data). However, it is likely that other members of the basic leucine zipper class of transcription factors are able to bind to this site. Thus this element remains a potentially important region of the SI gene for regulation of the promoter, either by the ubiquitous factor we cloned or by other unidentified proteins.

Another potentially interesting site is the conserved $(GA)_3$ repeat that is located between SIF3 and SIF4. A nuclear protein binds to the pentamer GAGAG, which is of functional importance in other genes. The GAGA protein binds to GA/CT-rich promoter regions in multiple *Drosophila* genes (85), the human CD11a gene (82), and the rat serine protease inhibitor 2.1 gene (43), creating DNase I hypersensitivity sites in DNA. The binding of the GAGA protein appears to disrupt the arrangement of nucleosomes, allowing access to the DNA for the initiation of transcription (20, 43, 47, 100). In *Drosophila*, the GAGA protein is bound constitutively to the promoter region of the uninduced hsp70 and hsp26 genes. After heat shock, the GAGA protein binds to the DNA in a 5' to 3' progression during transcription. The recruitment of GAGA protein to the induced hsp70 and hsp26 genes has kinetics similar to that found previously for RNA polymerase 11. The distribution of the GAGA protein and its pattern of binding to genes during transcription suggest that the protein may be necessary for transcription by opening the nucleosome structure allowing RNA polymerase 11 binding and transcription (61). Experimental evidence of a role for this protein in the SI promoter is not available.

## Function of the SI Promoter

It is clear that no one transcriptional protein identified to date is sufficient to direct the intestine-specific pattern found in the −201 to +54 mSI transgene. The *Cdx* genes are clearly insufficient because they are expressed in both small intestine and colon in adult animals and are expressed at the time of the endoderm-intestinal epithelial junction, when there is little SI gene expression. Therefore, the patterns of SI gene transcription are likely modulated by the combinatorial effects of multiple transcription factors. In addition, protein modifications including phosphorylation during development and in various cell lineages may be important for stage- or cell-specific function. Most importantly, there are likely protein cofactors that interact with the DNA-binding proteins to functionally link them to the basal transcriptional apparatus. Such cofactors could be envisioned to act by binding to a single DNA-binding protein, such as Cdx2, or to a complex of interacting proteins simultaneously bound to the SI promoter. An important example of such a cofactor in the determination of cell-specific transcriptional activation is the OCA-B protein in lymphocytes (48). This transcriptional cofactor is expressed specifically in B-lymphocytes and interacts with either the OCT1 or OCT2 proteins, presumably linking them to key factors in the basal transcriptional apparatus (48). Thus the expression of the cofactor in B-lymphocytes leads to activation of the immunoglobulin heavy chain promoter in only these cells rather than in other cells that also express the octamer proteins. In conclusion, once the majority of DNA-binding proteins that interact with specific elements are identified and functionally characterized, a great deal of work will remain to properly fit the pieces of the transcription factor puzzle together on the SI promoter.

## Other Intestine-Specific Promoters

The promoters of rat fabpi and mouse ilbp contain in sequences −103 to +28 and −145 to +48, respectively, the elements sufficient to restrict human growth hormone (hGH) reporter expression to intestinal enterocytes in transgenic adult mice. Although there is currently little functional information on regulatory elements for these promoters and their cognate DNA-binding proteins, some analysis has been performed. In both promoters there is one copy of a 14-bp element, conserved in mouse and human fabpi, that binds HNF-4 and apolipoprotein regulatory protein-1 (ARP-1) (14, 75). Cotransfection studies in CV-1 (monkey kidney cell line) and Caco-2 cells with fabpi linked to the hGH reporter and either HNF-4 or ARP-1, showed that HNF-4 can activate transcription from the promoter in CV-1 cells, and APR-1 activates transcription in Caco-2 cells.

Nucleotides −277 to −185 of fabpi contain part of a domain (−212 to −188) conserved between the three orthologous fabpi genes that binds nuclear factors present in colonic but not small intestinal epithelial cells. Removal of −277 to −185 results in inappropriate expression of hGH in proliferating epithelial cells located in the small intestine and colon (12). It appears that elements within −277 to −185 suppress expression in proliferating enterocytes. These data on fabpi and ilbp, when compared with data on the SI promoter, show that there are likely differences in how individual intestine-specific promoters are regulated.

## Function of Transcription Proteins in Development

A remarkable outgrowth of the characterization of transcription factors that direct tissue-specific gene transcription is that, in many cases, these same factors have important regulatory roles in development of the complete tissue or organ. Examples include the function of GATA proteins in hematopoietic development (64, 98); myoD, myogenin, and myf-5 in muscle development (102); and Pit1 in development of the anterior pituitary (101). The GATA-1 protein, which was isolated by virtue of its binding to regulatory elements in the β-globin gene, may be used to expand this concept. When a null mutation of the GATA-1 gene was produced in embryonic stem cells using homologous recombination, the entire hematopoietic lineage failed to develop in cultures of embryoid bodies or in homozygous null mice (64). Similarly, GATA-2 has a functional role in hematopoiesis (98). These data show that GATA genes are important for the overall process of hematopoiesis and not simply for activation of globin gene transcription in hematopoietic cells.

The discovery that Cdx2 is an important transcriptional protein for the SI promoter raises the issue of whether the *caudal*-related genes may have a more general function in intestinal development. Although *caudal*-related genes are found in many animal species and the patterns of expression have been carefully explored in some of these species, their function and gene targets have not been well described. In *Drosophila*, knockout of *cad* leads to impaired formation of posterior structures including the proctodeum and hindgut and portions of the distal midgut (49). From these and other data, the *cad* gene appears to play a role in axial pattern formation in early *Drosophila* development. An important gene target for *cad* in *Drosophila* is the segmentation gene *fuzi tarazu* (*ftz*), which has a number of functional *cad*-binding sites in its promoter (15).

In other animals, including mice, the functional role of caudal-related proteins has not been established, although developmental patterns of expression suggest important roles in early embryonic development. *Cdx1* mRNA and protein are first expressed in mouse embryos at day 7.5 in the region of the primitive streak, predominantly in nuclei of ectoderm and mesoderm and some in visceral endoderm (55). At day 7.75, expression extends to the entire posterior area, but there is no expression in definitive endoderm. Between embryonic day 8.25 and 12 there is variable expression of Cdx1 in a number of tissues including the neural tube, somites, the mesoderm, and limb buds. By day 12 there is marked reduction in expression, which correlates with undetectable levels of mRNA between days 11 and 14 (18). At approximately day 14, which is the time when the pseudostratified endoderm undergoes a transition to a columnar epithelium organized in nascent villi, *Cdx1* mRNA is expressed in embryonic intestine (18). Although the early embryonic expression of *Cdx2* has not been reported, Cdx2 protein is also expressed around the time of the endoderm-intestinal epithelial transition and continues to be expressed in adult mice along the entire crypt-villus axis of the small intestine and in crypts of the colon (37). We have preliminary evidence that Cdx2 expression precedes that of Cdx1 (83); however, no careful comparison of the expression of these two proteins in early intestinal development has been published. Finally, Cdx4 is expressed in posterior structures early in embryogenesis, but it is not expressed in the intestinal epithelium (24). Therefore, the currently available data on the pattern of expression of *Cdx* genes in mice suggests roles in both early developmental events and those occurring later during morphogenesis of the visceral endoderm into intestinal epithelium.

Recently, we have obtained preliminary evidence that Cdx2 has effects on both proliferation (87) and differentiation (E-R Suh & PG Traber, unpublished data) in an intestinal cell line. When expressed in IEC-6 cells using a conditional expression construct, Cdx2 caused an initial cessation of proliferation followed by growth to a high density, with evidence of morphologic and molecular differentiation. Thus the circumstantial data on the temporal pattern of expression in endoderm combined with this functional data in undifferentiated intestinal epithelial cells makes *caudal*-related genes an important target for study to elucidate the mechanisms of intestinal development.

## SUMMARY

The spectrum of DNA elements and their cognate-binding proteins that regulate the transcription of each gene expressed in the intestine is likely to be great. In fact, accumulating evidence shows that different regulatory regions act in complex patterns during intestinal development and maintenance of the intestinal phenotype. We believe that the degree of complexity being established for the few intestinal genes that have been studied will be applicable to most other intestinal genes. For this reason, it will be a challenge to find the similarities and common mechanisms between the regulation of different intestinal genes. However, the most progress will be made by using creative approaches to find commonality between the processes that govern expression of different gene products. We have attempted to point out common features of the regulation of transgenes, which should guide hypotheses for future investigation. One specific area of study related to transgenic experiments requires additional attention. It appears from most of the reported transgenic experiments that the chromosomal environment, or site of insertion of transgenic constructs, has a significant effect on the expression of the transgene. Additional exploration of the DNA regions flanking the regulatory elements already studied may provide evidence of locus control or matrix attachment regions that act to modulate and insulate regulatory elements from the effects of surrounding chromatin (62, 103). Moreover, we suggest that the addition of these types of regulatory elements may modulate the function of the currently described promoters in ways that are not predictable.

Conceptually, the comparison of genes that are expressed in both the intestine and liver provide an opportunity to understand molecular similarities and differences in these two organs. Well characterized genes that will continue to be important for this purpose include fabpl and ornithine transcarbamylase.

Understanding the integrated mechanism of intestine-specific transcription for even a single gene will require careful analysis of each regulatory element in a promoter that has been shown to be intestine-specific in transgenic animals. Moreover, each functional element that is characterized in cell lines must be validated in the context of the whole animal before ascribing its importance in the process. After the characterization of all elements and cognate-binding proteins, the even more involved task of the integration of transcription factor complexes, identification of functional posttranslational modifications, and the cloning of transcriptional cofactors must be tackled. Even though this daunting task awaits investigators in this field before a complete understanding of transcription of intestinal genes is gained, information regarding the function of transcription factors such as Cdx will likely provide a continual stream of important findings for intestinal biology and development.

## Literature Cited

1. Arceci RJ, King AAJ, Simon MC, Orkin SH, Wilson DB. 1993. Mouse GATA-4: a retinoic acid-inducible GATA-binding transcription factor expressed in endodermally derived tissues and heart. *Mol. Cell. Biol.* 13:2235–46
2. Baumhueter S, Courtois G, Crabtree GR. 1988. A variant nuclear protein in dedifferentiated hepatoma cells binds to the same functional sequences in the β fibrinogen gene promoter as HNF-1. *EMBO J.* 7:2485–93
3. Baumhueter S, Mendel DB, Conley PB, Kuo CJ, Turk C, et al. 1990. HNF-1 shares three sequence motifs with the POU domain proteins and is identical to LF-B1 and APF. *Genes Dev.* 4:372–79
4. Blumberg B, Wright CVE, DeRobertis EM, Cho KWY. 1991. Organizer-specific homeobox genes in *Xenopus laevis* embryos. *Science* 253:194–253
5. Bookstein C, Depaoli AM, Xie Y, Niu P, Musch MW, et al. 1994. Na$^+$/H$^+$ exchangers, NHE-1 and NHE-3, of rat intestine: expression and localization. *J. Clin. Invest.* 93:106–13
6. Bry L, Falk P, Huttner K, Ouellette A, Midtvedt T, Gordon JI. 1994. Paneth cell differentiation in the developing intestine of normal and transgenic mice. *Proc. Natl. Acad. Sci. USA* 91:10335–39
7. Burglin TR, Finney M, Coulson A, Ruvkun G. 1989. *Caenorhabditis elegans* has scores of homeobox-containing genes. *Nature* 341:239–43
8. Cheng H, Leblond CP. 1974. Origin, differentiation and renewal of the four main epithelial cell types in the mouse small intestine. 1. Columnar cell. *Am. J. Anat.* 141:461–80
9. Cheng H, Leblond CP. 1974. Origin, differentiation and renewal of the four main epithelial cell types in the mouse small intestine. V. Unitarian theory of the origin of the four epithelial cell types. *Am. J. Anat.* 141:537–62
10. Chinery R, Poulsom R, Rogers LA, Jeffery RE, Longcroft JM, et al. 1992. Localization of intestinal trefoil-factor mRNA in rat stomach and intestine by hybridization in situ. *Biochem. J.* 285:5–8
11. Cohn SM, Roth KA, Birkenmeier EH, Gordon JI. 1991. Temporal and spatial patterns of transgene expression in aging adult mice provide insights about the origins, organization, and differentiation of the intestinal epithelium. *Proc. Natl. Acad. Sci. USA* 88:1034–38
12. Cohn SM, Simon TC, Roth KA, Birkenmeier EH, Gordon JI. 1992. Use of transgenic mice to map *cis*-acting elements in the intestinal fatty acid binding protein gene (Fabpi) that control its cell lineage-specific and regional patterns of expression along the duodenal-colonic and crypt-villus axes of the gut epithelium. *J. Cell Biol.* 119:27–44
13. Cowell IG, Skinner A, Hurst HC. 1992. Transcriptional repression by a novel member of the bZIP family of transcription factors. *Mol. Cell. Biol.* 12:3070–77
14. Crossman MW, Hauft SM, Gordon JI. 1994. The mouse ileal lipid-binding protein gene: a model for studying axial patterning during gut morphogenesis. *J. Cell Biol.* 126:1547–64
15. Dearolf CR, Topol J, Parker CS. 1989. The *caudal* gene product is a direct activator of *fushi tarazu* transcription during *Drosophila* embryogenesis. *Nature* 341:340–43
16. De Simone V, De Magistris L, Lazzaro D, Gerstner J, Monaci P, Cortese R. 1991. LFB3, a heterodimer-forming homeodomain of the LFB1 family, is expressed in specialized epithelia. *EMBO J.* 10:1435–43
17. Dobbins WO, Austin LL. 1991. Electron microscopic definition of intestinal endocrine cells: immunogold localization and review. *Ultrastruct. Pathol.* 15:15–39
18. Duprey P, Chowdhury K, Dressler GR, Balling R, Simon D, et al. 1988. A mouse gene homologous to the *Drosophila* gene *caudel* is expressed in epithelial cells from the embryonic intestine. *Genes Dev.* 2:1647–54
19. Evans RM. 1988. The steroid and thyroid hormone receptor superfamily. *Science* 240:889–95
20. Farkas G, Gausz J, Galloni M, Reuter G, Gyurkovics H, Karch R. 1994. The trithorax-like gene encodes the *Drosophila* GAGA factor. *Nature* 371:806–8
21. Frain M, Swart G, Monaci P, Nicosia A, Stampfli S, et al. 1989. The liver-specific transcription factor LF-B1 contains a highly diverged homeobox DNA binding domain. *Cell* 59:145–57
22. Freund J-N, Boukamel R, Benazzouz A. 1992. Gradient expression of *cdx* along the rat intestine throughout postnatal development. *FEBS Lett.* 314:163–66
23. Frumkin A, Rangini Z, En-Yehuda A, Gruenbaum Y, Fainsod A. 1991. A chicken *caudal* homologue, *CHox-cad*,

is expressed in the epiblast with posterior localization and in the early endodermal lineage. *Development* 112:207–19

24. Gamer LW, Wright CVE. 1993. Murine *Cdx-4* bears striking similarities to the *Drosophila caudal* gene in its homeodomain sequence and early expression pattern. *Mech. Dev.* 43:71–81

25. Gavrieli Y, Sherman Y, Ben-Sasson SA. 1992. Identification of programed cell death in situ via specific labeling of nuclear DNA fragmentation. *J. Cell Biol.* 119:493–501

26. German MS, Wang J, Chadwick RB, Rutter WJ. 1992. Synergistic activation of the insulin gene by a LIM-homeo domain protein and a basic helix-loop-helix protein: building a functional insulin minienhancer complex. *Genes Dev.* 6:2165–76

27. Gordon JI. 1989. Intestinal epithelial differentiation: new insights from chimeric and transgenic mice. *J. Cell Biol.* 108:1187–94

28. Gordon JI. 1993. Understanding gastrointestinal epithelial cell biology: lessons from mice with help from worms and flies. *Gastroenterology* 104:315–24

29. Gordon JI, Schmidt GH, Roth KA. 1992. Studies of intestinal stem cells using normal, chimeric, and transgenic mice. *FASEB J.* 6:3039–50

30. Hansbrough JR, Lublin DM, Roth KA, Birkenmeier EH, Gordon JI. 1991. Expression of a liver fatty acid binding protein/human decay-accelerating factor/HLA-B44 chimeric gene in transgenic mice. *Am. J. Physiol.* 260: G929–39

31. Hauft SM, Kim SH, Schmidt GH, Pease S, Rees S, et al. 1992. Expression of SV-40 T antigen in the small intestinal epithelium of transgenic mice results in proliferative changes in the crypt and reentry of villus-associated enterocytes into the cell cycle but has no apparent effect on cellular differentiation programs and does not cause neoplastic transformation. *J. Cell Biol.* 117:825–39

32. Henning SJ. 1985. Ontogeny of enzymes in the small intestine. *Annu. Rev. Physiol.* 47:231–45

33. Henning SJ. 1987. Functional development of the gastrointestinal tract. In *Physiology of the Gastrointestinal Tract,* ed. LR Johnson, 2:285–300. New York: Raven

34. Hermiston ML, Gordon JI. 1993. Use of transgenic mice to characterize the multipotent intestinal stem cell and to analyze regulation of gene expression

in various epithelial cell lineages as a function of their position along the cephalocaudal and crypt-to-villus (or crypt-to-surface epithelial cuff) axes of the gut. *Semin. Dev. Biol.* 4:275–91

35. Hwang E-S, Hirayama BA, Wright EM. 1991. Distribution of the SGLT1 Na+/glucose cotransporter and mRNA along the crypt-villus axis of rabbit small intestine. *Biochem. Biophys. Res. Commun.* 181:1208–17

36. Iseki S, Kondo H, Hitomi M, Ono T. 1990. Localization of liver fatty acid-binding protein and its mRNA in the liver and jejunum of rats: an immunohistochemical and in situ hybridization study. *Mol. Cell Biochem.* 98:27–33

37. James R, Erler T, Kazenwadel J. 1994. Structure of the murine homeobox gene *cdx-2:* expression in embryonic and adult intestinal epithelium. *J. Biol. Chem.* 269:15229–37

38. James R, Kazenwadel J. 1991. Homeobox gene expression in intestinal epithelium of adult mice. *J. Biol. Chem.* 266:3246–51

39. Joly J-S, Maury M, Joly C, Duprey P, Boulekbache H, Condamine H. 1992. Expression of a zebrafish caudal homeobox gene correlates with the establishment of posterior cell lineages at gastrulation. *Differentiation* 50:75–87

40. Jones SN, Grompe M, Munir MI, Veres G, Craigen WJ, Caskey CT. 1990. Ectopic correction of ornithine transcarbamylase deficiency in sparse fur mice. *J. Biol. Chem.* 265:14684–90

41. Kuo CJ, Conley PB, Hsieh C-L, Francke U, Crabtree GR. 1990. Molecular cloning, functional expression, and chromosomal localization of mouse hepatocyte nuclear factor 1. *Proc. Natl. Acad. Sci. USA* 87:9838–42

42. Laverriere AC, MacNeill C, Mueller C, Poelmann RE, Burch JBE, Evans T. 1994. GATA-4/5/6, a subfamily of three transcription factors transcribed in developing heart and gut. *J. Biol. Chem.* 269:23177–84

43. LeCam A, Pantescu V, Paquereau L, Legraverend C, Fauconnier G, Asins G. 1994. *cis*-acting elements controlling transcription from rat serine protease inhibitor 2.1 gene promoter. *J. Biol. Chem.* 269:21532–39

44. Lichtsteiner S, Schibler U. 1989. A glycosylated liver-specific transcription factor stimulates transcription of the albumin gene. *Cell* 57:1179–87

45. Lipson KE, Baserga R. 1989. Transcriptional activity of the human thymidine kinase gene determined by a method using the polymerase chain reaction and

an intron-specific probe. *Proc. Natl. Acad. Sci. USA* 86:9774–77

46. Lopez MJ, Upchurch BH, Rindi G, Leiter AB. 1995. Studies in transgenic mice reveal potential relationships between secretin-producing cells and other endocrine cell types. *J. Biol. Chem.* 270: 885–91

47. Lu Q, Wallrath LL, Granok H, Elgin SCR. 1993. (CT)n (GA)n repeats and heat shock elements have distinct roles in chromatin structure and transcriptional activation of the *Drosophila* hsp26 gene. *Mol. Cell. Biol.* 13:2802–14

48. Luo Y, Fujii H, Gerster T, Roeder RG. 1992. A novel B cell-derived coactivator potentiates the activation of immunoglobulin promoters by octamer-binding transcription factors. *Cell* 71:231–41

49. Macdonald PM, Struhl G. 1986. A molecular gradient in early *Drosophila* embryos and its role in specifying the body pattern. *Nature* 324:537–45

50. Markowitz AJ, Wu GD, Bader A, Cui Z, Chen L, Traber PG. 1995. Regulation of the sucrase-isomaltase gene in transgenic mice and cell lines suggest that transcriptional repression is important for appropriate cell-lineage expression in the intestinal epithelium. *Am. J. Physiol.* In press

51. Markowitz AJ, Wu GD, Birkenmeier EH, Traber PG. 1993. The human sucrase-isomaltase gene directs complex patterns of gene expression in transgenic mice. *Am. J. Physiol.* 265:G526–39

52. Mendel DB, Crabtree GR. 1991. HNF-1, a member of a novel class of dimerizing homeodomain proteins. *J. Biol. Chem.* 266:677–80

53. Mendel DB, Hansen LP, Graves MK, Conley PB, Crabtree GR. 1991. HNF-1α and HNF1β (vHNF-1) share dimerization and homeo domains, but not activation domains, and form heterodimers in vitro. *Genes Dev.* 10:1042–56

54. Mendel DB, Khavari PA, Conley PB, Graves MK, Hansen LP, et al. 1991. Characterization of a cofactor that regulates dimerization of a mammalian homeodomain protein. *Science* 254: 1762–67

55. Meyer BI, Gruss P. 1993. Mouse *cdx-1* expression during gastrulation. *Development* 117:191–203

56. Miura N, Iwai K, Miyamoto I. 1993. Immunological characterization of hepatocyte nuclear factor 1 protein: appearance of hepatocyte nuclear factor 1 protein in developing mouse embryos. *Eur. J. Cell Biol.* 60:376–82

57. Mlodzik M, Fjose A, Gehring WJ. 1985. Isolation of *caudal*, a *Drosophila* homeo box-containing gene with maternal expression, whose transcripts for a concentration gradient at the pre-blastoderm stage. *EMBO J.* 4:2961–69

58. Mlodzik M, Gehring WJ. 1987. Expression of the caudal gene in the germ line of Drosophila: formation of an RNA and protein gradient during early embryogenesis. *Cell* 48:465–78

59. Mlodzik M, Gibson G, Gehring WJ. 1990. Effects of ectopic expression of *caudal* during *Drosophila* development. *Development* 109:271–77

60. Noren O, Dabelsteen E, Hoyer PE, Olsen J, Sjostrom H, Hansen GH. 1989. Onset of transcription of the aminopeptidase N (leukemia antigen CD 13) gene at the crypt/villus transition zone during rabbit enterocyte differentiation. *FEBS Lett.* 259:107–12

61. O'Brien T, Wilkins RC, Giardina C, Lis JT. 1995. Distribution of GAGA protein on *Drosophila* genes in vivo. *Genes Dev.* 9:1098–110

62. Orkin SH. 1990. Globin gene regulation and switching: circa 1990. *Cell* 63:665–72

63. Ouellette AJ, Greco RM, James M, Frederick D, Naftilan J, Fallon JT. 1989. Developmental regulation of cryptdin, a corticostatin/defensin precursor mRNA in mouse small intestinal crypt epithelium. *J. Cell Biol.* 108:1687–95

64. Pevny L, Simon MC, Robertson E, Klein WH, Tsai SF, et al. 1991. Erythroid differentiation in chimeric mice blocked by a targeted mutation in the gene for transcription factor GATA-1. *Nature* 349:257–60

65. Pinto M, Robine-Leon S, Appay M-D, Kedinger M, Triadou N, et al. 1983. Enterocyte-like differentiation and polarization of the human colon carcinoma cell line caco-2 in culture. *Biol. Cell* 47:323–30

66. Ponder BAJ, Schmidt GH, Wilkinson MM, Wood MJ, Monk M, Reid A. 1985. Derivation of mouse intestinal crypts from single progenitor cells. *Nature* 313: 689–91

67. Potten CS, Loeffler M. 1990. Stem cells: attributes, cycles, spirals, pitfalls and uncertainties. Lessons from the crypt. *Development* 110:1001–20

68. Rand EB, Depaoli AM, Davidson NO, Bell GI, Burant CF. 1993. Sequence, tissue distribution, and functional characterization of the rat fructose transporter GLUT5. *Am. J. Physiol.* 264: G1169–76

69. Rey-Campos J, Chouard T, Yaniv M, Cereghini S. 1991. vHNF1 is a homeoprotein that activates transcription and

forms heterodimers with HNF1. *EMBO J.* 10:1445–57

70. Rings EHHM, DeBoar PAJ, Moorman AFM, VanBeers EH, Deller J, et al. 1992. Lactase gene expression during early development of rat small intestine. *Gastroenterology* 103:1154–61

71. Roth KA, Hermiston ML, Gordon JI. 1991. Use of transgenic mice to infer the biological properties of small intestinal stem cells and to examine the lineage relationships of their descendants. *Proc. Natl. Acad. Sci. USA* 88:9407–11

72. Roth KA, Hertz JM, Gordon JL. 1990. Mapping enteroendocrine cell populations in transgenic mice reveals an unexpected degree of complexity in cellular differentiation within the gastrointestinal tract. *J. Cell Biol.* 110:1791–801

73. Roth KA, Kim S, Gordon JI. 1992. Immunocytochemical studies suggest two pathways for enteroendocrine cell differentiation in the colon. *Am. J. Physiol.* 263:G174–80

74. Roth KA, Rubin DC, Birkenmeier EH, Gordon JI. 1991. Expression of liver fatty acid-binding protein/human growth hormone genes within the enterocyte and enteroendocrine cell populations of fetal transgenic mice. *J. Biol. Chem.* 266:5949–54

75. Rottman JN, Gordon JI. 1993. Comparison of the patterns of expression of rat intestinal fatty acid binding protein/human growth hormone fusion genes in cultured intestinal epithelial cell lines and in the gut epithelium of transgenic mice. *J. Biol. Chem.* 268:11994–2002

76. Rubin DC, Ong DE, Gordon JI. 1989. Cellular differentiation in the emerging fetal rat small intestinal epithelium: mosaic patterns of gene expression. *Proc. Natl. Acad. Sci. USA* 86:1278–82

77. Sands BE, Haruhiko O, Lynch-Devaney K, deBeaumont M, Ezzell RM, Podolsky DK. 1995. Molecular cloning of the rat intestinal trefoil factor gene: characterization of an intestinal goblet cell-associated promoter. *J. Biol. Chem.* 270:9353–61

78. Sawada S, Scarborough JD, Killeen N, Littman DR. 1994. A lineage-specific transcriptional silencer regulates CD4 gene expression during T lymphocyte development. *Cell* 77:917–29

79. Schmidt GH, Wilkinson MM, Ponder BAJ. 1985. Cell migration pathway in the intestinal epithelium: an in situ marker system using mouse aggregation chimeras. *Cell* 40:425–29

80. Serfas MS, Tyner AL. 1993. HNF-1α and HNF-1β expression in mouse intestinal crypts. *Am. J. Physiol.* 265:G506–13

81. Serrano J, Scavo L, Roth J, de la Rosa EJ, de Pablo F. 1993. A novel chicken homeobox-containing gene expressed in neurulating embryos. *Biochem. Biophys. Res. Commun.* 190:270–76

82. Shelley CS, Farokhzad OC, Arnaout MA. 1993. Identification of cell-specific and developmentally regulated nuclear factors that direct myeloid and lymphoid expression of the CD11a gene. *Proc. Natl. Acad. Sci. USA* 90:5364–68

83. Silberg DG, Traber PG. 1995. Developmental expression of the *caudal* related homeodomain transcription factors Cdx-1 and Cdx-2. *Gastroenterology* 108:A753

84. Simon TC, Roth KA, Gordon JI. 1993. Use of transgenic mice to map *cis*-acting elements in the liver fatty acid-binding protein gene (*Fabpl*) that regulate its cell lineage-specific differentiation-dependent and spatial patterns of expression in the gut epithelium and in the liver acinus. *J. Biol. Chem.* 268:18345–58

85. Soeller WC, Oh CE, Kornberg TB. 1993. Isolation of cDNAs encoding the *Drosophila* GAGA transcription factor. *Mol. Cell. Biol.* 13:7961–70

86. Suh E-R, Chen L, Taylor J, Traber PG. 1994. A homeodomain protein related to caudal regulates intestine-specific gene transcription. *Mol. Cell. Biol.* 14:7340–51

87. Suh E-R, Traber PG. 1995. The intestine-specific homeobox gene *Cdx-2* regulates cell growth in intestinal cells (IEC-6). *Gastroenterology* 108:A541

88. Sweetser DA, Birkenmeier EH, Hoppe PC, McKeel DW, Gordon JI. 1988. Mechanisms underlying generation of gradients in gene expression within the intestine: an analysis using transgenic mice containing fatty acid binding protein-human growth hormone fusion genes. *Genes Dev.* 2:1318–32

89. Sweetser DA, Hauft SM, Hoppe PC, Birkenmeier EH, Gordon JI. 1988. Transgenic mice containing intestinal fatty acid-binding protein-human growth hormone fusion genes exhibit correct regional and cell-specific expression of the reporter gene in their small intestine. *Proc. Natl. Acad. Sci. USA* 85:9611–15

90. Thompson EM, Price YE, Wright NA. 1990. Kinetics of enteroendocrine cells with implications for their origin: a study of the cholecystokinin and gastrin

subpopulations combining tritiated thymidine labelling with immunocytochemistry. *Gut* 31:406–11

91. Traber PG. 1990. Regulation of sucrase-isomaltase gene expression along the crypt-villus axis of rat small intestine. *Biochem. Biophys. Res. Commun.* 173: 765–73

92. Traber PG, Wang W, Yu L. 1992. Differential regulation of P450 genes along the rat intestinal crypt-villus axis. *Am. J. Physiol.* 263:G215–23

93. Traber PG, Wu GD. 1995. Intestinal development and differentiation. In *Gastrointestinal Cancers: Biology, Diagnosis, and Therapy*, ed. AK Rustgi, pp. 21–43. New York: Raven

94. Traber PG, Wu GD, Wang W. 1992. Novel DNA-binding proteins regulate intestine-specific transcription of the sucrase-isomaltase gene. *Mol. Cell. Biol.* 12:3614–27

95. Traber PG, Yu L, Wu GD, Judge TA. 1992. Sucrase-isomaltase gene expression along the crypt-villus axis of human small intestine is regulated at the level of mRNA abundance. *Am. J. Physiol.* 262:G123–30

96. Trahair JF, Neutra MR, Gordon JI. 1989. Use of transgenic mice to study the routing of secretory proteins in intestinal epithelial cells: analysis of human growth hormone compartmentalization as a function of cell type and differentiation. *J. Cell Biol.* 109: 3231–34

97. Troelsen JT, Mehlum A, Olsen J, Spodsberg N, Hansen GH, et al. 1994. 1 kb of the lactase-phlorizin hydrolase promoter directs post-weaning decline and small intestinal-specific expression in transgenic mice. *FEBS Lett.* 342:291–96

98. Tsai F-Y, Keller G, Kuo FC, Weiss M, Chen JZ, et al. 1994. An early haematopoietic defect in mice lacking the transcription factor GATA-2. *Nature* 371:221–26

99. Tsai S-F, Martin DIK, Zon LI, D'Andrea AD, Wong GG, Orkin SH. 1989. Cloning of cDNA for the major DNA-binding protein of the erythroid lineage through expression in mammalian cells. *Nature* 339:446–51

100. Tsukiyama T, Becker PB, Wu C. 1994. ATP-dependent nucleosome disruption at a heat-shock promoter mediated by binding of GAGA transcription factor. *Nature* 367:525–31

101. Voss JW, Rosenfeld MG. 1992. Anterior pituitary development: short tales from dwarf mice. *Cell* 70:527–30

102. Weintraub H. 1993. The myoD family and myogenesis: redundancy, networks, and thresholds. *Cell* 75:1241–44

103. Wilson C, Bellen HJ, Gehring WJ. 1990. Position effects on eukaryotic gene expression. *Annu. Rev. Cell Biol.* 6:679–714

104. Wu GD, Chen L, Forslund K, Traber PG. 1994. Hepatocyte nuclear factor 1α (HNF-1α) and HNF-1β regulate transcription via two elements in an intestine-specific promoter. *J. Biol. Chem.* 269:17080–85

105. Wu GD, Wang W, Traber PG. 1992. Isolation and characterization of the human sucrase-isomaltase gene and demonstration of intestine-specific transcriptional elements. *J. Biol. Chem.* 267: 7863–70

106. Wu GD, Wang W, Traber PG. 1993. Molecular cloning of a transcriptional repressor protein (SIRP-1) which binds to the intestine-specific promoter region of the sucrase-isomaltase gene. *Gastroenterology* 104:A290

107. Xu G, Wang D, Huan LJ, Cutz E, Forstner GG, Forstner JF. 1992. Tissue-specific expression of a rat intestinal mucin-like peptide. *Histochem. J.* 286: 335–38

*Annu. Rev. Physiol. 1996. 58:299–327*

# QUEER CURRENT AND PACEMAKER: The Hyperpolarization-Activated Cation Current in Neurons

*Hans-Christian Pape*

Institut für Physiologie, Medizinische Fakultät, Otto-von-Guericke-Universität, D-39120 Magdeburg, Germany

KEY WORDS:     anomalous rectification, inward rectification, ionic currents, rhythmogenesis, cyclic AMP, nervous system

### ABSTRACT

The cation conductance activated upon hyperpolarization of the membrane beyond the resting value appears to represent an ubiquitous type of membrane channel. Our understanding of the respective membrane current, termed $I_h$, in neurons has matured from that of a "queer" current toward that of a highly regulated mechanism that is particularly important in determining integrative behavior near rest and providing the pacemaker depolarization during rhythmic-oscillatory activity.

## INTRODUCTION

The rich variety and complexity of functions of the nervous system are largely attained by a fine-tuned interplay between the intrinsic neuronal properties and the quality of synaptic interconnections. Intrinsic electrophysiological characteristics, in turn, reflect the type, location, and density of voltage- and ligand-gated ion channels that regulate the flow of ionic currents across the neuronal plasma membrane and that are controlled by a large variety of transmitter substances and intracellular messenger systems (67). In view of the highly specific—albeit dynamic—electroresponsiveness required of the neuronal elements, it is not unexpected that neurons possess a rich repertoire of ion channels, including classical types such as those producing voltage-dependent sodium ($Na^+$) and potassium ($K^+$) currents during the generation of an action potential (70), as well as a number of less conventional ionic conductances (85). A rather peculiar intrinsic mechanism, originally observed by Ito and

299

co-workers (4, 72) in cat motoneurons, is evident as a slow relaxation of the potential change induced by hyperpolarizing current, producing non-ohmic behavior of the current/voltage (I/V) relation in the hyperpolarizing direction. The underlying, time-dependent membrane conductance was first identified in rod photoreceptors as a caesium ($Cs^+$)-sensitive, slow inward current that is turned on by hyperpolarization and is capable of depolarizing the membrane, which results in the typical sequence of an initial transient hyperpolarization followed by a slowly decaying component in response to bright flashes of light (5, 7, 8, 52). The current in photoreceptors was termed $I_h$ (or $I_A$; 5) because of its activation by hyperpolarization. At about the same time, a similar current system was discovered in sino-atrial node cells and in Purkinje fibers of the mammalian heart (16, 17, 30, 31, 139), and it became apparent that the slow inward current represents a cation conductance permeable to $Na^+$ and $K^+$ ions. To underline its anomalous behavior, i.e. being an inward current activated by hyperpolarization that looked funnily similar to the presumed $K^+$ conductance $I_{K2}$, the current was named "funny" current ($I_f$). This current has since gained significant interest because of its involvement in the generation and control of spontaneous cardiac activity (see 20, 34, 36). Evidence for the existence of an equivalent current in central neurons was first reported by Halliwell & Adams (64). They observed in hippocampal pyramidal cells a slow inward current activation upon membrane hyperpolarization, which was termed "queer" current ($I_q$) in view of its odd electrophysiological behavior and its undefined functional significance. A current with similar properties was later found in a wide variety of neuronal and non-neuronal cells, and this hyperpolarization-activated current was recognized as an ubiquitous phenomenon within cells of the nervous system. It was called $I_q$, $I_f$, $I_{AR}$ (anomalous rectifier), or $I_{IR}$ (inward rectifier). However, to differentiate this current from the classical $K^+$ inward rectifier, the term hyperpolarization-activated current ($I_h$) is now preferred for use in the nervous system (67).

Although the respective neuronal channels were initially thought to be resistant to modulatory influences, accumulating data indicate that they are important targets for neurotransmitter and second messenger systems, which implies important physiological roles in the control of cellular electrical activities. The aim of this review is to summarize the experimental data on the most relevant biophysical properties of the hyperpolarization-activated channels and to discuss the mechanisms of regulatory influences that may contribute to the functional significance of $I_h$ within the nervous system.

## BIOPHYSICAL PROPERTIES OF $I_h$

The $I_h$ current is typically seen as a slowly developing inward current activation upon hyperpolarization of the membrane beyond the resting potential. The rate of activation and the amplitude of $I_h$ increase with increasing hyperpolarization, which is apparent as a region of anomalous inward rectification when the current magnitude is plotted against membrane potential in an I/V relation. In an initial attempt to characterize the slow inward current relaxation, it was important to demonstrate that it behaved in a way expected of a time- and voltage-dependent membrane conductance, as opposed to arising from a shift in driving force due to ion accumulation or depletion. The strongest evidence in favor of a conventional ionic current comes from the work of DiFrancesco (35), who identified single-channel events of low conductance (approximately 1 pS) that underlie $I_f$ in rabbit sino-atrial node cells. Although single $I_h$ channels remain to be identified in neurons, studies of the macroscopic currents strongly suggest mediation by a voltage-gated membrane conductance (cf 134) in showing that (a) activation and deactivation are associated with increases and decreases in membrane conductance, respectively (e.g. 1, 91, 94, 122); (b) the envelope of tail currents closely matches the kinetics of current activation (e.g. 5, 66, 76, 91, 94), as is predicted by Hodgkin-Huxley (70) formalism for a voltage-dependent conductance; (c) the voltage dependence of steady-state activation is well described by a Boltzmann function in most preparations (e.g. 6, 10, 46, 66, 76, 83, 87, 91, 94, 115, 118, 128); and (d) the reversal potential does not change even in response to very large and long periods of current activation (e.g. 1, 6, 94, 125). Second, it is clear that anomalous rectification due to $I_h$ is different from classical inward rectification, originally described by Katz (78) as a higher conductance for inward than for outward current in frog skeletal muscle fibers, and which has since been found in a large number of biological membranes (107). Different from $I_h$, the classical inward rectifier (a) is a pure $K^+$ conductance with no significant contribution of $Na^+$; (b) is sensitive to external barium ions ($Ba^{2+}$), in addition to $Cs^+$; (c) is active mainly negative to the $K^+$ equilibrium potential, with the activation range depending on the extracellular $K^+$ concentration; (d) activates within a few milliseconds of an appropriate change in membrane potential; and (e) is ohmic in nature with its voltage dependence arising secondary to voltage-dependent block by internal magnesium ions ($Mg^{2+}$) or polyamines (53, 58). Furthermore, inwardly rectifying $K^+$ channels have been cloned (e.g. 82), whereas the gene that encodes the $I_h$ channel has not been identified. Both types of inward rectification, the $K^+$ conductance and the mixed $Na^+/K^+$ conductance underlying $I_h$, can exist in parallel in biological membranes (e.g. 124, 135, 137).

## Gating of the $I_h$ Channels

One peculiar property that distinguishes the hyperpolarization-activated inward current from many other voltage-activated conductances pathways is the slow, complex time course of activation and deactivation (for a review on $I_f$ in cardiac tissue, see 34, 36). Following hyperpolarizing voltage steps negative to approximately −50 mV, there is first an instantaneous current that is resistant to extracellular $Cs^+$ and possesses linear I/V relationships, which probably reflects the passage of current through multiple "leakage" conductance pathways. The $I_h$ inward current turns on with a delay and slowly relaxes to a steady-state value, resulting in a characteristic sigmoidal shape of the current waveform (3, 7, 11, 30, 33, 46, 66, 91, 116). The delay is voltage dependent, decreasing with more negative membrane potentials, and reflects a process intrinsic to $I_h$ activation (33, 116). The slow inward current following the delay is a function of voltage and time, with the rate of activation increasing with more negative values of the membrane potential. Current kinetics are satisfactorily described by slow single-exponential processes in most neuronal cell types in mammals (25, 51, 76, 94, 96a, 117, 128, 137) and non-mammals (3, 24, 79, 125). Time constants are generally strongly voltage dependent (but see 118, 120), averaging (at 35°C) around 1 to 2 s at potentials near activation threshold and around 200 to 400 ms at the potential of maximal activation of $I_h$, if a $Q_{10}$ of 3 to 4 (3, 48, 64, 125) is assumed. Two kinetically distinct components of $I_h$ with time constants in the range of hundreds of milliseconds and seconds, respectively, whose relative amplitudes are not correlated, may indicate the existence of two distinct populations of $I_h$ channels (10, 18, 116). This view is supported by the finding that the two kinetically different current components can be differentially expressed in one type of neuron (114). The relatively fast time course of activation of $I_h$ in some classes of neurons (64, 87, 96a) may then reflect a predominance of the fast-current component. Two examples at the extreme end indicate the wide range of $I_h$ kinetics: Descriptions assuming double exponential functions with time constants between tens and hundreds of milliseconds (at room temperature) have been found to be sufficient for $I_h$ in rod (5, 66) and cone (88) photoreceptors, whereas the kinetics of $I_h$ activation range within the order of tens of seconds in slowly adapting lobster stretch receptor neurons (46).

Termination of the hyperpolarizing voltage steps evoke outward relaxations of the membrane current, indicating deactivation of the conductance underlying $I_h$. Envelopes of these tail currents, measured following hyperpolarizing steps of various durations, closely match the time course of the onset of $I_h$ (5, 33, 66, 76, 91, 94, 134), as is expected for a voltage-dependent conductance (70). The deactivation of $I_h$ exhibits a voltage dependence roughly opposite to that of activation kinetics, in that deactivation becomes faster as the membrane potential is depolarized, yielding a roughly bell-shaped voltage dependence of the rates of $I_h$ on- and off-relaxations, with maximal time constants near the potential of 50% steady-state activation (11, 12, 46, 47, 66, 76, 91, 94, 116, 125). Kinetics of tail currents are mostly described by single-exponential functions, with time constants ranging in the order of hundreds of milliseconds, although the exact kinetics were difficult to determine largely because of contamination by other voltage-dependent currents (12, 76, 91, 94, 116, 125). Detailed analyses of the kinetics in cardiac cells (33, 89, 134) and photoreceptors (46, 66) demonstrated that both activation and deactivation processes are sigmoidal functions of time at high negative and positive voltages, whereas exponential processes with one or two time constants satisfactorily describe the current kinetics in the vicinity of the half-activation voltage.

Decrements of the current during maintained hyperpolarization or alterations in the current waveform following activation after long depolarizing steps were not observed (6, 46, 94, 116, 125, 134), indicating a lack of inactivation of the underlying channels from open or closed states, respectively. Because $I_h$ does not inactivate, measurement of the voltage dependence of steady-state activation is straightforward in that tail currents evoked upon return to various membrane potentials following maximal activation of $I_h$ can be used. The steady-state activation of $I_h$ is well described by a Boltzmann function in most preparations. The $I_h$ currents begin to activate between −45 and −60 mV, and generally, half-activation is seen between −75 and −85 mV (3, 6, 10, 12, 18, 27, 46, 71, 83, 88, 91, 94, 96a, 115, 117, 118, 137), although closer to −65 mV in rod photoreceptors (66) and closer to −95 mV in some types of central and peripheral neurons (76, 87, 122, 125, 128). The $I_h$ conductance is generally maximal at membrane potentials negative to −110 mV (but see 3). Maximal amplitudes vary between different types of neurons, with reported conductance values ranging in the order 2–10 nS (115, 125, 128). From available data with regard to total current production and surface area (19, 32), it can be inferred that at voltage levels of maximal activation, the density of $I_h$ is between 1 and 5 $\mu A/cm^2$ (46). In view of a single-channel conductance at around 1 pS (35), the average channel density would be below 0.5 $\mu m^{-2}$, which is to be compared with an average $Na^+$ channel density of about 500 $\mu m^{-2}$ (46). The steepness of the activation curve, however, will ensure that even small changes in membrane polarization result in activation of a substantial part of the channels, which can be assumed to largely account for the anomalous inward rectification observed in the whole-cell I/V-relation. The activated conductance itself is not rectifying, as indicated by the nearly linear I/V-relation of the fully activated current (3, 6, 38, 46, 87, 101, 115). Comparative interpretation and estimates of channel densities in different types of cells are complicated, however, largely because of the relative uncertainty about the cells' geometry and membrane surface area. Additional constraints in the interpretation of these quantitative measurements derive from the reported influence of external ions, transmitters, and second messenger systems on the $I_h$ conductance or activation curve (as is described in detail below). These biological variables may help to explain the high variability of $I_h$ observed in neurons of the same type (e.g. 51, 83) and the reported wide range of $I_h$ activation in various preparations.

Another phenomenon to be considered in evaluating the voltage dependence of $I_h$ is current rundown, attributable to the loss of intracellular elements that make the channels available to voltage-dependent activation and that are associated with a voltage range of activation of $I_h$ different from that of a physiologically more intact cell (142).

The quantitative descriptions of $I_h$ facilitated a variety of reaction schemes to account for the rather complex current kinetics. A modified Hodgkin-Huxley (70) scheme of second order largely described the sigmoidicity of current onset and deactivation in sino-atrial node cells (134), although a more complex model involving voltage-dependent transitions between five open states and three closed states more fully accounted for the current waveforms in cardiac Purkinje fibers (33). Modeling of $I_h$ activation in corticotectal neurons of the rat, using a product of Hodgkin-Huxley type multistate reaction sequences, indicated the involvement of non-identical gating subunits and/or non-independence (cooperativity) in the gating reaction, with a minimum of two energetically non-equivalent conformational changes required for channel opening (116). Empirical quantifications of $I_h$ activation kinetics in photoreceptors included Hodgkin-Huxley formalism involving three states with voltage-dependent and voltage-independent transitions (46) or transitions between two closed and three open states governed by voltage-dependent rate constants (11). Other theories found the simple summation of two independent exponential components of opposite polarity (66) or a kinetic scheme based on the cooperation of fast and slow current components (28) sufficient to account for the kinetics of $I_h$. The conclusion drawn from these models is that opening of the $I_h$ channel requires prior transitions through multiple closed states and that the channel passes through several open states before closing; inactivated states are not significant. Furthermore, protein subunits may cooperatively interact within the gating processes.

## Ionic Nature of $I_h$

The $I_h$ current is a mixed cation current. The $I_h$ channels are not, however, nonselective. For example, although the channel is permeable to $Na^+$, it is almost impermeable to the very similar ion lithium ($Li^+$) (permeability ratio $P_{Li}/P_{Na} = 0.06$; 136), which is unique in that no other type of channel can discriminate $Li^+$ from $Na^+$ (68). The permeability of $I_h$ channels to $K^+$ is high compared with that of the similar ion rubidium ($Rb^+$) ($P_{Rb}/P_K = 0.55$; 136). Choline, protonated Tris, or larger amines such as tetramethylammonium or tetraethylammonium cannot pass through the $I_h$ channel, and there is little permeability to ammonium ions, but $I_h$ channels are permeable to thallium ions ($Tl^+$) ($P_{Tl}/P_K > 1.55$; 47, 136). Based upon permeabilities to organic cations, the apparent pore diameter of $I_h$ channels has been estimated to be between 4 and 4.6 Å (136). Thus it appears that the $I_h$ channel is highly selective for $Na^+$ and $K^+$, and the $I_h$ current will be carried by both $Na^+$ and $K^+$ under normal conditions. Reversal potentials of $I_h$ are between approximately $-50$ and $-20$ mV and thus in a region positive to the normal resting potential, as has been estimated from analyses of tail currents or fully activated I/V-relations in different types of cells under physiologic conditions (6, 10, 12, 18, 25, 27, 30, 46, 66, 76, 79, 91, 94, 96a, 101, 115, 118, 122, 125, 128, 134). When the ratio of $P_{Na}/P_K$ was explicitly calculated, values from 0.2 to 0.4 were found (46, 66, 88, 115) for moderate changes of $Na^+$ and $K^+$ concentrations from physiological levels, although the ratio can increase with more extreme changes in the extracellular levels of $Na^+$ and $K^+$ (46, 47). A prominent aspect of $I_h$ characteristics implying a deviation of the conductance mechanism from the independence principle is an increase in current amplitude upon increases in the external $K^+$ concentration that is independent of the effects on the $I_h$ reversal potential and that results in an increased slope of the I/V relation (6, 25, 27, 32, 47, 66, 76, 87–89, 94, 115, 118, 122, 124). The kinetic parameters and the steady-state voltage dependence of $I_h$ are generally not affected (but see 88), suggesting a regulation of the conductance mechanism underlying $I_h$ with no change in the gating properties (32, 47). A model of this phenomenon in corticotectal neurons predicted an approximately $\pm20\%$ variation in $I_h$ conductance during only a 1 mM change in extracellular $K^+$ concentration, and an ability of $K^+$ to maximally increase the $I_h$ conductance approximately tenfold over basal levels (115). In contrast, current modifications upon changes in extracellular $Na^+$ levels are merely the result of the altered driving force, or may reflect changes in the $K^+$ gradient secondary to a severe reduction in the external $Na^+$ concentration (118). A quantitative analysis performed in rod photoreceptors (66) demonstrated that the maximal $I_h$ conductance depends on the square root of the external $K^+$ concentration, with the flux of both $Na^+$ and $K^+$ ions being affected (see also 47). Following from this is the peculiar situation that $Na^+$ is necessary as the carrier of inward current in $I_h$ channels at a range of membrane potential where $I_h$ is important physiologically, yet $K^+$ is required for the channels to carry any current (32, 56, 56a, 136). Our understanding of the underlying permeation pathway is incomplete. The $I_h$ channel is considered a multi-ion pore possessing a high-affinity external binding site, the affinity of which is modulated by $K^+$ (32, 66, 68). Based on the efficacy of block by different ions and the degree to which $Na^+$ and $K^+$ antagonize the block, the permeation pathway of the $I_h$ channel was seen to contain at least two binding sites: one having a higher affinity for $K^+$ and another having a higher affinity for $Na^+$ (135a).

Experiments aimed at examining the permeability of chloride ions ($Cl^-$) through the $I_h$ channels were initially puzzling. Shifts in the $Cl^-$ equilibrium potential through replacement of extracellular choline chloride with sucrose or mannitol, or injection of $Cl^-$ into the cells, did not significantly affect $I_h$ (25, 115, 118), whereas substitution of external $Cl^-$ by larger anions such as isethionate resulted in a substantial reduction in current amplitude and no effects on the I/V relation (76, 91, 94, 122, 139). Because the current amplitude decreased, despite an increase in driving force on $Cl^-$, the large anion substitutes were thought to exert an unspecific blocking action on the $I_h$ conductance. A study of the equivalent conductance in isolated sino-atrial node cells (56) corroborated the reduction in current amplitude by large anions and in addition demonstrated that replacement of $Cl^-$ by small anions such as iodide or nitrate supported an intact current. The underlying conductance was found to be a saturating function of the extracellular $Cl^-$ concentration, indicating an activating effect of small anions rather than a blocking effect of large anions (56). Therefore, it appears that the $I_h$ conductance is unique because it is carried by $Na^+$ and $K^+$, yet it is dependent on an extracellular anion ($Cl^-$). $Cl^-$ may perform a screening role for cations bound at external sites of the multi-ion channel and thereby represent a necessary step in channel permeation by cations (56). Although the response of $I_h$ to changes in the ionic environment supports the notion that the channels' gating action and ion conduction are associated with operationally independent channel structures (48), the proposed mechanisms and models await further experimental clarification (e.g by single-channel analysis) and thus far can only be regarded as a useful description of available results (32).

## Blockade of the $I_h$ Channels

As originally described in photoreceptor cells (52), a general feature of the $I_h$ current is its sensitivity to low concentrations (0.1–5 mM) of extracellular $Cs^+$. In fact, the blockade by extracellular $Cs^+$ and the relative insensitivity to $Ba^{2+}$ has largely facilitated the isolation of the hyperpolarization-activated cation current and the evaluation of its physiological roles in a large variety of preparations. Internal $Cs^+$ does not block (11, 91, 96a, 118), whereas external $Cs^+$ results in a concentration- and voltage-dependent blockade, with dissociation contants at zero membrane potential ranging between 0.5 and 3.7 mM in cardiac cells (32). $Cs^+$ presumably binds to a blocking site inside the channel that is different from the externally located regulatory site to which $K^+$ binds (32). $Cs^+$ blocks current in negative regions of the I/V-curve, but has no effect or even enhances current positive to the reversal potential (32). These findings, and the known effect of $Cs^+$ to block other types of voltage-dependent conductances, such as delayed rectifier and $K^+$ inward rectifier channels (67, 107), put some constraints on the exclusive use of $Cs^+$ when the contribution of the $I_h$ current to electrical neuronal activity is to be quantitatively analyzed. In addition, manganese ($Mn^{2+}$) and $Ba^{2+}$, at mil-limolar concentrations often used to block contaminating $Ca^{2+}$ and $K^+$ cur-rents during the study of $I_h$, induce a positive and negative shift in the activation curve of the respective current in sino-atrial node myocytes (40). This result may help to explain reported reductions in $I_h$ amplitude following application of $Ba^{2+}$ (12, 14, 76, 122). Strontium also blocks $I_f$ in cardiac cells, whereas $Ca^{2+}$ is a very weak blocker (but may modulate $I_h$ activation), and $Mg^{2+}$ has little effect on the hyperpolarization-activated current (99). The neuronal $I_h$ has proven to be largely unaffected by extracellular tetro-dotoxin, cobalt ($Co^{2+}$), tetraethylammonium, and 4-aminopyridine in concen-trations that effectively blocked $Na^+$ and $K^+$ conductances (25, 27, 46, 88, 96a, 115, 120, 122, 125, 128), although intracellular tetraethylammonium at <15 mM blocked $I_h$ in cultured neocortical neurons (18). Volatile anesthetics, such as enflurane and halothane, evoke a negative shift in the $I_h$ activation curve and reduce the maximal $I_h$ conductance in bullfrog sensory neurons (126), and intracellular QX-314 (5-10 mM), a quaternary derivative of the local anesthetic lidocaine, blocks $I_h$ completely throughout its activation range in hippocampal CA1 pyramidal cells (103a). $Rb^+$ induces a voltage-independent block of the $I_h$ conductance in photoreceptor and cardiac cells (32, 47), although $Rb^+$ is far less potent than $Cs^+$ (32), and $Rb^+$ can also permeate the $I_h$ channel (136). An agent, 9-amino-1,2,3,4-tetrahydroacridine, was found to block the hyperpolarization-activated current in hippocampal pyramidal neurons (65) and cardiac cells (41) in a voltage-independent man-ner and at lower concentrations than other known $I_h$ channel blockers ($IC_{50}$ at 20 and 300 μM in the two preparations, respectively), although it similarly reduced agonist-induced or delayed rectifier $K^+$ conductances. A group of substances termed specific bradycardiac agents in view of their negative chronotropic effects exert a potent inhibition of the hyperpolarization-acti-vated cation current in cardiac cells (37, 131–133) and mammalian central neurons (101). Depending on the type of drug, inhibition results from a reduction in $I_h$ conductance and a negative shift of $I_h$ activation or a use-de-pendent block of the open channels, with no alteration in the gating proper-ties. Although these drugs potently inhibit $I_h$, their selectivity under various experimental conditions is still a matter of controversy (101, 131). Finally, a depressant effect on the gating process of $I_h$ with some physiological significance was obtained with $H^+$ ions in lobster stretch receptor neurons (48), which may underlie reported alterations in anomalous inward rectifica-tion upon manipulations of the buffered extracellular medium (22).

The complete pharmacological profile of the neuronal $I_h$ channels remains to be developed in detail, and a more specific and efficient $I_h$ blocker would be desirable for a quantitative analysis of the physiological roles of the $I_h$ conductance in the different classes of cells.

# REGULATION OF $I_h$

An important and physiologically significant property of $I_h$ channels is their ability to be regulated by neurotransmitters and metabolic stimuli. Although the control of cardiac $I_f$ channels through the intracellular cyclic adenosine monophosphate (cAMP) system has been known for several years (34, 36), early studies on neuronal $I_h$ found no changes attributable to neurotransmitters (e.g. 11, 64). However, the conclusions relied on the test of a relatively small number of cells and compounds. In fact, later experiments in thalamo-cortical neurons (103) and neurons of the brain stem nucleus prepositus hypoglossi (15) presented evidence of an increase in $I_h$ activation upon stimulation of β-adrenergic and serotonergic receptors. The modulation relies on a positive shift of the voltage dependence of the $I_h$ activation curve by up to +10 mV, with no changes in the steepness of the curve or in the fully activated I/V-relation. The intracellular messenger system mediating this response most likely involves stimulation of adenylyl cyclase and a resulting increase in intracellular cAMP level, as was indicated by the mimicking effects exerted by membrane-permeable analogues of cAMP (8-bromo-cAMP; dibutyryl-cAMP), a stimulant of adenylyl cyclase activity (forskolin; Figure 1A), or a phosphodiesterase inhibitor (3-isobutyl-1-methyl-xanthine) (15, 51, 95, 103, 125). Subsequent studies suggested that this intracellular pathway and associated modulation of $I_h$ channels is shared by a subset of receptor types that are positively coupled to adenylyl cyclase activity in various types of cells (Figure 1B), including serotonergic receptors of an as yet unclassified subtype in mammalian and crustacean motoneurons (58, 79, 83, 123), substantia nigra pars compacta neurons (97) and salivary gland cells of the leech (138), noradrenergic receptors of the β-subtype in neurons of the medial nucleus of the trapezoid body (10), and histaminergic $H_2$ receptors in thalamic neurons (96).

Furthermore, nitric oxide (NO), a gaseous messenger molecule known to induce a rise in the intracellular level of cyclic guanosine monophosphate (cGMP) through direct stimulation of guanylyl cyclase activity (26), induced a positive shift in $I_h$ activation similar to that observed after stimulation of the more classical receptors in thalamic neurons (102) and endothelial cells of the blood-brain barrier (73). These findings raise the interesting possibility that the cAMP and the cGMP systems are synergistically controlling the $I_h$ conductance (Figure 1B; 102), for example, via a direct modulation of the channels (42) or a cGMP-regulated isozyme of cyclic nucleotide phosphodiesterase (13). In support of this hypothesis is the finding that the NO effect on $I_h$ is imitated by membrane permeable analogues of both cAMP and cGMP (73, 102) and prevented by an inhibitor of adenylyl cyclase activity (102).

Receptors that are negatively coupled to adenylyl cyclase, in turn, are capable of negatively shifting $I_h$ activation by up to −10 mV along the voltage

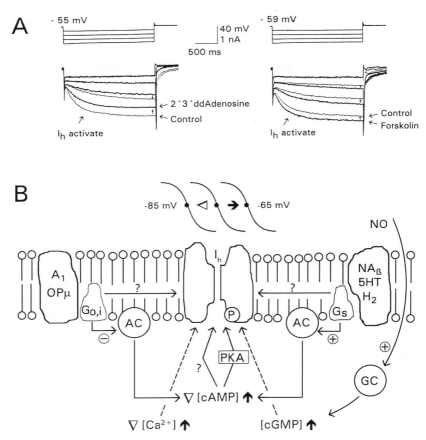

*Figure 1* Regulation of I_h. (*A*) The I_h current in a thalamic neuron is decreased by the adenylyl cyclase (AC) inhibitor 2′,3′-dideoxyadenosine and increased by the AC activator forskolin (modified from Reference 100). (*B*) Pathways of I_h regulation. Stimulation of receptors that are negatively (adenosine A₁, μ-opioid receptor) and positively (β-adrenergic, serotonergic, histamine H₂ receptor) coupled to AC activity induce a negative and positive shift in the I_h activation curve along the voltage axis, mediated via decreases and increases in the intracellular cAMP level, respectively. Whether cAMP directly modulates the channel or relies on PKA activity and phosphorylation (P) is undetermined. NO, through guanylyl cyclase (GC) activation and a rise in cGMP level, and presumably internal $Ca^{2+}$, regulate I_h activation via as yet unknown pathways (*dashed lines*). G_s and G_{o,i} are stimulatory and inhibitory G proteins that may directly or indirectly infuence the I_h channel. Stimulation, +; inhibition, −.

axis (Figure 1*B*), as has been shown for adenosine A₁ receptors in thalamic (100) and mesopontine neurons (105), and μ-opioid receptors in nodose ganglion cells (71). That this modulation occurs via adenylyl cyclase is indicated by two observations. First, opioids had no effect on I_h alone or during the presence of cAMP analogues but reversed the effects of forskolin on $I_h$ (71). Second, the negative shift in $I_h$ activation upon $A_1$ receptor stimulation functionally antagonized the β-adrenergic response; it also occurred without prior activation of adenylyl cyclase activity and was imitated by the adenylyl cyclase inhibitor 2′,3′-dideoxyadenosine (Figure 1A), indicating mediation through a decrease in basal activity of adenylyl cyclase (100). A negative shift in $I_h$ activation was also obtained with serotonin in cerebellar Purkinje cells (84), and there is evidence that hyperpolarization-activated currents are controlled through corticosteroid (77) or bradykinin action (80), although the mediating receptor subtypes and second messenger systems remain largely unknown. From these findings, it seems that the neuronal hyperpolarization-activated cation current is predominantly regulated through the basal activity of adenylyl cyclase and hence the intracellular concentration of cAMP. Stimulation of receptors that are negatively and positively coupled to adenylyl cyclase activity reciprocally shifts the $I_h$ activation curve along the voltage axis, thereby controlling the availability of the $I_h$ channels over a wide range of membrane potentials without changing the maximal conductance (Figure 1B). A similar relationship is known for cardiac sino-atrial node cells, where an opposite regulation of the cAMP level by muscarine or catecholamine regulates the voltage dependence of the equivalent current, $I_f$ (17, 43–45). Studies of single $I_f$ channels support this conclusion in that cAMP was found to shift the probability curve of first openings to shorter times without modification of the single-channel conductance (35, 39). Interestingly, as is the case in neurons, the $I_f$ current in the heart is enhanced after stimulation of histamine $H_2$ receptors (109) and decreased during action of adenosine (108). Notable exceptions from this unifying principle include dopamine $D_2$ and $GABA_B$ receptors in ventral tegmental neurons, whose stimulation induces a reduction in maximal $I_h$ current with no changes in kinetics or voltage dependence and with no apparent involvement of the adenylyl cyclase system (74).

The shift in the $I_h$ activation curve suggests that receptor stimulation modulates $I_h$ through an alteration in the voltage dependence of the underlying channels. Whether the change in voltage dependence results from activation of a cAMP-dependent protein kinase (PKA) cannot be deduced unambiguously from available data. The protein kinase inhibitor H-8 decreased the peak amplitude of $I_h$ in dissociated bullfrog sympathetic neurons, which suggests channel regulation through protein kinase activity (125), but it did not influence β-adrenergic activation of $I_h$ in thalamic neurons (100). A selective inhibitor of PKA (Walsh peptide) blocked the effect of β-adrenergic agonists and cAMP on the $Ca^{2+}$-dependent $K^+$ current $I_{AHP}$, but not on $I_h$, in hippocampal CA1 pyramidal cells, which suggested modulation of $I_h$ in a kinase-independent manner (119a). Conflicting results were also obtained from cardiac tissue. Two microelectrode voltage-clamp recordings in a multicellular Purkinje fiber preparation demonstrated that the cAMP-induced increase in $I_f$ is reversed by protein kinase inhibition through H-7 and H-8, whereas application of H-8 in the absence of activators of the cAMP cascade does not influence the current, which suggests that phosphorylation of the channels takes place down-stream of cAMP action (21). However, recordings in inside-out macro-patches from enzymatically isolated sino-atrial node myocytes suggest a direct cAMP-dependent gating of the $I_f$ channels independent of phosphorylation by a protein kinase (42): (a) The cAMP-induced shift of the activation curve occurred regardless of the presence of unspecific (H-7) or specific (pseudosubstrate peptide inhibitor) PKA inhibitors; (b) the application of PKA or active catalytic subunit did not activate the current; and (c) the action of addition or removal of cAMP in macro-patches was identical both qualitatively and quantitatively to the action of neurotransmitters on $I_f$ in whole cells, thereby implying that cAMP by itself produces the range of changes induced by neurotransmitters. The exact reasons for these discrepancies remain unclear but may be related to the different experimental approaches, i.e. the use of inside-out macro-patches, which allows a strict control of substrate conditions, but which involves enzymes for dissociation of cells (cf 18), or dialysis by a patch pipette with heavily buffered intracellular $Ca^{2+}$ level (cf 114), as opposed to the use of sharp microelectrodes in a multicellular preparation (21). However, the latter experiments that relied on the use of protein kinase inhibitors could not fully rule out the possibility of a direct blocking action of the inhibitors on the channels (cf 69) or of a reduction in $I_h$ secondary to a lowered cAMP level due to a decrease in adenylyl cyclase activity upon generalized protein kinase inhibition (cf 106). An alternative explanation for the action of kinase inhibitors on $I_h$ comes from the observation in rods (61) that the affinity of cGMP binding to light-activated channels is modulated by protein phosphatase activity. In conclusion, whether cAMP directly modulates the $I_h$ channels or relies on protein kinase activity is still an open issue, although stronger evidence appears to favor a direct action of cAMP on the channels not involving protein phosphorylation.

There is also evidence from studies in excised membrane patches of sino-atrial node cells that the hyperpolarization-activated current is increased by the GTP-binding protein $G_s$ and decreased by $G_{o,i}$, specifically by the $\alpha$-subunits, which indicates that the channels may be directly regulated by the G proteins in addition to indirect cytoplasmic pathways via cAMP (140). The possible existence of a direct membrane delimited pathway between receptors and $I_h$ channels in neurons is still unclear but appears unlikely for the following reasons: First, if adenosine $A_1$ receptors were directly coupled to $I_h$ channels, the component of $I_h$ modulation should have a time course similar to that for the $A_1$ receptor-induced increase in $K^+$ conductance, which is known to be directly mediated through a G protein (98). This is not the case, as indicated by the substantially slower rate of $I_h$ reduction compared with the increase in $K^+$ conductance upon stimulation of $A_1$ receptors in thalamic neurons (figure 5C in Reference 100). Second, although the non-hydrolyzable GTP analogue GTP-γ-S, applied intracellularly, irreversibly reduced $I_h$ and occluded the inhibitory effect of baclofen and dopamin on $I_h$ in ventral tegmental neurons, the results do not necessarily indicate a direct pathway between G proteins and $I_h$ channels because it would be necessary to assume that GTP-γ-S predominantly activates $G_{o,i}$ rather than $G_s$ in these cells (74). Another unresolved issue in the regulation of the $I_h$ channels concerns the intracellular $Ca^{2+}$ concentration. A whole-cell voltage-clamp study in single sino-atrial node cells revealed a positive shift in the $I_f$ activation upon increasing the $Ca^{2+}$ concentration of the pipette solution, which was unaffected by protein kinase or calmodulin inhibitors and thus assumed to reflect a direct action of $Ca^{2+}$ on the channels (63). However, recording of $I_f$ activity in inside-out macro-patches failed to demonstrate a modulating action of $Ca^{2+}$ on the $I_f$ current (141). Although these results weigh against direct control of the channels by internal $Ca^{2+}$, they do not rule out the possibility that increases in intracellular $Ca^{2+}$ concentration modify the activity of protein kinases and/or alter the levels of cAMP (141), thereby indirectly controlling $I_h$ (Figure 1B). The influence of intracellular $Ca^{2+}$ on $I_h$ in neurons has not been studied systematically. The positive shift in $I_h$ activation that was observed upon increases in the extracellular $Ca^{2+}$ or cobalt ($Co^{2+}$) concentration in lobster stretch receptor neurons (48) appears to be attributable to surface charge effects (cf 67) rather than a direct action of the ions on the gating parameters. In any case, an influence of internal $Ca^{2+}$ may help to explain findings of $I_h$ modulation by receptors or pathways that are rather unexpected, e.g. the positive shift in $I_h$ activation curve upon stimulation of muscarinic receptors and associated inositol phospholipid metabolism (23). However, alternative explanations are possible, and the exact mechanisms of $I_h$ regulation in the nervous system will only be revealed through further detailed biophysical and biochemical experiments, for instance, by utilizing excised inside-out patches that allow a more direct access of intracellular agents to the channels.

# PHYSIOLOGICAL ROLES OF $I_h$ IN NEURONS

Ionic currents similar to $I_h$ have been found in a diverse group of cell types in various species, including cardiac (34, 36) and smooth (113) muscle cells, salivary gland cells of the leech (138), blood-brain barrier endothelial cells (73), rod and cone photoreceptors in tiger salamander and lizard (5–8, 11, 66, 88, 136), olfactory and stretch receptor neurons in lobster (24, 46), heart

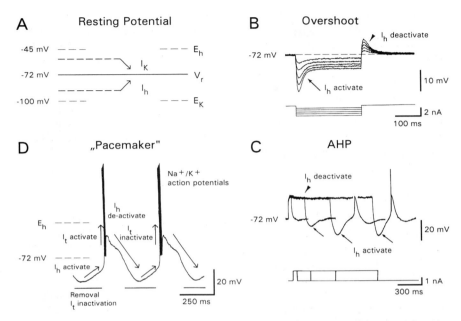

*Figure 2* Physiological roles of I$_h$ in neurons. Contribution of I$_h$ to (*A*) resting potential, V$_r$, during interaction with a K$^+$ current, I$_K$; (*B*) overshoots in membrane potential to hyper- and depolarizing stimuli; (*C*) development of a slow AHP following depolarization; and (*D*) rhythmogenesis as a pacemaker current during interaction with a Ca$^{2+}$ current, I$_t$. E$_h$ and E$_K$ indicate I$_h$ reversal potential and K$^+$ equilibrium potential, respectively. (*B* is modified from Reference 12; *C*, *D* are modified from Reference 94.) See text for details.

interneurons of the leech (3), crustacean motor neurons (60, 79), bullfrog sympathetic neurons (125), rat spinal root axons (9, 14, 62), rat optic nerves (50), presynaptic nerve terminals of chick ciliary ganglion (54), neurons in avian thalamus, and parasympathetic and sensory ganglia (111, 120), as well as in neurons in wide regions of the mammalian peripheral and central nervous system (1, 2, 10, 12, 15, 18, 25, 27, 51, 58, 64, 74, 76, 83, 84, 87, 91, 96a, 97, 103, 115, 117, 118, 122, 128, 129, 135, 137). The degree of anomalous rectification, or depolarizing sag of the membrane during hyperpolarizing responses, representing the activation of I$_h$ during current clamp recordings, is a widely used parameter in the characterization of electrogenic neuronal behavior and the classification of different types of neuronal elements. This ubiquitous phenomenon may also play an important role in the integrative performance of the neurons, as suggested by the strong developmental increase in anomalous rectification during embryonal and early postnatal periods (12, 111; see also 110) and the regulation of I$_h$ by extracellular ions, transmitters, and intracellular messenger systems. Anomalous rectification is modified during certain pathological conditions, for example, following peripheral axotomy (57), infection with herpes simplex viruses (90), or specific antigen challenge (130). Modulation of the voltage dependence of $I_h$, in addition, may be involved in increased primary afferent excitability during inflammation and its subsequent reduction through $\mu$-opioid receptor stimulation (71).

The unique property of $I_h$, e.g. an inward current activated upon hyperpolarization beyond resting potential, makes it a particularly useful mechanism for determining integrative behavior near rest and providing pacemaker depolarization during generation of rhythmic-oscillatory activity (Figure 2).

## Assistance to Integrative Behavior Near Rest

The normal resting potential is distinctively positive to the presumed $K^+$ equilibrium potential in many types of neurons, indicating a contribution of depolarizing currents, even in the absence of synaptic inputs. Because typical resting potentials lie within the voltage range of $I_h$ activation between $-50$ and $-100$ mV, and the $I_h$ current does not inactivate, a sustained inward $I_h$ current is likely to assist in determining resting potential and input resistance. Application of $Cs^+$ or specific bradycardic agents to resting neurons indeed resulted in hyperpolarization and increase in apparent input resistance averaging 30% (87, 94, 101, 128). Quantitatively similar results were obtained during intracellular (94, 101) or whole-cell (87, 128) recordings, and the blockers were specific for $I_h$ under the respective experimental conditions (87, 101), strongly suggesting a contribution of an inward current carried through $I_h$ channels to resting parameters. Because 10 to 15% of the $I_h$ conductance is active at the resting potential in these neurons, the recruitment of only this fraction of channels contributes about 30% to the total resting conductance and participates in moving the membrane potential positive to the $K^+$ equilibrium potential. Several observations support of this view. Neurons in the basolateral amygdala lacking an $I_h$ current were found to possess a resting potential substantially closer to the $K^+$ equilibrium potential compared with their counterparts displaying a strong $I_h$ (137). Among two populations of facial motoneurons, those with the more negative $I_h$ activation range had a significantly more negative resting potential (83). In thalamo-cortical neurons, the recruitment of $I_h$ supports the establishment of a true resting condition between two modes of electrogenic activity because its depolarizing influence moves the membrane potential from a range of $Ca^{2+}$-mediated burst activity at around $-75$ mV into a region still subthreshold to the generation of $Na^+/K^+$-mediated action potentials (94, 101). Thus $I_h$ appears to assist in determining the resting potential in many types of neurons, although additional conductances are also involved (e.g. 75, 96a). In any case, because the net current at the resting potential is zero, the $I_h$ inward current must be balanced by an outward current. This current could be contributed by a resting leakage current with an equilibrium potential negative to rest (118), an outwardly directed pump current (46, 49) or, as has been suggested for hippocampal pyramidal (64) and sensory ganglion cells (91), a noninactivating $K^+$ current such as $I_M$. The $I_M$ current, with its activation range positive to approximately $-60$ mV and slow dynamic responses, appears to be well adapted to functionally balance the effects of $I_h$ (Figure 2A). Transient outward currents would seem unlikely contributors to a steady current, but a small window current arising from the overlap of activation and inactivation curves is conceivable (75). Therefore, the uniform I/V-slope around the resting potential displayed by many neurons does not necessarily reflect the passive properties of the membrane, but rather may be due to the counterbalancing action of voltage-sensitive membrane conductances (91). This idea is supported by the observation, for instance in amygdaloid pyramidal neurons (104), that the apparent input resistance is maximal around the normal resting potential and decreases with either hyperpolarization or depolarization. A balancing outward current may also help to explain the observation in hypoglossal motoneurons that a developmental increase in $I_h$ current, which normally contributes to the resting potential, is not associated with a shift in membrane potential (12).

The assistance of $I_h$ in the determination of the resting potential has two major consequences: First, the $I_h$ current is able to lower the cell's apparent input resistance significantly at potentials negative to rest and, thereby, may effectively counteract any fluctuations to membrane polarization due to disturbing influences (49). Such changes may include extracellular $K^+$ accumulation and variations in pH and temperature, whose influences on membrane potential and excitability were markedly reduced by a functioning $I_h$ in lobster stretch receptor neurons (49). The properties of $I_h$, including its steep voltage dependence, slow activation kinetics, and regulation by $H^+$ and $K^+$, support a relatively efficient stabilization of the resting potential in the case of slow changes in resting conditions (46). Second, the depolarizing action of $I_h$ could be naturally exploited by the neurons as an excitability promoting factor during integration of synaptic inputs. These conclusions should take into consideration, however, the voltage-dependent properties of $I_h$ and the capability of transmitters and intracellular messenger systems to shift the activation range of $I_h$ (95). A positive shift of $I_h$ activation will increase the amount of $I_h$ current that is active at rest, thereby leading to a depolarization of the cell towards the reversal potential of $I_h$, i.e. closer to firing threshold. Although the steepness of the activation curve ensures that even small changes in the voltage dependence of the conductance underlying $I_h$ will result in large changes in the amount active at resting membrane potentials, the amplitude of the resulting depolarization is small due to the close proximity of the normal resting potential and the reversal potential of $I_h$. Whether the depolarization evokes spike activity (e.g. 15, 123) or remains subthreshold (e.g. 103) is largely dependent upon the position of the $I_h$ activation curve relative to threshold for the generation of $Na^+/K^+$-mediated action potentials. In addition, enhancement of the $I_h$ conductance at rest will have larger effects on the slow components of hyperpolarizing vs depolarizing inputs. Hyperpolarization will increase the driving force on $I_h$ and therefore will be partially offset by compensatory movements of $Na^+$ and $K^+$ through $I_h$ channels. The enhancement of the $I_h$ conductance at rest and resulting decrease in apparent input resistance will, in addition, ensure that hyperpolarizing inputs of all durations will be reduced. By comparison, the negative shift in $I_h$ activation will result in a slight hyperpolarization of the membrane, an increase in apparent input resistance, and a predominant enhancement of neuronal responses to hyperpolarizing influences.

In contrast to the regulatory potency of the $I_h$ conductance near resting membrane potentials, modulation of $I_h$ while the neurons are tonically depolarized into a region of spike firing will have distinctly different effects. Because the threshold for generation of $Na^+/K^+$ spikes is largely out of the range of $I_h$ activation, modulation will result in little or no change in membrane potential or firing frequency. However, upon hyperpolarization, the rate of repolarization of the membrane will be enhanced, thereby limiting prolonged hyperpolarizations. These effects of $I_h$ modulation are sometimes difficult to distinguish from additional or secondary mechansims activated by receptor stimulation. For example, (a) the $I_h$ activation induced by serotonin only partly contributes to the initial phase of serotonergic plateau potentials in crustacean dorsal gastric motoneurons during processing of motor behavior (79); (b) inhibition of $I_h$ is just one effect among a number of pre- or postsynaptic mechanisms through which the ambient level of adenosine keeps the resting potential in mesopontine brain stem neurons at a relatively hyperpolarized level (105); and (c) in auditory brain stem neurons, the activation of $I_h$ and associated small depolarization upon stimulation of noradrenergic receptors is supposed to be a merely supportive mechanism in the recruitment of a transient $K^+$ current, which in turn shapes synaptic potentials for improving auditory signal processing during arousal (10).

## Contribution to Overshoots in Membrane Voltage

Because the reversal potential of $I_h$ is positive to the normal resting potential, hyperpolarizing membrane responses from rest evoke a net $Na^+/K^+$ current that is inward both during activation and deactivation. The effect of current activation on a maintained hyperpolarization is a depolarizing sag toward the resting potential, which has been widely noted as anomalous rectification, whereas subsequent return to rest will cause a transient depolarizing overshoot of the original potential level (Figure 2B; see e.g. 12, 91, 115). Low concentrations of $Cs^+$ potently block $I_h$, the sag, and the overshoot phenomena. Sag and overshoot are generally not symmetrical because of the differences in driving force on $I_h$ (Figure 2B). Although the depolarizing overshoot is small due to the close proximity of the resting potential and the $I_h$ reversal potential, $I_h$ may act in concert with a low-threshold $Ca^{2+}$ conductance in triggering action potentials (1) or phasic burst discharges (24, 25, 55). $I_h$ could also contribute to the repolarization of $Na^+/K^+$-mediated spikes because, as deduced from a theoretical model (118), the $I_h$ current possessing its slow kinetics will only partially deactivate and increasingly become outward during the action potential. Another role of $I_h$ involves production of an after-hyperpolarization (AHP)-like waveform following a depolarization that deactivates the $I_h$ conductance (87, 94, 112). Deactivation of $I_h$ increases the apparent input resistance, and during repolarization, the membrane potential overshoots the original value in a hyperpolarizing direction, which in turn activates $I_h$ to induce a slow depolarization to the original potential value (Figure 2C). The findings that the AHP is sensitive to extracellular $Cs^+$, does not occur in a voltage region outside $I_h$ activation, and is increasingly present after a passive depolarization of increasing duration are in agreement with this view (94). $I_h$ can also contribute to the time course of AHPs mediated through $K^+$ conductances or electrogenic pump activity (87, 118).

The depolarizing sag owing to activation of $I_h$ effectively limits duration and/or amplitude of hyperpolarizing membrane responses. $I_h$ turns on slowly enough for clamping of the membrane potential to be prevented. $I_h$ thus is able to contribute to the integrative behavior of neuronal networks comprising interconnected excitatory and inhibitory neuronal elements (see below). There are two additional, conceptually different functions of $I_h$. First, in photoreceptors, $I_h$ does not contribute to the dark potential nor to responses to dim flashes of light. However, a bright flash of light can hyperpolarize the membrane well into the range of $I_h$ activation, resulting in the typical peak-plateau response thought to represent an adaptive mechanism for the maintenance of synaptic transmission during strong sensory stimuli (5, 52, 66). Second, in nerves the most likely function of $I_h$ is to limit the electrogenic hyperpolarization from activation of $K^+$ conductances or electrogenic pump activity following intense action potential activity (9, 14, 50, 62). This function may be of critical importance to prevent conduction failure, not only in damaged nerves, but also at regions of normally reduced safety factors, such as branch points (9, 14). In presynaptic nerve terminals (54), a similar function of $I_h$ may counteract impulse blockade and thereby help to protect synaptic transmission during massive invasion of action potentials. The midpoint voltage of $I_h$ activation near the most negative membrane potential normally reached by the respective cells (cf 11) and the control of the $I_h$ activation curve by transmitter and intracellular messenger systems are consistent with these roles for $I_h$.

## Support of Rhythmogenesis

The unique nature of $I_h$ as an inward current activated upon hyperpolarization beyond resting potential makes it a particularly useful mechanism in providing the pacemaker depolarization during rhythmic-oscillatory activity, as has been noted in cardiac tissue for several years (20, 34, 36). Different from the regenerative effects of voltage-gated $Na^+$ or $Ca^{2+}$ conductances, the depolarization from activation of $I_h$ reaches a plateau level on a slow time course, largely due to the slow response kinetics of the channels and their deactivation upon depolarization. Although the inward current carried by $I_h$ is generally not sufficient to bring the membrane back to the original level, it can reach threshold for activation of a persistent $Na^+$ current. The interaction of both currents may reinforce membrane resonance at 6–10 Hz that dominates potential fluctuations in a range subthreshold to spike activity (2, 121). A striking contribution of $I_h$ to rhythmic activity has been noticed in the thalamus (94, 117). Thalamo-cortical neurons can act as intrinsic oscillators, cycling slowly at around 0.5–4 Hz between a depolarization that triggers a burst of fast $Na^+/K^+$ spikes and a subsequent hyperpolarization that reaches well within the range of $I_h$ activation. The respective $I_h$ inward current induces a slow depolarization that reaches threshold for activation of a transient $Ca^{2+}$ current with low-threshold of activation, termed $I_t$. The resulting regenerative $Ca^{2+}$ response in turn triggers the burst of fast spikes. The depolarization deactivates $I_h$. During repolarization caused by inactivation of $I_t$, the lessened depolarizing influence of $I_h$ creates a hyperpolarizing overshoot. This hyperpolarization removes inactivation of $I_t$ and activates $I_h$, and the cycle starts again (Figure 2D).

Although this scenario may not include all the mechanisms involved in rhythmogenesis, the contribution of the $I_h$ conductance is fundamental in that it causes the afterhyperpolarization following the generation of the burst, determines the overall range of membrane potential within which the neuron oscillates, and affects the input conductance of the cell, thereby determining the responsiveness of the membrane potential to fluctuations in current flow (94). These conclusions are supported by the findings that the slow oscillatory activity is sensitive to extracellular $Cs^+$, possesses a voltage dependence roughly corresponding to that expected for a contribution of $I_h$, is largely unaffected by blocking $Na^+/K^+$ spikes or synaptic activity (94), and is reproduced by Hodgkin-Huxley-like models that include $I_h$, $I_t$, and a leakage conductance (29, 93, 127). In this manner, the intrinsic ability of thalamo-cortical neurons to generate oscillations of the membrane potential is largely determined by an equilibrium between $I_t$ and $I_h$. The single-cell oscillators are embedded into synaptic network interactions, which synchronize and sculpture rhythmic activity and, in addition, enable their regulation (92, 119). In vivo, two predominant forms of rhythmic activity are observed in the thalamocortical system, evident as spindling or slow/delta oscillations on the electroencephalogram (EEG) during early and late periods of slow-wave sleep, respectively. While the intrinsic capability of thalamo-cortical neurons to oscillate contributes significantly to slow/delta activity, spindle waves appear to rely mostly on synaptic interactions (119). During spindling oscillation, rhythmically recurring inhibitory postsynaptic potentials (IPSPs) in thalamocortical neurons are thought to provide the membrane hyperpolarization necessary for deinactivation of $I_t$, which in turn is activated during the decaying phase of the IPSPs and results in rhythmic rebound burst discharges. Because the range of deinactivation of $I_t$ widely overlaps with that of activation of $I_h$, the respective hyperpolarization will also activate $I_h$. The inward $I_h$ current will limit the duration and/or amplitude of the IPSPs, thereby strongly influencing the pattern of rhythmic rebound activity (94, 95, 100). Theoretical studies of a thalamic network model demonstrated that intermittent burst firing in thalamo-cortical neurons can be explained by a temporal integration of rhythmic IPSPs by $I_h$, provided that gating kinetics of $I_h$ are slower than the rhythmicity (134a). The $I_h$ channels may also directly support the generation of populations rhythms in a network of excitatory and inhibitory neurons that are reciprocally interconnected, even though none possesses endogenous oscillatory properties (81).

$I_h$ also regulates rhythmic pattern generation in other neuronal networks of similar architecture. Reported examples include (a) rhythmic breathing movements in mammals, where $I_h$ currents in bulbospinal neurons are thought to antagonize late expiratory phase synaptic inhibition (27); (b) rhythmic activity of the crustacean stomatogastric ganglion, where $I_h$ in lateral pyloric neurons controls phase relationships in the pyloric network (59, 60); and (c) slow oscillatory activity of interneurons that control heartbeat in the leech, where $I_h$ may mediate the escape from inhibition that times the phase transition of two interconnected neurons (3).

The fundamental involvement of $I_h$ in rhythmogenesis makes the $I_h$ channel an attractive target for neurotransmitter systems able to regulate the different forms of oscillatory activity. In general, rhythmic activity involving $I_h$ can be controlled by moving the membrane potential in and out of the range of $I_h$ activation, by regulating hyperpolarizing responses (e.g. to synaptic inputs), or by a more direct influence on the pacemaking apparatus. The reciprocal control of the voltage dependence of the $I_h$ channels via regulation of the intracellular cAMP level in thalamo-cortical neurons indeed appears to enable transmitters of ascending activation systems, such as serotonin, noradrenaline, histamine, NO, and adenosine, to specifically dampen or to promote oscillatory activity in the thalamus in a manner that is dependent upon various states of sleep and arousal and governed by the metabolic state of the cells (95, 96, 100–103). A similar system involving the equivalent current, $I_f$, in sino-atrial node cells enables the regulation of cardiac pacemaking through catecholamines and acetylcholine (34, 36). It is important to add that a number of mechanisms other than the modulation of $I_h$ are involved in the regulation of firing patterns in thalamo-cortical circuits (92, 119) For example, most of the respective transmitters evoke additional effects mediated via different receptor subtypes in thalamo-cortical neurons, such as a strong depolarization or hyperpolarization from rest owing to a decrease or increase in membrane $K^+$ conductance, respectively (92). Although the strong deflections in membrane potential can also shift the mode of activity in the thalamo-cortical system, the involvement of the $I_h$ channels in the regulatory apparatus is advantageous from a teleological point of view. Modulation of $I_h$ has significantly less influence on tonically depolarized neurons and associated generation of $Na^+/K^+$ spikes, which may support the selective termination of synchronized rhythmic activity patterns, for instance upon arousal from slow-wave sleep or pathological forms of synchronization (119), and the initiation of a state of activity that allows a more faithful transfer of synaptic signals without interfering with this state once it has been established.

## CONCLUDING REMARKS

Anomalous inward rectification upon hyperpolarization negative to the resting potential is a phenomenon present in neurons within wide areas of the peripheral and central nervous system. Our understanding of the underlying hyperpolarization-activated cation current $I_h$ has matured from that of a queer current to a mechanism that contributes significantly to the resting potential, the limitation of excessive hyperpolarization, the shaping of firing patterns, and the generation of rhythmic oscillations of the membrane potential. The most important biological variable to control the function of $I_h$ appears to be the voltage dependence of the activation, which can be regulated by extrinsic and metabolic stimuli via the intracellular cAMP pathway. The existence of $I_h$-like currents and the conservation of their regulation in a variety of tissues suggest that the respective channels are rather old in evolutionary terms (34). $I_h$ currents, in addition, display some peculiar properties different from those of other voltage-gated currents. They possess a steep voltage dependence and activate with a sigmoidal time course, thereby resembling voltage-gated $Na^+$, $Ca^{2+}$, and delayed rectifier $K^+$ currents, but unlike the latter, they also deactivate with sigmoidal kinetics and activation occurs upon membrane hyperpolarization. The activation at negative potentials and blockade by $Cs^+$ is reminiscent of the inwardly rectifying $K^+$ conductance. Many characteristics of $I_h$, however, are strikingly different from those of inward rectifiers: The activation kinetics are slower, the activation range is more positive and independent of the external $K^+$ concentration, the conductance is largely insensitive to external $Ba^{2+}$, and the $I_h$ channels are permeable to $Na^+$ in addition to $K^+$. Unlike other cation channels, such as ligand-gated cation channels, the $I_h$ channels are highly selective for $Na^+$ and $K^+$, and they have steeply voltage-dependent gating. Although the gene that encodes the $I_h$ channel has not been identified, it is tempting to put the $I_h$ channels in a class of their own within the superfamily of voltage-gated channels (136).

ACKNOWLEDGMENTS

Thanks are due to DA McCormick for an exciting collaboration, to UT Eysel for encouraging support, and to D DiFrancesco for critical comments on an earlier version of the manuscript. The research in my laboratory is supported by the Deutsche Forschungsgemeinschaft (DFG), the Kulturministerium des Landes Sachsen-Anhalt, the Bundesministerium für Bildung und Forschung, and the European Science Foundation.

## Literature Cited

1. Akasu T, Shoji S, Hasuo H. 1993. Inward rectifier and low-threshold calcium currents contribute to the spontaneous firing mechanism in neurons of the rat suprachiasmatic nucleus. *Pflügers Arch.* 425:109–16

2. Alonso A, Llinás R. 1989. Subthreshold $Na^+$-dependent theta-like rhythmicity in stellate cells of entorhinal cortex layer. II. *Nature* 342:175–77

3. Angstadt JD, Calabrese RL. 1989. A hyperpolarization-activated inward current in heart interneurons of the medicinal leech. *J. Neurosci.* 9:2846–57

4. Araki T, Ito M, Oshima T. 1962. Potential changes produced by application of current steps in motoneurones. *Nature* 191:1104–5

5. Attwell D, Wilson M. 1980. Behaviour of the rod network in the tiger salamander retina mediated by membrane properties of individual rods. *J. Physiol.* 309:287–315

6. Bader CR, Bertrand D. 1984. Effect of changes in intra- and extracellular sodium on the inward (anomalous) rectification in salamander photoreceptors. *J. Physiol.* 347:611–31

7. Bader CR, Bertrand D, Schwartz EA. 1982. Voltage-activated and calcium-activated currents studied in solitary rod inner segments from the salamander retina. *J. Physiol.* 331:253–84

8. Bader CR, MacLeish PR, Schwartz EA. 1979. A voltage-clamp study of the light response in solitary rods of the tiger salamander. *J. Physiol.* 296:1–26

9. Baker M, Bostock H, Grafe P, Martius P. 1987. Function and distribution of three types of rectifying channel in rat spinal root myelinated axons. *J. Physiol.* 383:45–67

10. Banks MI, Pearce RA, Smith PH. 1993. Hyperpolarization-activated cation current ($I_h$) in neurons of the medial nucleus of the trapezoid body: voltage-clamp analysis and enhancement by norepinephrine and cAMP suggest a modulatory mechanism in the auditory brain stem. *J. Neurophysiol.* 70:1420–32

11. Barnes S, Hille B. 1989. Ionic channels of the inner segment of tiger salamander cone photoreceptors. *J. Gen. Physiol.* 94:719–43

12. Bayliss DA, Viana F, Bellingham MC, Berger AJ. 1994. Characteristics and

postnatal development of a hyperpolarization-activated inward current in rat hypoglossal motoneurons in vitro. *J. Neurophysiol.* 71:119–28

13. Beavo JA. 1988. Multiple isozymes of cyclic nucleotide phosphodiesterase. In *Advances in Second Messenger and Phosphoprotein Research,* ed. P Greengard, GA Robinson, 22:1–7. New York: Raven

14. Birch BD, Kocsis JD, DiGregorio F, Bhisitkul RB, Waxman SG. 1991. A voltage- and time-dependent rectification in rat dorsal spinal root axons. *J. Neurophysiol.* 66:719–28

15. Bobker DH, Williams JT. 1989. Serotonin augments the cationic current $I_h$ in central neurons. *Neuron* 2:1535–40

16. Brown HF, DiFrancesco D. 1980. Voltage clamp investigations of currents underlying pacemaker activity in rabbit sino-atrial node. *J. Physiol.* 308:331–51

17. Brown HF, DiFrancesco D, Noble SJ. 1979. How does adrenaline accelerate the heart? *Nature* 280:235–36

18. Budde T, White JA, Kay AR. 1994. Hyperpolarization-activated $Na^+$-$K^+$ current ($I_h$) in neocortical neurons is blocked by external proteolysis and internal TEA. *J. Neurophysiol.* 72:2737–42

19. Callewaert G, Carmeliet E, Vereecke J. 1984. Single cardiac Purkinje cells: general electrophysiology and voltage-clamp analysis of the pace-maker current. *J. Physiol.* 349:643–61

20. Campbell DL, Rasmusson RL, Strauss HC. 1992. Ionic current mechanisms generating vertebrate primary cardiac pacemaker activity at the single cell level: an integrative view. *Annu. Rev. Physiol.* 54:279–302

21. Chang F, Cohen IS, DiFrancesco D, Rosen MR, Tromba C. 1991. Effects of protein kinase inhibitors on canine Purkinje fibre pacemaker depolarization and the pacemaker current $I_f$. *J. Physiol.* 440:367–84

22. Church J. 1992. A change from $HCO_3^-$-(-)-$CO_2$-to HEPES-buffered medium modifies membrane properties of rat CA1 pyramidal neurones in vitro. *J. Physiol.* 455:51–71

23. Colino A, Halliwell JV. 1993. Carbachol potentiates Q current and activates a calcium-dependent non-specific conductance in rat hippocampus, in vitro. *Eur. J. Neurosci.* 5:1198–209

24. Corotto FS, Michel WC. 1994. A hyperpolarization-activated cation conductance in lobster olfactory receptor neurons. *J. Neurophysiol.* 72:360–65

25. Crepel F, Penit-Soria J. 1986. Inward rectification and low threshold calcium conductance in rat cerebellar Purkinje cells. An in vitro study. *J. Physiol.* 372:1–23

26. Dawson TM, Snyder SH. 1994. Gases as biological messengers: nitric oxide and carbon monoxide in the brain. *J. Neurosci.* 14:5147–59

27. Dekin MS. 1993. Inward rectification and its effects on the repetitive firing properties of bulbospinal neurons located in the ventral part of the nucleus solitarius. *J. Neurophysiol.* 70:590–601

28. Destexhe A, Babloyantz A. 1993. A model of the inward current $I_h$ and its possible role in thalamocortical oscillations. *NeuroReport* 4:223–26

29. Destexhe A, Babloyantz A, Sejnowski TJ. 1993. Ionic mechanisms for intrinsic slow oscillations in thalamic relay neurons. *Biophys. J.* 65:1538–52

30. DiFrancesco D. 1981. A new interpretation of the pace-maker current in calf Purkinje fibres. *J. Physiol.* 314:359–76

31. DiFrancesco D. 1981. A study of the ionic nature of the pace-maker current in calf Purkinje fibres. *J. Physiol.* 314:377–93

32. DiFrancesco D. 1982. Block and activation of the pace-maker channel in calf Purkinje fibres: effects of potassium, caesium and rubidium. *J. Physiol.* 329:485–507

33. DiFrancesco D. 1984. Characterization of the pace-maker current kinetics in calf Purkinje fibres. *J. Physiol.* 348:341–67

34. DiFrancesco D. 1985. The cardiac hyperpolarizing-activated current, $i_f$. Origins and developments. *Prog. Biophys. Mol. Biol.* 46:163–83

35. DiFrancesco D. 1986. Characterization of single pacemaker channels in cardiac sino-atrial node cells. *Nature* 324:470–73

36. DiFrancesco D. 1993. Pacemaker mechanisms in cardiac tissue. *Annu. Rev. Physiol.* 55:455–72

37. DiFrancesco D. 1994. Some properties of the UL-FS 49 block of the hyperpolarization-activated current (i(f)) in sino-atrial node myocytes. *Pflügers Arch.* 427:64–70

38. DiFrancesco D, Ferroni A, Mazzanti M, Tromba C. 1986. Properties of the hyperpolarization-activated current ($I_f$) in cells isolated from the rabbit sino-atrial node. *J. Physiol.* 377:61–88

39. DiFrancesco D, Mangoni M. 1994. Modulation of single hyperpolarization-activated channels ($I_f$) by cAMP in the rabbit sino-atrial node. *J. Physiol.* 474:473–82

40. DiFrancesco D, Porciatti F, Cohen IS. 1991. The effects of manganese and barium on the cardiac pacemaker current, $I_f$, in rabbit sino-atrial node myocytes. *Experientia* 47:449–52

41. DiFrancesco D, Porciatti F, Janigro D, Maccaferri G, Mangoni M, et al. 1991. Block of the cardiac pacemaker current ($I_f$) in the rabbit sino-atrial node and in canine Purkinje fibres by 9-amino-1,2, 3,4-tetrahydroacridine. *Pflügers Arch.* 417:611–15

42. DiFrancesco D, Tortora P. 1991. Direct activation of cardiac pacemaker channels by intracellular cyclic AMP. *Nature* 351:145–47

43. DiFrancesco D, Tromba C. 1987. Acetylcholine inhibits activation of the cardiac hyperpolarizing-activated current, $I_f$. *Pflügers Arch.* 410:139–42

44. DiFrancesco D, Tromba C. 1988. Inhibition of the hyperpolarization-activated current ($I_f$) induced by acetylcholine in rabbit sino-atrial node myocytes. *J. Physiol.* 405:477–91

45. DiFrancesco D, Tromba C. 1988. Muscarinic control of the hyperpolarization-activated current ($I_f$) in rabbit sino-atrial node myocytes. *J. Physiol.* 405:493–510

46. Edman A, Gestrelius S, Grampp W. 1987. Current activation by membrane hyperpolarization in the slowly adapting lobster stretch receptor neurone. *J. Physiol.* 384:671–90

47. Edman A, Grampp W. 1989. Ion permeation through hyperpolarization-activated membrane channels (Q-channels) in the lobster stretch receptor neurone. *Pflügers Arch.* 413:249–55

48. Edman A, Grampp W. 1991. Ion ($H^+$, $Ca^{2+}$, $Co^{2+}$) and temperature effects on a hyperpolarization-activated membrane current in the lobster stretch receptor neurone. *Acta Physiol. Scand.* 141:251–61

49. Edman A, Theander S, Grampp W. 1992. Functional effects of a hyperpolarization-activated membrane current in the lobster stretch receptor neurone. *Acta Physiol. Scand.* 146:221–32

50. Eng DL, Gordon TR, Kocsis JD, Waxman SG. 1990. Current-clamp analysis of a time-dependent rectification in rat optic nerve. *J. Physiol.* 421: 185–202

51. Erickson KR, Ronnekleiv OK, Kelly MJ. 1993. Electrophysiology of guinea-pig supraoptic neurones: role of a hyperpolarization-activated cation current in phasic firing. *J. Physiol.* 460:407–25

52. Fain GL, Quandt FN, Bastian BL. 1978. Contribution of a caesium-sensitive conductance increase to the rod photoresponse. *Nature* 272:467–69

53. Ficker E, Taglialatela M, Wible BA, Henley CM, Brown AM. 1994. Spermine and spermidine as gating molecules for inward rectifier $K^+$ channels. *Science* 266:1068–72

54. Fletcher GH, Chiappinelli VA. 1992. An inward rectifier is present in presynaptic nerve terminals in the chick ciliary ganglion. *Brain Res.* 575:103–12

55. Foehring RC, Waters RS. 1991. Contributions of low-threshold calcium current and anomalous rectifier ($I_h$) to slow depolarizations underlying burst firing in human neocortical neurons in vitro. *Neurosci. Lett.* 124:17–21

56. Frace AM, Maruoka F, Noma A. 1992. Control of the hyperpolarization-activated cation current by external anions in rabbit sino-atrial node cells. *J. Physiol.* 453:307–18

56a. Frace AM, Maruoka F, Noma A. 1992. External $K^+$ increases $Na^+$ conductances of the hyperpolarization-activated current in rabbit cardiac pacemakers cells. *Pflügers Arch.* 421:94–96

57. Gallego R, Ivorra I, Morales A. 1987. Effects of central or peripheral axotomy on membrane properties of sensory neurones in the petrosal ganglion of the cat. *J. Physiol.* 391:39–56

58. Garrat JC, Alreja M, Aghajanian GK. 1993. LSD has high efficay relative to serotonin in enhancing the cationic current $I_h$: intracellular studies in rat facial motoneurons. *Synapse* 13:123–34

59. Golowasch J, Buchholtz F, Epstein IR, Marder E. 1992. Contribution of individual ionic currents to activity of a model stomatogastric ganglion neuron. *J. Neurophysiol.* 67:341–49

60. Golowasch J, Marder E. 1992. Ionic currents of the lateral pyloric neuron of the stomatogastric ganglion of the crab. *J. Neurophysiol.* 67:318–31

61. Gordon SE, Brautigan DL, Zimmerman AL. 1992. Protein phosphatases modulate the apperent agonist affinity of the light-regulated ion channel in retinal rods. *Neuron* 9:739–48

62. Gordon TR, Kocsis JD, Waxman SG. 1991. TEA-sensitive potassium channels and inward rectification in regenerated rat sciatic nerve. *Muscle Nerve* 14:640–46

63. Hagiwara N, Irisawa H. 1989. Modulation by intracellular $Ca^{2+}$ of the hyperpolarization-activated inward current in rabbit single sino-atrial node cells. *J. Physiol.* 409:121–41

64. Halliwell JV, Adams PR. 1982. Voltage-clamp analysis of muscarine exci-

tation in hippocampal neurons. *Brain Res.* 250:71–92

65. Halliwell JV, Grove EA. 1989. 9-amino-1,2,3,4-tetrahydroacridine (THA) blocks agonist-induced potassium conductance in rat hippocampal neurones. *Eur. J. Pharmacol.* 163:369–72

66. Hestrin S. 1987. The properties and function of inward rectification in rod photoreceptors of the tiger salamander. *J. Physiol.* 390:319–33

67. Hille B. 1992. *Ionic Channels of Excitable Membranes.* Sunderland, MA: Sinauer. 607 pp. 2nd ed.

68. Ho WK, Brown HF, Noble D. 1994. High selectivity of the $I_f$ channel to $Na^+$ and $K^+$ in rabbit isolated sinoatrial node cells. *Pflügers Arch.* 426:68–74

69. Hockberger B, Toselli M, Swandulla D, Lux HD. 1989. A diacylglycerol analogue reduces neuronal calcium currents independently of protein kinase C activation. *Nature* 338:340–42

70. Hodgkin AL, Huxley AF. 1952. A quantitative description of membrane current and its application to conduction and excitation in nerve. *J. Physiol.* 117:500–44

71. Ingram SL, Williams JT. 1994. Opioid inhibition of $I_h$ via adenyl cyclase. *Neuron* 13:179–86

72. Ito M, Oshima T. 1965. Electrical behaviour of the motoneurone membrane during intracellularly applied current steps. *J. Physiol.* 180:607–35

73. Janigro D, West A, Nguyen TS, Winn HR. 1994. Regulation of blood-brain barrier endothelial cells by nitric oxide. *Circ. Res.* 75:528–38

74. Jiang ZG, Pessia M, North RA. 1993. Dopamine and baclofen inhibit the hyperpolarization-activated cation current in rat ventral tegmental neurones. *J. Physiol.* 462:753–64

75. Jones SW. 1989. On the resting potential of isolated frog sympathetic neurons. *Neuron* 3:153–61

76. Kamondi A, Reiner PB. 1991. Hyperpolarization-activated inward current in histaminergic tuberomammillary neurons of the rat hypothalamus. *J. Neurophysiol.* 66:1902–11

77. Karst H, Wadman WJ, Joels M. 1993. Long-term control by corticosteroids of the inward rectifier in rat CA1 pyramidal neurons, in vitro. *Brain Res.* 612:172–79

78. Katz B. 1949. Les consantes electriques de la membrane du muscle. *Arch. Sci. Physiol.* 3:285–99

79. Kiehn O, Harris-Warrick RM. 1992. 5-HT modulation of hyperpolarization-activated inward current and calcium-dependent outward current in a crustacean motor neuron. *J. Neurophysiol.* 68:496–508

80. Kitakoga O, Kuba K. 1993. Bradykinin-induced ion currents in cultured rat trigeminal ganglion cells. *Neurosci. Res.* 16:79–93

81. Kopell N, LeMasson G. 1994. Rhythmogenesis, amplitude modulation, and multiplexing in a cortical architecture. *Proc. Natl. Acad. Sci. USA* 91:10586–90

82. Kubo Y, Baldwin TJ, Jan YN, Jan LY. 1993. Primary structure and functional expression of a mouse inward rectifier potassium channel. *Nature* 362:127–33

83. Larkman PM, Kelly JS. 1992. Ionic mechanisms mediating 5-hydroxytryptamine- and noradrenaline-evoked depolarization of adult rat facial motoneurones. *J. Physiol.* 456:473–90

84. Li SJ, Wang Y, Strahlendorf HK, Strahlendorf JC. 1993. Serotonin alters an inwardly rectifying current ($I_h$) in rat cerebellar Purkinje cells under voltage clamp. *Brain Res.* 617:87–95

85. Llinás RR. 1988. The intrinsic electrophysiological properties of mammalian neurons: insights into central nervous system function. *Science* 242:1654–64

86. Lopatin AN, Makhina EN, Nichols CG. 1994. Potassium channel block by cytoplasmic polyamines as the mechanism of intrinsic rectification. *Nature* 372:366–69

87. Maccaferri G, Mangoni M, Lazzari A, DiFrancesco D. 1993. Properties of the hyperpolarization-activated current in rat hippocampal CA1 pyramidal cells. *J. Neurophysiol.* 69:2129–36

88. Maricq AV, Korenbrot JI. 1990. Inward rectification in the inner segment of single retinal cone photoreceptors. *J. Neurophysiol.* 64:1917–28

89. Maruoka F, Nakashima Y, Takano M, Ono K, Noma A. 1994. Cation-dependent gating of the hyperpolarization-activated cation current in the rabbit sino-atrial node cells. *J. Physiol.* 477:423–35

90. Mayer ML. 1986. Selective block of inward but not outward rectification in rat sensory neurones infected with herpes simplex virus. *J. Physiol.* 375:327–38

91. Mayer ML, Westbrook GL. 1983. A voltage-clamp analysis of inward (anomalous) rectification in mouse spinal sensory ganglion neurons. *J. Physiol.* 340:19–45

92. McCormick DA. 1992. Neurotransmitter actions in the thalamus and cerebral cortex and their role in neuromodulation

of thalamocortical activity. *Progr. Neurobiol.* 39:337–88

93. McCormick DA, Huguenard JR. 1992. A model of the electrophysiological properties of thalamocortical relay neurons. *J. Neurophysiol.* 68:1384–400

94. McCormick DA, Pape HC. 1990. Properties of a hyperpolarization-activated cation current and its role in rhythmic oscillation in thalamic relay neurones. *J. Physiol.* 431:291–318

95. McCormick DA, Pape HC. 1990. Noradrenergic and serotonergic modulation of a hyperpolarization-activated cation current in thalamic relay neurones. *J. Physiol.* 431:319–42

96. McCormick DA, Williamson A. 1991. Modulation of neuronal firing mode in cat and guinea pig LGNd by histamine: possible cellular mechanisms of histaminergic control of arousal. *J. Neurosci.* 11:3188–99

96a. Mercury NB, Bonci A, Calabresi P, Stefani A, Bernardi G. 1995. Properties of the hyperpolarization-activated cation current I<sub>h</sub> in rat midbrain dopaminergic neurons. *Eur. J. Neurosci.* 7:462–69

97. Nedergaard S, Flatman JA, Engberg I. 1991. Excitation of substantia nigra pars compacta neurones by 5-hydroxy-tryptamine in vitro. *NeuroReport* 2:329–32

98. Nicoll RA, Malenka RC, Kauer JA. 1990. Functional comparison of neurotransmitter receptor subtypes in mammalian central nervous system. *Physiol. Rev.* 70:513–65

99. Ono K, Maruoka F, Noma A. 1994. Voltage- and time-dependent block of I(f) by Sr$^{2+}$ in rabbit sino-atrial node cells. *Pflügers Arch.* 427:437–43

100. Pape HC. 1992. Adenosine promotes burst activity in guinea-pig geniculocortical neurones through two different ionic mechanisms. *J. Physiol.* 447:729–53

101. Pape HC. 1994. Specific bradycardic agents block the hyperpolarization-activated cation current in central neurons. *Neuroscience* 59:363–73

102. Pape HC, Mager R. 1992. Nitric oxide controls oscillatory activity in thalamocortical neurons. *Neuron* 9:441–48

103. Pape HC, McCormick DA. 1989. Noradrenaline and serotonin selectively modulate thalamic burst firing by enhancing a hyperpolarization-activated cation current. *Nature* 340:715–18

103a. Perkins KL, Wong RKS. 1995. Intracellular QX-314 blocks the hyperpolarization-activated inward current I<sub>q</sub> in hippocampal CA1 pyramidal cells. *J. Neurophysiol.* 73:911–15

104. Rainnie DG, Asprodini EK, Shinnick-Gallagher P. 1991. Excitatory transmission in the basolateral amygdala. *J. Neurophysiol.* 66:986–97

105. Rainnie DG, Grunze HC, McCarley RW, Greene RW. 1994. Adenosine inhibition of mesopontine cholinergic neurons: implications for EEG arousal. *Science* 263:689–92

106. Richards JM, Tierney JM, Swislowski NI. 1981. ATP-dependent activation of adenylate cyclase. *J. Biol. Chem.* 256:8889–91

107. Rudy B. 1988. Diversity and ubiquity of K channels. *Neuroscience* 25:729–49

108. Satoh H. 1993. Electrophysiological actions of adenosine and aminophylline in spontaneously beating and voltage-clamped rabbit sino-atrial node preparations. *Naunyn-Schmiedebergs Arch. Pharmacol.* 347:197–204

109. Satoh H. 1993. Modulation of the automaticity by histamine and cimetidine in rabbit sino-atrial node cells. *Gen. Pharmacol.* 24:1213–22

110. Satoh H, Sperelakis N. 1993. Hyperpolarization-activated inward current in embryonic chick cardiac myocytes: developmental changes and modulation by isoproterenol and carbachol. *Eur. J. Pharmacol.* 240:283–90

111. Schlichter R, Bader CR, Bernheim L. 1991. Development of anomalous rectification (I<sub>h</sub>) and of a tetrodotoxin-resistant sodium current in embryonic quail neurones. *J. Physiol.* 442:127–45

112. Schwindt PC, Spain WJ, Crill WE. 1988. Influence of anomalous rectifier activation on afterhyperpolarizations of neurons from cat sensorimotor cortex in vitro. *J. Neurophysiol.* 59:468–81

113. Siegenbeek van Heukelom J. 1991. Role of the anomalous rectifier in determining membrane potentials of mouse muscle fibres at low extracellular K$^+$. *J. Physiol.* 434:549–60

114. Solomon JS, Doyle JF, Burkhalter A, Nerbonne JM. 1993. Differential expression of hyperpolarization-activated currents reveals distinct classes of visual cortical projection neurons. *J. Neurosci.* 13:5082–91

115. Solomon JS, Nerbonne JM. 1993. Hyperpolarization-activated currents in isolated superior colliculus-projecting neurons from rat visual cortex. *J. Physiol.* 462:393–420

116. Solomon JS, Nerbonne JM. 1993. Two kinetically distinct components of hyperpolarization-activated current in rat superior colliculus-projecting neurons. *J. Physiol.* 469:291–313

117. Soltesz I, Lightowler S, Leresche N, Jassik-Gerschenfeld D, Pollard CE,

Crunelli V. 1991. Two inward currents and the transformation of low-frequency oscillations of rat and cat thalamo-cortical cells. *J. Physiol.* 441:175–97

118. Spain WJ, Schwindt PC, Crill WE. 1987. Anomalous rectification in neurons from cat sensorimotor cortex in vitro. *J. Neurophysiol.* 57:1555–76

119. Steriade M, McCormick DA, Sejnowski TJ. 1993. Thalamocortical oscillations in the sleeping and aroused brain. *Science* 262:679–85

119a. Storm JF, Pedarzani P. 1995. Norepinephrine and cyclic AMP modulate the G/H-current independently of protein kinase A in hippocampal neurons. *Soc. Neurosci. Abstr.* 21:In press

120. Ströhmann B, Schwarz DWF, Puil E. 1994. Mode of firing and rectifying properties of nucleus ovoidalis neurons in the avian auditory thalamus. *J. Neurophysiol.* 71:1351–60

121. Ströhmann B, Schwarz DWF, Puil E. 1994. Subthreshold frequency selectivity in avian auditory thalamus. *J. Neurophysiol.* 71:1361–72

122. Takahashi T. 1990. Inward rectification in neonatal rat spinal motoneurones. *J. Physiol.* 423:47–62

123. Takahashi T, Berger AJ. 1990. Direct excitation of rat spinal motoneurones by serotonin. *J. Physiol.* 423:63–76

124. Tanaka E, Higashi H, Nishi S. 1991. Membrane properties of guinea pig cingulate cortical neurons in vitro. *J. Neurophysiol.* 65:808–21

125. Tokimasa T, Akasu T. 1990. Cyclic AMP regulates an inward rectifying sodium-potassium current in dissociated bull-frog sympathetic neurones. *J. Physiol.* 420:409–29

126. Tokimasa T, Sugiyama K, Akasu T, Muteki T. 1990. Volatile anaesthetics inhibit a cyclic AMP-dependent sodium-potassium current in cultured sensory neurones of bullfrog. *Br. J. Pharmacol.* 101:190–200

127. Tóth T, Crunelli V. 1992. Computer simulation of the pacemaker oscillations of thalamocortical cells. *NeuroReport* 3:65–68

128. Travagli RA, Gillis RA. 1994. Hyperpolarization-activated currents, $I_H$ and $I_{KIR}$, in rat dorsal motor nucleus of the vagus neurons in vitro. *J. Neurophysiol.* 71:1308–17

129. Uchimura N, Cherubini E, North RA. 1990. Cation current activated by hyperpolarization in a subset of rat nucleus accumbens neurons. *J. Neurophysiol.* 64:1847–50

130. Undem BJ, Hubbard W, Weinrich D. 1993. Immunologically induced neuromodulation of guinea pig nodose ganglion neurons. *J. Auton. Nerv. Syst.* 44:35–44

131. VanBogaert PP, Goethals M. 1987. Pharmacological influence of specific bradycardic agents on the pacemaker current of sheep cardiac Purkinje fibres. A comparison between three different molecules. *Eur. Heart J. Suppl.* 8:35–42

132. VanBogaert PP, Goethals M. 1992. Blockade of the pacemaker current by intracellular application of UL-FS 49 and UL-AH 99 in sheep cardiac Purkinje fibers. *Eur. J. Pharmacol.* 229:55–62

133. VanBogaert PP, Goethals M, Simoens C. 1990. Use- and frequency-dependent blockade by UL-FS 49 of the $I_f$ pacemaker current in sheep cardiac Purkinje fibres. *Eur. J. Pharmacol.* 187:241–56

134. VanGinneken ACG, Giles W. 1991. Voltage clamp measurements of the hyperpolarization-activated inward current $I_f$ in single cells from rabbit sino-atrial node. *J. Physiol.* 434:57–83

134a. Wang XJ, Golomb D, Rinzel F. 1995. Emergent spindle oscillations and intermittent burst firing in a thalamic model: specific neuronal mechanisms. *Proc. Natl. Acad. Sci. USA* 92:5577–81

135. Williams JT, Colmers WF, Pan ZZ. 1988. Voltage- and ligand-activated inwardly rectifying currents in dorsal raphe neurons in vitro. *J. Neurosci.* 8:3499–506

135a. Wollmuth LP. 1995. Multiple ion binding sites in $I_h$ channels of rod photoreceptors from tiger salamander. *Pflügers Arch.* 430:34–43

136. Wollmuth LP, Hille B. 1992. Ionic selectivity of $I_h$ channels of rod photoreceptors in tiger salamanders. *J. Gen. Physiol.* 100:749–65

137. Womble MD, Moises HC. 1993. Hyperpolarization-activated currents in neurons of the rat basolateral amygdala. *J. Neurophysiol.* 70:2056–65

138. Wuttke WA, Berry MS. 1992. Modulation of inwardly rectifying $Na^+$-$K^+$ channels by serotonin and cyclic nucleotides in salivary gland cells of the leech, haementaria. *J. Membr. Biol.* 127:57–68

139. Yanagihara K, Irisawa H. 1980. Inward current activated during hyperpolarization in the rabbit sino atrial node cell. *Pflügers Arch.* 385:11–19

140. Yatani A, Okabe K, Codina J, Birnbaumer L, Brown AM. 1990. Heart rate regulation by G proteins acting on the cardiac pacemaker channel. *Science* 249:1163–66

141. Zaza A, Maccaferri G, Mangoni M, DiFrancesco D. 1991. Intracellular calcium does not directly modulate cardiac pacemaker ($I_f$) channels. *Pflügers Arch.* 419:662–64

142. Zhou Z, Lipsius SL. 1993. Effect of isoprenaline on $I_f$ current in latent pacemaker cells isolated from cat right atrium: ruptured vs. perforated patch whole-cell recording methods. *Pflügers Arch.* 423:442–47

Annu. Rev. Physiol. 1996. 58:329–48

# LOW-THRESHOLD CALCIUM CURRENTS IN CENTRAL NERVOUS SYSTEM NEURONS

*J. R. Huguenard*

Department of Neurology and Neurological Sciences, Stanford University School of Medicine, Stanford, California 94305

KEY WORDS: LVA current, T current, low-threshold spike, calcium-dependent burst firing, oscillations

## ABSTRACT

The low-threshold calcium current, or T current, has recently been demonstrated with voltage-clamp recordings in a variety of central nervous system (CNS) neurons. It is especially prominent in the soma and dendrites of neurons with robust calcium-dependent burst firing behaviors such as thalamic relay neurons and cerebellar Purkinje cells. Single-channel and macroscopic current behavior have been carefully investigated and kinetic schemes devised to completely describe the activation and inactivation processes. The kinetic properties of T current lead to activation of low-threshold spikes subsequent to transient membrane hyperpolarizations. Putative functional roles for T current include generation of low-threshold spikes that lead to burst firing, promotion of intrinsic oscillatory behavior, boosting of calcium entry, and synaptic potentiation.

## INTRODUCTION AND HISTORY

In an elegant series of in vitro intracellular studies in cat thalamus, Eccles and collaborators (3) discovered that some central neurons displayed a form of paradoxical excitation. In contrast to the typical responses in most cells where depolarized membrane potentials are normally associated with enhanced excitability, hyperpolarizations such as those produced by inhibitory synaptic potentials resulted in increased responsiveness. This period of enhanced excitability following membrane hyperpolarizations was termed post-anodal exaltation. Llinás and colleagues carefully examined this property using intracellular recordings with in vitro slice preparations of inferior olive (65, 66) and thalamus (55, 56, 64). They noted that intracellular current injections, which hyperpolarized the membrane to levels more negative than rest (around

329

−65 to −70 mV), resulted in a rebound plateau excitation. The rebound potential exceeded the threshold for $Na^+$-dependent action potentials with the result that a burst of $Na^+$ spikes rode the crest of the plateau.

Further studies identified the likely mechanisms for the burst response. Blockade of $Na^+$ channels by tetrodotoxin revealed an underlying plateau potential. The activation threshold was around −55 mV, approximately 15 mV more negative than the threshold for $Na^+$ spikes. Therefore, the plateau was described as a low-threshold spike or LTS. The LTS was dramatically reduced by removing $Ca^{2+}$ from the extracellular solution or by adding inorganic $Ca^{2+}$ antagonists such as $Co^{2+}$. Substitution of $Ba^{2+}$ for $Ca^{2+}$ in the perfusate did not alter the time course of the LTS, thus indicating a lack of $Ca^{2+}$-dependent inactivation. These findings led to the suggestion that a specialized type of $Ca^{2+}$ current, the low-threshold $Ca^{2+}$ current (LTCC), was responsible for rebound burst firing in these neurons.

The pioneering current-clamp studies have been followed in detail over the last ten years with the direct identification of such a low-threshold, inactivating $Ca^{2+}$ current in several central neuronal types. The low-threshold calcium current was first fully described in cultured sensory neurons from rat and chick (12, 29, 79). In these neurons, it was clear that the current was not due to an alternative form of gating of a high-threshold channel. Evidence for an independent entity included metabolic stability compared with the lability of high-voltage-activated (HVA) $Ca^{2+}$ currents (14, 32, 63, 77), differential pharmacological sensitivity of the $I_T$ as opposed to HVA currents (13, 32, 77), and identification of a unique single-channel entity with activation properties complementary to those expected for macroscopic low-threshold $Ca^{2+}$ currents (12, 79).

Various nomenclatures have been devised to describe the multiple types of $Ca^{2+}$ currents in excitable cells, but complete classification will depend on identification of the molecular structure of the channels (94). In the most common usage, LTCC is equivalent to T (for tiny or transient) current (79). Other synonyms are the low-voltage activated (LVA) current (12), type I current (77), or the low-threshold-inactivating (LTI) current (63). In this review we restrict ourselves to the common terminology: T current or $I_T$.

Since the early intracellular studies that revealed a role for a specialized $Ca^{2+}$-dependent conductance in burst firing, subsequent reports have provided information regarding other functional roles of $I_T$ channels. Here we review several aspects of T current in a variety of central neurons (and a few other cell types where comparison is appropriate), with emphasis on biophysical properties, localization, modulation, heterogeneity, and proposed function(s).

## BIOPHYSICS

The voltage dependence of activation and inactivation of $I_T$ has been described in a number of preparations. Comparison of these studies is complicated by the different recording conditions used in each study. Voltage-dependent membrane conductances are dramatically affected by membrane-screening charges, especially those resulting from extracellular divalent cations (13, 29, 34, 44, 97, 98). An e-fold increase in extracellular $[Ca^{2+}]$ will shift gating curves by approximately +5 – +12 mV. These differences in screening charges must be accounted for when comparing the results of studies performed with various concentrations of $Ca^{2+}$ or when the charge carrier is $Ba^{2+}$, which is less effective at charge screening than $Ca^{2+}$ (13, 29, 52). The results from selected voltage-clamp studies that have provided relatively complete biophysical characterization of $I_T$ in a number of cell types are presented in Table 1. These studies were performed mostly at room temperature (near 22°C). Both the kinetics and amplitude of $I_T$ are highly dependent, with $Q_{10}$ values of 2 to 3 (21, 29, 78). The time constants of activation and inactivation would be approximately three to four times shorter at physiological temperatures (37°C).

## Activation

Voltage dependence of activation has been determined by a variety of methods including plotting the normalized peak current vs membrane potential (e.g. 24, 35, 43, 57) or by converting peak current to peak conductance by dividing by the driving force $(E-E_{Ca})$ (e.g. 40, 110). However, because $I_T$ has non-instantaneous activation and inactivation kinetics, these methods do not provide an independent measure of the macroscopic activation process. Two alternatives have been used. One, based on the original methods of Hodgkin & Huxley (47), involves fitting kinetic functions to whole-cell currents. Some assumptions underlying the original theory have been disproved by modern single-channel recordings, most notably the lack of independence between activation and inactivation (e.g. 1). Thus although the results do not provide complete information about microscopic gating mechanisms (see Single-Channel Studies below), these methods provide an excellent means of completely describing the time- and voltage-dependent activation and inactivation of macroscopic currents. The equations thus generated can be used in simulations of neuronal behavior (51, 72).

The generic Hodgkin-Huxley equation for an inactivating current is

$$g_t = g' \, [1-\exp(-t/\tau_m)]^n \, \exp(-t/\tau_h), \qquad\qquad 1.$$

where $g_t$ is the conductance at time t; $g' = \bar{g} \, (m)_\infty{}^n \, h_o$; $\bar{g}$ is the total conductance available; $\tau_m$ and $\tau_h$ are the time constants of activation and inactivation, respectively; $n$ is the power of the activation function (equivalent to the number of closed states through which a channel must traverse before opening); $m_\infty$ is the relative steady-state activation at a given membrane potential; and $h_o$ is the relative level of inactivation at the initial holding potential. With a holding

**Table 1** Voltage-dependent kinetics for T current in a variety of neurons

| Cell Type | Charge Carrier | Inactivation | | | | Activation | | | Reference |
|---|---|---|---|---|---|---|---|---|---|
| | | $V_{1/2}^a$ | $k^b$ | $\tau_h^c$ | $\tau_{recovery}^c$ | $V_{1/2}^2$ | $k^b$ | $\tau_m^c$ | |
| Isolated hippocampal L-M cells | 2 Ca | -94 | 6.3 | 25-10 | ~90 ms/-100 mV | -47 | 6 | ttp | (35) |
| Isolated rat VB | 3 Ca | -81 | 4.0 | 130-30 | 250 ms/-100mV | -57 | 6 | 15-2 | (51, 52) |
| Isolated rat nRt | 3 Ca | -80 | 5.3 | 100-80 | 500ms/-100mV | -50 | 7 | 11-3 | (52) |
| Isolated rat dLGN | 5 Ca | -64 | 7.8 | 70-20 | 750ms/-98mV | -45 | 6 | ttp | (43) |
| Cat and rat dLGN in slice | 1 Ca | -87 | 3.9 | 100-25 | ~300ms/-95mV | -60 | 2 | | (24) |
| Rat spinal dorsal horn in slice | 2 Ba | -86 | 8.0 | 80-10 | | -45 | 7 | | (86) |
| Isolated rat basal forebrain | 2.5 Ca | -49 | 3.9 | 82-16 | | -40 | 4.8 | ttp | (2) |
| Isolated rat lateral habenula | 3 Ca | -81 | 4.4 | 150, 50-30$^d$ | 510ms/-90mV | -58 | 3.4 | 8-2 | (50) |
| Isolated rat dorsal horn neurons | 5 Ca | -82 | 3.7 | 43-16 | | -50 | 6 | | (49) |
| Isolated rat neostriatum | 5 Ca | -88 | 6.1 | | 288ms/-100mV | -53 | 6 | ttp | (48) |
| Isolated rat Purkinje cells | 5 Ba | -93 | 8.2 | 100-25 | | -46 | 9 | | (84) |
| Xenopus neurons in culture | 2 Ca | -79 | 6.9 | 55-20 | | -49 | 6 | ttp | (40) |
| Neuroblastoma | 50 Ba | -51 | 4.0 | 400-20 | ~150ms/-80mV | -20 | 11 | 8-2 | (110) |
| GH3 cells | 10 Ca | -71 | | 100-20 | 250, 1000ms$^d$/-100mV | -33 | 7 | 10-2 | (44) |
| Chick drg | 10 Ca | -78 | 5.0 | 50-20 | | -51 | 7 | ttp | (32) |

Charge carrier concentrations are in mM. $^a$: half-activation or inactivation voltage; $^b$: slope of activation/inactivation curve, mV/efold; $^c$: all values for $\tau$ (time constant) in ms. $\tau_{recovery}$ is the time constant for recovery at the indicated potential; $^d$: Two exponential components; ttp: time to peak is voltage dependent.

potential sufficiently negative that $h_o \approx 0$, $g'$ is determined primarily by $m_\infty$. From Ohms law $g = I/E$; therefore, $g_t$ can be obtained by dividing the current by the driving force $(E-E_{Ca})$ or by the constant field equation (21, 44, 46, 51). Relative values for $m_\infty$ at a series of command potentials can then be obtained. Alternatively, activation can be approximated by measuring tail current amplitudes after a brief activating voltage step (e.g. 50–52, 84, 104). If an appropriate step duration is chosen, activation will be nearly complete while inactivation has not yet become significant. Thus tail current amplitude will closely reflect the maximum activation $[(m_\infty)^n]$ and has the advantage that the driving force is the same for each step.

Under physiological recording conditions, the apparent activation threshold for $I_T$ is near resting membrane potential, −50 to −60 mV, with activation normally complete at −20 to −30 mV. Activation is relatively gradual in most cases, with an e-fold increase in conductance normally requiring about 6–7 mV depolarization (Table 1). Exceptions include cat and rat thalamic relay (24) and rat lateral habenular cells (50), which have very steep activation curves (2–3.4 mV/efold) that would promote rapid regenerative $Ca^{2+}$-dependent responses. However, one of these studies was performed in slices where neurons retain extensive dendritic trees, and as indicated by the authors, voltage-clamp control was probably compromised (24). Thus T current activation slope is probably a relatively constant feature in neurons from several brain areas. The voltage at which $I_T$ is half-activated ($V_{1/2}$) is also comparable in many cell types, with values ranging between −45 and −60 mV in most cases. The differences in half-activation voltage between cell types (Table 1) cannot be completely explained by methodological differences. In a few experiments, direct comparison of activation properties between cell types was obtained with the same recording conditions (50, 52). In these cases, clear differences in $V_{1/2}$ were obtained, with thalamic reticular neurons showing half-activation 9 mV more depolarized than thalamic relay cells or lateral habenular neurons.

The rate of $I_T$ activation is highly voltage dependent. In every case where it has been measured (Table 1), the time to peak (ttp) current becomes shorter with depolarization. Furthermore, the time constant of activation ($\tau_m$) has been directly measured in many cases by fitting Equation 1 to whole-cell current traces. At threshold, $\tau_m$ is relatively slow (8–15 ms) and decreases to around 2 ms at maximal activation (Table 1). Comparison between cell types reveals that differences in the rate of activation are largely accounted for by shifts in the voltage dependence. For example, the relationship between $\tau_m$ and voltage is similar for thalamic relay and reticular neurons, but it is shifted about 20 mV in the positive direction for the latter (52). Functionally this means that at LTS threshold, ~ −50 mV, the rate of onset of T current is approximately twice as fast in relay cells compared with reticular cells. This slow onset of

$I_T$ in reticular neurons may help explain the gradually accelerating $Na^+$ spike frequency found on the rising phase of the LTS (26, 53).

There is a significant delay to the onset of the current, indicating that $I_T$ channels must traverse several closed states before opening (44). The sigmoid onset kinetics of macroscopic records can be best described by Equation 1, with the power factor $n$ set to 2 or 3. Studies in thalamus (21) and GH3 cells (44) have shown that a power factor of 3 is most appropriate to describe T current activation. However, in most other studies (29, 51, 77, 81, 110), including a follow-up study in thalamic neurons performed under slightly different experimental conditions than the original (51, 52), a value of 2 provided a better fit to the data.

The reverse activation process—deactivation—is relatively fast and becomes more rapid with hyperpolarization. The time constant of this process is on the order of 2–12 ms (50–52, 84). Deactivation can become physiologically significant following brief depolarizations that activate $I_T$. Upon repolarization, the T channels remain open for a finite time governed by $\tau_m$. The driving force at deactivation potentials (mainly –60 mV and below) is large so that significant $Ca^{2+}$ entry can occur until the channels are completely deactivated. Thus $I_T$ may serve to promote $Ca^{2+}$ influx during the repolarization phase of action potentials (71, 104).

## Inactivation

Inactivation is one of the main features that distinguishes $I_T$ from the various components of HVA. Inactivation of $Ca^{2+}$ currents are normally complete with voltage-clamp commands that are subthreshold for HVA activation. Three properties related to inactivation have significant functional impact on neurons containing $I_T$: time-dependent inactivation, steady-state inactivation, and recovery from inactivation. Membrane depolarizations into the activation range evoke a current that is slowly inactivating at threshold (time constant, $\tau_h$, around 50–100 ms) (Table 1). Currents activated by stronger depolarizations decay more rapidly, with $\tau_h$ approaching values of 10–20 ms. This feature promotes the self-termination of the LTS (see below). In most cells inactivation can be described by a single, exponential decay process that is highly voltage dependent. By contrast, neurons from the thalamic reticular nucleus exhibit a T current whose inactivation is nearly voltage independent (52), with values between 80 and 100 ms across a wide voltage range. Similarly, cells from the lateral habenula are characterized by a slowly inactivating $I_T$, but in this case the decay is biexponential, with a fast voltage-dependent phase and a slow voltage-independent phase (50).

Steady-state inactivation approximates the availability of T channels as a function of resting membrane potential. Experimentally, it is determined by using long voltage-clamp conditioning pulses that approach steady state, followed by test pulses of fixed amplitude. There is considerably more cell-type heterogeneity of the inactivation process compared with the activation functions described above. Half-inactivation values vary between −50 and −100 mV, although several types of cells have $V_{1/2}$ values near −80 mV (Table 1). The slope of steady-state inactivation is also quite variable, ranging from a low of 3.7 in dorsal horn neurons (49) to a high of 8.2 in cerebellar Purkinje cells (84). Thus weak hyperpolarizations to −60 mV can remove inactivation of a large fraction of $I_T$ in cholinergic forebrain neurons, for example (2), while having little effect on hippocampal interneurons (35) or Purkinje cells (84). Thus the differences in $I_T$ among neurons result in very different operational ranges of membrane potential in which burst firing can be generated. T currents in thalamic neurons have been carefully examined in a number of studies (21, 24, 43, 52, 96). These results indicate that with physiological levels of $[Ca^{2+}]_o$ T channels begin to become available around resting potential and more negative (−60 to −65 mV), reaching maximal levels around −100 mV.

The process of removal of inactivation is highly voltage dependent in almost all cell types (13, 16, 21, 43, 52, 58, 98, 110, but see 44). In some cases, the recovery process has been described as biphasic, with a slow phase up to several seconds in duration (21, 43, 44, 98). The rate of recovery, or deinactivation, determines the absolute and relative refractory periods for LTS generation. Some cell types exhibit very slow recovery processes, with time constants over 1 s (13, 98), whereas others are characterized by very rapid recovery, on the order of 90 ms (35). Deinactivation is expected to have a strong influence on whether a cell is capable of $I_T$-dependent rhythmic oscillatory behavior (see below).

## Permeation

Under normal conditions, $I_T$ channels are selectively permeable to $Ca^{2+}$ and other divalent ions, including $Ba^{2+}$ and $Sr^{2+}$. Peak current amplitude is a saturable function of $[Ca^{2+}]$. Concentration-response curves can be fitted by a single-site model with an apparent $K_d$ of 3.3–10 mM (9, 13, 44, 98). Whole-cell voltage-clamp recordings demonstrate that, in general, $Ba^{2+}$ permeates about the same (29, 59, 84), or not quite as well, as $Ca^{2+}$ (9, 13, 43, 52, 76, 80, 87, 108), whereas $Sr^{2+}$ current amplitudes are comparable to those obtained with $Ba^{2+}$ (29, 110) or slightly larger (98). One exception to this rule is in thalamic reticular neurons, where macroscopic $I_T$ amplitude is increased by about 50% when extracellular $Ca^{2+}$ (3 mM) is replaced by $Ba^{2+}$ (52). Whether this reflects differences in the permeation of single $I_T$ channels or alteration in gating properties will require single-channel studies or nonstationary fluctuation analysis (see below).

## Single-Channel Studies

T current channels have a very low conductance (5–9 pS) compared with HVA channels (14, 33, 63). In most studies, isotonic $BaCl_2$ was used as the charge carrier to maximize the conductance. Reported values of single-channel conductance include 8 pS in rat sensory neurons (79); 7.2 pS (60 mM $Ba^{2+}$) in mouse sensory neurons (63); 8 pS in rat retinal ganglion cells (59); 8 pS in rat and guinea pig hippocampal neurons (80); 9 pS (20 mM $Ba^{2+}$) in rat CA1 pyramidal cells (68); 8 pS (95 $BaCl_2$) in guinea pig hippocampal CA1, CA3, and dentate gyrus neurons (31); 5.2 pS, with a subconductance state of 3.6 pS (50 mM $Ca^{2+}$) in rat and chick dorsal root ganglion neurons (14); 7 pS in rat motoneurons (105); 9 pS in cerebellar Purkinje cells (8); and 8 pS in guinea pig basal forebrain neurons (39). $I_T$ channels in sensory neurons are approximately equally permeable to $Ca^{2+}$, $Ba^{2+}$, and $Sr^{2+}$ (14) or slightly less for $Sr^{2+}$ compared with $Ba^{2+}$ (63). Single-channel conductance was dependent on $[Ca^{2+}]_o$, with a value of $K_d$ around 10 mM and a maximum permeability of 5.7 pS (14). At physiological $[Ca^{2+}]_o$ near 2 mM, the expected conductance would be about 1 pS, yielding single-channel currents on the order of 0.1 pA at $-40$ mV. Estimates of single-channel current amplitudes (0.13–0.15 pA) from nonstationary fluctuation analysis in thalamic relay neurons (23) and cranial sensory neurons (9) are consistent with this value. Interestingly, when $[Ca^{2+}]_o$ is reduced to less than 100 μM (67), $I_T$ channels become permeable to monovalent cations including $Na^+$ and $Li^+$. Single-channel conductance is approximately two to four times larger (12–20 pS) under these conditions (14, 80).

Single-channel gating has been characterized in rat (14) and mouse (63) sensory neurons and in transformed 3T3 fibroblasts (16), but little information is available concerning gating of these channels in central neurons. In preliminary studies it appears that some features of $I_T$ gating are common in a number of cell types. In each case, the channels tend to open in bursts with several intraburst closures before final inactivation (8, 14, 16, 63, 68, 80). The open time distributions of $I_T$ channels are exponentially distributed with mean open times on the order of 1–2 ms (16, 33, 39, 63). In sensory neurons, the distribution of first latencies peaks significantly earlier than the macroscopic current (14). The time course of macroscopic activation and inactivation could be reproduced by evaluating the convolution integral of first latency distribution with the burst open probability. From these results it was concluded that activation and inactivation are only weakly coupled. A kinetic model was developed with two open, two closed, and one inactivated state that assumed to be absorbing (1). The open states were based on the two conductance states of the channel. At least two closed states were required based on the biexponential distribution of closed times and the first opening latency distribution, which was consistent with multiple closed states. Similar results were obtained in 3T3 cells (16). Macroscopic currents could be described by convolving first opening latencies with burst duration. A cyclical Markov model with two closed, one open, and two inactivated states was developed in which inactivation was not voltage dependent. The only transitions that required voltage dependence were between the two closed states, and one of the steps between the inactivated states and the closed state. This model provided a good fit to macroscopic currents in 3T3 cells, but was inadequate to describe $I_T$ in neuronal cells, even with modified rate constants. What is clear from these studies is that, in spite of relatively brief openings, slow inactivation of macroscopic $I_T$ can be explained by delayed opening and multiple reopenings of $I_T$ channels.

## PHARMACOLOGY

Both up- and down-modulation of $I_T$ has been demonstrated with a variety of neurotransmitters and peptides. Furthermore, T current is susceptible to blockade by organic and inorganic antagonists, many of which have some selectivity for $I_T$ over other $Ca^{2+}$ currents. However, in general there are not highly specific antagonists or toxins for T current, and thus there are few pharmacological tools available to demonstrate a functional role for $I_T$ in neuronal behaviors. There is general agreement that specific toxins such as ω-conotoxin GVIA and agatoxin IIIa have no effect on T currents (e.g. 2, 27, 28, 32, 52).

### Antagonists

Divalent and trivalent cations, including $La^{3+}$, $Ni^{2+}$, $Cd^{2+}$, and $Zn^{2+}$, are effective blockers of $I_T$ (e.g. 58, 74, 77). Further evidence for heterogeneity of $I_T$ channels among various neuronal types is provided by different potency series. For example, in rat frontal cortical neurons, the potency series was $La^{3+}>Cd^{2+}>Zn^{2+}>Ni^{2+}$ (109), whereas in rat amygdaloid neurons it was $La^{3+}>Ni^{2+}>Zn^{2+}=Cd^{2+}$ (57). A selective block of $I_T$ was observed with low doses (<100 μM) of $Ni^{2+}$ in rat sensory neurons (32), whereas 20–50 μM $Cd^{2+}$ strongly depressed HVA $Ca^{2+}$ currents with little effect on $I_T$. In general, this selectivity has not been observed in central neurons (Table 2). The concentration of $Ni^{2+}$, which blocks 50% of the current ($EC_{50}$), varies between 30 and 780 μM; the corresponding value for $Cd^{2+}$ ranges from 15 to 650 μM. Therefore, a voltage-clamp analysis of $Ca^{2+}$ current antagonism (obtained under similar ionic conditions) should be performed before a low concentration of $Cd^{2+}$ or $Ni^{2+}$ can be used as a probe for HVA or $I_T$ function in a cellular response.

Dihydropyridines and related compounds can also block $I_T$. Nicardipine and flunarizine are especially potent in this regard with $EC_{50}$s of 1–3 μM in

**Table 2**  Blockade of T current by $Cd^{2+}$ and $Ni^{2+}$

| Cell type | Charge carrier | $Ni^{2+}$ | $Cd^{2+}$ | Reference |
|---|---|---|---|---|
| Rat hippocampal L-M | 2 Ca | 400 | 260 | (35) |
| Rat Purkinje | 10 Ca | 110 | 70 | (58) |
| Rat Purkinje | 5 Ba | 52 | | (84) |
| Rat amygdala | 10 Ca | 30 | 650 | (57) |
| Rat frontal cortex pyramids | 10 Ca | 260 | 15 | (109) |
| Rat CA1 pyramids | 10 Ca | 230 | 80 | (97) |
| Rat dorsal horn | 5 Ca | 230 | 240 | (49) |
| Neuroblastoma | 50 Ba | 47 | 160 | (77) |
| GH3 | 10 Ca | 777 | 188 | (44) |

Charge carrier concentrations are in mM. Values for $Ni^{2+}$ and $Cd^{2+}$ are $EC_{50}$ in $\mu M$.

hippocampal CA1 neurons (97), cerebellar Purkinje cells (58), amygdaloid neurons (57), and in mouse sensory neurons (85). Other organic $Ca^{2+}$ channel antagonists, including D-600 and diltiazem, block $I_T$ at 100-fold higher concentrations (57, 58). An experimental diphenylmethylpiperazine derivative, U-92032, has recently been shown to be a more potent blocker of $I_T$ than flunarizine and is ineffective in reducing HVA in a neuronal cell line (54).

Succinimides and related compounds include a class of antiepileptic drugs that are specifically effective in the treatment of absence-type epilepsy (19). Ethosuximide, or 2-ethyl-2-methylsuccinimide, effectively controls absence seizures when blood levels are between 200 and 700 $\mu M$. In this same concentration range, ethosuximide reduces $I_T$ in thalamic relay (19, 20, 53) and reticular (53) neurons, without having any effect on activation or inactivation kinetics. At these concentrations, ethosuximide has no effect on HVA (19, 20) or on other voltage-dependent conductances (53). Two related compounds, methyl-phenylsuccinimide and dimethadione (active metabolites of anti-absences drug methsuximide and tridione), also reduce $I_T$ in thalamic neurons (19, 22), but these drugs are not as selective as ethosuximide in that they also reduce HVA current. Furthermore, the unsubstituted succinimide ring compound is not active in either $I_T$ current blockade or absence seizure reduction. The mechanism of block by methylphenylsuccinimide, as tested by nonstationary fluctuation analysis methods, was a reduction in the number of channels without a change in single-channel conductance (23), which suggests that succinimides block $I_T$ channels without affecting their gating or permeation. Taken together, these results indicate that T current blockade in thalamic neurons is a likely mechanism for the antiepileptic action of this class of drugs. Consistent with this theory is the finding that in an animal model of absence epilepsy the amplitude of $I_T$ in thalamic reticular neurons is increased compared with that in nonepileptic controls (103). Additionally, an unrelated antiabsence compound, valproic acid, has also been shown to exert weak antagonistic effects on $I_T$ (61).

Amiloride is a relatively specific blocker of $I_T$ in neuroblastoma cells (101), with an $EC_{50}$ of ~50 μM. In central neurons, however, the effects are highly variable. For example, in hippocampal CA1 cells, 300 μM amiloride reduces $I_T$ by ~40% but also significantly reduces some components of HVA (99). In other studies of hippocampal cells, the $EC_{50}$s were ~250–500 μM (60, 102). By contrast, in amphibian spinal (40) and basal forebrain (2) neurons, the $EC_{50}$ was ~100 μM, whereas in rat spinal motoneurons, 1 mM amiloride produced only 27% block (104). Octanol has been reported to be a specific antagonist of $I_T$ (92). In cultured rat sensory neurons, 1 μM 1-octanol strongly inhibits $I_T$ without affecting HVA (90). However, in hippocampal neurons, 300 μM octanol reduced all components of $Ca^{2+}$ current (99), and in GH3 cells, the $EC_{50}$ for $I_T$ reduction was ~250 μM (44). Volatile anesthetics (45, 100) and neuroleptics (81) have all been shown to reduce the amplitude of $I_T$ in various preparations.

## Modulators

A prominent and common difference between $I_T$ and HVA $Ca^{2+}$ currents is metabolic stability. In contrast to HVA currents, $I_T$ is stable during whole-cell dialysis (6, 13, 21, 29, 32, 35, 77, 82), persists with intracellular $F^-$ (13, 35, 44, 98) or $Ca^{2+}$ (13, 52) perfusion, without intracellular ATP or GTP (29), and in cell-free patches (14, 63). Given the relatively stable metabolic state of $I_T$ channels, this may explain why there are fewer reports of $I_T$ modulation than for HVA currents.

Examples of modulatory actions include cholinergic and serotonergic increases, as well as baclofen-dependent blockade, of $I_T$ in hippocampal interneurons (35). Muscarine and carbachol, but not the β-adrenergic agonist isoproterenol, increase channel open probability in cell-attached patch recordings of hippocampal CA3 neurons (30). Substance P enhances $I_T$ in dorsal horn neurons (86). Dopamine and norepinephrine slightly decrease $I_T$ in chick sensory and sympathetic neurons (70). Angiotensin II causes a small (20%) depression of $I_T$ in a neuronal cell line through a G protein-dependent process (10, 11). An activator of protein kinase C (1-oleoyl-2-acetyl-*sn*-glycerol, OAG) reduces both $I_T$ and HVA currents in GH3 cells, with half-maximal effects near 25 μM (69). In sensory neurons, $I_T$ is selectively downregulated by another protein kinase C activator, phorbol 12-myristate-13-acetate (88), but only at temperatures of 29°C and higher, whereas $I_T$ and the inactivating components of HVA are both reduced by opiates acting at the μ receptor (89). The general rule in each of these cases of T current modulation is a reduction in peak current with little effect on kinetics. One possible explanation for this result is that modulation alters the number of available channels but does not affect their time- and voltage-dependent gating.

## LOCALIZATION

The specific location of $I_T$ channels within the somadendritic membrane has significant influence on neuronal function. As far as LTS generation in thalamic relay neurons is concerned, it is clear that $I_T$ channels are present in the somatic membrane at high density because large T currents are recorded in acutely isolated relay cells that have had most of their dendritic tree truncated (21, 43, 96). By contrast, thalamic reticular cells are capable of generating robust LTSs in vitro (53) and in vivo (75), yet only a relatively small conductance is observed in isolated and truncated neurons (52). This is consistent with a putative concentration of $I_T$ channels in dendrites of thalamic reticular cells (75, 91). Dendritic localization in hippocampal CA1 cells has recently been directly demonstrated by dendrite-attached recordings up to 300 μm from the soma (68). Furthermore, a calcium-imaging study demonstrated that spike trains produced a $Ni^{2+}$-sensitive increase in $[Ca^{2+}]_i$ that was more pronounced in dendritic than somatic regions, which indicates that $I_T$ channels may be somewhat restricted to dendritic membranes (17). Recordings of $Ca^{2+}$ current from intact hippocampal CA1 neurons in slices demonstrated a transient $Ca^{2+}$ current that resembles $I_T$, but the voltage-dependence of steady-state inactivation was very hyperpolarized with a $V_{1/2}$ value around $-106$ mV (60). This was interpreted as being the result of dendritic $I_T$ channels that could not be adequately voltage clamped from a somatic site. In support of this idea was the finding that the amplitude of $I_T$ became progressively smaller with cuts that removed increasing amounts of the apical dendritic tree. Intradendritic recording of rat cerebellar Purkinje cells in culture reveal a low-threshold, inactivating $Ca^{2+}$ current present at moderate densities (7).

## FUNCTION

Besides promoting $Ca^{2+}$-dependent burst firing, several additional functional roles for $I_T$ have been proposed. These include intrinsic neuronal oscillations, promotion of $Ca^{2+}$ entry, boosting of synaptic signals, and lowering threshold for high-threshold spike generation. By contrast, one role for T channels that appears unlikely is $Ca^{2+}$ entry at synaptic terminals leading to synaptic release. A voltage-clamp study of excitatory synaptic connections in cultured thalamic neurons demonstrated that $Cd^{2+}$-dependent block of excitatory synapses was correlated with the level of HVA current blockade (83). For example, 10 μM

$Cd^{2+}$ reduced HVA and evoked synaptic currents by greater than 60%, but only reduced $I_T$ by 20%. Furthermore, 50 μM $Cd^{2+}$ completely blocked synaptic transmission and HVA currents while leaving more than 50% of $I_T$ unblocked. It appears that $I_T$ channels cannot by themselves support excitatory neurotransmission, at least in thalamic cells.

Perhaps the most obvious functional role of T channels is to promote LTS generation, which can lead to burst firing in several cell types that include thalamic reticular (75) and relay cells (25, 64), inferior olive cells (65), hippocampal interneurons (35), lateral habenular neurons (107), a subpopulation of pontine reticular formation cells (37), and neocortical neurons (36). Within the neocortex, T channels seem to be found mainly in pyramidal neurons but not in interneurons (38, 42).

Several biophysical features of T current kinetics promote regenerative LTSs. Activation of $I_T$ begins approximately at rest, around −65 mV and more positive, so that brief hyperpolarizing sojourns can result in return of the membrane potential to the activation range. The relatively hyperpolarized activation region for this current means that when $I_T$ is deinactivated, the threshold for regenerative responses becomes much closer to the resting potential (~ −60 mV), compared with the normal threshold for $Na^+$-spike generation (~ −45 mV). Another feature is the voltage-dependent activation rate (Table 1) that contributes to robust regenerative responses in a manner similar to, but slower than, that which occurs with fast $Na^+$ spikes. When the threshold for LTS generation is crossed, the activation rate is slow but becomes progressively faster, leading to more and more depolarization (21).

Inactivation in general, and specifically a voltage-dependent inactivation rate, leads to a LTS that is self limiting in time (21). During the LTS, the rate of macroscopic inactivation becomes progressively faster, largely as a result of shortening of the time to first opening. Thus a separate repolarization mechanism may not be necessary for the LTS. This explains why LTS duration is not affected by $Ba^{2+}$ substitution for $Ca^{2+}$ (55). An exception occurs in thalamic reticular neurons (52), where the rate of inactivation is relatively slow and not very dependent on voltage. Along with dendritic localization of $I_T$, this may be one factor that promotes relatively long duration bursts in nRt cells (75, 91).

The steady-state inactivation function will determine the necessary hyperpolarization for repriming or deinactivation of sufficient $I_T$ channels to lead to subsequent activation of an LTS. Given the variability in the position and steepness of this function among different cell types (Table 1), it appears that some neurons are poised to fire LTSs with minimal provocation, whereas others require substantial hyperpolarization. Interestingly, thalamic neurons have a large reserve of T channels, more than would be necessary to produce a full-fledged LTS. Specific blockade of approximately 40% of T channels by succinimides does not reduce the size or duration of $Ca^{2+}$-dependent bursts in thalamic neurons, even though the probability of obtaining a LTS from a given stimulus is reduced (53).

One other feature of inactivation pertinent to burst generation is recovery from inactivation or deinactivation. This process describes the voltage- and time-dependence of the repriming process. Corrected for temperature, the time constant governing this process in somatosensory thalamic relay cells would be on the order of 60–80 ms at approximately −100 mV (21). This time is much shorter than the duration of inhibitory synaptic potentials mediated by $GABA_B$ receptors in thalamic neurons (200–300 ms), thus ensuring that synaptic inhibitory responses are effective in producing rebound LTSs (53).

As a secondary consequence of burst generation, the presence of significant $I_T$ can promote intrinsic single-cell oscillatory activity (4, 5, 41, 107). The 15–25 mV depolarization and relatively long duration (20–150 ms) of the LTS can lead to activation or inactivation of other voltage- or $Ca^{2+}$-dependent conductances that can interact with $I_T$ to produce repetitive bursts. For example, the depolarization associated with an LTS in thalamic relay cells can deactivate a hyperpolarization-activated inward current ($I_H$) that normally contributes to resting conductance (72, 73, 93). Following the LTS, the membrane hyperpolarizes because of the deactivated $I_H$, and this leads to deinactivation of $I_T$, followed by reactivation of $I_H$ so that the cycle repeats (72). Similarly, LTS generation in thalamic reticular cells leads to $Ca^{2+}$ entry, a $Ca^{2+}$-dependent burst after hyperpolarization (4, 5) that deinactivates $I_T$, and a $Ca^{2+}$-activated nonspecific cation conductance (5), which can return the membrane potential to the activation threshold for LTS generation and continue the cycle. Relatively slow inactivation of $I_T$ in thalamic reticular and lateral habenular cells should lead to long duration LTSs, which would be especially powerful in promoting these types of secondary conductance changes and oscillatory behaviors (41, 50).

Another putative function for $I_T$ in central neurons is boosting of synaptic potentials. As mentioned above, T channels have been shown by several methods to exist in the dendrites of hippocampal CA1 neurons. Therefore, these channels are present at the major site of synaptic input. Dendrite-attached patch recordings have been used to demonstrate that the depolarization associated with a dendritic synaptic input is sufficient to activate $I_T$ channels (68). This would lead to an increase in the local depolarizing potential and potentially insure the active propagation of the synaptic potential to the soma. A similar boosting role has been proposed for $I_T$ in neocortical neurons (95).

Significant $Ca^{2+}$ entry may be promoted by the presence of $I_T$ channels in neuronal membranes, which would lead to $Ca^{2+}$-dependent secondary responses. Voltage-clamped spike waveforms have been used to assess the contribution of various $Ca^{2+}$ channels to total $Ca^{2+}$ entry during action potentials in sensory neurons (71). Selective blockade by $Cd^{2+}$ or amiloride was used to demonstrate that entry through $I_T$ channels is relatively independent of the duration of the spike. This is largely a result of the slow deactivation kinetics of $I_T$, which leads to a large fraction of $Ca^{2+}$ entry occurring during the repolarizing phase of the action potential. A depolarizing after-potential (DAP), which follows single $Na^+$ spikes in dentate gyrus (111) and neocortical neurons (62), is thought to result from $I_T$ in these neurons, based on its sensitivity to holding potential and $Ni^{2+}$ and $Co^{2+}$. Interestingly, it has been postulated that $Ca^{2+}$ entry resulting from the DAP is responsible for long-term potentiation (LTP) in kitten neocortical neurons (62) because manipulations that block the DAP, such as alteration of the membrane potential (either hyperpolarization or depolarization) or addition of $Ni^{2+}$, also block the induction of LTP. Finally, in amphibian spinal neurons in culture, $I_T$ appears to promote spontaneous fluctuations in intracellular $Ca^{2+}$, possibly by lowering the threshold for spontaneous high-threshold spikes (40). Concentrations of amiloride and $Ni^{2+}$, which selectively block $I_T$ in these neurons, reduce the number of cells with spontaneous $Ca^{2+}$ fluctuations by about one third.

## CONCLUSIONS

T currents in central neurons are heterogeneous among different neuronal types, with different antagonist profiles, voltage-dependent kinetics, and modulation. A common feature of T current is that if present in neuronal membranes at sufficient density, robust rebound burst firing is insured. The localization of $I_T$ channels in dendrites will likely boost input or lead to burst generation during synaptic input (68, 91).

Important future directions in T channel research include identification of the molecular structure, including subunit composition (15, 106), and identification and development of specific pharmacological blockers or toxins. Furthermore, because neuronal T channel densities are upregulated by acute injury (18), investigation of regulatory mechanisms that control expression and trafficking of the channel protein is warranted.

*Literature Cited*

1. Aldrich RW, Corey DP, Stevens CF. 1983. A reinterpretation of mammalian sodium channel gating based on single channel recording. *Nature* 306:436–41
2. Allen TG, Sim JA, Brown DA. 1993. The whole-cell calcium current in acute-ly dissociated magnocellular cholinergic basal forebrain neurones of the rat. *J. Physiol.* 460:91–116
3. Andersen P, Eccles JC, Sears TA. 1964. The ventro-basal complex of the thalamus: types of cells, their responses and

their functional organization. *J. Physiol.* 174:370–99

4. Avanzini G, de Curtis M, Panzica F, Spreafico R. 1989. Intrinsic properties of nucleus reticularis thalami neurones of the rat studied in vitro. *J. Physiol.* 416:111–22

5. Bal T, McCormick DA. 1993. Mechanisms of oscillatory activity in guinea-pig nucleus reticularis thalami in vitro: a mammalian pacemaker. *J. Physiol.* 468:669–91

6. Berger AJ, Takahashi T. 1990. Serotonin enhances a low-voltage-activated calcium current in rat spinal motoneurons. *J. Neurosci.* 10:1922–28

7. Bossu JL, Dupont JL, Feltz A. 1989. Calcium currents in rat cerebellar Purkinje cells maintained in culture. *Neuroscience* 30:605–17

8. Bossu JL, Fagni L, Feltz A. 1989. Voltage-activated calcium channels in rat Purkinje cells maintained in culture. *Pflügers Arch.* 414:92–94

9. Bossu JL, Feltz A, Thomann JM. 1985. Depolarization elicits two distinct calcium currents in vertebrate sensory neurons. *Pflügers Arch.* 403:360–68

10. Buisson B, Bottari SP, de Gasparo M, Gallo-Payet N, Payet MD. 1992. The angiotensin AT2 receptor modulates T-type calcium current in non-differentiated NG108–15 cells. *FEBS Lett.* 309:161–64

11. Buisson B, Laflamme L, Bottari SP, de Gasparo M, Gallo-Payet N, Payet MD. 1995. A G protein is involved in the angiotensin AT2 receptor inhibition of the T-type calcium current in non-differentiated NG108–15 cells. *J. Biol. Chem.* 270:1670–74

12. Carbone E, Lux HD. 1984. A low voltage-activated, fully inactivating Ca channel in vertebrate sensory neurones. *Nature* 310:501–2

13. Carbone E, Lux HD. 1987. Kinetics and selectivity of a low-voltage-activated calcium current in chick and rat sensory neurons. *J. Physiol.* 386:547–70

14. Carbone E, Lux HD. 1987. Single low-voltage-activated calcium channels in chick and rat sensory neurones. *J. Physiol.* 386:571–601

15. Catterall WA. 1991. Functional subunit structure of voltage-gated calcium channels. *Science* 253:1499–500

16. Chen CF, Hess P. 1990. Mechanism of gating of T-type calcium channels. *J. Gen. Physiol.* 96:603–30

17. Christie BR, Eliot LS, Ito K-I, Miyakawa H, Johnston D. 1995. Different $Ca^{2+}$ channels in soma and dendrites of hippocampal pyramidal neurons mediate

spike-induced $Ca^{2+}$ influx. *J. Neurophysiol.* 73:2553–57

18. Chung JM, Huguenard JR, Prince DA. 1993. Transient enhancement of low-threshold calcium current in thalamic relay neurons after corticectomy. *J. Neurophysiol.* 70:20–27

19. Coulter DA, Huguenard JR, Prince DA. 1989. Characterization of ethosuximide reduction of low-threshold calcium current in thalamic neurons. *Ann. Neurol.* 25:582–93

20. Coulter DA, Huguenard JR, Prince DA. 1989. Specific petit mal anticonvulsants reduce calcium currents in thalamic neurons. *Neurosci. Lett.* 98:74–78

21. Coulter DA, Huguenard JR, Prince DA. 1989. Calcium currents in rat thalamocortical relay neurones: kinetic properties of the transient, low-threshold current. *J. Physiol.* 414:587–604

22. Coulter DA, Huguenard JR, Prince DA. 1990. Differential effects of petit mal anticonvulsants and convulsants on thalamic neurones: calcium current reduction. *Br. J. Pharmacol.* 100:800–6

23. Coulter DA, Huguenard JR, Prince DA. 1991. Mechanism of block of thalamic "T"-type $Ca^{2+}$ channels by petit mal anticonvulsants. *Exp. Brain Res.* 20:201–4

24. Crunelli V, Lightowler S, Pollard CE. 1989. A T-type $Ca^{2+}$ current underlies low-threshold $Ca^{2+}$ potentials in cells of the cat and rat lateral geniculate nucleus. *J. Physiol.* 413:543–61

25. Deschênes M, Roy JP, Steriade M. 1982. Thalamic bursting mechanism: an inward slow current revealed by membrane hyperpolarization. *Brain Res.* 239:289–93

26. Domich L, Oakson G, Steriade M. 1986. Thalamic burst patterns in the naturally sleeping cat: a comparison between cortically projecting and reticularis neurones. *J. Physiol.* 379:429–49

27. Eliot LS, Johnston D. 1994. Multiple components of calcium current in acutely dissociated dentate gyrus granule neurons. *J. Neurophysiol.* 72:762–77

28. Ertel EA, Warren VA, Adams ME, Griffin PR, Cohen CJ, Smith MM. 1994. Type III omega-agatoxins: a family of probes for similar binding sites on L- and N-type calcium channels. *Biochemistry* 33:5098–108

29. Fedulova SA, Kostyuk PG, Veselovsky NS. 1985. Two types of calcium channels in the somatic membrane of newborn rat dorsal root ganglion neurones. *J. Physiol.* 359:431–46

30. Fisher R, Johnston D. 1990. Differential modulation of single voltage-gated cal-

cium channels by cholinergic and adrenergic agonists in adult hippocampal neurons. *J. Neurophysiol.* 64:1291–302

31. Fisher RE, Gray R, Johnston D. 1990. Properties and distribution of single voltage-gated calcium channels in adult hippocampal neurons. *J. Neurophysiol.* 64:91–104

32. Fox AP, Nowycky MC, Tsien RW. 1987. Kinetic and pharmacological properties distinguishing three types of calcium currents in chick sensory neurones. *J. Physiol.* 394:149–72

33. Fox AP, Nowycky MC, Tsien RW. 1987. Single-channel recordings of three types of calcium channels in chick sensory neurones. *J. Physiol.* 394:173–200

34. Frankenhaeuser B, Hodgkin AL. 1957. The action of calcium on the electrical properties of squid axons. *J. Physiol.* 137:218–44

35. Fraser DD, MacVicar BA. 1991. Low-threshold transient calcium current in rat hippocampal lacunosum-moleculare interneurons: kinetics and modulation by neurotransmitters. *J. Neurosci.* 11: 2812–20

36. Friedman A, Gutnick MJ. 1987. Low-threshold calcium electrogenesis in neocortical neurons. *Neurosci. Lett.* 81: 117–22

37. Gerber U, Greene RW, McCarley RW. 1989. Repetitive firing properties of medial pontine reticular formation neurones of the rat recorded in vitro. *J. Physiol.* 410:533–60

38. Giffin K, Solomon JS, Burkhalter A, Nerbonne JM. 1991. Differential expression of voltage-gated calcium channels in identified visual cortical neurons. *Neuron* 6:321–32

39. Griffith WH, Taylor L, Davis MJ. 1994. Whole-cell and single-channel calcium currents in guinea pig basal forebrain neurons. *J. Neurophysiol.* 71:2359–76

40. Gu X, Spitzer NC. 1993. Low-threshold Ca$^{2+}$ current and its role in spontaneous elevations of intracellular Ca$^{2+}$ in developing *Xenopus* neurons. *J. Neurosci.* 13:4936–48

41. Gutnick MJ, Yarom Y. 1989. Low threshold calcium spikes, intrinsic neuronal oscillation and rhythm generation in the CNS. *J. Neurosci. Methods* 28:93–99

42. Hamill OP, Huguenard JR, Prince DA. 1991. Patch-clamp studies of voltage-gated currents in identified neurons of the rat cerebral cortex. *Cereb. Cortex* 1:48–61

43. Hernandez-Cruz A, Pape HC. 1989. Identification of two calcium currents in acutely dissociated neurons from the rat lateral geniculate nucleus. *J. Neurophysiol.* 61:1270–83

44. Herrington J, Lingle CJ. 1992. Kinetic and pharmacological properties of low voltage-activated Ca$^{2+}$ current in rat clonal (GH3) pituitary cells. *J. Neurophysiol.* 68:213–32

45. Herrington J, Stern RC, Evers AS, Lingle CJ. 1991. Halothane inhibits two components of calcium current in clonal (GH3) pituitary cells. *J. Neurosci.* 11: 2226–40

46. Hille B. 1992. *Ionic Channels of Excitable Membranes.* Sunderland, MA: Sinauer. 607 pp.

47. Hodgkin AL, Huxley AF. 1952. A quantitative description of membrane current and its application to conduction and excitation in nerve. *J. Physiol.* 117:500–44

48. Hoehn K, Watson TWJ, MacVicar BA. 1993. Multiple types of calcium channels in acutely isolated rat neostriatal neurons. *J. Neurosci.* 13:1244–57

49. Huang L-YM. 1989. Calcium channels in isolated rat dorsal horn neurones, including labelled spinothalamic and trigeminothalamic cells. *J. Physiol.* 411: 161–77

50. Huguenard JR, Gutnick MJ, Prince DA. 1993. Transient Ca$^{2+}$ currents in neurons isolated from rat lateral habenula. *J. Neurophysiol.* 70:158–66

51. Huguenard JR, McCormick DA. 1992. Simulation of the currents involved in rhythmic oscillations in thalamic relay neurons. *J. Neurophysiol.* 68:1373–83

52. Huguenard JR, Prince DA. 1992. A novel T-type current underlies prolonged Ca(2+)-dependent burst firing in GABAergic neurons of rat thalamic reticular nucleus. *J. Neurosci.* 12:3804–17

53. Huguenard JR, Prince DA. 1994. Intrathalamic rhythmicity studied in vitro: nominal T current modulation causes robust anti-oscillatory effects. *J. Neurosci.* 14:5485–502

54. Ito C, Im WB, Takagi H, Takahashi M, Tsuzuki K, et al. 1994. U-92032, a T-type Ca$^{2+}$ channel blocker and antioxidant, reduces neuronal ischemic injuries. *Eur. J. Pharmacol.* 257:203–10

55. Jahnsen H, Llinás R. 1984. Ionic basis for the electro-responsiveness and oscillatory properties of guinea-pig thalamic neurones in vitro. *J. Physiol.* 349: 227–47

56. Jahnsen H, Llinás R. 1984. Electrophysiological properties of guinea-pig thalamic neurones: an in vitro study. *J. Physiol.* 349:205–26

57. Kaneda M, Akaike N. 1989. The low-threshold Ca current in isolated amyg-

daloid neurons in the rat. *Brain Res.* 497:187–90

58. Kaneda M, Wakamori M, Ito C, Akaike N. 1990. Low-threshold calcium current in isolated Purkinje cell bodies of rat cerebellum. *J. Neurophysiol.* 63:1046–51

59. Karschin A, Lipton SA. 1989. Calcium channels in solitary retinal ganglion cells from post-natal rat. *J. Physiol.* 418:379–96

60. Karst H, Joels M, Wadman WJ. 1993. Low-threshold calcium current in dendrites of the adult rat hippocampus. *Neurosci. Lett.* 164:154–58

61. Kelly KM, Gross RA, Macdonald RL. 1990. Valproic acid selectively reduces the low-threshold (T) calcium current in rat nodose neurons. *Neurosci. Lett.* 116:233–38

62. Komatsu Y, Iwakiri M. 1992. Low-threshold $Ca^{2+}$ channels mediate induction of long-term potentiation in kitten visual cortex. *J. Neurophysiol.* 67:401–10

63. Kostyuk PG, Shuba YaM, Savchenko AN. 1988. Three types of calcium channels in the membrane of mouse sensory neurons. *Pflügers Arch.* 411:661–69

64. Llinás R, Jahnsen H. 1982. Electrophysiology of mammalian thalamic neurones in vitro. *Nature* 297:406–8

65. Llinás R, Yarom Y. 1981. Properties and distribution of ionic conductances generating electroresponsiveness of mammalian inferior olivary neurones in vitro. *J. Physiol.* 315:569–84

66. Llinás R, Yarom Y. 1981. Electrophysiology of mammalian inferior olivary neurones in vitro. Different types of voltage-dependent ionic conductances. *J. Physiol.* 315:549–67

67. Lux HD, Carbone E, Zucker H. 1990. $Na^+$ currents through low-voltage-activated $Ca^{2+}$ channels of chick sensory neurones: block by external $Ca^{2+}$ and $Mg^{2+}$. *J. Physiol.* 430:159–88

68. Magee JC, Johnston D. 1995. Synaptic activation of voltage-gated channels in the dendrites of hippocampal pyramidal neurons. *Science* 268:301–4

69. Marchetti C, Brown AM. 1988. Protein kinase activator 1-oleoyl-2-acetyl-*sn*-glycerol inhibits two types of calcium currents in GH3 cells. *Am. J. Physiol.* 254:C206–10

70. Marchetti C, Carbone E, Lux HD. 1986. Effects of dopamine and noradrenaline on Ca channels of cultured sensory and sympathetic neurons of chick. *Pflügers Arch.* 406:104–11

71. McCobb DP, Beam KG. 1991. Action potential waveform voltage-clamp commands reveal striking differences in calcium entry via low and high voltage-activated calcium channels. *Neuron* 7:119–27

72. McCormick DA, Huguenard JR. 1992. A model of the electrophysiological properties of thalamocortical relay neurons. *J. Neurophysiol.* 68:1384–400

73. McCormick DA, Pape H-C. 1990. Properties of a hyperpolarization-activated cation current and its role in rhythmic oscillation in thalamic relay neurones. *J. Physiol.* 431:291–318

74. Mlinar B, Enyeart JJ. 1993. Block of current through T-type calcium channels by trivalent metal cations and nickel in neural rat and human cells. *J. Physiol.* 469:639–52

75. Mulle C, Madariaga A, Deschênes M. 1986. Morphology and electrophysiological properties of reticularis thalami neurons in cat: in vivo study of a thalamic pacemaker. *J. Neurosci.* 6:2134–45

76. Muller TH, Misgeld U, Swandulla D. 1992. Ionic currents in cultured rat hypothalamic neurones. *J. Physiol.* 450:341–62

77. Narahashi T, Tsunoo A, Yoshii M. 1987. Characterization of two types of calcium channels in mouse neuroblastoma cells. *J. Physiol.* 383:231–49

78. Nobile M, Carbone E, Lux HD, Zucker H. 1990. Temperature sensitivity of Ca currents in chick sensory neurones. *Pflügers Arch.* 415:658–63

79. Nowycky MC, Fox AP, Tsien RW. 1985. Three types of neuronal calcium channel with different calcium agonist sensitivity. *Nature* 316:440–43

80. O'Dell TJ, Alger BE. 1991. Single calcium channels in rat and guinea-pig hippocampal neurons. *J. Physiol.* 436:739–67

81. Ogata N, Narahashi T. 1990. Potent blocking action of chlorpromazine on two types of calcium channels in cultured neuroblastoma cells. *J. Pharmacol. Exp. Ther.* 252:1142–49

82. Ozawa S, Tsuzuki K, Iino M, Ogura A, Kudo Y. 1989. Three types of voltage-dependent calcium current in cultured rat hippocampal neurons. *Brain Res.* 495:329–36

83. Pfrieger FW, Veselovsky NS, Gottmann K, Lux HD. 1992. Pharmacological characterization of calcium currents and synaptic transmission between thalamic neurons in vitro. *J. Neurosci.* 12:4347–57

84. Regan LJ. 1991. Voltage-dependent calcium currents in Purkinje cells from rat

cerebellar vermis. *J. Neurosci.* 11:2259–69

85. Richard S, Diochot S, Nargeot J, Baldy-Moulinier M, Valmier J. 1991. Inhibition of T-type calcium currents by dihydropyridines in mouse embryonic dorsal root ganglion neurons. *Neurosci. Lett.* 132:229–34

86. Ryu PD, Randic M. 1990. Low- and high-voltage-activated calcium currents in rat spinal dorsal horn neurons. *J. Neurophysiol.* 63:273–85

87. Sayer RJ, Schwindt PC, Crill WE. 1990. High- and low-threshold calcium currents in neurons acutely isolated from rat sensorimotor cortex. *Neurosci. Lett.* 120:175–78

88. Schroeder JE, Fischbach PS, McCleskey EW. 1990. T-type calcium channels: heterogeneous expression in rat sensory neurons and selective modulation by phorbol esters. *J. Neurosci.* 10:947–51

89. Schroeder JE, Fischbach PS, Zheng D, McCleskey EW. 1991. Activation of mu opioid receptors inhibits transient high- and low-threshold Ca$^{2+}$ currents, but spares a sustained current. *Neuron* 6:13–20

90. Scott RH, Wootton JF, Dolphin AC. 1990. Modulation of neuronal T-type calcium channel currents by photoactivation of intracellular guanosine 5′-O(3-thio) triphosphate. *Neuroscience* 38:285–94

91. Sejnowski TJ, Destexhe A, Contreras D, Steriade M, Huguenard JR. 1995. In vivo, in vitro and computational analysis of dendritic currents in thalamic reticular neurons. *Soc. Neurosci. Abstr.* 21:1187

92. Sinton CM, Krosser BI, Walton KD, Llinás RR. 1989. The effectiveness of different isomers of octanol as blockers of harmaline-induced tremor. *Pflügers Arch.* 414:31–36

93. Soltesz I, Lightowler S, Leresche N, Jassik-Gerschenfeld D, Pollard CE, Crunelli V. 1991. Two inward currents and the transformation of low-frequency oscillations of rat and cat thalamocortical cells. *J. Physiol.* 441:175–97

94. Spedding M, Paoletti R. 1992. Classification of calcium channels and the sites of action of drugs modifying channel function. *Pharmacol. Rev.* 44:363–76

95. Sutor B, Zieglgansberger W. 1987. A low-voltage activated, transient calcium current is responsible for the time-dependent depolarizing inward rectification of rat neocortical neurons in vitro. *Pflügers Arch.* 410:102–11

96. Suzuki S, Rogawski MA. 1989. T-type calcium channels mediate the transition between tonic and phasic firing in thalamic neurons. *Proc. Natl. Acad. Sci. USA* 86:7228–32

97. Takahashi K, Akaike N. 1991. Calcium antagonist effects on low-threshold (T-type) calcium current in rat isolated hippocampal CA1 pyramidal neurons. *J. Pharmacol. Exp. Ther.* 256:169–75

98. Takahashi K, Ueno S, Akaike N. 1991. Kinetic properties of T-type Ca$^{2+}$ currents in isolated rat hippocampal CA1 pyramidal neurons. *J. Neurophysiol.* 65:148–54

99. Takahashi K, Wakamori M, Akaike N. 1989. Hippocampal CA1 pyramidal cells of rats have four voltage-dependent calcium conductances. *Neurosci. Lett.* 104:229–34

100. Takenoshita M, Steinbach JH. 1991. Halothane blocks low-voltage-activated calcium current in rat sensory neurons. *J. Neurosci.* 11:1404–12

101. Tang CM, Presser F, Morad M. 1988. Amiloride selectively blocks the low threshold (T) calcium channel. *Science* 240:213–15

102. Thompson SM, Wong RK. 1991. Development of calcium current subtypes in isolated rat hippocampal pyramidal cells. *J. Physiol.* 439:671–89

103. Tsakiridou E, Bertollini L, de Curtis M, Avanzini G, Pape H-C. 1995. Selective increase in T-type calcium conductance of reticular thalamic neurons in a rat model of absence epilepsy. *J. Neurosci.* 15:3110–17

104. Umemiya M, Berger AJ. 1994. Properties and function of low- and high-voltage-activated Ca$^{2+}$ channels in hypoglossal motoneurons. *J. Neurosci.* 14:5652–60

105. Umemiya M, Berger AJ. 1995. Single-channel properties of four calcium channel types in rat motoneurons. *J. Neurosci.* 15:2218–24

106. Varadi G, Mori Y, Mikala G, Schwartz A. 1995. Molecular determinants of Ca$^{2+}$ channel function and drug action. *Trends Pharmacol. Sci.* 16:43–49

107. Wilcox KS, Gutnick MJ, Christoph GR. 1988. Electrophysiological properties of neurons in the lateral habenula nucleus: an in vitro study. *J. Neurophysiol.* 59:212–25

108. Yaari Y, Hamon B, Lux HD. 1987. Development of two types of calcium channels in cultured mammalian hippocampal neurons. *Science* 235:680–82

109. Ye JH, Akaike N. 1993. Calcium currents in pyramidal neurons acutely dissociated from the rat frontal cortex: a

study by the nystatin perforated patch technique. *Brain Res.* 606:111–17

110. Yoshii M, Tsunoo A, Narahashi T. 1988. Gating and permeation properties of two types of calcium channels in neuroblastoma cells. *Biophys. J.* 54:885–95

111. Zhang L, Valiante TA, Carlen PL. 1993. Contribution of the low-threshold T-type calcium current in generating the post-spike depolarizing afterpotential in dentate granule neurons of immature rats. *J. Neurophysiol.* 70:223–31

Annu. Rev. Physiol. 1996. 58:349–62

# PERSISTENT SODIUM CURRENT IN MAMMALIAN CENTRAL NEURONS

*Wayne E. Crill*

Department of Physiology and Biophysics, University of Washington, Seattle, Washington 98195

KEY WORDS:    sodium channels, persistent sodium current, neurons

## ABSTRACT

Neurons from the mammalian CNS have a noninactivating component of the tetrodotoxin-sensitive sodium current ($I_{NaP}$). Although its magnitude is <1% of the transient sodium current, $I_{NaP}$ has functional significance because it is activated about 10 mV negative to the transient sodium current, where few voltage-gated channels are activated and neuron input resistance is high. $I_{NaP}$ adds to synaptic current, and evidence indicates that it is present in dendrites where relatively small depolarizations will activate $I_{NaP}$, thereby increasing effectiveness of distal depolarizing synaptic activity. The mechanism for $I_{NaP}$ is not known. Research in striated muscle and neurons suggests a modal change in gating of conventional sodium channels, but it is also possible that $I_{NaP}$ flows through a distinct subtype of noninactivating sodium channels. Modulation of $I_{NaP}$ could have a significant effect on the transduction of synaptic currents by neurons.

## INTRODUCTION

The ionic model proposed in 1952 by Hodgkin & Huxley (31) continues to serve as the foundation for our understanding of excitability. Depolarization evokes all-or-nothing action potentials by activating the voltage-dependent opening of sodium channels. With maintained polarization, the sodium conductance inactivates within a millisecond or so and this, together with activation of potassium conductances, leads to rapid repolarization of the action potentials in neurons. The Hodgkin-Huxley model (31) also explains how voltage-dependent inactivation of sodium channels causes spike threshold accommodation and anodal break excitation. At present, biophysicists are designing experiments to understand the molecular mechanism for selective

349

0066-4278/96/0315-0349$08.00

permeability and the voltage-dependent gating of sodium channels. Excellent recent reviews cover the rapid progress in this field (12, 13, 55, 73).

Many types of excitable cells also have a voltage-dependent noninactivating component of the inward depolarizing sodium current. It has been detected in striated cardiac and skeletal muscle (8, 9, 23, 25, 28, 38, 39, 40, 42, 51, 56–58, 64, 74, 76) and explains some disease processes. Patients with hyperkalemic periodic paralysis have sodium channels in skeletal muscle that often fail to inactivate when $[K^+]_o$ is increased (11). Ischemia increases noninactivating sodium current in cardiac muscle and could contribute to arrythmias (PW Gage, personal communication). Slowly inactivating sodium channels are even present in squid axon (26). In mammalian neurons, a small portion of the overall sodium current flows through noninactivating sodium channels ($I_{NaP}$). The persistent noninactivating sodium current in neurons is the topic of this review. A noninactivating or slowly inactivating sodium current has been found in mammalian neurons located in neocortex (6, 14, 65–67), thalamus (37), entorhinal cortex (3, 22), hippocampus (24), and cerebellum (44). Recently, $I_{NaP}$ was recorded in human neocortical neurons (18). Although electrical responses consistent with a noninactivating subthreshold sodium current were described nearly two decades ago, recent experiments in several laboratories have provided new insights into possible mechanisms for noninactivation and the putative integrative role of $I_{NaP}$ in neurons.

## EARLY OBSERVATIONS AND GENERAL PROPERTIES Of $I_{NaP}$

The first observations indicating a subthreshold noninactivating sodium current came from brain slice studies using the guinea pig hippocampus, cerebellum, and neocortex. Intracellular recording is stable in brain slices, and the extracellular environment of impaled neurons is easily changed. The Prince laboratory measured an increase in slope resistance at potentials 10 to 15 mV positive to resting potential in hippocampal CA1 neurons (32) and neocortical neurons (14). This inward rectification had the pharmacological characteristics of voltage-dependent sodium channels. It was blocked by extracellular tetrodotoxin (TTX) or intracellular injection of the lidocaine derivative QX-314 (15), and it disappeared when choline replaced extracellular sodium.

A depolarizing intracellular current applied to cerebellar Purkinje cells evokes a plateau potential that outlasts the intracellular stimulus by several hundred milliseconds (44). Such an electrogenic response could be caused by a depolarizing high-threshold calcium current, but the plateau potentials were not blocked by the calcium channel blocker $CdCl_2$. The plateau potential was abolished by removing extracellular sodium or adding TTX. This response was detected only near the soma. Llinás & Sugamori (44) proposed that fast action potentials and plateau responses in the same Purkinje cell arose from two different sodium conductance mechanisms: a Hodgkin-Huxley inactivating transient sodium conductance (31) responsible for spikes and a noninactivating sodium conductance underlying plateau responses.

Noninactivating subthreshold inward sodium currents were first recorded in layer V pyramidal neurons from cat sensorimotor cortex, using the single-electrode voltage clamp (65–67). A persistent inward current first detected about 10 mV positive to resting potential was revealed by either a ramp voltage–clamp command that slowly depolarized the soma or voltage-step commands (Figure 1). The subthreshold inward current was blocked by TTX and intracellular QX-314 but was not blocked by the calcium channel blocker $CoCl_2$. Activation of $I_{NaP}$ was rapid and occurred within the settling time of the single-electrode voltage clamp (3–4 ms). In these studies, the membrane potential trajectory between spikes, even at the slowest repetitive firing rates, traversed the potentials at which $I_{NaP}$ was activated. The inward rectification measured with single-electrode voltage clamp was compared with current clamp records to insure that the noninactivating current was not an artifact of a poor space clamp in dendritic neurons (76). When the slice was bathed in $CoCl_2$ and tetraethylammonium (TEA) to block calcium channels and potassium currents, $I_{NaP}$ was opposed only by residual repolarizing potassium currents and the leakage current. Under these conditions, a brief depolarizing current evoked one or two action potentials followed by a plateau potential 50 mV positive to resting potential, which persisted for hundreds of milliseconds after the stimulating current was terminated. As expected, the evoked plateau response was blocked by TTX (66).

In these early studies, the pharmacology of $I_{NaP}$ and transient sodium current was nearly identical. $I_{NaP}$ is blocked by $10^{-7}$ to $10^{-6}$ M extracellular TTX or the intracellular iontophoresis of QX-314 (14, 32, 65, 66). Divalent cations like $Mn^{2+}$, $Co^{2+}$, and $Cd^{2+}$ block calcium channels and have no appreciable effect on $I_{NaP}$. There is no pharmacological agent that selectively distinguishes $I_{Na}$ from $I_{NaP}$. In cat pyramidal neurons, intracellular QX-314 reduces $I_{NaP}$ more effectively than it reduces the maximal rate of rise of the action potential (66), but this could reflect a nonlinear relationship between transient sodium current and the rate of rise of the action potential.

## Biophysical Properties of $I_{NaP}$

Acutely isolated mammalian neurons have only small dendritic remnants, and they can be reliably voltage clamped with patch electrodes (5, 10, 22, 24, 29, 34, 63). This preparation largely eliminates artifacts from poor voltage control of the dendrites. Acutely isolated neuron studies have given us some quantitative whole-cell measurements of $I_{NaP}$ from several CNS neuron types. The steady-state activation curve for the noninactivating sodium conductance ($g_{NaP}$)

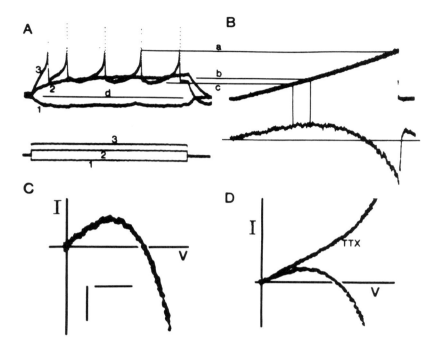

*Figure 1* The noninactivating sodium current recorded from a cat layer V pyramidal neuron. (*A*) Top trace is response to depolarizing and hyperpolarizing constant current stimulation (*bottom trace*). Action potentials are clipped. (*B*) Slowly rising ramp voltage–clamp command (*top trace*) and recorded current (*bottom trace*) in the same neuron using single-electrode voltage clamp. Recorded membrane potentials in *A* correspond to values in *B*, as indicated by horizontal lines. Note interspike trajectory in *A* corresponds to membrane potentials in *B* where inward rectification occurs. (*C*) I-V curve generated from ramp command potential as shown in *B*. (*D*) Superimposed I-V relationships, before and after application of 1 μM TTX, generated by slowly rising ramp as in *B*. Records in *A-D* from same neurons. Origin in *C* and *D* is resting potential. Calibrations in *C*: vertical bar I 20 mV, 2 nA for *A*; 20 mV and 1 nA for *B*; 0.5 nA for *C*; and 1 nA for *D*. Horizontal bar is 50 ms for *A*, 100 ms for *B*, and 10 mV for *C* and *D*. (From *Brain Res.* 1982. 236:221–26, with permission.).

is half-activated at approximately −50 mV (24). Nearly identical values have been found in hippocampal CA1 neurons (10, 24) and pyramidal neurons of the neocortex (10). The Gage group (24) found similar values for half-activation of the noninactivating current in acutely dissociated neurons and in the same neuron type studied in brain slices.

Steady-state inactivation of $I_{NaP}$ has been measured in hippocampal CA1 neurons (24). Conditioning potentials from −90 to −70 mV had little effect on $I_{NaP}$, but conditioning pulses of −30 to −20 mV decreased $I_{NaP}$ by about 40%.

Whole-cell voltage-clamp steps in acutely isolated neurons reveal no detectable decrease in the persistent sodium current during steps lasting several hundred milliseconds. The kinetics of $I_{NaP}$ activation have not been measured in neurons. $I_{NaP}$ is fully activated by the time the transient sodium current inactivates.

## MECHANISM FOR NONINACTIVATING SODIUM CHANNELS

Three general hypotheses about the origin of the noninactivating current have been presented: first, the window current hypothesis based on Hodgkin-Huxley whole-cell current properties (31); second, the possibility that $I_{NaP}$ is generated by an unusual subtype of sodium channels that does not inactivate (24, 66); and third, recent evidence of a modal change in the inactivation properties of the transient sodium channels (4).

The concept of a window current comes directly from the model of Hodgkin & Huxley (31). Plots of h, the probability that a sodium channel is not inactivated, and m, the probability that a sodium channel is activated, vs membrane potential overlap over a small potential range, predicting a steady sodium conductance over this range. Using measurements of h and m from CA1 hippocampal pyramidal cells, French et al (24) calculated the steady-state window $g_{Na}$ and compared it with $g_{NaP}$ measured from the same neuron type. In hippocampal neurons, the activation curve for $g_{NaP}$ increases monotonically following a Boltzmann curve with a $V_{1/2}$ about $-50$ mV and does not decrease, even at potentials positive to zero. In contrast, the predicted window current peaks at about $-50$ mV and rapidly falls to zero with further depolarization. In neocortical neurons, the evoked prolonged plateaus caused by a noninactivating sodium current (with calcium currents and much of the repolarizing potassium currents blocked) reached a depolarizing potential where expected window current should be minimal (66).

$I_{NaP}$ could be mediated by a noninactivating subtype of sodium channels that would allow a different spatial distribution in a neuron for transient and noninactivating sodium channels. Llinás and Sugimori (43) found the noninactivating sodium current at or near the soma of Purkinje cells. Moreover, Westenbroek et al (75) measured a high concentration of the immunologically distinct RI subtype on neuron somata, whereas the subtype RII was located primarily in axons, which suggests that the RI channel subtype could be responsible for the noninactivating current.

Results from a number of laboratories have consistently found that the noninactivating sodium current is activated about 10 mV negative to the transient sodium current (10, 24, 66). This finding appears to support the hypothesis that $I_{NaP}$ flows through a subset of channels different than those underlying the transient current. The more negative activation of $I_{NaP}$ allowed its detection in early voltage-clamp studies (65, 66), and as discussed below, the activation of $I_{NaP}$ in isolation at negative potentials likely contributes to its functional importance.

Details of the inactivation process in sodium channels are not well understood. For example, there is abundant evidence (7, 30) that the activation and inactivation processes described by Hodgkin & Huxley (31) are not independent. Inactivation appears to require partial activation of sodium channels. Moreover, at least in some types of excitable cells, the microscopic rate constant for inactivation is much faster than the macroscopic relaxation of the transient sodium conductance, and the microscopic inactivation rate constant is not highly voltage dependent, in contrast to macroscopic whole-cell currents (1, 2). The apparent voltage dependence of whole-cell sodium current inactivation actually reflects the voltage dependence of late-activating channels. Our incomplete understanding of inactivation is discussed in detail by Hille (30). Gonoi & Hille (27) demonstrated that removing inactivation with papain and other agents will prolong the rising phase of the sodium current and shift the activation curve along the voltage axis in the negative direction if the sodium channels obey the Aldrich-Corey-Stevens (1, 2) model of gating, with its rapid and largely voltage-independent inactivation. Because sodium channel activation is slow at small depolarizations, the rapid inactivation does not allow detection of a macroscopic inward current until an appreciable number of sodium channels can open rapidly. The relaxing transient current is not caused by inactivation. It is caused by the slow, first opening of sodium channels. Experimentally removing inactivation with papain reveals activation at more negative potentials. If mammalian central neurons have properties like those of the cell lines studied by Gonoi & Hille (27), the more negative activation curve for $I_{NaP}$ compared with $I_{Na}$ could be explained by this mechanism. Brown et al (10) found the activation curve for $I_{NaP}$ about 7 mV negative to the activation curve for transient $I_{Na}$ in neocortical neurons. When papain was injected into the neuron to remove inactivation of the transient channels, the inward sodium current was prolonged and the activation curve for $I_{Na}$ shifted to more negative potentials where $I_{NaP}$ was activated. In fact, transient sodium channels with inactivation pharmacologically removed activate at the same membrane potentials as $I_{NaP}$. Therefore, we need not interpret the difference in activation curve for $I_{NaP}$ and $I_{Na}$ as evidence for multiple subtypes of sodium channels.

The hypothesis that $I_{NaP}$ flows through a noninactivating subtype of sodium channels is best tested by direct isolation of the channels. Noninactivating channels have been recorded in cultured hippocampal neurons (48) and from Purkinje cells (72). In nearly 40% of the patches from cultured hippocampal neurons, noninactivating channel activity with a single-channel conductance of 15–25 pS carried a $Cd^{2+}$- and $Co^{2+}$-insensitive inward current (48). The channel has long open times. In Purkinje cells studied with cell-attached patches in slices from guinea pig cerebellum, the noninactivating channels have a single-channel conductance of only 7 pS (72). The interpretation is that Purkinje cells have a subtype of sodium channel that fails to inactivate. Surprisingly, in some patches the depolarizing voltage pulse only randomly caused persistent opening.

The channel carrying $I_{NaP}$ could also carry transient $I_{Na}$. That is, most of the time the channel would behave like a transient sodium channel, but infrequently the channel would fail to inactivate. These inactivation failures would carry the persistent sodium current. If this type of modal behavior explains $I_{NaP}$, it must occur infrequently because the noninactivating current is much smaller than $I_{Na}$. Modal gating is not a new idea and has been observed for calcium and sodium channels in a number of nonneural tissues (16, 17, 55–59, 61).

Alzheimer et al (4) used the on cell-patch technique on neocortical pyramidal cells in thin slices (21) and in acutely isolated neurons to search for noninactivating sodium channels that could explain the persistent current. None of their patches contained a single channel; the usual number was 4 to 12 channels, but all patches showed the same behavior. Voltage steps that depolarized the patch for 400 ms revealed two types of late openings (Figure 2). Minibursts lasting 10–40 ms occurred with a low frequency, giving a low open–probability of less than 0.01. In addition, less than 1% of the depolarizations evoked reopening by an individual sodium channel (Figure 2), which usually lasted throughout the duration of the depolarization (400 ms). The unitary amplitude and slope conductance of the brief late openings, sustained openings, and early openings were nearly identical, which supports the authors' contention that a single electrophysiologically uniform population of channels is responsible for early and recurrent openings. Identical late openings were present in inside-out patches. Therefore, the cytoskeletal structures or the cytosol were not required for late openings. To estimate whether the observed late-opening modes could explain the measured whole-cell $I_{NaP}$, Alzheimer et al calculated the magnitude of a noninactivating current, using measured values for the probability of occurrence of late openings and single-channel current, and estimated the number of sodium channels in a neuron. These rough calculations indicate that the recorded late openings provide a reasonably sized noninactivating persistent sodium current.

The experimental weakness of the above studies was the inability to study a patch with only a single channel. Nonetheless, a modal change in gating is the simplest explanation for the late openings. If the rare reopenings were the activity of a separate noninactivating subtype of sodium channel, its properties are unusual. Depolarizations from −70 to near zero mV would only activate the noninactivating channel less than 1% of the time. The modal interpretation

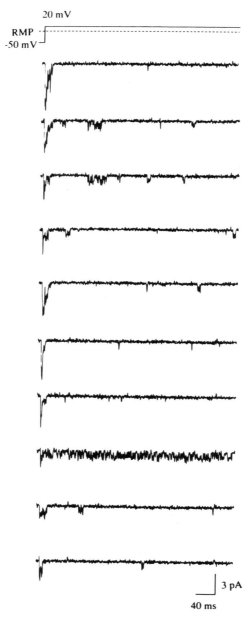

*Figure 2* Voltage-clamp recordings from a cell-attached patch on a visually identified layer V rat neocortical pyramidal neuron in a thin slice. Successive recorded traces evoked by a step-voltage command from −50 to 20 mV. Each trace shows early-opening channels. Delayed brief openings occur in trace 2 and 3, and a prolonged burst is present in trace 8. (From *J. NeuroSci.* 1993. 13:600–73, with permission.)

for persistent reopenings was first made by Patlak & Oritz (56) in skeletal muscle. Nilius (51), using cardiac tissue, and Zhou et al (77), recording from the $\mu$I sodium channel from skeletal muscle, also found modal changes in inactivation gating. Moorman et al (50) injected *Xenopus* oocytes with rat brain type-III sodium channel mRNA and found both fast and slow gating.

To summarize, it is unlikely that a Hodgkin-Huxley (31) window current explains the noninactivating current; two laboratories have reported (48, 72) a population of channels with only slow gating, and a number of laboratories using biophysical measurements and molecular biological techniques report slow gating that is best explained by more than one gating mode. The mechanism for $I_{NaP}$ will be settled by recording from a single, isolated channel subtype.

## Integrative Properties of $I_{NaP}$

Regardless of the exact mechanism, $I_{NaP}$ has been found in a number of different neuron types, and in rat neocortical neurons, $I_{NaP}$ increases during the first 20 postnatal days (5, 49). $I_{NaP}$ is small compared with the transient current; in neocortical neurons, it is estimated to represent only 0.25% of the transient current. But $I_{NaP}$ is activated negative to the transient sodium current where the input resistance of neurons is high. Alzheimer et al (4) calculated that the small $I_{NaP}$ could depolarize the cell 26 mV at −50 mV membrane potential in neocortical pyramidal neurons. Studies on neocortical neurons and hippocampal neurons revealed activation of $I_{NaP}$ at membrane potentials typical of the interspike trajectory (Figure 1). That is, during repetitive firing, $I_{NaP}$ would be activated during both action potentials and the interspike interval and would add a depolarizing current to synaptic currents. Moreover, $I_{NaP}$ is rapidly activated and would be expected to contribute to the synaptic depolarization caused by a brief synchronous excitatory volley. Deisz et al (20) found a QX-314-sensitive enhancement of EPSPs (but the time-dependent change in EPSPs was not affected).

There is now abundant evidence for transient sodium channels in the dendrites of many neuron types (35, 68, 69). If noninactivating sodium currents flow through neuronal transient sodium channels, we would expect depolarization of the dendritic tree to also activate $I_{NaP}$. Jack et al (36) noted the effects of inward rectification in dendrites upon electrical length and, therefore, the transmission of synaptic current to spike-generating regions. A dendritic current need not generate a spike to amplify distal synaptic effects. Inward rectification that does not cause a net inward current would decrease the slope conductance of the dendrite, allowing a much smaller decrement of distal synaptic potentials along the dendritic cable than would occur if the dendrite were passive. That is, dendritic inward rectification would markedly shorten the electrical length of the dendrite and could be a mechanism for increasing the effectiveness of distal dendritic excitation. $I_{NaP}$ is rapidly activated at small depolarizations, and this effect could occur even during brief excitation. P Schwindt (unpublished observations) used distal focal application of glutamate to the dendrites (33) to show a persistent TTX-sensitive inward rectification ($I_{NaP}$) in dendrites of neocortical neurons. Any voltage-dependent inward current could decrease the electrical length of dendrites. In neocortical neurons, a large component of the calcium current has a high-voltage threshold (63) requiring large dendritic depolarizations. Thalamic neurons (37) and inferior olive neurons (45) have large, low-threshold calcium currents, which would have an amplifying effect on tonic distal synaptic depolarization.

Many neurons of the CNS show subthreshold oscillating activity. Single-neuron oscillations in thalamocortical circuits appear to control behavioral states like sleep-wakefulness. Llinás (43) has suggested an additional role of neuronal oscillations in motor coordination and connectivity during development. $I_{NaP}$ contributes to oscillation in subthreshold membrane potential in the entorhinal cortex (3) and in neocortical neurons (6). The voltage-dependent subthreshold oscillation in these neurons is blocked by TTX. Neuronal oscillations, therefore, are not caused exclusively by the activation of voltage-dependent calcium currents and calcium-activated potassium currents (43).

A noninactivating sodium conductance could serve as a critical link between anoxia and injury in central white matter. Stys et al (70) showed that TTX caused hyperpolarizing shifts in optic nerve axons depolarized in high potassium solution, which was interpreted as evidence for a persistent sodium current in central axons. In gray matter, synaptic terminals release glutamate, and its neurotoxic effects cause extensive calcium influx into neuron somata and dendrites. This mechanism cannot cause white matter ischemic lesions because there are few synaptic stores of excitotoxic neurotransmitters. The Waxman & Ransom (71) group suggest that sodium entry through noninactivating sodium channels causes anoxic injury in axons by reversing the sodium-calcium exchanger and thereby increasing intracellular calcium concentration. TTX provides axon protection to anoxic injury in white matter.

There is no direct evidence that noninactivating sodium channels contribute to epileptic behavior. Nonetheless, a direct increase in the noninactivating component of sodium current would amplify the responses of neurons to excitation and could lead to an avalanche of activity in an affected population of neurons. Commonly used anticonvulsants such as phenytoin and carbamazapine reduce the probability of sodium channel opening (47, 62). The hypothetical increased current flowing through noninactivating channels would change the balance of depolarizing sodium and hyperpolarizing potassium currents. The steady inward current need not be net inward or support all-or-nothing prolonged responses. Any relative increase in $I_{NaP}$ could lead to hyperactive aggregates of neurons.

## MODULATION OF $I_{NaP}$

The modulation of neuron activity by either physiological or pathological changes in $I_{NaP}$, therefore, could markedly change neuron function. Protein kinase C (PKC) phosphorylates chick (19, 52, 60) and rat brain sodium channels. The peak transient sodium current is reduced and inactivation is slowed. In single-channel studies, openings were prolonged and reopenings were evident (52). No change in single-channel conductance or changes in voltage dependence of activation or inactivation were detected. The functional significance of these observations is uncertain. The large decrease in the transient sodium current would guard against hyperexcitability, but if the late openings increased the noninactivating current, increased repetitive firing to an excitatory input would be expected. cAMP-dependent protein kinase also phosphorylates brain sodium channels (41). Whole-cell sodium currents are decreased by 40 to 80%. Single-channel conductance or the voltage dependence of activation or inactivation were not changed. In cardiac ventricular myocytes, forskolin increases sodium channel bursting (53, 54), but this effect occurred when cAMP-dependent phosphorylation was inhibited by the protein kinase inhibitor H-89. Ono et al (54) postulate that forskolin acts directly on the sodium channels.

Guanine nucleotide-binding proteins can modulate channels directly through a membrane-delimited mechanism (46). Ma et al (46) have shown that a G protein–coupled pathway markedly increases whole-cell sodium current by shifting both the voltage dependence of activation and inactivation 8 to 10 mV in the negative direction.

In summary, sodium channels are modulated by both diffusible second messengers and membrane-delimited G protein channel interactions. The functional significance of this modulation of sodium channels and possible changes in $I_{NaP}$ remains a subject for future investigation.

## Literature Cited

1.  Aldrich RW, Corey DP, Stevens CF. 1983. A reinterpretation of mammalian sodium channel gating based on single channel recording. *Nature* 306:436–41

2.  Aldrich RW, Stevens CF. 1987. Voltage-dependent gating of single sodium channels from mammalian neuroblastoma cells. *J. Neurosci.* 7:4118–31

3. Alonso A, Llinás RR. 1989. Subthreshold Na+ dependent theta-like rhythmicity in stellate cells of entorhinal cortex layer II. *Nature* 342:1175–77

4. Alzheimer C, Schwindt PC, Crill WE. 1993. Modal gating of Na+ channels as a mechanism of persistent Na+ current in pyramidal neurons from rat and cat sensorimotor cortex. *J. Neurosci.* 13:660–73

5. Alzheimer C, Schwindt PC, Crill WE. 1993. Postnatal development of a persistent Na+ current in pyramidal neurons from rat sensorimotor cortex. *J. Neurophysiol.* 69:290–92

6. Amitai Y. 1994. Membrane potential oscillations underlying firing patterns in neocortical neurons. *Neuroscience* 63:151–61

7. Armstrong CM. 1992. Voltage-dependent ion channels and their gating. *Physiol. Rev.* 72:S5–14

8. Attwell D, Cohen I, Eisner D, Ohba M, Ojeda C. 1979. The steady state TTX-sensitive ("window") sodium current in cardiac Purkinje fibres. *Pflügers Arch.* 379:137–42

9. Böhle T, Benndorf K. 1995. Multimodal action of single Na+ channels in myocardial mouse cells. *Biophys. J.* 68:121–30

10. Brown AM, Schwindt PC, Crill WE. 1994. Different voltage dependence of transient and persistent Na+ currents is compatible with modal-gating hypothesis for sodium channels. *J. Neurophysiol.* 71:2562–65

11. Cannon SC, Brown RH, Corey DP. 1991. A sodium channel defect in hyperkalemic periodic paralysis: potassium-induced failure of inactivation. *Neuron* 6:619–26

12. Catterall WA. 1988. Structure and function of voltage-sensitive ion channels. *Science* 242:50–61

13. Catterall WA. 1992. Cellular and molecular biology of voltage-gated sodium channels. *Physiol. Rev.* 72:S15–48

14. Connors BW, Gutnick MJ, Prince DA. 1982. Electrophysiological properties of neocortical neurons in vitro. *J. Neurophysiol.* 48:1302–20

15. Connors W, Prince DA. 1982. Effects of local anesthetic QX-314 on the membrane properties of hippocampal pyramidal neurons. *J. Pharm. Exp.* 220:476–81

16. Correa AM, Benzanilla F. 1994. Gating of the squid axon sodium channel at positive potentials: II. Single channels reveal two open states. *Biophys. J.* 66:1864–78

17. Correa AM, Bezanilla F, Agnew WS. 1990. Voltage activation of purified eel sodium channels reconstituted into artificial liposomes. *Biochemistry* 29:6230–40

18. Cummins TR, Xia Y, Haddad GG. 1994. Functional properties of rat and human neocortical voltage-sensitive sodium currents. *J. Neurophysiol.* 71:1052–64

19. Dascal N, Lotan I. 1991. Activation of protein kinase C alters voltage dependence of a Na+ channel. *Neuron* 6:165–75

20. Deisz RA, Fortin G, Zielgänsberger W. 1991. Voltage dependence of excitatory postsynaptic potentials of rat neocortical neurons. *J. Neurophysiol.* 63:371–82

21. Edwards FA, Konnerth A, Sakmann B, Takahashi T. 1989. A thin slice preparation for patch clamp recordings from neurones of the mammalian central nervous system. *Pflügers Arch.* 414:600–12

22. Fan S, Stewart M, Wong RKS. 1994. Differences in voltage-dependent sodium currents exhibited by superficial and deep layer neurons of guinea pig entorhinal cortex. *J. Neurophysiol.* 71:1986–91

23. Fozzard HA, Hanck DA, Makielski JC, Scanley BE, Sheets MF. 1987. Sodium channels in cardiac Purkinje cells. *Experientia* 43:1162–68

24. French CR, Sah P, Buckett KJ, Gage PW. 1990. A voltage-dependent persistent sodium current in mammalian hippocampal neurons. *J. Gen. Physiol.* 95:1139–57

25. Gage PW, Lamb GD, Wakefield BT. 1989. Transient and persistent sodium currents in normal and denervated mammalian skeletal muscle. *J. Physiol.* 418:427–39

26. Gilly WF, Armstrong CM. 1985. Threshold channels—a novel type of sodium channel in squid giant axon. *Nature* 309:448–50

27. Gonoi T, Hille B. 1987. Gating of sodium channels: inactivation modifiers discriminate among models. *J. Gen. Physiol.* 89:253–74

28. Grant AO, Starmer CF. 1987. Mechanisms of closure of cardiac sodium channels in rabbit ventricular myocytes: single-channel analysis. *Circ. Res.* 60:897–913

29. Hamill OP, Marty A, Neher E, Sakmann B, Sigworth FJ. 1981. Improved patch-clamp techniques for high-resolution current recording from cells and cell-free membrane patches. *Pflügers Arch.* 391:85–100

30. Hille B. 1992. *Ionic Channels of Excitable Membranes.* Sunderland, MA: Sinauer. 607 pp.

31. Hodgkin AL, Huxley AF. 1952. A quantitative description of membrane current and its application to conduction and excitation in nerve. *J. Physiol.* 117:500–544

32. Hotson JR, Prince DA, Schwartzkroin PA. 1979. Anomalous inward rectification in hippocampal neurons. *J. Neurophysiol.* 42:889–95

33. Hu G-Y, Hvalby Ø. 1992. Glutamate-induced action potentials are preceded by regenerative prepotentials in rat hippocampal pyramidal cells in vitro. *Exp. Brain Res.* 88:485–94

34. Huguenard JR, Hamill OP, Prince DA. 1988. Developmental changes in $Na^+$ conductances in rat neocortical neurons: appearance of a slowly inactivating component. *J. Neurophysiol.* 59:778–95

35. Huguenard JR, Hamill OP, Prince DA. 1989. Sodium channels in dendrites of rat cortical pyramidal neurons. *Proc. Natl. Acad. Sci. USA* 86:2473–77

36. Jack JJB, Noble D, Tsien RW. 1975. *Electric Current Flow in Excitable Cells.* London: Oxford Univ. Press. 518 pp.

37. Jahnsen H, Llinás R. 1984. Ionic basis for the electro-responsiveness and oscillatory properties of guinea-pig thalamic neurons in vitro. *J. Physiol.* 349:227–47

38. Kiyosue T, Arita M. 1989. Late sodium current and its contribution to action potential configuration in guinea pig ventricular myocytes. *Circ. Res.* 64:389–97

39. Kohlhardt M, Fröbe U, Herzig JW. 1987. Properties of normal and non-inactivating single cardiac $Na^+$ channels. *Proc. R. Soc. London Ser. B* 232:71–93

40. Kunze DL, Lacerda AE, Wilson DL, Brown AM. 1985. Cardiac Na currents and the inactivating, reopening, and waiting properties of single cardiac Na channels. *J. Gen. Physiol.* 86:691–719

41. Li M, West JW, Lai Y, Scheuer T, Catterall WA. 1992. Functional modulation of brain sodium channels by cAMP-dependent phosphorylation. *Neuron* 8:1151–59

42. Liu Y-M, DeFelice LH, Mazzanti M. 1992. Na channels that remain open throughout the cardiac action potential plateau. *Biophys. J.* 63:654–62

43. Llinás RR. 1988. The intrinsic electrophysiological properties of mammalian neurons: insights into central nervous system function. *Science* 242:1654–64

44. Llinás RR, Sugimori M. 1980. Electrophysiological properties of in vitro Purkinje cell somata in mammalian cerebellar slices. *J. Physiol.* 305:171–95

45. Llinás RR, Yarom Y. 1981. Electrophysiology of mammalian inferior olivary neurones in vitro. Different types of voltage-dependent ionic conductances. *J. Physiol.* 315:549–67

46. Ma J, Li M, Catterall WA, Scheuer T. 1994. Modulation of brain $Na^+$ channels by a G-protein-coupled pathway. *Proc. Natl. Acad. Sci. USA* 91:12351–55

47. Macdonald RL, Kelly KM. 1993. Antiepileptic drug mechanisms of action. *Epilepsia Suppl.* 534:S1–8

48. Masukawa LM, Hansen AJ, Shepherd G. 1991. Distribution of single-channel conductances in cultured rat hippocampal neurons. *Cell. Mol. Neurobiol.* 11:231–43

49. McCormick DA, Prince DA. 1987. Postnatal development of electrophysiological properties of rat cerebral cortical pyramidal neurones. *J. Physiol.* 393:743–62

50. Moorman JR, Kirsch GE, VanDongen AMJ, Joho RH, Brown AM. 1990. Fast and slow gating of sodium channels encoded by a single mRNA. *Neuron* 4:243–52

51. Nilius B. 1988. Modal gating behavior of cardiac sodium channels in cell-free membrane patches. *Biophys. J.* 53:857–62

52. Numann R, Catterall WA, Scheuer T. 1991. Functional modulation of brain sodium channels by protein kinase C phosphorylation. *Science* 254:115–18

53. Ono K, Fozzard H, Hanck D. 1993. Mechanism of cAMP-dependent modulation of cardiac sodium channel current kinetics. *Circ. Res.* 72:807–15

54. Ono K, Fozzard HA, Hanck DA. 1995. A direct effect of forskolin on sodium channel bursting. *Pflügers Arch.* 429:561–69

55. Patlak J. 1991. Molecular kinetics of voltage-dependent $Na^+$ channels. *Physiol. Rev.* 71:1047–80

56. Patlak JB, Ortiz M. 1985. Slow currents through single sodium channels of the adult rat heart. *J. Gen. Physiol.* 86:89–104

57. Patlak JB, Ortiz M. 1986. Two modes of gating during late $Na^+$ channel currents in frog sartorius muscle. *J. Gen. Physiol.* 87:305–26

58. Patlak JB, Ortiz M. 1989. Kinetic diversity of $Na^+$ channel bursts in frog skeletal muscle. *J. Gen. Physiol.* 94:279–301

59. Plummer MR, Hess P. 1991. Reversible uncoupling of inactivation in N-type calcium channels. *Nature* 351:657–59

60. Qu Y, Rogers J, Tanada T, Scheuer T, Catterall WA. 1994. Modulation of car-

diac Na+ channels expressed in a mammalian cell line and in ventricular myocytes by protein kinase C. *Proc. Natl. Acad. Sci. USA* 91:3289–93

61. Quandt FN. 1987. Burst kinetics of sodium channels which lack fast inactivation in mouse neuroblastoma cells. *J. Physiol.* 392:563–83

62. Quandt FN. 1988. Modification of slow inactivation of single sodium channels by phenytoin in neuroblastoma cells. *Mol. Pharmacol.* 34:557–65

63. Sayer RJ, Schwindt PC, Crill WE. 1990. High- and low-threshold calcium currents in neurons acutely isolated from rat sensorimotor cortex. *Neurosci. Lett.* 120:175–78

64. Scanley BE, Hanck DA, Chay T, Fozzard HA. 1990. Kinetic analysis of single sodium channels from canine cardiac Purkinje cells. *J. Gen. Physiol.* 95:411–37

65. Stafstrom CE, Schwindt PC, Crill WE. 1982. Negative slope conductance due to a persistent subthreshold sodium current in cat neocortical neurons in vitro. *Brain Res.* 236:221–26

66. Stafstrom CE, Schwindt PC, Chubb MC, Crill WE. 1985. Properties of persistent sodium conductance and calcium conductance of layer V neurons from cat sensorimotor cortex in vitro. *J. Neurophysiol.* 53:153–70

67. Stafstrom CE, Schwindt PC, Flatman JA, Crill WE. 1984. Properties of subthreshold response and action potential recorded in layer V neurons from cat sensorimotor cortex in vitro. *J. Neurophysiol.* 52:244–63

68. Stuart G, Hausser M. 1994. Initiation and spread of sodium action potentials in cerebellar Purkinje cells. *Neuron* 13:703–12

69. Stuart GJ, Sakmann B. 1994. Active propagation of sodium action potentials into neocortical pyramidal cell dendrites. *Nature* 367:69–72

70. Stys PK, Sontheimer H, Ransom BR, Waxman SG. 1993. Noninactivating, tetrodotoxin-sensitive Na+ conductance in rat optic nerve axons. *Proc. Natl. Acad. Sci. USA* 90:6976–80

71. Stys PK, Waxman SG, Ransom BR. 1992. Ionic mechanisms of anoxic injury in mammalian CNS white matter: role of Na+ channels and Na+-Ca2+ exchanger. *J. Neurosci.* 12:430–39

72. Sugimori M, Kay AR, Llinás R. 1994. The persistent Na+ current in cerebellar Purkinje cells has a single channel conductance distinct from the inactivating current. *Soc. Neurosci. Abst.* 20:63

73. Taylor CP. 1993. Na+ currents that fail to inactivate. *Trends Neurosci.* 116:455–60

74. Ukomadu C, Zhou S, Sigworth FJ, Agnew WS. 1992. μI Na+ channels expressed transiently in human embryonic kidney cells: biochemical and biophysical properties. *Neuron* 8:663–76

75. Westenbroek RE, Merrick DK, Catterall WA. 1989. Differential sub-cellular localization of the $R_1$ and $R_2$ Na+ channel subtypes in central neurons. *Neuron* 3:695–704

76. White JA, Sekar NS, Kay AR. 1995. Errors in persistent inward currents generated by space-clamp errors: a modeling study. *J. Neurophysiol.* 73:2369–77

77. Zhou J, Potts JF, Trimmer JS, Agnew WS, Sigworth FJ. 1991. Multiple gating modes and the effect of modulating factors on the μI sodium channel. *Neuron* 7:775–85

Annu. Rev. Physiol. 1996. 58:363–94

# MYOCARDIAL POTASSIUM CHANNELS: Electrophysiological and Molecular Diversity

## Dianne M. Barry and Jeanne M. Nerbonne

Department of Molecular Biology and Pharmacology, Washington University
Medical School, St. Louis, Missouri 63110

KEY WORDS:    outward rectifiers, inward rectifiers, $K^+$ channels, atria and ventricles,
              molecular cloning of ion channels

## ABSTRACT

Myocardial $K^+$ currents function to control resting membrane potentials, the heights and durations of action potentials, and refractoriness and automaticity. They are important targets for the actions of transmitters and hormones or drugs known, or postulated, to modulate cardiac functioning. A variety of $K^+$ currents that subserve these functions have now been identified in myocardial cells isolated from different species, as well as in cells isolated from different regions of the heart in the same species. These currents include the voltage-gated $K^+$ types, such as the transient outward ($I_{to}$) and delayed rectifier ($I_K$) currents, as well as the inwardly rectifying currents, $I_{K1}$, $I_{K(ACh)}$, and $I_{K(ATP)}$. The physiological and functional properties of the various $K^+$ currents/channels expressed in different myocardial cell types are the focus of this review. Advances made in cloning $K^+$ channel subunits of the Kv, *eag*, Kir, and $I_{sK}$ families are discussed, and progress made in identifying the $K^+$ channel subunits expressed in the mammalian myocardium is summarized. The relationships between the various cloned $K^+$ channel subunits and the functional $K^+$ channels characterized electrophysiologically in myocardial cells are explored.

## INTRODUCTION

A variety of $K^+$ currents with differing time- and voltage-dependent properties and pharmacological sensitivities have been identified in myocardial cells isolated from different species, as well as in cells isolated from different regions of the heart in the same species (1, 3, 36, 64, 99, 126, 166, 173, 183). Similar to findings in other cells, $K^+$ channels are more numerous and more diverse than other types of ion channels expressed in myocardial cells.

363

Individual myocardial cells express multiple types of K⁺ channels. Differences in the types and/or densities of K⁺ channels expressed contribute to determining the variability in action potential waveforms recorded in different regions of the heart (Figure 1A). It is now well documented that changes in the densities and/or the properties of K⁺ currents occur during normal development and as a result of damage or disease and that these changes have profound physiological consequences. In this review, we focus on the electrophysiological diversity of K⁺ channels in the mammalian myocardium and on the molecular mechanisms underlying this diversity; space does not permit discussion of K⁺ channel regulation and modulation by transmitters or drugs during normal development or as a result of damage or disease. Molecular studies have revealed even more potential for diversity than was expected, on the basis of the electrophysiology, and we are only beginning to understand the relationship between cloned K⁺ channel subunits and functional cardiac K⁺ channels.

## ELECTROPHYSIOLOGICAL DIVERSITY OF DEPOLARIZATION-ACTIVATED K⁺ CHANNELS IN MYOCARDIAL CELLS

Depolarization-activated K⁺ currents function to control the height and duration of action potentials. In several myocardial preparations, two basic types of voltage-gated K⁺ currents have been distinguished based on differing time- and voltage-dependent properties and pharmacological sensitivities: (a) 4-aminopyridine (4-AP) -sensitive, rapidly activating and inactivating currents, referred to as $I_{to}$ (transient outward) and (b) delayed, slowly activating and slowly inactivating outward currents that are sensitive to tetraethylammonium (TEA) and referred to as $I_K$ (delayed rectifier). The differing kinetic and voltage-dependent properties of $I_{to}$ and $I_K$ subserve distinct functions in action potential repolarization. $I_{to}$, for example, underlies the early phase (1) of repolarization, whereas $I_K$ contributes to the later phase (3) of repolarization (Figure 1B). These are broad classifications, however, and the detailed properties of the currents referred to as $I_{to}$ and $I_K$ vary in different species, as well as in cells isolated from different regions of the heart in the same species. In addition, there is evidence that other types of depolarization-activated K⁺ currents, not readily classified as $I_{to}$ or $I_K$, are also expressed in some myocardial cells.

### Transient Outward K⁺ Currents/Channels: $I_{to}$

Transient outward currents, first described in sheep Purkinje fibers, were thought to be carried primarily by Cl⁻ (41, 46, 59). Subsequent work revealed

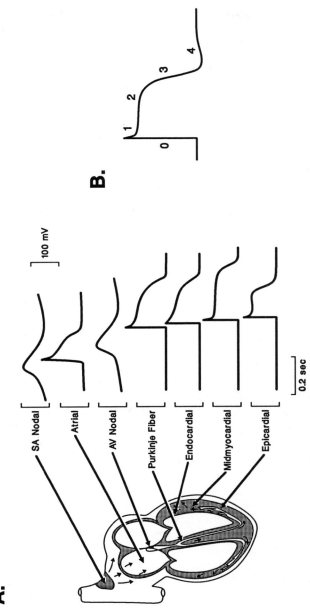

*Figure 1* Myocardial cardiac action potential waveforms. (*A*) Schematic of the variations in the waveforms of the action potentials recorded in different regions of the heart; action potentials are displaced in time to reflect the temporal sequence of propagation through the heart. (*B*) The phases of the ventricular action potential: phase 0, rapid depolarization; phase 1, early repolarization; phase 2, plateau; phase 3, late repolarization; phase 4, return to the resting membrane potential.

the presence of two components: $I_{to1}$, which is $Ca^{2+}$-independent and 4-AP-sensitive; and $I_{to2}$, which is 4-AP-insensitive and $Ca^{2+}$-dependent (35, 90). Considerable evidence now demonstrates that $I_{to2}$ is $Cl^-$, not $K^+$, selective (89, 90, 209–211). Therefore, we focus on $I_{to1}$ and refer to this current as $I_{to}$ for simplicity. At the macroscopic level, $I_{to}$ has been extensively characterized in cat (63), dog (106, 179, 180), ferret (24), human (92, 187, 199, 200), mouse (13, 14), rabbit (65, 70) and rat (4, 84, 199) ventricular myocytes, as well as in rabbit (33, 54, 65), dog (206) and human (48, 49, 54, 67, 161, 187) atrial myocytes, and in rabbit nodal (124) and crista terminalis (66) cells (Table 1). In each of these preparations, the currents termed $I_{to}$ are similar in that their activation and inactivation are rapid; in addition $I_{to}$ is $Ca^{2+}$ insensitive, blocked by 4-AP, and $K^+$ selective (64). Although not studied extensively to date, the single-channel correlates of $I_{to}$ ($\gamma = 20$–$27$ pS) in different cells are also similar (12, 124).

The finding that the properties of the currents termed $I_{to}$ are similar suggests that the molecular correlates of $I_{to}$ in different species and cell types likely are the same. Nevertheless, there are some subtle differences in the detailed time- and voltage-dependent properties of $I_{to}$ in different cells. In the rat heart, for example, $I_{to}$ is prominent in ventricular myocytes (4), whereas two 4-AP-sensitive, rapidly activating, slowly inactivating $K^+$ currents, termed $I_{Kf}$ and $I_{Ks}$, are expressed in atrial myocytes (19). At physiological temperatures, however, the time constant of $I_{Kf}$ inactivation is increased 20-fold to ~30 ms (184), indicating that $I_{Kf}$ functions as a transient outward current. In addition, although recovery of $I_{to}$ from steady-state inactivation is rapid (tau ~25–30 ms) in mouse (13, 14), rat (4), and human (54, 199) myocytes, recovery of rabbit atrial $I_{to}$ requires seconds (54, 65). This slow recovery underlies the marked change in the early phase of repolarization seen in rabbit, but not in human, atrial myocytes at high stimulation frequencies (54). Although guinea pig atrial and ventricular myocytes reportedly lack $I_{to}$ (155, 156), removal of extracellular $Ca^{2+}$ reveals an $I_{to}$-like current (76). This intriguing result suggests that $I_{to}$ channels are expressed in guinea pig cells but that they are largely nonfunctional under physiological conditions.

Marked differences in $I_{to}$ density are evident in cells isolated from different regions of the heart. In human, rabbit, and rat, for example, $I_{to}$ density is substantially higher in atrial than in ventricular myocytes (18, 19, 65, 187). In dog heart, $I_{to}$ density is also higher in myocytes isolated from the right (rather than the left) ventricular epicardium (42). In addition, $I_{to}$ density varies across the thickness of the ventricular wall in dog (106, 108), cat (63), human (199), rabbit (52), and rat (32). In dog ventricle, for example, $I_{to}$ density is five- to sixfold higher in cells isolated from the epicardium or midmyocardium (M cells) than in cells from the endocardium (108). The high density of $I_{to}$ under-

**Table 1** Diversity of myocardial $K^+$ currents

| Current | Activation | Inactivation | Blocker | Cell type | Species | References |
|---|---|---|---|---|---|---|
| $I_{to}$ ($I_{K1}$) | Fast | Fast | 4-AP[1] | Atrial | Dog, human, rabbit, rat | 19, 33, 48, 54, 65, 67, 161, 187, 199, 200, 206 |
| | | | | Ventricular | Cat, dog, ferret, human, mouse, rabbit, rat | 4, 13, 14, 24, 63, 65, 70, 84, 92, 106, 179, 180, 187, 199, 200 |
| | | | | Nodal | Rabbit | 124 |
| $I_{Kr}$ | Moderate | Slow | E-4031 Dofetilide Lanth-anum | Atrial | Dog, guinea pig, human | 72, 156, 195, 206 |
| | | | | Ventricular | Cat, dog, guinea pig, human, rabbit | 10, 16, 58, 107, 155, 188, 189 |
| | | | | Nodal | Rabbit | 160 |
| $I_{Ks}$ | Very slow | Very, Very slow | NE-10064 NE-10133 | Atrial | Dog, guinea pig, human | 72, 156, 195, 206 |
| | | | | Ventricular | Dog, guinea pig | 107, 155 |
| | | | | Nodal | Guinea pig | 2, 60 |
| $I_K$ | Moderate | Slow | TEA[2] | Ventricular | Rat | 4 |
| $I_{Kslow}$ | Fast | Very slow | 4-AP[1] DTX[3] | Atrial | Human, rat | 19, 184, 193 |
| $I_{sus}$, $I_{ss}$ | Fast | No | 4-AP[1] | Atrial | Human, rat | 19, 184, 193, 194 |
| $I_{Kp}$ | Fast | No | $Ba^{2+}$ | Ventricular | Guinea pig | 8, 205 |
| $I_{K1}$ | | | $Ba^{2+}$ | Atrial | Guinea pig, human, rabbit, | 65, 69, 75, 187 |
| | | | | Ventricular | Cat, dog, guinea pig, human, rabbit, rat | 62, 65, 75, 83, 131, 151, 180, 187 |
| $I_{K(ACh)}$ | | | Atropine PTX[4] | Atrial | Guinea pig, human, rabbit | 69, 93, 100, 163 |
| | | | | Ventricular | Cat, guinea pig, human | 93 |
| | | | | Nodal | Rabbit | 133, 132, 151 |
| $I_{K(ATP)}$ | | | Sulphonyl-ureas | Atrial | Guinea pig, human, rabbit | 69, 130 |
| | | | | Ventricular | Guinea pig, rabbit, rat | 56, 73, 86, 127, 130, 177 |
| | | | | Nodal | Rabbit | 85 |

[1]4-AP, 4-aminopyridine; [2]TEA, tetraethylammonium; [3]DTX, dendrotoxin; [4]PTX, pertussis toxin

lies the "spike and dome" configuration of the action potential that is prominent in epicardial and M, but not in endocardial, cells (108).

## Delayed Rectifier $K^+$ Currents/Channels: $I_K$

Slowly activating $K^+$ currents ($I_K$), also first described in sheep Purkinje fibers (129), have been characterized in dog (107, 180, 206), cat (58, 62), guinea pig (2, 10, 60, 72, 155–157, 190), human (16, 189, 195), rabbit (160, 188), and rat (4) myocardium (Table 1). In contrast to $I_{to}$, however, there are multiple components of $I_K$ that display differing time- and voltage-dependent properties and pharmacological sensitivities. For example, two components of $I_K$, referred to as $I_{Kr}$ (rapid $I_K$) and $I_{Ks}$ (slow $I_K$), have been distinguished in guinea pig atrial and ventricular myocytes (155, 156) (Table 1). $I_{Kr}$ activates faster and at more negative potentials than $I_{Ks}$, and $I_{Kr}$ displays marked inward rectification at potentials positive to 0 mV (155, 156). In addition, the pharmacological sensitivities of $I_{Kr}$ and $I_{Ks}$ are distinct (10, 22, 25, 155, 156). $I_{Kr}$ is selectively blocked by lanthanum and by several class III antiarrhythmics, including dofetilide, E-4031, and sotalol (25, 155, 156); $I_{Ks}$, although unaffected by these agents, is selectively blocked by other class III antiarrhythmics, such as NE-10064 and NE-10133 (22). $I_{Kr}$ and $I_{Ks}$ can also be distinguished at the single-channel level. In symmetrical $K^+$, the single-channel conductances of $I_{Kr}$ and $I_{Ks}$ channel are 10–13 and 3–5 pS, respectively (10, 72, 160, 188). These results suggest that $I_{Kr}$ and $I_{Ks}$ reflect the expression of distinct molecular entities. Similar currents have been described in dog atrial (206) and ventricular (107) cells and in human atrial (195) myocytes (Table 1).

In several preparations including guinea pig (2, 60) and rabbit (160) nodal cells and cat (58), rabbit (188), and rat (4) ventricular myocytes, there appears to be a single component of delayed rectification. In guinea pig nodal cells, this current corresponds to $I_{Ks}$ (2, 60), whereas in cat (58), human (16, 189), and rabbit (188) ventricular myocytes and rabbit nodal cells (160), only E-4031-sensitive $I_{Kr}$-like currents are readily distinguished. The single component of $I_K$ in rat ventricular myocytes, in contrast, appears to be distinct from both $I_{Ks}$ and $I_{Kr}$ (4). Interestingly, no currents resembling $I_{Ks}$ or $I_{Kr}$ have been described in rat (4) ventricular myocytes.

Similar to the findings with $I_{to}$, $I_{Ks}$ and $I_{Kr}$ densities vary in different myocardial cell types and in different regions of the ventricle. In guinea pig, for example, $I_{Kr}$ and $I_{Ks}$ densities are approximately twofold higher in atrial than in ventricular myocytes, likely contributing to the shortening of action potentials in atrial myocytes (155, 156). In addition, in the dog ventricle, $I_{Ks}$ density is higher in epicardial and endocardial cells than in the M cells (107). The lower density of $I_{Ks}$ underlies the finding that action potentials are prolonged and more sensitive to rate of stimulation in M cells, as compared with epicardial and endocardial cells (107).

## Other Depolarization-Activated K$^+$ Currents/Channels

In several myocardial preparations, voltage-gated K$^+$ currents/channels have been described that cannot readily be classified as $I_{to}$- or $I_K$-like currents. In rat atrial myocytes, for example, a rapidly activating, slowly inactivating, 4-AP-sensitive K$^+$ current, referred to as $I_{Kslow}$ has been described (19). In addition to differences in inactivation (19), $I_{Kslow}$ is distinguished from the rapidly inactivating ($I_{Kf}$ or $I_{to}$) and the noninactivating ($I_{ss}$) outward currents (Table 1) in these cells by its dendrotoxin sensitivity (184). In guinea pig ventricular myocytes, rapidly activating, noninactivating, 12–14 pS K$^+$-selective channels that are quite distinct from $I_{Kr}$ and $I_{Ks}$ channels have also been described and referred to as $I_{Kp}$ ($I_K$, plateau, persistent, or potential-sensitive) channels (205). $I_{Kp}$ is sensitive to mM concentrations of Ba$^{2+}$ (8). In rat (19) and human (193, 194) atrial myocytes, K$^+$ currents with similar kinetics have also been described and referred to as $I_{ss}$ (rat, 19) and $I_{sus}$ (human, 193, 194). The similarity in their properties and the finding that both currents are blocked by phenylephrine suggests that related proteins underlie these currents (184). Furthermore, because the properties of guinea pig ventricular $I_{Kp}$ (8, 205) are very similar to the atrial currents ($I_{ss}$ and $I_{sus}$), it is tempting to speculate that the molecular correlates of $I_{Kp}$, $I_{ss}$, and $I_{sus}$ are all the same.

## ELECTROPHYSIOLOGICAL DIVERSITY OF INWARDLY RECTIFYING K$^+$ CHANNELS IN MYOCARDIAL CELLS

Inwardly rectifying K$^+$ currents are important in setting the resting membrane potential and in controlling myocardial cell excitability. The channels that underlie these currents are distinct from those discussed above in that they are open over the entire physiological voltage range and pass current preferentially in the inward direction. Three types of inwardly rectifying K$^+$ currents have been distinguished in cardiac cells: $I_{K1}$, $I_{K(ACh)}$, and $I_{K(ATP)}$ (Table 1). They differ in their regulation by acetylcholine (ACh) and G proteins ($I_{K(ACh)}$) or intracellular ATP ($I_{K(ATP)}$) and in the degree of inward rectification ($I_{K1}$ > $I_{K(ACh)}$ > $I_{K(ATP)}$). In addition, they display different single-channel properties, which suggests that distinct molecular entities underlie these channels.

## Strong Inwardly Rectifying K$^+$ Currents/Channels: $I_{K1}$

Strong inwardly rectifying K$^+$ currents ($I_{K1}$) are readily detected in cardiac Purkinje fibers and in atrial and ventricular myocytes but appear to be absent in nodal cells (65, 74, 83, 131, 151, 152, 162). At the macroscopic level, $I_{K1}$ has been characterized in guinea pig (74), human (69, 187), and rabbit (65) atrial and ventricular myocytes (Table 1), and the properties of the currents in these preparations are similar in that they are $K^+$ selective, blocked by extracellular $Cs^+$ and $Ba^{2+}$, and strongly rectifying (183). $I_{K1}$ plays a prominent role in setting the resting membrane potential and contributes to phase 3 repolarization (Figure 1B). When action potentials are elicited in the presence of extracellular $Ba^{2+}$, for example, phase 3 repolarization is slowed markedly (65).

At the microscopic level, $I_{K1}$ channels are readily distinguished from other types of inwardly rectifying $K^+$ channels. In guinea pig atrial and ventricular myocytes, for example, 27 pS channels predominate in symmetrical $K^+$, although there is also evidence for subconductance states (69, 115, 152). Experiments on excised membrane patches suggest that the rectification of $I_{K1}$ channels can result from block by intracellular $Mg^{2+}$ (115, 117, 182). In the presence of μM intracellular $Mg^{2+}$, two distinct subconductance states (spaced 7 pS apart), as well as the fully open and fully closed $I_{K1}$ channels, are resolved (115). These observations suggest that functional $I_{K1}$ channels comprise three identical, but independent, units (115, 116). There is also a time-dependent component of inward rectification (78, 98, 134) that accounts for the steepness of steady-state rectification and the negative slope region of the current-voltage relationship for $I_{K1}$. Recent studies on cloned inwardly rectifying $K^+$ channel subunits suggest that this intrinsic rectification reflects block by polyamines (51, 55, 110). In addition, although it has not been demonstrated directly that this mechanism underlies intrinsic rectification of myocardial $I_{K1}$ channels, it was recently reported that spermine does block the strongly rectifying $I_{K(ACh)}$, but not the weakly rectifying $I(K_{ATP})$, channels (204) in rabbit atrial myocytes.

Similar to the voltage-gated $K^+$ currents, the densities and the detailed properties of the currents termed $I_{K1}$ vary in different myocardial cell types. $I_{K1}$ is larger in rabbit ventricular than in atrial myocytes and undetectable in rabbit sinoatrial and atrioventricular cells (65, 131, 151). The presence of $I_{K1}$ is reflected in the negative slope region (between −50 and −10 mV) that is prominent in ventricular myocytes but is small or absent in atrial cells (65). Similar regional differences in $I_{K1}$ density are evident in human and guinea pig heart. In human heart, $I_{K1}$ density is approximately two and one half times greater in ventricular than in atrial myocytes (187). In guinea pig, the properties of the currents referred to as $I_{K1}$ in atrial and ventricular myocytes are also distinct: $I_{K1}$ inactivates during maintained hyperpolarization in ventricular, but not in atrial, myocytes (74). In addition, elevation of $[K^+]_o$ substantially increases the magnitude of the outward currents through ventricular $I_{K1}$ channels, but has little effect on atrial $I_{K1}$ channels (74). Interestingly, although the mean slope conductances are indistinguishable, the mean open time of ventricular

$I_{K1}$ channels is significantly longer (tau ~1 s) than that of atrial $I_{K1}$ channels (tau ~220 ms) (74). Taken together, these results suggest the interesting possibility that the molecular compositions of atrial and ventricular $I_{K1}$ channels are not identical.

## *Acetylcholine-Activated K$^+$ Currents/Channels: $I_{K(ACh)}$*

Acetylcholine, released on vagal stimulation, produces negative inotropic and chronotropic effects that are mediated through the activation of m2 muscarinic acetylcholine receptors (mAChR) (99). The negative chronotropic effect probably results in part from the opening of a novel class of inwardly rectifying K$^+$ channels ($I_{K(ACh)}$) in atrial and nodal cells, and several lines of evidence suggest that these channels are directly activated by mAChR occupation (133, 132). Consistent with these suggestions, ACh (or adenosine) activates channels in excised patches from nodal and atrial cells that are distinct from $I_{K1}$ (and $I_{K(ATP)}$) channels (100, 101, 151, 163). Under some experimental conditions, activation of mAChR (or adenosine receptors) can also result in the activation of $I_{K(ATP)}$ channels in guinea pig (81) and cat (192) atrial cells and in rat ventricular myocytes (91), but it appears that this effect involves an intracellular messenger pathway different from that underlying the activation of $I_{K(ACh)}$ channels (192). $I_{K(ACh)}$ channels have been extensively characterized in rabbit nodal (151) cells and in human (69), guinea pig (69), and rabbit (163) atrial myocytes (Table 1). In each of these preparations, application of ACh reveals large conductance (40 pS in symmetrical K$^+$) channels with similar gating properties (69, 151, 163). Intracellular GTP is required for $I_{K(ACh)}$ channel activation; nonhydrolyzable GTP analogues mimic the effect of GTP, which is mediated through a pertussis toxin-sensitive G protein (20, 101, 102, 138). Subsequent work has demonstrated that the βγ subunits of heterotrimeric G proteins directly activate $I_{K(ACh)}$ (31, 109, 202).

Although the expression of $I_{K(ACh)}$ is well documented in pacemaker cells, atrial myocytes, and cardiac Purkinje fibers (69, 93, 132, 151), recent work also demonstrated $I_{K(ACh)}$ in cat, guinea pig, and human ventricular myocytes (93). Ventricular $I_{K(ACh)}$ is also activated through a pertussis toxin–sensitive G protein, and single atrial and ventricular $I_{K(ACh)}$ channels display similar single-channel conductances and kinetic properties (93). Interestingly, ventricular $I_{K(ACh)}$ ($K_d$ 0.13 µM) is significantly less sensitive to ACh than atrial $I_{K(ACh)}$ ($K_d$ 0.03 µM). This difference, rather than a difference in the properties of the underlying $I_{K(ACh)}$ channels, appears to account for the relatively low current density of $I_{K(ACh)}$ in ventricular cells (93). Taken together, the single-channel data suggest that the same molecule underlies the expression of $I_{K(ACh)}$ in different species, as well as in different cell types in the same species.

## ATP-Sensitive $K^+$ Currents/Channels: $I_{K(ATP)}$

A clear link between cardiac metabolic and electrical activity was established with the identification of inwardly rectifying $K^+$ channels in ventricular myocytes that are inhibited by intracellular ATP ($ATP_i$) and referred to as $I_{K(ATP)}$ channels (130, 176, 177). When $ATP_i$ is reduced during hypoxia or ischemia or following treatment with metabolic inhibitors such as cyanide or DNP, $ATP_i$ drops and large conductance, weakly inwardly rectifying $K^+$-selective ($I_{K(ATP)}$) channels are revealed (126, 166, 173). Opening of $I_{K(ATP)}$ channels during metabolic stress results in action potential shortening (103), an effect that can be blocked by tolbutamide, a $I_{K(ATP)}$ channel blocker (50). Interestingly, $I_{K(ATP)}$ channels are closed by ATP in the μM range (130), whereas intracellular ATP is in the mM range, which suggests that under physiological conditions $I_{K(ATP)}$ channels will be substantially inhibited. Detailed examination of the relationship between action potential duration and $I_{K(ATP)}$ conductance has revealed that slight reductions in $ATP_i$ (128), corresponding to the opening of ~1% of the total number of $I_{K(ATP)}$ channels (50), lead to marked action potential shortening.

At potentials positive to $E_K$, $I_{K(ATP)}$ channels are also blocked by $Mg^{2+}$ and $Na^+$ (73). In the absence of these cations, the current-voltage relationship is nearly linear, although a slight (intrinsic) inward rectification is evident at more positive potentials (56, 73). Inhibition of $I_{K(ATP)}$ channels by ATP is achieved by decreasing the open-state probability (86). ATP inhibits $I_{K(ATP)}$ channels in the absence of $Mg^{2+}$ and nonhydrolyzable ATP analogues mimic the effect (86, 144). In experiments producing rapid concentration jumps of ATP, Qin and coworkers (144) demonstrated that the time-course for inhibition of $I_{K(ATP)}$ channels by ATP is rapid, suggesting that no intermediate steps are required for ATP-induced channel block. It is now generally accepted that ATP binds directly to either the channel protein or to a protein closely associated with the channels (125, 144, 166), and detailed analyses and modeling suggest that four ATP molecules are needed (127). Although these findings indicate that the inhibition of $I_{K(ATP)}$ by ATP does not require hydrolysis (86), ATP hydrolysis may play a role in the regulation of $I_{K(ATP)}$ channels. Following patch excision, $I_{K(ATP)}$ channel activity decreases—a process referred to as rundown. This process can be reversed by adding Mg-ATP and requires ATP hydrolysis (167). $ATP_i$, therefore, appears to play two roles in regulating $I_{K(ATP)}$ channels: (a) reduction of open probability of $I_{K(ATP)}$ channels by binding directly to the channels or to a closely associated regulatory component and (b) maintenance of active $I_{K(ATP)}$ channels via ATP hydrolysis, an effect that may involve protein phosphorylation (126, 166, 173).

In cell-attached and excised patch recordings from human and guinea pig atrial myocytes, $I_{K(ATP)}$ channels are readily distinguished from $I_{K1}$ and $I_{K(ACh)}$

channels based on sensitivity to $ATP_i$ and markedly differing conductances and gating properties (69). In symmetrical K⁺, large conductance (~70 pS) channels that are sensitive to $ATP_i$ have been characterized in guinea pig (69, 130), human (69), and rabbit (130) atrial myocytes, as well as in guinea pig (73, 86, 130, 177), rabbit (130), and rat (56, 125, 127) ventricular myocytes, and in rabbit nodal cells (85) (Table 1). In each of these preparations, the gating properties of the channels referred to as $I_{K(ATP)}$ are also quite similar, displaying clusters of burst openings separated by long closed periods (69, 73, 85, 86, 126, 166, 173, 177). In human ventricular myocytes, however, 100 pS $I_{K(ATP)}$ channels with somewhat different gating properties have also been described (7), suggesting that there is molecular heterogeneity among $I_{K(ATP)}$ channels, a suggestion supported by the finding that $I_{K(ATP)}$ channels in neonatal rat ventricular myocytes display differing sensitivities to guanine nucleotides (15).

# MOLECULAR DIVERSITY OF VOLTAGE-GATED K⁺ CHANNEL α SUBUNITS

## The Kv Family of Voltage-Gated K⁺ Channel α Subunits

The first voltage-gated K⁺ channel subunit cloned was from the *Shaker* (88) locus in *Drosophila* (87, 135, 143). Examination of the deduced amino acid sequence revealed *Shaker* to be an integral membrane protein of approximately 70 kDa (172), and hydropathy plots suggested the presence of six transmembrane regions with both the N- and C-termini located intracellularly (Figure 2A). Sequence analysis further revealed a high degree of homology between an arginine-rich region in the fourth membrane-spanning domain of *Shaker* and a corresponding region in voltage-gated Na⁺ channels believed to be important in voltage sensing (172). This region is commonly referred to as S4, and channel subunits containing it are considered part of the S4 superfamily of channel genes that includes voltage-gated Na⁺, $Ca^{2+}$, and K⁺ channels, as well as some cyclic nucleotide-gated channels (82, 141). The (P or H5) loop between S5 and S6 contributes to forming the K⁺-selective pore (82, 141, 142). Injection of *Shaker* cRNA into *Xenopus* oocytes results in the expression of rapidly activating and inactivating K⁺ currents (174). The fact that the *Shaker* protein is much smaller than the voltage-gated Na⁺ and $Ca^{2+}$ channel proteins (70 kDa for *Shaker* compared with 180–240 kDa for $Ca^{2+}$ and Na⁺ channel pore-forming subunits) and appears similar to one of the four homologous domains of Na⁺ ($Ca^{2+}$) channel proteins led to early suggestions (174) that functional *Shaker* K⁺ channels are oligomeric proteins, composed of several subunits. Consistent with this hypothesis, heterologous expression of *Shaker* produces voltage-gated K⁺ channels comprising four subunits (112).

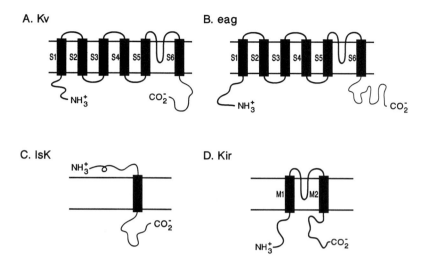

*Figure 2* Simplified illustration of the proposed membrane topology of $K^+$ channel α subunits. (*A*) Kv family members have six transmembrane domains (S1 through S6) and a hydrophobic pore (P or H5) region between S5 and S6; both the N- and C-termini are intracellular. The arginine-rich fourth membrane-spanning domain (S4) contributes to voltage-dependent channel gating. (*B*) Similar to the Kv family, *eag* family members have six transmembrane domains (S1 through S6), a pore region between S5 and S6, and a voltage-sensing S4. The cytoplasmic C-terminal domain of *eag* family members is substantially larger than that found in the Kv family and contains a cyclic nucleotide-binding site. (*C*) The $I_{sK}$ protein has a single transmembrane domain and is illustrated with the N-terminus extracellular and the C-terminus intracellular. (*D*) Members of the Kir family have two putative transmembrane domains (M1 and M2) separated by a pore region; M1 and M2 are homologous to S5 and S6 in the Kv (*A*) and *eag* (*B*) families. Kir subunits do not contain the S4 voltage-sensing domain found in the Kv1 (*A*) and *eag* (*B*) families.

Salkoff and colleagues later identified three other subfamilies of voltage-gated $K^+$ channel subunit genes, which they referred to as *Shab, Shaw,* and *Shal* genes (23). These genes encode proteins of 100, 56.5, and 56 kDa, respectively; they share 50% amino acid identity with one another and with *Shaker* (198), and the predicted membrane topology is the same as that of *Shaker* (Figure 2A). Heterologous expression of *Shab, Shaw,* or *Shal* also reveals voltage-gated $K^+$ currents, albeit with differing time- and voltage-dependent properties (198). Homology screening has led to the identification of a number of members of each subfamily in vertebrates, and a somewhat more systematic terminology was suggested (27) and is now widely used: $K^+$ channel subunit genes of the *Shaker, Shab, Shaw,* and *Shal* subfamilies are referred to as Kv1.x, Kv2.x, Kv3.x, and Kv4.x, respectively (Table 2). In vertebrates, a number of $K^+$ channel subunit proteins are formed either as a result of alternative splicing or the presence of multiple genes in each subfamily, designated by a number in place of the x in the Kv terminology (for review of the diversity and the properties of heterologously expressed Kv subunits, see 28, 141). Alternative splicing is the common mechanism in *Drosophila* (158, 198), whereas multiple subfamily genes appear to be the more common mechanism for generating K$^+$ channel diversity (Table 2) in vertebrates (82, 141, 153).

Another potential mechanism for generating K$^+$ channel diversity is through the formation of heteromultimeric channels. Coinjection experiments have revealed that heteromultimeric Kv channels can and do form in oocytes following injection of two different cRNAs belonging to the same subfamily and, interestingly, the properties of heteromultimeric channels are distinct from those of the corresponding homomultimeric channels produced by injection of either cRNA alone (30, 77, 150). However, heteromultimeric channels do not form between the protein products of two different subfamily genes (37). Although not quantitative, these experiments have revealed that coinjection of equal amounts of two cRNAs results in a predominance of heteromultimeric channels (30, 37, 77, 150), which might suggest that heteromultimeric channels are actually formed in preference to homomultimeric channels. Indeed, two recent studies have demonstrated that some Kv subunits are assembled as heteromultimers in the nervous system (159, 191).

## Kv Subunit Expression in the Mammalian Heart

Several laboratories have reported the cloning of Kv subunits from cardiac cDNA libraries and the expression of Kv subunits in the mammalian heart (34, 38, 53, 136, 140, 148, 149, 170, 181). Six different K$^+$ channel subunits were found by Northern blot analysis in the rat heart; four, Kv1.1, Kv1.2, Kv1.4, and Kv1.5, belong to the *Shaker* subfamily; one, Kv4.2, belongs to the *Shal* subfamily; and one, Kv2.1, belongs to the *Shab* subfamily (149) (Table 2). Subsequent quantitative RNAase protection assays confirmed the presence of Kv1.2, Kv1.4, Kv1.5, Kv2.1, and Kv4.2 in adult rat atria and ventricles, but failed to detect Kv1.1 (43). The simplest interpretation of the latter finding is that the Northern blot analysis included some neuronal mRNA (perhaps isolated from the intrinsic cardiac ganglia). Importantly, Dixon & McKinnon (43) showed that of the 15 K$^+$ channel subunit sequences probed, only Kv1.2, Kv.1.4, Kv1.5, Kv2.1, and Kv4.2 were detectable at the mRNA level in adult rat atria and ventricles. In addition, they demonstrated that the level of Kv4.2 expression varied through the thickness of the ventricular wall in a manner similar to that seen for $I_{to}$ (32, 52, 63, 106, 108, 200), which suggests that Kv4.2 might underlie $I_{to}$ (43).

Some progress has also been made in identifying the Kv subunits expressed

**Table 2** Diversity of K$^+$ channel $\alpha$ subunits and relation to functional myocardial K$^+$ channels[a]

| | Subunit | Activation | Inactivation | Blocker | Endogenous current |
|---|---|---|---|---|---|
| **Kv family** | | | | | |
| Kv1 (Shaker) | Kv 1.1 | | | | |
| | Kv 1.2 | Fast | Very slow | 4-AP DTX | $I_{Kslow}$? |
| | Kv 1.3 | | | | |
| | Kv 1.4 | Fast | Fast | 4-AP | ? |
| | Kv 1.5 | Fast | Very slow | 4-AP | $I_{sus}/I_{ss}/I_{Kp}$ |
| | Kv 1.6 | | | | |
| | Kv 1.7 | | | | |
| | Kv 1.8 | | | | |
| Kv2 (Shab) | Kv2.1 | Slow | Very slow | TEA | $I_K$? |
| | Kv2.2 | | | | |
| Kv3 (Shaw) | Kv3.1 | | | | |
| | Kv3.2 | | | | |
| | Kv3.3 | | | | |
| | Kv3.4 | | | | |
| Kv4 (Shal) | Kv4.1 | | | | |
| | Kv4.2 | Fast | Fast | 4-AP | $I_{to}$ |
| IsK family | IsK | Very slow | Very, Very slow | NE-10064 NE-10133 | $I_{Ks}$ |
| **eag family** | | | | | |
| eag | eag | | | | |
| elk | elk | | | | |
| h-erg | h-erg | Fast | Fast | Lanthanum | $I_{Kr}$ |
| **Kir family** | | | | | |
| Kir1 (ROMK) | Kir 1.1 | | | | ? |
| Kir2 (IRK) | Kir2.1 | | | | $I_{K1}$? |
| | Kir2.2 | | | | $I_{K1}$? |
| | Kir2.3 | | | | $I_{K1}$? |
| Kir3 (GIRK) | Kir3.1 | | | | $I_{K\ (ACh)}$ (with Kir3.4) |
| | Kir3.2 | | | | |
| | Kir3.3 | | | | |
| | Kir3.4 | | | | $I_{K\ (ACh)}$ (with Kir3.1) |
| Kir4 (BIR10) | Kir 4.1 | | | | — |
| Kir5 (BIR9) | Kir 5.1 | | | | — |
| Kir6 (uK$_{ATP1}$) | Kir 6.1 | | | | $I_{K(ATP)}$? |

[a] Boxes indicate subunits expressed in heart.

in other species. Kv1.4, for example, has been cloned from human (170) and ferret (34) ventricular libraries. The human and ferret clones are 98% identical to rat Kv1.4 (34, 170, 181), and when expressed in *Xenopus* oocytes, both produce rapidly activating and inactivating K⁺ currents (34, 139, 140), similar to rat Kv1.4 (181). Kv1.5 has also been cloned from human heart (38, 53, 170); human Kv1.5 is 85% identical to rat Kv1.5 (149) and has been localized to the short arm of chromosome 12 (38). Northern blot analysis indicates that Kv1.4 is more abundant in human ventricles, whereas Kv1.5 is more abundant in atria (170). Expression of human Kv1.5 (53) reveals currents similar to the rapidly activating, noninactivating component of the outwardly rectifying K⁺ current ($I_{ss}$ or $I_{sus}$) in rat (19, 184) and human (182, 193, 194) atrial myocytes (Table 2). To date, no other Kv subfamily cDNAs have been cloned from human or ferret heart or, for that matter, from the hearts of other species.

## The eag, elk, and h-erg Family

*Drosophila* genetics also led to the cloning and identification of *eag* (196), the gene that is mutated in *ether-a-go-go* flies, which (like *Shaker* flies) shake in response to ether anesthesia (88). Electrophysiological studies suggest that mutations in the *eag* gene affect multiple K⁺ currents in larval (*Drosophila*) muscle (207, 208). The cloning of *eag* by Ganetsky and co-workers (45, 196) revealed a protein of 1174 amino acids with seven hydrophobic domains (Figure 2B). The fourth membrane-spanning region (S4) and the putative pore (H5) region are similar to those in the Kv family of voltage-gated K⁺ channel subunits, consistent with the suggestion that *eag* contributes to the formation of functional K⁺ channels (196, 207, 208). The homology between *eag* and the Kv subfamilies overall, however, is very low (10–17% amino acid identity), which indicates that *eag* represents a novel family of K⁺ channel subunit genes (Table 2). *Eag* is also homologous to cyclic nucleotide-gated channels (68), which are nonselective cation channels. In addition, when *eag* is expressed in *Xenopus* oocytes, K⁺- and Ca²⁺-permeable channels are observed, and these channels are modulated by cAMP, which suggests that *eag* may form homomeric channels (21) and, perhaps, heteromultimeric channels (207, 208).

Screening a *Drosophila* (head) cDNA library with probes based on *eag* led to the isolation of a novel cDNA encoding an *eag*-like (*elk*) protein, indicating that there are additional subfamilies of K⁺ channel subunit genes of the *eag* family (197). In addition, the mouse (197) and rat (111) homologues of *eag* (*m-eag* and *r-eag*, respectively) have been cloned from brain libraries, and an *eag*-related molecule (*h-erg*) has been cloned from a human hippocampal library (197).

## *eag Subunit Expression in the Mammalian Heart*

Although there have been no reports of cloning *eag* or *elk* from cardiac cDNA libraries to date, it has been demonstrated that *h-erg* is expressed in human heart (39). *h-erg* maps to chromosome 7 (197) and has recently been identified as the locus of one form of long QT-syndrome, LQT2 (39), which is associated with abnormal repolarization and had long been assumed to involve a mutation in a voltage-gated $K^+$ channel or a closely associated $K^+$ channel regulatory protein. Although the functional consequences of *h-erg* expression in the human myocardium have not been explored directly, it has recently been demonstrated that heterologous expression of *h-erg* reveals strongly rectifying $K^+$-selective channels (154, 178) that are similar to $I_{Kr}$.

## *The Minimal, minK or $I_{sK}$ Subunit*

A completely different type of $K^+$ channel subunit was expression cloned from rat kidney and named $I_{sK}$ or minK (123, 169). $I_{sK}$ encodes a protein of only 130 amino acids with a single membrane–spanning domain; the N-terminus is thought to be extracellular and the C-terminus intracellular (Figure 2C). Clearly, $I_{sK}$ lacks the S4 sequence found in all of the Kv and *eag* family members and, in fact, is unrelated to other $K^+$ (or $Na^+$, $Ca^{2+}$, etc) channel subunits cloned to date. Although identified in neonatal heart (57), $I_{sK}$ is undetectable in adult rat atria or ventricles (43). It has been reported, however, that $I_{sK}$ is expressed in adult mouse (104) and human (164) heart. Because of the very small size of $I_{sK}$ and the fact that this protein shares no homology to any other channel subunit proteins, there has been considerable discussion surrounding $I_{sK}$ and whether it is a channel-forming peptide (6). Heterologous expression of $I_{sK}$ reveals very slowly activating, $K^+$-selective currents (57), and mutations in the transmembrane domain of $I_{sK}$ alter the permeation properties of the channels expressed in oocytes (168), consistent with the idea that $I_{sK}$ forms channels. As is discussed further below, cardiac physiologists have found the idea that $I_{sK}$ encodes a channel attractive primarily because expressed $I_{sK}$ currents closely resemble the very slowly activating, delayed $K^+$ currents characterized extensively in guinea pig atrial and ventricular myocytes (155, 156) and, more recently, in human atrial (195) myocytes. Nevertheless, at least one report has shown that injection of $I_{sK}$ cRNA into *Xenopus* oocytes increases expression of $Cl^-$ as well as $K^+$ currents (6), consistent with the suggestion that $I_{sK}$ might be a channel-regulatory protein rather than a channel-forming protein per se. Recent work, however, demonstrates that chemical cross-linking of $I_{sK}$ subunits results in the expression of rapidly activating $K^+$ currents (186), further supporting the suggestion that $I_{sK}$ is a channel-forming polypeptide.

# MOLECULAR DIVERSITY OF INWARDLY RECTIFYING K$^+$ CHANNEL SUBUNITS

## *ROMK, IRK, and GIRK*

Unlike work done to classify the Kv and *eag* families of K$^+$ channel subunit genes, efforts to probe the molecular diversity of inwardly rectifying K$^+$ channels have advanced without the benefit of *Drosophila* genetics. The first inwardly rectifying K$^+$ channel subunits were cloned in 1993: one, ROMK1, was cloned from rat kidney (71) and another, IRK1, was cloned from a mouse macrophage cell line (96). ROMK1 and IRK1 encode proteins of 391 and 428 amino acids, respectively (71, 96), and they share approximately 45% amino acid identity. Hydropathy plots suggest the presence of three hydrophobic domains; the predicted membrane topology of these subunits is illustrated in Figure 2D. In contrast to the Kv and *eag* families of K$^+$ channel $\alpha$ subunits, there are two predicted transmembrane domains and, importantly, IRK1 and ROMK1 lack the S4 sequence characteristic of the voltage-gated K$^+$, Na$^+$, and Ca$^{2+}$ channel pore-forming $\alpha$ subunits.

Although heterologous expression of either ROMK1 or IRK1 in *Xenopus* oocytes reveals inwardly rectifying K$^+$ currents that are blocked by extracellular Cs$^+$ and Ba$^{2+}$ (71, 96), there are marked differences in the properties of the channels formed. For example, IRK1 channels strongly rectify, whereas ROMK1 channels are weakly rectifying, and the single-channel conductances of ROMK1 and IRK1 channels (39 and 23 pS, respectively) are distinct (71, 96). Although the fact that ROMK1 has a potential nucleotide-binding domain suggests that this subunit underlies $I_{K(ATP)}$ channels, this possibility seems unlikely given that expressed ROMK1 currents are actually increased rather than decreased [as would be expected for $I_{K(ATP)}$ channels (126, 166, 173)] by application of ATP (71). Nevertheless, it is certainly possible that ROMK1 contributes to the formation of $I_{K(ATP)}$ channels. To date, this possibility has not been explored directly.

Homology screening subsequently led to the identification of a G protein–coupled inwardly rectifying K$^+$ channel $\alpha$ subunit, termed GIRK1 (97). The same clone was identified in rat atria by expression cloning and referred to as KGA (40). At the amino acid level, GIRK1 is 43 and 37% identical to IRK1 and ROMK1, respectively (97). Heterologous expression of GIRK1 with m2 muscarinic acetylcholine receptors reveals inwardly rectifying K$^+$ channels that are activated by ACh and by nonhydrolyzable analogues of GTP (97). Subsequent experiments revealed that expressed GIRK1 channels are directly activated by the $\beta\gamma$ subunits of heterotrimeric G proteins (147), as has been clearly demonstrated for $I_{K(ACh)}$ (31, 109, 202). Although these results suggest that GIRK1 underlies $I_{K(ACh)}$, more recent work (95) proposes that $I_{K(ACh)}$ is a heteromultimer of GIRK and another related subunit CIR (cardiac inward rectifier) rather than a homomultimer of GIRK1 subunits.

The distinct sequences and proposed structures of ROMK1, IRK1, and GIRK suggest that inwardly rectifying $K^+$ channel $\alpha$ subunits constitute a new superfamily of ion channel genes (71, 96, 97). Consistent with this speculation, several laboratories have demonstrated that there are homologous IRK and GIRK subunits (94, 105, 114, 121, 137, 165, 171), and more recently, additional related subunits, BIR9, BIR10, and BIR11, have been cloned from rat brain (18). To facilitate comparison of clones identified in different laboratories and/or in different species, a more uniform terminology has been suggested (29): In this scheme, ROMK, IRK, GIRK, BIR10, and BIR9 subfamily members are referred to as Kir1.x, Kir2.x, Kir3.x, Kir4.x, and Kir5.x, respectively (Table 2). Unlike the Kv terminology for the voltage-gated $K^+$ channel $\alpha$ subunits, however, the Kir designators are only beginning to be widely used (44). By analogy to the Kv family of $K^+$ channel $\alpha$ subunits, it has been assumed that four subunits combine to form functional inwardly rectifying channels (96), although this has not been directly demonstrated.

## Kir Subunit Expression in the Mammalian Heart

Three homologous IRK subfamily members have now been cloned from mouse (121, 165), rat (94), and human (114, 137, 171) brain cDNA libraries. In terminology suggested by Chandy & Gutman (29), these are referred to as Kir2.1, Kir2.2, and Kir2.3 (44). Each has subsequently been cloned from or shown to be expressed in heart (79, 137, 145, 201) (Table 2). Heterologous expression of these subunits reveals inwardly rectifying $K^+$ channels with distinct single-channel conductances (22 pS for Kir2.1, 36 pS for Kir2.2, and 10 pS for Kir2.3) and kinetic properties (94, 96, 114, 121, 137, 165, 171). Several GIRK subfamily members have also been cloned from mouse brain (105), and recently a new member of the GIRK (Kir3) subfamily has been identified in heart (95). Although is is unclear if Kir4 or Kir5 subfamily members are expressed in heart, a novel ATP-sensitive inwardly rectifying $K^+$ channel subunit, termed $uK_{ATP}$, recently cloned from rat pancreas has been shown to be expressed in heart (75). The reported ATP sensitivity of this subunit (75) suggests that it may contribute to $I_{K(ATP)}$ (Table 2). The extent of Kir1, Kir2, Kir 3 (Kir4, Kir5), and Kir6 subfamily subunit heterogeneity in the heart and the role each plays in the formation of functional inwardly rectifying $K^+$ channels remain to be defined.

## ACCESSORY ($\beta$) SUBUNITS OF VOLTAGE-GATED $K^+$ CHANNELS

In addition to the pore-forming ($\alpha$) $K^+$ channel subunits, biochemical studies completed several years ago suggested that accessory $\beta$ subunits of brain voltage-gated K$^+$ channels of the Kv1 (122) and Kv2 (175) subfamilies also exist. By analogy to the functioning of accessory subunits of voltage-gated Na$^+$ and Ca$^{2+}$ channels, K$^+$ channel $\beta$ subunits were assumed to associate with the pore-forming $\alpha$ subunits and influence their properties (80). Two homologous Kv1 subfamily $\beta$ subunits, referred to as Kv$\beta_1$ and Kv$\beta_2$, have been cloned from brain (146). The deduced sequences of these clones revealed proteins of approximately 45 kDA (Kv$\beta_1$) and 40 kDA (Kv$\beta_2$), and the homology (85%) resides entirely in the C-terminus (146). Sequence analysis also revealed the lack of membrane-spanning domains and glycosylation sites (146), consistent with Kv$\beta_1$ and Kv$\beta_2$ being cytoplasmic proteins (80). Although these $\beta$ subunits do not show any sequence similarity to voltage-gated Na$^+$ or Ca$^{2+}$ channel $\beta$ subunits (80), they are homologous to the aldol-ketoreductase family of enzymes (119), a finding of unknown significance.

Coexpression of Kv$\beta_1$ with Kv1.1 increases the apparent rate of inactivation of expressed Kv1.1 currents (146). The finding that Kv$\beta_2$ is without effects on Kv1.1 suggests that the unique N-terminal domain of Kv$\beta_1$ underlies the functional inactivation observed on coexpression of this subunit. Another $\beta$ subunit, Kv$\beta_3$, recently cloned from ferret heart (120) and from human ventricular (47) and atrial (113) cDNA libraries, is highly homologous to Kv$\beta_1$ (100% in the C-terminal 329 amino acids and 25% in the N-terminal 79 amino acids), suggesting that they reflect alternative splice variants of the same gene (47, 113, 120). It is unclear if there are cardiac-specific variants of Kv$\beta_2$. In contrast to the findings with Kv$\beta_1$ (146), coexpression of Kv$\beta_3$ has no effect on the properties of expressed Kv1.1 currents (120). Coexpression of cardiac Kv$\beta_3$, however, does alter inactivation and deactivation of Kv1.4 (26, 113, 120) and the time- and voltage-dependent properties of Kv1.5 (47, 120). It is important to point out, however, that in spite of the cloning of Kv$\beta_3$ from heart and the interesting effects of Kv$\beta_3$ coexpression on Kv1.4 and Kv1.5, it is not known which K$^+$ channel $\alpha$ subunit(s) Kv$\beta_3$ associates with in the myocardium. In addition, the possibility that there are also $\beta$ subunits associated with Kv2 and/or Kv4 subfamily $\alpha$ subunits or with *eag* or Kir family members in the myocardium has not been explored.

## RELATIONSHIP BETWEEN CLONED SUBUNITS AND FUNCTIONAL MYOCARDIAL K$^+$ CHANNELS

The cloning of cardiac K$^+$ channel $\alpha$ and $\beta$ subunits has provoked much interest in determining which subunits contribute to the formation of the various types of K$^+$ currents/channels characterized electrophysiologically in myocardial cells (Table 1). Perhaps the simplest approach to exploring these relationships is to compare the time- and voltage-dependent properties and the pharmacological sensitivities of the K$^+$ currents formed on heterologous expression of the various cloned subunits (or combinations of subunits) with those of myocardial $K^+$ currents. Although not always, this approach has met with some success, and some clear insights have been provided (Table 2).

## minK ($I_{sK}$) Underlies $I_{Ks}$

Heterologous expression of $I_{sK}$ in *Xenopus* oocytes results in the expression of delayed, very slowly activating, noninactivating outward $K^+$ currents that closely resemble $I_{Ks}$ in guinea pig ventricular myocytes (57, 61, 185, 186). The pharmacological properties of expressed $I_{sK}$ and guinea pig ventricular $I_{Ks}$ are also very similar (22). In addition, it has been demonstrated that $I_{sK}$ protein is expressed in these cells (61). Taken together, these results argue that the minK protein underlies $I_{Ks}$ (Table 2) in guinea pig ventricular myocytes (22, 61, 185, 186) and suggest that $I_{sK}$ also underlies the currents referred to as $I_{Ks}$ in other species, including human.

## Kv1.5 Underlies $I_{ss}$ and $I_{sus}$

Heterologous expression of Kv1.5 yields 4-AP-sensitive rapidly activating, noninactivating outwardly rectifying $K^+$ currents that are quite similar to the rapidly activating, sustained component ($I_{sus}$ or $I_{ss}$) of the outward current in rat (19, 184) and human (182, 193, 194) atrial myocytes. In addition, Kv1.5 is expressed in rat and human myocytes at the RNA (43, 149, 170) and protein levels (11, 118), consistent with the hypothesis that Kv1.5 underlies $I_{sus}$ and $I_{ss}$ (11, 53, 118, 184, 194). The fact that the properties of guinea pig ventricular $I_{Kp}$s (8, 205) are similar to the atrial $I_{sus}/I_{ss}$ currents further suggests that Kv1.5 also underlies $I_{Kp}$ (Table 2).

## h-erg Underlies $I_{Kr}$

A quite different experimental strategy has resulted in the recent suggestion that *h-erg* forms the molecular basis of myocardial $I_{Kr}$. As discussed above, *h-erg* was cloned from a human hippocampal library and shown to map to human chromosome 7 (197). Molecular genetic analysis led to the identification of *h-erg* as the locus of one form of long QT syndrome, LQT2 (39). Interestingly, expression of *h-erg* in *Xenopus* oocytes reveals voltage-gated, $K^+$-selective channels that display marked inward rectification (154, 178). Therefore, the time- and voltage-dependent properties of expressed *h-erg* channels are similar to the cardiac current $I_{Kr}$ (154) that has been extensively characterized in guinea pig atrial and ventricular myocytes (10, 155, 156), as well as in human atrial (195), and dog, human, and rabbit ventricular (16, 107, 188, 189) cells, which suggests that *h-erg* underlies the formation of functional $I_{Kr}$ channels (Table 2). The detailed kinetic properties of expressed *h-erg* and endogenous $I_{Kr}$ channels, however, are not identical (154). Furthermore, expressed *h-erg* channels, although sensitive to lanthanum, are reportedly insensitive to class III antiarrhythmics such as E-4031 and dofetilide (154), and sensitivity to these agents is a hallmark of cardiac $I_{Kr}$ (25, 155, 156). Although these differences may reflect the effects of cellular environment, it is also possible that *h-erg* combines with other K$^+$ channel $\alpha$ and/or $\beta$ subunits to produce $I_{Kr}$ channels. Alternative experimental strategies will be necessary to test these hypotheses directly and to define the molecular composition of functional myocardial $I_{Kr}$ channels.

## Kv4.2 Underlies $I_{to}$

Attempts to define the subunits underlying cardiac $I_{to}$ channels have been confounded by the finding that heterologous expression of either Kv1.4 (181) or Kv4.2 (9, 17) reveals rapidly activating and inactivating K$^+$ currents similar to $I_{to}$. Recovery from steady-state inactivation of heterologously expressed Kv1.4 (181) or Kv4.2 (9, 17), however, is much slower than that of $I_{to}$ (4, 13, 14, 54, 199). Coexpression of either Kv1.2 or Kv1.5 with Kv1.4 increases the rate of recovery, which suggests that functional $I_{to}$ channels might be heteromultimeric, composed of Kv1.4 with Kv1.2 and/or Kv1.5 (139). However, the recovery rates for heteromeric Kv1.2-Kv1.4 and Kv1.4-Kv1.5 channels are also much slower than for myocardial $I_{to}$. Subsequent studies by Dixon & McKinnon (43) revealed that Kv4.2 message levels vary through the thickness of the ventricular wall in a manner similar to that seen for $I_{to}$ (32, 52, 63, 106, 108, 200), which suggests that Kv4.2 more likely underlies $I_{to}$ than Kv1.4.

In experiments aimed at determining the relationship between the various K$^+$ channel $\alpha$ subunits and the voltage-gated K$^+$ currents in rat cardiac myocytes (4, 18, 19), we exploited K$^+$ channel subunit-specific antibodies to examine the distributions of Kv $\alpha$ subunits in adult (11) and developing rat heart (203). These experiments, using both immunohistochemistry and Western blot analysis, revealed that Kv1.4 is barely detectable in the membranes of adult rat ventricular myocytes, which suggests that Kv1.4 does not contribute to rat ventricular $I_{to}$ (11). Kv4.2, on the other hand, is abundant in rat ventricular membranes, supporting the idea that Kv4.2 underlies $I_{to}$ (11, 43) (Table 2). Because Kv4.1 message levels are insignificant in adult rat ventricle (43), one can further speculate that $I_{to}$ is homomeric, composed of four copies of Kv4.2. It is possible, however, that there are accessory $\beta$ subunits associated with Kv4.2 in vivo that contribute to determining the properties of functional $I_{to}$ channels in rat ventricular myocytes. Experiments designed to test this hypothesis directly are clearly warranted. It is tempting to speculate that Kv4.2 also underlies $I_{to}$ in atrial and ventricular myocytes in other species. The similarities between the properties and the pharmacological sensitivities of rat ventricular $I_{to}$ (4, 84, 199) and $I_{to}$ channels of cat, dog, ferret, human, mouse, and rabbit clearly support this hypothesis (13, 14, 24, 63, 65, 70, 92, 106, 179, 180, 187, 199, 200). Nevertheless, to date it has not been demonstrated that either Kv4.2 (or other members of the *Shal*-subfamily) have been expressed in ventricular/atrial cells in these species. This possibility clearly warrants further investigation.

## $I_{K(ACh)}$ is a Heteromultimer of GIRK and CIR

Biochemical studies have also been exploited to explore the molecular composition of myocardial $I_{K(ACh)}$ channels. Following the cloning of GIRK1 (97), it was demonstrated that expressed GIRK1 channels can be modulated directly by the $\beta\gamma$ subunits of heteromeric G proteins (147), as has been clearly demonstrated for endogenous atrial $I_{K(ACh)}$ channels (31, 99, 109, 202). These observations are consistent with the hypothesis that GIRK1 underlies $I_{K(ACh)}$. Detailed comparison of the properties of expressed GIRK (Kir3.1; Table 2) with atrial $I_{K(ACh)}$ channels, however, revealed some subtle, but real, differences.

Speculating that these differences might reflect the presence of auxiliary or accessory subunits, Clapham and coworkers developed antibodies against GIRK1 and used these to immunoprecipitate $I_{K(ACh)}$ channels from isolated, purified bovine atrial membranes (95). These experiments revealed the presence of an additional subunit, which they referred to as CIR (cardiac inward rectifier), that coimmunoprecipitates with GIRK1 (95). In the Kir terminology suggested by Chandy & Gutman (29), CIR is referred to as Kir3.4 (44) (Table 2). Subsequent sequencing and cloning revealed CIR to be a 45-kDa protein that is identical (except for one amino acid) to rcKATP1, which was previously cloned from rat heart (5) and suggested to contribute to the formation of $I_{K(ATP)}$ channels. The sequence of this subunit, however, does not contain an obvious nucleotide-binding domain (5), and subsequent work has shown that heterologous expression of CIR does not result in the expression of currents that are modulated directly by ATP (95). Although these results indicate that $I_{K(ATP)}$ does not arise from homomultimeric assembly of CIR, it is certainly possible that CIR combines with other Kir $\alpha$ or $\beta$ subunits to give rise to functional $I_{K(ATP)}$ channels. More importantly, heterologous expression of GIRK1 (Kir3.1) with CIR (Kir3.4) reveals G protein–gated $K^+$ channels that are indistinguishable from native $I_{K(ACh)}$ channels (95), consistent with the suggestion that functional $I_{K(ACh)}$ channels are heteromultimers of Kir3.1 and Kir 3.4 (Table 2).

## SUMMARY

Electrophysiological studies have clearly demonstrated the presence of diverse types of $K^+$ channels in cardiac cells isolated from different species, as well as cardiac cells isolated from different regions of the heart in the same species. Molecular biological studies have revealed unexpected diversity of K$^+$ channel subunits, and several K$^+$ channel $\alpha$ and, more recently, $\beta$ subunits have now been cloned from or shown to be expressed in ferret, guinea pig, rat, and human myocardium. Comparison of the properties of the channels formed on heterologous expression of some of these subunits or combinations of subunits with those of endogenous cardiac K$^+$ channels has provided insights into the likely subunits contributing to the formation of some of the K$^+$ channels characterized in cardiac cells. As discussed above, this approach has led to the suggestion that $I_{sK}$ underlies $I_{Ks}$ and similarly to the postulate that Kv1.5 underlies rat and human atrial $I_{ss}/I_{sus}$, as well possibly, as guinea pig ventricular $I_{Kp}$. Although these suggestions are quite reasonable based on the available data, it is important to note that the molecular compositions of $I_{Ks}$ and $I_{ss}/I_{sus}$ channels have not been defined directly. Gleaning molecular insights by comparing the properties of heterologously expressed K$^+$ channel subunits and endogenous K$^+$ channels has proven to be more difficult in other cases, primarily because the properties of expressed and endogenous K$^+$ channels, although often similar, are not identical. Interpretation of the results from any expression system is complicated because it is possible that the oocytes/cell lines used in the expression experiments contain endogenous K$^+$ channel $\alpha$ and/or $\beta$ subunits that can co-assemble with the exogenous subunit. It is also difficult because posttranslational processing occurs differently in oocytes/cell lines than it does in cardiac myocytes. Adding to this, it is possible that more than one cloned subunit will display properties similar to the endogenous current, as was the case with Kv4.2 and Kv1.4 discussed above. It seems reasonable, therefore, that defining the molecular composition of the functional K$^+$ channels in myocardial cells will require a combination of physiological, molecular, immunohistochemical, and biochemical approaches. With the combination of these approaches, it seems certain that in the next several years cardiac physiologists will succeed in defining the molecular structures of the various types of K$^+$ channels expressed in myocardial cells. Once this goal is accomplished, it will be possible to explore the molecular mechanisms controlling the regulation and modulation of myocardial K$^+$ channel expression and functioning in great detail.

ACKNOWLEDGMENTS

We thank Colin Nichols for many helpful comments and discussions and for his careful and critical reading of this manuscript. Preparation of this review and work from this laboratory have been supported by the National Heart, Lung, and Blood Institute of the National Institutes of Health (HL-34161); by the Monsanto/Searle/Washington University Biomedical Research Agreement; and by the American Heart Association National Office and Missouri Affiliate.

JMN is an Established Investigator of the American Heart Association and DMB is the recipient of an American Heart Association Predoctoral Fellowship.

Any *Annual Review* chapter, as well as any article cited in an *Annual Review* chapter, may be purchased from the Annual Reviews Preprints and Reprints service. 1-800-347-8007; 415-259-5017; email: arpr@class.org

## Literature Cited

1. Anumonwo JMB, Freeman LC, Kwok WM, Kass RS. 1991. Potassium channels in the heart: electrophysiology and pharmacological regulation. *Cardiovasc. Drug Rev.* 9:299–316
2. Anumonwo JMB, Freeman LC, Kwok WM, Kass RS. 1992. Delayed rectification in single cells isolated from guinea pig sinoatrial node. *Am. J. Physiol.* 262:H921–25
3. Antzelevitch C, Sicouri S, Lukas A, Nesterenko VV, Liu D-W, Di Diego JM. 1994. Regional differences in the electrophysiology of ventricular cells: physiological implications. In *Cardiac Electrophysiology: From Cell To Bedside,* ed, DP Zipes, J Jalife, pp. 228–45. Philadelphia: Saunders
4. Apkon M, Nerbonne JM. 1991. Characterization of two distinct depolarization-activated $K^+$ currents in isolated adult rat ventricular myocytes. *J. Gen. Physiol.* 97:973–1011
5. Ashford MLJ, Bond CT, Blair TA, Adelman JP. 1994. Cloning and functional expression of a rat heart KATP channel. *Nature* 370:456–59
6. Attali B, Guillemare E, Lesage F, Honore E, Romey G, et al. 1993. The protein $I_{SK}$ is a dual activator of $K^+$ and $Cl^-$ channels. *Nature* 365:850–52
7. Babenko AP, Samoilov VO, Kazantseva ST, Shevchenko YL. 1992. ATP-sensitive $K^+$ channels in the human ventricular cardiomyocytes membrane. *FEBS Lett.* 313:148–50
8. Backx PH, Marban E. 1993. Background potassium current active during the plateau of the action potential in guinea pig ventricular myocytes. *Circ. Res.* 72:890–900
9. Baldwin TJ, Tsaur M-L, Lopez GA, Jan YN, Jan LY. 1991. Characterization of a mammalian cDNA for an inactivating voltage-sensitive $K^+$ channel. *Neuron* 7:471–83
10. Balser JR, Bennett PB, Roden DM. 1990. Time dependent outward currents in guinea pig ventricular myocytes: gating kinetics of the delayed rectifier. *J. Gen. Physiol.* 96:835–63
11. Barry DM, Trimmer JS, Merlie JP, Nerbonne JM. 1995. Differential expression of voltage-gated $K^+$ channel subunits in adult rat heart: relationship to functional $K^+$ channels. *Circ. Res.* 77:361–69
12. Benndorf K. 1988. Three types of single K channels contribute to the transient outward current in myocardial mouse cells. *Biochim. Biomed. Acta* 47:401–16
13. Benndorf K, Markwardt F, Nilius B. 1987. Two types of transient outward currents in cardiac ventricular cells of mice. *Pflügers Arch.* 409:641–43
14. Benndorf K, Nilius B. 1988. Properties of an early outward current in single cells of the mouse ventricle. *Gen. Physiol. Biophys.* 7:449–66
15. Benz I, Kohlhardt M. 1992. Differential sensitivity of cardiac $K^+(ATP)$ channels to guanine nucleotides. *Pflügers Arch.* 21:299–302
16. Beuckelmann DJ, Näbauer M, Erdmann E. 1993. Alterations in $K^+$ currents in isolated human ventricular myocytes from patients with terminal heart failure. *Circ. Res.* 73:379–85
17. Blair TA, Roberds SL, Tamkun MM, Hartshorne RP. 1991. Functional characterization of RK5, a voltage-gated $K^+$ channel cloned from the rat cardiovascular system. *FEBS. Lett.* 295:211–13
18. Bond CT, Pessia M, Xia X-M, Lagrutta A, Kavanaugh MP, Adelman JP. 1994. Cloning and expression of a family of inward rectifier potassium channels. *Receptors Channels* 2:183–91
19. Boyle WA, Nerbonne JM. 1992. Two functionally distinct 4-aminopyridine-sensitive outward $K^+$ currents in adult rat atrial myocytes. *J. Gen. Physiol.* 100:1047–61
20. Breitwieser GE, Szabo G. 1985. Uncoupling of cardiac muscarinic and β-adrenergic receptors from ion channels by

a guanine nucleotide analogue. *Nature* 317:538–40

21. Brüggemann A, Pardo LA, Stühmer W, Pongs O. 1993. *Ether-a-go-go* encodes a voltage-gated channel permeable to K⁺ and Ca²⁺ and modulated by cAMP. *Nature* 365:445–48

22. Busch AE, Malloy K, Groh WJ, Varnum MD, Adelman JP, Maylie J. 1994. The novel class III antiarrhythmics NE-10064 and NE-10133 inhibit I$_{sK}$ channels expressed in *Xenopus* oocytes and I$_{Ks}$ in guinea pig ventricular myocytes. *Biochem. Biophys. Res. Commun.* 202:265–70

23. Butler A, Wei A, Baker K, Salkoff L. 1989. A family of putative potassium channel genes in *Drosophila*. *Science* 243:943–47

24. Campbell DL, Rasmusson RL, Comer MB, Strauss, HC. 1993. The calcium-independent transient outward potassium current in isolated ferret right ventricular myocytes. I. Basic characterization, and kinetic analysis. *J. Gen. Physiol.* 101:571–601

25. Carmeliet E. 1992. Voltage- and time-dependent block of the delayed K⁺ current in cardiac myocytes by dofetilide. *J. Pharmacol. Exp. Ther.* 262:809–17

26. Castellino RC, Morales MJ, Strauss HC, Rasmusson RL. 1995. Time- and voltage-dependent modulation of a Kv1.4 channel by a β subunit (Kvβ3) cloned from ferret ventricle. *Am. J. Physiol.* 38:H385–91

27. Chandy KG. 1991. Simplified gene nomenclature. *Nature* 352:26

28. Chandy KG, Gutman GA. 1995. Voltage-gated K⁺ channels. In *Handbook of Receptors and Channels: Ligand and Voltage-Gated Channels*, ed, RA North, pp. 1–71. Boca Raton, FL: CRC Press

29. Chandy KG, Gutman GA. 1995. Nomenclature for mammalian potassium channel genes. *Trends Pharmacol. Sci.* 14:434–35

30. Christie MJ, North RA, Osborne PB, Douglass J, Adelman JP. 1990. Heteropolymeric potassium channels expressed in *Xenopus* oocytes from cloned subunits. *Neuron* 2:405–11

31. Clapham DE, Neer EJ. 1993. New roles for G-protein βγ-dimers in transmembrane signalling. *Nature* 365:403–6

32. Clark RB, Bouchard RA, Salinas-Stefanson E, Sanchez-Chalupa J, Giles WR. 1993. Heterogeneity of action potential waveforms and potassium currents in rat ventricle. *Cardiovasc. Res.* 27:1795–99

33. Clark RB, Giles WR, Imaizumi Y. 1988. Properties of the transient outward current in rabbit atrial cells. *J. Physiol.* 405:147–68

34. Comer MB, Campbell DL, Rasmusson RL, Lamson DR, Morales MJ, et al. 1994. Cloning and characterization of an I$_{to}$-like potassium channel from ferret ventricle. *Am. J. Physiol.* 267:H1388–95

35. Coraboeuf E, Carmeliet E. 1982. Existence of two transient outward currents in sheep cardiac Purkinje fibers. *Pflügers Arch.* 392:352–59

36. Coraboeuf E, Nargeot J. 1993. Electrophysiology of human cardiac cells. *Cardiovasc. Res.* 27:1713–25

37. Covarrubias M, Wei A, Salkoff L. 1991. *Shaker, Shal, Shab,* and *Shaw* express independent K⁺ current systems. *Neuron* 7:763–73

38. Curran ME, Landis GM, Keating MT. 1992. Molecular cloning, characterization, and genomic localization of a human potassium channel gene. *Genomics* 12:729–37

39. Curran ME, Splawski I, Timothy KW, Vincent GM, Green ED, Keating MT. 1995. A molecular basis for cardiac arrhythmia: *herg* mutations cause long QT syndrome. *Cell* 80:795–803

40. Dascal N, Lim NF, Schriebmayer W, Wang W, Davidson N, Lester HA. 1993. Expression of an atrial G-protein-activated potassium channel in *Xenopus* oocytes. *Proc. Natl. Acad. Sci. USA* 90:6596–600

41. Deck KA, Trautwein W. 1964. Ionic currents in cardiac excitation. *Pflügers Arch.* 280:63–80

42. Di Diego JM, Antzelevitch C. 1995. Electrophysiological distinctions between right and left ventricular epicardium in the canine heart. *Am. J. Physiol.* Submitted

43. Dixon JE, McKinnon D. 1994 Quantitative analysis of mRNA expression in atrial and ventricular muscle of rats. *Circ. Res.* 75:252–60

44. Doupnik CA, Davidson N, Lester HA. 1995. The inward rectifier potassium channel family. *Curr. Opin. Neurobiol.* 5:268–77

45. Drysdale R, Warmke J, Kreber R, Ganetsky B. 1991. Molecular characterization of *eag*: a gene affecting potassium channels in *Drosophila melanogaster*. *Genetics* 127:497–505

46. Dudel J, Peper K, Rudel R, Trautwein W. 1967. The dynamic chloride component of membrane current in Purkinje fibers. *Pflügers Arch.* 295:197–212

47. England SK, Uebele VN, Shear H, Kodali K, Bennett PB, Tamkun MM. 1995. Characterization of a novel K⁺ channel

β subunit expressed in human heart. *Proc. Natl. Acad. Sci. USA.* 92:6309–13

48. Escande D, Coulombe A, Faivre JF, Deroubaix E, Coraboeuf E. 1987. Two types of transient outward currents in adult human atrial cells. *Am. J. Physiol.* 252:H142–48

49. Escande D, Loisance D, Planche C, Coraboeuf E. 1985. Age-related changes of the action potential plateau shape in isolated human atrial fibers. *Am. J. Physiol.* 249:H843–50

50. Faivre J-F, Findlay I. 1990. Action potential duration and activation of ATP-sensitive potassium current in isolated guinea-pig ventricular myocytes. *Biochim. Biophys. Acta* 1029:167–72

51. Fakler B, Brändle U, Glowatzki E, König C, Bond C, Adelman JP, Zenner H-P, Ruppersberg JP. 1994. A structural determinant of differential sensitivity of cloned inward-rectifier K⁺ channels to intracellular spermine. *FEBS Lett.* 356:199–203

52. Fedida D, Giles WR. 1991. Regional variations in action potentials and transient outward current in myocytes isolated from rabbit left ventricle. *J. Physiol.* 442:191–209

53. Fedida D, Wible B, Wang Z, Fermini B, Faust F, et al. 1993. Identity of a novel delayed rectifier current from human heart with a cloned K⁺ channel current. *Circ. Res.* 73:210–16

54. Fermini B, Wang Z, Duan D, Nattel S. 1992. Differences in rate dependence of the transient outward current in rabbit and human atrium. *Am. J. Physiol.* 263:H1747–54

55. Ficker E, Tagliatella M, Wible BA, Henley CM, Brown AM. 1994. Spermine and spermidine as gating molecules for inward rectifier K⁺ currents. *Science* 266:1068–72

56. Findlay I. 1987. ATP-sensitive K⁺ channels in rat ventricular myocytes are blocked and inactivated by internal divalent cations. *Pflügers Arch.* 410:313–20

57. Folander K, Smith JS, Antanavage J, Bennett C, Stein RB, Swanson R. 1990. Cloning and expression of the delayed rectifier I_sK channel from neonatal rat heart and diethylstilbestrol-primed rat uterus. *Proc. Natl. Acad. Sci. USA* 87:2975–79

58. Follmer CH, Colatsky TJ. 1990. Block of delayed rectifier potassium current, I_K, by flecainide and E-4031 in cat ventricular myocytes. *Circulation* 82:289–93

59. Fozzard HA, Hiraoka M. 1973. The positive dynamic current and its inactivation properties in cardiac Purkinje fibres. *J. Physiol.* 234:569–86

60. Freeman LC, Kass RS. 1993. Delayed rectifier potassium channels in ventricle and sinoatrial node of guinea pig: molecular and regulatory properties. *Cardiovasc. Drugs Ther.* 7:627–35

61. Freeman LC, Kass RS. 1993. Expression of a minimal K⁺ channel protein in mammalian cells and immunolocalization in guinea pig heart. *Circ. Res.* 73:968–73

62. Furukawa T, Kimura S, Furukawa N, Bassett AL, Myerburg RJ. 1992. Potassium rectifier currents differ in myocytes of endocardial and epicardial origin. *Circ. Res.* 70:91–103

63. Furukawa T, Myerburg RJ, Furukawa N, Bassett AL, Kimura S. 1990. Differences in transient outward currents of feline endocardial and epicardial myocytes. *Circ. Res.* 67:1287–91

64. Giles WR, Clark RB, Braun A. 1995. Ca²⁺-independent transient outward current in mammalian heart. In *Molecular Physiology and Pharmacology of Cardiac Ion Channels and Transporters,* ed. M Morad, Y Kurachi, Y Hosoda, W Trautwein. Amsterdam: Kluwer Academic. In press

65. Giles WR, Imaizumi Y. 1988. Comparison of potassium currents in rabbit atrial and ventricular cells. *J. Physiol.* 405:123–45

66. Giles WR, van Ginneken AC. 1985. A transient outward current in isolated cells from the crista terminalis of rabbit heart. *J. Physiol.* 368:243–64

67. Gross GJ, Burke RP, Castle NA. 1995. Characterisation of transient outward current in young human myocytes. *Cardiovasc. Res.* 29:112–17

68. Guy HR, Durell SR, Warmke J, Drysdale R, Ganetsky B. 1991. Similarities in amino acid sequence of *Drosophila* eag and cyclic nucleotide-gated channels. *Science* 254:730

69. Heidbüchel H, Vereecke J, Carmeliet E. 1990. Three different potassium channels in human atria. Contribution to the basal potassium conductance. *Circ. Res.* 66:1277–86

70. Hiraoka M, Kawano S. 1989. Calcium-sensitive and insensitive transient outward current in rabbit ventricular myocytes. *J. Physiol.* 410:187–212

71. Ho K, Nichols CG, Lederer WJ, Lytton J, Vasselev PM, et al. 1993. Cloning and expression of an inwardly rectifying ATP-regulated potassium channel. *Nature* 362:31–38

72. Horie M, Hayashi S, Kawai C. 1990. Two types of delayed rectifying K⁺

channels in atrial cells of guinea pig heart. *Jpn. J. Physiol.* 40:479–90

73. Horie M, Irisawa H, Noma A. 1987. Voltage-dependent magnesium block of adenosine-triphosphate-sensitive potassium channel in guinea-pig ventricular cells. *J. Physiol.* 387:251–72

74. Hume JR, Uehara A. 1985. Ionic basis of the different action potential configurations of single guinea-pig atrial and ventricular myocytes. *J. Physiol.* 368:525–44

75. Inagaki N, Tsuura Y, Namba N, Masuda K, Gonoi T, et al. 1995. Cloning and functional characterization of a novel ATP-sensitive potassium channel ubiquitously expressed in rat tissues, including pancreatic islets, pituitary, skeletal muscle and heart. *J. Biol. Chem.* 270:5691–94

76. Inoue M, Imanaga I. 1993. Masking of A-type K⁺ channel in guinea pig cardiac cells by extracellular $Ca^{2+}$. *Am. J. Physiol.* 264:C1434–38

77. Isacoff EY, Jan YN, Jan LY. 1990. Evidence for the formation of heteromultimeric potassium channels in *Xenopus* oocytes. *Nature* 345:530–34

78. Ishihara K, Mitsuiye T, Noma A, Takano M. 1989. The $Mg^{2+}$ block and intrinsic gating underlying inward rectification of the K⁺ current in guinea pig cardiac myocytes. *J. Physiol.* 419:297–320

79. Ishii K, Yamagishi T, Taira N. 1994. Cloning and functional expression of a cardiac inward rectifier K⁺ channel. *FEBS Lett.* 338:107–11

80. Isom LL, DeJongh KS, Catterall WA. 1994. Auxiliary subunits of voltage-gated ion channels. *Neuron* 12:1183–94

81. Ito H, Tung RT, Sugimoto T, Kobayashi I, Takahashi K, et al. 1992. On the mechanism of G protein βγ subunit activation of the muscarinic K⁺ channel in guinea pig atrial cell membrane. *J. Gen. Physiol.* 99:961–83

82. Jan LY, Jan YN. 1992. Structural elements involved in specific K⁺ channel functions. *Annu. Rev. Physiol.* 54:537–55

83. Josephson IR, Brown AM. 1986. Inwardly rectifying single-channel and whole cell K⁺ currents in rat ventricular myocytes. *J. Membr. Biol.* 94:19–35

84. Josephson IR, Sanchez-Chapula J, Brown AM. 1984. Early outward current in rat single ventricular cells. *Circ. Res.* 54:157–62

85. Kakei M, Noma A. 1984. Adenosine-5′-triphosphate-sensitive single potassium channel in the atrioventricular node cell of the rabbit heart. *J. Physiol.* 352:265–84

86. Kakei M, Noma A, Shibasaki T. 1985. Properties of adenosine-triphosphate-regulated potassium channels in guinea-pig ventricular cells. *J. Physiol.* 363:441–62

87. Kamb A, Tseng-Crank J, Tanouye MA. 1988. Multiple components of the *Drosophila Shaker* gene may contribute to potassium channel diversity. *Neuron* 1:421–30

88. Kaplan WD, Trout WE. 1969. The behavior of four neurological mutations of *Drosophila. Genetics* 61:399–409

89. Kenyon JL, Gibbons WR. 1979. Influence of chloride, potassium, and tetraethylammonium on the early outward current of sheep cardiac Purkinje fibers. *J. Gen. Physiol.* 73:117–38

90. Kenyon JL, Gibbons WR. 1979. 4-Aminopyridine and the early outward current of sheep cardiac Purkinje fibers. *J. Gen. Physiol.* 73:139–57

91. Kirsch GE, Codina J, Birnbaumer L, Brown AM. 1990. Coupling of ATP-sensitive K⁺ channels to A1 receptors by G proteins in rat ventricular myocytes. *Am. J. Physiol.* 28:H820–26

92. Konarzewska H, Peeters GA, Sanguinetti MC. 1995. Repolarizing K⁺ currents in non-failing human hearts: similarities between right-septal subendocardial and left epicardial ventricular myocytes. *Circulation* 92:1179–87

93. Koumi S-I, Wasserstrom JA. 1994. Acetylcholine-sensitive muscarinic K⁺ channels in mammalian ventricular myocytes. *Am. J. Physiol.* 266:H1812–21

94. Koyama H, Morishige K-I, Takahashi N, Zanelli JS, Fass DN, Kurachi Y. 1994. Molecular cloning, functional expression and localization of a novel inward rectifier potassium channel in the rat brain. *FEBS Lett.* 341:303–7

95. Krapivinsky G, Gordon EA, Wickman K, Velimiroviç B, Krapivinsky L, Clapham DE. 1995. The G-protein-gated atrial K⁺ channel $I_{KACh}$ is a heteromultimer of two inwardly rectifying K⁺ channel proteins. *Nature* 374:135–41

96. Kubo Y, Baldwin T, Jan YN, Jan LY. 1993. Primary structure and functional expression of a mouse inward rectifier potassium channel. *Nature* 362:127–33

97. Kubo Y, Reuveny E, Slesinger PA, Jan YN, Jan LY. 1993. Primary structure and functional expression of a rat G-protein-coupled muscarinic potassium channel. *Nature* 364:802–6

98. Kurachi Y. 1985. Voltage-dependent activation of the inward rectifier potassium channel in the ventricular cell membrane

of guinea pig heart. *J. Physiol.* 366:365–85

99. Kurachi Y. 1995. G protein regulation of cardiac muscarinic potassium channel. *Am. J. Physiol.*

100. Kurachi Y, Nakajima T, Sugimoto T. 1986. Acetylcholine activation of $K^+$ channels in cell-free membrane of atrial cells. *Am. J. Physiol.* 251:H681–84

101. Kurachi Y, Nakajima T, Sugimoto T. 1986. On the mechanism of activation of muscarinic $K^+$ channels by adenosine in isolated atrial cells: involvement of GTP-binding proteins. *Pflügers Arch* 407:264–74

102. Kurachi Y, Tung RT, Ito H, Nakajima T. 1992. G-protein activation of cardiac muscarinic $K^+$ channels. *Prog. Neurobiol.* 39:229–46

103. Lederer WJ, Nichols CG, Smith GL. 1989. The mechanism of early contractile failure of isolated rat ventricular myocytes subjected to complete metabolic inhibition. *J. Physiol.* 413:329–49

104. Lesage F, Attali B, Lazdunski M, Barhanin J. 1992. $I_{sK}$, a slowly activating voltage-sensitive $K^+$ channel. Characterization of multiple cDNAs and gene organization in the mouse. *FEBS. Lett.* 301:168–72

105. Lesage F, Duprat F, Fink M, Guillemare E, Coppola T, et al. 1994. Cloning provided evidence for a family of inward rectifier and G-protein coupled $K^+$ channels in the brain. *FEBS Lett.* 353:37–42

106. Litovsky SH, Antzelevitch C. 1988. Transient outward current prominent in canine ventricular epicardium but not endocardium. *Circ. Res.* 72:1092–103

107. Liu D-W, Antzelevitch C. 1995. Characterisics of the delayed rectifier current ($I_{Kr}$ and $I_{Ks}$) in canine ventricular epicardial, midmyocardial, and endocardial myocytes. *Circ. Res.* 76:351–65

108. Liu D-W, Gintant GA, Antzelevitch C. 1993. Ionic basis for electrophysiological distinctions among epicardial, midmyocardial and epicardial myocytes. *Circ. Res.* 72:671–87

109. Logothetis DE, Kurachi Y, Galper J, Neer EJ, Clapham DE. 1987. The βγ subunits of GTP-binding proteins activate the muscarinic $K^+$ channel in heart. *Nature* 325:321–26

110. Lopatin AN, Makhina EN, Nichols CG. 1994. Potassium channel block by cytoplasmic polyamines as the mechanism of intrinsic rectification. *Nature* 372:366–69

111. Ludwig J, Terlau H, Wunder F, Brüggemann A, Pardo LA, et al. 1994. Functional expression of a rat homologue of the voltage-gated *ether-a-go-go* potas-sium channel reveals differences in selectivity and activation kinetics between the *Drosophila* channel and its mammalian counterpart. *EMBO J.* 13:4451–58

112. MacKinnon R. 1991. Determination of the subunit stoichiometry of a voltage-activated potassium channel. *Nature* 350:232–35

113. Majumder K, DeBiasi M, Wang Z, Wible B. 1995. Molecular cloning and functional expression of a novel potassium channel β subunit from human atrium. *FEBS Lett.* 361:13–16

114. Makhina EN, Kelly AJ, Lopatin AN, Mercer RW, Nichols CG. 1994. Cloning and expression of a novel human brain inward rectifier potassium channel. *J. Biol. Chem.* 269:20468–74

115. Matsuda H. 1988. Open-state substructure of inwardly rectifying potassium channels revealed by magnesium block in guinea pig heart cells. *J. Physiol.* 397:237–58

116. Matsuda H, Matsuura H, Noma A. 1989. Triple-barrel structure of inwardly rectifying $K^+$ channels revealed by $Cs^+$ and $Rb^+$ block in guinea pig heart cells. *J. Physiol.* 413:139–57

117. Matsuda H, Saigusa A, Irisawa H. 1987. Ohmic conductance through the inwardly rectifying K channel and blocking by internal $Mg^{2+}$. *Nature* 325:156–59

118. Mays DJ, Foose JM, Philipson LH, Tamkun MM. 1995. Localization of the Kv1.5 $K^+$ channel protein in explanted cardiac tissue. *J. Clin. Invest.* 96:282–92

119. McCormack T, McCormack K. 1994. *Shaker* $K^+$ channel beta subunits belong to an NAD(P)H-dependent oxidoreductase superfamily. *Cell* 79:1133–35

120. Morales MJ, Castellino RC, Crews AL, Rasmusson RL, Strauss HC. 1995. A novel β subunit increases the rate of inactivation of specific voltage-gated potassium channel α subunits. *J. Biol. Chem.* 270:6272–77

121. Morishige K-I, Takahashi N, Jahangir A, Yamada M, Koyama H, et al. 1994. Molecular cloning and functional expression of a novel brain-specific inward rectifier potassium channel. *FEBS Lett.* 346:251–56

122. Muniz ZM, Parcej DN, Dolly JO. 1992. Characterization of monoclonal antibodies against voltage-dependent $K^+$ channels raised using α-dendrotoxin acceptors purified from bovine brain. *Biochemistry* 31:12297-303

123. Murai T, Kakizuka A, Takumi T, Ohkubo H, Nakanishi S. 1989. Molecular cloning and sequence analysis of human

genomic DNA encoding a novel membrane protein which exhibits slowly activating potassium channel activity. *Biochem. Biophys. Res. Commun.* 61: 176–81

124. Nakayama T, Irisawa H. 1985. Transient outward current carried by potassium and sodium in quiescent atrioventricular node cells of rabbits. *Circ. Res.* 57:65–73

125. Nichols CG, Lederer WJ. 1991. The mechanism of $K_{ATP}$ channel inhibition by ATP. *J. Gen. Physiol.* 97:1095–98

126. Nichols CG, Lederer WJ. 1991. Adenosine triphosphate-sensitive potassium channel in the cardiovascular system. *Am. J. Physiol.* 261:H1675–86

127. Nichols CG, Lederer WJ, Cannell MB. 1991. ATP dependence of $K_{ATP}$ channel kinetics in isolated membrane patches from rat ventricle. *Biophys. J.* 60:1164–77

128. Nichols CG, Ripoll C, Lederer WJ. 1991. ATP-sensitive potassium channel modulation of the guinea pig ventricular action potential and contraction. *Circ. Res.* 68:280–87

129. Noble D, Tsien RW. 1969. Outward membrane currents activated in the plateau range of potentials in cardiac Purkinje fibres. *J. Physiol.* 200:205–31

130. Noma A. 1983. ATP-regulated K⁺ channels in cardiac muscle. *Nature* 305:147–48

131. Noma A, Nakayama T, Kurachi Y, Irisawa H. 1984. Resting K conductances in pacemaker and non-pacemaker heart cells of the rabbit. *Jpn. J. Physiol.* 34:245–54

132. Noma A, Peper K, Trautwein W. 1979. Acetylcholine-induced potassium current fluctuations in the rabbit sino-atrial node. *Pflügers Arch.* 381:255–62

133. Noma A, Trautwein W. 1978. Relaxation of the ACh-induced potassium current in the rabbit sinoatrial node cell. *Pflügers Arch.* 377:193–200

134. Oliva C, Cohen IS, Pennefather P. 1990. The mechanism of rectification of $I_{K1}$ in canine Purkinje myocytes. *J. Gen. Physiol.* 96:299–318

135. Papazian DM, Schwarz TL, Temple BL, Jan YN, Jan LY. 1987. Cloning of genomic and complementary DNA from *Shaker,* a putative potassium channel gene from *Drosophila. Science* 237:749–53

136. Paulmichl M, Nasmith P, Hellmiss R, Reed K, Boyle WA, et al. 1991. Cloning and expression of a cardiac delayed rectifier potassium channel RAK. *Proc. Natl. Acad. Sci. USA* 88:7892–95

137. Perier F, Radeke CM, Vandenberg CA.

138. 1994. Primary structure and characterization of a small-conductance inwardly rectifying potassium channel from human hippocampus. *Proc. Natl. Acad. Sci. USA* 91:6240–44

138. Pfaffinger PJ, Martin JM, Hunter DD, Nathanson NM, Hille B. 1985. GTP-binding proteins couple cardiac muscarinic receptors to a K channel. *Nature* 317:536–38

139. Po S, Roberds S, Snyders DJ, Tamkun MM, Bennett PB. 1993. Heteromultimeric assembly of human potassium channels. Molecular basis of a transient outward current? *Circ. Res.* 72:1326–36

140. Po S, Snyders DJ, Baker R, Tamkun MM, Bennett PB. 1992. Functional expression of an inactivating potassium channel cloned from human heart. *Circ. Res.* 71:732–36

141. Pongs O. 1992. Molecular biology of voltage-dependent potassium channels. *Physiol. Rev.* 72:S69–88

142. Pongs O. 1993. Structure-function studies on the pore of potassium channels. *J. Membr. Biol.* 136:1–8

143. Pongs O, Kecskemethy N, Muller R, Krah-Jentgens I, Baumann A, et al. 1988. *Shaker* encodes a family of putative potassium channel proteins in the nervous system. *EMBO J.* 7:1087–96

144. Qin D, Takano M, Noma A. 1989. Kinetics of ATP-sensitive K⁺ channel revealed with oil-gate concentration jump method. *Am. J. Physiol.* 257: H1624–33

145. Raab-Graham KF, Radeke CM, Vandenberg CA. 1994. Molecular cloning and expression of a human heart inward rectifier potassium channel. *Neuro. Rep.* 5:2501–5

146. Rettig J, Heinemann SH, Wunder F, Lorra C, Parcej DN, et al. 1994. Inactivation properties of voltage-gated K⁺ channels altered by presence of β-subunit. *Nature* 369:289–94

147. Reuveny E, Slesinger PA, Inglese J, Morales JM, Iñiguez-Lluhi JA, et al. 1994. Activation of the cloned muscarinic potassium channel by G protein beta-gamma subunits. *Nature* 370:143–46

148. Roberds SL, Knoth KM, Po S, Blair TA, Bennett PB, et al. 1993. Molecular biology of the voltage-gated potassium channels of the cardiovascular system. *J. Cardiovasc. Electrophysiol.* 4:68–80

149. Roberds SL, Tamkun MM. 1991. Cloning and tissue-specific expression of five voltage-gated potassium channel cDNAS expressed in rat heart. *Proc. Natl. Acad. Sci. USA* 88:1798–802

150. Ruppersberg JP, Schroter KH, Sakmann

B, Stocker M, Sewing S, Pongs O. 1990. Heteromultimeric channels formed by rat brain potassium-channel proteins. *Nature* 345:535–37

151. Sakmann B, Noma A, Trautwein W. 1983. Acetylcholine activation of single muscarinic $K^+$ channels in isolated pacemaker cells of the mammalian heart. *Nature* 303:250–53

152. Sakmann B, Trube G. 1984. Conductance properties of single inwardly rectifying potassium channels in ventricular cells from guinea-pig heart. *J. Physiol.* 347:641–57

153. Salkoff L, Baker K, Butler A, Covarrubias M, Pak MV, Wei A. 1992. An essential set of $K^+$ channels conserved in flies, mice and men. *Trends Neurosci.* 15:161–66

154. Sanguinetti MC, Jiang C, Curran ME, Keating MT. 1995. A mechanistic link between an inherited and an acquired cardiac arrhythmia: *HERG* encodes the $I_{Kr}$ potassium channel. *Cell* 81:299–307

155. Sanguinetti MC, Jurkiewicz NK. 1990. Two components of cardiac delayed rectifier $K^+$ current. *J. Gen. Physiol.* 96:195–215

156. Sanguinetti MC, Jurkiewicz NK. 1991. Delayed rectifier outward $K^+$ current is composed of two currents in guinea pig atrial cells. *Am. J. Physiol.* 260:H393–99

157. Sanguinetti MC, Jurkiewicz NK. 1992. Role of external $Ca^{2+}$ and $K^+$ in gating of cardiac delayed rectifier $K^+$ currents. *Pflügers Arch.* 420:180–86

158. Schwarz TL, Temple BL, Papazian DM, Jan YN, Jan LY. 1988. Multiple potassium-channel components are produced by alternative splicing at the *Shaker* locus in *Drosophila*. *Nature* 331:137–42

159. Sheng M, Liao YJ, Jan YN, Jan LY. 1993. Presynaptic A-current based on heteromultimeric $K^+$ channels detected in vivo. *Nature* 365:72–75

160. Shibasaki T. 1987. Conductance and kinetics of delayed rectifier potassium channels in nodal cells of the rabbit heart. *J. Physiol.* 387:227–50

161. Shibata EF, Drury T, Refsum H, Aldrete V, Giles W. 1989. Contributions of a transient outward current to repolarization in human atrium. *Am. J. Physiol.* 257:H1773–81

162. Shimoni Y, Clark RB, Giles WR. 1992. Role of an inwardly rectifying potassium current in rabbit ventricular action potential. *J. Physiol.* 448:709–27

163. Soejima M, Noma A. 1984. Mode of regulation of the ACh-sensitive K-channel by the muscarinic receptor in rabbit atrial cells. *Pflügers Arch.* 400:424–31

164. Swanson R, Folander K, Antanavage J, Smith J. 1991. The $I_{sK}$ gene is expressed in the human heart. *Biophys. J.* 59:452a (Abst.)

165. Takahashi N, Morishige K-I, Jahangir A, Yamada M, Findlay I, et al. 1994. Molecular cloning and functional expression of cDNA encoding a second class of inward rectifier potassium channels in the mouse brain. *J. Biol. Chem.* 269:23274–79

166. Takano M, Noma A. 1993. The ATP-sensitive $K^+$ channel. *Prog. Neurobiol.* 41:21–30

167. Takano M, Qin D, Noma A. 1990. ATP-dependent decay and recovery of $K^+$ channels in guinea pig cardiac myocytes. *Am. J. Physiol.* 258:H45–50

168. Takumi T, Moriyoshi K, Aramori Y, Ishii T, Oiki S, et al. 1991. Alteration of channel activities and gating by mutations of slow $I_{sK}$ potassium channel. *J. Biol. Sci.* 266:22192–98

169. Takumi T, Ohkubo H, Nakinishi S. 1988. Cloning of a membrane protein that induces a slow voltage-gated potassium current. *Science* 242:1042–45

170. Tamkun MM, Knoth KM, Walbridge JA, Kroemer H, Roden DM, Glover DM. 1991. Molecular cloning and characterization of two voltage-gated $K^+$ channel cDNAs from human ventricle. *FASEB J.* 5:331–37

171. Tang W, Yang XC. 1994. Cloning of a novel human brain inward rectifier potassium channel and its functional expression in *Xenopus* oocytes. *FEBS Lett.* 348:239–43

172. Tempel BL, Papazian DM, Schwarz TL, Jan YN, Jan LY. 1987. Sequence of a probable potassium channel component encoded at the *Shaker* locus in *Drosophila*. *Science* 237:770–74

173. Terzic A, Jahangir A, Kurachi Y. 1995. Cardiac ATP-sensitive $K^+$ channels: regulation by intracellular nucleotides and potassium channel opening drugs. *Am. J. Physiol.* 38:C525–45

174. Timpe LC, Schwarz TL, Temple BL, Papazian DM, Jan YN, Jan LY. 1988. Expression of functional potassium channels from *Shaker* cDNA in *Xenopus* oocytes. *Nature* 331:143–45

175. Trimmer JS. 1991. Immunological identification and characterization of a delayed rectifier $K^+$ channel polypeptide in rat brain. *Proc. Natl. Acad. Sci. USA* 88:10764–68

176. Trube G, Hescheler J. 1983. Potassium channels in isolated patches of cardiac cell membrane. *Naunyn-Schmiedebergs Arch. Pharmacol.* 322:R64

177. Trube G, Hescheler J. 1984. Inward-rec-

tifying channels in isolated patches of the heart cell membrane: ATP-dependence and comparison with cell-attached patches. *Pflügers Arch.* 401:178–84

178. Trudeau MC, Warmke JW, Ganetsky B, Robertson GA. 1995. *H-erg*, a human inward rectifier with structural and functional homology to voltage-gated K⁺ channels. *Science* 269:92–95

179. Tseng G-N, Hoffman BF. 1989. Two components of transient outward current in canine ventricular myocytes. *Circ. Res.* 64:633–47

180. Tseng G-N, Robinson RB, Hoffman BF. 1987. Passive properties and membrane currents of canine ventricular myocytes. *J. Gen. Physiol.* 90:671–701

181. Tseng-Crank JCL, Tseng GN, Schwartz A, Tanouye MA. 1990. Molecular cloning and functional expression of a potassium channel cDNA isolated from a rat cardiac library. *FEBS Lett.* 268:63–68

182. Vandenberg CA. 1987. Inward rectification of a potassium channel in cardiac ventricular cells depends on internal magnesium ions. *Proc. Natl. Acad. Sci. USA* 84:2560–64

183. Vandenberg CA. 1994. Cardiac inward rectifier potassium channel. In *Ion Channels in the Cardiovascular System: Function and Dysfunction,* ed. PM Spooner, AM Brown, WA Catterall, GJ Kaczorowski, HC Strauss, pp. 145–67. Mt Kisco, NY: Futura

184. Van Wagoner DR, Lamorgese M. 1995. Phenylephrine suppresses distinct outward K⁺ currents in rat and human atrial myocytes. *Am. J. Physiol.* In press

185. Varnum MD, Busch AE, Bond CT, Maylie J, Adelman JP. 1993. The minK channel underlies the cardiac current I_{Ks} and mediates species-specific responses to protein kinase C. *Proc. Natl. Acad. Sci. USA* 90:11528–32

186. Varnum MD, Maylie J, Busch AE, Adelman JP. 1995. Persistent activation of min K channels by chemical crosslinking. *Neuron* 14:407–12

187. Varro A, Nanasi PP, Lathrop DA. 1993. Potassium currents in isolated human atrial and ventricular cardiocytes. *Acta Physiol. Scand.* 149:133–42

188. Veldkamp MW, van Ginneken ACG, Bouman LN. 1993. Single delayed rectifier channels in the membrane of rabbit ventricular myocytes. *Circ. Res.* 72:865–78

189. Veldkamp MW, van Ginneken ACG, Opthof T, Bouman LN. 1995. Delayed rectifier channels in human ventricular myocytes. *Circulation.* In press

190. Walsh KB, Arena JP, Kwok WM, Free-man L. 1991. Delayed-rectifier potassium channel activity in isolated membrane patches of guinea pig ventricular myocytes. *Am. J. Physiol.* 260:H1390–93

191. Wang H, Kunkel DD, Martin TM, Schwartzkroin PA, Tempel BL. 1993. Heteromultimeric K⁺ channels in terminal and juxtaparanodal regions of neurons. *Nature* 365:75–79

192. Wang YG, Lipsius SL. 1995. Acetylcholine activates a glibenclamide-sensitive K⁺ current in cat atrial myocytes. *Am. J. Physiol.* 37:H1322–34

193. Wang Z, Fermini B, Nattel S. 1993. Delayed rectifier outward current and repolarization in human atrial myocytes. *Circ. Res.* 73:276–85

194. Wang Z, Fermini B, Nattel S. 1993. Sustained depolarization-induced outward current in human atrial myocytes. Evidence for a novel delayed rectifier K⁺ current similar to Kv1.5 cloned channel currents. *Circ. Res.* 73:1061–76

195. Wang Z, Fermini B, Nattel S. 1994. Rapid and slow components of delayed rectifier current in human atrial myocytes. *Cardiovasc. Res.* 28:1540–46

196. Warmke JE, Drysdale R, Ganetsky B. 1991. A distinct potassium channel polypeptide encoded by the *Drosophila eag* locus. *Science* 252:1560–64

197. Warmke JE, Ganetsky B. 1994. A family of potassium channel genes related to eag in *Drosophila* and mammals. *Proc. Natl. Acad. Sci. USA* 91:3438–42

198. Wei A, Covarrubias M, Butler A, Baker K, Pak M, Salkoff L. 1990. K⁺ current diversity is produced by an extended gene family conserved in *Drosophila* and mouse. *Science* 248:599–603

199. Wettwer E, Amos G, Gath J, Zerkowski H-R, Reidemeister J-C, Ravens U. 1993. Transient outward current in human and rat ventricular myocytes. *Cardiovasc. Res.* 27:1662–69

200. Wettwer E, Amos G, Posival H, Ravens U. 1994. Transient outward current in human and ventricular myocytes of subepicardial and subendocardial origin. *Circ. Res.* 75:473–82

201. Wible BA, DeBiasi M, Majumder K, Tagliattella AM, Brown AM. 1995. Cloning and functional expression of an inwardly rectifying K⁺ channel from human atrium. *Circ. Res.* 76:343–50

202. Wickman KD, Iñiguez-Lluhi JA, Davenport PA, Taussig R, Krapivinsky GB, et al. 1994. Recombinant G-protein βγ-subunits activate the muscarinic-gated

atrial potassium channel. *Nature* 368: 255–57

203. Xu H, Dixon JE, Barry DM, Trimmer JS, McKinnon D, et al. 1995. Developmental expression of K⁺ channel α subunits and voltage-gated K⁺ channel currents in rat ventricular myocytes. *J. Gen. Physiol.* Submitted

204. Yamada M, Kurachi Y. 1995. Spermine gates inward-rectifying muscarinic but not ATP-dependent K⁺ channels in rabbit atrial myocytes—intracellular substance mediated mechanism of inward rectification. *J. Biol. Chem.* 270:9289–94

205. Yue DT, Marban E. 1988. A novel cardiac potassium channel that is active and conductive at depolarized potentials. *Pflügers Arch.* 413:127–33

206. Yue L, Feng J, Li G-R, Nattel S. 1995. A characterization of transient outward and delayed rectifier currents in canine atrial myocytes: properties of currents and the role of cell isolation methods. *Circulation.* In press

207. Zhong Y, Wu C-F. 1991. Alteration of four identified K⁺ currents in *Drosophila* muscle by mutations in *eag*. *Science* 252:1562–64

208. Zhong Y, Wu C-F. 1993. Modulation of different K⁺ currents in *Drosophila*: a hypothetical role for the eag subunit in multimeric K⁺ channels. *J. Neurosci.* 13:4669–79

209. Zygmunt AC. 1994. Intracellular calcium activates a chloride current in canine ventricular myocytes. *Am. J. Physiol.* 267:H1984–95

210. Zygmunt AC, Gibbons WR. 1991. Calcium-activated chloride current in rabbit ventricular myocytes. *Circ. Res.* 68: 424–37

211. Zygmunt AC, Gibbons WR. 1992. Properties of the calcium-activated chloride current in heart. *J. Gen. Physiol.* 99: 391–414

*Annu. Rev. Physiol. 1996. 58:395–426*

# CYCLIC NUCLEOTIDE-GATED ION CHANNELS: An Extended Family With Diverse Functions

*John T. Finn[1–3], Maria E. Grunwald[2,3], and King-Wai Yau[2,3]*

[1]Thomas C. Jenkins Department of Biophysics [2]Department of Neuroscience and [3]Howard Hughes Medical Institute, Johns Hopkins University School of Medicine, Baltimore, Maryland 21205

KEY WORDS:    cGMP ion channel channel gating, permeation and modulation, cyclic-nucleotide binding, ligand-gated ion channels, structure and function of ion channels

---

## ABSTRACT

An ion channel directly activated by cGMP was first discovered about ten years ago. Since then, a number of ion channels with the same property (cyclic nucleotide-activated channels) have been reported that are involved in a variety of cell functions. In addition, other channels have been found that are not primarily controlled by cyclic nucleotides but are modulated by them (cyclic nucleotide-modulated channels). These channels likewise have diverse functions and tissue distributions. Both channel classes are reviewed here. Coverage includes the cyclic-nucleotide binding site on these channels, ion permeation, pharmacological blockers, channel gating and modulation, and physiological functions of the channels.

---

## INTRODUCTION

Cyclic nucleotide-gated ion channels are a relatively recent discovery. Their identification began in the mid-1980s when the cation channel (the "light-sensitive" conductance) mediating visual transduction in retinal rod photoreceptors was found to be directly activated by guanosine 3′,5′-cyclic monophosphate (cGMP) (49, 236; see also 107). Before that time, cyclic nucleotides were thought to affect ion channel function only through cyclic nucleotide-dependent protein kinases and channel phosphorylation. Direct binding, however, allows rapid control of channel function. Soon after the discovery of the rod cGMP-activated channel, a similar channel was identified in cone photoreceptors (29, 84). Subsequently, a cation channel activated roughly equally by

395

cAMP and cGMP was identified on the cilia of olfactory receptor neurons (154). It is now clear that ion channels directly activated by cyclic nucleotides are not unique to visual and olfactory receptor neurons. In this review, we refer to these channels collectively as cyclic nucleotide-activated channels because they generally require the binding of cyclic nucleotide in order to open. Other channels have been found that are not primarily controlled by cyclic nucleotides but are modulated by them. We refer to these as cyclic nucleotide-modulated channels. Both classes are described here.

## CYCLIC NUCLEOTIDE-ACTIVATED CHANNELS

The gating of these channels is primarily controlled by the binding of cyclic nucleotide. Their mode of operation is similar to that of ligand-activated channels at chemical synapses, except that the ligand-binding site for cyclic nucleotide-activated channels resides on the cytoplasmic side of the protein.

### Retinal Rod and Cone cGMP-Activated Channels

The cGMP-activated channels in retinal rod and cone photoreceptors have a central role in visual transduction. This transduction process is particularly well understood in rods (101, 103, 122, 173, 232). In darkness, a relatively high concentration of cGMP in the cell's light-transducing outer segment maintains cGMP-activated cation channels in the open state. These open channels keep the cell depolarized and maintain a steady release of neurotransmitter (glutamate) from the cell's synaptic terminal. Upon absorbing light, the visual pigment rhodopsin isomerizes into an active form and catalyzes the exchange of GTP for GDP bound to the G protein transducin. With GTP bound, transducin stimulates a cGMP-phosphodiesterase to accelerate the hydrolysis of cGMP. The consequent decrease in cytoplasmic cGMP concentration leads to the closure of the cGMP-activated channels, producing a membrane hyperpolarization. This light-induced hyperpolarization reduces or stops the release of glutamate from the photoreceptor to second-order visual neurons. The phototransduction mechanism in cones is similar, except for quantitative differences such as a lower light sensitivity and faster response kinetics. The cGMP-activated channel in cones is a different isoform from the rod channel and has somewhat different electrical properties (see below).

An interesting characteristic of the rod and cone cGMP-activated channels is that, unlike most ligand-activated channels, they show no desensitization to the steady presence of ligand (234: see also 223). This property allows the channels to stay open in darkness, and to be closed only by light. Additionally, the channels are activated by cGMP with a Hill coefficient larger than unity (~2–2.5 in approximately physiological conditions); this feature renders the channels highly sensitive to changes in cGMP concentration and hence to light intensity. The half-activation constant, $K_{1/2}$, for both channels measured near physiological conditions is ~50 μM cGMP. Finally, these channels are permeable to $Ca^{2+}$, a feature that is crucial for the ability of photoreceptors to adapt to steady light. In darkness, the steady inward current through the rod channel is roughly 80% $Na^+$ and 15% $Ca^{2+}$ (with the rest apparently carried by $Mg^{2+}$). The dark $Ca^{2+}$ influx is balanced by an equal $Ca^{2+}$ efflux through a $Na^+/Ca^{2+},K^+$ exchanger. In light, the closure of the channels stops the $Ca^{2+}$ influx, but the $Ca^{2+}$ efflux continues, leading to a decline in the cytoplasmic $Ca^{2+}$ concentration. This $Ca^{2+}$ decrease triggers elaborate negative-feedback pathways that diminish the effect of illumination, producing adaptation (111). $Ca^{2+}$ is approximately 100-fold less concentrated than $Na^+$ in the extracellular medium, yet, as mentioned above, it carries as much as 15% of the inward current through the channel. Thus the channel actually selects $Ca^{2+}$ over $Na^+$. For the cone cGMP-activated channel, the fraction of inward current carried by $Ca^{2+}$ appears to be even higher (57, 165, 169).

## Cyclic Nucleotide-Activated Channel in Vertebrate Olfactory Receptor Neurons

There is now good evidence that a cyclic nucleotide-activated cation channel is also involved in olfactory transduction in the cilia of vertebrate olfactory receptor neurons (53–55, 117, 133; for review, see 244). In this process, some odorants are known to activate a G protein-mediated signaling cascade that leads to the stimulation of an adenylate cyclase and the production of cAMP, which in turn opens cyclic nucleotide-activated cation channels and depolarizes the receptor cell (120a, 123, 177, 244). (Other odorants are thought to activate a phosphoinositide pathway; see 177.) The olfactory cyclic nucleotide-activated channel has properties similar to those of the rod and cone cGMP-activated channels, except that it is activated by a much lower cyclic nucleotide concentration (154). Also, whereas the photoreceptor channels are activated much more readily by cGMP than cAMP (~30-fold difference in $K_{1/2}$), the olfactory channel is only slightly more sensitive to cGMP than cAMP, with both $K_{1/2}$ values at 1–20 μM (56, 118, 154). The effectiveness of cGMP on the olfactory channel is peculiar because the second messenger in olfactory transduction is thought to be cAMP, not cGMP. One explanation is that there is no need for the channel to be selective for cAMP if the basal cGMP level in olfactory receptor cells is very low and not affected by odorants. Alternatively, because the olfactory channel is also present in other tissues (see below), cGMP may be the physiological activator at some of these locations. Similar to the photoreceptor channels, the olfactory channel is highly permeable to $Ca^{2+}$. The $Ca^{2+}$ influx through the open channel activates a $Ca^{2+}$-activated $Cl^-$ channel that amplifies the olfactory response (106a, 120, 134). Simultaneously, the $Ca^{2+}$ influx leads to olfactory adaptation as a result of a rise in cytoplasmic $Ca^{2+}$ concentration (119). One mechanism in this adaptation appears to be a modulation of the channel itself by $Ca^{2+}$ (28, 113; see below).

## Molecular Structure and Function of the Visual and Olfactory Cyclic Nucleotide-Activated Channels

Molecular studies of cyclic nucleotide-activated channels became possible when the rod cGMP-activated channel was successfully purified from bovine retina (33, 34) and the cDNA cloned (102). When expressed in the *Xenopus* oocyte, the cloned cGMP-activated channel broadly resembles the native channel in properties. The apparent molecular mass of the purified protein is around 63 kDa, vs a calculated 80 kDa (690 amino acids) based on the cDNA. A good part of this discrepancy appears to arise from post- or cotranslational removal of the 92 N-terminal amino acids of the native rod channel (151). The cloned channel has a domain of slightly over 100 amino acids near the C-terminus that shows homology to the cGMP-binding domains in cGMP-dependent protein kinase (PKG), as well as homology to the cAMP-binding domains in the regulatory subunits of cAMP-dependent protein kinase (PKA) and the catabolite gene activator protein, CAP, in *Escherichia coli* (102). A region similar to the voltage-sensing S4 domain of voltage-activated channels has also been recognized (96, 97), even though the rod cGMP-activated channel is not voltage-gated. Nonetheless, the open probability of the channel does increase slightly at positive voltages in the presence of cyclic nucleotide (see 234). It is suggested that the S4 region is part of the core structure of an ancestor common to both voltage- and cyclic nucleotide-activated channels and has evolved into the voltage sensor in voltage-activated channels (96, 97). Finally, a domain resembling the pore-forming region of voltage-activated $K^+$ channels is also present in the rod cGMP-activated channel (78). These homologies, together with the hydropathy profile of the amino acid sequence and evidence from immunological staining (151, 228) and gene fusion experiments (87a), suggest a folding pattern of the rod channel in the membrane similar to that of many voltage-activated $K^+$ channels such as the Shaker $K^+$ channel (Figure 1*a*): with cytoplasmic N- and C-termini, six putative transmembrane domains (including the S4 domain; see Figure 1*b*), and a pore-forming loop (Figure 1*c*) dipping into the membrane between the last two transmembrane domains. The cyclic-nucleotide binding site is located in the cytoplasmic C-terminal segment. There is a single N-glycosylation site situated between the fifth transmembrane domain and the pore region (228). Mutations in the rod channel gene have been linked to certain cases of retinitis pigmentosa, a retinal degenerative disease (46).

    In addition to bovine retina, the rod channel has been cloned from human,

a.

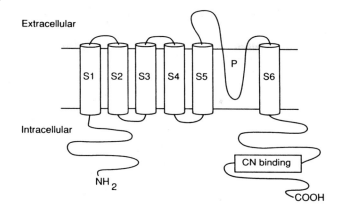

b.                        S4 region

Shaker    L A I L Ṙ V I Ṙ L V Ṙ V F Ṙ I Ḟ K L S Ṙ H S K̇ G
bRCNC     Y P E I R L N R L L R I S R M F E F F Q R T E T

c.                        Pore region

bRCNC    L Y **W** S **T L T** L **T T** I **G** - - **E** T P
Shaker   F W **W** A V V **T** M **T T** V **G** Y G D M T
CaB1I    F A V L **T** V F Q C I T M - - **E** G W
II       A A I M **T** V F Q I L **T** **G** - - **E** D W
III      W A L L **T L** F T V S **T** **G** - - **E** G W
IV       Q A L M L **L** F R S A T **G** - - **E** A W

*Figure 1*   (*a*) Putative folding pattern of a cyclic nucleotide-activated channel. S1–6 are the putative transmembrane domains. P indicates the pore region, and CN binding indicates the cyclic-nucleotide binding domain. Lengths of N- and C-termini are drawn roughly to scale. (*b*) Alignment of the amino acid sequences of the S4 region in the Shaker K⁺ channel (212) and the α-subunit of the bovine rod cGMP-activated channel, bRCNC (102). Identical amino acids are shown in boldface. Dots mark the repeated basic residues characteristic of the S4 region. (*c*) Alignment of the sequences of the putative pore region in bRCNC (α-subunit), Shaker, and each of the four repeats (I-IV) in the calcium channel CaB1 (152). Amino acids identical to the bRCNC sequence are indicated in boldface. (Adapted from 86.)

mouse, and chicken retinae (17, 38, 171). The olfactory cyclic nucleotide-activated channel, with a similar structure and about 60% amino acid identity, has been cloned from rat, cattle, and catfish (39, 73, 135). The cone channel was first cloned from chicken retina (17). The bovine counterpart was serendipitously cloned from the testis (227) and the kidney (15). The cone channel bears about 60% sequence identity to the rod and olfactory channels, and proteolytic cleavage of its N-terminus also appears to take place in the retina (17).

It is now known that the rod and olfactory cyclic nucleotide-activated channels are hetero-oligomers. The native rod channel has at least two different subunits. Subunit 1 (or $\alpha$) is the originally purified and cloned 63-kDa protein (102). Subunit 2 (or $\beta$) is a homologous protein with a similar folding pattern but is unable to form functional channels by itself; nonetheless, it imparts specific properties to the hetero-oligomeric channel complex (26, 27; see below). When originally cloned, the $\beta$-subunit was thought to have a molecular mass of under 100 kDa. The latest evidence, however, suggests that it is considerably larger (26, 109), being a 240-kDa protein co-purified with the 63-kDa protein from retinal tissue (150; see also 7a, 22, 23). The olfactory channel likewise has a second subunit (18, 129) and so may the cone channel. Different combinations of the subunits allow functional diversity. This diversity may be further increased by the coassembly of, for example, rod and olfactory channel subunits to form hybrid, functional complexes (51). In this review, unless otherwise stated, the term rod channel or olfactory channel refers to the $\alpha$-subunit of the respective channel.

By analogy to the Shaker $K^+$ channel (125, 139), the visual and olfactory cyclic nucleotide-activated channels are most likely tetramers. This assumption is strengthened by mutational experiments showing that the pore structures of the two kinds of channels are closely related (see below). The $\alpha/\beta$ subunit stoichiometries in the native channels are unknown.

ION PERMEATION    The rod channel was originally thought to be selective for $Na^+$. Subsequently, it was found to be permeable to a variety of monovalent cations (reviewed in 234; see also 31, 58, 147, 166, 189, 193). Still more surprisingly, the channel appears to be more permeable to divalent cations such as $Ca^{2+}$ (reviews in 234; also 31, 58, 147, 169, 189). The nonselectivity among cations also applies to the cone and olfactory channels (56, 82, 83, 116, 119, 156, 165, 167, 169). Indeed, the relative $Ca^{2+}$ permeability is even higher for the cone and olfactory channels than for the rod channel (57, 165, 169), which may implicate these channels as an important pathway for $Ca^{2+}$ influx specifically controlled by cyclic nucleotides. Not only do divalent cations permeate the channels, but in the process they also partially block them (reviewed in 234; 83, 99, 105, 106, 163, 169, 194, 210, 240, 242). In this manner, these channels somewhat resemble $Ca^{2+}$ channels. $Ca^{2+}$ channels are permeable to monovalent cations when divalent cations are absent, but in their presence, this conductivity to monovalent cations is blocked (4, 88). An important site underlying the divalent cation block of cyclic nucleotide-activated channels has been identified as a glutamate residue (Glu-363 in the bovine rod channel; see Figure 1c) presumably located near the extracellular side of the pore region (47, 180). When this glutamate is mutated into a neutral residue such as glutamine, the sensitivity of the channel to block by divalent cations is reduced by two orders of magnitude (47, 180). For a homotetrameric channel complex, there should be four such glutamate residues, but these appear to interact to effectively produce two identical and independent binding sites for metal cations or protons (181; for the phenomenon of proton block, see also 208). A glutamate residue is also present in the corresponding positions in all four repeats of the $Ca^{2+}$ channel, with similar functional characteristics (152, 231; see Figure 1c). For the native rod channel, there should be a weaker sensitivity to divalent cations because the $\beta$-subunit has a glycine instead of a glutamate at the corresponding position; this has been supported by a comparison of the current-voltage relations for the expressed homomeric and heteromeric channels (27).

As stated above, homology in the pore region also exists between cyclic nucleotide-activated channels and $K^+$ channels. Unlike $K^+$ channels, the cGMP-activated channels do not discriminate between $Na^+$ and $K^+$. This difference in conduction properties arises mostly from the presence of two additional amino acid residues, tyrosine and glycine, in the pore region of $K^+$ channels (Figure 1c). When these residues are deleted, the $K^+$ channel shows little selectivity among monovalent cations; at the same time, it is subject to blockage by $Ca^{2+}$ (86). The pore region of voltage-gated $Ca^{2+}$ channels also lacks these two amino acid residues (Figure 1c). In addition, both the rod and olfactory channels can be blocked from the cytoplasmic side by synthetic peptides that are derived from the N-terminus of the Shaker $K^+$ channel and produce rapid inactivation of the latter by interacting with its pore (112; see also 74).

In summary, there is strong evidence for an evolutionary link between cyclic nucleotide-activated channels and voltage-activated channels. Recently, experiments using cysteine scanning mutagenesis have suggested that the loop forming the pore of the rod channel may not project transversely into in the membrane (206; ZP Sun et al, personal communication). This finding may change our picture of the pore of voltage-gated channels as well.

PHARMACOLOGICAL BLOCKERS    Several chemicals have been found to block the visual and olfactory cyclic nucleotide-activated channels, although not with very high affinity. The most well-known among these is L-cis-diltiazem, which at physiological pH blocks the native rod and cone channels at micromolar concentrations from the cytoplasmic side (81, 107, 144, 145, 174, 203). The degree of block increases with depolarization, which suggests a binding site situated in the transmembrane electric field. At least for the rod channel, the potency of this drug depends on the β-subunit; in its absence, the drug's effectiveness decreases by almost 100-fold (27). The D-*cis* isomer, which blocks Ca²⁺ channels, is much less effective than the L-*cis* isomer on the rod channel (107). The effect of L-*cis*-diltiazem on the native olfactory channel is weaker than on the rod channel by perhaps an order of magnitude (56). Several other $Ca^{2+}$-channel antagonists likewise have an effect from the cytoplasmic side: Pimozide blocks the rod channel with a potency similar to that of L-*cis*-diltiazem (161), whereas D-600 and nifedipine block the olfactory channel in the 20–50 μM range at positive voltages (56, 242). In addition, the $Na^+$ channel blocker amiloride inhibits the olfactory channel, and its derivative 3',4'-dichlorobenzamil inhibits the rod channel at micromolar concentrations from the cytoplasmic side, also at positive voltages (56, 162). Finally, the rod channel is moderately sensitive to block by the local anesthetic tetracaine (94, 174, 188, 189).

CYCLIC-NUCLEOTIDE BINDING AND CHANNEL GATING    The cyclic-nucleotide binding sites on the rod and olfactory channels bear structural homology to those on the PKA and PKG enzymes, as well as to those on the catabolite gene activator protein (CAP). The crystal structure of the CAP dimer, with two cAMP molecules bound, has been solved (142, 143). It suggests that each of the two cAMP-binding sites envelops a cAMP molecule in a pocket composed of multiple β-strands and an α-helix (labeled the C-helix in CAP; see Figure 2*a*). The cAMP molecule is stabilized in the pocket by hydrogen bonds and nonpolar interactions with the protein. Key arginine, glutamate, and glycine residues have been identified in CAP that interact with the cyclic nucleotide ribose phosphate moiety (143); the same residues are present in PKA (226), PKG (225), and the rod cGMP-activated channel (Arg-559, Glu-544 and Gly-543 in the bovine channel) (see Figure 2*b*). In addition, a threonine residue has been identified in PKG with a hydroxyl group that likely forms a hydrogen bond with the amino group of cGMP (225). The corresponding residue in PKA is alanine, which cannot form the same hydrogen bond. This threonine/alanine difference is thought to help discriminate between cGMP and cAMP at the binding pocket (225); converting the alanine residue to threonine in PKA markedly increases the cGMP affinity of the enzyme (195). In the rod cGMP-activated channel, the threonine residue (Thr-560) is likewise present. When this residue is mutated into alanine, the expressed channel shows, as expected, a decrease in sensitivity to cGMP but not to cAMP (5). Although this experiment indicates that the threonine residue participates in cGMP binding, it has not provided a basis for

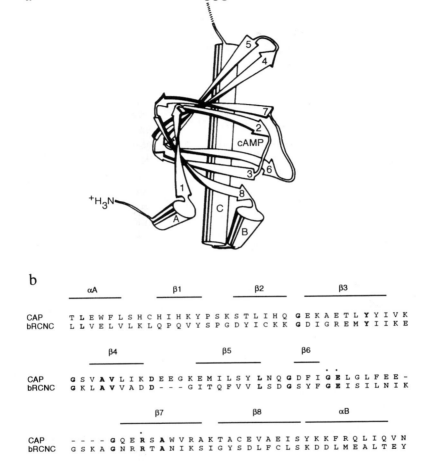

*Figure 2*  (*a*) A three-dimensional, schematic drawing of the cyclic nucleotide-binding site of the CAP monomer in the closed form (i.e. with cAMP bound). The α-helices, shown as tubes, are lettered A through C. The β-sheets, represented by arrows, are numbered 1 through 8. The approximate position of the cAMP in the β roll is shown. (Adapted from 143.) (*b*) Alignment of the amino acid sequences of the cyclic nucleotide-binding domains of CAP and the α-subunit of the bovine rod cGMP-activated channel, bRCNC. Identical residues are indicated in boldface. Dots mark some of the key residues for cyclic nucleotide-binding. The elements of secondary structure are overlined and marked αA through αC for α-helices and β1 through β8 for β-sheets (see panel *a*). (Adapted from 115.)

the relative preference of a channel for cGMP or cAMP. For example, the cloned catfish olfactory channel has the relevant threonine residue (Thr-530), but it shows roughly equal apparent affinities for cAMP and cGMP (73), indicating that other parts of the protein are also involved in the discrimination. Several studies have further examined the binding pocket, using molecular modeling (115) or cyclic nucleotide analogues (21, 191, 209; see also 241). Recently, evidence also indicates that the C-helix is important for cGMP or cAMP discrimination (75, 218a).

For the visual and olfactory channels, the dependence of channel activation on cyclic nucleotide concentration shows a Hill coefficient typically in the 1.5–3 range (reviewed in 234; see also 56, 118, 154). These values can be accounted for by a tetrameric channel model with a cyclic-nucleotide binding site on each subunit. In gating studies, one approach has been to assume, largely for simplicity, that the channel cannot open unless all the cyclic-nucleotide binding sites are occupied (85, 100). In reality, the channels probably can open, although with very low probability, when the sites are occupied only partially or even not at all (170, 213). Single-channel recordings have revealed subconductance states; these are possibly associated with partially liganded states (reviewed in 234; also 85, 94, 211). A quantitative understanding of the behavior of fully liganded vs partially liganded channels, however, will require elaborate molecular biological manipulations combined with detailed single-channel analysis.

The openings and closings of the native visual channels are very brief (reviewed in 234; also 85, 95, 140, 168, 211, 214, 224), a feature described as flicker (85, 140, 211, 214). The flicker of the olfactory channel is perhaps slower (118, 243). In both the visual and olfactory channels, this flicker appears to arise from the β-subunit (18, 27, 51, 129). Homomeric channels formed by the α-subunit alone show openings that have a much more rectangular appearance, reflecting longer open times (27, 38, 102). The mechanism underlying this flicker is still unclear; it is perhaps related to the transient block by protons reported for the α-subunit of the olfactory channel (181). The native rod and olfactory channels respond rapidly to changes in cyclic nucleotide concentration, which should allows them to serve as fast sensors of these second messengers during sensory transduction (30, 134), although this view is not unanimous in the case of the olfactory channel (245).

Although the visual and olfactory channels can be activated by various cyclic nucleotides (cGMP and cAMP being the most common), the ligands are not equally effective. Apart from a possible difference in affinity for different ligands, the open probability (i.e. the gating) of a channel also depends on the bound species. For example, the maximum macroscopic current elicited from native rod channels by cAMP is only about one third of that elicited by cGMP (209). Because the single-channel current is the same with either ligand (37a, 95), this reflects a smaller open probability for the cAMP-bound channel than for the cGMP-bound channel. From the law of mass action, the opening and closing of a liganded channel is coupled to the ligand-binding step. Thus, in general, the measured $K_{1/2}$ for the macroscopic activation of a channel by a ligand depends on both the intrinsic affinity of the binding site and the ease with which the liganded channel opens, and it is not always possible to separate the two contributions (32). The binding and gating parameters may also change with subunit composition of the channel complex. For example, the $K_{1/2}$ for the activation of the rat olfactory channel by cAMP decreases by more than tenfold in the presence of the β-subunit (18, 129). Transition metals such as $Ni^{2+}$ have been found to increase the potency of cyclic nucleotides in activating the rod channel (95, 99). This effect appears to arise from the binding of these cations to the C-terminus of the channel and a consequent favoring of its open state, i.e. an influence on the gating step (50, 68). Sufhydryl reagents also increase the potency of cyclic nucleotides on the rod and olfactory channels (10, 43, 50, 192a, 205), apparently through a similar mechanism (50).

MODULATION    An interesting modulation of these channels is produced by the binding of of $Ca^{2+}$-calmodulin ($Ca^{2+}$-CaM). The rod channel shows a mild effect of $Ca^{2+}$-CaM, which consists of a twofold increase in its cGMP $K_{1/2}$ (67, 91, 92, 155) that is apparently conferred by the β-subunit (26). The polarity of this effect suggests that it should contribute to light adaptation of the rod photoreceptor (91), although weakly (110). The effect of $Ca^{2+}$-CaM on the olfactory channel is much stronger and results in a maximal 20-fold increase in its $K_{1/2}$ for cAMP (28). The polarity and strength of this modulation suggest that it is important for adaptation of olfactory receptor neurons (28). The increase in $K_{1/2}$ appears to result from $Ca^{2+}$-CaM favoring the closed state of the channel, i.e. an influence again on the gating step (131). Unlike in the rod channel, $Ca^{2+}$-CaM affects the olfactory channel through its α-subunit. The binding site is situated on the cytoplasmic N-terminal segment (131), which implicates the latter domain in the gating process. Experiments employing rod/olfactory chimeric channels have likewise identified this region as having an influence on channel gating (69, 75). One idea (75) is that this region, together with the first two transmembrane domains, is involved in intersubunit interactions (by analogy to potassium channels; see 8, 124, 196), which in turn determine the ease with which the channel opens (216, 217). In addition to a modulation through CaM, other modulations of the olfactory channel by $Ca^{2+}$ have been reported (137, 246), but these findings may be confounded by residual CaM. The cone channel, at least in catfish, does not appear to be modulated by $Ca^{2+}$-CaM (LW Haynes, personal communication).

For the rod channel, modulation by phosphorylation has been described, which may affect its $K_{1/2}$ (65, 132). Diacylglycerol analogues also appear to have some effect on this channel, but the implications are unclear (66).

## Visual and Olfactory Cyclic Nucleotide-Activated Channels in Cell Types Other than Sensory Receptors

Originally thought to be unique to sensory transduction, cyclic nucleotide-activated channels now appear to have fairly widespread tissue distributions. Northern blotting at high stringency has detected mRNA for the rod cGMP-activated channel in heart and kidney (3). Indeed, the cDNA has also been cloned from the M-1 line of kidney cells (1). In addition, the cDNA for the olfactory channel has been cloned from the aorta (14) and the heart (182). As pointed out above, the cDNA encoding the cone channel was originally cloned from the testis (227) and the kidney (15), and it appears to be present also in the heart and colon (15, 42). In some of these tissues such as heart and kidney, there is not yet any physiological evidence for cyclic nucleotide-activated channel activity, but ion channels modulated by the direct binding of cyclic nucleotide have been reported (see sections below). Possibly, these modulations by cyclic nucleotides are conferred by rod, cone, or olfactory channel subunits forming part of the channels in question. On the other hand, excised-patch recordings revealed cGMP-activated channels on the plasma membrane of sperm, a finding consistent with the cloning results from testis (227). Chemotaxis in sperm involves activation of a membrane-bound guanylate cyclase and an internal $Ca^{2+}$ rise (60). Because cGMP-activated channels are permeable to $Ca^{2+}$ ions, they could provide a causal link between the rises in cGMP and $Ca^{2+}$ (227). Based on evidence from in situ hybridizations, polymerase chain reaction (PCR), and whole-cell recordings with cGMP infusion, retinal ganglion cells may also have a cyclic nucleotide-activated channel identical, or very similar, to the rod channel (2). Similar approaches combined with immunocytochemistry and excised-patch recordings have likewise implicated the presence of the olfactory channel in hippocampal and cerebellar neurons (19, 47a), as well as the olfactory bulb and the pituitary gland (47a). The details of the signaling pathways coupled to the channels in these last two locations, and their functional significance, are unclear. The sensory cyclic nucleotide-activated channels may still be present elsewhere (see below).

## Sensory Cyclic Nucleotide-Activated Channels in Invertebrates

PHOTORECEPTORS    The majority of invertebrate photoreceptors have a light-sensitive rhabdomeric structure. Unlike vertebrate rods and cones, these photoreceptors show a depolarizing response to light, through mechanisms still not entirely clear (7, 79, 130, 164, 175). In *Limulus* and *Drosophila* photoreceptors, on which most work has been done, $Ca^{2+}$ (regulated by a phosphoinositide pathway) and cGMP are thought to be important, but their relationship is unknown. In the *Limulus* ventral photoreceptor, excised-patch experiments have indicated the presence of a cGMP-activated channel with single-channel conductance, reversal potential (near 0 mV), and mean open time like those of the light-activated channels recorded from cell-attached patches (9, 98, 130). There is only limited information on the cGMP dependence of this channel, with the $K_{1/2}$ value possibly in the 10–30 μM cGMP range. Recently, the cDNA for a homologue of vertebrate cyclic nucleotide-activated channels was cloned from *Drosophila* (11). The expressed protein is more effectively activated by cGMP than cAMP and shows $K_{1/2}$ values intermediate between the vertebrate rod and olfactory channels. Northern blotting shows mRNA in the eyes and the antennae of the insect, implicating roles for the channel in both vision and olfaction (11). Although the vertebrate rod, cone, and olfactory channels are encoded by distinct genes, Southern analysis of *Drosophila* genomic DNA has not detected additional genes homologous to the one already cloned (11). If this is confirmed, the divergence between the visual and olfactory channels may be a late event in evolution. The cloning of a cGMP-activated channel, nonetheless, has not clarified the visual transduction mechanism in *Drosophila* photorecep-tors; thus far, there is no report of a light-induced change in cGMP content in these cells and little evidence in other invertebrate photoreceptors as well (20). Knowing the cellular localization of the *Drosophila* channel protein may help answering this question. For other rhabdomeric photoreceptors, such as in squid and scallop, experiments using bilayer reconstitution methods have also raised the possibility of the presence of a cGMP-activated channel (157, 158).

The situation is somewhat different for invertebrate photoreceptors with a ciliary structure. Unlike rhabdomeric photoreceptors, these cells produce hy-perpolarizing light responses, apparently the result of the opening of a $K^+$ channel (62, 63, 146). Surprisingly, this $K^+$-selective conductance was recently found to be directly activated by cGMP (64). A cyclic nucleotide-activated channel selective for $K^+$ represents a departure from the other members of this channel family described above. A similar channel has recently been reported to underlie the light response of an extraocular, photosensitive neuron in the abdominal ganglion of the mollusc *Onchidium verrunculatum*, except in this case, the channel closes in the light to depolarize the cell (70–72). Thus several variations of a motif based on a cGMP pathway and a cGMP-activated channel appear to operate as phototransduction mechanisms. Other cyclic nucleotide-activated $K^+$ channels are described below.

OLFACTORY RECEPTOR CELLS    Olfaction in invertebrates, as in vertebrates, involves both the cAMP and the phosphoinositide pathways. In the lobster, odorants activate at least two transduction pathways: One excites and the other inhibits olfactory receptor cells (149, 187). The excitatory pathway appears to involve an inositol trisphosphate (IP₃) -activated cation channel on the plasma membrane, with properties similar to intracellular IP$_3$ receptor channels in other cells (48, 80), whereas the inhibitory pathway appears to involve a cyclic nucleotide-activated channel that, like that in ciliary photoreceptors, is also K$^+$-selective (80, 148). Excised-patch recordings indicate that both the IP$_3$-activated and the cyclic nucleotide-activated channels may be present on the same olfactory receptor cell (80). There is no quantitative information on the activation of the latter channels by cyclic nucleotides.

## Other Cyclic Nucleotide-Activated Channels

Here we briefly describe several other ion channels; some have been clearly demonstrated to be directly activated by cyclic nucleotides, and others are speculated to be controlled by them. The molecular identity is not known for any of these channels.

In fish and bird, the neurons in the pineal gland are sensitive to light. In lamprey, for example, pineal photoreceptors give a hyperpolarizing response just like those of retinal rods and cones (172, 207). It thus seems possible that pineal and retinal photoreceptor neurons have a common phototransduction pathway, including the presence of a cGMP-activated channel. This is indeed the case, as indicated by excised-patch recordings from dissociated chick pineal photoreceptors (44, 45). The activation of the pineal channel by cGMP shows a $K_{1/2}$ value similar to that of the retinal photoreceptor channels, i.e. around 50 µM, cAMP is ineffective. Molecular cloning of the channel has not been carried out. In mammals, the pinealocytes are not photosensitive. Nonetheless, PCR amplification indicates that these cells may have a cGMP-activated channel like that found in rods (185); this pineal channel appears to be linked to a signaling pathway activated by vasoactive intestinal peptide (VIP).

In addition to lateral eyes, the lizard has a third (parietal) eye on its forehead. This eye, structurally simpler, projects to nonvisual areas of the midbrain and may function as a dawn/dusk detector (202). Like rods and cones, the parietal-eye photoreceptors have a light-sensitive outer segment of ciliary origin. Unlike rods and cones, however, the latter give depolarizing responses to light in the dark-adapted state (202). Still, they have a cGMP-activated channel with properties similar to the rod channel (52). The phototransduction pathway involving this channel remains to be examined.

In the longitudinal ventrolateral muscle of larval *Drosophila*, there is a tetraethylammonium (TEA)-sensitive, K$^+$-selective channel that is activated by cAMP (37). The half-maximal activation constant is about 50 µM cAMP, and the Hill coefficient is near 3; cGMP is ineffective at 80 µM. In the pedal and buccal ganglia of the mollusc *Pleurobranchaea californica,* there is a cAMP-activated Na$^+$ current (204). In cultured carrot cells, there appears to be a cAMP-activated cation channel that is permeable to Ca$^{2+}$ and modulated by Ca$^{2+}$-CaM (121). Finally, the first example of an anion channel seemingly directly activated by cGMP was also recently reported (36). Found on cultured proximal convoluted tubule cells from kidney, this channel has a 150-pS conductance and is voltage independent. It has a half-maximal activation constant of close to 1 mM cGMP, and cAMP appears to be ineffective. One peculiarity is that it takes minutes for cGMP to open this channel even in excised patches, which raises concerns about its true activation mechanism. The activation of this $Cl^-$ channel by cGMP is supposedly triggered by the hormone atrial natriuretic peptide and is thought to affect transepithelial potential and consequently reduce $Na^+$ reabsorption (hence increase its excretion) via apical cation channels (see below).

A putative cGMP-activated channel is present in retinal on-bipolar cells. Retinal bipolar cells receive synaptic inputs from photoreceptors and are of two types: On-bipolar cells depolarize, and off-bipolar cells hyperpolarize in response to illumination. Off-bipolar cells have glutamate receptor channels on their dendrites so that they are depolarized in darkness by the steady release of glutamate from the photoreceptors. On-bipolar cells, on the other hand, are unusual in that they typically have a nonselective cation channel that is closed in darkness and opens in the light (201, 219, 230). This cation channel, surprisingly, may be opened by cytoplasmic cGMP (159, 197, 198). The present picture is that in darkness glutamate released from photoreceptors stimulates a G protein-coupled metabotropic glutamate receptor (mGLuR6; see 153), which in turn activates a cGMP-phosphodiesterase to remove cGMP and keep the channels closed (160,198). Light stops this cascade, allowing the channels to be opened by cGMP (160, 198). This cascade is strongly reminiscent of the phototransduction pathway, although different protein isoforms are involved (199, 218). One wonders why there is such an elaborate mechanism for the photoreceptor/on-bipolar cell synapse. One possibility is that because the electrical response of photoreceptors to light is relatively slow (12), coupling this light response to a matched, slow synapse will remove any fast noise associated with, for example, random openings of the cGMP-activated channels in the photoreceptors in darkness (see 13, 16, 76), thus improving the signal-to-noise ratio for light detection. This synaptic filtering is particularly critical for the rod on-pathway, which is able to detect dim light down to single-photon levels. At this point, however, it remains to be proven by excised-patch recording that the cation channel in question is indeed directly activated by cGMP. There is no evidence that the rod, cone, or olfactory channel is in on-bipolar cells (see, for example, 222), which suggests the presence of a distinct molecular species. This possibility is supported by the insensitivity of the bipolar cell channel to blockage by extracellular divalent cations (200, 219).

In cone synaptic terminals, there is preliminary evidence for a cGMP-activated channel participating in synaptic transmission by virtue of its $Ca^{2+}$

permeability (178). This channel somewhat resembles the cone phototransduction channel in its current-voltage relation, but its detailed properties, especially pertaining to activation by cGMP, remain to be studied. Finally, a cGMP-activated cation channel may be present in skeletal muscle (141).

# CYCLIC NUCLEOTIDE-MODULATED CHANNELS

We describe here several ion channels that are not activated primarily by the binding of a cyclic nucleotide but the open probability of which is affected by cyclic-nucleotide binding. We refer to these channels as cyclic nucleotide-modulated channels.

## Renal cGMP-Modulated Channel

The hormone atrial natriuretic peptide increases $Na^+$ excretion by the kidney via cGMP as a second messenger. One target of cGMP was proposed to be the cGMP-activated $Cl^-$ channel described above. Another better-studied target appears to be a cGMP-inhibited cation channel in the apical membrane of renal inner medullary collecting duct cells (138, 237). This inhibition suppresses $Na^+$ absorption across the collecting duct. This channel is not voltage dependent, is selective for monovalent cations, and is inhibited by micromolar concentrations of amiloride (127). In excised, inside-out membrane patches, the open probability of this channel decreases moderately (from about 0.7 to 0.5) in the presence of cGMP, with half-maximal effect occurring at ~7 μM cGMP (128). The hydrolysis-resistant analogue 8-bromo-cGMP has the same effect. cAMP up to 1 mM has no effect. This was the first example of an ion channel the open probability of which declined upon binding of cyclic nucleotide. In addition to being directly inhibited by cGMP, this channel is also inhibited by a cGMP-dependent protein kinase, which instead of phosphorylating the channel may act through a G protein (126). The dual action of cGMP is proposed to provide both a fast modulation through direct binding and a slow modulation through the kinase (126). Recently, a nonselective cation channel in the M-1 mouse cortical collecting duct cell line has likewise been found to be directly inhibited by cGMP (1). This channel may be the same as the one in the inner medullary collecting duct. PCR cloning has further found expression of the α-subunit of the rod cGMP-activated channel in the M-1 cells (1), a result consistent with Northern blot experiments on kidney tissue described above. In this context, it may be recalled that the cone homologue of the rod cGMP-activated channel was originally cloned from kidney. It is presently unclear whether one or more of the visual channel subunits constitute part of the cGMP-modulated channel in question. The inhibitory effect of cGMP would tend to argue against this possibility, but other subunits in an hetero-oligomeric channel complex might alter the polarity of cGMP action.

## cAMP-Modulated Pacemaker (I_f) Channel in Cardiac Pacemaker Cells

In pacemaker cells of the cardiac sinoatrial node, there is a hyperpolarization-activated, nonselective cationic current ($I_f$) involved in the slow diastolic depolarization underlying spontaneous electrical activity (40). This current is modulated by adrenaline and acetylcholine in opposite ways. Adrenaline increases $I_f$ and leads to acceleration of pacemaker activity by enhancing adenylate cyclase activity and raising cAMP. Acetylcholine, on the other hand, decreases $I_f$ and decelerates pacemaker activity by decreasing adenylate cyclase activity and lowering cAMP. The modulation of $I_f$ by cAMP appears to involve, instead of phosphorylation of the channel, a direct binding of the cyclic nucleotide (41). cAMP activates $I_f$ by shifting its activation curve (maximal by 10 mV) to less negative voltages, making the current more readily activated upon hyperpolarization of the cell; the fully activated current is not affected by cAMP (41). The cAMP effect is half-maximal at 0.2 μM cAMP, with a Hill coefficient of 0.85. The Hill coefficient of less than unity is interesting because it suggests that there is only one cyclic-nucleotide binding site on the channel, unlike the cyclic nucleotide-activated channels in sensory neurons. cGMP and cCMP act similarly but are less effective, with $K_{1/2}$ values of 8 and 12 μM, respectively. This channel is the first example of an ion channel that is dually gated by voltage and cyclic nucleotide. Preliminary evidence from cDNA library screening suggests that a protein highly homologous to the α-subunits of the rod and olfactory channels is present in the sinoatrial node (93). Again, it is possible that the $I_f$ channel is a hetero-oligomer, composed of cyclic nucleotide-activated channel subunits and others that confer the voltage sensitivity. It is also possible that the $I_f$ channel is related to the Eag family of ion channels described below, which likewise are dually controlled by voltage and cyclic-nucleotide binding.

## $Ca^{2+}$-Activated, cAMP-Modulated, Nonselective Cation Channel in a Pancreatic Islet Cell Line

Recently, a $Ca^{2+}$-activated, nonselective cation channel in a rat insulinoma cell line, CRI-G1, has been reported to be modulated by cAMP (176, 176a). This modulation is complex, consisting of an enhancement at low cAMP concentrations (0.1–1.0 μM) and an inhibition at higher concentrations. It was proposed that different binding sites mediate the two effects, with the inhibitory site strongly preferring cAMP over cGMP, and the stimulatory site showing roughly equal preference for cAMP and cGMP. In addition, this channel is also modulated by noncyclic nucleotides such as AMP and ADP. The physiological function of this channel is unclear.

## Cyclic Nucleotide-Suppressible Cation Current in Taste Receptor Cells

A cGMP-modulated cation channel appears to be involved in taste transduction. Taste in vertebrates has four primary sensations: salty, sour, sweet, and bitter. (Umami, a distinct taste produced by certain amino acids such as glutamate, has often been referred to as a fifth sensation.) These sensations involve a variety of transduction mechanisms (61, 104). Recent experiments have suggested that a cyclic nucleotide-suppressible cation channel may be involved in bitter or sweet taste transduction in frog (108). Half-maximal inhibition of the channel occurs at ~100 nM cAMP or fivefold lower cGMP, even though cAMP is probably the native second messenger (183). The proposed pathway involving this channel is that certain taste receptors, upon activation by tastants, stimulate a G protein (apparently identical to rod transducin), which in turn activates a cAMP-specific phosphodiesterase to decrease cAMP concentration, with the resulting removal of inhibition from the cyclic nucleotide-suppressible channel leading to its opening and depolarization of the cell (108). This scheme seems highly speculative, however, because this channel was found to be moderately $K^+$ selective (108), and its opening could, therefore, lead to a hyperpolarization instead of depolarization. In any case, this cyclic nucleotide-suppressible channel is the second example of its kind reported so far.

## Eag $K^+$ Channel Family

The *eag* (*ether-a-go-go*) mutants in *Drosophila* have a leg-shaking phenotype; physiologically, they show spontaneous, repetitive firing of motor neurons and increased neurotransmitter release at the larval neuromuscular junction (59). Voltage-clamp experiments on larvae have indicated that several distinct $K^+$ currents are diminished, but not eliminated, by *eag* mutations; these currents include a transient $K^+$ current, a delayed noninactivating $K^+$ current, and a fast and a slow $Ca^{2+}$-activated $K^+$ current (229, 238). At the same time, modulations of these currents by cGMP, for example, are affected by *eag* mutations (239). These findings suggest that the Eag protein is a subunit common to different $K^+$ channels. The cloned *eag* gene was found to encode a protein homologous to Shaker $K^+$ channels, with approximately 25% amino acid identity in the transmembrane domains (220). Interestingly, the Eag protein (with ~1200 amino acid residues) is about twice as large as the Shaker channel protein, with the non-overlapping part situated at the C-terminus. This protein bears even higher homology to cyclic nucleotide-activated channels; in particular, it has a putative cyclic-nucleotide binding domain on the C-terminal segment (78, 221). The cDNAs for the mouse and rat homologues (m-Eag and r-Eag) of the *Drosophila* Eag protein have recently been cloned (136, 221), as have those for two related but distinct channel proteins in *Drosophila* (Elk) and human (HERG) (221). Thus it appears that Eag is only one member of a new family of K$^+$ channels. When heterologously expressed in *Xenopus* oocytes, the *Drosophila* and vertebrate Eag proteins can form functional homomeric channels (24, 136, 179; GA Robertson et al, personal communication). These channels give voltage-activated K$^+$ currents that show either no or only some inactivation. One unusual feature of the Eag channels (in particular the vertebrate forms) is that their activation kinetics depend on the holding potential; namely, a more negative holding potential slows the activation kinetics (136; GA Robertson et al, personal communication). It has been reported that cAMP can shift the voltage dependence of the *Drosophila* Eag channel and that the channel is permeable to Ca$^{2+}$ in addition to K$^+$ (24), but these findings have not yet been independently confirmed (GA Robertson et al, personal communication). The vertebrate Eag channel is predominantly located in the central nervous system, particularly in the hippocampus and the cerebellum (136). The presence of this channel in hippocampus is interesting because *eag* mutants in *Drosophila* have learning deficits (77).

The best understood member of this channel family is the HERG channel. Although it was originally cloned from human hippocampus (221), it appears to be also highly expressed in the heart, and its defects have recently been associated with an inherited form of a cardiac disease called long-QT syndrome (LQT) (35). This disease is characterized by a prolonged QT interval in the electrocardiogram arising from abnormally slow repolarizations of the action potentials and can cause sudden death from ventricular arrhythmia. A LQT syndrome can also be induced by certain anti-arrhythmic drugs that block the rapidly activating delayed-rectifier K$^+$ current, $I_{Kr}$, in the heart (25). Together, these results suggest a link between LQT and $I_{Kr}$. Indeed, when expressed in *Xenopus* oocytes, the HERG channel resembles $I_{Kr}$ in several properties (184, 215). Thus HERG is probably a component of the $I_{Kr}$ channel known to be important for initiating the repolarization of the cardiac action potential. An interesting feature of both HERG and $I_{Kr}$ is that the outward K$^+$ current decreases with membrane depolarizations above 0 mV (184). At the same time, HERG can behave like an inward rectifier (215). In these respects, HERG is functionally different from the other members of the Eag family.

## AKT1 and KAT1 Channels in Plants

Plant cells are generally exposed to extremely low extracellular K$^+$ concentrations (often in the micromolar range). For various cell functions, these cells accumulate $K^+$ from the external environment through either high-affinity $K^+$ transport systems or $K^+$ channels (190). This uptake is facilitated by a generally very negative membrane potential of $-120$ to $-250$ mV, maintained by an electrogenic $H^+$-ATPase. Using suppression of the mutant phenotype of a $K^+$ uptake-deficient yeast strain as an assay, two cDNAs have been independently isolated from the plant *Arabidopsis thaliana* (6, 192). These cDNAs, designated AKT1 and KAT1, are derived from separate genes but are highly homologous. They show homology to cyclic nucleotide-activated channels and Shaker $K^+$ channels, including similar predicted folding patterns in the membrane, the presence of a S4 domain, a homologous pore region, and a cyclic-nucleotide binding domain in the cytoplasmic C-terminal segment. The KAT1 cDNA has been expressed in the *Xenopus* oocyte (90, 186), producing a noninactivating, inwardly rectifying $K^+$-selective channel that is activated by hyperpolarizations more negative than $-100$ mV. Submillimolar concentrations of cGMP (but not cAMP) shift the activation curve to more negative voltages (90). These plant channels are structurally different from the inwardly rectifying $K^+$ channels in animal cells, which, based on recent cloning studies, belong to a new family of $K^+$ channels by having only two instead of six putative transmembrane domains (89, 114). The mechanism underlying their inward rectification is unknown. These plant channels lend additional support to the notion that there is an ancient common ancestor of voltage-gated and cyclic nucleotide-gated channels (96). Sequence analysis suggests that the AKT1 and KAT1 channels are particularly closely related to the Eag family of channels (221).

## SUMMARY

It is remarkable that in just ten years since the first ion channel directly gated by cyclic nucleotide was discovered, numerous other channels have been found with similar or related properties and involved in a great diversity of cell functions. Together, these channels constitute an extended family with members all sharing the property of binding cyclic nucleotide (149a, 221) and consequently being affected in various ways. A summary of these channels is given in Table 1. Undoubtedly, many more members of this extended family will be discovered.

ACKNOWLEDGMENTS

This review is an updated and expanded version of earlier reviews by one of the authors (233, 235). We thank Drs. Dietmar Krautwurst and Kei Nakatani for comments on the manuscript. Supported by grant EY 06837 from the National Eye Institute.

**Table 1**  Summary of known cyclic nucleotide-gated channels

|  | Location | Reference |
|---|---|---|
| **Cyclic nucleotide-activated channels** |  |  |
| Vertebrates |  |  |
| cGMP-activated nonselective cation channel | Retinal rods and ganglion cells, heart, kidney | 2, 3, 26, 27, 49, 102, 109, 236 |
| cGMP-activated nonselective cation channel | Retinal cones, kidney, testis (sperm), heart, colon | 15, 17, 42, 84, 227 |
| Cyclic nucleotide-activated nonselective cation channel | Olfactory receptor neurons, aorta, heart, hippocampus | 14, 18, 19, 39, 73, 129, 135, 154, 182 |
| cGMP-activated cation channel[a,b] | Pineal photoreceptors | 44 |
| cGMP-activated cation channel[a,b] | Lizard parietal-eye photoreceptors | 52 |
| cGMP-activated anion channel[a] | Cultured renal proximal convoluted tubule cells | 36 |
| cGMP-activated nonselective cation channel(?) | Retinal on-bipolar cells | 159, 197 |
| cGMP-activated nonselective cation channel(?) | Retinal cone synaptic terminals | 178 |
| cGMP-activated cation channel(?) | Skeletal muscle | 141 |
| Invertebrates |  |  |
| cGMP-activated nonselective cation channel | Rhabdomeric photoreceptors | 11, 130 |
| cGMP-activated $K^+$ channel[a] | Ciliary photoreceptors | 62, 64 |
| cGMP-activated $K^+$ channel[a] | Molluscan extraocular photoreceptor | 72 |
| Cyclic nucleotide-activated $K^+$ channel[a] | Olfactory receptor neurons | 80, 148 |
| cAMP-activated $K^+$ channel[a] | Larval *Drosophila* muscle | 37 |
| cAMP-activated $Na^+$ channel[a,b] | Molluscan ganglia | 204 |
| Plant |  |  |
| cAMP-activated cation channel[a,b] | Cultured carrot cells | 121 |
| **Cyclic nucleotide-modulated channels** |  |  |
| Vertebrates |  |  |
| cGMP-suppressible cation channel[a] | Renal inner medullary collecting duct cells | 128 |
| $I_f$ channel[a] | Cardiac sinoatrial node | 41 |
| Cyclic nucleotide-modulated non-selective cation channel[a] | Insulinoma cell line | 176 |
| Cyclic nucleotide-suppressible, mostly $K^+$-selective channel[a] | Taste receptor cells | 108 |
| Eag $K^+$ channel | Brain | 136, 221 |
| Erg $K^+$ channel | Heart, brain | 221 |

**Table 1**  *(Continued)*

|  | Location | Reference |
|---|---|---|
| Invertebrates |  |  |
| Eag $K^+$ channel | *Drosophila* tissue | 220 |
| Elk $K^+$ channel[c] | *Drosophila* tissue | 221 |
| Plant |  |  |
| AKT1, KAT1 $K^+$ channels | *Arabidopsis* tissue | 6, 192 |

[a] Molecular identity unknown.
[b] Selectivity among various cations not yet examined.
[c] No functional expression yet.
A question mark indicates that direct gating by cyclic nucleotide remains to be confirmed by excised-patch recordings.

## *Literature Cited*

1. Ahmad I, Korbmacher C, Segal AS, Cheung P, Boulpaep EL, et al. 1992. Mouse cortical collecting duct cells show nonselective cation channel activity and express a gene related to the cGMP-gated rod photoreceptor channel. *Proc. Natl. Acad. Sci. USA* 89:10262–66

2. Ahmad I, Leinders-Zufall T, Kocsis JD, Shepherd GM, Zufall F, et al. 1994. Retinal ganglion cells express a cGMP-gated cation conductance activatable by nitric oxide donors. *Neuron* 12:155–65

3. Ahmad I, Redmond LJ, Barnstable CJ. 1990. Developmental and tissue-specific expression of the rod photoreceptor cGMP-gated ion channel gene. *Biochem. Biophys. Res. Commun.* 173:463–70

4. Almers W, McCleskey EW, Palade PT. 1984. A non-selective cation conductance in frog muscle membrane blocked by micromolar external calcium ions. *J. Physiol.* 353:565–83

5. Altenhofen W, Ludwig J, Eismann E, Kraus W, Bönigk W, et al. 1991. Control of ligand specificity in cyclic nucleotide-gated channels from rod photoreceptors and olfactory epithelium. *Proc. Natl. Acad. Sci. USA* 88:9868–72

6. Anderson JA, Huprikar SS, Kochian LV, Lucas WJ, Gaber RF. 1992. Functional expression of a probable *Arabidopsis thaliana* potassium channel in *Saccharomyces cerevisiae*. *Proc. Natl. Acad. Sci. USA* 89:3736–40

7. Anderson RE, Brown JE. 1988. Phosphoinositides in the retina. *Prog. Retinal Res.* 8:211–28

7a. Ardell MD, Makhija AK, Oliveira L, Miniou P, Viegas-Péquignot E, Pittler SJ. 1995. cDNA, gene structure, and chromosomal localization of human GAR1 (CNCG13L), a homolog of the third subunit of bovine photoreceptor cGMP-gated channel. *Genomics* 28:32–38

8. Babila T, Moscucci A, Wang H, Weaver FE, Koren G. 1994. Assembly of mammalian voltage-gated potassium channels: evidence for an important role of the first transmembrane segment. *Neuron* 12:615–26

9. Bacigalupo J, Johnson EC, Vergara C, Lisman JE. 1991. Light-dependent channels from excised patches of *Limulus* ventral photoreceptors are opened by cGMP. *Proc. Natl. Acad. Sci. USA* 88:7938–42

10. Balakrishnan K, Padgett J, Cone RA. 1990. Calcium flux in rod outer segment membranes: NEM potentiates the effects of cGMP. *Biophys. J.* 57:A371 (Abstr.)

11. Baumann A, Frings S, Godde M, Seifert R, Kaupp UB. 1994. Primary structure and functional expression of a *Drosophila* cyclic nucleotide-gated channel present in eyes and antennae. *EMBO J.* 13:5040–50

12. Baylor DA. 1987. Photoreceptor signals and vision. *Invest. Ophthal. Vis. Sci.* 28:34–49

13. Baylor DA, Matthews G, Yau K-W. 1980. Two components of electrical dark noise in toad retinal rod outer segments. *J. Physiol.* 309:591–621

14. Biel M, Altenhofen W, Hullin R, Ludwig J, Freichel M, et al. 1993. Primary structure and functional expression of a cyclic nucleotide-gated channel from rabbit aorta. *FEBS Lett.* 329:134–38

15. Biel M, Zong X, Distler M, Bosse E, Klugbauer N, et al. 1994. Another member of the cyclic nucleotide-gated channel family expressed in testis, kidney, and heart. *Proc. Natl. Acad. Sci. USA* 91:3505–9

16. Bodoia RD, Detwiler PB. 1985. Patch-clamp recordings of the light-sensitive dark noise in retinal rods from the lizard and frog. *J. Physiol.* 367:183–216

17. Bönigk W, Altenhofen W, Müller F, Dòse A, Illing M, et al. 1993. Rod and cone photoreceptor cells express distinct genes for cGMP-gated channels. *Neuron* 10:865–77

18. Bradley J, Li J, Davidson N, Lester HA, Zinn K. 1994. Heteromeric olfactory cyclic nucleotide-gated channels: a subunit that confers increased sensitivity to cAMP. *Proc. Natl. Acad. Sci. USA* 91:8890–94

19. Bradley J, Li J, Zhang Y, Bakin R, Matsuzaki O, et al. 1995. Expression and analysis of subunits of olfactory cyclic nucleotide-gated channel. *Am. Chem. Soc. Abstr.* 17:222

20. Brown JE, Faddis M, Combs A. 1992. Light does not induce an increase in cyclic-GMP content of squid or *Limulus* photoreceptors. *Exp. Eye Res.* 54:403–10

21. Brown RL, Bert RJ, Evans FE, Karpen JW. 1993. Activation of retinal rod cGMP-gated channels: what makes for an effective 8-substituted derivative of cGMP? *Biochemistry* 32:10089–95

22. Brown RL, Gerber WV, Karpen JW. 1993. Specific labeling and permanent activation of the retinal rod cGMP-activated channel by the photoaffinity analog 8-*p*-azidophenacylthio-cGMP. *Proc. Natl. Acad. Sci. USA* 90:5369–73

23. Brown RL, Gramling R, Bert RJ, Karpen JW. 1995. Cyclic GMP contact points within the 63-kDa subunit and a 240-kDa associated protein of retinal rod cGMP-activated channels. *Biochemistry* 34:8365–70

24. Brüggemann A, Pardo LA, Stühmer W, Pongs O. 1993. *Ether-a-go-go* encodes a voltage-gated channel permeable to $K^+$ and $Ca^{2+}$ and modulated by cAMP. *Nature* 365:445–48

25. Buchanan LV, Kabell G, Brunden MN, Gibson JK. 1993. Comparative assessment of Ibutilide, d-Sotalol, Clofilium, E-4031, and UK-68,798 in a rabbit model of proarrhythmia. *J. Cardiovasc. Pharmacol.* 22:540–49

26. Chen T-Y, Illing M, Molday LL, Hsu Y-T, Yau K-W, et al 1994. Subunit 2 (or β) of retinal rod cGMP-gated cation channel is a component of the 240-kDa channel-associated protein and mediates $Ca^{2+}$-calmodulin modulation. *Proc. Natl. Acad. Sci. USA* 91:11757–61

27. Chen T-Y, Peng Y-W, Dhallan RS, Ahamed B, Reed RR, Yau K-W. 1993. A new subunit of the cyclic nucleotide-gated cation channel in retinal rods. *Nature* 362:764–67

28. Chen T-Y, Yau K-W. 1994. Direct modulation by $Ca^{2+}$-calmodulin of cyclic nucleotide-activated channel of rat olfactory receptor neurons. *Nature* 368:545–48

29. Cobbs WH, Barkdoll AE III, Pugh EN Jr. 1985. Cyclic GMP increases photocurrent and light sensitivity of retinal cones. *Nature* 317:64–66

30. Cobbs WH, Pugh EN Jr. 1987. Kinetics and components of the flash photocurrent of isolated retinal rods of the larval salamander, *Ambystoma tigrinum*. *J. Physiol.* 394:529–72

31. Colamartino G, Menini A, Torre V. 1991. Blockage and permeation of divalent cations through the cyclic GMP-activated channel from tiger salamander retinal rods. *J. Physiol.* 440:189–206

32. Colquhoun D, Farrant M. 1993. The binding issue. *Nature* 366:510–11

33. Cook NJ, Hanke W, Kaupp UB. 1987. Identification, purification, and functional reconstitution of the cyclic GMP-dependent channel from rod photoreceptors. *Proc. Natl. Acad. Sci. USA* 84:585–89

34. Cook NJ, Zeilinger C, Koch K-W, Kaupp UB. 1986. Solubilization and functional reconstitution of the cGMP-dependent cation channel from bovine rod outer segments. *J. Biol. Chem.* 261:17033–39

35. Curran ME, Splawski I, Timothy KW, Vincent GM, Green ED, et al. 1995. A molecular basis for cardiac arrhythmia: HERG mutations cause long QT syndrome. *Cell* 80:795–803

36. Darvish N, Winaver J, Dagan D. 1995. A novel cGMP-activated $Cl^-$ channel in renal proximal tubules. *Am. J. Physiol.* 268:F323–29

37. Delgado R, Hidalgo P, Diaz F, Latorre R, Labarca P. 1991. A cyclic AMP-activated $K^+$ channel in *Drosophila* larval muscle is persistently activated in *dunce*. *Proc. Natl. Acad. Sci. USA* 88:557–60

37a. Dhallan RS, Haynes LW, Yau K-W. 1990. Openings of single rod cGMP-gated channels induced by cAMP. *Biophys. J.* 57:367a (Abstr.)

38. Dhallan RS, Macke JP, Eddy RL, Shows TB, Reed RR, et al. 1992. Human rod photoreceptor cGMP-gated channel:

amino acid sequence, gene structure, and functional expression. *J. Neurosci.* 12:3248–56

39. Dhallan RS, Yau K-W, Schrader KA, Reed RR. 1990. Primary structure and functional expression of a cyclic nucleotide-activated channel from olfactory neurons. *Nature* 347:184–87

40. DiFrancesco D. 1993. Pacemaker mechanisms in cardiac tissue. *Annu. Rev. Physiol.* 55:451–67

41. DiFrancesco D, Tortora P. 1991. Direct activation of cardiac pacemaker channels by intracellular cyclic AMP. *Nature* 351:145–47

42. Distler M, Biel M, Flockerzi V, Hofmann F. 1994. Expression of cyclic nucleotide-gated cation channels in nonsensory tissues and cells. *Neuropharmacology* 33:1275–82

43. Donner K, Hemila S, Kalamkarov G, Koskelainen A, Pogozheva I, et al. 1990. Sulfhydryl binding reagents increase the conductivity of the light-sensitive channel and inhibit phototransduction in retinal rods. *Exp. Eye Res.* 51:97–105

44. Dryer SE, Henderson D. 1991. A cyclic GMP-activated channel in dissociated cells of the chick pineal gland. *Nature* 353:756–58

45. Dryer SE, Henderson D. 1993. Cyclic GMP-activated channels of the chick pineal gland: effects of divalent cations, pH, and cyclic AMP. *J. Comp. Physiol. A* 172:271–79

46. Dryja TP, Finn JT, Peng Y-W, McGee TL, Berson EL, et al. 1995. Mutations in the gene encoding the α subunit of the rod cGMP-gated channel in autosomal recessive retinitis pigmentosa. *Proc. Natl. Acad. Sci. USA* 92:10177–81

47. Eismann E, Müller F, Heinemann SH, Kaupp UB. 1994. A single negative charge within the pore region of a cGMP-gated channel controls rectification, $Ca^{2+}$ blockage, and ionic selectivity. *Proc. Natl. Acad. Sci. USA* 91:1109–13

47a. El-Husseini AE, Bladen C, Vincent SR. 1995. Expression of the olfactory cyclic nucleotide-gated channel (CNG1) in the rat brain. *NeuroReport* 6:1131–35

48. Fadool DA, Ache BW. 1992. Plasma membrane inositol 1,4,5-trisphosphate-activated channels mediate signal transduction in lobster olfactory receptor neurons. *Neuron* 9:907–18

49. Fesenko EE, Kolesnikov SS, Lyubarsky AL. 1985. Induction by cyclic GMP of cationic conductance in plasma membrane of retinal rod outer segment. *Nature* 313:310–13

50. Finn JT, Li J, Yau K-W. 1995. C-terminus involvement in the gating of cyclic nucleotide-activated channels as revealed by $Ni^{2+}$ and NEM. *Biophys. J.* 68:A385 (Abstr.)

51. Finn JT, Schroeder JE, Chen T-Y, Yau K-W. 1994. Hybrid channels formed from co-assembly of retinal rod and olfactory cyclic nucleotide-gated channel proteins. *Biophys. J.* 66:A350 (Abstr.)

52. Finn JT, Solessio E, Yau K-W. 1995. cGMP-activated channel in photoreceptors of lizard parietal eye. *Invest. Ophthal. Vis. Sci.* 36:1262 (Abstr.)

53. Firestein S, Darrow B, Shepherd GM. 1991. Activation of the sensory current in salamander olfactory receptor neurons depends on a G protein-mediated cAMP second messenger system. *Neuron* 6:825–35

54. Firestein S, Zufall F, Shepherd GM. 1991. Single odor-sensitive channels in olfactory receptor neurons are also gated by cyclic nucleotides. *J. Neurosci.* 11:3565–72

55. Frings S, Lindemann B. 1991. Current recording from sensory cilia of olfactory receptor cells in situ. I. The neuronal response to cyclic nucleotides. *J. Gen. Physiol.* 97:1–16

56. Frings S, Lynch JW, Lindemann B. 1992. Properties of cyclic nucleotide-gated channels mediating olfactory transduction: activation, selectivity and blockage. *J. Gen. Physiol.* 100:45–67

57. Frings S, Seifert R, Godde M, Kaupp UB. 1995. Profoundly different calcium permeation and blockage determine the specific function of distinct cyclic nucleotide-gated channels. *Neuron* 15:169–79

58. Furman RE, Tanaka JC. 1990. Monovalent selectivity of the cyclic guanosine monophosphate-activated ion channel. *J. Gen. Physiol.* 96:57–82

59. Ganetzky B, Wu CF. 1985. Genes and membrane excitability in *Drosophila.* *Trends Neurosci.* 8:322–26

60. Garbers DL. 1989. Molecular basis of fertilization. *Annu. Rev. Biochem.* 58:719–42

61. Gilbertson T. 1993. The physiology of vertebrate taste reception. *Curr. Opin. Neurobiol.* 3:532–39

62. Gomez MD, Nasi E. 1994. The light-sensitive conductance of hyperpolarizing invertebrate photoreceptors: a patch-clamp study. *J. Gen. Physiol.* 103:939–56

63. Gomez MD, Nasi E. 1994. Blockage of the light-sensitive conductance in hyperpolarizing photoreceptors of the scallop: effects of tetraethylammonium and

4-aminopyridine. *J. Gen. Physiol.* 104: 487–505

64. Gomez MD, Nasi E. 1995. Activation of light-dependent potassium channels in ciliary invertebrate photoreceptors involves cGMP but not the IP$_3$/Ca cascade. *Neuron.* 15:607–18

65. Gordon SE, Brautigan DL, Zimmerman AL. 1992. Protein phosphatases modulate the apparent agonist affinity of the light-regulated ion channel in retinal rods. *Neuron* 9:739–48

66. Gordon SE, Downing-Park J, Tam B, Zimmerman AL. 1995. Diacylglycerol analogs inhibit the rod cGMP-gated channel by a phosphorylation-independent mechanism. *Biophys. J.* 69: 409–17

67. Gordon SE, Downing-Park J, Zimmerman AL. 1995. Modulation of the cGMP-gated ion channel in frog rods by calmodulin and an endogenous inhibitory factor. *J. Physiol.* 486:533–46

68. Gordon SE, Zagotta WN. 1995. A histidine residue associated with the gate of the cyclic nucleotide-activated channels in rod photoreceptors. *Neuron* 14: 177–83

69. Gordon SE, Zagotta WN. 1995. Localization of regions affecting an allosteric transition in cyclic nucleotide-activated channels. *Neuron* 14:857–64

70. Gotow T. 1989. Photoresponse of an extraocular photoreceptor associated with a decrease in membrane conductance in an opisthobranch mollusc. *Brain Res.* 479:120–29

71. Gotow T, Nishi T. 1991. Roles of cyclic GMP and inositol trisphosphate in phototransduction of the molluscan extraocular photoreceptor. *Brain Res.* 557: 121–28

72. Gotow T, Nishi T, Kijima H. 1994. Single K$^+$ channels closed by light and opened by cyclic GMP in molluscan extraocular photoreceptor cells. *Brain Res.* 662:268–72

73. Goulding EH, Ngai J, Kramer RH, Colicos M, Axel R, et al. 1992. Molecular cloning and single-channel properties of the cyclic nucleotide-gated channel from catfish olfactory neurons. *Neuron* 8:45–58

74. Goulding EH, Tibbs GR, Liu D, Siegelbaum SA. 1993. Role of H5 domain in determining pore diameter and ion permeation through cyclic nucleotide-gated channels. *Nature* 364:61–64

75. Goulding EH, Tibbs GR, Siegelbaum SA. 1994. Molecular mechanism of cyclic-nucleotide-gated channel activation. *Nature* 372:369–74

76. Gray P, Attwell D. 1985. Kinetics of light-sensitive channel in vertebrate photoreceptors. *Proc. R. Soc. London Ser. B* 223:379–88

77. Griffith LC, Wang J, Zhong Y, Wu C-F, Greenspan RJ. 1994. Calcium/calmodulin-dependent protein kinase II and potassium channel subunit Eag similarly affect plasticity in *Drosophila*. *Proc. Natl. Acad. Sci. USA* 91:10044–48

78. Guy HR, Durell SR, Warmke J, Drysdale R, Ganetzky B. 1991. Similarities in amino acid sequences of *Drosophila eag* and cyclic nucleotide-gated channels. *Science* 254:730

79. Hardie RC, Minke B. 1993. Novel Ca$^{2+}$ channels underlying transduction in *Drosophila* photoreceptors: implications for phosphoinositide-mediated Ca$^{2+}$ mobilization. *Trends Neurosci.* 19: 371–76

80. Hatt H, Ache BW. 1994. Cyclic nucleotide- and inositol phosphate-gated ion channels in lobster olfactory receptor neurons. *Proc. Natl. Acad. Sci. USA* 91:6264–68

81. Haynes LW. 1992. Block of the cyclic GMP-gated channel of vertebrate rod and cone photoreceptors by L-*cis*-diltiazem. *J. Gen. Physiol.* 100:783–801

82. Haynes LW. 1995. Permeation of internal and external monovalent cations through the catfish cone photoreceptor cGMP-gated channel. *J. Gen. Physiol.* 106:485–505

83. Haynes LW. 1995. Permeation and block by internal and external divalent cations of the catfish cone photoreceptor cGMP-gated channel. *J. Gen. Physiol.* 106:507–23

84. Haynes LW, Yau K-W. 1985. Cyclic GMP-sensitive conductance in outer segment membrane of catfish cones. *Nature* 317:61–64

85. Haynes LW, Yau K-W. 1990. Single-channel measurement from the cyclic GMP-activated conductance of catfish retinal cones. *J. Physiol.* 429: 451–81

86. Heginbotham L, Abramson T, MacKinnon R. 1992. A functional connection between the pores of distantly related ion channels as revealed by mutant K$^+$ channels. *Science* 258:1152–55

87. Henn DK, Baumann A, Kaupp UB. 1995. Probing the transmembrane topology of cyclic nucleotide-gated ion channels with a gene fusion approach. *Proc. Natl. Acad. Sci. USA* 92:7425–29

88. Hess P, Tsien RW. 1984. Mechanism of ion permeation through calcium channels. *Nature* 309:453–56

89. Ho K, Nichols CG, Lederer WJ, Lytton J, Vassilev PM, et al. 1993. Cloning and expression of an inwardly rectifying

ATP-regulated potassium channel. *Nature* 362:31–38

90. Hoshi T. 1995. Regulation of voltage dependence of the KAT1 channel by intracellular factors. *J. Gen. Physiol.* 105:309–28

91. Hsu Y-T, Molday RS. 1993. Modulation of the cGMP-gated channel of rod photoreceptor cells by calmodulin. *Nature* 361:76–79

92. Hsu Y-T, Molday RS. 1994. Interaction of calmodulin with the cyclic GMP-gated channel of rod photoreceptor cells. *J. Biol. Chem.* 269:29765–70

93. Hundal SP, DiFrancesco D, Mangoni M, Brammar WJ, Conley EC. 1993. An isoform of the cGMP-gated retinal photoreceptor channel gene expressed in the sinoatrial node (pacemaker) region of rabbit heart. *Biochem. Soc. Trans.* 21: 119S (Abstr.)

94. Ildefonse M, Bennett N. 1991. Single-channel study of the cGMP-dependent conductance of retinal rods from incorporation of native vesicles into planar lipid bilayers. *J. Membr. Biol.* 123:133–47

95. Ildefonse M, Crouzy S, Bennett N. 1992. Gating of retinal rod cation channel by different nucleotides: comparative study of unitary currents. *J. Membr. Biol.* 130: 91–104

96. Jan LY, Jan YN. 1990. A superfamily of ion channels. *Nature* 345:672

97. Jan LY, Jan YN. 1992. Tracing the roots of ion channels. *Cell* 69:715–18

98. Johnson EC, Bacigalupo J. 1992. Spontaneous activity of the light-dependent channel irreversibly induced in excised patches from *Limulus* ventral photoreceptors. *J. Membr. Biol.* 130:33–47

99. Karpen JW, Brown RL, Stryer L, Baylor DA. 1993. Interactions between divalent cations and the gating machinery of cyclic GMP-activated channels in salamander retinal rods. *J. Gen. Physiol.* 101:1–25

100. Karpen JW, Zimmerman AL, Stryer L, Baylor DA. 1988. Gating kinetics of the cyclic-GMP-activated channel of retinal rods: flash photolysis and voltage-jump studies. *Proc. Natl. Acad. Sci. USA* 85: 1287–91

101. Kaupp UB, Koch K-W. 1992. Role of cGMP and $Ca^{2+}$ in vertebrate photoreceptor excitation and adaptation. *Annu. Rev. Physiol.* 54:153–75

102. Kaupp UB, Niidome T, Tanabe T, Terada S, Bönigk W, et al. 1989. Primary structure and functional expression from complementary DNA of the rod photoreceptor cyclic GMP-gated channel. *Nature* 342:762–66

103. Kawamura S. 1993. Molecular aspects of photoreceptor adaptation in vertebrate retina. *Intern. Rev. Neurobiol.* 35: 43–86

104. Kinnamon SC, Cummings TA. 1992. Chemosensory transduction mechanism in taste. *Annu. Rev. Physiol.* 54:715–31

105. Kleene SJ. 1993. The cyclic nucleotide-activated conductance in olfactory cilia: effects of cytoplasmic $Mg^{2+}$ and $Ca^{2+}$. *J. Membr. Biol.* 131:237–43

106. Kleene SJ. 1995. Block by external calcium and magnesium of the cyclic-nucleotide-activated current in olfactory cilia. *Neuroscience* 66:1001–8

106a. Kleene SJ, Gesteland RC. 1991. Calcium-activated chloride conductance in frog olfactory cilia. *J. Neurosci.* 11: 3624–29

107. Koch K-W, Kaupp UB. 1985. Cyclic GMP directly regulates a cation conductance in membranes of bovine rods by a cooperative mechanism. *J. Biol. Chem.* 260:6788–800

108. Kolesnikov SS, Margolskee RF. 1995. A cyclic-nucleotide-suppressible conductance activated by transducin in taste cells. *Nature* 376:85–88

109. Körschen H, Illing M, Seifert R, Sesti F, Williams A, et al. 1995. A 240kDa protein represents the complete β-subunit of the cyclic nucleotide-gated channel from rod photoreceptor. *Neuron.* In press

110. Koutalos Y, Nakatani K, Yau K-W. 1995. The cGMP-phosphodiesterase and its contribution to sensitivity regulation in retinal rods. *J. Gen. Physiol.* In press

111. Koutalos Y, Yau K-W. 1995. Sensitivity regulation in rod photoreceptors by calcium. *Trends Neurosci.* In press

112. Kramer RH, Goulding E, Siegelbaum SA. 1994. Potassium channel inactivation peptide blocks cyclic nucleotide-gated channels by binding to the conserved pore domain. *Neuron* 12: 655–62

113. Kramer RH, Siegelbaum SA. 1992. Intracellular $Ca^{2+}$ regulates the sensitivity of cyclic nucleotide-gated channels in olfactory receptor neurons. *Neuron* 9: 897–906

114. Kubo Y, Baldwin TJ, Jan YN, Jan LY. 1993. Primary structure and functional expression of a mouse inward rectifier potassium channel. *Nature* 362:127–33

115. Kumar VD, Weber IT. 1992. Molecular model of the cyclic GMP-binding domain of the cyclic GMP-gated ion channel. *Biochemistry* 31:4643–49

116. Kurahashi T. 1989. Activation by odorants of cation-selective conduc-

tance in the olfactory receptor cell isolated from the newt. *J. Physiol.* 419: 177–92

117. Kurahashi T. 1990. The response induced by intracellular cyclic AMP in isolated olfactory receptor cells of the newt. *J. Physiol.* 430:355–71

118. Kurahashi T, Kaneko A. 1993. Gating properties of the cAMP-gated channel in toad olfactory receptor cells. *J. Physiol.* 466:287–302

119. Kurahashi T, Shibuya T. 1990. Ca²⁺-dependent adaptive properties in the solitary olfactory cell of the newt. *Brain Res.* 515:261–68

120. Kurahashi T, Yau K-W. 1993. Co-existence of cationic and chloride components in the odorant-induced current of vertebrate olfactory receptor cells. *Nature* 363:71–74

120a. Kurahashi T, Yau K-W. 1994. Tale of an unusual chloride current. *Curr. Biol.* 4:256–58

121. Kurosaki F, Kaburaki H, Nishi A. 1994. Involvement of plasma membrane-located calmodulin in the response decay of cyclic nucleotide-gated cation channel of cultured carrot cells. *FEBS Lett.* 340:193–96

122. Lagnado L, Baylor DA. 1992. Signal flow in visual transduction. *Neuron* 8: 995–1002

123. Lancet DA. 1986. Vertebrate olfactory reception. *Annu. Rev. Neurosci.* 9:329–55

124. Li M, Jan YN, Jan LY. 1992. Specification of subunit assembly by the hydrophilic amino-terminal domain of the Shaker potassium channel. *Science* 257: 1225–30

125. Li M, Unwin N, Stauffer KA, Jan Y-N, Jan LY. 1994. Images of purified Shaker potassium channels. *Curr. Biol.* 4:110–15

126. Light DB, Corbin JD, Stanton BA. 1990. Dual ion-channel regulation by cyclic GMP and cyclic GMP-dependent protein kinase. *Nature* 344:336–39

127. Light DB, McCann FV, Keller TM, Stanton BA. 1988. Amiloride-sensitive cation channel in apical membrane of inner medullary collecting duct. *Am. J. Physiol.* 255:F278–86

128. Light DB, Schwiebert EM, Karlson KH, Stanton BA. 1989. Atrial natriuretic peptide inhibits a cation channel in renal inner medullary collecting duct cells. *Science* 243:383–85

129. Liman ER, Buck LB. 1994. A second subunit of the olfactory cyclic nucleotide-gated channel confers high sensitivity to cAMP. *Neuron* 13:611–21

130. Lisman J, Erickson MA, Richard EA,

Cote RH, Bacigalupo J, et al. 1992. Mechanisms of amplification, deactivation, and noise reduction in invertebrate photoreceptors. In *Sensory Transduction*, ed. DP Corey, SD Roper, pp. 175–99. New York: Rockefeller Univ. Press

131. Liu M, Chen T-Y, Ahamed B, Li J, Yau K-W. 1994. Calcium-calmodulin modulation of the olfactory cyclic nucleotide-gated cation channel. *Science* 266: 1348–54

132. Liu M, Li J, Yau K-W. 1994. Phosphorylation of the N-terminal domain of human rod cyclic nucleotide-gated channel by protein kinase C and the cAMP-dependent protein kinase. *Invest. Ophthal. Vis. Sci.* 35:1474 (Abstr.)

133. Lowe G, Gold GH. 1993. Contribution of the ciliary cyclic nucleotide-gated conductance to olfactory transduction in the salamander. *J. Physiol.* 462:175–96

134. Lowe G, Gold GH. 1993. Nonlinear amplification by calcium-dependent chloride channels in olfactory receptor cells. *Nature* 366:283–86

135. Ludwig J, Margalit T, Eismann E, Lancet D, Kaupp UB. 1990. Primary structure of cAMP-gated channel from bovine olfactory epithelium. *FEBS Lett.* 270:24–29

136. Ludwig J, Terlau H, Wunder F, Bruggemann A, Pardo LA, et al. 1994. Functional expression of a rat homologue of the voltage gated ether a go-go potassium channel reveals differences in selectivity and activation kinetics between the *Drosophila* channel and its mammalian counterpart. *EMBO J.* 13:4451–58

137. Lynch JW, Lindemann B. 1994. Cyclic nucleotide-gated channels of rat olfactory cells: divalent cations control the sensitivity to cAMP. *J. Gen. Physiol.* 103:87–106

138. Maack T, Kleinert HD. 1986. Renal and cardiovascular effects of atrial natriuretic factor. *Biochem. Pharmacol.* 35: 2057–64

139. MacKinnon R. 1991. Determination of the subunit stoichiometry of a voltage-activated potassium channel. *Nature* 350:232–35

140. Matthews G, Watanabe SI. 1988. Activation of single ion channels from toad retinal rod inner segments by cyclic GMP: concentration dependence. *J. Physiol.* 403:389–405

141. McGeoch JEM, Guidotti G. 1992. An insulin-stimulated cation channel in skeletal muscle: inhibition by calcium causes oscillation. *J. Biol. Chem.* 267: 832–41

142. McKay DB, Steitz TA. 1981. Structure

of catabolite gene activator protein at 2.9-Å resolution suggests binding to left-handed B-DNA. *Nature* 290:744–49

143. McKay DB, Weber IT, Steitz TA. 1982. Structure of catabolite gene activator protein at 2.9-Å resolution. *J. Biol. Chem.* 257:9518–24

144. McLatchie LM, Matthews HR. 1992. Voltage-dependent block by L-*cis*-diltiazem of the cyclic GMP-activated conductance of salamander rods. *Proc. R. Soc. London Ser. B* 247:113–19

145. McLatchie LM, Matthews HR. 1994. The effect of pH on the block by L-*cis*-diltiazem and amiloride of the cyclic GMP-activated conductance of salamander rods. *Proc. R. Soc. London Ser. B* 255:231–36

146. McReynolds JS. 1976. Hyperpolarizing photoreceptors in invertebrates. In *Neural Principles in Vision*, ed. F Zettler, R Weiler, pp. 394–409. Berlin: Springer-Verlag

147. Menini A. 1990. Currents carried by monovalent cations through cyclic GMP-activated channels in excised patches from salamander rods. *J. Physiol.* 424:167–85

148. Michel WC, Ache BW. 1992. Cyclic nucleotides mediate an odor-evoked potassium conductance in lobster olfactory receptor cells. *J. Neurosci.* 12:3979–84

149. Michel WC, McClintock TS, Ache BW. 1991. Inhibition of lobster olfactory receptor cells by an odor-activated potassium conductance. *J. Neurophysiol.* 65:446–53

149a. Milkman R. 1994. An *Escherichia coli* homologue of eukaryotic potassium channel proteins. *Proc. Natl. Acad. Sci. USA* 91:3510–14

150. Molday LL, Cook NJ, Kaupp UB, Molday RS. 1990. The cGMP-gated cation channel of bovine rod photoreceptor cells is associated with a 240-kDa protein exhibiting immunochemical cross-reactivity with spectrin. *J. Biol. Chem.* 265:18690–95

151. Molday RS, Molday LL, Dosé A, Clark-Lewis I, Illing M, et al. 1991. The cGMP-gated channel of the rod photoreceptor cell: characterization and orientation of the amino terminus. *J. Biol. Chem.* 266:21917–22

152. Mori Y, Friedrich T, Kim MS, Mikami A, Nakai J, et al. 1991. Primary structure and functional expression from complementary DNA of a brain calcium channel. *Nature* 350:398–402

153. Nakajima Y, Iwakabe H, Akazawa C, Nawa H, Shigemoto R, et al. 1993. Molecular characterization of a novel retinal metabotropic glutamate receptor mGluR6 with a high agonist selectivity for L-2-amino-4-phosphonobutyrate. *J. Biol. Chem.* 268:11868–73

154. Nakamura T, Gold GH. 1987. A cyclic nucleotide-gated conductance in olfactory receptor cilia. *Nature* 325:442–44

155. Nakatani K, Koutalos Y, Yau K-W. 1995. Ca²⁺ modulation of the cGMP-gated channel of bullfrog retinal rod photoreceptors. *J. Physiol.* 484:69–76

156. Nakatani K, Yau K-W. 1989. Sodium-dependent calcium extrusion and sensitivity regulation in retinal cones of the salamander. *J. Physiol.* 409:525–48

157. Nasi E, Gomez M. 1990. Recording from solitary photoreceptors and reconstituted rhabdomeric membranes of the squid. *Biophys. J.* 57(2):368 (Abstr.)

158. Nasi E, Gomez M. 1991. Light-activated channels in scallop photoreceptors: recordings from cell-attached and perfused excised patches. *Biophys. J.* 59(2):540 (Abstr.)

159. Nawy S, Jahr CE. 1990. Suppression by glutamate of cGMP-activated conductance in retinal bipolar cells. *Nature* 346:269–71

160. Nawy S, Jahr CE. 1991. cGMP-gated conductance in retinal bipolar cells is suppressed by the photoreceptor transmitter. *Neuron* 7:677–83

161. Nicol GD. 1993. The calcium channel antagonist, pimozide, blocks the cyclic GMP-activated current in rod photoreceptors. *J. Pharmacol. Exp. Ther.* 265:626–32

162. Nicol GD, Schnetkamp PPM, Saimi Y, Cragoe EJ, Bownds MD. 1987. A derivative of amiloride blocks both the light- and cyclic GMP-regulated conductances in rod photoreceptors. *J. Gen. Physiol.* 90:651–70

163. Nizzari M, Sesti F, Giraudo MT, Virginio C, Cattaneo A, et al. 1993. Single-channel properties of cloned cGMP-activated channels from retinal rods. *Proc. R. Soc. London Ser. B* 254:69–74

164. Payne R, Walz B, Levy S, Fein A. 1988. The localization of calcium release in *Limulus* ventral photoreceptors and its control by negative feedback. *Philos. Trans. R. Soc.* 320:359–79

165. Perry RJ, McNaughton PA. 1991. Response properties of cones from the retina of the tiger salamander. *J. Physiol.* 433:561–87

166. Picco C, Menini A. 1993. The permeability of the cGMP-activated channel to organic cations in retinal rods of the tiger salamander. *J. Physiol.* 460:741–58

167. Picones A, Korenbrot JI. 1992. Permeation and interaction of monovalent cations with the cGMP-gated channel of cone photoreceptors. *J. Gen. Physiol.* 100:647–73

168. Picones A, Korenbrot JI. 1994. Analysis of fluctuations in the cGMP-dependent currents of cone photoreceptor outer segments. *Biophys. J.* 66:360–65

169. Picones A, Korenbrot JI. 1995. Permeability and interaction of $Ca^{2+}$ with cGMP-gated ion channels differ in retinal rod and cone photoreceptors. *Biophys. J.* 69:120–27

170. Picones A, Korenbrot JI. 1995. Spontaneous, ligand-independent activity of the cGMP-gated ion channels in cone photoreceptors of fish. *J. Physiol.* 485:699–14

171. Pittler SJ, Lee AK, Altherr MR, Howard TA, Seldin MF, et al. 1992. Primary structure and chromosomal localization of human and mouse rod photoreceptor cGMP-gated cation channel. *J. Biol. Chem.* 267:6257–62

172. Pu GA, Dowling JE. 1981. Anatomical and physiological characteristics of pineal photoreceptor cell in the larval lamprey, *Petromyzon marinus*. *J. Neurophysiol.* 46:1018–38

173. Pugh EN Jr, Lamb TD. 1993. Amplification and kinetics of the activation steps in phototransduction. *Biochim. Biophys. Acta* 1141:111–49

174. Quandt FN, Nicol GD, Schnetkamp PPM. 1991. Voltage-dependent gating and block of the cyclic-GMP-dependent current in bovine rod outer segments. *Neuroscience* 42:629–38

175. Ranganathan R, Malicki DM, Zuker CS. 1995. Signal transduction in *Drosophila* photoreceptors. *Annu. Rev. Neurosci.* 18:283–17

176. Reale V, Hales CN, Ashford MLJ. 1994. Nucleotide regulation of a calcium-activated cation channel in the rat insulinoma cell line, CRI-G1. *J. Membr. Biol.* 141:101–12

176a. Reale V, Hales CN, Ashford MLJ. 1995. Regulation of calcium-activated nonselective cation channel activity by cyclic nucleotides in the rat insulinoma cell line, CRI-G1. *J. Membr. Biol.* 145:267–78

177. Reed RR. 1992. Signaling pathways in odorant detection. *Neuron* 8:205–29

178. Rieke F, Schwartz EA. 1994. A cGMP-gated current can control exocytosis at cone synapses. *Neuron* 13:863–73

179. Robertson GA, Warmke JW, Ganetzky B. 1993. Functional expression of the *Drosophila EAG* $K^+$ channel gene. *Biophys. J.* 64(2):340 (Abstr.)

180. Root MJ, MacKinnon R. 1993. Identification of an external divalent cation-binding site in the pore of a cGMP-activated channel. *Neuron* 11:459–66

181. Root MJ, MacKinnon R. 1994. Two identical noninteracting sites in an ion channel revealed by proton transfer. *Science* 265:1852–56

182. Ruiz ML. 1994. *The cloning of an olfactory channel from mouse heart*. PhD thesis. Harvard, Cambridge, MA. 93 pp.

183. Ruiz-Avila L, McLaughlin SK, Wildman D, McKinnon PJ, Robichon A, et al. 1995. Coupling of bitter receptor to phosphodiesterase through transducin in taste receptor cells. *Nature* 376:80–85

184. Sanguinetti MC, Jiang C, Curran ME, Keating MT. 1995. A mechanistic link between an inherited and an acquired cardiac arrhythmia: HERG encodes the $I_{kr}$ potassium channel. *Cell* 81:299–307

185. Schaad NC, Vanecek J, Rodriguez IR, Klein DC, Holtzclaw L, et al. 1995. Vasoactive intestinal peptide elevates pinealocyte intracellular calcium concentrations by enhancing influx: evidence for involvement of a cyclic GMP-dependent mechanism. *Mol. Pharmacol.* 47:923–33

186. Schachtman DP, Schroeder JI, Lucas WJ, Anderson JA, Gaber RF. 1992. Expression of an inward-rectifying potassium channel by the *Arabidopsis KAT1* cDNA. *Science* 258:1654–58

187. Schmiedel-Jacob I, Michel WC, Anderson PAV, Ache BW. 1990. Whole cell recording from lobster olfactory receptor cells: multiple ionic bases for the receptor potential. *Chem. Senses* 15:397–405

188. Schnetkamp PPM. 1987. Sodium ions selectively eliminate the fast component of guanosine cyclic 3',5'-phosphate induced $Ca^{2+}$ release from bovine rod outer segment disks. *Biochemistry* 26:3249–53

189. Schnetkamp PPM. 1990. Cation selectivity of and cation binding to the cGMP-dependent channel in bovine rod outer segment membranes. *J. Gen. Physiol.* 96:517–34

190. Schroeder JI, Hedrich R. 1989. Involvement of ion channels and active transport in osmoregulation and signaling of higher plant cells. *Trends Biochem. Sci.* 14:187–92

191. Scott S-P, Tanaka JC. 1995. Molecular interactions of 3',5'-cyclic purine analogues with the binding site of retinal rod ion channels. *Biochemistry* 34:2338–47

192. Sentenac H, Bonneaud N, Minet M, Lacroute F, Salmon J-M, et al. 1992.

Cloning and expression in yeast of a plant potassium ion transport system. *Science* 256:663–65

192a. Serre V, Ildefonse M, Bennett N. 1995. Effects of cysteine modification on the activity of the cGMP-gated channel from retinal rods. *J. Membr. Biol.* 146: 145–62

193. Sesti F, Eismann E, Kaupp UB, Nizarri M, Torre V. 1995. The multi-ion nature of the cGMP-gated channel from vertebrate rods. *J. Physiol.* 487:17–36

194. Sesti F, Straforini M, Lamb TD, Torre V. 1994. Gating, selectivity and blockage of single channels activated by cyclic GMP in retinal rods of the tiger salamander. *J. Physiol.* 474:203–22

195. Shabb JB, Ng L, Corbin JD. 1990. One amino acid change produces a high affinity cGMP-binding site in cAMP-dependent protein kinase. *J. Biol. Chem.* 265:16031–34

196. Shen NV, Chen X, Boyer MM, Pfaffinger PJ. 1993. Deletion analysis of $K^+$ channel assembly. *Neuron* 11:67–76

197. Shiells RA, Falk G. 1990. Glutamate receptors of rod bipolar cells are linked to a cyclic GMP cascade via a G-protein. *Proc. R. Soc. London Ser. B* 242:91–94

198. Shiells RA, Falk G. 1992. The glutamate-receptor linked cGMP cascade of retinal on-bipolar cells is pertussis and cholera toxin-sensitive. *Proc. R. Soc. London Ser. B* 247:17–20

199. Shiells RA, Falk G. 1992. Retinal on-bipolar cells contain a nitric oxide-sensitive guanylate cyclase. *NeuroReport* 3:845–48

200. Shiells RA, Falk G. 1992. Properties of the cGMP-activated channel of retinal on-bipolar cells. *Proc. R. Soc. London Ser. B* 247:21–25

201. Slaughter MM, Miller RF. 1981. 2-Amino-4-phosphonobutyric acid: a new pharmacological tool for retina research. *Science* 211:182–85

202. Solessio E, Engbretson GA. 1993. Antagonistic chromatic mechanisms in photoreceptors of the parietal eye of lizards. *Nature* 364:442–45

203. Stern JH, Kaupp UB, MacLeish PR. 1986. Control of the light-regulated current in rod photoreceptors by cyclic GMP, calcium and L-*cis*-diltiazem. *Proc. Natl. Acad. Sci. USA* 83:1163–67

204. Sudlow LC, Huang R-C, Green DJ, Gillette R. 1993. cAMP-activated $Na^+$ current of molluscan neurons is resistant to kinase inhibitors and is gated by cAMP in the isolated patch. *J. Neurosci.* 13:5188–93

205. Sun Z-P, Akabas MH, Karlin A, Siegelbaum SA. 1993. Covalent modification of cysteines by MTSEA changes cGMP responses of a cyclic nucleotide-gated channel. *Soc. Neurosci. Abstr.* 19:713

206. Sun Z-P, Goulding EH, Akabas M, Karlin A, Siegelbaum SA. 1995. State dependent accessibility of the amino acid residues lining the pore of a cyclic nucleotide-gated channel. *Biophys. J.* 68: A264 (Abstr.)

207. Tamotsu S, Morita Y. 1986. Photoreception in pineal organs of larval and adult lampreys, *Lampetra japonica*. *J. Comp. Physiol. A* 159:1–5

208. Tanaka JC. 1993. The effects of protons on 3′,5′-cGMP-activated currents in photoreceptor patches. *Biophys. J.* 65: 2517–23

209. Tanaka JC, Eccleston JF, Furman RE. 1989. Photoreceptor channel activation by nucleotide derivatives. *Biochemistry* 28:2776–84

210. Tanaka JC, Furman RE. 1993. Divalent effects on cGMP-activated currents in excised patches from amphibian photoreceptors. *J. Membr. Biol.* 131:245–56

211. Taylor WR, Baylor DA. 1995. Conductance and kinetics of single cGMP-activated channels in salamander rod outer segments. *J. Physiol.* 483:567–82

212. Tempel BL, Papazian DM, Schwarz TL, Jan YN, Jan LY. 1987. Sequence of a probable potassium channel component encoded at *Shaker* locus of *Drosophila*. *Science* 237:770–75

213. Tibbs GR, Goulding EH, Siegelbaum SA. 1995. Spontaneous opening of cyclic nucleotide-gated channels supports an allosteric model of activation. *Biophys. J.* 68:A253 (Abstr.)

214. Torre V, Straforini M, Sesti F, Lamb TD. 1992. Different channel-gating properties of two classes of cyclic GMP-activated channel in vertebrate photoreceptors. *Proc. R. Soc. London Ser. B* 250:209–15

215. Trudeau MC, Warmke JW, Ganetzky B, Robertson GA. 1995. HERG, a human inward rectifier in the voltage-gated potassium channel family. *Science* 269: 92–95

216. Unwin N. 1995. Acetylcholine receptor channel imaged in the open state. *Nature* 373:37–43

217. Unwin PNT, Ennis PD. 1984. Two configurations of a channel-forming membrane protein. *Nature* 307:609–13

218. Vardi N, Matesic DF, Manning DR, Liebman PA, Sterling P. 1993. Identification of a G-protein in depolarizing rod bipolar cells. *Vis. Neurosci.* 10:473–78

218a. Varnum MD, Black KD, Zagotta WN, 1995. Molecular mechanism for ligand

discrimination of cyclic nucleotide-gated channels. *Neuron* 15:619–25
219. Villa P, Kurahashi T, Kaneko A. 1995. L-glutamate-induced responses and cGMP-activated channels in three subtypes of retinal bipolar cells dissociated from the cat. *J. Neurosci.* 15:3571–82
220. Warmke JW, Drysdale R, Ganetzky B. 1991. A distinct potassium channel polypeptide encoded by the *Drosophila eag* locus. *Science* 252:1560–62
221. Warmke JW, Ganetzky B. 1994. A family of potassium channel genes related to *eag* in *Drosophila* and mammals. *Proc. Natl. Acad. Sci. USA* 91: 3438–42
222. Wässle H, Grunert U, Cook NJ, Molday RS. 1992. The cGMP-gated channel of rod outer segments is not localized in bipolar cells of the mammalian retina. *Neurosci. Lett.* 134:199–202
223. Watanabe SI, Matthews G. 1990. Cyclic GMP-activated channels of rod photoreceptors show neither fast nor slow desensitization. *Vis. Neurosci.* 4:481–87
224. Watanabe SI, Murakami M. 1991. Similar properties of cGMP-activated channels between cones and rods in the carp retina. *Vis. Neurosci.* 6:563–68
225. Weber IT, Shabb JB, Corbin JD. 1989. Predicted structures of the cGMP binding domains of the cGMP-dependent protein kinase: a key alanine/threonine difference in evolutionary divergence of cAMP and cGMP binding sites. *Biochemistry* 28:6122–27
226. Weber IT, Steitz TA, Bubis J, Taylor SS. 1987. Predicted structures of cAMP binding domains of type I and II regulatory subunits of cAMP-dependent protein kinase. *Biochemistry* 26:343–51
227. Weyand I, Godde M, Frings S, Weiner J, Müller F, et al. 1994. Cloning and functional expression of a cyclic-nucleotide-gated channel from mammalian sperm. *Nature* 368:859–63
228. Wohlfart P, Haase W, Molday RS, Cook NJ. 1992. Antibodies against synthetic peptides used to determine the topology and site of glycosylation of the cGMP-gated channel from bovine rod photoreceptors. *J. Biol. Chem.* 267: 644–48
229. Wu CF, Ganetzky B, Haugland FN, Liu AX. 1983. Potassium currents in *Drosophila:* different components affected by mutations of two genes. *Science* 220: 1076–78
230. Yamashita M, Wässle H. 1991. Responses of rod bipolar cells isolated from the rat retina to the glutamate agonist 2-amino-4-phosphonobutyric acid (APB). *J. Neurosci.* 11:2372–82

231. Yang J, Ellinor PT, Sather WA, Zhang J-F, Tsien RW. 1993. Molecular determinants of Ca$^{2+}$ selectivity and ion permeation in L-type Ca$^{2+}$ channels. *Nature* 366:158–61
232. Yau K-W. 1994. Phototransduction mechanism in retinal rods and cones. The Friedenwald Lecture. *Invest. Ophthal. Vis. Sci.* 35:9–32
233. Yau K-W. 1994. Cyclic nucleotide-gated channels: an expanding new family of ion channels. *Proc. Natl. Acad. Sci. USA* 91:3481–83
234. Yau K-W, Baylor DA. 1989. Cyclic GMP-activated conductance of retinal photoreceptor cells. *Annu. Rev. Neurosci.* 12:289–327
235. Yau K-W, Chen T-Y. 1995. Cyclic nucleotide-gated channels. In *Handbook of Receptors and Channels: Ligand- and Voltage-Gated Ion Channels*, ed. RA North, pp. 307–35. Boca Raton, FL: CRC
236. Yau K-W, Nakatani K. 1985. Light-suppressible, cyclic GMP-sensitive conductance in the plasma membrane of a truncated rod outer segment. *Nature* 317:252–55
237. Zeidel ML, Silva P, Brenner BM, Seifter JL. 1987. cGMP mediates effects of atrial peptides on medullary collecting duct cells. *Am. J. Physiol.* 252:F551–59
238. Zhong Y, Wu CF. 1991. Alteration of four identified K$^+$ currents in *Drosophila* muscle by mutations in *eag. Science* 252:1562–64
239. Zhong Y, Wu CF. 1993. Modulation of different K$^+$ currents in *Drosophila*: a hypothetical role for the Eag subunit in multimeric K$^+$ channels. *J. Neurosci.* 13:4669–79
240. Zimmerman AL, Baylor DA. 1992. Cation interactions within the cyclic GMP-activated channel of retinal rods from the tiger salamander. *J. Physiol.* 449: 759–83
241. Zimmerman AL, Yamanaka G, Eckstein F, Baylor DA, Stryer L. 1985. Interaction of hydrolysis-resistant analogs of cyclic GMP with the phosphodiesterase and light-sensitive channel of retinal rod outer segments. *Proc. Natl. Acad. Sci. USA* 82:8813–17
242. Zufall F, Firestein S. 1993. Divalent cations block the cyclic nucleotide-gated channel of olfactory receptor neurons. *J. Neurophysiol.* 69:1758–68
243. Zufall F, Firestein S, Shepherd GM. 1991. Analysis of single cyclic nucleotide-gated channels in olfactory receptor cells. *J. Neurosci.* 11:3573–80
244. Zufall F, Firestein S, Shepherd GM. 1994. Cyclic nucleotide-gated ion chan-

nels and sensory transduction in olfactory receptor neurons. *Annu. Rev. Biophys. Biomol. Struct.* 23:577–607

245. Zufall F, Hatt H, Firestein S. 1993. Rapid application and removal of second messengers to cyclic nucleotide-gated channels from olfactory epithelium. *Proc. Natl. Acad. Sci. USA* 90:9335–39

246. Zufall F, Shepherd GM, Firestein S. 1991. Inhibition of the olfactory cyclic nucleotide-gated ion channel by intracellular calcium. *Proc. R. Soc. London Ser. B* 246:225–30

*Annu. Rev. Physiol. 1996. 58:427–45*

# PHYSIOLOGY AND BIOCHEMISTRY OF THE KIDNEY VACUOLAR H$^+$-ATPase

*Stephen L. Gluck, David M. Underhill, Masahiro Iyori, L. Shannon Holliday, Tatiana Y. Kostrominova, and Beth S. Lee*

Departments of Medicine and Cell Biology and Physiology, and the George M. O'Brien Kidney and Urological Diseases Center, Washington University School of Medicine, St. Louis, Missouri 63110

KEY WORDS:    urinary acidification, H$^+$ transport, collecting tubule, proximal tubule

## ABSTRACT

Vacuolar H$^+$-ATPases have an essential role in renal hydrogen ion secretion in the proximal tubule, collecting duct, and other segments of the nephron. Control of H$^+$ transport is achieved by variations in the intrinsic properties of the renal H$^+$-ATPases and by several cellular regulatory mechanisms, including redistribution of the enzyme both by vesicular traffic and regulated assembly and disassembly, and cytosolic regulatory proteins that interact directly with H$^+$-ATPase. These mechanisms may provide a means for fine control of net acid excretion and for regulating vacuolar H$^+$-ATPases residing on the plasma membrane independently from those in intracellular compartments.

## INTRODUCTION

During its daily maintenance of acid-base balance, the kidney reabsorbs 4500 millimoles of bicarbonate filtered by the glomerulus and regenerates the approximately 70 millimoles of bicarbonate consumed by metabolic proton generation (69, 93). The renal tubule reabsorbs and regenerates bicarbonate by hydrogen ion secretion (93). Vacuolar ATPases (V-ATPases) residing on the plasma membrane of renal tubular epithelial cells have an essential role in H$^+$ secretion in both proximal and distal nephron segments (51, 92, 129).

The kidney has the greatest number and most activity of plasma membrane V-ATPases of any mammalian tissue. V-ATPases are responsible for up to half of total renal H$^+$ secretion and over 1% of daily ATP consumption.

427

0066-4278/96/0315-0427$08.00

428    GLUCK ET AL

# STRUCTURE OF THE MAMMALIAN V-ATPases

V-ATPases are electrogenic proton translocating ATPases that acidify endosomes, lysosomes, and other intracellular compartments of the vacuolar
system of all eukaryotic cells, including fungal, protist, plant, and animal. They
are large multisubunit proteins, evolutionarily related and structurally similar
to the $F_0F_1$ H⁺-ATPases (85), composed of more than ten different polypeptides
(29). As illustrated in Figure 1, V-ATPases contain a catalytic ($V_1$) domain,
composed of peripheral membrane proteins, and a transmembrane ($V_0$) domain, composed of intrinsic membrane proteins (30) that transmit protons
through the lipid bilayer. The principal structural components of the $V_0$ domain
are a 15-kDa proteolipid subunit (9, 84) and a 19-kDa subunit (126). In
addition, either a 110- or 116-kDa polypeptide, and 38-kDa transmembrane
polypeptide, designated accessory proteins (86, 87), are associated with the
V-ATPase in some preparations (8, 78, 80, 124).

The $V_1$ domain contains a catalytic head consisting of three pairs of A (70
kDa) and B (56 kDa) subunits arrayed as a hexagon (9) around a central D
(33 kDa) subunit (82). The A subunit, a homologue of the $F_0F_1$ catalytic
subunit, contains the site of ATP hydrolysis (8, 28, 79). The B subunit, a
homologue of the $F_0F_1$ regulatory β subunit, may have a regulatory role (2,
120); there are two isoforms of this subunit (B1 and B2), encoded by different
genes, that have unique amino and carboxyl terminal sequences and are expressed in different renal tubular epithelial cells (see below). The D subunit
is a homologue of the subunit of the $F_0F_1$ H⁺-ATPases (82) and, by analogy,
may reside in the center of the hexagonal catalytic head. Other subunits in the

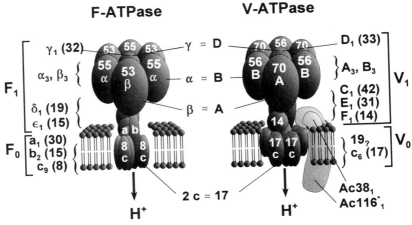

*Figure 1* Structural comparison of the $F_0F_1$ H⁺-ATPase (F-ATPase) with the V-ATPase.

$V_1$ domain of the enzyme include one each of the C (42 kDa) and E (31 kDa) subunits (8, 41, 80)). An additional 14-kDa subunit, designated the F subunit, was found originally in the $V_1$ domain of the V-ATPase from insect intestine (48) and was shown to be an essential subunit of the *Saccharomyces cerevisiae* V-ATPase (49, 81). Although a mammalian homologue has not been reported, it is likely that the mammalian V-ATPase also has an F subunit. The C, E, and F subunits have no amino acid sequence similarity to any subunits of the $F_0F_1$ H$^+$-ATPases (48, 58, 83); it is likely that they reside in a stalk domain attaching the catalytic head of the enzyme to the $V_0$ domain, as do the $\delta$ and $\varepsilon$ subunits of the $F_0F_1$ H$^+$-ATPases.

## DISTINCTIVE PROPERTIES OF RENAL PLASMA MEMBRANE V-ATPases

The plasma membrane V-ATPases of hydrogen ion-transporting renal epithelial cells have several features that distinguish them from V-ATPases of intracellular organelles: (*a*) They reside at densities as great as 1000 times those in intracellular membranes (16); (*b*) their amplified expression occurs in a cell-specific manner (18, 88); (*c*) they have a polarized distribution (17, 18) that allows for vectorial secretion of hydrogen ion across the epithelial layer; and (*d*) the plasma membrane V-ATPases of the nephron are subject to physiologic regulation (51, 77, 107), enabling the kidney to preserve acid-base balance.

## SITES OF V-ATPases IN THE NEPHRON AND THEIR ROLE IN BICARBONATE REABSORPTION AND H$^+$ SECRETION

The distribution of V-ATPases in the nephron has been determined by immunocytochemical and physiologic methods (summarized in Table 1). The proximal tubule, serving primarily for mass bicarbonate transport, reabsorbs 80% of the filtered bicarbonate (6). V-ATPases are highly abundant in the initial segments of the proximal tubule brush border, in agreement with physiologic measurements indicating that they account for 30–40% of proximal tubule H$^+$ secretion (11, 92). The thick ascending limb (20, 47) and distal convoluted tubule (19, 114) also contribute significantly to bicarbonate reabsorption. V-ATPases are present at moderate levels in the thick ascending limb of Henle's loop and in the distal convoluted tubule, in accord with direct measurements suggesting that they contribute 10–15% and 20-40%, respectively, of H$^+$ secretion in these segments (20, 21, 31, 47, 119).

The collecting duct is responsible for reabsorption of the remaining bicarbonate in the tubular fluid and for additional secretion of hydrogen ions titrated

**Table 1**  Distribution of V-ATPase in rat kidney and contribution to H$^+$ secretion

| Segment | HCO$_3^-$ reabsorption (H$^+$ secretion) | V-ATPase distribution and staining intensity[a] | |
|---|---|---|---|
| Proximal tubule: S1 | Total: 80%[b] | Brush border microvilli | 3+ |
| | | Sub-villar invaginations and en-dosomes | 2+ |
| Proximal tubule: S2 | | Brush border microvilli | 2+ |
| | V-ATPase: 3–40%[c] | Sub-villar invaginations and en- | 2+ |
| Proximal tubule: S3 | (25–30% of total) | dosomes | 0 |
| | | Brush border microvilli | 2+ |
| | | Sub-villar invaginations and en-dosomes | |
| Loop: cortical thin descend-ing limb | Total: 0% | Apical membrane | 1+ |
| | | Basolateral membrane | 1+ |
| Loop: medullary thin limb | Total: 0% | Apical membrane | 0.00 |
| | | Basolateral membrane | |
| Loop: thick ascending limb | Total: 10–15% V-ATPase: ≤20% (1–2% of total) | Apical membrane and apical vesi-cles | 1+ |
| Distal convoluted tubule | Total: 1–5% V-ATPase: 30–40% (1–2% of total) | Apical membrane | 1+ |
| Connecting | — | Principal cells: apical membrane | 1+ |
| | | Intercalated cells (plasma mem-brane and vesicles) | 4+ |
| Cortical collecting tubule | Total: 5–10% | Principal cells: | 0 |
| | | Intercalated cells (plasma mem-brane and vesicles) | 4+ |
| Outer medullary collecting tubule: outer stripe | V-ATPase: ≥590%[d] (5–10% of total) | Principal cells: | 0 |
| | | Intercalated cells (plasma mem-brane and vesicles) | 4+ |
| Outer medullary collecting tubule: inner stripe | — | Principal cells: apical membrane | 0 |
| | | Intercalated cells (plasma mem-brane and vesicles) | 4+ |
| Inner medullary collecting tubule | Total? ≤5% V-ATPase: ≥0%[d] (≤5% of total) | Principal cells: apical membrane (B1 subunit only) | 1+ |
| | | | 4+ |
| | | Intercalated cells (present in first third only) | |

[a] The distribution is derived from immunocytochemical studies in rat kidney (18). The distribution of H$^+$-ATPase in rabbit kidney is largely similar, although differences are present (100).
[b] Percent of filtered bicarbonate reabsorbed in the segment.
[c] Percent of segmental bicarbonate reabsorption derived from V-ATPase.
[d] The quantity of H$^+$ secretion derived from an H$^+$-K$^+$-ATPase in these segments remains unresolved.

by non-bicarbonate luminal buffers, which results in the generation of new bicarbonate. The collecting duct is comprised of several distinct segments with a mosaic of two major cell types, principal cells and intercalated cells. The intercalated cells, comprising 40%, have densely packed V-ATPases both on their plasma membranes and in a specialized intracellular tubulovesicular system (17, 18, 111) and are responsible for most of the hydrogen ion transport in these segments. [In the inner stripe of the outer medulla in the rabbit kidney, the principal cells also have a luminal membrane vacuolar H$^+$-ATPase that may contribute to H$^+$ secretion (121).] The cortical portion of the collecting duct has both acid-secreting ($\alpha$ or type A) and bicarbonate-secreting ($\beta$ or type B) subtypes of intercalated cells (99). [There may be additional phenotypic forms of intercalated cells (5, 27, 103); in the rabbit cortical collecting tubule, a third type of intercalated cell ($\gamma$) has been found by physiologic assays (27).]

V-ATPases in the intercalated cells reach densities estimated at 14,000 pumps/$\mu$m$^2$ (16) and are probably responsible for most of the acid secretion (52, 55, 59, 65, 109; reviewed in 99). Intercalated cells also have an H$^+$-K$^+$-ATPase that secretes H$^+$ and reabsorbs potassium (123). The H$^+$-K$^+$-ATPase probably has an important function during potassium depletion (122). The enzyme may also contribute substantially to H$^+$ secretion (10), although the extent of its role remains unresolved.

The outer medullary collecting tubule has two functionally distinct segments, the outer and inner stripes. Similar to the cortical collecting tubule, the outer medullary collecting tubule is composed of principal and intercalated cells; however, these segments have only $\alpha$ (acid-secreting) intercalated cells and no bicarbonate-secreting cells (reviewed in 99). The inner stripe has the highest rate of H$^+$ secretion of the collecting duct segments (70).

Hence, V-ATPases are important contributors to proton transport throughout the nephron, with particular importance in proximal tubule and collecting duct intercalated cells, and are responsible for as much as 45 to 50% of total renal bicarbonate reabsorption and H$^+$ secretion.

## MECHANISMS FOR CONTROL OF RENAL H$^+$ SECRETION

Renal epithelial cells face the task of controlling H$^+$ secretion by V-ATPases on the plasma membrane while maintaining the activity of V-ATPases in intracellular compartments as required for constitutive cellular functions. Several mechanisms participate in this process.

### V-ATPase Polarity as a Determinant of Transport Phenotype

In the kidney collecting duct, polarity in the distribution of V-ATPases provides a means for controlling H$^+$ secretion. As shown in Figure 2, V-ATPases

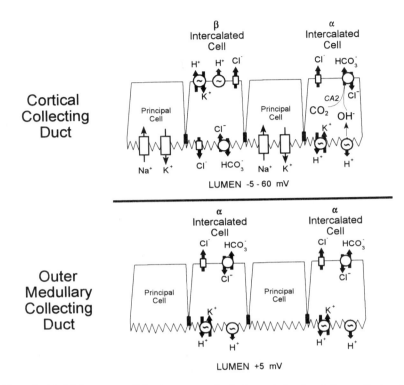

*Figure 2*    Model for proton and bicarbonate secretion in the cortical and medullary collecting duct.

may be polarized to the luminal plasma membrane, producing a proton-secreting $\alpha$ cell, or to the basolateral membrane, yielding a bicarbonate-secreting $\beta$ cell (17). Rates of $H^+$ and $HCO_3^-$ transport can be varied independently in the two cell types (73, 97, 98), enabling the tubule to secrete bicarbonate during metabolic alkalosis and to reabsorb bicarbonate during acidosis (99).

In the outer medullary collecting duct, intercalated cells have V-ATPases only in the luminal pole (12, 18), consistent with physiologic evidence (99) that no bicarbonate secretion occurs in these segments.

## Variations in V-ATPase Intrinsic Enzymatic Properties and Structure

V-ATPases, isolated by immunoaffinity purification from other membrane fractions of mammalian kidney (41, 120; S Gluck et al, in preparation), have distinctive enzymatic properties. The pH optimum of the brush border V-

ATPase is 7.2, close to the steady-state intracellular pH of the proximal tubule cell (6), and is therefore optimal for constitutive H$^+$ transport in the proximal tubule, whose primary function is bulk reabsorption of bicarbonate. In contrast, the pH optimum of V-ATPase from microsomes enriched for intercalated cell membranes is 6.3, well below the steady-state intracellular pH of about 7.2 in intercalated cells (15, 32, 56, 65, 96, 102, 121). Activity would increase with cytosolic acidification, but the magnitude of such changes would be small, only 20–25% over a physiologic pH range of 6.2 to 7.5 (41), well below the capacity of the kidney to adjust net acid excretion. As discussed below, intercalated cells employ other mechanisms to adjust H$^+$ secretion.

The V-ATPases from brush border and microsomes differ in the effect of lipids on catalytic activity (41, 120). Although the physiologic significance of such differences is not clear, the apical membrane of epithelia maintains a lipid composition different from that of the basolateral membrane and intracellular membrane compartments (105, 106, 115). Changes in the lipid environment of the plasma membrane could be a means for physiologic regulation, but this has not been demonstrated directly.

Among the V-ATPases of different compartments, there is striking diversity in the ability of divalent and trivalent cations to support or inhibit ATPase activity (41, 120; S Gluck et al, in preparation).

The V-ATPases from different membrane compartments also vary in their nucleotide specificity, which indicates that they differ in the structure of the catalytic site. On the basis of structural similarities with the $F_0F_1$ H$^+$-ATPases, for which crystallographic information is available (1), it is likely that the catalytic site of the V-ATPases is at the juncture of the A and B subunits, which implies that variations in structure of either of the subunits could contribute to functional differences.

V-ATPase isolated from bovine kidney membranes by ion exchange or immunoaffinity chromatography (41, 42, 120) has a polypeptide composition similar to that reported for other mammalian vacuolar H$^+$-ATPases (29) but notably lacks the $M_r$ 110,000 or 116,000 intrinsic membrane polypeptides observed in other H$^+$-ATPase preparations; however, this may result from the different conditions for membrane protein solubilization (41, 124). Ion exchange chromatography of kidney V-ATPase reveals two peaks of activity (41), which represent complexes with slightly different relative molecular masses (42). The polypeptide composition of the two peaks differs; two B subunit polypeptides, $M_r$ 58,000 and 56,000, now known to be the B1 and B2 isoforms of the B subunit, segregate separately into the peaks (41).

On two-dimensional polyacrylamide gels, V-ATPases isolated from kidney microsomes and brush border by immunoaffinity chromatography show a single A subunit polypeptide but have different isoforms of the B subunit (120). These findings have been confirmed by immunocytochemistry using antisera specific for individual B subunit isoforms. The B1 isoform is located predominantly in the intercalated cells and is not present in the proximal tubule; the B2 isoform is abundant in the proximal tubule but undetectable in the intercalated cells (88; RD Nelson et al, submitted). Variations have also been found in the E subunit. On immunoblots with a monoclonal antibody, V-ATPase purified from brush border had multiple lower-mobility immunoreactive E subunits, whereas V-ATPase from renal microsomes had only a single detectable E subunit polypeptide (57).

These findings indicate that intrinsic differences in V-ATPases, manifest as distinct structural forms of the V-ATPase, with different distributions in the nephron and significant differences in enzymatic properties, provide one means for specificity in the control of V-ATPase proton transporting activity.

## Cellular Regulation of the Renal Epithelial Cell V-ATPase

The control of renal $H^+$ transport may be classified into acute responses, occurring in minutes to hours, and usually readily reversible, and chronic responses, occurring in hours to days and often requiring major changes in cell architecture. In principle, three types of mechanism could participate in regulation.

V-ATPase RECRUITMENT    *Recruitment by vesicular traffic*    The distribution of V-ATPases in intercalated cells is dynamic, responding to physiologic stimuli. V-ATPases have variable distributions in apical membrane, basolateral membrane, or cytosolic vesicles among the intercalated cells (12, 18). In normal rat kidneys, $\alpha$ intercalated cells in the medullary collecting duct have some V-ATPase on the luminal membrane, but most of the enzyme is distributed in a specialized intracellular tubulovesicular system in the apical pole of the cell. In rats subjected to a sustained increase in nonvolatile acid intake (given as oral $NH_4Cl$), the V-ATPase undergoes a profound redistribution; after 14 days, the intercalated cells have most of the V-ATPase on the plasma membrane (12, 111) and exhibit a profound loss of intracellular tubulovesicles from the apical cytoplasm (111). These morphologic changes are thought to reflect an increase in $H^+$ secretory state of the cell (66). Similar changes, although less extreme, occur in $\alpha$ intercalated cells of the cortical collecting duct in response to acid administration (12).

Vesicular traffic as a mechanism for V-ATPase recruitment has been demonstrated most convincingly in the apical membrane of $H^+$-secreting intercalated cells. There is some evidence that V-ATPase recruitment by vesicular traffic occurs in the basolateral membrane of intercalated cells and in the proximal tubule brush border. In metabolic alkalosis induced by chloride depletion, loss of V-ATPase-containing vesicles from the cytoplasm of intercalated cells and an increase in V-ATPase staining on the basolateral membrane were observed (116). Chronic metabolic acidosis produced an increase in apparent brush border V-ATPase activity without changing the total cellular content of V-ATPase, which was interpreted to represent recruitment of V-ATPase from intracellular compartments (22).

*Recruitment by assembly and disassembly*    Regulated assembly and disassembly is a newly discovered mechanism that controls the number of functional V-ATPases in a membrane. Following the assembly of a complete V-ATPase protein, the $V_1$ domain of the V-ATPase may detach and release a subcomplex of A and B subunits that may reassemble with newly synthesized stalk subunits such as the E subunit (D Underhill & S Gluck, submitted). In LLC-PK1 cells, disassembly of half of the cellular V-ATPases may be induced by lowering extracellular pH to 5.5 for 60 min; disassembly is pH dependent, ATP dependent, and rapidly and completely reversible. Reassembly does not require new protein synthesis (D Underhill & S Gluck, submitted). This process is not unique to LLC-PK1 cells and occurs in several cultured cell lines.

No experiments have yet demonstrated directly that regulated assembly and disassembly participates in controlling renal H$^+$ secretion. Studies in tubules taken from acidotic animals (33, 68, 74) and in vitro in isolated perfused tubules bathed in acidic buffers (76, 125) have demonstrated that cortical collecting tubule bicarbonate secretion is lost rapidly without any detectable change in H$^+$ secretion. These observations suggest that the mechanism controlling bicarbonate secretion by $\beta$ intercalated cells is fundamentally different from the mechanisms (such as vesicular traffic) that control H$^+$ secretion in $\alpha$ intercalated cells. V-ATPase disassembly, induced by low extracellular pH, is an attractive candidate for a mechanism controlling bicarbonate secretion because it could account for the rapid loss of bicarbonate secretion observed in acid-bathed tubules in vitro.

V-ATPase KINETIC REGULATION    An adverse proton electrochemical gradient across the membrane in which the V-ATPase resides suppresses the rate of electrogenic H$^+$ transport in tight urinary epithelia (108), whether the proton-motive force is generated by pH gradients or by electrical gradients (4, 7). This inhibition is thought to represent a direct influence on the turnover rate of the V-ATPase (7).

Kidney cytosol contains proteins that modify the activity of the purified kidney V-ATPase (127, 128). A V-ATPase inhibitor has been purified to a high degree using several precipitation, ion exchange, and size separation steps (128), eluting from a gel filtration column with an apparent $M_r$ of 14,000–20,000. Its inhibitory effect is irreversible and pH dependent, showing an increase above pH 7.5. The pH dependence is such that the inhibitor would reduce H$^+$-ATPase activity with an increase in cytosolic pH above the normal physiologic range. The inhibitor has equal potency (at maximal concentrations) on V-ATPases purified from several kidney membrane compartments (128).

A cytosolic V-ATPase activator has been partially purified by precipitation, ion exchange, and gel filtration chromatography (127), eluting from a gel filtration column with an apparent $M_r$ of 35,000. V-ATPase activation is also highly pH dependent. In the pH range $\leq 6.6$, the activator stimulates activity up to 1200-fold; at pH values $\geq 6.6$, activity increases only 1–2-fold. The pH dependence is therefore such that the activator would increase $H^+$-ATPase activity if cytosolic pH were to fall below the normal physiologic range. The activator increased microsomal and brush border V-ATPase activity more than twice as much as lysosomal V-ATPase activity, thus demonstrating significant selectivity in its effect on different kidney V-ATPases and implying that the activator could exert selective regulatory effects on $H^+$-ATPases residing on the plasma membrane (127).

CHANGES IN V-ATPase CONTENT    The expectation that V-ATPase content might be regulated is based on the well-documented observation that changes in $Na^+$-$K^+$-ATPase density occur during chronic adaptation in various physiologic settings (13). Chronic administration of acid to rats produces no detectable increase in V-ATPase content of the kidney as measured by immunoassay (12). Several investigators have found changes in $N$-ethylmaleimide (NEM)-inhibitable or bafilomycin-sensitive ATPase in kidney under various pathophysiologic conditions (23, 34, 94), but the specificity of these assays as an index of V-ATPase remains unproven.

Assays of whole-cell $Na^+$-$K^+$-ATPase activity (using inhibitor ouabain) and pump density (using $^3$H-ouabain) in different nephron segments have provided useful information because (a) ouabain is highly specific, and (b) nearly all the $Na^+$-$K^+$-ATPase resides on the plasma membrane. In contrast, several problems beset attempts to measure changes in vacuolar $H^+$-ATPase activity. First, the validity of NEM sensitivity (24–26, 35–40, 61–64, 94, 95) and bafilomycin sensitivity (22) as assays for vacuolar $H^+$-ATPase remains unproven. For example, no studies have determined if immunodepletion of V-ATPase from these preparations removes all NEM- or bafilomycin-sensitive activity. The sulfhydryl reagent NEM inhibits various transport ATPases, and its presumed specificity relies on assay conditions that minimize the other activities. The high-affinity inhibitor bafilomycin inhibits V-ATPases with an $IC_{50}$ in the low nanomolar range, orders of magnitude below that for other ATPases (14, 60). However, when used at the concentrations needed to fully inhibit vacuolar $H^+$-ATPase, it does inhibit other ATPases and may have additional effects. The second problem with assaying vacuolar $H^+$-ATPase in intact tubule segments is that the enzyme resides mainly in intracellular compartments (18, 72, 111, 117, 118). No study of total NEM-sensitive ATPase in intact cells has ascertained whether the activity arises from the plasma membrane. It has been proposed that in permeabilized cells the activity measured represents the total enzyme content of the cell (3, 35, 95) However, colchicine inhibits nearly completely the NEM-sensitive ATPase activity in permeabilized kidney cells (61), presumably by preventing microtubule-mediated insertion of H$^+$-ATPase in the plasma membrane. This suggests that the cellular location or redistribution of the enzyme powerfully influences the measured NEM-sensitive activity. Thirdly, it cannot be resolved whether an increase in total activity represents an increase in the number of H$^+$-ATPase molecules or a kinetic activation of extant enzyme.

The work of Sabatini et al (95) underscores the the pitfalls of using whole tubule NEM-sensitive ATPase assays. They showed that the pH optimum and $K_m$ (ATP) were entirely different from those of the purified kidney H$^+$-ATPase (41, 42, 120), which are in good agreement with those for other purified V-ATPases (29, 43) and for proton transport in kidney membrane vesicles (104). Additionally, in four studies, the NEM-sensitive ATPase activity in the thick ascending limb exceeded that in all segments of the collecting duct (3, 35, 38, 94) despite immunocytochemical evidence for far lower H$^+$-ATPase density in the former. Despite clear physiologic evidence that increased acid secretion in the thick ascending limb is mainly mediated by Na$^+$-H$^+$ exchange activity (45–47), two studies (62, 94) found that chronic acid administration caused NEM-sensitive ATPase to increase about twofold, more than in any other nephron segment. At this writing, there is no convincing evidence that alteration in V-ATPase content is used to regulate H$^+$ transport.

*Acute and chronic regulation of V-ATPase activity*   Of the several factors that have acute effects on collecting duct H$^+$ secretion (53, 91), aldosterone, carbon dioxide, and bicarbonate are the most significant. Aldosterone stimulates distal nephron H$^+$ secretion (69, 90) in part by increasing luminal sodium permeability (69, 50, 90) and hence the lumen-negative potential difference, and in part by direct stimulation of H$^+$ secretion (54, 110). Chronic administration of mineralocorticoids also increases the H$^+$ secretory capacity of α intercalated cells (66, 121). The mechanisms of both the acute direct stimulation of H$^+$ secretion and the chronic stimulation are unknown; none of the regulatory mechanisms discussed above has been excluded.

Acutely lowering or raising basolateral bicarbonate at constant PCO$_2$ stimulates or inhibits H$^+$ secretion, respectively (59), and lowering (59) or raising the PCO$_2$ (75) at a constant basolateral bicarbonate concentration, respectively, inhibits or stimulates H$^+$ secretion. As discussed above, in intact rats subjected to sustained NH$_4$Cl intake, V-ATPase is recruited to the luminal membrane of α intercalated cells by vesicular traffic (12, 111), changes thought to reflect an increase in H$^+$ secretory state of the cell (66). In contrast, several studies have demonstrated either in collecting tubules removed from acid-loaded animals and examined in vitro (33, 70) or in tubules subjected to an acidic bath in vitro (125) that $H^+$ secretion is unchanged (although bicarbonate secretion is markedly suppressed). These findings suggest that unidentified factors in the intact animal, missing in tubules studied in vitro, are required to evoke the acidosis-induced recruitment of V-ATPases to the luminal membrane by vesicular traffic.

In support of this concept, our laboratory examined the determinants of vesicle-mediated·V-ATPase recruitment to the luminal membrane in $\alpha$ intercalated cells in vivo and in vitro (M Iyori & S Gluck, submitted). Administration of $NH_4Cl$ to rats induced redistribution of cell V-ATPase from cytosolic vesicles to the apical membrane that was detectable at 2 h, over half-maximal by 24 h, and reached a maximum by 5 days. Following the administration of $NH_4Cl$, the kidneys were removed and 0.75-$\mu$m medullary slices were prepared and incubated in vitro. $\alpha$ Intercalated cell V-ATPase polarization, assayed as the percent of intercalated cells with plasma membrane staining, was 10.9, 9.6, and 12.1% of the initial values at 1, 2, and 3 h, indicating that loss of V-ATPase polarization occurs rapidly during in vitro incubation. Because reducing bath $HCO_3^-$ concentration in vitro stimulates $H^+$ secretion (59), the response may arise from mechanisms other than recruitment of V-ATPase by vesicular traffic, such as changes in the kinetics of the V-ATPase. Future work may reveal whether cytosolic regulatory proteins have a role.

In the intact animal, acute alterations in $PCO_2$ appear to change the rate of $H^+$ secretion in the $\alpha$ intercalated cell by altering the number of luminal V-ATPases through membrane fusion or internalization (71). In contrast, in the isolated collecting tubule incubated in high $PCO_2$ buffers, no evidence for fusion of cytoplasmic tubulovesicles with the luminal membrane was observed (75). Schwartz & Al-Awqati (101) showed that intercalated cells in rabbit medullary collecting tubules internalize FITC-dextran into acidic compartments. A 24 to 27% reduction of the fluorescence intensity in the cells in each segment upon changing from $CO_2$-free to $HCO_3^-/CO_2$ buffers was interpreted to represent $CO_2$-induced release of the dextran by exocytosis because it was inhibited by colchicine, but release of dextran into the lumen was not demonstrated, and other possible causes for loss of fluorescence intensity, such as increased scatter or cell volume changes, were not excluded. Thus unidentified factors in the intact animal, not found in tubules studied in vitro, may be required to elicit the $CO_2$-induced recruitment of V-ATPases to the luminal membrane by vesicular traffic. Supporting this model, no change in tubular $H^+$ secretion was observed in vitro in medullary collecting tubules removed from rabbits subjected to hypercapnia (67). (An increase in total net transtubular $H^+$ secretion was observed in cortical collecting tubules from these animals, but this may have been due to suppression of bicarbonate secretion.) Because reducing the bath $PCO_2$ concentration in vitro suppresses $H^+$ secretion (59), the response again may originate from changes in the kinetics of the V-ATPase.

Recent studies suggest that angiotensin II (113) and nitric oxide (112) may inhibit V-ATPase activity in permeabilized cortical collecting tubules; the mechanism of the effects and physiologic significance of the findings have not been established.

## SUMMARY

In specialized proton-transporting renal epithelial cells, most of the V-ATPase resides on the plasma membrane and in plasmalemma-associated tubulovesicles, where it functions in the bicarbonate reabsorption, regeneration, and

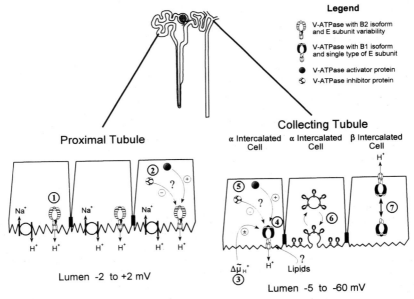

*Figure 3* Summary of mechanisms for cell-specific regulation of the V-ATPase in the nephron. (1) The proximal tubule expresses V-ATPase with distinct enzymatic properties containing the B2 isoform and variable E subunit polypeptides. (2) Cytosolic regulatory proteins may affect proximal tubule V-ATPase activity by altering its kinetics directly; effect may be selective for specific structural variants. (3) The proton electrochemical gradient $\Delta\bar{\mu}_H$ + across the luminal membrane alters V-ATPase kinetics. (4) The collecting tubule expresses V-ATPase with distinct enzymatic properties containing the B1 isoform and a single detectable E subunit polypeptide. (5) Cytosolic regulatory proteins may affect collecting tubule V-ATPase activity by altering its kinetics directly; effect may be selective for specific structural variants. (6) In the α intercalated cell, the number of active V-ATPases on the luminal membrane is controlled in vivo, in response to changes in $PaCO_2$ or plasma bicarbonate, by membrane vesicle-mediated traffic that may require unidentified mediators. (7) In the β intercalated cell, the number of active V-ATPases on the basolateral membrane may be controlled by regulated assembly and disassembly, responding directly to extracellular pH.

bicarbonate secretion required for acid-base homeostasis. Studies to date have provided a model of the distinct mechanisms used to regulate V-ATPase-driven $H^+$ secretion in different cell types (Figure 3). (a) Renal epithelial cells have the capacity to express different structural forms of V-ATPase that have intrinsic differences in their enzymatic properties. (b) The kidney produces cytosolic regulatory proteins capable of interacting directly with the V-ATPase that may modify its activity. V-ATPases in different cell types may differ in the degree to which their activity is affected by regulatory factors as a result of variations in V-ATPase structure. (c) In the α intercalated cell, the number of active V-ATPase molecules on the luminal membrane is controlled in vivo by membrane vesicle-mediated traffic that may require unidentified mediators. In the intercalated cell, the number of active V-ATPase molecules on the basolateral membrane may be controlled by regulated assembly and disassembly, responding directly to extracellular pH.

ACKNOWLEDGMENT

We thank Dr. Raoul Nelson for his many contributions to the experiments discussed. This work was supported by National Institutes of Health grants DK38848, DK09976, AR32087, and DK45181. BLS was supported in part by a research grant from the Arthritis Foundation.

## Literature Cited

1. Abrahams JP, Leslie AG, Lutter R, Walker JE. 1994. Structure at 2.8 Å resolution of F1-ATPase from bovine heart mitochondria. *Nature* 370:621–28
2. Adachi I, Arai H, Pimental R, Forgac M. 1990. Proteolysis and orientation on reconstitution of the coated vesicle proton pump. *J. Biol. Chem.* 265:960–66
3. Ait-Mohamed AK, Marsy S, Barlet C, Khadouri C, Doucet A. 1986. Characterization of *N*-ethylmaleimide-sensitive proton pump in the rat kidney. Localization along the nephron. *J. Biol. Chem.* 261:12526–33
4. Al-Awqati Q, Mueller A, Steinmetz PR. 1977. Transport of $H^+$ against electrochemical gradients in turtle urinary bladder. *Am. J. Physiol.* 233:F502–8
5. Alper SL, Natale J, Gluck S, Lodish HF, Brown D. 1989. Subtypes of intercalated cells in rat kidney collecting duct defined by antibodies against ery-

throid band 3 and renal vacuolar $H^+$-ATPase. *Proc. Natl. Acad. Sci. USA* 86:5429–33
6. Alpern RJ. 1990. Cell mechanisms of proximal tubule acidification. *Physiol. Rev.* 70:79–114
7. Andersen OS, Silveira JE, Steinmetz PR. 1985. Intrinsic characteristics of the proton pump in the luminal membrane of a tight urinary epithelium. The relation between transport rate and delta-mu-H. *J. Gen. Physiol.* 86:215–34
8. Arai H, Berne M, Terres G, Terres H, Puopolo K, Forgac M. 1987. Subunit composition and ATP site labeling of the coated vesicle proton-translocating adenosinetriphosphatase. *Biochemistry* 26:6632–38
9. Arai H, Terres G, Pink S, Forgac M. 1988. Topography and subunit stoichiometry of the coated vesicle proton pump. *J. Biol. Chem.* 263:8796–802

10. Armitage FE, Wingo CS. 1994. Luminal acidification in K-replete OMCDi: contributions of H-K-ATPase and bafilomycin-A1-sensitive H-ATPase. *Am. J. Physiol.* 267:F450–58

11. Bank N, Aynedjian HS, Mutz BF. 1989. Proximal bicarbonate absorption independent of $Na^+-H^+$ exchange: effect of bicarbonate load. *Am. J. Physiol.* 256:F577–82

12. Bastani B, Purcell H, Hemken P, Trigg D, Gluck S. 1991. Expression and distribution of renal vacuolar proton-translocating adenosine triphosphatase in response to chronic acid and alkali loads in the rat. *J. Clin. Invest.* 88:126–36

13. Bertorello AM, Katz AI. 1993. Short-term regulation of renal Na-K-ATPase activity: physiological relevance and cellular mechanisms. *Am. J. Physiol.* 265:F743–55

14. Bowman EJ, Siebers A, Altendorf K. 1988. Bafilomycins: a class of inhibitors of membrane ATPases from microorganisms, animal cells, and plant cells. *Proc. Natl. Acad. Sci. USA* 85:7972–76

15. Breyer MD, Jacobson HR. 1989. Regulation of rabbit medullary collecting duct cell pH by basolateral $Na^+/H^+$ and $Cl^-$/base exchange. *J. Clin. Invest.* 84:996–1004

16. Brown D, Gluck S, Hartwig J. 1987. Structure of the novel membrane-coating material in proton-secreting epithelial cells and identification as an H⁺ATPase. *J. Cell Biol.* 105:1637–48

17. Brown D, Hirsch S, Gluck S. 1988. An H⁺-ATPase in opposite plasma membrane domains in kidney epithelial cell subpopulations. *Nature* 331:622–24

18. Brown D, Hirsch S, Gluck S. 1988. Localization of a proton-pumping ATPase in rat kidney. *J. Clin. Invest.* 82:2114–26

19. Capasso G, Jaeger P, Giebisch G, Guckian V, Malnic G. 1987. Renal bicarbonate reabsorption in the rat. II. Distal tubule load dependence and effect of hypokalemia. *J. Clin. Invest.* 80:409–14

20. Capasso G, Unwin R, Agulian S, Giebisch G. 1991. Bicarbonate transport along the loop of Henle. I. Microperfusion studies of load and inhibitor sensitivity. *J. Clin. Invest.* 88:430–37

21. Capasso G, Unwin R, Giebisch G. 1991. Role of the loop of Henle in urinary acidification. *Kidney Int. Suppl.* 33:S33–S35

22. Chambrey R, Paillard M, Podevin RA. 1994. Enzymatic and functional evidence for adaptation of the vacuolar H(+)-ATPase in proximal tubule apical membranes from rats with chronic metabolic acidosis. *J. Biol. Chem.* 269:3243–50

23. Doucet A, Khadouri C, Cheval L, Marsy S, Barlet-Bas C. 1993. Renal proton adenosine triphosphatases. *Adv. Nephrol. Necker Hosp.* 22:287–304

24. Eiam-Ong S, Dafnis E, Spohn M, Kurtzman NA, Sabatini S. 1993. H-K-ATPase in distal renal tubular acidosis: urinary tract obstruction, lithium, and amiloride. *Am. J. Physiol.* 265:F875–80

25. Eiam-Ong S, Kurtzman NA, Sabatini S. 1993. Regulation of collecting tubule adenosine triphosphatases by aldosterone and potassium. *J. Clin. Invest.* 91:2385–92

26. Eiam-Ong S, Lonis B, Kurtzman NA, Sabatini S. 1992. The biochemical basis of hypokalemic metabolic alkalosis. *Trans. Assoc. Am. Physicians* 105:157–64

27. Emmons C, Kurtz I. 1994. Functional characterization of three intercalated cell subtypes in the rabbit outer cortical collecting duct. *J. Clin. Invest.* 93:417–23

28. Feng Y, Forgac M. 1992. Cysteine 254 of the 73-kDa A subunit is responsible for inhibition of the coated vesicle (H⁺)-ATPase upon modification by sulfhydryl reagents. *J. Biol. Chem.* 267:5817–22

29. Forgac M. 1989. Structure and function of vacuolar class of ATP-driven proton pumps. *Physiol. Rev.* 69:765–96

30. Forgac M. 1992. Structure and properties of the coated vesicle (H⁺)-ATPase. *J. Bioenerg. Biomembr.* 24:341–50

31. Froissart M, Borensztein P, Houillier P, Leviel F, Poggioli J, et al. 1992. Plasma membrane $Na(+)-H^+$ antiporter and H(+)-ATPase in the medullary thick ascending limb of rat kidney. *Am. J. Physiol.* 262:C963–70

32. Furuya H, Jacobson HR, Breyer MD. 1993. Evidence for basolateral membrane $Ca^{2+}/H^+$ exchange in outer medullary collecting duct. *Am. J. Physiol.* 264:F88–93

33. Garcia-Austt J, Good DW, Burg MB, Knepper MA. 1985. Deoxycorticosterone-stimulated bicarbonate secretion in rabbit cortical collecting ducts: effects of luminal chloride removal and in vivo acid loading. *Am. J. Physiol.* 249:F205–12

34. Garg LC. 1991. Respective roles of H-ATPase and H-K-ATPase in ion transport in the kidney. *J. Am. Soc. Nephrol.* 2:949–60

35. Garg LC, Narang N. 1985. Stimulation

of an N-ethylmaleimide-sensitive ATP-ase in the collecting duct segments of the rat nephron by metabolic acidosis. *Can. J. Physiol. Pharmacol.* 63:1291–96

36. Garg LC, Narang N. 1987. Effects of potassium bicarbonate on distal nephron Na-K-ATPase in adrenalectomized rabbits. *Pflügers Arch.* 409:126–31

37. Garg LC, Narang N. 1988. Effects of aldosterone on NEM-sensitive ATPase in rabbit nephron segments. *Kidney Int.* 134:13–17

38. Garg LC, Narang N. 1990. Decrease in N-ethylmaleimide-sensitive ATPase activity in collecting duct by metabolic alkalosis. *Can. J. Physiol. Pharmacol.* 68:1119–23

39. Garg LC, Narang N. 1990. Effects of low-potassium diet on N-ethylmaleimide-sensitive ATPase in the distal nephron segments. *Renal Physiol. Biochem.* 13:129–36

40. Garg LC, Narang N. 1991. Changes in H-ATPase activity in the distal nephron segments of the rat during metabolic acidosis and alkalosis. *Contrib. Nephrol.* 92:39–45

41. Gluck S, Caldwell J. 1987. Immunoaffinity purification and characterization of vacuolar H+ATPase from bovine kidney. *J. Biol. Chem.* 262:15780–89

42. Gluck S, Caldwell J. 1988. Proton-translocating ATPase from bovine kidney medulla: partial purification and reconstitution. *Am. J. Physiol.* 254:F71–F79

43. Gluck SL. 1993. The vacuolar H(+)-ATPases: versatile proton pumps participating in constitutive and specialized functions of eukaryotic cells. *Int. Rev. Cytol.* 137:105–37

44. Deleted in proof

45. Good DW. 1990. Adaptation of $HCO_3^-$ and $NH_4^+$ transport in rat MTAL: effects of chronic metabolic acidosis and Na+ intake. *Am. J. Physiol.* 258:F1345–53

46. Good DW. 1990. Bicarbonate absorption by the thick ascending limb of Henle's loop. *Semin. Nephrol.* 10:132–38

47. Good DW. 1993. The thick ascending limb as a site of renal bicarbonate reabsorption. *Semin. Nephrol.* 13:225–35

48. Graf R, Lepier A, Harvey WR, Wieczorek H. 1994. A novel 14-kDa V-ATPase subunit in the tobacco hornworm midgut. *J. Biol. Chem.* 269:3767–74

49. Graham LA, Hill KJ, Stevens TH. 1994. VMA7 encodes a novel 14-kDa subunit of the *Saccharomyces cerevisiae* vacuolar H(+)-ATPase complex. *J. Biol. Chem.* 269:25974–77

50. Gross JB, Kokko JP. 1977. Effects of aldosterone and potassium-sparing diuretics on electrical potential differences across the distal nephron. *J. Clin. Invest.* 59:82–89

51. Hamm LL, Hering-Smith KS. 1993. Acid-base transport in the collecting duct. *Semin. Nephrol.* 13:246–55

52. Hayashi M, Iyori M, Yamaji Y, Saruta T. 1993. Effects of in vivo and in vitro alkali treatment on intracellular pH regulation of OMCDi cells. *Am. J. Physiol.* 265:F729–35

53. Hays S, Kokko JP, Jacobson HR. 1986. Hormonal regulation of proton secretion in rabbit medullary collecting duct. *J. Clin. Invest.* 78:1279–86

54. Hays SR. 1992. Mineralocorticoid modulation of apical and basolateral membrane $H^+/OH^-/HCO_3^-$ transport processes in the rabbit inner stripe of outer medullary collecting duct. *J. Clin. Invest.* 90:180–87

55. Hays SR, Alpern RJ. 1990. Apical and basolateral membrane $H^+$ extrusion mechanisms in inner stripe of rabbit outer medullary collecting duct. *Am. J. Physiol.* 259:F628–35

56. Hays SR, Alpern RJ. 1990. Basolateral membrane Na(+)-independent $Cl^-/HCO_3^-$ exchange in the inner stripe of the rabbit outer medullary collecting tubule. *J. Gen. Physiol.* 195:347–67

57. Hemken P, Guo XL, Wang ZQ, Zhang K, Gluck S. 1992. Immunologic evidence that vacuolar $H^+$ ATPases with heterogeneous forms of $M_r = 31,000$ subunit have different membrane distributions in mammalian kidney. *J. Biol. Chem.* 267:9948–57

58. Hirsch S, Strauss A, Masood K, Lee S, Sukhatme V, Gluck S. 1988. Isolation and sequence of a cDNA clone encoding the 31-kDa subunit of bovine kidney vacuolar $H^+$-ATPase. *Proc. Natl. Acad. Sci. USA* 85:3004–8

59. Jacobson HR. 1984. Medullary collecting duct acidification. Effects of potassium, $HCO_3^-$ concentration, and $pCO_2$. *J. Clin. Invest.* 74:2107–14

60. Jehmlich K, Sablotni J, Simon BJ, Burckhardt G. 1991. Biochemical aspects of H(+)-ATPase in renal proximal tubules: inhibition by N,N'-dicyclohexylcarbodiimide, N-ethylmaleimide, and bafilomycin. *Kidney Int. Suppl.* 33:S64–S70

61. Khadouri C, Cheval L, Marsy S, Barlet-Bas C, Doucet A. 1991. Characterization and control of proton-ATPase along the nephron. *Kidney Int. Suppl.* 33:S71–S78

62. Khadouri C, Marsy S, Barlet-Bas C, Cheval L, Doucet A. 1992. Effect of

metabolic acidosis and alkalosis on NEM-sensitive ATPase in rat nephron segments. *Am. J. Physiol.* 262:F583–90

63. Khadouri C, Marsy S, Barlet-Bas C, Doucet A. 1987. Effect of adrenalectomy on NEM-sensitive ATPase along rat nephron and on urinary acidification. *Am. J. Physiol.* 253:F495–99

64. Khadouri C, Marsy S, Barlet-Bas C, Doucet A. 1989. Short-term effect of aldosterone on NEM-sensitive ATPase in rat collecting tubule. *Am. J. Physiol.* 257:F177–81

65. Kuwahara M, Sasaki S, Marumo F. 1990. Cell pH regulation in rabbit outer medullary collecting duct cells: mechanisms of $HCO_3(-)$-independent processes. *Am. J. Physiol.* 259:F902–9

66. Kuwahara M, Sasaki S, Marumo F. 1992. Mineralocorticoids and acidosis regulate $H^+/HCO_3^-$ transport of intercalated cells. *J. Clin. Invest.* 89:1388–94

67. Laski ME, Kurtzman NA. 1990. Collecting tubule adaptation to respiratory acidosis induced in vivo. *Am. J. Physiol.* 258:F15–F20

68. Levine DZ, Iacovitti M, Harrison V. 1991. Bicarbonate secretion in vivo by rat distal tubules during alkalosis induced by dietary chloride restriction and alkali loading. *J. Clin. Invest.* 87:1513–18

69. Levine DZ, Jacobson HR. 1986. The regulation of renal acid secretion: new observations from studies of distal nephron segments. *Kidney Int.* 29:1099–109

70. Lombard WE, Kokko JP, Jacobson HR. 1983. Bicarbonate transport in cortical and outer medullary collecting tubules. *Am. J. Physiol.* 244:F289–96

71. Madsen KM, Tisher CC. 1983. Cellular response to acute respiratory acidosis in rat medullary collecting duct. *Am. J. Physiol.* 245:F670–79

72. Madsen KM, Verlander JW, Kim J, Tisher CC. 1991. Morphological adaptation of the collecting duct to acid-base disturbances. *Kidney Int. Suppl.* 33:S57–S63

73. McKinney TD, Burg MB. 1977. Bicarbonate transport by rabbit cortical collecting tubules. Effect of acid and alkali loads in vivo on transport in vitro. *J. Clin. Invest.* 60:766–68

74. McKinney TD, Burg MB. 1978. Bicarbonate secretion by rabbit cortical collecting tubules in vitro. *J. Clin. Invest.* 61:1421–27

75. McKinney TD, Davidson KK. 1988. Effects of respiratory acidosis on $HCO_3^-$ transport by rabbit collecting tubules. *Am. J. Physiol.* 255:F656–65

76. Mehrgut FM, Satlin LM, Schwartz GJ.

1990. Maturation of $HCO_3^-$ transport in rabbit collecting duct. *Am. J. Physiol.* 259:F801–8

77. Moe OW, Preisig PA, Alpern RJ. 1990. Cellular model of proximal tubule NaCl and $NaHCO_3^-$ absorption. *Kidney Int.* 38:605–11

78. Moriyama Y, Nelson N. 1987. The purified ATPase from chromaffin granule membranes is an anion-dependent proton pump. *J. Biol. Chem.* 262:9175–80

79. Moriyama Y, Nelson N. 1987. Nucleotide binding sites and chemical modification of the chromaffin granule proton ATPase. *J. Biol. Chem.* 262:14723–29

80. Moriyama Y, Nelson N. 1989. Lysosomal $H^+$-translocating ATPase has a similar subunit structure to chromaffin granule $H^+$-ATPase complex. *Biochim. Biophys. Acta* 980:241–47

81. Nelson H, Mandiyan S, Nelson N. 1994. The *Saccharomyces cerevisiae VMA7* gene encodes a 14-kDa subunit of the vacuolar H(+)-ATPase catalytic sector. *J. Biol. Chem.* 269:24150–55

82. Nelson H, Mandiyan S, Nelson N. 1995. A bovine cDNA and a yeast gene (*VMA8*) encoding the subunit D of the vacuolar H(+)-ATPase. *Proc. Natl. Acad. Sci. USA* 92:497–501

83. Nelson H, Mandiyan S, Noumi T, Moriyama Y, Miedel MC, Nelson N. 1990. Molecular cloning of cDNA encoding the C subunit of H(+)-ATPase from bovine chromaffin granules. *J. Biol. Chem.* 265:20390–93

84. Nelson H, Nelson N. 1989. The progenitor of ATP synthases was closely related to the current vacuolar $H^+$-ATPase. *FEBS Lett.* 247:147–53

85. Nelson N. 1992. Evolution of organellar proton-ATPases. *Biochim. Biophys. Acta* 1100:109–24

86. Nelson N. 1992. Organellar proton-ATPases. *Curr. Opin. Cell Biol.* 24:654–60

87. Nelson N. 1992. Structure and function of V-ATPases in endocytic and secretory organelles. *J. Exp. Biol.* 172:149–53

88. Nelson RD, Guo XL, Masood K, Brown D, Kalkbrenner M, Gluck S. 1992. Selectively amplified expression of an isoform of the vacuolar H(+)-ATPase 56-kilodalton subunit in renal intercalated cells. *Proc. Natl. Acad. Sci. USA* 89:3541–45

89. Deleted in proof

90. Paillard M. 1977. Effects of aldosterone on renal handling of sodium, potassium and hydrogen ions. *Adv. Nephrol. Necker Hosp.* 27:83–104

91. Paillard M, Bichara M. 1989. Peptide hormone effects on urinary acidifica-

tion and acid-base balance: PTH, ADH, and glucagon. *Am. J. Physiol.* 256: F973–85

92. Preisig PA, Alpern RJ. 1990. Pathways for apical and basolateral membrane $NH_3$ and $NH_4^+$ movement in rat proximal tubule. *Am. J. Physiol.* 259:F587–93

93. Rector F Jr. 1981. Renal regulation of acid-base balance. *Aust. NZ J. Med.* 11:1–5

94. Sabatini S, Laski ME, Kurtzman NA. 1990. NEM-sensitive ATPase activity in rat nephron: effect of metabolic acidosis and alkalosis. *Am. J. Physiol.* 258: F297–304

95. Sabatini S, Laski ME, Spohn M, Kurtzman NA. 1991. Characterization of the $N$-ethylmaleimide-sensitive ATPase in rat cortical and medullary collecting tubule. *Miner. Electrolyte Metab.* 17:324–30

96. Satlin LM, Schwartz GJ. 1987. Postnatal maturation of rabbit renal collecting duct: intercalated cell function. *Am. J. Physiol.* 253:F622–35

97. Satlin LM, Schwartz GJ. 1989. Cellular remodeling of $HCO_3(-)$-secreting cells in rabbit renal collecting duct in response to an acidic environment. *J. Cell Biol.* 109:1279–88

98. Schuster VL. 1991. Cortical collecting duct bicarbonate secretion. *Kidney Int. Suppl.* 33:S47–S50

99. Schuster VL. 1993. Function and regulation of collecting duct intercalated cells. *Annu. Rev. Physiol.* 55:267–88

100. Schuster VL, Fejes-Toth G, Naray-Fejes-Toth A, Gluck S. 1991. Colocalization of H(+)-ATPase and band 3 anion exchanger in rabbit collecting duct intercalated cells. *Am. J. Physiol.* 260: F506–17

101. Schwartz GJ, Al-Awqati Q. 1985. Carbon dioxide causes exocytosis of vesicles containing $H^+$ pumps in isolated perfused proximal and collecting tubules. *J. Clin. Invest.* 75:1638–44

102. Schwartz GJ, Barasch J, Al-Awqati Q. 1985. Plasticity of functional epithelial polarity. *Nature* 318:368–71

103. Schwartz GJ, Satlin LM, Bergmann JE. 1988. Fluorescent characterization of collecting duct cells: a second H+-secreting type. *Am. J. Physiol.* 255:F1003–14

104. Simon BJ, Burckhardt G. 1990. Characterization of inside-out oriented H(+)-ATPases in cholate-pretreated renal brush-border membrane vesicles. *J. Membr. Biol.* 117:141–51

105. Simons K, Dupree P, Fiedler K, Huber LA, Kobayashi T, et al. 1992. Biogenesis of cell-surface polarity in epithelial cells and neurons. *Cold Spring Harbor Symp. Quant. Biol.* 57:611–19

106. Simons K, Wandinger-Ness A. 1990. Polarized sorting in epithelia. *Cell* 62: 207–10

107. Steinmetz PR. 1986. Cellular organization of urinary acidification. *Am. J. Physiol.* 251:F173–87

108. Steinmetz PR, Andersen OS. 1982. Electrogenic proton transport in epithelial membranes. *J. Membr. Biol.* 65: 155–74

109. Stone DK, Seldin DW, Kokko JP, Jacobson HR. 1983. Anion dependence of rabbit medullary collecting duct acidification. *J. Clin. Invest.* 71:1505–8

110. Stone DK, Seldin DW, Kokko JP, Jacobson HR. 1983. Mineralocorticoid modulation of rabbit medullary collecting duct acidification. A sodium-independent effect. *J. Clin. Invest.* 2872: 77–83

111. Tisher CC, Madsen KM, Verlander JW. 1991. Structural adaptation of the collecting duct to acid-base disturbances. *Contrib. Nephrol.* 95:168–77

112. Tojo A, Guzman NJ, Garg LC, Tisher CC, Madsen KM. 1994. Nitric oxide inhibits bafilomycin-sensitive H(+)-ATPase activity in rat cortical collecting duct. *Am. J. Physiol.* 267:F509–15

113. Tojo A, Tisher CC, Madsen KM. 1994. Angiotensin II regulates H(+)-ATPase activity in rat cortical collecting duct. *Am. J. Physiol.* 267:F1045–51

114. Vandorpe DH, Levine DZ. 1989. Distal tubule bicarbonate reabsorption in $NH_4Cl$ acidotic rats. *Clin. Invest. Med.* 12:224–29

115. van Meer G, Simons K. 1988. Lipid polarity and sorting in epithelial cells. *J. Cell. Biochem.* 36:51–58

116. Verlander JW, Madsen KM, Galla JH, Luke RG, Tisher CC. 1992. Response of intercalated cells to chloride depletion metabolic alkalosis. *Am. J. Physiol.* 262: F309–19

117. Verlander JW, Madsen KM, Larsson L, Cannon JK, Tisher CC. 1989. Immunocytochemical localization of intracellular acidic compartments: rat proximal nephron. *Am. J. Physiol.* 257:F454–62

118. Verlander JW, Madsen KM, Tisher CC. 1991. Structural and functional features of proton and bicarbonate transport in the rat collecting duct. *Semin. Nephrol.* 11:465–77

119. Wang T, Malnic G, Giebisch G, Chan YL. 1993. Renal bicarbonate reabsorption in the rat. IV. Bicarbonate transport mechanisms in the early and late distal tubule. *J. Clin. Invest.* 91:2776–84

120. Wang ZQ, Gluck S. 1990. Isolation

and properties of bovine kidney brush border vacuolar H(+)-ATPase. A proton pump with enzymatic and structural differences from kidney microsomal H(+)-ATPase. *J. Biol. Chem.* 265: 21957–65

121.  Weiner ID, Wingo CS, Hamm LL. 1993. Regulation of intracellular pH in two cell populations of inner stripe of rabbit outer medullary collecting duct. *Am. J. Physiol.* 265:F406–15

122.  Wingo CS, Armitage FE. 1993. Potassium transport in the kidney: regulation and physiological relevance of H$^+$, K(+)-ATPase. *Semin. Nephrol.* 13:213–24

123.  Wingo CS, Cain BD. 1993. The renal H-K-ATPase: physiological significance and role in potassium homeostasis. *Annu. Rev. Physiol.* 3255:323–47

124.  Xie XS, Stone DK. 1988. Partial resolution and reconsitution of the subunits of the clathrin-coated vesicle proton ATPase responsible for Ca$^{2+}$-activated ATP hydrolysis. *J. Biol. Chem.* 263: 9859–67

125.  Yasoshima K, Satlin LM, Schwartz GJ. 1992. Adaptation of rabbit cortical collecting duct to in vitro acid incubation. *Am. J. Physiol.* 263:F749–56

126.  Zhang J, Feng Y, Forgac M. 1994. Proton conduction and bafilomycin binding by the V0 domain of the coated vesicle V-ATPase. *J. Biol. Chem.* 269: 23518–23

127.  Zhang K, Wang ZQ, Gluck S. 1992. Identification and partial purification of a cytosolic activator of vacuolar H(+)-ATPases from mammalian kidney. *J. Biol. Chem.* 267:9701–5

128.  Zhang K, Wang ZQ, Gluck S. 1992. A cytosolic inhibitor of vacuolar H(+)-ATPases from mammalian kidney. *J. Biol. Chem.* 267:14539–42

129.  Zimolo Z, Montrose MH, Murer H. 1992. H$^+$ extrusion by an apical vacuolar-type H(+)-ATPase in rat renal proximal tubules. *J. Membr. Biol.* 126:19–26

*Annu. Rev. Physiol. 1996. 58:447–81*

# THIN FILAMENT–MEDIATED REGULATION OF CARDIAC CONTRACTION

*Larry S. Tobacman*

Departments of Internal Medicine and Biochemistry, The University of Iowa, Iowa City, Iowa 52242

KEY WORDS:    troponin, tropomyosin, muscle proteins, cooperativity, actin

### ABSTRACT

Cardiac and skeletal muscle contraction are activated by $Ca^{2+}$ binding to specific regulatory sites on the striated muscle thin filament. The thin filament is a large allosteric assembly, containing multiple copies of actin, tropomyosin, and the three troponin subunits (troponin C, troponin I, and troponin T). This review describes recent developments in understanding the structure and dynamics of these proteins and how they function to regulate contraction. Emphasis is placed on the cardiac thin filament and on the features that distinguish it from the skeletal muscle system. The discussion also emphasizes current knowledge of the protein-protein interactions involved in the cooperative processes of thin filament assembly and regulation.

## INTRODUCTION

Cardiac contraction is regulated by $Ca^{2+}$ binding to a remarkable allosteric system, the thin filament. As a result of interactions among the subunits of this multimeric assembly, muscle contraction is turned on and off by a very small change in the $Ca^{2+}$ concentration. The isometric tension of skinned cardiac muscle fibers and of single cardiac myocytes is low in the absence of $Ca^{2+}$ and reaches 50% of maximum in the presence of $\sim 2 \times 10^6$ $M^{-1}$ $Ca^{2+}$, depending upon the experimental conditions (35). Twofold deviations from the $Ca^{2+}$ midpoint result in at least 90% activation or inhibition in most studies, corresponding to a Hill coefficient of 3 or more (4, 119, 166). Thin filament regulation of fast skeletal muscle contraction is even more cooperative, with Hill coefficients of 5–7 (4, 8, 123).

One of the more interesting attributes of this cooperative system is the low stoichiometry of regulatory subunits, i.e. troponin (33), relative to the number

447

of functional subunits, i.e. actin. There is only one troponin molecule for every seven actins, which are the sites for force generation with myosin. This stoichiometry is attributable to the effects of tropomyosin, a highly extended α-helical coiled coil protein. Tropomyosin spans seven actins, binds and specifically positions one troponin for each tropomyosin on the thin filament, and is a primary mediator of the long-range regulatory effect of $Ca^{2+}$ binding to troponin. Considering the separation between troponin molecules, it is all the more remarkable that the response of the system to $Ca^{2+}$ evidences so much cooperativity. The activation of the thin filament is therefore a complex process involving long-range cooperative effects, effects in which several types of protein-protein interactions are likely to be significant. Several other reviews of various aspects of thin filament–mediated regulation have appeared (3, 20, 98, 136, 206). This review describes recent developments in understanding thin filament–based regulation of striated muscle contraction, with emphasis where possible on the cardiac thin filament, on features that distinguish it from skeletal muscle, and with particular attention to the allosteric properties of the thin filament.

Although the thin filament is unlike other allosteric systems in that its function is primarily mechanical rather than enzymatic or ligand binding, cooperative muscle regulation ought to be explicable on a level similar to other systems such as hemoglobin or aspartate transcarbamylase. That is, ligand binding results in definable conformational changes that not only influence other binding sites within the same subunit, but also affect other subunits by alterations at protein-protein interfaces. Functionally important alterations in protein-protein interactions are a key feature of allosteric systems and underlie both classical (202) and contemporary (1, 68) models of cooperative systems. Thin filament regulation, in other words, includes relatively direct and relatively indirect changes in structure. $Ca^{2+}$ binding to the regulatory sites of the troponin C subunit (TnC) is accompanied by a conformational change in the N-domain of this molecule (42, 65). Tight myosin binding to actin is believed sterically to require a rotational movement of tropomyosin relative to the axis of the actin filament, so that the tropomyosin does not block the myosin-binding site on actin (99). These are relatively direct effects. The cooperative properties of the system arise from the propagation of these events to other protein-protein interfaces resulting in structural changes and functional consequences physically remote from the original binding site. Importantly, such interactions are often directly measurable by assembling an allosteric system from its constituent subunits.

## THE ACTIN FILAMENT

Actin is one of several contractile proteins for which high resolution structures are now available. Because of its tendency to form filaments, actin has not been crystallized in the absence of other proteins, but X-ray structures of monomeric actin in complex with pancreatic DNAse I (89), gelsolin (115), and profilin (157) are all available. The actin conformation is very similar in all three of these complexes, except for small regions that directly contact the other proteins in the co-crystals. Actin has two domains of roughly equal size, each of which has two subdomains. The well-known requirement of a metal-nucleotide complex for actin stability (93) is readily explained by the positioning of this complex between the two domains, with contacts to both of them.

Coincident with the publication of the actin-DNAse I structure, an atomic model for the actin filament was also presented (81), using data from X-ray diffraction of oriented actin gels to help fit the actin monomers into a filament. These data were subsequently refined (110). The resulting model for F-actin indicates that the larger of the two actin domains is located more toward the center of the two-stranded filament helix. The smaller domain, which includes both the N-and C-termini in subdomain 1, is more solvent exposed. However, neither domain is buried within the filament. Significantly for allosteric models of thin filament behavior, the precise contacts between monomers are not well defined. However, there appear to be more sites of interaction along each of the two longitudinal strands, in comparison with the proposed number of contacts between the strands. Strand-strand association is hypothesized to be mediated, in significant part, by a repositioning (relative to its position in the X-ray structure) of a loop in domain 2 so that it can form a hydrophobic interaction with the other strand. In support of this model, mutagenesis of the loop resulted in a temperature-sensitive destabilization of yeast F-actin (23).

Studies of conformational changes within F-actin may prove highly pertinent for understanding thin filament regulation but are difficult to accomplish at high resolution. Based upon transitions in the profilin-actin crystal structure, an alternative model for the packing of monomers into F-actin has been proposed (158). This relatively radical proposal for specific alterations in F-actin is controversial. More subtle changes were recently proposed by Orlova et al (132, 133). Thin filament three-dimensional reconstructions were created from electron micrographs of F-actin polymerized under different conditions. Significant differences were found depending upon whether $Ca^{2+}$ G-actin or $Mg^{2+}$ G-actin was polymerized. Proteolytic removal of three C-terminal residues caused a reduction in strand-strand connectivity. Surprisingly, binding of gelsolin at the end of the actin filament seemed to change its overall structure. This interesting long-range effect of gelsolin is indirectly supported by the studies of Muhlrad et al (125). Substoichiometric concentrations of $BeFl_3$, a phosphate analogue, alter the proteolytic susceptibility of specific sites on F-actin. The alteration of the proteolytic rate is in considerable disproportion to the amount of $BeFl_3$ added, which implies propagated conformational changes in the thin filament. BeFl$_3$ also alters the rigidity of F-actin (86), and any of several phosphate analogues can stabilize actin-actin bonds (19) and reduce disorder in F-actin (131). Tirion & ben-Avraham have investigated the normal mode vibrations of G-actin (176), which provided a more dynamic picture of actin than previously demonstrated. These are very disparate studies, and many have no direct relationship to movement, force generation, or regulation. However, the accumulating evidence of variability within F-actin suggests that changes in troponin and tropomyosin may not be a sufficient structural explanation for thin filament activation. Functionally significant alterations in polymeric actin itself may also be occurring. Additional evidence for this possibility is provided below.

## TROPOMYOSIN

Actin, the most essential molecule in the thin filament, is the protein directly involved in force production, and troponin is the primary site of regulation. Regulation would not occur, however, without the physical and functional link between these proteins that is provided by tropomyosin. Tropomyosin is a highly extended, $\alpha$-helical coiled coil (144, 145, 193). The continuous tropomyosin strand spans seven actin monomers and forms an indirect connection between troponins that otherwise are so far apart as to make regulation problematic. The steric blocking model (59, 83, 99, 137), in which Ca$^{2+}$ binding to troponin causes tropomyosin to move away from a position that interferes with myosin binding to actin, is an attractive and enduring solution to the dilemma of the relatively sparse number of troponin molecules on the thin filament. In large mammals, cardiac tropomyosin is predominantly one isoform, $\alpha$-tropomyosin, which has the same amino acid sequence as $\alpha$-tropomyosin found in skeletal muscle (105). In smaller mammals, cardiac tropomyosin more closely resembles fast skeletal muscle tropomyosin, with an equal mixture of $\alpha$- and $\beta$-isoforms. The structure of tropomyosin has been discussed in previous thin filament reviews [see especially Leavis & Gergely (98)]. The role of tropomyosin in thin filament–mediated regulation is discussed below.

## TROPONIN C

### Structure and Regulation of Skeletal Muscle Troponin C

Striated muscle contraction is most directly regulated by Ca$^{2+}$ binding to TnC, which has four metal-binding EF-hand motifs, although not all are active in every TnC isoform. In vertebrate cardiac muscle, site I (the most N-terminal site) lacks crucial sequence requirements for Ca$^{2+}$ binding (183) and is inactive.

Site II is the primary site for regulation of cardiac contraction, whereas both sites I and II are regulatory in fast skeletal muscle (see below). The high resolution X-ray structure of avian skeletal muscle TnC (64, 164) presents an asymmetric molecule with two globular domains connected by a long central helix. Each domain contains a pair of $Ca^{2+}$-binding sites, but at the low pH of the crystal only the higher affinity sites III and IV are occupied. The protein is highly $\alpha$-helical, and the helices entering and leaving each of the four EF-hand sites are designated helices A through H. The long helix connecting the two domains extends from site II to site III and, accordingly, is designated helix D/E.

Herzberg et al proposed that $Ca^{2+}$ binding to the regulatory sites is accompanied by a conformational change in the N-domain of TnC that results in a structure similar to the metal-filled C-domain of the crystal structure (65). This would involve a reorganization of the relative positions of the helices in the N-domain, with the B and C helices moving as a unit relative to the A and D helices. Some residues would be repositioned 10 to 15 Å by this proposed regulatory conformational change. Subsequent to the publication of this model, site-directed mutagenesis of TnC by several laboratories produced functional alterations consistent with the proposed structural change upon $Ca^{2+}$ binding. Targeted insertion of Cys residues in TnC permitted formation of a disulfide between helix D and the B/C linker, which resulted in weaker $Ca^{2+}$ affinity as predicted by the model (48). The mutant TnC also displayed impaired regulatory function in myofibrils. Similarly, creation of a salt bridge between Glu57 and Glu88 by mutating either residue to Lys was predicted to oppose the $Ca^{2+}$-induced conformational change and was shown to weaken the $Ca^{2+}$ affinity of sites I and II (40). Perhaps more convincing are the results using mutant TnCs with increased rather than decreased $Ca^{2+}$ affinity. The Herzberg et al model suggests that several hydrophobic residues, buried in the 2-$Ca^{2+}$ X-ray crystal structure, become exposed to solvent in the 4-$Ca^{2+}$ state. Pearlstone et al studied five mutant TnCs in which the side chain apolar surface area of selected residues was changed (138). The results were generally consistent with the model; $Ca^{2+}$ affinity was increased where predicted, although the magnitude of the change was not entirely explained. Interestingly, two of these mutants (V45T and M48A) were exchanged into skinned fibers and were shown to decrease the $Ca^{2+}$ concentration required for tension activation (30). How the other troponin subunits, especially TnI, may alter the solvent exposure of these residues is not known. Nevertheless, the results in skinned fibers parallel the results for TnC alone.

A recent NMR spectroscopy study by Gagné et al has provided direct structural evidence for the nature of the $Ca^{2+}$-induced conformational change in the regulatory N-domain of skeletal muscle TnC (Figure 1) (42). There is high $\alpha$-helical content in the N-domain, regardless of whether $Ca^{2+}$ is present.

*Figure 1* Schematic representation of the $Ca^{2+}$-induced conformational change in the $NH_2$-terminal regulatory domain of skeletal muscle TnC. Model I is the $Ca^{2+}$-free crystal structure (64); model II shows the predicted $Ca^{2+}$-saturated structure (65), and model III shows the $Ca^{2+}$-saturated structure based on NMR data. (From 42, with permission.)

However, the B-helix leading out of $Ca^{2+}$-binding site I is bent in $Ca^{2+}$-free TnC but converted to a continuous, straighter helix when $Ca^{2+}$ is bound to sites I and II. This straightening of the B-helix is sufficient to cause the overall relative movement of the N-domain helices, as predicted in the Herzberg & James model. It will be important to determine whether the same mechanism is operative in cardiac TnC, which has an inactive site I.

## Structure and Regulation of Cardiac Troponin C

Like skeletal muscle TnC, cardiac TnC has two classes of $Ca^{2+}$-binding sites (71, 82, 92). A large amount of evidence suggests that $Ca^{2+}$-binding site II in the TnC N-domain is responsible for regulating cardiac contraction. In the ternary cardiac troponin complex, the TnC C-domain sites III and IV bind $Ca^{2+}$ with high affinity ($3 \times 10^8$ $M^{-1}$), but they also bind $Mg^{2+}$ ($3 \times 10^3$ $M^{-1}$) (82) so that few of these sites are metal free, even in relaxed muscle. Sites III and IV influence the N-domain of TnC from cardiac or skeletal muscle (47, 108, 167, 189), but kinetic evidence suggests this has limited regulatory importance. Skeletal muscle relaxes much faster than the dissociation rate of $Ca^{2+}$ from sites III and IV (155) and the C-domain sites in cardiac TnC and skeletal TnC are similar in metal affinity. Furthermore, activation of myofibrillar ATPase (82) and fiber tension (135) correlate with titration of site II, not sites III and IV. Finally, targeted mutations of the cardiac TnC N-domain have shown that a functional site II is necessary for contraction (56, 152, 165), that functional (i.e. mutant) site I cannot replace an inactivated (also mutant) site II (165), and that mutations in sites III and IV weaken TnC thin filament affinity without abolishing regulation (31, 127). Interestingly, although skeletal muscle TnC requires both active site I and active site II for normal function when exchanged into cardiac or skeletal muscle fibers (56, 159, 163), normal cardiac regulation occurred with a chimeric TnC containing sites II-IV from skeletal TnC and the N-terminal portion (including inactive site I) from cardiac TnC (56). From these results it seems clear that the primary regulation of cardiac contraction involves the reversible binding of $Ca^{2+}$ to TnC site II.

One consequence of the regulatory primacy of the TnC N-domain is that there is only one regulatory site per cardiac troponin, in contrast to fast skeletal muscle troponin, which has two sites. Recent studies of the skeletal TnC F29W mutant suggest that sites I and II bind $Ca^{2+}$ with high cooperativity (138). Although this was not seen with earlier studies (46, 150, 156), the recent result is consistent with the proposed 4-$Ca^{2+}$ structure (65). Also, mutagenesis studies of sites I or II suggest interactions between the sites (152, 159). Regardless of whether sites I and II cooperatively bind $Ca^{2+}$ in fast skeletal muscle, this mechanism is not present in cardiac muscle, which lacks site I but nevertheless responds cooperatively to $Ca^{2+}$ (4, 119, 135, 166). As stated previously (177, 180), this makes cardiac muscle an appealing system for elucidating the mechanism of cooperative muscle activation.

The TnC X-ray structure employed skeletal muscle TnC, and there is as yet no high resolution structure for the cardiac protein. However, a $Ca^{2+}$-induced increase in accessibility of cardiac TnC Cys84 parallels the predicted conformational change at this position in skeletal muscle TnC (84). Much more detailed analysis comes from the work of Rosevear and co-workers who have used NMR of wild-type and mutant cardiac TnCs to acquire significant structural information. (*a*) The mutation D65A, which inactivates site II and produces an inhibitory form of TnC (152), results in only minor structural changes in TnC (13). This result validates the various functional studies of this mutant protein (31, 152, 165). (*b*) The aromatic C-domain nuclear Overhauser effects (NOEs) are nearly identical for the two proteins, regardless of whether $Ca^{2+}$, $Mg^{2+}$, or no metal was present. Similarly, $^{13}C$ Met resonances in the C-domain are unaffected by the mutation in site II (108). Site II $Ca^{2+}$ binding has little effect on the C-domain. (*c*) On the other hand, comparison between the wild-type and mutant protein indicates that $Ca^{2+}$ binding to the C-domain has significant effects on the chemical shifts of epsilon H Met47 and Met81 in the N-domain (108). This implies a domain-domain interaction in cardiac TnC, as suggested earlier by fluorescence studies (189). (*d*) $Ca^{2+}$ binding to the N-domain causes large changes in N-domain Met chemical shifts and also changes the chemical shifts of several identified Phe residues that form a hydrophobic cluster in the N-domain. Inter-residue NOEs among these Phe residues do not change on $Ca^{2+}$ binding (13). However, they are all located in helices A and D, so their lack of relative movement is consistent with the Herzberg & James model. (*e*) The amide protons of the Gly at position 6 of the $Ca^{2+}$ sites were studied with $^{15}N$-enriched amino acids and multidimensional NMR (95). The resonances are downfield shifted in $Ca^{2+}$ TnC, except Gly70 is not seen in the

*D65A* mutant. The H-bond between positions 1 and 6 appears essential for $Ca^{2+}$ binding and requires an Asp at position 1, consistent with other mutagenesis studies of position 1 (5). (*f*) The expected β-sheet between sites I and II is present in apo TnC but poorly formed between sites III and IV unless metal is present (12, 95). In the presence of $Ca^{2+}$, the β-sheet between sites III and IV can still form if only one of these two sites is activated. A detailed understanding of cardiac regulation will require comprehensive knowledge of TnC structure, as these studies have begun to provide.

# TROPONIN I

## Inhibitory Function of Troponin I

Troponin I (TnI) is the troponin subunit essential for inhibiting muscle contraction in the absence of $Ca^{2+}$. The amino acid sequence of cardiac TnI (49) identifies a protein of molecular weight 23, 800, with a 27–33 residue N-terminal extension not found in skeletal muscle TnI (49, 102a). Deletion of the extension by mutagenesis has little functional effect, but phosphorylation of the extension by cAMP-dependent protein kinase results in lower $Ca^{2+}$ affinity for the TnC regulatory site II (57). Skeletal muscle TnI inhibits the actin-myosin MgATPase rate in vitro in the absence of tropomyosin or the other troponin subunits (50, 51, 169). This inhibition requires lower concentrations of TnI in the presence of tropomyosin (143). TnI binding to actin is reversed by the addition of TnC plus $Ca^{2+}$ (73, 149). These results suggest that the MgATPase inhibition by tropomyosin plus TnI may be similar to what occurs in the complete thin filament with its well-defined stoichiometry. However, cardiac TnI is considerably less effective as an inhibitor than skeletal muscle TnI, requiring higher concentrations and achieving less striking inhibition even at apparent saturation (57, 168, 171). The functional correlation between inhibition by TnI and inhibition by whole troponin must be viewed as incomplete and as yet unsubstantiated by structural data.

On the other hand, it is notable that the inhibitory effects of TnI can be mimicked by a positively charged fragment of TnI, known as the inhibitory peptide. The inhibitory region of TnI was first identified by Syska et al as a cyanogen bromide fragment, residues 96–116 (169, 196). The inhibitory effect of this skeletal muscle peptide can be reversed by the addition of TnC plus $Ca^{2+}$ (169). Talbot & Hodges demonstrated that residues 95–104 could be deleted from the peptide without loss of function (172). Van Eyk & Hodges performed detailed structure-function studies of the inhibitory peptide and concluded that Arg115 and Val114 were most essential, but each residue in the 104–115 region was important (184). The inhibitory peptide differs in cardiac and fast skeletal muscles in one position; the cardiac sequence has Thr at the position corresponding to Pro110 in skeletal muscle TnI. Although whole cardiac TnI inhibits less well than its skeletal muscle counterpart, the Pro to Thr change makes no difference in the inhibitory function of the inhibitory peptide (171). However, one study suggests that the cardiac and skeletal muscle peptides have opposite effects on the $Ca^{2+}$ affinity of the regulatory domain of their corresponding TnC isoforms (185). In the skeletal muscle system, the peptide increased N-, as well as C-domain, $Ca^{2+}$ affinity (22, 167). The contrasting result that the peptide decreases N-domain $Ca^{2+}$ affinity in cardiac troponin (185) has not yet been confirmed but may reflect the more complex picture of TnI-TnC interactions suggested by recent studies (36, 129).

## The Troponin I-Troponin C Binary Complex

The stability of the TnI-TnC binary complex is sensitive to the presence of $Ca^{2+}$ (24, 85, 106), and the TnI-TnC interface is likely a primary site for transmission of the effects of regulatory site $Ca^{2+}$ to the remainder of the thin filament. In skeletal muscle, the affinities of 2-$Mg^{2+}$-TnC and 4-$Ca^{2+}$-TnC for TnI differ by 15- to 100-fold. This large effect of $Ca^{2+}$ suggests that a change in the TnI-TnC interaction may be the best candidate for the propagation of the effects of $Ca^{2+}$ binding. However, $Ca^{2+}$ binding has a relatively small effect on the stability of the cardiac TnC-TnI complex. Cardiac TnI and TnC bind with an affinity of $4 \times 10^7$ $M^{-1}$ in the presence of $Mg^{2+}$, vs $1.3 \times 10^8$ $M^{-1}$ in the presence of $Ca^{2+}$ (106).

Recent results strongly imply there are multiple interaction sites between skeletal muscle TnI and TnC, as was also suggested earlier by Grabarek et al (45). TnC and TnI are readily cross-linked by heterobifunctional reagents (175). Cys98 in the distal E helix of TnC cross-links to the TnI inhibitory peptide (residues 96–116) (102). The interaction of the inhibitory peptide with the TnC C-domain is also shown by cross-linking between TnI Gly104 and TnC Met155 (128). However, other studies have shown proximity between TnC N-domain position 57 and TnI peptide 113–121 (91), between TnC position 12 and TnI Cys133 (90), and between TnC peptide 46–78 and TnI Lys 105 and Lys107 (with a zero-length cross-linker) (104). It is interesting to compare these cross-linking studies implying that the inhibitory peptide binds to both TnC domains with the fluorescence studies of Swenson & Fredrickson (167). The inhibitory peptide binds with 1:1 stoichiometry and comparable affinities to the TnC N-domain, the C-domain, or whole TnC (167). Therefore, it is unclear whether the structure of the inhibitory peptide, when bound to skeletal muscle TnC (16) or cardiac TnC (17), represents a peptide bound to the N-domain, the C-domain, or both.

The most comprehensive structure-function study of TnI as of this writing is the 1994 report of Farah et al (36), which describes the properties of seven recombinant forms of TnI, in combination with actin, tropomyosin, myosin subfragment 1, troponin T (TnT), and several site-specific mutants of TnC. The results show that the regulatory N-domain of TnC binds in a $Ca^{2+}$-sensitive manner to the C-terminal region of TnI. Furthermore, TnC-binding of C-terminal TnI fragment 103–182, which includes the inhibitory peptide, is much tighter than TnC-binding of TnI 120–182, which does not. Similarly, TnI 1–98 binds only to the C-domain of TnC, but inclusion of the inhibitory peptide (TnI 1–116) results in a TnI fragment that will also bind (albeit weakly) to the TnC regulatory domain. TnI binding to the C-domain of TnC is promoted by $Ca^{2+}$ or by $Mg^{2+}$, as would be expected from the properties of TnC sites III and IV. A 1995 mutagenesis report from the same investigative group provides further evidence that all four metal-binding sites in TnC contribute to TnC thin filament binding (163). The combined results of Reinach and co-workers clearly imply an anti-parallel arrangement between TnI and TnC, with multiple sites of interaction between the two subunits. The results also support the importance of the TnI-inhibitory peptide for regulation because only TnI fragments including this region were able to produce $Ca^{2+}$-sensitive MgATPase regulation in a reconstituted thin filament. The authors propose that a $Ca^{2+}$-insensitive attachment exists between TnI and TnC via their N- and C-regions, respectively, and that regulation involves a reversible, $Ca^{2+}$-sensitive binding of the regulatory domain of TnC to the C-terminal portion of TnI. Although these conclusions were based upon experiments with skeletal muscle troponin, a recent NMR study indicates that cardiac troponin also has an anti-parallel arrangement for the TnI-TnC complex (96).

The results of Farah et al are in excellent agreement with the proposed structure of the skeletal muscle TnI-TnC complex. From small angle X-ray and neutron scattering, Olah & Trewella concluded that the TnI-TnC complex has overall dimensions of 115 Å, even larger than the 72 Å span of the fully extended TnC X-ray structure. Because the TnI and TnC centers of mass are approximately coincident, portions of TnI must lie beyond the opposite, most distal portions of the TnC structure (Figure 2). The results of Farah et al suggest the polarity of TnI in this proposed structure. The N-terminal region of TnI presumably contacts the TnC C-domain; the C-terminal region of TnI contacts the TnC regulatory domain; and a linker extends between these two regions of the complex. The position of the inhibitory peptide is unclear. The NMR structure of the inhibitory region in complex with TnC (16, 17) suggests a bent, α-helical conformation, which is consistent with the conformation of Olah & Trewella's proposed 70–80 residue mid-TnI linker region. However, a highly extended TnI-TnC complex appears inconsistent with extensive contacts between the inhibitory peptide and both N- and C-domains of TnC.

It is notable that cardiac TnC-TnI binding is increased only threefold by regulatory site $Ca^{2+}$ binding (106). This is a relatively small change for a

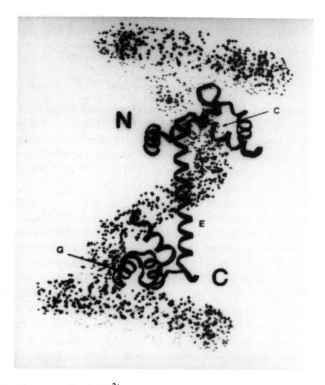

*Figure 2*   Model structure for the $Ca^{2+}$-saturated TnC-TnI complex. TnI is stippled, and the solid line indicates the position of the TnC backbone atoms. (From 129, with permission.)

process believed crucial for the propagation of TnC site II $Ca^{2+}$ binding to the conformation of the remainder of the thin filament. The resolution of this apparent paradox may lie in the skeletal muscle results of Swenson & Fredrickson, who studied the thermodynamics of the interactions of $Ca^{2+}$, $Mg^{2+}$, and TnI with whole TnC and with the TnC N- and C-domains (167). TnI binds to either the N- or C-domains of TnC with a 1:1 stoichiometry and similar affinities. The summed free energy for binding to the two domains is much greater than the free energy for binding to whole TnC, which suggests a positive free energy of interaction between the domains within the TnI-TnC complex. Furthermore, the replacement of $Mg^{2+}$ by $Ca^{2+}$ has a much smaller effect on the affinity of TnI for each domain than its effect on TnI binding to whole TnC. This suggests that $Ca^{2+}$ binding to the regulatory sites(s) of the TnI-TnC complex is influenced by $Ca^{2+}$-sensitive, unfavorable domain-domain interactions in TnC. A large $Ca^{2+}$-induced increase in the association of TnI with the TnC regulatory domain (36, 167) would not necessarily cause a large change in overall cardiac TnI-TnC affinity, because there may also be a change in the interaction between TnI and the TnC C-domain.

## *Troponin I Binding to Tropomyosin and to Troponin T*

TnI binds weakly to immobilized tropomyosin and has little effect on the association of TnT to tropomyosin (142, 173). However, TnI promotes tropomyosin-actin binding (32), and tropomyosin promotes TnI-actin binding (72, 149), which suggests that TnI and tropomyosin may directly interact. TnI also binds to TnT, with an association constant of $8 \times 10^6$ M$^{-1}$ (85). Several lines of evidence, mostly obtained with skeletal muscle proteins, suggest this involves the N-terminal portion of TnI. TnI Cys48 and Cys64 become inaccessible to reaction with iodoacetamide when TnT is present (27). In the presence of a photoaffinity cross-linker, these same residues can be cross-linked to TnT (28). TnI C-terminal fragment 103–182 fails to form a ternary troponin complex with TnT and TnC (36). The reactivity (to acetic anhydride) of TnI lysines 40, 65, 70, 78, and 90 is suppressed in the TnT-TnI complex or in whole troponin (75). Significantly, these lysine reactivities are influenced by the presence of $Mg^{2+}$ instead of $Ca^{2+}$. This is understandable in the context of the more recent demonstration that this same region of TnI interacts with the C-domain of TnC (36), which binds $Ca^{2+}$ or $Mg^{2+}$. Finally, some analogous results have been obtained with cardiac subunits. Cardiac TnI Cys75 and Cys92 are buried by TnT, becoming unreactive to iodoacetamide in whole troponin or in the TnT-TnI complex (84). It seems clear that the N-terminal region of TnI binds to TnT as well as to the C-domain of TnC.

## TROPONIN T AND THE TROPONIN COMPLEX

The remaining troponin subunit to be discussed, troponin T (TnT), binds to tropomyosin (111, 112, 122, 140, 141, 174); TnI (28, 74, 174); TnC (74, 102, 112, 174, 175); and actin (29, 63). It is hardly an exaggeration to call TnT the glue that holds the regulatory system together. A schematic representation of the thin filament, including the Tn-T1 (residues 1–158) and Tn-T2 (residues 159–259) regions of TnT, is shown in Figure 3. Skeletal muscle TnT is a highly elongated, rod-like protein, with a length of $185 \pm 35$ Å, according to the electron microscopic study of Flicker et al (38). Cardiac TnT is approximately 20 Å longer (15), due to a longer amino acid sequence in the hypervariable region near the N-terminus (103). The predominant TnT isoform is 284 amino acids in length in bovine heart (103) and 259 residues in rabbit fast skeletal muscle (41, 139). Amino acids 1–158 of skeletal muscle TnT are 68% α-helical

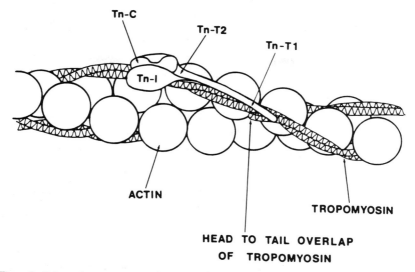

*Figure 3*   Schematic representation of a small region of the thin filament. The rabbit skeletal muscle TnT proteolytic fragment Tn-T1 (residues 1–158) spans the tropomyosin-tropomyosin overlap joint. TnT fragment Tn-T2 (residues 159–259) interact with TnC and TnI. (From Reference 62, with permission.)

(140, 174) and may extend through much of the considerable length of this molecule. However, the tertiary structure of TnT is unknown.

Interestingly, the globular head region of skeletal muscle troponin has an estimated dimension of 105 Å (38), a value similar to the 115 Å span of the TnI-TnC complex in the Olah & Trewella model (129). TnT is rod-like and approximately 25 Å longer than the length of the tail in the ternary troponin complex (38). Evidently, the globular region consists of TnI, TnC, and a small portion of TnT. However, it is not clear what part(s) of the TnT sequence form the region interacting with the other two subunits. Tanokura et al reported that skeletal muscle TnT fragment 159–227 binds much more tightly to TnI than does TnT fragment 159–222 (174). Because the two fragments are similarly folded according to their circular dichroism spectra, the results suggest that TnT residues 223–227 are important for binding to TnI. Similarly, TnC Cys98 cross-links to TnT region 176–230 (102) when all three subunits are present. In the binary TnT-TnC complex, TnT residues 175–178 are implicated. Chong & Hodges showed that Cys residues in the N-terminal region of TnI can be cross-linked to the 176–230 region of TnT (28). These studies can be summarized to implicate the 176–230 region of skeletal muscle TnT as the primary site of interaction with the TnI-TnC complex. However, TnI cross-linking to the TnT 71–151 region was also found (28). Furthermore, formation of the troponin complex greatly diminishes the accessibility of selected TnT Lys residues spanning positions 114 through 223, a very wide region (74). It is hard to reconcile these results with the available low-resolution structural data, as discussed above, which imply that a relatively small region of TnT interacts directly with TnI-TnC.

An important study of troponin-tropomyosin structure involved the binding of skeletal muscle troponin or TnT fragments to glutaraldehyde-treated tropomyosin crystals (195). The globular region of troponin was not well seen, but bound weakly to the 150–180 region of tropomyosin (which has 284 residues). Similarly, other studies have shown that tropomyosin near Cys190 interacts weakly with the globular region of troponin (37, 38, 97, 122, 175). The co-crystal studies also show that the distal end of the TnT tail, which binds near the C-terminus of tropomyosin, has the tightest observed binding to tropomyosin and is most clearly seen. This is consistent with the observation that TnT fragment 1–151 blocks iodination of tyrosines near the C-terminus of tropomyosin (Tyr261 and 267), but has no effect on Tyr60, 162, 214, or 221 (111). Also, alteration of the tropomyosin C-terminus by carboxypeptidase A digestion or by mutagenesis dramatically reduces the interaction of troponin (especially TnT 1–158) with tropomyosin (25, 62, 111, 141). The co-crystal studies (195) suggest that TnT fragment 1–158 constitutes two thirds of the TnT length, including the tight binding region. Finally, the most N-terminal region, fragment 1–70, was located at the junction between adjacent tropomyosins. However, fragment 71–151 was incompletely visualized (194), so part of this latter fragment may also lie near the tropomyosin-tropomyosin junction.

## THE THIN FILAMENT

### Structure and Dynamics

Since the publication of the first atomic structure for G-actin (89), the goal of high resolution models for the thin filament in various states has seemed achievable, although not without difficulty. Several kinds of information are available for informing attempts to move from the strucure of one actin monomor to the structure of the thin filament: X-ray diffraction of oriented F-actin gels, X-ray diffraction of muscle fibers stretched to eliminate thin and thick filament overlap, optical reconstruction from cryo-electron micrographs or negatively stained electron micrographs, and neutron scattering. These techniques are generally based on the periodic placement of the actin monomers within the thin filament. Tropomyosin is an α-helical coiled-coil, and can be embedded quite reasonably in the periodic actin structure. A similar approach cannot be used for troponin. It has a different periodicity within the actin filament, and its structure is unknown. This complicates and limits the interpretation of thin filament structure.

Lorenz and co-workers recently published an atomic model for F-actin-tropomyosin (109), based on three sources of data: X-ray diffraction of oriented thin filaments in the absence of troponin, a previous atomic model of F-actin (110), and a coiled coiled-coil structure for tropomyosin. In agreement with neutron scattering (6) and electron microscopic (120) studies, tropomyosin lies at a 39 Å radius from the center of F-actin. There is a 10.5 Å distance between side chains of tropomyosin and actin subdomains 3 and 4, implying weak electrostatic interactions between the two proteins. These studies do not show, but also do not exclude, a closer more specific contact between actin and a specific region of tropomyosin. For example, the amino terminus is crucial for tropomyosin function, including actin binding (26, 61, 76, 197).

Notably, the actin-tropomyosin atomic model implies that tropomyosin causes subtle conformational changes in the actin monomers, with a 1.5 Å rms movement of the actin $C^\alpha$ atoms (109) relative to their positions in the absence of tropomyosin. In particular, there is movement of the hydrophobic loop in the interior of the filament (F264-I274), repositioning of helices R183-T194 and F223-A230, and movement of the DNAse-binding loop toward a smaller radius. These results are consistent with the conclusion of Butters et al that conformational changes in actin occur on tropomyosin binding, because disruption of tropomyosin-tropomyosin end-to-end binding by several methods had only a small effect on the cooperativity of tropomyosin-actin binding (14). This effect had also been suggested as a possibility in earlier work (61, 62, 156). Lorenz and co-workers also calculated that rotation of tropomyosin about its own axis would have dramatic effects on its ability to bind to actin (109). This may explain the impaired binding of mutant tropomyosins with deletions of nonintegral portions of a putative actin-binding site (77). Finally, the atomic model for actin-tropomyosin (109) shows tropomyosin in a position similar to that in the invertebrate actin-tropomyosin-troponin-$Ca^{2+}$ structure (99). Most, but not all, of the actin site for myosin binding (80, 154) is unobstructed by the tropomyosin.

Two decades of structural studies of actin-troponin-tropomyosin were expertly reviewed in 1984 (98) and updated in 1992 (20). More recently, a $Ca^{2+}$-induced repositioning of tropomyosin was observed in three-dimensional reconstructions using electron micrographs of *Limulus* actin-troponin-tropomyosin (99). In separate studies, an atomic model for the vertebrate thin filament in the presence and absence of $Ca^{2+}$ is being developed (80, 99a, 146, 163a). These investigations imply that muscle activation does indeed involve a repositioning of tropomyosin, as suggested by earlier studies, and that steric effects of tropomyosin on actin-myosin binding are important in regulation. It is not yet clear how well the atomic models will successfully define the $Ca^{2+}$-induced changes in actin monomer structure that are implied to exist by several studies (147, 148, 163a, 203). Because tropomyosin alone alters actin monomer structure (109), and $Ca^{2+}$ causes tropomyosin to shift on actin in the presence of troponin, an effect of $Ca^{2+}$ on actin is expected. Changes in actin are also implied by the substantially increased flexibility of the thin filament in the presence of $Ca^{2+}$ (86, 130, 204), despite the tight binding of troponin-tropomyosin to actin in the presence and in the absence of $Ca^{2+}$ (29, 37, 66, 197). However, neither the nature of the actin conformational changes, nor their significance for the regulation of muscle contraction is known.

## Thin Filament Assembly

Troponin and tropomyosin each bind more tightly to actin in the presence of the other molecule than they do alone (72, 73, 149). Because of limited structural information, the mechanism for this is not completely clear. However, TnI and TnT bind to actin in the absence of tropomyosin (discussed above), and troponin probably binds simultaneously to both actin and tropomyosin, thereby tethering all three proteins together. Troponin may also increase tropomyosin-actin binding by promoting tropomyosin-tropomyosin end-to-end interactions. Troponin or TnT causes a large increase in tropomyosin viscosity at low ionic strength (88), implying troponin-induced polymerization of tropomyosin. Also, troponin-tropomyosin co-crystals indicate that TnT spans the tropomyosin-tropomyosin overlap joint (195). However, equilibrium studies of thin filament assembly suggest that neither skeletal muscle troponin (37, 66) nor cardiac muscle troponin (29) increases cooperative interactions between adjacent tropomyosins on the thin filament. This implies that troponin promotes tropomyosin actin-binding primarily by a direct local effect on the thin filament, such as binding simultaneously to actin and to tropomyosin. Whatever the specific protein-protein interactions may be at the atomic level, the thermodynamic effect is significant. As shown for the cardiac thin filament in Figure 4, troponin-tropomyosin binds 100- to 1000-fold more tightly to an isolated site on F-actin than does tropomyosin alone (14, 29, 37, 66). Furthermore, this effect of troponin is diminished only about twofold by $Ca^{2+}$, consistent with earlier studies (107, 156, 191). This has implications for the mechanism of regulation, as discussed below.

A primary feature of the assembly of troponin and tropomyosin onto the actin filament is the requirement that they be positioned precisely every seven actins along the thin filament. If tropomyosin or troponin-tropomyosin bound randomly to actin, gaps would be left between adjacent ligands that were less than seven actins long—too short for another tropomyosin to fit. This parking problem, i.e. the problem of how long ligands park on a linear lattice, applies

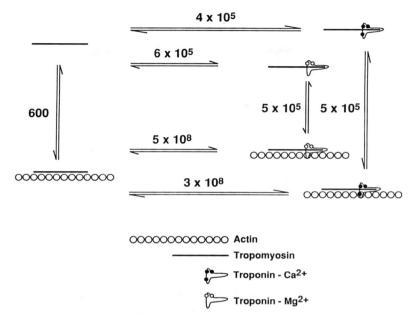

*Figure 4* Association constants (in units of $M^{-1}$) for the binding of cardiac troponin and tropomyosin to each other and to an isolated site on the actin filament. (Data from 29.)

equally to tropomyosin-actin binding and to the association of nonspecific DNA-binding proteins to DNA. The parameters crucial to this kind of process and their quantitative effects on binding curves were elucidated by several authors (68, 113, 182). This approach has been applied to thin filament assembly data, demonstrating that both tropomyosin and troponin-tropomyosin bind to actin with high cooperativity (29, 66, 170, 190). Two important parameters can be extracted from binding data: (*a*) $K_o$, the affinity of the ligand (tropomyosin or troponin-tropomyosin) for an isolated site on F-actin; and (*b*) *y*, which is equivalently either the equilibrium constant for an isolated actin-bound ligand to move to a position adjacent to another bound ligand (Figure 5), or the fold-increase in affinity when the ligand binds adjacent to another bound ligand instead of to an isolated site. If cooperativity promotes assembly, then the value of *y*, sometimes designated as $\omega$, is greater than 1. For tropomyosin-actin binding the value of *y* is in the 100 to 1000 range, implying high cooperativity. High cooperativity was also shown in an elegant synchrotron radiation study of the kinetics of tropomyosin binding to actin (192). The values of $K_o$ and *y* measured in equilibrium studies may be influenced by one consideration not included in the linear lattice model. The mathematical deri-

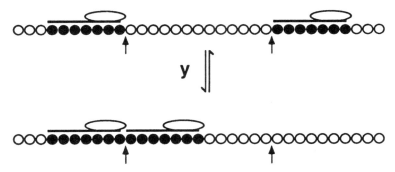

*Figure 5* Schematic representation of cooperative interactions between identical, actin-bound troponin-tropomyosin complexes. The strength of the interaction is defined by the equilibrium constant *y* for repositioning a troponin-tropomyosin complex from an isolated thin filament site to a position adjacent to another actin-bound complex. (From 14, with permission.)

vation of the tropomyosin-actin binding curve assumes that tropomyosins interact only if they are immediately adjacent on the actin filament. This may not be true if the effects of tropomyosin on actin conformation are propagated longitudinally or between the two strands of F-actin.

## $Ca^{2+}$ Binding to the Thin Filament

$Ca^{2+}$ binding to the thin filament is a complex process, and there are relatively few careful studies in cardiac muscle. In general such studies strongly support the view that site II is the regulatory site in cardiac TnC. Pan & Solaro found, as expected from data with TnC alone, two classes of $Ca^{2+}$-binding sites in skinned heart muscle fibers (135). The higher affinity class ($7 \times 10^7$ M$^{-1}$) competed significantly with $Mg^{2+}$ (900 M$^{-1}$) and $Ca^{2+}$ binding did not correlate with tension activation. The lower affinity $Ca^{2+}$ sites ($2.8–12 \times 10^5$ M$^{-1}$) bound $Mg^{2+}$ weakly ($K_{Mg}$ 110 M$^{-1}$), and $Ca^{2+}$ binding correlated with isometric tension.

The $Ca^{2+}$ affinity of cardiac TnC regulatory sites was increased 33% in unrestrained fibers, and three to fourfold in rigor (135). Morimoto & Ohtsuki obtained similar results (121), which indicates that cross-bridges increase $Ca^{2+}$ affinity in rigor and suggests the possibility of a (lesser) effect of cross-bridges in active muscle. In a separate study, Hoffman & Fuchs found that cycling cross-bridges do increase $Ca^{2+}$ affinity in the heart (78). Tobacman & Sawyer found that $Ca^{2+}$ binding to the TnC regulatory sites of isolated thin filaments is cooperative, even in the absence of myosin (180). Long-range cooperative interactions between troponin molecules were suggested as the explanation for this result.

The most extensive work on $Ca^{2+}$ binding to the thin filament has been done in skeletal muscle, and these results may have implications for the cardiac system. Bremel & Weber found that myosin increased the $Ca^{2+}$ affinity of reconstituted thin filaments, that a similar effect occurs in myofibrils when the ATP concentration is low, and that low ATP concentrations can activate the actin-myosin ATPase rate in the absence of $Ca^{2+}$ (10). Rosenfeld & Taylor reported an eightfold increase in regulatory site $Ca^{2+}$ affinity in the presence of rigor cross-bridges (156). Equilibrium titrations detected no cooperativity in $Ca^{2+}$ binding in the presence or in the absence of myosin, but the complexity of regulatory $Ca^{2+}$ site binding was demonstrated by biphasic kinetics that occurred only when the troponin was bound to actin-tropomyosin. Zot & Potter also found no cooperativity in equilibrium studies of regulatory site $Ca^{2+}$ binding (207). However, Grabarek et al did find cooperative binding to TnC sites I and II, but only when TnC was within the thin filament (46). The mechanism for this cooperativity (and for the complex kinetics of Rosenfeld & Taylor) was proposed to be either interactions between TnC sites I and II that are only apparent in the context of the thin filament, or else interactions between thin filament–bound troponin molecules. Regardless of which interpretation is correct, none of the above studies detected sufficient cooperativity in $Ca^{2+}$ binding to explain the very cooperative activation of muscle contraction.

Some of the most sensitive studies of regulatory site $Ca^{2+}$ binding in skeletal muscle fibers involve extraction of TnC and replacement by TnC labeled with a fluorophore. One caution in interpreting such data is the recent demonstration that TnC is preferentially extracted from non-overlap regions of the thin filament (205). Inattention to this problem may explain discrepancies in earlier studies. In different reports it was found that $Ca^{2+}$ binding occurs at lower (58) or approximately equal (2) concentrations as does force. X-ray probe microanalysis measurements indicate that rigor cross-bridges increase $Ca^{2+}$ affinity (18). Fluorescence data suggest this is a twofold effect (58). Interestingly, the X-ray probe data indicate the effect of rigor cross-bridges is not propagated through the non-overlap region of the thin filament, which indicates that any cooperative effects are short range. Cycling cross-bridges appear to have a smaller effect, consistent with the cardiac results discussed above (135). Direct binding results from Fuchs & Wang suggest no effect of cycling cross-bridges on $Ca^{2+}$ binding in skeletal muscle (39). A biochemical study by Wnuk et al (200) reached a similar conclusion for invertebrate striated muscle. One study did suggest a tenfold effect of cycling cross-bridges in skeletal muscle (58). However, this report also described no effect of filament overlap on the pCa/fluorescence relationship. The preponderance of the data suggests that cycling cross-bridges have a small effect on $Ca^{2+}$ binding to the regulatory sites of the thin filament.

# THE COOPERATIVE REGULATION OF MUSCLE CONTRACTION

## The Two-Site Model for Troponin-Mediated Regulation

In the early 1970s, several groups described what has proven to be a seminal model for the mechanism of regulation (73, 112, 149). Much of the troponin subunit data obtained in the last two decades, and summarized in other sections of this review, can still be interpreted in terms of the original proposal (73):

> This model states that there are two different classes of binding sites between troponin and the actin-tropomyosin structure, one which is $Ca^{2+}$ sensitive and operates in the absence of $Ca^{2+}$ but not in its presence, and a second binding site which is not $Ca^{2+}$ sensitive and is attached all the time.

Troponin I, particularly the inhibitory region, is generally considered to be the $Ca^{2+}$-sensitive site, and the $Ca^{2+}$-insensitive interaction is primarily between the N-terminal 151 residues of TnT and the C-terminus of tropomyosin.

A significant limitation to the adequacy of the two-site model is that the $Ca^{2+}$-sensitive region does not confer much $Ca^{2+}$ sensitivity to the overall process. In the absence of tropomyosin, $Ca^{2+}$ has a small effect on troponin binding to actin (72, 149). These results are less pertinent than whether $Ca^{2+}$ significantly changes troponin's affinity for actin-tropomyosin. One study reported a two and one half-fold effect of $Ca^{2+}$ on this process (107), but most authors have found troponin binding to the thin filament to be too tight to measure easily. Recently, a new approach to this problem was developed (29, 37), using the equilibrium linkage relationships among the association reactions of troponin, tropomyosin, and an isolated site on the actin filament (see Figure 4). The affinity of cardiac tropomyosin and troponin-tropomyosin for an isolated site on the actin filament ($K_o$; see section on Thin Filament Assembly) was determined in the presence of $Mg^{2+}$, with and without the addition of $Ca^{2+}$. The actin-affinity of troponin-tropomyosin was found to be three orders of magnitude greater than that of tropomyosin alone. From these values, and from measurements of troponin's affinity for tropomyosin, the binding constant of cardiac troponin for the thin filament was calculated to be $5 \times 10^8$ $M^{-1}$ in the absence of $Ca^{2+}$ and $3 \times 10^8$ $M^{-1}$ in the presence of $Ca^{2+}$. These results indicate that $Ca^{2+}$ has only a small effect on thin filament assembly. Furthermore, TnI was also shown not to be required for tight assembly of the regulatory proteins onto the thin filament. The affinity of TnT alone for actin-tropomyosin was $4 \times 10^8$ $M^{-1}$ and the TnT-tropomyosin complex bound at least as tightly to actin as did troponin-tropomyosin, with or without $Ca^{2+}$. These data complicate the two-site model of regulation. The small effects of $Ca^{2+}$ or TnI deletion are inconsistent with the idea that regulation can be understood as a $Ca^{2+}$-induced release of TnI from actin. Disruption of an actin-TnI protein-protein interface would be expected to produce a much larger energetic change. A $Ca^{2+}$-induced release of TnI can only be occurring if some other interaction(s) between troponin and the thin filament are strengthened by $Ca^{2+}$. Dahiya et al suggested TnT as one possibility for a $Ca^{2+}$-strengthened interaction with the thin filament (29), perhaps via the direct TnT-actin binding demonstrated by Heeley & Smillie (63). A recent report by Potter and co-workers similarly suggests that TnT is important in regulation, perhaps via direct TnT-TnC interactions (151).

A limitation to the above analysis of thin filament assembly is that the small effect of $Ca^{2+}$ on troponin-thin filament binding is not measured directly but instead is calculated from equilibrium linkage relationships. Also, the above results were obtained with cardiac troponin, whereas most of the data for the two-site model was obtained with skeletal muscle troponin. However, a similar equilibrium linkage analysis for skeletal muscle troponin binding to the thin filament also showed that $Ca^{2+}$ has only a twofold effect (37). Furthermore, truncation of the N-terminal region of TnT in this study did not increase the $Ca^{2+}$ sensitivity of thin filament assembly. Finally, the twofold effect of $Ca^{2+}$ has been confirmed in a completely different set of experiments, using cardiac troponin. The effect of $Ca^{2+}$ binding to TnC site II on troponin's affinity for the thin filament can be sensitively studied by the competitive assembly of thin filaments (116) with a mixture of wild-type troponin and troponin containing TnC mutated to inactivate site II. The results show a twofold effect of regulatory site $Ca^{2+}$ on troponin's affinity for the thin filament (83a).

## Cooperative Binding of Myosin Subfragment 1 (S-1) to the Thin Filament

The binding of rigor cross-bridges to the skeletal muscle thin filament, especially in the absence of $Ca^{2+}$, is so cooperative that it cannot be explained by the coincident association of seven myosin heads to the actin region contacting one tropomyosin (54, 181, 198). Fiber studies suggest that cardiac muscle may be even more cooperatively activated by myosin than is skeletal muscle (117), but this has not yet been explored in biochemical studies. To explain the biochemical results with skeletal muscle proteins, Hill et al proposed a theoretical model in which each seven-actin region of the thin filament exists in equilibrium between two states (strong myosin-binding and weak myosin-binding) (69). The model proposes that the equilibrium between the states is influenced not only by local binding of myosin and $Ca^{2+}$ but also by interactions with immediately adjacent regions. This suggestion logically follows from known features of thin filament structure, in particular the interactions between adjacent tropomyosins that are essential for thin filament assembly (see above). In fact, regardless of the degree of experimentally observed cooperativity, the possibility that these tropomysoin-tropomyosin interactions are perturbed by myosin binding must be considered in any model of myosin-thin filament binding. Cooperative myosin-thin filament binding is explained by two mechanisms in the model: a cooperative transition for the seven actins contacting the same tropomyosin, and cooperative interactions with immediately adjacent tropomyosin-seven-actin regions. The model is appealing in several respects. (a) It was analyzed quantitatively by a statistical mechanical approach, thereby allowing experimental data to be related to the equilibrium constants in the model. (b) It was consistent with several important features of thin filament structure, such as the troponin-tropomyosin-seven actin unit. Unlike other theoretical models (160, 161), it did not invoke assumptions about $Ca^{2+}$ binding that were inconsistent with subsequent experiments. (c) By proposing just two states for each local region of the thin filament, the model had a conceptual simplicity, even if it was mathematically complex. Also, the local protein-protein interactions of each region of the thin filament additively contribute to the energetics and behavior of the whole system. This a less restrictive assumption than treating the thin filament as one unit (7, 8, 126). (d) By equating the strong and weak myosin-binding states to on and off conformations, it has been possible to relate the model to muscle and/or thin filament activation. (e) Most importantly, the model has been used successfully to describe a considerable amount of experimental data (52, 87, 134, 198, 199).

Several interesting conclusions have been derived using the 1980 Hill et al model. $Ca^{2+}$ binding to the skeletal muscle thin filament alters the on/off equilibrium, without directly causing much change in cooperative interactions between adjacent regions (52, 87). The on/off equilibrium and the affinity of myosin S-1 for each state are the same for tropomyosin-actin and for $Ca^{2+}$-troponin-tropomyosin-actin (198). The affinity of myosin S-1 for the strong-binding state of the the thin filament is about eightfold greater than myosin S-1's affinity for actin alone (198). The on/off transition is accompanied by a change in the geometrical relationship between actin and a fluoresent probe on tropomyosin Cys190 (101). The effect of myosin S-1 on tropomyosin-tropomyosin interactions, important in cooperative myosin S-1 thin filament binding, is eliminated when tropomyosin-tropomyosin contacts are abolished by tropomyosin digestion with carboxypeptidase A (134). [On the other hand, this digestion of tropomyosin does not diminish cooperativity in $Ca^{2+}$-induced activation of the the thin filament-myosin S-1 ATPase rate (188).] In contrast to the results discussed so far that concern rigor-like cross-bridges, when ATP or an ATP analogue is present on the myosin S-1, it has nearly equal affinity for the on and off states (55). Binding is not cooperative under these conditions. The ability of rigor-like cross-bridges (e.g. N-ethylmaleimide-modified myosin S-1) to activate the ATPase rate of unmodified myosin S-1 can be quantitatively explained by the two-state Hill et al model (199). The rapid ATPase rate of the on state is characterized by ATPase activation at lower concentrations of the thin filament than are required for myosin S-1 binding to the thin filament, implying a different rate-limiting step for the ATPase cycle under these conditions.

An important implication derived from the fitting of binding isotherms to the Hill et al (69) model is that $Ca^{2+}$ alone causes only a small activation of the thin filament (53, 87). Only in the presence of strongly binding cross-bridges does the thin filament become more than 10–20% activated. This is a significant weakness of the model because structural studies of the thin filament show that $Ca^{2+}$ alone causes a major conformational change (80, 86, 94, 130, 147, 148, 203). The simplest way to reconcile these results is to suggest the existence of three states: relaxed, $Ca^{2+}$-induced, and myosin-induced. A statistical mechanical exploration of such a model is not difficult in principle (67, 68, 70) but involves more assumptions than are testable with present experimental data. Greene and co-workers found (53, 55) that the Hill et al two-state model (69) provided a better description of binding data than did the alternative, several state model proposed in 1983 (70). However, this result did not eliminate the problems of the two-state model, and overall the data suggest that neither model is completely successful. Perhaps the major limitation of theoretical models of myosin-thin filament binding is that the models are underdetermined by experimental information. That is, they are uninformed with regard to the distribution of myosin on the thin filament. The cooperative mechanisms put into mathematical form by the models imply specific statistical distributions of myosin along the thin filament. Until methods are available for measuring those distributions, no model can be well substantiated and all models must be viewed with caution.

## Cooperative Effects of $Ca^{2+}$ on Thin Filament Assembly

From a theoretical perspective, the effects of $Ca^{2+}$ on thin filament assembly have similarities to those of myosin. In each case it is the assembly and properties of a cooperative linear lattice that must be considered. The linkage between $Ca^{2+}$ and the binding of troponin-tropomyosin to the thin filament have been described experimentally for both the skeletal muscle (191) and cardiac muscle (83a, 116, 180) systems. The assembly and average properties of the thin filament were shown to depend in part upon interactions between adjacent regions (i.e. troponin-tropomyosin-seven actin regions). If these interactions are sensitive to $Ca^{2+}$, then the properties of the fully assembled thin filament will be affected. The published data suggest two conclusions. (a) The relative affinity of troponin rather than troponin-$Ca^{2+}$ for the thin filament is variable: It depends on the degree of $Ca^{2+}$ saturation of the thin filament. This indicates that thin filament–bound troponin molecules interact in a $Ca^{2+}$-sensitive manner. Furthermore, this result implies that cooperative interactions between troponin molecules cause cooperative binding of $Ca^{2+}$ to the regulatory sites of the thin filament. (b) The degree of demonstrated cooperativity is modest, corresponding to a Hill coefficient less than or equal to 2. This is not sufficient to explain the higher cooperativity in tension/pCa plots, but makes a significant contribution to the overall cooperative response.

## Muscle Fiber Studies of Thin Filament–Mediated Cooperativity

Although muscle fiber studies are generally beyond the scope of this review, a few reports require mention because of their close relationship to the biochemical studies of the thin filament. In the mid-1980s, two laboratories described the effects in skeletal muscle fibers of partial extraction of TnC (8, 124), which removes the site required for disinhibition of contraction. One investigative group found that partial TnC removal caused a disproportionately large fall in tension; thus only about 30% of $Ca^{2+}$-activated tension was produced when half of the TnC content remained (124). Furthermore, after partial TnC removal, the remaining tension responded less cooperatively to $Ca^{2+}$, and higher concentrations of $Ca^{2+}$ were required to produce this residual tension (8, 124). These results strongly suggest the importance of interactions between troponin molecules in muscle activation by $Ca^{2+}$. It is interesting to compare these results with data obtained upon removal of either whole troponin (123) or TnI-TnC (162). In these experiments, the unregulated portions of the thin filament are constitutively on instead of off. Maximum tension is unaffected, but there is substantial $Ca^{2+}$-insensitive tension. Thin filament–mediated cooperativity was again suggested because the fall in tension was not proportional to troponin extraction and because the tension/pCa curve for the residual $Ca^{2+}$-sensitive tension was shifted to lower $Ca^{2+}$ concentrations. However, there is an unresolved discrepancy between the TnC extraction experiments and the troponin extraction experiments. In the first case, inactivation of 50% of the sites resulted in 30% tension. In the second case, activation of 50% of the sites produced 100% $Ca^{2+}$-insensitive tension. Thus, it is unclear whether, in an unextracted fiber, 50% saturation of the thin filament troponin with $Ca^{2+}$ (i.e. 50% of the TnCs having empty sites I and II and 50% filled sites I and II) would produce closer to 30% tension or 100% tension. In a recent biochemical correlate of these experiments, thin filaments were prepared containing actin, tropomyosin, and defined mixtures of cardiac troponins with and without inactivation of TnC site II by mutagenesis (179). $Ca^{2+}$-activation of the MgATPase rate of myosin S-1 was not proportional to the fraction of troponin molecules binding $Ca^{2+}$. Substantially less than 50% MgATPase activation was produced by 50% $Ca^{2+}$ binding. This implies a complex cooperative mechanism for thin filament activation, even when very little myosin is present.

## The Three-State Model for Regulation

In an interesting series of recent papers, the equilibrium binding and the kinetics of binding of skeletal muscle myosin S-1 to the thin filament have been reexamined (43, 60, 100, 114). Both the kinetics and the equilibrium results are complex, and the authors propose that three states for each troponin-tropomyosin are required to explain the data. The on state is fully active and can bind myosin in any part of its cross-bridge cycle. The closed state can bind myosin weakly, in an initial complex that can undergo a transition to strong myosin binding (with coincident alteration of the local thin filament state to the on conformation). The blocked state does not bind myosin but exists in equilibrium with the closed and on states. $Ca^{2+}$ causes the equilibrium constant between the blocked and closed states to change from 70% blocked to <5% blocked. Therefore, in contrast to the Hill et al model (69), the three-state model is consistent with structural data indicating a large effect of $Ca^{2+}$ on thin filament structure. The blocked-closed equilibrium constant is independent of ionic strength unless the ionic strength is less than 50 mM. Under these conditions, the blocked state is not favored even in the absence of $Ca^{2+}$. The $Ca^{2+}$-induced transition between the blocked and the closed states is cooperative, with a Hill coefficient of 1.8. Strong myosin binding to the closed state is forbidden in the model, as is any myosin binding to the blocked state. Cooperative interactions between tropomyosins are not included, but they could be added, in principle, if enough experimental information were available. In fact, one of the studies points out that the seven-actin-troponin-tropomyosin unit may not precisely correspond to the region affected by a thin filament–bound cross-bridge (43). This relates, as discussed above, to the absence of data on the actual thin filament distribution of myosin S-1. The model successfully describes a large amount of complex data and strongly indicates that at least three states must be considered for a local region of the thin filament. It allows for a contribution of $Ca^{2+}$ to cooperative muscle activation, but as in the earlier models of Hill et al, thin filament activation is proposed to require strong binding of myosin cross-bridges.

As valuable as this new model is, its limitations should be mentioned. It does not consider cooperative interactions between neighboring troponin-tropomyosin complexes. As discussed above, the existence of these interactions is evident in thin filament assembly, and the sensitivity of these interactions to myosin binding is evident from the extreme cooperativity in myosin binding seen under some conditions. It is also important that, for experimental reasons, the model was not designed to describe the binding of myosin S-1-ATP to the thin filament but, rather, the binding of stronger-binding forms of myosin S-1. It is arguable whether the blocked state is really blocked with respect to cross-bridges with bound ATP. In one study performed in the presence of ATP, it was reported that the binding of heavy meromyosin to the thin filament at high ionic strength is not altered by $Ca^{2+}$ (34). However, most authors find that binding is too weak under such conditions for accurate measurements to be made. In the presence of low ionic strength, $Ca^{2+}$ regulates the cross-bridge-thin filament ATPase rate, regardless of whether the form of myosin is sub-fragment 1, which binds in a $Ca^{2+}$-insensitive manner (21, 178), or heavy meromyosin, which binds with tenfold greater affinity when $Ca^{2+}$ is present (186). It is not clear how this should be reconciled with the three-state model. Perhaps more significantly, the evident absence of $Ca^{2+}$ regulation of the blocked to closed transition (at low ionic strength) would require a different mechanism for regulation by $Ca^{2+}$ depending upon the ionic strength. This is possible but raises a note of caution about the three-state model in its present form.

## An Alternative Three-State Model of Regulation

Little serious consideration has been given to what might be the most obvious suggestion from the structural, biochemical, and physiological data, i.e. that $Ca^{2+}$ activates the thin filament, and cross-bridges can produce an additional conformational change resulting in even greater activation. This is similar to the concept of potentiation, proposed previously (9). Because other models have been only partially successful, it seems inappropriate to exclude this alternative. It remains plausible that rigor-like myosin binding is not required for thin filament activation, which can be produced by $Ca^{2+}$ alone. In this regard it is important to note that the biochemical properties of the thin filament when fully turned-on by strong-binding myosin do not resemble those of actin alone in the absence of troponin and tropomysin. This is significant because actin alone is sufficient for force and movement. The myosin-binding and MgATPase properties of actin alone resemble, in many respects, those of $Ca^{2+}$-saturated thin filaments in the presence of low concentrations of myosin S-1-ATP, rather than those of thin filaments activated by rigor-like cross-bridges (178, 199). Therefore, it is not unreasonable to suggest that there are two active states of the thin filament. One active state, corresponding to the structure induced by $Ca^{2+}$, interacts with myosin similarly to the way myosin interacts with actin alone. The other active state corresponds to the strong myosin-binding state of the thin filament deduced by many investigators. In this state, the MgATPase rate is higher, particularly in the presence of relatively low thin filament concentrations (199). A great advantage of this proposal is that it provides a mechanism for explaining a graded response to $Ca^{2+}$ in muscle fibers. Several muscle fiber studies have suggested that progressive muscle activation by $Ca^{2+}$ does more than recruit an increasing number of cross-bridges with identical kinetic behavior. The kinetics of cross-bridge behavior are also affected (11, 79, 118, 187, 201). This can most easily be explained by the existence of more than one active state for any region of the thin filament. A similar conclusion was suggested by Gordon & Ridgway (44). However, a detailed proposal for such a mechanism, incorporating the full complexity of the cooperative structure that is the thin filament, remains to be presented and subjected to experimental investigation.

ACKNOWLEDGMENTS

Space limitations have prevented discussion of many significant contributions: I apologize. I thank Dr. Charles Swenson for his insightful comments on an earlier version of this manuscript. I also thank the National Institutes of Health for grant support (HL38834).

*Literature Cited*

1. Ackers GK, Doyle ML, Myers D, Daugherty MA. 1992. Molecular code for cooperativity in hemoglobin. *Science* 255:54–63
2. Allen TS, Yates LD, Gordon AM. 1992. $Ca^{2+}$-dependence of structural changes in troponin-C in demembranated fibers of rabbit psoas muscle. *Biophys. J.* 61:399–409
3. Ashley CC, Mulligan IP, Lea TJ. 1991. $Ca^{2+}$ and activation mechanisms in skeletal muscle. *Q. Rev. Biophys.* 24:1–73
4. Babu A, Scordilis SP, Sonnenblick EH, Gulati J. 1987. The control of myocardial contraction with skeletal fast muscle troponin C. *J. Biol. Chem.* 262:5815–22
5. Babu A, Su H, Ryu Y, Gulati J. 1992. Determination of residue specificity in the EF-hand of troponin C for $Ca^{2+}$ coordination, by genetic engineering. *J. Biol. Chem.* 267:15469–74
6. Bivin DB, Stone DB, Schneider DK, Mendelson RA. 1991. Cross-helix separation of tropomyosin molecules in acto-tropomyosin as determined by neutron scattering. *Biophys. J.* 59:880–88
7. Brandt PW, Diamond MS, Rutchik JS, Schachat FH. 1987. Cooperative inter-

actions between troponin-tropomyosin units that extend the length of the thin filament in skeletal muscle. *J. Mol. Biol.* 195:885–96
8. Brandt PW, Diamond MS, Schachat FH. 1984. The thin filament of vertebrate skeletal muscle co-operatively activates as a unit. *J. Mol. Biol.* 180:379–84
9. Bremel RD, Murray JM, Weber A. 1972. Manifestations of cooperative behavior in the regulated actin filament during actin-activated ATP hydrolysis in the presence of calcium. *Cold Spring Harbor Symp. Quant. Biol.* 37:267–75
10. Bremel RD, Weber A. 1972. Cooperation within actin filament in vertebrate skeletal muscle. *Nature New Biol.* 238:97–101
11. Brenner B. 1988. Effect of $Ca^{2+}$ on cross-bridge turnover kinetics in skinned single rabbit psoas fibers: implications for regulation of muscle contraction. *Proc. Natl. Acad. Sci. USA* 85:3265–69
12. Brito RM, Krudy GA, Negele JC, Rosevear PR. 1993. Calcium plays distinctive structural roles in the N- and C-terminal domains of cardiac troponin C. *J. Biol. Chem.* 268:20966–73
13. Brito RM, Putkey JA, Strynadka NCJ,

James MNG, Rosevear PR. 1991. Comparative NMR studies on cardiac troponin C and a mutant incapable of binding calcium at site II. *Biochemistry* 30:10236–45

14. Butters CA, Willadsen KA, Tobacman LS. 1993. Cooperative Interactions between adjacent troponin-tropomyosin complexes may be transmitted through the thin filament. *J. Biol. Chem.* 268: 15565–70

15. Cabral-Lilly D, Tobacman LS, Mehegan JP, Cohen C. 1991. Polarity of troponin T in tropomyosin/troponin T cocrystals. *Biophys. J.* 59:581a

16. Campbell AP, Sykes BD. 1991. Interaction of troponin I and troponin C. Use of the two-dimensional nuclear magnetic resonance transferred nuclear Overhauser effect to determine the structure of the inhibitory peptide when bound to skeletal troponin C. *J. Mol. Biol.* 222:405–21

17. Campbell AP, Van Eyk JE, Hodges RS, Sykes BD. 1992. Interaction of troponin I and troponin C: use of the two-dimensional transferred nuclear Overhauser effect to determine the structure of a Gly-110 peptide analog when bound to cardiac troponin C. *Biochim. Biophys. Acta* 1160:35–54

18. Cantino ME, Allen TS, Gordon AM. 1993. Subsarcomeric distribution of calcium in demembranated fibers of rabbit psoas muscle. *Biophys. J.* 64:211–22

19. Carlier M-F. 1991. Actin: protein structure and filament dynamics. *J. Biol. Chem.* 266:1–4

20. Chalovich JM. 1992. Actin mediated regulation of muscle contraction. *Pharmacol. Ther.* 55:95–148

21. Chalovich JM, Eisenberg E. 1982. Inhibition of actomyosin ATPase activity by troponin-tropomyosin without blocking the binding of myosin to actin. *J. Biol. Chem.* 257:2432–37

22. Chandra M, McCubbin WD, Oikawa K, Kay CM, Smillie LB. 1994. $Ca^{2+}$, $Mg^{2+}$, and troponin I inhibitory peptide binding to a Phe-154 to Trp mutant of chicken skeletal muscle troponin C. *Biochemistry* 33:2961–69

23. Chen X, Cook RK, Rubenstein P. 1993. Yeast actin with a mutation in the "hydrophobic plug" between subdomains 3 and 4 (L266D) displays a cold-sensitive polymerization defect. *J. Cell Biol.* 123: 1185–95

24. Cheung HC, Wang CK, Malik NA. 1987. Interactions of troponin subunits: free energy of binary and ternary complexes. *Biochemistry* 26:5904–7

25. Cho Y-J, Hitchcock-DeGregori SE. 1990. Relationship between alternatively spliced exons and functional domains in tropomyosin. *Proc. Natl. Acad. Sci. USA* 88:10153–57

26. Cho Y-J, Liu J, Hitchcock-DeGregori SE. 1990. The amino terminus of tropomyosin is a major determinant for function. *J. Biol. Chem.* 265:545

27. Chong PCS, Hodges RS. 1982. Proximity of sulfhydryl groups to the sites of interaction between components of the troponin complex from rabbit skeletal muscle. *J. Biol. Chem.* 257:2549–55

28. Chong PCS, Hodges RS. 1982. Photochemical cross-linking between rabbit skeletal troponin subunits. Troponin I-troponin T interactions. *J. Biol. Chem.* 257:11667–72

29. Dahiya R, Butters CA, Tobacman LS. 1994. Equilibrium linkage analysis of cardiac thin filament assembly. Implications for the regulation of muscle contraction. *J. Biol. Chem.* 269:29457–61

30. da Silva ACR, de Araujo AHB, Herzberg O, Moult J, Sorenson M, Reinach FC. 1993. Troponin-C mutants with increased calcium affinity. *Eur. J. Biochem.* 213:599–604

31. Dotson DG, Putkey JA. 1993. Differential recovery of $Ca^{2+}$ binding activity in mutated EF-hands of cardiac troponin C. *J. Biol. Chem.* 268:24067–73

32. Eaton BL, Kominz DR, Eisenberg E. 1975. Correlation between the inhibition of the acto-heavy meromyosin ATPase and the binding of tropomyosin to F-actin: effects of $Mg^{2+}$, KCl, troponin I and troponin C. *Biochemistry* 14:2718–25

33. Ebashi S, Endo M, Ohtsuki I. 1969. Control of muscle contraction. *Q. Rev. Biophys.* 2:351–84

34. El-Saleh SC, Potter JD. 1985. Calcium-insensitive binding of heavy meromyosin to regulated actin at physiological ionic strength. *J. Biol. Chem.* 260:14775–79

35. Fabiato A, Fabiato F. 1978. Effects of pH on the myofilaments and the sarcoplasmic reticulum of skinned cells from cardiac and skeletal muscles. *J. Physiol.* 276:233–55

36. Farah CS, Miyamoto CA, Ramos CHI, da Silva ACR, Quaggio RB, et al. 1994. Structural and regulatory functions of the $NH_2$-and COOH-terminal regions of skeletal muscle troponin I. *J. Biol. Chem.* 269:5230–40

37. Fisher D, Wang G, Tobacman LS. 1995. N-terminal truncation of skeletal muscle troponin T does not alter the $Ca^{2+}$ sensitivity of thin filament assembly. *J. Biol. Chem.* 270:25455–60

38. Flicker PF, Phillips JGN, Cohen C. 1982. Troponin and its interactions with tropomyosin: an electron microscope study. *J. Mol. Biol* 162:495–501

39. Fuchs F, Wang YP. 1991. Force, length, and $Ca^{2+}$-troponin C affinity in skeletal muscle. *Am. J. Physiol.* 261:C787–92

40. Fujimori K, Sorenson M, Herzberg O, Moult J, Reinach FC. 1990. Probing the calcium-induced conformational transition of troponin C with site-directed mutants. *Nature* 345:182–84

41. Fujita S, Maeda K, Maeda Y. 1991. Complete coding sequences of cDNAs of four variants of rabbit skeletal muscle troponin T. *J. Muscle Res. Cell Motil.* 12:560–65

42. Gangé SM, Tsuda S, Li MX, Chandra M, Smillie LB, Sykes BD. 1994. Quantification of the calcium-induced secondary structural changes in the regulatory domain of troponin-C. *Protein Sci.* 3: 1961–74

43. Geeves MA, Lehrer SS. 1994. Dynamics of the muscle thin filament regulatory switch: the size of the cooperative unit. *Biophys. J.* 67:273–82

44. Gordon AM, Ridgway EB. 1993. Crossbridges affect both TnC structure and calcium affinity in muscle fibers. *Adv. Exp. Med. Biol.* 332:183–94

45. Grabarek Z, Drabikowski W, Leavis PC, Rosenfeld SS, Gergely J. 1981. Proteolytic fragments of troponin C. Interactions with the other troponin subunits and biological activity. *J. Biol. Chem.* 256:13121–27

46. Grabarek Z, Grabarek J, Leavis PC, Gergely J. 1983. Cooperative binding to the $Ca^{2+}$ -specific sites of troponin C in regulated actin and actomyosin. *J. Biol. Chem.* 258:14098–102

47. Grabarek Z, Leavis PC, Gergely J. 1986. Calcium binding to the low affinity sites in troponin C induces conformational changes in the high affinity domain: a possible route of information transfer in activation of muscle contraction. *J. Biol. Chem.* 261:608–13

48. Grabarek Z, Tan R-Y, Wang J, Tao T, Gergely J. 1990. Inhibition of mutant troponin C activity by an intra-domain disulfide bond. *Nature* 345:132–35

49. Grand RJA, Wilkinson JM, Mole LE. 1976. The amino acid sequence of rabbit cardiac troponin I. *Biochem. J.* 159:633–41

50. Greaser ML, Gergely J. 1971. Reconstitution of troponin activity from three protein components. *J. Biol. Chem.* 246: 4226–33

51. Greaser ML, Gergely J. 1973. Purification and properties of the components

52. Greene LE. 1982. The effect of nucleotide on the binding of myosin subfragment 1 to regulated actin. *J. Biol. Chem.* 257:13993–99

53. Greene LE. 1986. Cooperative binding of myosin subfragment 1 to regulated actin as measured by fluorescence changes of troponin I modified with different fluorophores. *J. Biol. Chem.* 261:1279–85

54. Greene LE, Eisenberg E. 1980. Cooperative binding of myosin subfragment-1 to the actin-troponin-tropomyosin complex. *Proc. Natl. Acad. Sci. USA* 77: 2616–20

55. Greene LE, Williams DL, Eisenberg E. 1987. Regulation of actomyosin ATPase activity by troponin-tropomyosin: effect of the binding of the myosin subfragment 1 (S-1)-ATP complex. *Proc. Natl. Acad. Sci. USA* 84:3102–6

56. Gulati J, Babu A, Su H. 1992. Functional delineation of the $Ca^{2+}$-deficient EF-hand in cardiac muscle, with genetically engineered cardiac-skeletal chimeric troponin C. *J. Biol. Chem.* 267: 25073–77

57. Guo X, Wattanapermpool J, Palmiter KA, Murphy AM, Solaro RJ. 1994. Mutagenesis of cardiac troponin I. Role of the unique $NH_2$-terminal peptide in myofilament activation. *J. Biol. Chem.* 269:15210–16

58. Guth K, Potter JD. 1987. Effect of rigor and cycling cross-bridges on the structure of troponin C and on the $Ca^{2+}$-specific regulatory sites in skinned rabbit psoas fibers. *J. Biol. Chem.* 262:13627–35

59. Haselgrove JC. 1972. X-ray evidence for a conformational change in the actin containing filaments of vertebrate striated muscle. *Cold Spring Harbor Symp. Quant. Biol.* 37:341–52

60. Head JG, Ritchie MD, Geeves MA. 1995. Characterization of the blocked and closed states of muscle thin filaments. *Eur. J. Biochem.* 227:694–99

61. Heald RW, Hitchcock-DeGregori SE. 1988. The structure of the amino terminus of tropomyosin is critical for binding to actin in the absence and presence of troponin. *J. Biol. Chem.* 263:5254–59

62. Heeley DH, Golosinska K, Smillie LB. 1987. The effects of troponin T fragments T1 and T2 on the binding of nonpolymerizable tropomyosin to F-actin in the presence and absence of troponin I and troponin C. *J. Biol. Chem.* 262:9971–78

63. Heeley DH, Smillie LB. 1988. Interaction of rabbit skeletal muscle troponin T and F-actin at physiological ionic strength. *Biochemistry* 27:8227–32

64. Herzberg O, James MNG. 1985. Structure of the calcium regulatory muscle protein troponin-C at 2.8 Å resolution. *Nature* 313:653–59

65. Herzberg O, Moult J, James MNG. 1986. A model for the $Ca^{2+}$-induced conformational transition of troponin C. A trigger for muscle contraction. *J. Biol. Chem.* 261:2638–44

66. Hill LE, Mehegan JP, Butters CA, Tobacman LS. 1992. Analysis of troponin-tropomyosin binding to actin. Troponin does not promote interactions between tropomyosin molecules. *J. Biol. Chem.* 267:16106–13

67. Hill TL. 1983. Two elementary models for the regulation of skeletal muscle contraction by calcium. *Biophys. J.* 44:383–96

68. Hill TL. 1985. *Cooperativity Theory in Biochemistry.* New York: Springer-Verlag

69. Hill TL, Eisenberg E, Greene LE. 1980. Theoretical model for cooperative equilibrium binding of myosin subfragment-1 to the actin-troponin-tropomyosin complex. *Proc. Natl. Acad. Sci. USA* 77:3186–90

70. Hill TL, Eisenberg E, Greene LE. 1993. Alternate model for the cooperative equilibrium binding of the myosin subfragment-1-nucleotide complex to actin-troponin-tropomyosin. *Proc. Natl. Acad. Sci. USA* 80:60–64

71. Hincke MT, McCubbin WD, Kay CM. 1978. Calcium-binding properties of cardiac and skeletal troponin C as determined by circular dichroism and ultraviolet difference spectroscopy. *Can. J. Biochem.* 56:384–95

72. Hitchcock SE. 1975. Regulation of muscle contraction: binding of troponin and its components to actin and tropomyosin. *Eur. J. Biochem.* 52:255–63

73. Hitchcock SE, Huxley HE, Szent-Gyorgyi AG. 1973. Calcium sensitive binding of troponin to actin-tropomyosin: a two-site model for troponin action. *J. Mol. Biol.* 80:825–36

74. Hitchcock SE, Zimmerman CJ, Smalley C. 1981. Study of the structure of troponin-T by measuring the relative reactivities of lysines with acetic anhydride. *J. Mol. Biol.* 147:125–51

75. Hitchcock-DeGregori SE. 1982. Study of the structure of troponin-I by measuring the relative reactivities of lysines with acetic anhydride. *J. Biol. Chem.* 257:7372–80

76. Hitchcock-DeGregori SE, Heald RW. 1987. Altered actin and troponin-binding of amino-terminal variants of chicken striated muscle α-tropomyosin expressed in *Escherichia coli. J. Biol. Chem.* 262:9730–35

77. Hitchcock-DeGregori SE, Varnell TA. 1990. Tropomyosin has discrete actin-binding sites with sevenfold and fourteenfold periodicities. *J. Mol. Biol.* 214:885–96

78. Hoffman PA, Fuchs F. 1987. Evidence for a force-dependent component of calcium binding to cardiac troponin C. *Am. J. Physiol.* 253:C541–46

79. Hoffman PA, Moss RL. 1992. Effects of calcium on shortening velocity in frog chemically skinned atrial myocytes and in mechanically disrupted ventricular myocardiaum from rat. *Circ. Res.* 70:885–92

80. Holmes KC. 1995. The actomyosin interaction and its control by tropomyosin. *Biophys. J.* 68:2s–7s

81. Holmes KC, Popp D, Gebhard W, Kabsch W. 1990. Atomic model of the actin filament. *Nature* 347:44–49

82. Holroyde MJ, Robertson SP, Johnson JD, Solaro RJ, Potter JD. 1980. The calcium and magnesium binding sites on cardiac troponin and their role in the regulation of myofibrillar adenosine triphosphatase. *J. Biol. Chem.* 255:11688–93

83. Huxley HE. 1972. Structural changes in the actin and myosin containing filaments during contraction. *Cold Spring Harbor Symp. Quant. Biol.* 37:361–76

83a. Huynh Q, Butters CA, Leiden JM, Tobacman LS. 1996. Effects of cardiac thin filament $Ca^{2+}$, statistical mechanical analysis of TnC site II mutant. *Biophys J.* In press

84. Ingraham RH, Hodges RS. 1988. Effects of $Ca^{2+}$ and subunit interactions on surface accessibility of cysteine residues in cardiac troponin. *Biochemistry* 27:5891–98

85. Ingraham RH, Swenson CA. 1984. Binary interactions of troponin subunits. *J. Biol. Chem.* 259:9544–88

86. Isambert H, Venier P, Maggs AC, Fattoum A, Kassab R, et al. 1995. Flexibility of actin filaments derived from thermal fluctuations. Effect of bound nucleotide, phalloidin, and muscle regulatory proteins. *J. Biol. Chem.* 270:11437–44

87. Ishii Y, Lehrer SS. 1990. Excimer fluorescence of pyrenyliodoacetamide-labeled tropomyosin: a probe of the state of tropomyosin in reconstituted muscle thin filaments. *Biochemistry* 29:1160–66

88. Jackson P, Amphlett GN, Perry SV. 1975. The primary structure of troponin T and the interaction with tropomyosin. *Biochem. J.* 151:85–97

89. Kabsch W, Mannerz HG, Suck D, Pai EF, Holmes KC. 1990. Atomic structure of the actin:DNase I complex. *Nature* 347:37–44

90. Kobayashi T, Tao T, Gergely J, Collins JH. 1994. Structure of the troponin complex. Implications of photocross-linking of troponin I to troponin C thiol mutants. *J. Biol. Chem.* 269:5725–29

91. Kobayashi T, Tao T, Grabarek Z, Gergely J, Collins JH. 1991. Cross-linking of residue 57 in the regulatory domain of a mutant rabbit skeletal muscle troponin C to the inhibitory region of troponin I. *J. Biol. Chem.* 266:13746–51

92. Kohama K. 1980. Role of the high affinity Ca binding sites of cardiac and fast skeletal troponins. *J. Biochem.* 88:591–99

93. Korn ED. 1982. Actin polymerization and its regulation by proteins from nonmuscle cells. *Physiol. Rev.* 62:672–737

94. Kress M, Huxley HE, Faruqi AR, Hendrix J. 1986. Structural changes during activation of frog muscle studied by time-resolved X-ray diffraction. *J. Mol. Biol.* 188:325–42

95. Krudy GA, Brito RM, Putkey JA, Rosevear PR. 1992. Conformational changes in the metal binding sites of cardiac troponin C induced by calcium binding. *Biochemistry* 31:1595–602

96. Krudy GA, Kleerekoper Q, Guo X, Howarth JW, Solaro RJ, Rosevear PR. 1994. NMR studies delineating spatial relationships within the cardiac troponin I-troponin C complex. *J. Biol. Chem.* 269:23731–35

97. Lamkin M, Tao T, Lehrer SS. 1983. Tropomyosin-troponin and tropomyosin-actin interactions: a fluorescence quenching study. *Biochemistry* 22:3053–58

98. Leavis PC, Gergely J. 1984. Thin filament proteins and thin filament-linked regulation of vertebrate muscle contraction. *CRC Crit. Rev. Biochem.* 16:235–305

99. Lehman W, Craig R, Vibert P. 1994. Ca$^{2+}$-induced tropomyosin movement in *Limulus* thin filaments revealed by three-dimensional reconstruction. *Nature* 368:65–67

99a. Lehman W, Vibert P, Uman P, Craig R. 1995. Steric-blocking by tropomyosin visualized in relaxed vertebrate muscle thin filaments. *J. Mol. Biol.* 251:191–96

100. Lehrer SS. 1994. The regulatory switch of the muscle thin filament: Ca$^{2+}$ or myosin heads? *J. Muscle Res. Cell Motil.* 15:232–36

101. Lehrer SS, Ishii Y. 1988. Fluorescence properties of acrylodan-labeled tropomyosin and tropomyosin-actin: evidence for myosin subfragment 1 induced changes in geometry between tropomyosin and actin. *Biochemistry* 27:5899–906

102. Leszyk J, Collins JH, Leavis PC, Tao T. 1988. Cross-linking of rabbit skeletal muscle troponin subunits: labeling of cysteine-98 of troponin-C with 4-maleimidobenzophenone and analysis of products formed in the binary complex with troponins I and T. *Biochemistry* 27:6983–87

102a. Leszyk J, Dumaswala R, Potter JD, Collins JH. 1988. Amino acid sequence of bovine cardiac troponin I. *Biochemistry* 27:2821–27

103. Leszyk J, Dumaswala R, Potter JD, Gusev NB, Verin AD, et al. 1987. Bovine cardiac troponin T: amino acid sequences of the two isoforms. *Biochemistry* 26:7035–42

104. Leszyk J, Grabarek Z, Gergely J, Collins JH. 1990. Characterization of zero-length cross-links between rabbit skeletal muscle troponin C and troponin I: evidence for direct interaction between the inhibitory region of troponin I and the NH$_2$-terminal, regulatory domain of troponin C. *Biochemistry* 29:299–304

105. Lewis WG, Smillie LB. 1980. The amino acid sequence of rabbit cardiac tropomyosin. *J. Biol. Chem.* 255:6854–59

106. Liao R, Wang C-K, Cheung HC. 1994. Coupling of calcium to the interaction of troponin I with troponin C from cardiac muscle. *Biochemistry* 33:12729–34

107. Lin T-I, Lambert P, Dowben RM. 1983. Calcium regulates troponin-tropomyosin binding to the reconstituted thin filament. *Biochem. Biophys. Res. Commun.* 114:447–51

108. Lin X, Krudy GA, Howarth J, Rosevear PR, Putkey JA. 1994. Assignment and calcium dependence of methionyl epsilon C and epsilon H resonances in cardiac troponin C. *Biochemistry* 33:14434–42

109. Lorenz M, Poole KJV, Popp D, Rosenbaum G, Holmes KC. 1995. An atomic model of the unregulated thin filament obtained by X-ray fiber diffraction on oriented actin-tropomyosin gels. *J. Mol. Biol.* 246:108–19

110. Lorenz M, Popp D, Holmes KC. 1993.

Refinement of the F-actin model against X-ray fiber diffraction data by the use of a directed mutation algorithm. *J. Mol. Biol.* 234:826–36

111. Mak AS, Smillie LB. 1981. Structural interpretation of the two-site binding of troponin on the muscle thin filament. *J. Mol. Biol.* 149:541–50

112. Margossian SS, Cohen C. 1973. Troponin subunit interactions. *J. Mol. Biol.* 81:409–13

113. McGhee JD, von Hippel PH. 1974. Theoretical aspects of DNA-protein interactions: cooperative and non-cooperative binding of large ligands to a one-dimensional lattice. *J. Mol. Biol.* 86:469–89

114. McKillop DFA, Geeves MA. 1993. Regulation of the interaction between actin and myosin subfragment 1: evidence for three states of the thin filament. *Biophys. J.* 65:693–701

115. McLaughlin PJ, Gooch JT, Mannerz H-G, Weeds AG. 1993. Structure of gelsolin segment 1-actin complex and the mechanism of filament severing. *Nature* 364:685–92

116. Mehegan JP, Tobacman LS. 1991. Cooperative interactions between troponin molecles bound to the cardiac thin filament. *J. Biol. Chem.* 266:966–72

117. Metzger JM. 1995. Myosin binding-induced cooperative activation of the thin filament in cardiac myocytes and skeletal muscle fibers. *Biophys. J.* 68:1430–42

118. Metzger JM, Moss RL. 1991. Kinetics of a $Ca^{2+}$-sensitive cross-bridge state transition in skeletal muscle fibers. Effects due to variations in thin filament activation by extraction of troponin C. *J. Gen. Physiol.* 98:233–48

119. Metzger JM, Parmacek MS, Barr E, Pasyk K, Lin W, et al. 1993. Skeletal troponin C reduces contractile sensitivity to acidosis in cardiac myocytes from transgenic mice. *Proc. Natl. Acad. Sci. USA* 90:9036–40

120. Milligan RA, Whittaker M, Safer D. 1990. Molecular structure of F-actin and location of surface binding sites. *Nature* 348:217–21

121. Morimoto S, Ohtsuki I. 1994. $Ca^{2+}$ binding to cardiac troponin C in the myofilament lattice and its relation to the myofibrillar ATPase activity. *Eur. J. Biochem.* 226:597–602

122. Morris EP, Lehrer SS. 1984. Troponin-tropomyosin interactions. Fluorescence studies of the binding of troponin, troponin T, and chymotryptic troponin T fragments to specifically labeled tropomyosin. *Biochemistry* 23:2214–20

123. Moss RL, Allen JD, Greaser ML. 1986. Effects of partial extraction of troponin complex upon the tension-pCa relation in rabbit skeletal muscle. Further evidence that tension development involves cooperative effects within the thin filament. *J. Gen. Physiol.* 87:761–74

124. Moss RL, Guilian GG, Greaser ML. 1985. The effects of partial extraction of TnC upon the tension-pCa relationship in skinned rabbit skeletal muscle fibers. *J. Gen. Physiol.* 86:585–600

125. Muhlrad A, Cheung P, Phan BC, Miller C, Reisler E. 1994. Dynamic properties of actin. Structural changes induced by beryllium fluoride. *J. Biol. Chem.* 269:11852–58

126. Nagashima H, Asakura S. 1982. Studies on cooperative properties of tropomyosin-actin and tropomyosin-troponin-actin complexes by the use of N-ethylmaleimide-treated and untreated species of myosin subfragment 1. *J. Mol. Biol.* 155:409–28

127. Negele JC, Dotson DG, Liu W, Sweeney HL, Putkey JA. 1992. Mutation of the high affinity calcium binding sites in cardiac troponin C. *J. Biol. Chem.* 267:825–31

128. Ngai S-M, Sonnichsen FD, Hodges RS. 1994. Photochemical cross-linking between native rabbit skeletal troponin C and benzoylbenzoyl-troponin I inhibitory peptide, residues 104–115. *J. Biol. Chem.* 269:2165–72

129. Olah GA, Trewella J. 1994. A model structure of the muscle protein complex $4Ca^{2+}$-troponin C-troponin I derived from small-angle scattering data: implications for regulation. *Biochemistry* 33:12800–6

130. Oosawa F, Fujime S, Ishiwata S, Mihashi K. 1972. Dynamic properties of F-actin and thin filament. *Cold Spring Harbor Symp. Quant. Biol.* 37:277–85

131. Orlova A, Egelman EH. 1992. Structural basis for the destabilization of F-actin by phosphate release following ATP hydrolysis. *J. Mol. Biol.* 227:1043–53

132. Orlova A, Egelman EH. 1995. Structural dynamics of F-actin: I. Changes in the C terminus. *J. Mol. Biol.* 245:582–97

133. Orlova A, Prochniewicz E, Egelman EH. 1995. Structural dynamics of F-actin: II. Cooperativity in structural transitions. *J. Mol. Biol.* 245:598–607

134. Pan B-S, Gordon AM, Luo Z. 1989. Removal of tropomyosin overlap modifies cooperative binding of myosin S-1 to reconstituted thin filaments of rabbit striated muscle. *J. Biol. Chem.* 264:8495–98

135. Pan B-S, Solaro RJ. 1987. Calcium-

binding properties of troponin C in detergent-skinned heart muscle fibers. *J. Biol. Chem.* 262:7839–49

136. Parmacek MS, Leiden JM. 1991. Structure, function, and regulation of troponin C. *Circulation* 84:991–1003

137. Parry DAD, Squire JM. 1973. Structural role of tropomyosin in muscle regulation: analysis of the X-ray diffraction patterns from relaxed and contracting muscles. *J. Mol. Biol.* 75:33–55

138. Pearlstone JR, Borgford T, Chandra M, Oikawa K, Kay CM, et al. 1992. Construction and characterization of a spectral probe mutant of troponin C: application to analyses of mutants with increased $Ca^{2+}$ affinity. *Biochemistry* 31:6545–53

139. Pearlstone JR, Johnson P, Carpenter MR, Smillie LB. 1977. Primary structure of rabbit skeletal muscle troponin-T. Sequence determination of the $NH_2$-terminal fragment CB3 and the complete sequence of troponin-T. *J. Biol. Chem.* 252:983–89

140. Pearlstone JR, Smillie LB. 1977. The binding site of rabbit skeletal α-tropomyosin on troponin-T. *Can. J. Biochem.* 55:1032–38

141. Pearlstone JR, Smillie LB. 1982. Binding of troponin-T fragments to several types of tropomyosin. Sensitivity to $Ca^{2+}$ in the presence of troponin-C. *J. Biol. Chem.* 257:10587–92

142. Pearlstone JR, Smillie LB. 1983. Effects of troponin-I plus -C on the binding of troponin-T and its fragments to α-tropomyosin. $Ca^{2+}$ sensitivity and cooperativity. *J. Biol. Chem.* 258:2534–42

143. Perry SV, Cole HA, Head JF, Wilson FJ. 1972. Localization and mode of action of the inhibitory protein component of the troponin complex. *Cold Spring Harbor Symp. Quant. Biol.* 37: 251–62

144. Phillips JGN, Fillers JP, Cohen C. 1986. Tropomyosin crystal structure and muscle regulation. *J. Mol. Biol.* 192:111–31

145. Phillips JGN, Lattman EE, Cummins P, Lee KY, Cohen C. 1979. Crystal structure and molecular interactions of tropomyosin. *Nature* 278:413–17

146. Poole KJV, Holmes KC, Rayment I, Lorenz M. 1994. Control of the actomyosin interaction. *Biophys. J.* 68: 348s

147. Popp D, Maeda Y. 1993. Calcium ions and the structure of muscle actin filament. An X-ray diffraction study. *J. Mol. Biol.* 229:279–85

148. Popp D, Maeda Y, Stewart AAE, Holmes KC. 1991. X-ray diffraction studies on muscle regulation. In *Dynamic Structural Views of Muscle Contraction and Its Control,* ed. M Kotani, pp. 89–103. Tokyo: Japan Sci. Soc.; Limerick: Elsevier

149. Potter JD, Gergely J. 1974. Troponin, tropomyosin, and actin interactions in the $Ca^{2+}$ regulation of muscle contraction. *Biochemistry* 13:2697–703

150. Potter JD, Gergely J. 1975. The calcium and magnesium binding sites on troponin and their role in the regulation of myofibrillar adenosine triphosphatase. *J. Biol. Chem.* 250:4628–33

151. Potter JD, Sheng Z, Pan B-S, Zhao J. 1995. A direct regulatory role for troponin T and a dual role for troponin C in the $Ca^{2+}$ regulation of muscle contraction. *J. Biol. Chem.* 270:2557–62

152. Putkey JA, Sweeney HL, Campbell ST. 1989. Site-directed mutation of the trigger calcium-binding sites in cardiac troponin C. *J. Biol. Chem.* 264:12370–78

153. Deleted in proof

154. Rayment I, Holden HM, Whittaker M, Yohn CB, Lorenz M, et al. 1993. Structure of the actin-myosin complex and its implications for muscle contraction. *Science* 261:58–65

155. Robertson SP, Johnson JD, Potter JD. 1981. The time-course of $Ca^{2+}$ exchange with calmodulin, troponin, parvalbumin, and myosin in response to transient increases in $Ca^{2+}$. *Biophys. J.* 34:559–69

156. Rosenfeld SS, Taylor EW. 1985. Kinetic studies of calcium binding to regulatory complexes from skeletal muscle. *J. Biol. Chem.* 260:252–61

157. Schutt CE, Myslik JC, Rozycki MD, Goonesekere NCW, Lindberg U. 1993. The structure of crystalline profilin:β-actin. *Nature* 365:810–16

158. Schutt CE, Rozycki MD, Chik JK, Lindberg U. 1995. Structural studies on the ribbon-to-helix transition in profilin:actin crystals. *Biophys. J.* 68:12s-18s

159. Sheng Z, Strauss WL, Francois J-M, Potter JD. 1990. Evidence that both $Ca^{2+}$-specific sites of skeletal muscle TnC are required for full activity. *J. Biol. Chem.* 265:21554–60

160. Shiner JS, Solaro RJ. 1982. Activation of thin-filament-regulated muscle by calcium ion: considerations based on nearest-neighbor lattice statistics. *Proc. Natl. Acad. Sci. USA* 79:4637–41

161. Shiner JS, Solaro RJ. 1984. The Hill coefficient for the $Ca^{2+}$-activation of striated muscle contraction. *Biophys. J.* 46:541–43

162. Shiraishi F, Yamamoto K. 1994. The effect of partial removal of troponin I and C on the $Ca^{2+}$-sensitive ATPase activity of rabbit skeletal myofibrils. *J. Biochem.* 115:171–73

163. Sorenson MM, da Silva ACR, Gouveia CS, Sousa VP, Oshima W, et al. 1995. Concerted action of the high affinity calcium binding sites in skeletal muscle troponin C. *J. Biol. Chem.* 270:9770–77

163a. Squire JM, Al-Khayat HA, Yagi N. 1993. Muscle thin filament structure and regulation: actin subdomain movements and the tropomyosin shift modelled from low angle X-ray diffraction. *J. Chem. Soc. Faraday Trans.* 89:2717–26

164. Sundaralingam M, Bergstrom R, Strasburg G, Rao ST, Roychowdhury P, et al. 1985. Molecular structure of troponin C from chicken skeletal muscle at 3 Å resolution. *Science* 227:945–48

165. Sweeney HL, Brito RM, Rosevear PR, Putkey JA. 1990. The low-affinity $Ca^{2+}$-binding sites in cardiac/slow skeletal muscle troponin C perform distinct functions: site I alone cannot trigger contraction. *Proc. Natl. Acad. Sci. USA* 87:9538–42

166. Sweitzer NK, Moss RL. 1990. The effect of altered temperature on $Ca^{2+}$-sensitive force in permeabilized myocardium and skeletal muscle. *J. Gen. Physiol.* 96:1221–45

167. Swenson CA, Fredrickson RS. 1992. Interaction of troponin C and troponin C fragments with troponin I and the troponin I inhibitory peptide. *Biochemistry* 31:3420–29

168. Syska H, Perry SV, Trayer IP. 1974. A new method of preparation of troponin I (inhibitory protein) using affinity chromatography. Evidence for three different forms of troponin I in striated muscle. *FEBS Lett.* 40:253–57

169. Syska H, Wilkinson JM, Grand RJA, Perry SV. 1976. The relationship between biological activity and primary structure of troponin I from white skeletal muscle of the rabbit. *Biochem. J.* 153:375–87

170. Szczesna D, Borovikov YS, Sobieszek A. 1989. Interaction of tropomyosin with F-actin-heavy meromyosin complex. *Biol. Chem. Hoppe-Seyler* 370:399–407

171. Talbot JA, Hodges RS. 1981. Synthetic studies on the inhibitory region of rabbit skeletal troponin I. Relationship of amino acid sequence to biological activity. *J. Biol. Chem.* 256:2798–802

172. Talbot JA, Hodges RS. 1981. Comparative studies on the inhibitory region of selected species of troponin-I. The use of synthetic peptide analogs to probe structure-function relationships. *J. Biol. Chem.* 256:12374–78

173. Tanokura M, Ohtsuki I. 1984. Interactions among chymotryptic troponin T subfragments, tropomyosin, troponin I, and troponin C. *J. Biochem.* 95:1417–21

174. Tanokura M, Tawada Y, Ono A, Ohtsuki I. 1983. Chymotryptic subfragments of troponin T from rabbit skeletal muscle. Interactions with tropomyosin, troponin I and troponin C. *J. Biochem.* 93:331–37

175. Tao T, Scheiner CJ, Lamkin M. 1986. Site-specific photo-cross-linking studies on interactions between troponin and tropomyosin and between subunits of troponin. *Biochemistry* 25:7633–39

176. Tirion MM, ben-Avraham D. 1993. Normal mode analysis of G-actin. *J. Mol. Biol.* 230:186–95

177. Tobacman LS. 1987. Activation of actin-cardiac myosin subfragment 1 MgATPase rate by $Ca^{2+}$ shows cooperativity intrinsic to the thin filament. *Biochemistry* 26:492–97

178. Tobacman LS, Adelstein RS. 1986. Mechanism of regulation of cardiac actin-myosin subfragment 1 by troponin-tropomyosin. *Biochemistry* 25:798–802

179. Tobacman LS, Butters CA. 1996. Thin filament activation is not proportional to TnC regulatory site $Ca^{2+}$ binding. Studies of cardiac thin filaments containing mixtures of TnC and regulatory site mutant TnC. *Biophys. J. Abstr.* In press

180. Tobacman LS, Sawyer D. 1990. Calcium binds cooperatively to the regulatory sites of the cardiac thin filament. *J. Biol. Chem.* 265:931–39

181. Trybus KM, Taylor EW. 1980. Kinetic studies of the cooperative binding of subfragment 1 to regulated actin. *Proc. Natl. Acad. Sci. USA* 77:7209–13

182. Tsuchiya T, Szabo A. 1982. Cooperative binding of n-mers with steric hindrance to finite and infinite one-dimensional lattices. *Biopolymers* 21:979–94

183. van Eerd J-P, Takahashi K. 1975. The amino acid sequence of bovine cardiac troponin C. Comparison with rabbit skeletal troponin C. *Biochem. Biophys. Res. Commun.* 64:122–27

184. Van Eyk JE, Hodges RS. 1988. The biological importance of each amino acid residue of the troponin I inhibitory sequence 104–115 in the interaction with troponin C and tropomyosin-actin. *J. Biol. Chem.* 263:1726–32

185. Van Eyk JE, Kay CM, Hodges RS. 1991. A comparative study of the interactions of synthetic peptides of the skeletal and cardiac troponin I inhibitory region wiht skeletal and cardiac troponin C. *Biochemistry* 30:9974–81

186. Wagner PD. 1984. Effect of skeletal muscle myosin light chain 2 on the

Ca$^{2+}$-sensitive interaction of myosin and heavy meromyosin with regulated actin. *Biochemistry* 23:5950–56

187. Walker JW, Lu Z, Moss RL. 1992. Effects of Ca$^{2+}$ on the kinetics of phosphate release in skeletal muscle. *J. Biol. Chem.* 267:2459–66

188. Walsh TP, Trueblood CE, Evans R, Weber A. 1984. Removal of tropomyosin overlap and the co-operative response to increasing calcium concentrations of the acto-subfragment-1 ATPase. *J. Mol. Biol.* 182:265–69

189. Wang C-LA, Leavis PC. 1990. Distance measurements in cardiac troponin C. *Arch. Biochem. Biophys.* 276:236–41

190. Wegner A. 1979. Equilibrium of the actin-tropomyosin interaction. *J. Mol. Biol.* 131:839–53

191. Wegner A, Walsh TP. 1981. Interaction of tropomyosin-troponin with actin filaments. *Biochemistry* 20:5633–42

192. Weigt C, Wegner A, Koch MHJ. 1991. Rate and mechanism of assembly of tropomyosin with actin filaments. *Biochemistry* 30:10700–7

193. Whitby FG, Kent H, Stewart F, Xie X, Hatch V, et al. 1992. Structure of tropomyosin at 9 angstroms resolution. *J. Mol. Biol.* 227:441–52

194. White SP. 1988. *Structure of cocrystals of tropomyosin and troponin.* PhD thesis. Univ. Illinois-Urbana-Champaign 69 pp.

195. White SP, Cohen C, Phillips JGN. 1987. Structure of co-crystals of tropomyosin and troponin. *Nature* 325:826–28

196. Wilkinson JM, Grand RJA. 1978. Comparison of amino acid sequence of troponin I from different striated muscles. *Nature* 271:31–35

197. Willadsen KA, Butters CA, Hill LE, Tobacman LS. 1992. Effects of the amino-terminal regions of tropomyosin and troponin T on thin filament assembly. *J. Biol. Chem.* 267:23746–52

198. Williams DL, Greene LE. 1983. Comparison of the effects of tropomyosin and troponin-tropomyosin on the binding of myosin subfragment 1 to actin. *Biochemistry* 22:2770–74

199. Williams DL, Greene LE, Eisenberg E. 1988. Cooperative turning on of myosin subfragment 1 adenosine triphosphatase activity by the troponin-tropomyosin-actin complex. *Biochemistry* 27:6897–993

200. Wnuk W, Schoechlin M, Stein EA. 1984. Regulation of actomyosin ATPase by a single calcium-binding site on troponin C from crayfish. *J. Biol. Chem.* 259:9017–23

201. Wolff MR, McDonald KS, Moss RL. 1995. Rate of tension development in cardiac muscle varies with level of activator calcium. *Circ. Res.* 76:154–60

202. Wyman J Jr. 1964. Linked functions and reciprocal effects in hemoglobin: a second look. *Adv. Protein Chem.* 19:223–86

203. Yagi N, Matsubara I. 1989. Structural changes in the thin filament during activation studied by X-ray diffraction of highly stretched skeletal muscle. *J. Mol. Biol.* 208:359–63

204. Yanagida T, Taniguchi M, Oosawa F. 1974. Conformational changes in F-actin in the thin filaments of muscle induced in vivo and in vitro by calcium ions. *J. Mol. Biol.* 90:509–22

205. Yates LD, Coby RL, Luo Z, Gordon AM. 1993. Filament overlap affects TnC extraction from skinned muscle fibres. *J. Muscle Res. Cell Motil.* 14:392–400

206. Zot AS, Potter JD. 1987. Structural aspects of troponin-tropomyosin regulation of skeletal muscle contraction. *Annu. Rev. Biophys. Biophys. Chem.* 16:535–59

207. Zot HG, Potter JD. 1987. Calcium binding and fluorescence measurements of dansylaziridine-labelled troponin C in reconstituted thin filaments. *J. Muscle Res. Cell Motil.* 8:428–36

*Annu. Rev. Physiol.* 1996. 58:483–507

# INHERITED DISEASES OF THE VASCULATURE

## Claire L. Shovlin

Department of Genetics, Harvard Medical School, Boston, Massachusetts 02115; and Department of Medicine, Royal Postgraduate Medical School, London W12 ONN, UK

## James Scott

Department of Medicine, Royal Postgraduate Medical School, London W12 ONN, UK

KEY WORDS:     genetic, blood vessels, aorta, malformations, telangiectasia

### ABSTRACT

This review focuses on a spectrum of inherited disorders in which recent genetic advances have made a significant contribution to our understanding of vascular pathology and homeostasis. They are discussed according to the type of blood vessel affected and the compounded physiological processes that include angiogenesis, vascular development, and defects in the structure and regulation of the mature vessel. Vascular malformations, arterial aneurysms and dissection, telangiectasia, infiltrative vascular disease, and inherited tumors and disorders of neovascularization are discussed in a variety of settings. Disease roles for endoglin, tissue inhibitor of metalloproteinases 3 (TIMP3), and vascular endothelial growth factor (VEGF) dysregulation are highlighted (175 references).

## INTRODUCTION

Inherited disorders provide a means to identify critical pathways in vascular biology. Innumerable molecules exhibit effects in vitro and in vivo that suggest they may play physiological roles, but confirmation of this is facilitated by identifying or creating states in which the activity of the molecules is altered. Such information may be derived without prior knowledge of the predicted components by using the genetic approaches of experimental mutagenesis or analysis of natural disease states. These may be complementary. Human vascular disease is detectable because embryogenesis during the first 12 weeks of gestation has been sufficiently normal to produce an individual in which

483

defects are apparent; embryonic-lethal phenotypes are more readily observed in experimental organisms.

The rationale for this review is therefore to identify diseases in which molecular approaches may elucidate critical components of the biology of the vasculature. It is restricted to those hereditary diseases with a primary vascular pathology in which a single gene defect is predicted from patterns of inheritance. Polygenic disorders with multiple hereditary and environmental components, such as atherosclerosis and hypertension, are not covered, and recent reviews (60, 68) are suggested. The first part of this review discusses the physiological processes involved in the subsequently discussed pathologies. Although these are brief overviews, the roles of molecules implicated in the diseases section are highlighted.

## THE BIOLOGY OF THE NORMAL VASCULATURE

Vascular structure, forces acting upon the vessel, and sites of pathological states are summarized in Figure 1. The mesoderm-derived components reflect the size of the vessel and functional requirements that, in turn, reflect the vessel's position in the vascular tree (79, 128).

### Vasculogenesis and Angiogenesis

Vasculogenesis, the generation of vessels from free angioblasts de novo, has been reviewed recently (132). Undifferentiated mesenchymal cells in the splanchnopleuric mesoderm condense, differentiate in situ into angioblasts, then form nests of isolated cords that develop lumens and coalesce to form the primitive capillary retiform plexus. Definitive peripheral vascular stems arise by regulated enlargement, fusion, and atrophy of areas of this plexus. Additional mesenchymal cells are recruited and incorporate into the vessel wall, differentiating to smooth muscle cells or pericytes. Subsequent morphogenesis of peripheral vessels requires blood flow to establish an appropriate pattern. Recent studies have delineated the importance of particular ligand-receptor interactions in induction between adjacent tissues in vascular development.

→

*Figure 1*   The gross anatomy of vessels at the extremes of the circulation is given (*A*). In small venules and capillaries, a single layer of endothelial cells is surrounded by a basement membrane, scattered pericytes, and occasional smooth muscle cells if a subendothelial layer is present. As vessels enlarge, these structures may become part of the tunica intima. Additional layers are observed, comprising smooth muscle cells, orderly arrangements of elastic and collagen fibers, and associated vasa vasorum and vasomotor nerves. The tunica media is more prominent in systemic arteries. The predominant mechanical forces acting on these vessels are illustrated as bold arrows. Diseases affecting different regions of the vasculature are given (*B*), with congenital malformations italicized.

## A) VASCULAR STRUCTURE AND MECHANICAL FORCES:

### LARGE ARTERIES

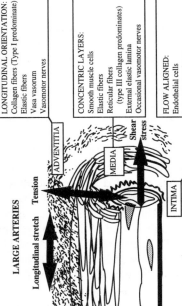

LONGITUDINAL ORIENTATION:
Collagen fibers (Type I predominate)
Elastic fibers
Vasa vasorum
Vasomotor nerves

CONCENTRIC LAYERS:
Smooth muscle cells
Elastic fibers
Reticular fibers
(type III collagen predominates)
External elastic lamina
Occasional vasomotor nerves

FLOW ALIGNED:
Endothelial cells
Basement membrane
Subendothelial layer
(occasional smooth muscle cells)
Internal elastic lamina

ADVENTITIA
MEDIA
INTIMA

Tension
Longitudinal stretch
Shear stress

### CAPILLARIES AND SMALL VENULES

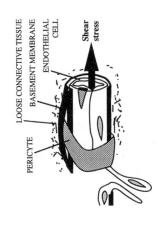

LOOSE CONNECTIVE TISSUE
BASEMENT MEMBRANE
ENDOTHELIAL CELL
PERICYTE
Shear stress

## B) INHERITED VASCULAR DISEASES:

### CAPILLARIES & VENULES

*Capillary-venous malformations*
*Bean syndrome*
Telangiectasia
HHT
Ataxia telangiectasia
Fabry's disease
Fucosidosis

ANGIOGENIC SPROUT
Von Hippel Lindau disease
Sorsby fundal dystrophy
? vitreoretinopathies

### MEDIUM & SMALL ARTERIES

*Moyamoya vessels*
Pseudoxanthoma elasticum
Cutis laxa
Neurofibromatosis
Polycystic kidney disease
Familial intracranial aneurysms
Migraine
Fabry's disease
Amyloid (HCHWA)
Subcortical arteriopathies

### AORTA & LARGE ARTERIES

Ehlers-Danlos syndrome type IV
Marfan syndrome
Supra-valvular aortic stenosis
Familial aortic aneurysms

### MULTIPLE SITES

*Complex combined malformations*
Von Willebrands disease
Sneddon syndrome

These include $\alpha_5$ integrin and fibronectin (57, 172), and endothelial cell receptor tyrosine kinases and their ligands (108).

Angiogenesis is the sprouting of new vessels from pre-existing, normally quiescent endothelium in a response modulated by growth factors, interstitial matrix or mechanical stress (50, 51, 108). The signals may converge on one common pathway resulting in extracellular matrix degradation, endothelial cell migration and proliferation, and the generation of new capillary tubules. Initial capillary buds have discontinuous basement membranes and are highly permeable (51), which is reflected clinically by hemorrhage from these vessels. Interestingly, the initial stages of angiogenesis do not depend on endothelial mitosis (144), but protease degradation of the matrix is a prerequisite. Regulation of a variety of proteolytic enzymes (serine proteases and the zinc matrix metalloproteinases) and their inhibitors, including tissue inhibitors of metalloproteinases (TIMPs) 1, 2 and 3, permits regulated local degradation. In vitro, TIMPs inhibit endothelial tube formation (139); in vivo, one has recently been associated with a vascular retinopathy. The acquisition of the migratory phenotype by the endothelial cell may be promoted by a variety of angiogenic stimuli (50, 108). Among those with direct effects, acidic and basic fibroblast growth factor have been reviewed recently (50, 52). Evidence for crucial angiogenic roles of the endothelial-specific vascular endothelial growth factor/vascular permeability factor, VEGF/VPF, is persuasive. VEGF is up-regulated during tumor- (118) and hypoxia- (142) induced angiogenesis. Furthermore, transgenic expression of VEGF induces angiogenesis (103), whereas anti-VEGF antibodies (84), or the expression of a defective VEGF receptor mutant (105), inhibit it.

## Regulation of Vessel Morphogenesis

The normal endothelium maintains a neutral state in a variety of settings but reserves the capacity for acute responses. The features involve an interplay between cells, external factors, and molecules of the extracellular matrix (49, 74). For example, the extracellular matrix mediates mechanical stresses (see below) and provides a reservoir of inactive growth factors that may be rapidly released and activated by local regulatory proteases. Transforming growth factor-$\beta$ (TGF-$\beta$) is an example of a growth factor regulated in this manner (170) and is implicated in the pathogenesis of hereditary hemorrhagic telangiectasia. Signaling from TGF-$\beta$ is mediated through the serine kinase receptors types I and II (168). Type III receptors (betaglycan and endoglin) can regulate TGF-$\beta$ responses: Endoglin appears to be the critical type III receptor in endothelial cells (22). TGF-$\beta$ induces the synthesis of matrix proteins, alters transcription of matrix-degrading enzymes and their inhibitors, and induces changes in the fibrinolytic system and adhesion molecules (see

18, 116 for recent discussions). Because TGF-β is up-regulated by shear stress (113), or may be released from proteoglycan matrix reservoirs by heparin and activated by plasminogen activator, it is poised to play critical roles in processes such as angiogenesis (75) and wound repair (97).

## Stress and Strain Considerations

Vessels need to withstand three different directional forces generated in the course of the cardiac cycle: radial compression/distension (tension), longitudinal stretch, and tangential shear stress (102, 110) (Figure 1). A failure to withstand these forces leads to vascular disruption, dilatation, and hemorrhage. The degree of shear stress applied to the vessel wall is proportional to the flow rate (governed by viscosity, turbulence, and non-Newtonian behavior of red and white blood cells) and vessel diameter, $d^{-3}$. Thus for a given flow, smaller vessels experience more shear stress than larger vessels, and it is likely that the contribution of flow to pathology in the microcirculation has been underestimated.

CONTAINMENT   As a result of an applied mechanical load, a structure deforms. The degree of strain (spatial variation of displacement) that occurs is determined by the strength and elasticity of the material. Radial compressive/distensive (tensile) stress constitutes the predominant mechanical load for larger arterial vessels and is carried by the medial and adventitial elements. At typical arterial pressures, all the elements combine to withstand the normal stress load, but individual wall components have specific roles. Elastic fibers allow tissues to recoil after stretch (1) and to withstand longitudinal stresses (38), aided by their circumferential arrangement in arteries. Their core contains elastin, the major biomechanical component, and fibulin. This core is associated with a microfibrillar sheath comprising fibrillin-1 and microfibril-associated proteins. The critical role of the sheath in its proposed roles during elastogenesis or core-stabilization is manifest in Marfan syndrome (94). The interstitial collagens withstand predominantly extending stresses (38). Complementary fiber arrangements in the media [which is unusually rich in type III collagen ($\alpha1(III)3$)] and interstitium permit modulation of distending and longitudinal stresses. Shear stresses are absorbed by the endothelial cell cytoskeleton, which transmits imposed forces to neighboring rigid structures or elastic elements (33). In vitro, the cytoskeleton (in the form of stress fibers comprised of actin filaments and myosin II) is anchored via linker proteins to integrins in the plasma membrane at regions of tight contact known as focal adhesions (117). Cells do not detach under shear stress because of a number of adhesive molecules, including integrins, immunoglobulin superfamily members, selectins, and cadherins (35, 43), that act between adjacent cell surfaces or between the cell and extracellular matrix molecules. Ligands may be other cell surface components or extracellular matrix molecules.

RESPONSES TO ACUTE FLUCTUATIONS    Repetitive mechanical stretching of endothelial cells in vitro leads to realignment in the direction of the stress, cytoskeletal alterations, and extracellular matrix changes (61, 102) that may help promote vascular integrity. Similar, but not identical, responses occur as a result of shear stress. These include endothelial cell elongation and alignment in the direction of flow, cytoskeletal reorganization (33, 151), up-regulation of intercellular adhesion molecules, vasodilatation, and modulation of the fibrinolytic and coagulation systems (34, 102, 110, 126). Many of the genes up-regulated in these processes have a shear stress response element in their promoter (126). Shear stress transmission through cytoskeleton filamentous actin (33) has been supported by the demonstration of direct mechanical coupling of the cytoskeleton to the luminal surface (160). This may be integrin mediated. Integrins are the predominant matrix receptors on cells (3) and function both as adhesion molecules and transducers of chemical or mechanical signals. Their signaling functions, recently reviewed (26), include pathways providing the potential for the observed cooperativity with signals from cell growth factor receptors and mechanotransduction leading to cytoskeletal reorganization (25). Smooth muscle cell responses are reviewed elsewhere (141).

CHRONIC RESPONSES    Early microscopic observations suggested that the size of the vessel lumen and wall thickness depended upon the rate of the blood flow (70, 73, 167). They also suggested flow-related changes in vascular type (27), although this remains a subject of controversy. Following a reduction in blood flow, extensive remodeling has been observed in the abdominal aorta (140) and the common carotid artery in an endothelium-dependent manner (91). These changes support a body of experimental and physiological evidence that arteries adopt wall diameters to maintain a constant shear stress of 15–20 dynes/cm$^2$ (82), which may rise to 100 dynes/cm$^2$ at branches and regions of sharp wall curvature (110). Additional factors may contribute to flow-mediated changes. For instance, during pregnancy there is a rise in cardiac output and vascular volume of up to 40% by term. The required acute vasodilatation is enhanced by estrogen and progesterone, either directly or via an attenuation in angiotensin II and endothelin responses (58). Chronic adaptive vascular effects may be promoted by estrogen- and progesterone-induced alterations in matrix proteins (46).

## INHERITED DISEASES OF THE VASCULATURE

For the purposes of this review, diseases are considered according to the type of blood vessel affected and, where possible, the compounded physiological processes (see Table 1 and Figure 1). Primary vascular diseases are emphasized, but examples of metabolic processes that result in secondary vascular pathology are given, particularly when they are relevant to diseases discussed elsewhere. Due to space considerations, certain diseases for which less information is available are listed in Table 1 but not covered in the text. The classification is somewhat arbitrary; for instance, certain processes affect several parts of the vascular tree, and there are clear overlaps, for example, between malformations and telangiectasia. It should also be noted that familial disorders represent only a subgroup of potential disease states, as sporadic occurrence is common. Finally, the emphasis on vascular pathology could render some systemic diseases barely recognizable. To minimize this inevitable bias, involvement of other systems that characterize the full disease picture are mentioned briefly.

## Inherited Malformations

A recent classification system for generalized vascular dilatations (sometimes referred to by the descriptive term angiodysplasia) has provided a framework from which pathogenic mechanisms become more evident (107). Lesions characterized by excessive endothelial proliferation (suffix, -oma), which are rarely familial, are distinguished from true vascular malformations, which undergo commensurate growth. Vascular malformations are proposed to arise from miscues during embryological development of the vascular bed, failure of regulated remodeling of the primitive capillary retiform plexus or subsequent vascular networks (173), with the precise nature of the anomaly reflecting the stage of development (6).

CAPILLARY-VENOUS MALFORMATIONS    Cerebral "cavernous angiomas" consist of endothelial-lined vascular channels, devoid of feeding or draining vessels but contiguous to one another. No arterial components are observed within the lesions (131). In two Hispanic families and one European family, a gene inherited as an autosomal-dominant has been mapped to chromosome 7q (40, 64). In addition, autosomal-dominant transmission of similar lesions in the non-cerebral circulation has been described in isolated families (115).

VENOUS MALFORMATIONS    *Bean syndrome*    Blue rubber-bleb nevus syndrome is recognized by distinctive "rubber nipple"-like venous malformations in the skin that are present at birth (8, 107). Vascular beds in other viscera, particularly the gastrointestinal tract, may be involved (8, 130). Due to the high incidence of sporadic cases, it is questionable if the disorder represents a single entity. However, familial occurence has allowed the localization of a gene for Bean syndrome to chromosome 9p (12).

**Table 1**   Inherited diseases of the vasculature

| Disease | Inheritance pattern | Gene Site | Identity | Reference |
|---|---|---|---|---|
| Inherited malformations | | | | |
| Capillary (Unna's nevus) | occ familial | ? | ? | (8) |
| Capillary venous, | aut dom | ? | ? | (115) |
| Non-cerebral cerebral | aut dom | 7q | ? | (40, 64) |
| Venous (Bean syndrome) | aut dom | 9p | ? | (12) |
| Arteriovenous[a] | aut dom | ? | ? | (39) |
| Complex combined[b] | occ familial | ? | ? | (2, 53) |
| Arterial (Moyamoya disease) | familial | ? | ? | (85) |
| Aberrant vascular course | occ familial | ? | ? | (56) |
| Vascular disruption sequences[c] | occ familial | ? | ? | (13, 72) |
| | | | | (153) |
| Large vessel disease | | | | |
| Common aortic involvement | | | | |
| Ehlers-Danlos syndrome Type IV | aut dom | 2q | Col3A1 | (121) |
| Marfan syndrome | aut dom | 15q | fibrillin 1 | (37) |
| Marfan-like syndrome | aut dom | 3p | ? | (28) |
| SVAS/Williams syndrome | aut dom | 7q | elastin | (32, 111) |
| Alpha-glucosidase deficiency | aut rec | 11q | same | (98) |
| Homocysteinemia | aut rec | 21q | c-$\beta$-synth | (29) |
| Tuberose sclerosis | aut dom | 16p | tuberin | (92) |
| | | 9q | ? | |
| Familial aortic aneurysms | varies | ? | ? | (89) |
| Rare aortic involvement | | | | |
| Pseudoxanthoma elasticum | aut dom | ? | ? | (134) |
| Cutis laxa | aut dom | ? | ? | (67, 174) |
| Neurofibromatosis | aut dom | 17q | neurofibromin | (5, 169) |
| Adult polycystic kidney | aut dom | 16p | PKD1 | (20, 41) |
| disease | aut dom | 4q | ? | (41) |
| Familial carotid aneurysms | varies | ? | ? | (133) |
| Microcirculation | | | | |
| Telangiectasia | | | | |
| Hereditary hemorrhage telangiectasia | aut dom | 9q | endoglin | (101, 119) |
| | aut dom | 12q | 1? | (76a, 159) |
| Ataxia telangiectasia | aut rec | 11q | ATM | (14, 137) |
| Fabry's disease[d] | X-linked rec | Xq | $\alpha$-N-AG | (14, 15) |
| Fucosidosis[d] | aut rec | 1p | $\alpha$-L-F | (14) |
| Occlusive disease | | | | |
| HCHWA (Icelandic-type) | aut dom | 20p | cystatin C | (76) |
| HCHWA (Dutch-type) | aut dom | ? | ? | (158) |
| Inherited subcortical | aut dom | 19q | ? | (7, 154) |
| arteriopathies | aut rec | ? | ? | (171) |
| Acid maltase deficiency | aut rec | 17q | same | (87) |
| Progressive hyalinosis | occ fam | ? | ? | (123) |

| | | | | |
|---|---|---|---|---|
| **Abnormalities of tone** | | | | |
| Familial hemiplegic migraine | aut dom | 19q | ? | (154) |
| **Familial tumors** | | | | |
| Chemodactomas | occ fam | ? | ? | (21) |
| Malignant hemangiopericytoma | occ fam | ? | ? | (120) |
| von Hippel-Lindau syndrome | aut dom | 3p | vHL | (19, 93) |
| **Coagulation (generalized)** | | | | |
| Von Willebrand's disease | aut dom | 12q | vWF[e] | (see text) |
| Sneddon's syndrome | aut dom | ? | ? | (59) |
| **Possible primary vascular** | | | | |
| Membranous lipodystrophy | aut rec | ? | ? | (81) |
| Sorsby's fundus dystrophy | aut dom | 22q | TIMP3 | (162) |
| Exudative familial vr | aut dom | 11q | ? | (96) |
| Familial inflammatory vr | aut dom | 11q | ? | (149) |

For each disease discussed in the text, and additional diseases not referred to, the familial inheritance pattern, chromosomal gene location, and causal gene (if known) are illustrated. References relate to the gene, or where no genetic information is available, the most useful papers: Additional references are given in the text. Abbreviations: aut, autosomal; dom, dominant; rec, recessive; familial, mode of inheritance not determined or varies; occ fam, occasionally familial; SVAS, supravalvular aortic stenosis; c-$\beta$-synth, cystathione-$\beta$-synthetase; $\alpha$-$N$-AG, $\alpha$-$N$-acetylgalactosaminidase; $\alpha$-L-F: $\alpha$-F-fucosidase; vr, vitreoretinopathy.
[a] Also occur in hereditary hemorrhagic telangiectasia.
[b] Possible spectrum including Klippel-Trenaunay, Parkes Weber, and Proteus syndromes.
[c] May include Poland sequence, Adams-Olivier, Klippel Feil and Mobius syndromes.
[d] Also causes occlusive disease
[e] Other loci contribute to disease.

ARTERIOVENOUS MALFORMATIONS (AVMS)    Whereas microscopic AVMs are normal components of the circulation, particularly in the skin (79), pathological AVMs occur throughout the circulation. Familial AVMs tend to be multiple. Although autosomal-dominant inheritance, with or without cutaneous lesions, has been detected (39), the molecular basis of these conditions is unknown. It is interesting that pathogenic mechanisms for AVMs in different parts of the body appear distinct. The most common cause of inherited AVMs is Hereditary Hemorrhagic Telangiectasia (HHT), in which up to 20% of affected individuals have pulmonary AVMs, and a significant number have cerebral involvement (119). However, in these individuals, not all cerebral vascular lesions are of the AVM type (44; PB Fayad, personal communication).

ARTERIAL MALFORMATIONS    Moyamoya disease (derived from Moya-moya, the Japanese word "puff of smoke") is the name given to an angiographic picture of intracranial arterial occlusion or stenosis, accompanied by a network of extensively developed collaterals between the extracranial and cerebral arteries, most prominent in the region of the basal ganglia. Seven percent of cases are familial (85); the remainder represent the secondary development of moyamoya collaterals. Because these collaterals develop only in a small proportion of such cases, especially in diseases where vasculopathies would be predicted, e.g. neurofibromatosis, it has been suggested that the moyamoya vessels reflect an aberrant, normally nonfunctional cerebrovascular congenital malformation (55).

## Large Vessel Disease

A healthy arterial wall fully compensates the periodic pulsations generated by the cardiac cycle. Diseased vessels may fail to generate the correct stress-strain response, despite attempts to restore homeostatic mechanisms by wall remodeling, and may rupture or fail to return to the resting state (dilatation). The process of remodeling may itself generate significant hemodynamic impairment. The focal dilatations of an arterial wall, termed aneurysms, are clinically interlinked with arterial dissection (138), in which a stream of blood generates a false lumen through the wall of an artery. Inherited arteriopathies provide information on the sites of stress generation, the ability of the vessel to withstand the imposed force, and particularly highlight the roles of elastic and collagen fibers in the arterial wall.

COMMON AORTIC INVOLVEMENT    *Ehlers-Danlos syndrome type IV*   The molecular basis for this autosomal-dominant disease is now well established (121), and only a brief summary is given. Vascular complications of this disease include spontaneous large artery or vena caval rupture and fistula formation. Some of the most dramatic examples have occurred at known periods of vascular stretching such as avulsion of the heart from the vena cava during cardiac massage. A skin capillary microangiopathy with aneurysms and hemorrhage also occurs. This is in contrast to the other Ehlers-Danlos syndromes in which nonvascular connective tissue disease is the rule. Type IV was shown to result from mutations in *COL3A1,* the gene for the $\alpha 1$ (III) propolypeptide collagen chain (reviewed in 121). The dominant effect of the observed mutations are explained by destabilization of the collagen triple helix; the catastrophic consequences confirm the critical contribution of type III collagen to the ability of the vascular wall to withstand distending and longitudinal mechanical stress.

*Marfan syndrome (MFS)*   Marfan syndrome results in a spectrum of defects affecting skeletal, ocular, and pulmonary systems, but it is the involvement of the cardiovascular system that accounts for the poor prognostic outlook in these individuals—most commonly progressive dilatation of the (thoracic) aortic root leading to dissection. The variation in severity of disease among members of the same family points to additional genetic or environmental modifiers (37). Histologically, the aorta displays so-called cystic medial necrosis, in which fragmented elastic fibers are replaced by amorphous ground substance. Linkage to chromosome 15 led to detection of mutations in the *fibrillin-1* (*FBN-1*) gene, reviewed recently in this series (37).

Fibrillin-1 is one of the microfilament proteins in elastic fibers, stabilizing the fiber via disulfide bonds between cysteine-rich regions. One mutated *fibrillin-1* allele is sufficient to generate the Marfan phenotype. Potential pathogenic mechanisms are a stoichiometric insufficiency of the wild-type allele, or mutant allele interference with the wild-type in a dominant-negative manner. Clinical evidence favors the latter because full transcription of a mutant allele tends to result in more severe disease than in cases where there is a reduction in mutant allele transcription (37). Furthermore, an allele predicted to produce no mutant protein has been found in a family with isolated skeletal findings of MFS (104). A dominant-negative effect at the stage of fibrillin protein deposition has been demonstrated for several mutations (4). There is some evidence that mutations in a particular region of *FBN-1* may be responsible for a severe neonatal form of MFS (80). However, this type of analysis has limitations in a disease with marked intrafamilial variation, which implies that the available family members may not represent the full range of phenotypes potentially associated with the mutation. Finally, additive mutational effects appear plausible, given the recent description of a homozygous case with a more severe phenotype than would be predicted from either allele (83). The cardiovascular and connective tissue effects of fibrillin may be distinct (104). This is highlighted by the recent report of a single family with Marfan-like vascular and skeletal phenotype without ocular involvement mapping to 3p24.2-p25 (28). Although there has been debate over the diagnosis of MFS (36, 11), this does at least raise the possibility that a gene other than *FBN-1* may generate the substantive vascular phenotype of Marfan syndrome, with differential effects in other tissues.

*Supra-valvular aortic stenosis (SVAS)*    SVAS results in significant narrowing of several major arteries, particularly the ascending aorta and pulmonary arteries, but including coronary and carotid arteries. It may be inherited as an isolated autosomal-dominant trait, or as part of Williams syndrome (24, 63), a multisystem developmental disorder associated with hypercalcemia, characteristic facies, and mental retardation. Microscopically, the stenoses exhibit medial disorganization with collagen deposition replacing the spaces between haphazard and fragmented elastic fibers (112). Isolated SVAS was mapped by genetic linkage to 7q11 and displayed no recombination events with a polymorphism within the elastin gene. Subsequently, several mutations in the 3′ region of elastin were shown to cosegregate with SVAS (32, 42). In the majority of Williams syndrome cases, deletion of an entire allele was observed (111). Because mild Williams syndrome and SVAS may cosegregate with the same elastin translocation mutant allele (32), and a number of coexisting SVAS/Williams/overlap pedigrees have been described (63), this supports the hypothesis that the two disorders reflect variable expression of the same mutation(s). However, the contribution of a particular critical region of the elastin gene or neighboring locus in the generation of the non-aortic features of Williams syndrome is not yet resolved.

IDIOPATHIC FAMILIAL ANEURYSMS    Thirteen to seventeen percent of aortic aneurysms have been associated with a familial contribution not due to other inherited disorders (89). To unmask the disease potential, additional risk factors (e.g. hypertension, smoking) may be required, but accelerated atherosclerosis is not supported as the sole factor in most cases (161). The involvement of *COL3A1* in aortic disease in Ehlers-Danlos syndrome led to the proposal that it may be involved in isolated aortic aneurysms, but a structural gene defect has been excluded as a major factor following mutational screening in 48 cases (155). Several groups have reported excessive elastase activity in aneurysms associated with atherosclerosis and Marfan syndrome (71, 150). If so, the primary insult in aneurysmal formation could be diverse, ranging from abnormal elastic fiber structure, as in Marfan syndrome, immune-mediated damage, or a primary abnormality of metalloproteinases or their inhibitors (as in TIMP3 in Sorsby's fundus dystrophy).

RARE AORTIC INVOLVEMENT    *Pseudoxanthoma elasticum (PXE) (134) and the cutis laxa syndromes (67)*    These diseases are occasionally observed with vascular abnormalities. In both diseases, abnormalities in collagen and elastic fibers are observed, but no defect in the structural genes has been described. The possibility that these disorders reflect a regulatory abnormality has been supported recently by the observation that TGF-β may reverse the posttranscriptional defect in elastin synthesis observed in vitro in cutis laxa-derived fibroblasts (174).

*Neurofibromatosis (NF)-1 (von Recklinghausen's disease)*    This is characterized by hamartomas and neoplastic proliferation of cells particularly of the peripheral and central nervous systems. The gene for NF-1 encodes neurofibromin, a GTPase-activating protein (GAP)-related protein (5, 169) mutated in human tumors (95). Vascular NF-1, first delineated in 1945 (127), affects up to 7% of NF-1 children (45). Involvement of the entire arterial tree has been described, but renal artery stenosis is the most common (129), with eccentric fibrohyalinization and lumen obliteration, loss of smooth muscle cells and elastin, and the formation of aneurysms. It has been suggested that these changes are a result of secondary degeneration (6, 135). However, the concept of a generalized vasculopathy is supported by the frequent incidence of moyamoya vessels (152), the occurrence of vascular changes without other characteristic features of NF-1 (86), and recent data on p120-rasGAP and neurofibromin null mice (175).

*Autosomal-dominant polycystic kidney disease*    (PKD) is characterized by the development of cystic kidneys and ultimately renal failure. It is also associated in 5% of cases with multiple intracranial aneurysms (20). Early biochemical data revealed cyst tissue to be deficient in heparan sulfate proteoglycans, with reduced TGF-β sensitivity (54, 165), which suggested a perturbed regulatory role of extracellular matrix. Following the recent identification of the PKD-1 gene (41) (which has no significant homologies), an antibody was produced to the extreme carboxyl-terminal domain of the putative PKD protein. This suggested that the gene product was an extracellular matrix protein (156), but a frame shift as a result of an erroneous 2bp deletion in the initially published sequence implies that the matrix protein identified may not be directly related to the PKD gene (66).

IDIOPATHIC FAMILIAL ANEURYSMS    Up to 10% of intracranial aneurysms may be familial, with known genetic disease accounting for only a small subgroup of these cases (133). Evidence for ultrastructural collagen alterations in cerebral aneurysmal walls (109) led to the proposal that *COL3A1* may be involved in idiopathic aneurysms. However, mutational screening in 58 cases excluded a structural gene defect as a major factor (88).

## Diseases of the Microcirculation

TELANGIECTASIA    Telangiectases are dilated capillaries, venules, or arterioles. The most common hereditary forms are those found in Anglo-Saxon skin after chronic exposure to sunlight (14). Nonhereditary forms include chronic telangiectases of radiation dermatitis (simulated at an accelerated rate by xeroderma pigmentosum); spider nevi, which appear to be estrogen-associated (8); cuticular telangiectases of vasculitic connective tissue diseases and the telangiectases on the border of basal cell carcinomas (reviewed 14, 48). However, the multitude of predisposing environmental and hereditary factors may not converge on common pathways because the resulting vessels exhibit distinctive morphological and ultrastructural appearances (15, 16).

*Hereditary hemorrhagic telangiectasia (HHT; Rendu-Osler-Weber syndrome)* This was first distinguished from hemophilia by Rendu 100 years ago (125).

The disease is characterized by nose bleeds, often commencing in childhood, mucocutaneous telangiectasia, and variable involvement of visceral vascular beds increasing with age (119). Profound variation in disease expression is seen between members of the same family, including phenotypic modification by the female hormones, which is beneficial in treatment of hemorrhage (157), but may adversely affect disease progression, particularly in the lungs and during pregnancy (146). The smallest HHT cutaneous telangiectatic lesion is a focal dilatation of the postcapillary venule in the upper horizontal plexus, with abnormal stress fibers in the venule pericytes (16). The lesions appear to progress by remodeling (27) via recruitment of mural cells, involvement of further vascular segments, and loss of the capillary bed (16).

Genetic mapping studies initially identified a locus on chromosome 9q, now known to be the endoglin gene, which mediates TGF-$\beta$ signaling (101). The initial mapping also revealed that HHT was genetically heterogeneous (145). A second locus has been recently identified on chromosome 12 (76a, 159), but support for a 3p22 locus (101) has been withdrawn because the disease gene in that family maps to the 12q locus (76a). Endoglin mutations to date (101; CL Shovlin, unpublished observations) have not demonstrated large genomic deletions in a total of over 100 HHT individuals. In addition to the three initially published mutations in exons 7 and 11 , two of which generated premature termination codons (101), point mutations and small deletions both in and out of frame have been detected. Comparably severe phenotypes are observed in all groups (CL Shovlin, unpublished observations). Although the initial report suggested a two-hit mechanism, with somatic loss of the normal allele required to generate the abnormal vessels, there is no direct evidence for this. Endoglin homodimerises as a transmembrane protein. It is therefore possible that the mutated protein would form a heterodimer with the normal protein, preventing either component from acting appropriately, or that haplo insufficiency occurs. Considerations of the role of TGF-$\beta$ in the vasculature (see above) and the site of onset in the postcapillary venule suggest possible initiating events, including wound healing or aberrant angiogenic signals. Associated endothelial effects have been suggested by reports of increased tissue plasminogen activator (tPA) associated with the lesions (90) and a link with von Willebrand's disease (see below).

*Ataxia telangiectasia (AT)*   The oculocutaneous telangiectasia in AT patients have contributed considerably more to the naming of this disease than to its study. Characteristic venous telangiectases develop between 3 and 6 years of age and consist of fine wiry vessels coursing from the corners of the eyes and fanning out over the eyeball. In addition, short, stubby vessels may appear on the upper chest and neck, back of the hands, fossae of knee and elbow (14). In many cases, the pattern is said to conform to areas of maximal sun exposure

(48). All classical AT families mapped to a site on chromosome 11q, where the ATM gene was recently described (137). This gene may point to potential pathogenic routes because it bears extensive homologies to PI-3 kinase and *rad3*, a yeast gene that prevents cell cycle progression in the presence of radiation-damaged DNA. It is recognized that telangiectasia are not invariantly present (100), and in one AT family with no telangiectasia and a relatively mild course, linkage to 11q appeared to be excluded (69).

*Fabry's disease and fucosidosis*    These diseases result in the accumulation of glycosphingolipids in vessel walls. One consequence is progressive development of skin telangiectasia (14, 48) resulting from dilatation of small collecting veins (15). Deposition also occurs in cerebral arterioles and small arteries resulting in occlusive disease.

OCCLUSIVE DISEASE *Hereditary cerebral hemorrhage with amyloid (HCHWA)*    A predominantly Icelandic angiopathy, HCHWA-I manifests with first strokes in young adults due to cerebral artery deposition of an amyloid protein corresponding to the extracellular cysteine proteinase inhibitor, cystatin C. One mutation (Leu68Glu) was found in all Icelandic families studied, which suggests a common founder effect (76). A similar disease, HCHWA-D, but with a later onset, has been detected in Dutch fishermen. These cases show no abnormalities of cystatin C, and the deposits found in the arteries have immunohistochemical characteristics of Alzheimer disease-related β-protein (158).

*Inherited subcortical arteriopathies*    These conditions present with recurrent stroke or transient ischemic attack in the third to seventh decade. Elastic lamina fragmentation in small cerebral arteries has been observed, associated with concentric thickening of the media due to deposits of collagen, elastic fragments, and an unidentified substance (7). An autosomal-dominant form of the disorder has now been mapped in two unrelated families to chromosome 19q12 (154).

DISORDERS OF TONE *Familial hemiplegic migraine*    This variety of migraine, characterized by hemiplegia during the aura, is genetically heterogeneous with loci on chromosome 19 (77) and at least one other site (78). It should be noted that nonhemiplegic migraine, while a common disorder in the general population, does show an increased incidence in other vascular disorders such as HHT (148). Familial occurrence has also been reported in other vasospastic states such as Raynaud's phenomenon and may represent underlying vascular pathology as in Sneddon's syndrome (59).

FAMILIAL TUMORS *von Hippel-Lindau disease*    This disease predisposes to a number of tumors, most commonly cerebellar hemangioblastoma, in addition to retinal angiomas, other central nervous system hemangioblastomas, highly vascularized tumors (particularly renal cell carcinomas), pheochromocytomas, and renal cysts (165, 166). Histologically, hemangioblastomas consist of dense networks of capillaries comprising normal endothelial cells and pericytes, with highly abnormal, as yet uncharacterized stromal cells (19, 147), and intratumoral cyst formation (166). It has been proposed that the lesions recapitulate primitive angioblasts in vasculogenesis (19). They are pathologically benign, nonmetastatic tumors. The disease-causing gene at the 3p25-p26 locus (143) has been determined (93) and displays no genetic homologies except to a surface glycoprotein of the procyclic form of *Trypanosoma brucei*. On clinical grounds, this gene is expected to encode a tumor suppress; this is supported by data citing loss of heterozygosity (31). All mutations to date have been located in the 3′ portion of the gene (164, 23); hemangioblastomas are associated with truncations and missense mutations, whereas Arg238Gln and Arg238Trp appear to correlate particularly with a pheochromocytoma predisposition (23, 31, 164). Recently, up-regulation of VEGF and its receptors has been observed in hemangioblastomas (166). Thus the von Hippel-Lindau gene may function as an angiogenesis inhibitor; inactivation of this gene directly or indirectly inducing VEGF and its receptors, possibly through a number of intervening steps (166).

COAGULATION DEFECTS    Most disorders of inadequate or excessive thrombosis result from defects in the coagulation cascade or circulating cells (see review in 9). However, aberrant endothelial expression of components of the fibrinolytic system, or coagulation cascade, particularly von Willebrand's factor, thrombomodulin, and tissue factor (99), are also potential mediators of such disease (9). While coagulation defects generally affect the entire vascular bed, two diseases with specific relevance to the microcirculation are discussed below.

*von Willebrand's disease (VWD)*    von Willebrand factor (VWF) is predominantly synthesized by endothelial cells. It promotes hemostasis by mediating initial platelet adherence to the subendothelium after vascular injury and by stabilizing factor VIII in the plasma to promote the intrinsic coagulation cascade. von Willebrand's disease results from structural gene mutations, defects in posttranslational processing or instability of the protein and leads to a hemorrhagic tendency (62). VWD is also associated with gastrointestinal telangiectasia, and possibly with hereditary hemorrhagic telangiectasia (122), although this may be somewhat misleading because telangiectasia occurs in only a subset of family members with VWD (30, 65, 122). Interestingly, the linkage interval for the HHT gene on 12q lies close to the von Willebrand factor (*VWF*) locus (159). This raises the possibility of linkage disequilibrium between the two loci. Alternatively, it has been proposed that VWD and the telangiectasia reflect a common endothelial defect owing to endothelial synthesis of VWF. A third possibility—that VWD predisposes to GI telangiectasia—has not been explored but may be considered because VWF mediates endothelial cell adhesion to the extracellular matrix (10).

*Sneddon's syndrome* This is an example of a thrombotic state that may be mediated by a primary vascular defect. Autosomal-dominant inheritance has been described in this condition, which presents with excessive vasoconstriction (Raynaud's phenomenon), peripheral ischemic changes, and early onset strokes (59, 124). Recent evidence suggests that it is mediated by in situ cerebrovascular thrombosis resulting in embolism, rather than a primary vasculitis, which was proposed previously (59).

POSSIBLE PRIMARY VASCULAR DISEASES In a number of inherited diseases that until now have not been considered as vasculopathies, evidence for a primary vascular mediation is accumulating.

*Sorsby's fundus dystrophy (SFD)* SFD, a form of macular degeneration, results in the loss of central vision through neovascularization and atrophy of the choroid, pigment epithelium, and retina. It is associated with the early accumulation of lipid material in Bruch's membrane, a multilayered basement membrane-like structure between the choroid and retinal pigment epithelium. New vessels subsequently grow from the choroid into the pigment epithelium. The disorder was initially linked to 22q (163) in one kindred. Subsequently, point mutations in the carboxyl-terminal domain of the tissue inhibitor of metalloproteinase-3 (TIMP3) gene were detected in affected members of two SFD pedigrees (162). In each case, the generation of a novel cysteine residue is predicted, suggesting the tertiary protein structure may be perturbed by the formation of additional disulfide bonds. It is still unclear whether neovascularization is a functional response to metabolic or regulatory impairment of Bruch's membrane, or whether alteration in the matrix directly generates a primary angiogenic stimulus (TIMP-like molecules have displayed antiangiogenic activity) (106).

FAMILIAL VITREORETINOPATHY *Exudative familial vitreoretinopathy (EVR)* This autosomal-dominant trait exhibits peripheral retinal cystoid degeneration and is characterized by temporal neovascularization leading to recurrent vitreous hemorrhages, intraretinal exudates, local retinal detachment, and the generation of fibrovascular masses (17). The vascular changes are similar in distribution and structure to those observed in retrolental fibroplasia of prematurity (17). EVR families were mapped to 11q13-23 (96), interestingly, the same region as a second vitreoretinopathy autosomal-dominant neovascular inflammatory vitreoretinopathy (149) in which there is early temporal retinal vessel closure associated with focal hyperpigmentation and neo-vascularization. The question of whether these two diseases are allelic variants or the result of a clustering of genes with similar effects has not been resolved.

## SUMMARY AND PERSPECTIVES

Coordinated interacting processes critical for optimal functioning of the vasculature may be assaulted by diverse pathogenic mechanisms. This review has highlighted structural and regulatory defects in the extracellular matrix, aberrant endothelial cell regulation, and abnormal angiogenesis. In some cases, the disease manifestations are in accordance with predictions regarding the functional biomechanics of the vascular wall, e. g. vascular rupture associated with type III collagen defects and predominantly dilating disease with fibrillin mutations. However, it is puzzling why the effects of disrupting the elastic fiber are so different in Marfan syndrome and supravalvular aortic stenosis, both in regard to extravascular phenotypic effects and the distinct functional differences within the vasculature.

It is tempting to speculate which currently identified genes will cause disease by considering mapping and functional-pathological correlations. The linkage interval for Bean syndrome is consistent with an intriguing candidate, the endothelial receptor tyrosine kinase tie-2 (TEK1), in which homozygous deletion is associated with abnormal embryonic vascular morphogenesis (136). A locus for inherited subcortical arteriopathy, maps adjacent to proteins implicated in amyloidosis, and the vitreoretinopathies map adjacent to two metalloproteinase genes on chromosome 11. In general terms, it appears that certain trends are apparent already. Defective genes responsible for viable disease states have encoded structural effectors (*COL3A1, elastin, fibrillin*) or relatively up-stream regulators (*endoglin* and *TIMP3*), which suggest crucial early developmental modulators or downstream signaling effectors may be responsible for embryological lethal states rather than disease phenotypes.

However, it should be noted that the majority of diseases covered in this review are autosomal-dominant traits. The complete absence of their causative genes as recessive traits may result in a lethal peturbation of embryogenesis, in contrast to the single mutant allele exposed only by dysregulation in response to physiological challenges in post-natal life. Furthermore, the role of redundancy in critical cellular mechanisms cannot be overlooked, which makes it difficult to predict the relative requirement for a particular protein during the different processes in which it is engaged. These considerations are supported by diseases in which the observed pathology seems somewhat sparse in the face of dysregulation of a critical vascular process (e.g. HHT and endoglin).

Thus the information derived from disease states should be complementary to the detection of lethal abnormalities in other organisms (47) or experimental modifications of bioactive molecules. We predict that animal models will be sought for most, if not all, molecules with proposed biological functions and disease states (114). For human disease, it remains to be seen how accurately these models will recapitulate disease, as the known sequence variations between homologous genes in different species may reflect significant biological differences. Such considerations will be important both in understanding pathogenesis and, perhaps more importantly, in determining their effectiveness as a means to develop new treatment modalities.

ACKNOWLEDGMENTS

CLS is a Wellcome Trust Training Fellow. The authors thank Drs. Luisa Iruela-Arispe, Timothy F Lane, and Michelle Letarte for their critical reviews of this manuscript.

## Literature Cited

1. Aaron, BB, Gosline JM. 1981. Elastin as a random network elastomer. *Biopolymers Biopolarity* 20: 1247–60
2. Aelvolet GE, Jorens PG, Roelen LM. 1992. Genetic aspects of the Klippel-Trenaunay syndrome. *Br. J. Dermatol.* 126:603–7
3. Albeda SM, Buck CA. 1990. Integrins and other cell adhesion molecules. *FASEB J.* 4:2868–80
4. Aoyama T, Francke U, Dietz HC, Furthmayr H. 1994. Quantitative differences in biosynthesis and extracellular deposition of fibrillin in cultured fibroblasts distinguish five groups of Marfan syndrome patients and suggest distinct pathogenetic mechanisms. *J. Clin. Invest.* 94:130–37
5. Ballester R, Marchuk D, Boguski M, Saulino A, Letcher R, et al. 1990. The *NF1* locus encodes a protein functionally related to mammalian GAP and yeast IRA proteins. *Cell* 63:851–59
6. Bartels C, Horsch S. 1995. Classification of congenital arterial and venous vascular malformations. *Angiology* 46: 191–200
7. Baudrimont M, Dubas F, Joutel A, Tournier-Lasserve E, Bousser M-G. 1993. Autosomal dominant leukoen-

cephalopathy and subcortical ischemic stroke. *Stroke* 24:122–25
8. Bean WB. 1958. *Vascular Spiders and Related Lesions of the Skin.* Springfield, Ill: Thomas
9. Beutler E, Lichtman MA, Coller BS, Kipps TJ. 1995. *Williams Hematology.* New York: McGraw-Hill. 5th ed.
10. Blann A. 1993. von Willebrand factor and the endothelium in vascular disease. *Br. J. Biomed. Sci.* 50:125–34
11. Boileau C, Junien C, Collod G, Jondeau G, Dubourg O, et al. 1995. The question of heterogeneity in Marfan syndrome-In reply. *Nat. Genet.* 9:230–31
12. Boon LM, Mulliken JB, Vikkula M, Watkins H, Seidman J, et al. 1994. Assignment of a locus for dominantly inherited venous malformation to chromosome 9p. *Hum. Mol. Genet.* 3:1583–87
13. BouwesBavinck JN, Weaver DW. 1986. Subclavian artery disruption sequence: hypothesis of a vascular etiology for Poland, Klippel-Feil and Mobius anomalies. *Am. J. Med. Genet.* 23:903–18
14. Braverman IM. 1981. *Skin Signs of Systemic Disease* Philadelphia: Saunders. 2nd ed.
15. Braverman IM, Keh-Yen A. 1986. Ul-

trastructure and three-dimensional reconstruction of several macular and papular telangiectases. *J. Invest. Dermatol.* 81:489–97

16. Braverman IM, Keh A, Jacobson BS. 1990. Ultrastructure and three-dimensional organisation of the telangiectases of hereditary hemorrhagic telangiectasia. *J. Invest. Dermatol.* 95:422–27

17. Canny CLB, Oliver GL. 1976. Fluorescein angiographic findings in familial exudative vitreretinopathy. *Arch. Ophthalmol.* 94:1114–20

18. Chang E, Goldberg H. 1995. Requirements for transforming growth factor-β regulation of the pro-α2(I) collagen and plasminogen activator inhibitor-1 promoters. *J. Biol. Chem.* 270:4473–77

19. Chaudhry AP, Montes M, Cohn GA. 1978. Ultrastructure of cerebellar hemangioblastoma. *Cancer* 42:1834–50

20. Chaveau D, Pirson Y, Verellen-Dumoulin C, Macnicol A, Gonzalo A, et al. 1994. Intracranial aneurysms in autosomal dominant polycystic disease. *Kidney Int.* 45:1140–46

21. Chedid A, Jao W. 1974. Hereditary bodies of the carotid bodies and chronic obstructive pulmonary disease. *Cancer* 33:1635–41

22. Cheifetz S, Bellon T, Cales C, Vera S, Bernabeus C, et al. 1992. Endoglin is a component of the transforming growth factor-β receptor system in human endothelial cells. *J. Biol. Chem.* 267:19027–30

23. Chen F, Kishida T, Yao M, Hustad T, Glavac D, et al. 1995. Germline mutations in the von Hippel-Lindau disease tumor suppressor gene: correlations with phenotype. *Hum. Mutat.* 5:66–75

24. Chiarella F, Bricarelli FD, Lupi G, Bellotti P, Domenicucci S, et al. 1989. Familial supravalvular aortic stenosis: a genetic study. *J. Med. Genet.* 26:86–92

25. Chong LD, Traynor-Kaplan A, Bokoch GM, Schwartz MA. 1994. The small GTP-binding protein rho regulates a phosphatidylinositol 4-phosphate 5-kinase in mammalian cells. *Cell* 79:507–13

26. Clark EA, Brugge JS. 1995. Integrins and signal transduction pathways: the road taken. *Science* 268:233–39

27. Clark ER, Clark EL. 1940. Microscopic observations on the extra-endothelial cells of living mammalian blood vessels. *Am. J. Anat.* 66:2–49

28. Collod G, Babron M-C, Jondeau G, Coulon M, Weissenbach J, et al. 1994. A second locus for Marfan syndrome maps to chromosome 3p24.2-p25. *Nat. Genet.* 8:264–68

29. Colwell N, Clarke R, Robinson K, Keane F, O'Briain S, et al. 1991. Hyperhomocysteinaemia and multiple aneurysms. *Postgrad. Med. J.* 67:186–88

30. Conlon CL, Weinger RS, Cimo PL, Moake JL, Olson JD. 1978. Telangiectasia and von Willebrand's disease in two families. *Ann. Int. Med.* 89:921–24

31. Crossey PA, Foster K, Richards FM, Phipps ME, Latif F, et al. 1994. Molecular genetic investigations of the mechanism of tumorigenesis in von Hippel-Lindau disease: analysis of allele loss in VHL tumours. *Hum. Genet.* 93:53–58

32. Curran ME, Atkinson DL, Ewart AK, Morris CA, Leppert MF, et al. 1993. The elastin gene is disrupted by a translocation associated with supravalvular aortic stenosis. *Cell* 73:159–68

33. Davies PF, Robotewskyj A, Griem ML. 1994. Quantitative studies of endothelial cell adhesion. *J. Clin. Invest.* 93:2031–38

34. Davies PF, Tripathi SC. 1993. Mechanical stress mechanisms and the cell: an endothelial paradigm. *Circ. Res.* 72:239–45

35. Dejana E, Corada M, Lampugnani MG. 1995. Endothelial cell-to-cell junctions. *FASEB J.* 9:910–18

36. Dietz H, Francke U, Furthmayr H, Francomano C, De Paepe A, et al. 1995. The question of heterogeneity in Marfan syndrome. *Nat. Genet.* 9:228–29

37. Dietz HC, Pyeritz RE. 1994. Molecular genetic approaches to the study of human cardiovascular disease. *Annu. Rev. Physiol.* 56:763–96

38. Dobrin PB, Schwarcz TH, Mrkvicka R. 1990. Longitudinal retractive force in pressurized dog and human arteries. *J. Surg. Res.* 48:116–20

39. Dobyns WB, Michels VV, Groover RV, Mokri B, Trautmann JC, et al. 1987. Familial cavernous malformations of the central nervous system and retina. *Ann. Neurol.* 21:578–83

40. Dubovsky J, Zabramski JM, Kurth J, Spetzler RF, Rich SS, et al. 1995. A gene responsible for cavernous malformations of the brain maps to chromosome 7q. *Hum. Mol. Genet.* 4:453–58

41. European Polycystic Kidney Disease Consortium. 1994. The polycystic kidney disease 1 gene encodes a 14kb transcript and lies within a duplicated region on chromosome 16. *Cell* 77:881–94

42. Ewart AK, Jin W, Atkinson D, Morris CA, Keating MT. 1994. Supravalvular aortic stenosis associated with a deletion

disrupting the elastin gene. *J. Clin. Invest.* 93:1071–77

43. Fawcett J, Buckley C, Holness CL, Bird IN, Spragg JH, et al. 1995. Mapping the homotypic binding sites in CD31 and the role of CD31 adhesion in the formation of interendothelial cell contacts. *J. Cell Biol.* 128:1229–41
44. Fayad PB, Fulbright RK, Chaloupka JC, Awad IA, White RI. 1994. A prospective neurological and magnetic resonance imaging evaluation of hereditary hemorrhagic telangiectasia. *Stroke* 26:160
45. Fienman NL, Yakovac WC. 1970. Neurofibromatosis in childhood. *J. Pediatrics* 76:339–46
46. Fisher GM, Swain ML. 1985. Effects of estradiol and progesterone on the increased synthesis of collagen in atherosclerotic rabbit aortas. *Atherosclerosis* 54:177–85
47. Fishman MC, Stainier DYR. 1994. Cardiovascular development. Prospects for a genetic approach. *Circ. Res.* 74:757–63
48. Fitzpatrick TB, Eisen AZ, Wolf FK, Freedberg IM, Austen KF. 1987. *Dermatology in General Medicine.* New York: McGraw-Hill. 3rd ed.
49. Flaumenhaft R, Rifkin DB. 1992. The extracellular regulation of growth factor action. *Mol. Biol. Cell* 3:1057–65
50. Folkman J, Shing Y. 1992. Angiogenesis. *J. Biol. Chem.* 267:10931–34
51. Form DM, Pratt BM, Madri JA. 1986. Endothelial cell proliferation during angiogenesis. *Lab. Invest.* 55:521–30
52. Friesel RE, Maciag T. 1995. Molecular mechanisms of angiogenesis. *FASEB J.* 9:919–25
53. Fryburg JS, Pelegano JP, Bennett MJ, Bebin EM. 1994. Long-chain 3-hydroxyacyl-coenzyme A dehydrogenase (L-CHAD) deficiency in a patient with the Bannayan-Riley-Ruvalcaba syndrome. *Am. J. Med. Genet.* 52:97–102
54. Gabow PA. 1991. Polycystic kidney disease: clues to pathogenesis. *Kidney Int.* 40:989–96
55. Gadoth N, Hirsch M. 1980. Primary and acquired forms of moyamoya disease. *Isr. J. Med. Sci.* 16:370–77
56. Gates RR. 1946. Congenital anomalies. In *Human Genetics,* ed. RR Gates, 2:1304. New York: Macmillin
57. George EL, Georges-Labouesse EN, Patel-King RS, Rayburn H, Hynes RO. 1993. Defects in mesoderm, neural tube and vascular development in mouse embryos lacking fibronectin. *Development* 119:1079–91
58. Gerhard M, Ganz P. 1995. How do we explain the clinical benefits of estrogen? *Circulation* 92:5–8
59. Gerschwind DH, FitzPatrick M, Mischel PS, Cummings JL. 1995. Sneddon's syndrome is a thrombotic vasculopathy: neuropathologic and neuroradiologic evidence. *Neurology* 45:557–60
60. Gibbons GH, Dzau VJ. 1994. The emerging concept of vascular remodelling. *New Engl. J. Med.* 330:1431–38
61. Gorfien SF, Howard PS, Myers JC, Macarak EJ. 1990. Cyclic biaxial strain of pulmonary artery endothelial cells causes an increase in cell layer-associated fibronectin. *Am. J. Resp. Cell. Mol. Biol.* 3:421–29
62. Gralnick HR, Ginsburg D. 1995. von Willebrand disease. See Ref. 9, pp. 1458–80
63. Grimm T, Wesselhoeft H. 1980. Zur Genetik des Williams-Beuren-Syndroms und der isolierten Form der supravalvularen Aortenstenose Untersuchungen von 128 Familien. *Z. Kardiol.* 69:168–72
64. Gunel M, Awad IA, Anson J, Lifton RP. 1995. Mapping a gene causing cerebral cavernous malformation to 7q11.2-q21. *Proc. Natl. Acad. Sci. USA* 92:6620–24
65. Hanna W, McCarroll D, Lin D, Chua W, McDonald TP, et al. 1984. A study of a Caucasian family with variant von Willebrand's disease in association with vascular telangiectasia and haemoglobinopathy. *Thromb. Haemostas.* 51:275–78
66. Harris PC, Germino G, Klinger K, Landes G, van Adelsberg J. 1995. The PKD1 gene product. *Nat. Med.* 1:493
67. Hayden JG, Talner NS, Klaus SN. 1968. Cutis laxa associated with pulmonary artery stenosis. *J. Pediatr.* 72:506–9
68. Hayden MR, Reidy M. 1995. Many roads lead to atheroma. *Nat. Med.* 1:22–23
69. Hernandez D, McConville CM, Stacey M, Woods CG, Brown MM, et al. 1993. A family showing no evidence of linkage between the ataxia telangiectasia gene and chromosome 11q22–23. *J. Med. Genet.* 30:135–40
70. Holman E. 1968. *Abnormal Arteriovenous Communications.* Spingfield, Ill: Thomas. 2nd ed.
71. Hornebeck W, Flores-Delgado G, Robert L. 1993. Elastin and elastases in the pathophysiology of the arterial wall. In *Vascular Medicine,* ed. H Boccalon, pp. 145–48. Amsterdam: Excerpta Medica
72. Hoyme HE, Der Kaloustian VM, Hogg H, Entin MA, Guttmacher AE. 1992.

Possible common pathogenetic mechanisms for Poland sequence and Adams-Olivier syndrome. *Am. J. Med. Genet.* 42:398–99

73. Hughes AFW. 1935. Studies on the area vasculosa of the embryo chick I. *J. Anat.* 70:76–129

74. Ingber DE, Folkman J. 1989. How does extracellular matrix control capillary morphogenesis? *Cell* 58:803–5

75. Iruela-Arispe ML, Sage EH. 1993. Endothelial cells exhibiting angiogenesis in vitro proliferate in response to TGF-β1. *J. Cell. Biochem.* 52:414–30

76. Jensson O, Palsdottir A, Thorsteinsson L, Arnason A. 1989. The saga of cystatin C gene mutation causing amyloid angiopathy and brain hemorrhage—clinical genetics in Iceland. *Clin. Genet.* 36:368–77

76a. Johnson DW, Berg JN, Gallione CJ, McAllister KA, Warner JP, et al. 1995. A second locus for hereditary hemorrhagic telangiectasia maps to chromosome 12. *Genome Res.* 5:21–28

77. Joutel A, Bousser M-G, Biousse V, Laberge P, Chabriat H, et al. 1993. A gene for familial hemiplegic migraine maps to chromosome 19. *Nat. Genet.* 5:40–45

78. Joutel A, Ducros A, Vahedi K, Labauge P, Delrieu O, et al. 1994. Genetic heterogeneity of familial hemiplegic migraine. *Am. J. Hum. Genet.* 55:1166–72

79. Junqueira LC, Carneiro J, Kelley RO. 1995. *Basic Histology*, pp. 202–17. Norwalk, CT: Appleton & Lange. 8th ed.

80. Kainulainen K, Karttunen L, Puhakka L, Sakai L, Peltonen L. 1994. Mutations in the fibrillin gene responsible for dominant ectopia lentis and neonatal Marfan syndrome. *Nat. Genet.* 6:64–69

81. Kalimo H, Sourander P, Jarvi O, Hakola P. 1994. Vascular changes in blood-brain barrier damage in the pathogenesis of polycystic lipomembranous osteodysplasia with sclerosing leukoencephalopathy (membranous lipodystrophy). *Acta Neurol. Scand.* 89:353–61

82. Kamiya A, Togawa T. 1980. Adaptive regulation of wall shear stress to flow change in the canine carotid artery. *Am. J. Physiol.* 239:H14–21

83. Karttunen L, Raghunath M, Lonnqvist L, Peltonen L. 1994. A compound-heterozygous Marfan patient: two defective fibrillin alleles result in a lethal phenotype. *Am. J. Hum. Genet.* 55:1083–91

84. Kim KJ, Li B, Winer J, Armanini M, Gillett N, et al. 1993. Inhibition of vascular endothelial growth factor-induced angiogenesis suppresses tumour growth in vivo. *Nature* 362:841–44

85. Kitaharo T, Ariga N, Yamaura A, Makino H, Maki Y. 1979. Familial occurence of moya-moya disease: report of three Japanese families. *J. Neurol. Neurosurg. Psych.* 42:208–14

86. Kousseff BG, Gilbert-Barness EF. 1989. "Vascular neurofibromatosis" and infantile gangrene. *Am. J. Med. Genet.* 34:221–26

87. Kretzschmar HA, Wagner H, Hubner G, Danek A, Witt TN, et al. 1990. Aneurysms and vacuolar degeneration of cerebral arteries in late-onset acid maltase deficiency. *J. Neurol. Sci.* 98: 169–83

88. Kuivaniemi H, Prockop DJ, Wu Y, Madhatheri SL, Kleinert C, et al. 1993. Exclusion of mutations in the gene for type III collagen (COL3A1) as a common cause of intracranial aneurysms or cervical artery dissections. *Neurology* 43:2652–58

89. Kuivaniemi H, Tromp C, Prockop DJ. 1991. Genetic causes of abdominal aortic aneurysms: unlearning at least part of what the textbooks say. *J. Clin. Invest.* 88:1441–44

90. Kwaan HC, Silverman S. 1973. Fibrinolytic activity in lesions of hereditary hemorrhagic telangiectasia. *Arch. Dermatol.* 107:571–73

91. Langille BL, O'Donnell F. 1986. Reductions in arterial diameter produced by chronic decreases in blood flow are endothelium-dependent. *Science* 231: 405–7

92. Larbre F, Loire R, Guibaud P, Lauras B, Weill B. 1971. Observation clinique et anatomique d'un anevrysme de l'aorte au cours d'une sclerose tubereuse de Bourneville. *Arch. Fr. Pediatr.* 28:975–84

93. Latif F, Tory K, Gnarra J, Yao M, Duh FM, et al. 1993. Identification of the von Hippel-Lindau disease tumor suppressor gene. *Science* 260:1317–20

94. Lee B, Godfrey M, Vitale E, Hori H, Mattei M-G, et al. 1991. Linkage of Marfan syndrome and a phenotyically related disorder to two different fibrillin genes. *Nature* 352:330–34

95. Li Y, Bollag G, Clark R, Stevens J, Conroy L, et al. 1992. Somatic mutations in the neurofibromatosis 1 gene in human tumours. *Cell* 69:275–81

96. Li Y, Muller B, Fuhrmann C, van Nouhuys CE, Laqua H, et al. 1992. The autosomal dominant familial exudative vitreoretinopathy locus maps on 11q and is closely linked to D11S533. *Am. J. Hum. Genet.* 51:749–54

97. Madri JA, Merwin JR, Bell L, Basson CT, Kocher O, et al. 1992. Interactions of matrix components and soluble fac-

tors in vascular responses to injury. In *Endothelial Cell Dysfunctions*, ed. N Simionescu M Simionescu, pp. 11–30. New York: Plenum

98. Makos MM, McComb RD, Hart MN, Bennett DR. 1987. Alpha-glucosidase deficiency and basilar artery aneurysm: report of a sibship. *Ann. Neurol.* 22:629–33

99. Martin DMA, Boys CWG, Ruf W. 1995. Tissue factor molecular recognition and cofactor function. *FASEB J.* 9:852–59

100. Maserati E, Ottolini A, Veggiotti P, Lanzi G, Pasquali F. 1988. Ataxia-without-telangiectasia in two sisters with rearrangements of chromosomes 7 and 14. *Clin. Genet.* 34:283–87

101. McAllister KA, Grogg KM, Johnson DW, Gallione CJ, Baldwin MA, et al. 1994. Endoglin, a TGF-β binding protein of endothelial cells, is the gene for hereditary haemorrhagic telangiectasia type 1. *Nat. Genet.* 8:345–51

102. McIntire LV. 1994. Bioengineering and vascular biology. *Ann. Biomed. Eng.* 22:2–13

103. Mesri EA, Federoff HJ, Brownlee M. 1994. Expression of vascular endothelial growth factor from a defective herpes simplex virus type I amplicon vector induces angiogenesis in mice. *Circ. Res.* 76:161–67

104. Milewicz DM, Grossfield J, Cao S-N, Kielty C, Covitz W, et al. 1995. A mutation in *FBN1* disrupts profibrillin processing and results in isolated skeletal features of the Marfan syndrome. *J. Clin. Invest.* 95:2373–78

105. Millauer B, Shawver LK, Plate KH, Risau W, Ullrich A. 1994. Glioblastoma growth inhibited in vivo by a dominant-negative Flk-1 mutant. *Nature* 367:576–79

106. Moses MA, Sudhalter J, Langer R. 1990. Identification of an inhibitor of neovascularisation from cartilage. *Science* 248:1408–10

107. Mulliken JB, Young AE. 1988. *Vascular Birthmarks: Hemangiomas and Malformations.* Philadelphia: Saunders

108. Mustonen T, Alitalo K. 1995. Endothelial cell receptor tyrosine kinases involved in angiogenesis. *J. Cell Biol.* 129:895–98

109. Neil-Dwyer G, Bartlett JR, Nicholls AC, Narcisi P, Pope FM. 1983. Collagen deficiency and ruptured cerebral aneurysms. A clinical and biochemical study. *J. Neurosurg.* 59:16–20

110. Nerem RM, Girard PR. 1990. Hemodynamic influences on vascular endothelial biology. *Toxicol. Pathol.* 18:572–82

111. Nickerson E, Greenberg F, Keating MT, McCaskill C, Shaffer LG. 1995. Deletions of the elastin gene at 7q11.23 occur in 90% of patients with Williams syndrome. *Am. J. Hum. Genet.* 56:1156–61

112. O'Connor WN, Davies JB, Geissler R, Cottrill CM, Noonan JA, et al. 1985. Supravalvular aortic stenosis: clinical and pathological observations in six patients. *Arch. Pathol. Lab. Med.* 109:179–85

113. Ohno M, Cooke JP, Dzau VJ, Gibbons GH. 1995. Fluid shear stress induces endothelial transforming growth factor β-1 transcription and production. *J. Clin. Invest.* 95:1363–69

114. Paigen K. 1995. A miracle enough: the power of mice. *Nat. Med.* 1:215–20

115. Pasyk KA, Argenta LC, Erickson RP. 1984. Familial vascular malformations. *Clin. Genet.* 26:221–27

116. Paulus W, Baur I, Huettner C, Schmausser B, Roggendorf W, et al. 1995. Effects of transforming growth factor-β₁ on collagen synthesis, integrin expression, adhesion and invasion of glioma cells. *J. Neuropath. Exp. Neurol.* 54:236–44

117. Pavalko FM, Otey CA. 1994. Role of adhesion molecule cytoplasmic domains in mediating interactions with the cytoskeleton. *Proc. Soc. Exp. Biol. Med.* 205:282–93

118. Plate KH, Breier G, Weich HA, Risau W. 1992. Vascular endothelial growth factor is a potent tumor angiogenesis factor in human gliomas in vivo. *Nature* 359:845–48

119. Plauchu H, de Chadarevian JPD, Bideau A, Robert J-M. 1989. Age-related profile of hereditary hemorrhagic telangiectasia in an epidemiologically recruited population. *Am. J. Med. Genet.* 32:291–97

120. Plukker JT, Koops HS, Molenaar I, Vermey A, ten Kate LP, et al. 1988. Malignant hemangiopericytoma in three kindred members of one family. *Cancer* 61:841–48

121. Pope FM. 1993. Molecular abnormalities of collagen. In *Oxford Textbook of Rheumatology*, ed. PH Maddison, DA Isenberg, P Woo, DN Glass, 1:204–32. Oxford: Oxford Univ. Press

122. Quick AJ. 1967. Telangiectasia: its relationship to the Minot-von Willebrand syndrome. *Am. J. Med. Sci.* 254:585–601

123. Rambaud J-C, Galian A, Touchard G, Morel-Maroger L, Mikol J, et al. 1986. Digestive tract and renal small vessel hyalinosis, idiopathic nonarteriosclerotic intracerebral calcifications, retinal

ischemic syndrome, and phenotypic abnormalities. *Gastroenterology* 90:930–38

124. Rebolla M, Val JF, Garijo F, Quintana F, Berciano J. 1983. Livido reticularis and cerebrovascular lesions (Sneddon's syndrome). *Brain* 106:965–79

125. Rendu H. 1896. Epistaxis repetees chez un sujet porteur de petits angiomes cutanes et muquez. *Gaz. Hop.* 135:132–33

126. Resnick N, Gimbrone MA. 1995. Hemodynamic forces are complex regulators of endothelial gene expression. *FASEB J.* 9:874–82

127. Reubi F. 1945. Neurofibromatose et lesions vasculaires. *Schweiz. Med. Wochenschr.* 21:463–65

128. Rhodin JAG. 1968. Ultrastructure of mammalian venous capillaries, venules and small collecting veins. *J. Ultrastruc. Res.* 25:452–500

129. Riccardi VM. 1992. Type I neurofibromatosis and the pediatric patient. *Curr. Prob. Pediatr.* 22:66–106

130. Rice JS, Fischer DS. 1962. Blue rubber-bleb nevus syndrome. *Arch. Dermatol.* 86:163–71

131. Rigamonti D, Hadley MN, Drayer BP, Johnson PC, Hoenig-Rigamonti K, et al. 1988. Cerebral cavernous malformations. Incidence and familial occurrence. *New Engl. J. Med.* 319:343–47

132. Risau W. 1995. Differentiation of endothelium. *FASEB J.* 9:926–33

133. Ronkainen A, Hernesniemi J, Ryynanen M. 1993. Familial subarachnoid hemorrhage in East Finland, 1977–1990. *Neurosurgery* 33:787–97

134. Ryder REJ, Mir MA, Freeman EA. 1986. *An Aid to the MRCP Short Cases.* Oxford: Blackwell Scientific

135. Salyer WR, Salyer DC. 1974. The vascular lesions of neurofibromatosis. *Angiology* 25:510–19

136. Sato TN, Tozawa Y, Deutsch U, Wolburg-Buchholz K, Fujiwara Y, et al. 1995. Distinct roles of the receptor tyrosine kinases Tie-1 and Tie-2 in blood vessel formation. *Nature* 376:70–74

137. Savitsky K, Bar-Shira A, Gilad S, Rotman G, Ziv Y, et al. 1995. A single ataxia telangiectasia gene with a product similar to PI-3 kinase. *Science* 268:1749–53

138. Schievink WI, Mokri B, Michels VV, Piepgras DG. 1991. Familial association of intracranial aneurysms and cervical artery dissections. *Stroke* 22:1426–30

139. Schnaper HW, Grant DS, Stetler-Stevenson WG, Fridman R, D'Orazi G, et al. 1993. Type IV collagenase(s) and TIMPs modulate endothelial cell morphogenesis in vitro. *J. Cell. Physiol.* 156:235–46

140. Schwartz SM, Benditt EP. 1973. Cell replication in the aortic endothelium. *Lab. Invest.* 28:699–707

141. Schwartz SM, Liaw L. 1993. Growth control and morphogenesis in the development and pathology of arteries. *J. Cardiovasc. Pharmacol.* 2:S31–49

142. Schweiki D, Itin A, Soffer D, Keshet E. 1992. Vascular endothelial growth factor induced by hypoxia may mediate hypoxia-initiated angiogenesis. *Nature* 359:843–45

143. Seizinger BR, Rouleau GA, Ozelius LJ, Lane AH, Farmer GE, et al. 1988. Von Hippel-Lindau disease maps to the region of chromosome 3 associated with renal cell carcinoma. *Nature* 332:268–69

144. Sholley MM, Ferguson GP, Seibel HR, Montour JL, Wilson JD. 1984. Mechanisms of neovascularisation: vascular sprouting can occur without proliferation of endothelial cells. *Lab. Invest.* 51:624–34

145. Shovlin CL, Hughes JMB, Tuddenham EGD, Temperley I, Perembelon YFN, et al. 1994. A gene for hereditary haemorrhagic telangiectasia maps to chromosome 9q3. *Nat. Genet.* 6:205–9

146. Shovlin CL, Winstock AR, Peters AM, Jackson JE, Hughes JMB. 1995. Medical complications of pregnancy in hereditary haemorrhagic telangiectasia. *Q. J. Med.* 88:In press

147. Spence AM, Rubenstein LJ. 1975. Cerebellar capillary hemangioblastoma: its histogenesis studied by organ culture and electron microscopy. *Cancer* 35:326–41

148. Steele JG, Nath PU, Burn J, Porteous MEM. 1993. An association between migrainous aura and hereditary haemorrhagic telangiectasia. *Headache* 33:145–48

149. Stone EM, Kimura AE, Folk JC, Bennett SR, Nichols BE, et al. 1992. Genetic linkage of autosomal dominant neovascular inflammatory vitreoretinopathy to chromosome 11q13. *Hum. Mol. Genet.* 1:685–89

150. Thompson RW, Holmes DR, Mertens RA, Liao S, Botney MD, et al. 1995. Production and localisation of 92-Kilodalton gelatinase in abdominal aortic aneurysms. *J. Clin. Invest.* 96:318–26

151. Thurston G, Baldwin AL. 1994. Endothelial actin cytoskeleton in rat mesentery microvasculature. *Am. J. Physiol.* 266:H1896–H1909

152. Tomsick TA, Lukin RR, Chambers AA, Benton C. 1976. Neurofibromatosis and

intracranial arterial occlusive disease. *J. Neuroradiol.* 11:229–34

153. Toriello HV, Graff RG, Florentine MF, Lacina S, Moore WD. 1988. Scalp and limb defects with cutis marmorata telangiectica congenita: Adams-Olivier syndrome? *Am. J. Med. Genet.* 29:269–76

154. Tournier-Lasserve E, Joutel A, Melki J, Weissenbach J, Lathrop GM, et al. 1993. Cerebral autosomal dominant arteriopathy with subcortical infarcts and leukoencephalopathy maps to chromosome 19q12. *Nat. Genet.* 3:256–59

155. Tromp G, Wu Y, Prockop DJ, Madhatheri SL, Kleinert C, et al. 1993. Sequencing of cDNA from 50 unrelated patients reveals that mutations in the triple-helical domain of type III procollagen are an infrequent cause of aortic aneurysms. *J. Clin. Invest.* 91:2539–45

156. van Adelsberg JS, Franck D. 1995. The *PKD1* gene produces a developmentally regulated protein in mesenchyme and vasculature. *Nat. Med.* 1:359–64

157. Van Cutsem E. 1993. Oestrogen-progesterone, a new therapy of bleeding gastrointestinal vascular malformations. *Acta Gastro-Enterol. Belg.* 56:2–10

158. van Duinen SG, Castano EM, Prelli F, Bots GTAB, Luyendijk W, et al. 1987. Hereditary cerebral hemorrhage with amyloidosis in patients of Dutch origin is related to Alzheimer's disease. *Proc. Natl. Acad. Sci. USA* 84:5991–94

159. Vincent P, Plauchu H, Hazan J, Faure S, Weissenbach J, et al. 1995. A third locus for hereditary haemorrhagic telangiectasia maps to chromosome 12q. *Hum. Mol. Genet.* 4:945–49

160. Wang N, Butler JP, Ingber DE. 1993. Mechanotransduction across the cell surface and through the cytoskeleton. *Science* 260:1124–27

161. Ward AS. 1992. Aortic aneurysmal disease. A general dilating diathesis? *Arch. Surg.* 127:990–91

162. Weber BHF, Vogt G, Pruett RC, Stohr H, Felbor U. 1994. Mutations in the tissue inhibitor of metalloproteinases-3 (TIMP3) in patients with Sorsby's fundus dystrophy. *Nat. Genet.* 8:352–56

163. Weber BHF, Vogt G, Wolz W, Ives EJ, Ewing CC. 1994. Sorsby's fundal dystrophy is genetically linked to chro-

mosome 22q13-qter. *Nat. Genet.* 7:158–61

164. Whaley JM, Naglich J, Gelbert L, Hsai YE, Lamiell JM, et al. 1994. Germ-line mutations in the von Hippel-Lindau tumor supressor gene are similar to somatic von Hippel-Lindau aberrations in sporadic renal cell carcinoma. *Am. J. Hum. Genet.* 55:1092–102

165. Wilson PD, Sherwood AC. 1991. Tubulocystic epithelium. *Kidney Int.* 39:450–63

166. Wizigmann-Voos S, Breier G, Risau W, Plate KH. 1995. Up-regulation of vascular endothelial growth factor and its receptors in von Hippel-Lindau disease-associated and sporadic hemangioblastomas. *Cancer Res.* 55:1358–64

167. Woollard HH, Harpman JA. 1937. The relation between the size of the artery and the capillary bed in the embryo. *J. Anat.* 72:18–22

168. Wrana JL, Attisano L, Wieser R, Ventura F, Massagué J. 1994. Mechanism of activation of the TGF-β receptor. *Nature* 370:341–47

169. Xu G, O'Connell P, Viskochil D, Cawthon R, Robertson M, et al. 1990. The neurofibromatosis type 1 gene encodes a protein related to GAP. *Cell* 62:599–608

170. Yamaguchi Y, Mann DM, Ruoslahti E. 1990. Negative regulation of transforming growth factor-β by the proteoglycan decorin. *Nature* 346:281–84

171. Yamamura T, Nishimura M, Shirabe T, Fujita M. 1987. Subcortical vascular encephalopathy in a normotensive, young adult with premature baldness and spondylitis deformans: a clinicopathological study and review of the literature. *J. Neurol. Sci.* 78:175–88

172. Yang JT, Rayburn H, Hynes RO. 1993. Embryonic mesodermal defects in $\alpha_5$ integrin-deficient mice. *Development* 119:1093–105

173. Young AE. 1988. Pathogenesis of vascular malformations. See Ref. 107, pp. 107–13.

174. Zhang MC, Giro M, Quaglino D, Davidson JM. 1995. Transforming growth factor-β reverses a posttranscriptional defect in elastin synthesis in a cutis laxa skin fibroblast strain. *J. Clin. Invest.* 95:986–94

## ADDED IN PROOF

175. Henkemeyer M, Rossi DJ, Holmyard DP, Puri MC, Mbamalu G, et al. 1995. Vascular system defects and neuronal apoptosis in mice lacking Ras ATPase-activating protein. *Nature* 377:695–701

Annu. Rev. Physiol. 1996. 58:509–21

# THE POLYCLONAL ORIGIN OF MYOCYTE LINEAGES

## Takashi Mikawa and Donald A. Fischman

Department of Cell Biology and Anatomy, Cornell University Medical College, 1300 York Avenue, New York, NY 10021

KEY WORDS:   heart development, retrovirus, atrium, ventricle, Purkinje fiber

### ABSTRACT

The heart beat is coordinated by the integrated activities of three myocyte subpopulations: atrial myocytes, ventricular myocytes, and cells of the cardiac conduction system. In this review we discuss the classic fate map and recent retroviral cell lineage studies to better understand the origin, timing, and mechanisms regulating (a) the formation of these three myocyte lineages and (b) the morphogenetic plan underlying formation of the myocardial walls and the conduction system.

## Heart Morphogenesis

The first morphogenetic event of heart development is the formation of two endothelial tubes by cells segregating from splanchnic mesodermal plates (the cardiogenic mesoderm), which form an anterolateral crescent flanking Hensen's node (58, 59, 62; Figure 1.). As a consequence of neurulation and ventral convergence of the lateral body folds, the two endothelial tubes, which contain epithelioid cardiac mesoderm, fuse at the midline. This fusion of bilateral cardiac primordia gives rise to a single tubular heart consisting of two epithelial layers: a central endocardium and a peripheral myocardium, the two separated by a gelatinous extracellular matrix, termed cardiac jelly, a secretory product of the myocardial cells (43). Vascular and connective tissue cells are absent from the heart at this stage, entering later as the epicardial mantle enfolds the myocardium (see below). Myocardial contractions begin during this double-walled stage of heart formation; initial pulsations are observed on the right convex surface of the heart at stage 10 in the chicken (26), spreading over the whole myocardium by stage 11. With continued development, the epithelioid myocardium undergoes a series of morphogenetic steps: (a) Asymmetric elongation of the tubular heart, greater on the right than the left, creates a dextral, S-shaped loop; (b) septation of the tubular heart by endocardial cushions

509

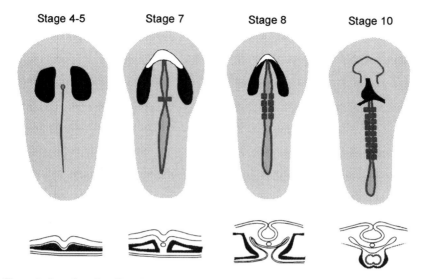

*Figure 1*   Location of cardiogenic cells in the early chicken embryo (modified from Reference 13). Ventral views of embryos (*top*) and cross-sections of heart-forming region of each embryonic stage (*bottom*) are presented. Undifferentiated cardiogenic primordia (stages 4–8) and differentiated myocytes (stage 10) are marked (*solid*).

generates two chambers—atrial and ventricular—which later partition into the four compartments characteristic of the adult heart; (*c*) trabeculation accompanies marked thickening of the ventricular walls; and (*d*) the atrial chambers shift posteriorly and cranially to assume their adult position rostral and dorsal to the ventricles.

## Separate Origin of Atrial and Ventricular Myocyte Lineages

Fate mapping studies with chicken/quail chimeras, dye marking, or grafts of tissues labeled with [3H]-thymidine, have shown that a subset of cells in the rostral half of the primitive streak migrate during early gastrulation to the cardiogenic area rostrolateral to Hensen's node (14, 59). This caudal-to-rostral migration of cardiac mesoderm is directed by the underlying endoderm and involves a fibronectin network that forms between the two embryonic layers (39, 40). During fusion of the bilateral heart primordia, cells in the epithelioid myocardium begin expression of muscle-specific genes and proteins, substantially before initiation of the heart beat (3, 27, 41). By this stage, cells in the caudal region of the presumptive myocardium can be distinguished as atrial myocytes from those in the rostral region differentiating as ventricular myocytes, based on electrophysiological properties (11, 31) and the expression of contractile protein genes (51, 76). Thus two distinct myocyte lineages, atrial and ventricular, both arise from a portion of mesoderm migrating to the cardiogenic area through the rostral half of the primitive streak at early gastrulation.

These results raise an important question concerning the timing and mechanisms generating two myocyte lineages within the cardiogenic mesoderm. It has been shown that more rostral cells of the primitive streak form more rostral outflow regions of the tubular heart and that the more caudal cells form the more caudal inflow regions (14, 59). However, this spatial relationship is not absolute; the region of the primitive streak where cardiogenic mesoderm arises contains progenitors of endothelial cells that form the extracardiac vessels (14). Thus the fate map based on migration patterns of a group of cells does not provide sufficiently high resolution to settle the question of whether the atrial and ventricular lineages segregate at the time of gastrulation or if both lineages arise from a common progenitor present in cardiogenic mesoderm.

A direct answer to this question was obtained in cell lineage studies using single cell-tagging procedures in chicken (45) and zebrafish (63) embryos. Retroviral-mediated genetic marking and subsequent fate analyses of individual cells present in the cardiogenic mesoderm proved that ventricular myocytes arise from cell populations that are distinct from those generating the atrial myocyte lineage during chicken embryogenesis (45). The rostral cardiogenic mesoderm only generated the ventricular myocyte lineage, whereas cells in the caudal region entered the atrial myocyte lineage. In no case did a single cell in the cardiogenic area produce both cell lineages. Clone-based fate maps based on vital dye injections of single blastomeres in zebrafish embryos showed that atrial and ventricular myocyte lineages separate at the midblastula stage (63). Furthermore, mesodermal explants isolated from the caudal region of the cardiogenic area just after gastrulation differentiate into atrial but not ventricular myocytes in culture (75). These results indicate that these two myocyte lineages are already established when mesodermal cells migrate into the cardiogenic area; the ventricular myocytes arise from a subpopulation residing in the rostral regions of the cardiogenic mesodermal plates, whereas the atrial myocyte lineage originates from cells present in the caudal regions of cardiogenic mesoderm.

To date, neither extracellular signals nor intracellular *trans*-acting factors that induce these two cardiomyocyte lineages have been identified. However, caudal cardiac mesoderm (atrial progenitor) undergoes a change in beat rate to that characteristic of prospective ventricular myocytes if placed in the rostral heart-forming region (61). Ectopic retinoic acid treatment of chicken embryos soon after formation of cardiogenic mesoderm induces the expression of atrial myosin heavy chain in presumptive ventricular myocytes (74). Such plasticity is lost after atrial and ventricular myocyte phenotypes become apparent. These observations suggest that myogenic progenitors within the cardiogenic mesoderm remain bipotential until overt myocyte differentiation is evident; terminal differentiation into either atrial or ventricular phenotypes may occur in response to positionally defined extracellular signal(s).

## Multi-Layered Myocardial Wall Formation from the Epithelioid Myocardium

Although cardiogenic progenitors retain a limited degree of plasticity during terminal differentiation, their migration within the mesodermal plates appears limited (10). Cells within the cardiogenic plates became epithelialized soon after their migration from the primitive streak (38, 56), minimizing the intermixing of myogenic cells within the mesoderm and refining the rostral-caudal boundaries defining the zones forming ventricular and atrial myocytes. Epithelial characteristics of the cardiac mesoderm are maintained during fusion of the bilateral mesodermal plates and until all cells in the outer myocardium of the heart tube differentiate into either atrial or ventricular contractile myocytes (43). Once these two myocyte lineages complete their terminal differentiation, the epithelioid, contractile myocytes generate daughter cells that delaminate basally and migrate within the cardiac jelly toward the endocardium. This active proliferation and cellular migration generates the trabeculated pattern characteristic of the avascular ventricular myocardium. Retroviral cell lineage procedures have been useful in defining the fate of individual myocytes during trabeculation, subsequent thickening and multi-layering of the ventricular myocardial wall (44–46).

Myocardial wall morphogenesis can be divided into four major steps (Figure 2). (a) The differentiated, epithelioid myocytes give rise to a series of progeny that undergo an epithelial-mesenchymal transformation and migrate more vertically than horizontally within the cardiac jelly, creating ridge-like protrusions (trabeculae) into the endocardial lumen. During this migration, intermingling of progeny from different parental myocytes occurs to a limited extent in the looping tubular heart. (b) Daughter cells of these intermingled progenitors then form expanding subcolonies that exhibit less migratory activity. Continued cell division further enlarges these subcolonies to form overlapping sectors that span the entire thickness of the myocardium. The orientation of the elongated myocytes within each growth sector changes at different depths of the myocardium. (c) Gradients of myocyte proliferation are evident across the myocardial wall, greater at peripheral than deeper layers, which results in the formation of the cone- or wedge-shaped sectors that are the fundamental growth units of the myocardial wall. Sector sizes are larger in the left than in the right ventricle. The interventricular septum consists of cones of more

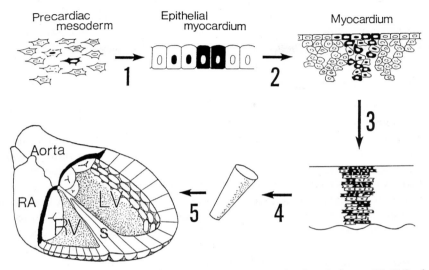

*Figure 2*  Proposed model for myocardial wall formation (modified from Reference 44). Cells of the precardiac mesoderm are labeled with the retrovirus-expressing cytoplasmic β-galactosidase (*black cells*) or the virus-expressing nuclear-targeted β-galactosidase (*black nuclei*). These cells form an epithelium in cardiogenic primodia at HH-stages 5–7 (step 1). As the cells continue to proliferate and the myocardium develops (step 2), the *trans*-mural growth units become apparent. Note that the growth units contain intermingled cytoplasmic and nuclear-tagged clones. The cells then differentiate and form intercalated discs (step 3), and cell migrations now cease. The mature cone-shaped growth units enlarge (step 4) and these form the mature myocardial walls. Note the elongated shape of the cones in the septum, the smaller growth units in the RV as compared with the LV. Abbreviations: RA, right atrium; RV, right ventricle; LV, left ventricle; S, septum.

axially elongated dimensions than those in the lateral walls. (*d*) Two-dimensional arrays of these cone-shaped growth units give rise to the three-dimensional ovoid structure of the ventricular walls.

Thus the thickened and multi-layered ventricular myocardium is defined by the locally regulated migration and proliferation of progeny derived from individual epithelioid parental myocytes. Among growth factors expressed in the heart, receptor-mediated fibroblast growth factor (FGF) signaling appears to be an endogenous mitogen necessary for myocyte proliferation. Cardiogenic mesodermal cells exhibit a decrease in proliferation in culture when they are incubated with antisense-oligonucleotides to FGF (64). Blockage of FGF-receptor functions with a dominant-negative mutant or antisense RNA results in suppression of myocyte proliferation in vivo during chicken embryonic heart development (50). N-cadherin, a calcium-dependent cell adhesion molecule

(65), plays a role in the regulation of myocyte migration (53), in addition to its know functions as a molecular component of the intercalated discs, which are sites for connexin-mediated electrical coupling between contractile myocytes and the anchorage of myofibrils at the cell membrane (16).

## Cardiac Conduction System

After formation of the tubular heart but before it begins contraction, the epithelioid myocytes become electrically active. Action potentials are first detected in the posterior inflow tract, the presumptive sinus venosus and atrium, and impulses propagate to the rostral end of the heart through gap junctions between the presumptive myocytes (31). At this stage, the pacemaker regions are localized in both right and left inflow tracts, later being restricted to the left side (31, 74). Although all myocytes of the tubular heart have the potential to generate spontaneous action potentials, this caudal-to-rostral pattern of electrical propagation, initiated by sino-atrial pacemakers, produces a caudal-to-rostral contractile wave in the tubular heart that permits effective pumping of the blood prior to the formation of cardiac valves.

Unlike the tubular heart, rhythmic contraction of the mature heart is coordinated by a specialized tissue called the cardiac conduction system (CCS). This system consists of four major components: (*a*) the sinoatrial node (SA-node) and its variably organized short branches in the wall of the right atrium; (*b*) the atrioventricular node (AV-node) lying in the posterior-inferior part of the interatrial septum just above the opening of the coronary sinus; (*c*) the atrioventricular bundle (AV-bundle, bundle of His) arising from the AV-node, which separates into right and left branches traversing the dense connective tissue barrier of the cardiac skeleton that separates atria and ventricles, thereby entering the muscular, interventricular septum; (*d*) the Purkinje fibers, a network of conducting fibers in the ventricular myocardium. For convenience, components (*a*), (*b*), and (*c*) are termed central elements of the CCS; the Purkinje fibers are considered peripheral elements of this system. Pacemaker function in the mature heart resides in the SA-node. Action potentials initiated by the SA-node spread through the contractile myocytes of both atria initiating their contraction. Unlike the tubular heart, electrical signals of the atrial myocytes do not propagate directly to the ventricular mycocytes. Instead, the impulses first converge on the AV-node, where after a brief delay, they propagate rapidly through AV-bundle and its branched limbs, finally spreading into ventricular muscle via the intramural network of Purkinje fibers (36, 69). Mechanisms governing the differentiation and morphogenesis of the CCS have been poorly understood, largely because of uncertainties concerning the origin and lineage relationships of its cellular components.

## Neural Crest vs Myocyte Origin of the Conduction System

In addition to their anatomical properties, cells of the CCS can be distinguished from contractile myocytes with appropriate molecular probes. Conduction cells contain a unique set of $K^+$ and $Ca^{2+}$ channels for pacemaker activity (5, 6, 25) and unique connexins found at their gap-junctional electrical connections (1, 22–24, 32). Conduction cells express genes usually restricted to neurons or skeletal muscle fibers, e.g. neurofilament proteins, brain-associated glycoproteins, and slow-type skeletal myosin heavy chain (17, 19, 60). In the chicken, these unique molecular characteristics of the conduction cells become evident at embryonic day E10 (21), long after neural crest-derived autonomic cells (33) and coronary vascular cells (47, 57) migrate into the heart at E3–4. The coexpression of neural and muscle genes together with arrival of these migratory cell populations has led to suggestions of two possible origins, myogenic (54) and neural crest (18, 19), for this specialized tissue.

In the human embryonic heart, a ring-like cluster of cells near the AV junction has been mapped as an initiation site for the conduction system (73). In the chicken heart, expression of a homeobox gene *Msx-2* at E2 is restricted to a ring-like cluster of cells, the primary ring, near the AV junction that colocalizes with the developing central conduction system (7). Differentiation of the Purkinje fiber network first becomes evident at E10 (21), but *Msx-2* expression is absent from the peripheral components of the conduction system (7). Based on this central-to-peripheral sequence of conduction system development, and the expression pattern of *Msx-2*, the cells forming the primary ring of the tubular heart are thought to provide the precursors for both central and peripheral elements of the CCS (7, 36, 73). A clear resolution of these lineage relationships has now been provided with retroviral cell-labeling procedures (23).

## Purkinje Fibers Arise from Contractile Ventricular Myocytes

In the chicken heart, the Purkinje fiber network is identified as a tissue branching in close association with peripheral branches of the coronary arterial bed (9, 36, 68). In the embryonic heart, the differentiating Purkinje fibers can first be detected as cells expressing abundant levels of connexin, Cx42, in close association with the growing coronary arteries at E10, but not earlier (21, 23). As described above, all cells in the epithelioid myocardium of the tubular heart differentiate into contractile myocytes by the end of E2 (43). However, cells of the cardiac neural crest begin their migration from the embryonic hind brain at E2–3, entering the heart at E4 to form cardiac ganglia (33). Therefore, if Purkinje fibers are of neural crest origin, their precursors must be absent from the heart before E3. On the other hand, if the conduction cells are of myogenic origin, the precursors must be present in the beating tubular heart at E3.

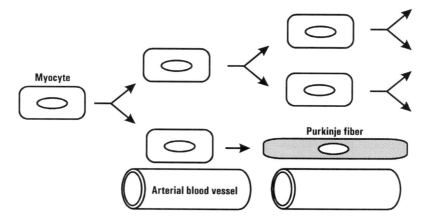

Myocyte

Purkinje fiber

Arterial blood vessel

*Figure 3* Morphogenetic steps involved in the terminal differentiation of Purkinje fibers within the myocyte lineage (23). (*a*) Vasculogenic formation of coronary blood vessels (44, 47) occurs mainly in the post-septation phase of heart development. (*b*) Only subpopulations of the clonally related, beating myocytes undergo Purkinje fiber differentiation in the perivascular region of developing coronary arteries. (*c*) Working myocardial cells increase in number by cell division, whereas Purkinje cells soon withdraw from the mitotic cycle.

Retroviral tagging of single contractile myocytes in the E3 tubular heart and their analysis at E14 and E18 have revealed that a subset of clonally related myocytes differentiates into conductile Purkinje fibers, invariably in close spatial association with developing coronary arteries (23). Importantly, in no case did a clone containing both contractile myocytes and Purkinje fibers include cells of the central conduction system such as the AV-bundles or SA components. These data indicate that Purkinje fibers arise from a subpopulation of contractile myocytes in close proximity to the developing coronary arterial bed; the peripheral CCS appears to have a different parental lineage from that of the central conduction system (Figure 3).

Unfortunately, direct cell-lineage data for the origin of the central conduction system are not yet available. Although a number of morphological studies have suggested that the primary ring provides progenitors for both the central and peripheral conduction systems (7, 36, 73), cells in this region cease their proliferation very early in development (66). Taken together with evidence of the local recruitment of Purkinje fibers from contractile myocytes (23), these data do not support an hypothesis that the branched network of the entire CCS is established by outgrowth from the primary ring. Rather, the lineage data suggest independent origins for central and peripheral elements of the CCS. It remains to be seen how the central and peripheral components link in situ to form an integrated conduction system.

## Potential Involvement of Coronary Arteries and Neural Crest Derivatives in Purkinje Fiber Differentiation

Based on the close spatio-temporal relationship between Purkinje fiber differentiation and coronary blood vessel development, an inductive role of the coronary vasculature on Purkinje fiber differentiation has been proposed (23). It has been shown that coronary arteries do not arise by an angiogenic outgrowth from the root of the aorta. Coronary precursors migrate into the tubular heart from extracardiac mesenchyme (47, 57) along with the proepicardial sheet (28, 29). In the avian embryo, movement of these coronary precursors into the heart begins at E3 (47, 57). Retroviral cell lineage (47) and histological studies (4, 72) have revealed that following inward migration, vasculogenic cells initially form discontinuous endothelial channels; later fusion of these endothelial channels and their connection to the aorta establishes the closed coronary vascular network. Smooth muscle cells migrate to and ensheathe the primary endothelial channels. Coincident with this early vasculogenic process, induction of Cx42 becomes apparent exclusively in myocyte subpopulations juxtaposed to developing coronary arteries but not to veins (23). If coronary arteries play a role in the recruitment of Purkinje fibers from contractile myocytes, the vessel network may be a key factor in defining the branching pattern of the peripheral conduction system.

Evidence also exists that neural crest-derived cells affect the development of coronary arteries. Ablation of the cardiac neural crest alters the pattern of the coronary arterial tree (15, 30). Apparently, association of neural crest derivatives with developing blood vessels is necessary for the survival of branches of the coronary artery system (71). Thus cell-lineage studies prove a myogenic origin for the Purkinje fibers, but neural crest-derived cells may indirectly contribute to their differentiation and network patterning. It remains to be seen if Purkinje fiber development is altered in concert with the rearrangement of coronary arteries following ablation of the cardiac neural crest.

## Gene Expression During Conversion of Contractile to Conductile Myocytes

The evidence for Purkinje fiber differentiation from beating myocytes provides the first insight into mechanisms governing a unique tissue-specific pattern of gene expression in the conduction system. As noted above, genes usually restricted to neurons or skeletal muscle fibers are induced in a subset of contractile cardiomyocytes that diversify into the Purkinje fiber lineage. It is well known that the expression of many muscle-specific proteins is regulated by the binding of a *trans*-acting *MyoD* gene family member to a *cis*-element, the E-box, residing in an enhancer/promoter region of the muscle structural genes (12, 52). In contrast, no member of the *MyoD* gene family has been identified as a transcription factor within cardiac myocytes (41, 44), suggesting that different *trans*-activation mechanisms function in these two striated muscle tissues. Evidence does exist, however, for common gene-activating mechanisms in skeletal muscle and cardiac conduction but not in contractile myocytes (37): Transgenic mice carrying a reporter gene fused to a portion of the *cis*-element of the desmin gene, a member of the intermediate filament protein gene family, exhibited restricted expression of the transgene to cardiac conduction and skeletal muscle fibers. No transgene expression was observed in contractile cardiomyocytes, even though the endogenous desmin gene was expressed in all myogenic lineages (skeletal, cardiac, and smooth muscles). These results indicate that as contractile myocytes undergo the terminal diversification into conduction cells, they may induce the *trans*-acting factors that recognize *cis*-sequences functioning in the skeletal muscle lineage. Skeletal muscle-specific gene products that have now been identified in Purkinje fibers include skeletal muscle myosin heavy chain (17, 60) and myosin-binding protein H (MyBP-H) (8). Interestingly, the expression of heart muscle-specific TnI, an inhibitory subunit of troponin, is shut down in the Purkinje system (19). Identification of these *cis*-element sequences shared by skeletal muscle and Purkinje fibers would substantially improve our understanding of gene regulatory mechanisms during the formation of the CCS.

## Concluding Remarks

Except for central elements of the CCS, the origin and lineage relationships of all three myocyte subtypes in the heart—atrial, ventricular, and Purkinje fibers—have now been identified. Questions that remain to be addressed are (*a*) What extracellular factors restrict bipotential cardiogenic mesoderm to either atrial or ventricular myocytes and do so in a spatially defined pattern? (*b*) How are the proliferative and migratory activities of contractile myocytes locally regulated to form the left, right, and interventricular walls of the myocardium? (*c*) Which signals and cell types of the developing coronary arteries are responsible for conversion of contractile ventricular myocytes into Purkinje fibers? (*d*) How are the branching patterns of Purkinje fibers and coronary arteries defined? What is the role of the cardiac neural crest in this process? (*e*) What mechanisms govern linkage of the Purkinje fiber network to the central conduction system?

Answering these questions will contribute significantly to our understanding of the development and integrated function of the vertebrate heart.

## Literature Cited

1. Bastide B, Neyses L, Ganten D, Paul M, Willecke K, Traub O. 1993. Gap junction protein connexin40 is preferentially expressed in vascular endothelium and conductive bundles of rat myocardium and is increased under hypertensive conditions. *Circ. Res.* 73: 1138–49
2. Beyer EC. 1990. Molecular cloning and developmental expression of two chick embryo gap junction proteins. *J. Biol. Chem.* 265:14439–43
3. Bisaha JG, Bader D. 1991. Identification and characterization of a ventricular-specific avian myosin heavy chain VMHC1: expression in differentiating cardiac and skeletal muscle. *Dev. Biol.* 148:355–64
4. Bogers AJJC, de Groot AC, Poelmann RE, Huysmans HA. 1989. Development of the origin of the coronary arteries, a matter of ingrowth or outgrowth? *Anat. Embryol.* 180:437–41
5. Callewaert G, Vereecke J, Carmeliet E. 1986. Existence of a calcium-dependent potassium channel in the membrane of cow cardiac Purkinje cells. *Pflügers Arch.* 406:424–26
6. Cavalie A, Ochi R, Pelzer D, Trautwein W. 1983. Elementary currents through Ca²⁺ channels in guinea pig myocytes. *Pflügers Arch.* 398:284–97
7. Chan-Thomas PS, Thompson RP, Robert B, Yacoub M, Barton PJR. 1993. Expression of homeobox genes *Msx-1* (*Hox-7*) and *Msx-2* (*Hox-8*) during cardiac development in the chick. *Dev. Dynam.* 197:203–16
8. Cohen-Gould L, Alyonycheva T, Fischman DA, Mikawa T. 1994. Conducting fibers in the chicken myocardium express skeletal muscle-type myosin-binding protein H (MyBP-H). *FASEB J.* 8:A609
9. Davies F. 1930. The conducting system of the bird's heart. *J. Anat.* 64:129–46
10. DeHaan RL. 1963. Migration patterns of the precardiac mesoderm in the early chick embryo. *Exp. Cell Res.* 29:544–60
11. DeHaan RL. 1965. Morphogenesis of the vertebrate heart. In *Organogenesis,* ed. RL DeHaan, H Ursprung, pp. 377–419. New York: Holt, Rinehart, & Winston
12. Emerson CP Jr. 1993. Embryonic signals for skeletal myogenesis: arriving at the beginning. *Curr. Opin. Cell Biol.* 5:1057–64
13. Gannon M. 1995. *Differentiation and diversification of cardiac mesoderm in the avian embryo: the role of anterior endoderm.* PhD thesis. Cornell Univ. New York. 126 pp.
14. Garcia-Martinez V, Schoenwolf GC. 1993. Primitive-streak origin of the cardiovascular system in avian embryos. *Dev. Biol.* 159:706–19
15. Gittenberger de Groot AC Bartelings NM, Bokenkamp R, Kirby ML. 1993. Neural crest and coronary artery development. *J. Cell. Biochem.* 17D:211 (Suppl.)
16. Goncharova EJ, Kam Z, Geiger B. 1992. The involvement of adherens junction components in myofibrillogenesis in cultured cardiac myocytes. *Development* 114:173–82
17. Gonzalez-Sanchez A, Bader D. 1985. Characterization of a myosin heavy chain in the conductive system of the adult and developing chicken heart. *J. Cell Biol.* 100:270–75
18. Gorza L, Schiaffino S, Vitadello M. 1988. Heart conduction system: a neural crest derivative. *Brain Res.* 457:360–66
19. Gorza L, Vettore S, Vitadello M. 1994. Molecular and cellular diversity of heart conduction system myocytes. *Trends Cardiol. Med.* 4:153–59
20. Gorza L, Vitadello M. 1989. Distribution of conduction system fibers in the developing and adult rabbit heart revealed by an antineurofilament antibody. *Circ. Res.* 65:360–69
21. Gourdie RG, Green CR, Severs NJ, Anderson RH, Thompson RP. 1993. Evidence for a distinct gap-junctional phenotype in ventricular conduction tissues of the developing and mature avian heart. *Circ. Res.* 72:278–89
22. Gourdie RG, Green CR, Severs NJ, Thompson RP. 1992. Immunolabelling patterns of gap junction connexins in the developing and mature rat heart. *Anat. Embryol.* 185:363–78
23. Gourdie RG, Mima T, Thompson RP, Mikawa T. 1995. Terminal diversification of the myocyte lineage generates Purkinje fibers of the cardiac conduction system. *Development* 121:1423–31
24. Gros D, Jarry-Guichard T, Ten-Velde I, de-Maziere A, van Kempen MJ, et al. 1994. Restricted distribution of connexin40, a gap junctional protein, in mammalian heart. *Circ. Res.* 74:839–51
25. Hagiwara N, Irisawa H, Kameyama M. 1988. Contribution of two types of calcium currents to the pacemaker potentials of rabbit sino-atrial node cells. *J. Physiol.* 395:233–53

26. Hamburger V, Hamilton HL. 1951. A series of normal stages in the development of the chick embryo. *J. Morphol.* 88:49–92

27. Han Y, Dennis JE, Cohen-Gould L, Bader DM, Fischman DA. 1992. Expression of sarcomeric myosin in the presumptive myocardium of chicken embryos occurs within six hours of myocyte commitment. *Dev. Dynam.* 193:257–65

28. Hiruma T, Hirakow R. 1989. Epicardial formation in embryonic chick heart: computer-aided reconstruction, scanning, and transmission electron microscopic studies. *Am. J. Anat.* 184:129–38

29. Ho E, Shimada Y. 1988. Formation of the epicardium studied with the scanning electron microscope. *Dev. Biol.* 66:579–85

30. Hood LA, Rosenquist TH. 1992. Coronary artery development in the chick: origin and development of smooth muscle cells, and effects of neural crest ablation. *Anat. Rec.* 234:291–300

31. Kamino K, Hirota A, Fujii S. 1981. Localization of pacemaking activity in early embryonic heart monitored using voltage-sensitive dye. *Nature* 290:595–97

32. Kanter HL, Laing JG, Beau SL, Beyer EC, Saffitz JE. 1993. Distinct patterns of connexin expression in canine Purkinje fibers and ventricular muscle. *Circ. Res.* 72:1124–31

33. Kirby MIL. 1988. Role of extracardiac factors in heart development. *Experientia* 44:944–51

34. Deleted in proof

35. Deleted in proof

36. Lamers WH, De Jong F, De Groot IJM, Moorman AFM. 1991. The Development of the avian conduction system, a review. *Eur. J. Morphol.* 29:233–53

37. Li Z, Marchand P, Humbert J, Babinet C, Paulin D. 1993. Desmin sequence elements regulating skeletal muscle-specific expression in transgenic mice. *Development* 117:947–59

38. Linask KK. 1992. N-cadherin localization in early heart development and polar expression of $Na^+$, $K^+$-ATPase, and integrin during pericardial coelom formation and epithelialization of the differentiating myocardium. *Dev. Biol.* 151:213–24

39. Linask KK, Lash JW. 1986. Precardiac cell migration: fibronectin localization at mesoderm-endoderm interface during directional movement. *Dev. Biol.* 114:87–101

40. Linask KK, Lash JW. 1988. A role for fibronectin in the migration of avian precardiac cells. II. Rotation of the heart-forming region during different stages and its effects. *Dev. Biol.* 129:324–29

41. Litvin J, Montgomery M, Gonzalez-Sanchez A, Bisaha JG, Bader D. 1992. Commitment and differentiation of cardiac myocytes. *Trends Cardiovasc. Med.* 2:27–32

42. Lyons GE. 1994. In situ analysis of the cardiac muscle gene program during embryogenesis. *Trends Cardiovasc. Med.* 4:70–77

43. Manasek FJ. 1968. Embryonic development of the heart: a light and electron microscopic study of myocardial development in the early chick embryo. *J. Morphol.* 125:329–66

44. Mikawa T. 1995. Retroviral targeting of FGF and FGFR in cardiomyocytes and coronary vascular cells during heart development. *Ann. NY Acad. Sci.* 752:506–16

45. Mikawa TA, Borisov AMC, Brown DA, Fischman DA. 1992. Clonal analysis of cardiac morphogenesis in the chicken embryo using a replication-defective retrovirus: I. Formation of the ventricular myocardium. *Dev. Dynam.* 193:11–23

46. Mikawa T, Cohen-Gould L, Fischman DA. 1992. Clonal analysis of cardiac morphogenesis in the chicken embryo using a replication-defective retrovirus. III: Polyclonal origin of adjacent ventricular myocytes. *Dev. Dynam.* 195:133–41

47. Mikawa T, Fischman DA. 1992. Retroviral analysis of cardiac morphogenesis: discontinuous formation of coronary vessels. *Proc. Natl. Acad. Sci. USA* 89:9504–8

48. Deleted in proof

49. Deleted in proof

50. Mima T, Ueno H, Fischman DA, Williams LT, Mikawa T. 1995. FGF-receptor is required for in vivo cardiac myocyte proliferation at early embryonic stages of heart development. *Proc. Natl. Acad. Sci. USA* 92:467–71

51. O'Brien TX, Lee KJ, Chien KR. 1993. Positional specification of ventricular myosin light chain 2 expression in the primitive murine heart tube. *Proc. Natl. Acad. Sci. USA* 90:5157–61

52. Olson EN. 1992. Interplay between proliferation and differentiation within the myogenic lineage. *Dev. Biol.* 154:261–72

53. Ong L, Mima T, Cohen-Gould L, Mikawa T. 1994. A dominant negative mutant of N-cadherin activates migra-

tion of cardiac myocytes in the embryonic chicken heart. *FASEB J.* 8:A609

54. Pattern BM. 1956. The development of the sinoventricular conduction system. *Univ. Mich. Med. Bull.* 22:1–21

55. Pattern BM, Kramer TC. 1933. The initiation of contraction in the embryonic chick heart. *Am. J. Anat.* 53:349–75

56. Peng I, Dennis JE, Rodriguez-Boulan E, Fischman DA. 1990. Polarized release of enveloped viruses in the embryonic chick heart: demonstration of epithelial polarity in the presumptive myocardium. *Dev. Biol.* 141:164–72

57. Poelmann RE, Gutenberger de Groot AC, Mentink MT, Bokenkamp R, Hogers B. 1993. Development of the cardiac coronary vascular endothelium studied with anti-endothelial antibodies, in chicken-quail chimeras. *Circ. Res.* 73:559–68

58. Rawles ME. 1943. The heart forming regions of the early chick blastoderm. *Physiol. Zool.* 16:22–42

59. Rosenquist GC, DeHaan RL. 1966. Migration of precardiac cells in the chick embryo: a radioautographic study. *Embryology* 38:111–21

60. Sartore S, Pierobon-Bormioli S, Schiaffino S. 1978. Immuno-histochemical evidence for myosin polymorphism in the chicken heart. *Nature* 274:82–83

61. Satin J, Fujii S, DeHaan RL. 1988. Development of cardiac beat rate in early chick embryos is regulated by regional cues. *Dev. Biol.* 129:103–13

62. Stalsberg H, DeHaan RL. 1969. The precardiac areas and formation of the tubular heart in the chick embryo. *Dev. Biol.* 19:128–59

63. Stanier DYR, Lee RK, Fishman MC. 1993. Cardiovascular development in the zebrafish 1. Mocardial fate and heart tube formation. *Development* 119:31–40

64. Sugi Y, Sasse J, Lough J. 1993. Inhibition of precardiac mesoderm cell proliferation by antisense oligodeoxynucleotide complementary to fibroblast growth factor-2 (FGF-2). *Dev. Biol.* 157:28–37

65. Takeichi M. 1991. Cadherin cell adhesion receptors as a morphogenetic regulator. *Science* 251:1451–55

66. Thompson RP, Lindroth JR, Wong Y-MM. 1990. Regional differences in DNA-synthetic activity in the preseptation myocardium of the chick. In *Developmental Cardiology; Morphogenesis and Function,* ed. E Clark, A Takao, pp. 219–34. New York: Futura

67. van Kempen MJ, Fromaget C, Gros D, Moorman AF, Lamers WH. 1991. Spatial distribution of connexin43, the major cardiac gap junction protein, in the developing and adult rat heart. *Circ. Res.* 68:1638–51

68. Vassal-Adams PR. 1982. The development of the atrioventricular bundle and its branches in the avian heart. *J. Anat.* 134:169–83

69. Viragh SZ, Challice CE. 1982. The development of the conduction system in the mouse embryo heart. IV. Differentiation of the atrioventricular conduction system. *Dev. Biol.* 89:25–40

70. Deleted in proof

71. Waldo KL, Kumiski DH, Kirby ML. 1994. Association of the cardiac neural crest with development of the coronary arteries in the chick embryo. *Anat. Rec.* 239:315–31

72. Waldo KL, Willner W, Kirby ML. 1990. Origin of the proximal coronary artery stems and a review of ventricular vascularization in the chick embryo. *Am. J. Anat.* 188:109–20

73. Wessels A, Vermeulen JLM, Verbeek FJ, Viragh S, Kalman F, et al. 1992. Spatial distribution of "tissue-specific" antigens in the developing human heart. *Anat. Rec.* 232:97–1 11

74. Yada T, Sakai T, Komuro H, Jirota A, Kamino K. 1985. Development of electrical rhythmic activity in early embryonic cultured chick double heart monitored with a voltage-sensitive dye. *Dev. Biol.* 110:455–66

75. Yutzey KE, Gannon M, Bader D. 1995. Diversification of cardiomyogenic cell lineages in vitro. *Dev. Biol.* 170:531–41

76. Yutzey KE, Rhee JT, Bader D. 1994. Expression of the atrial-specific myosin heavy chain AMHC1 and the establishment of anteroposterior polarity in the developing chicken heart. *Development* 120:871–83

*Annu. Rev. Physiol. 1996. 58:523–38*

# MULTIPLE ROLES OF CARBONIC ANHYDRASE IN CELLULAR TRANSPORT AND METABOLISM

*Raymond P. Henry*

Department of Zoology and Wildlife Science, 101 Cary Hall, Auburn University, Auburn, Alabama 36849–5414

KEY WORDS:    carbon dioxide excretion, ammonia excretion, ureagenesis, gluconeogenesis

### ABSTRACT

Carbonic anhydrase (CA) is a central enzyme to both transport and metabolic processes at the cellular level. In metabolically active tissue such as muscle, CA in the cytoplasm and on the sarcolemma appears to be important in facilitating $CO_2$ transport out of the cell. Membrane-associated CA, with an extracellular orientation, also appears to be important in acidifying the outer boundary layer through the catalyzed hydration of excreted $CO_2$. This facilitates cellular ammonia transport by providing $H^+$ ions for the protonation of $NH_3$, thus maintaining the *trans*-membrane $NH_3$ gradient. Mitochondrial CA is known to supply $HCO_3^-$ for the initial reactions of gluconeogenesis and ureagenesis in mammalian tissues, but systematic comparative studies of CA as a metabolic enzyme are lacking. CA probably evolved as an enzyme of *trans*-membrane facilitated $CO_2$ transport and took on a secondary metabolic role later in metazoan evolution.

## INTRODUCTION

Carbonic anhydrase (CA) is a primitive and ubiquitous enzyme found in virtually every tissue and cell type, in many subcellular organelles, and in organisms ranging from unicellular cyanobacteria through mammals (3, 23, 48, 50, 56, 57, 70, 93, 98). The enzyme catalyzes the reversible hydration/dehydration of $CO_2$ and water:

$$CO_2 + H_2O \; \underset{\longleftarrow}{\overset{CA}{\longrightarrow}} \; H^+ + HCO_3^- \, .$$

Because the reactants and products include both gaseous and ionic chemical species, CA could potentially be important for any physiological or biochemi-

0066–4278/96/0315–0523$08.00

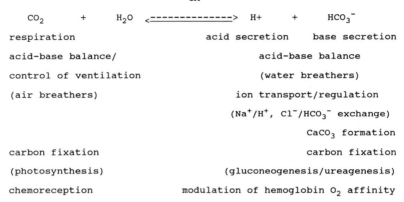

*Figure 1* Suggested multiple physiological and biochemical roles of carbonic anhydrase. The physiological and biochemical processes in which CA may play a role are listed under the chemical species believed to be the net product of the catalyzed reaction. (Modified and expanded from Reference 50.)

cal process in which these species are used. Indeed, a large body of evidence supports the role of CA in a wide variety of processes from respiration to intermediary metabolism (see Figure 1 for a summary).

The two most heavily investigated areas of CA function, respiration ($CO_2$ transport and excretion) and ion transport, have been studied primarily on the systemic level. In the former the roles of erythrocyte and vascular CA have been well documented in the transport of $CO_2$ in the extracellular fluid (ECF) and its excretion across the respiratory epithelium (7, 30, 80, 83, 84). Ion transport has been most commonly studied in relation to the role of CA in systemic mechanisms of extracellular fluid ion regulation (48, 50, 61).

The limiting step in $CO_2$ transport, however, is known to occur at the cellular level. Although $CO_2$ gas is freely permeable across biological membranes, the more abundant chemical species in the ECF under physiological conditions, $HCO_3^-$, is not (25, 81, 92). The large ECF bicarbonate pool must first be mobilized to $CO_2$ gas before it can be excreted by diffusion. The uncatalyzed dehydration of $HCO_3^-$ is very slow ($t\ 1/2 = 25$ s at 37°C) (24), and thus the limiting step becomes the conversion of $HCO_3^-$ to $CO_2$. This was shown experimentally by Gutknecht et al (44): In the absence of CA, the limiting step in $CO_2$ transport across a membrane was the uncatalyzed dehydration of $HCO_3^-$ to $CO_2$ in the boundary layer on the upstream side of the membrane. With CA present, $HCO_3^-$ and $CO_2$ were maintained in instantaneous equilibrium, sustaining a high $PCO_2$ in the boundary layer, thus allowing the process to proceed at the rate of $CO_2$ diffusion through the membrane.

Therefore, the underlying principles that govern $CO_2$ transport are (*a*) the permeability differences between $CO_2$ and $HCO_3^-$ and (*b*) the subsequent need for the rapid conversion of $HCO_3^-$ to $CO_2$ gas. Two conclusions can be drawn from this information that bear directly on the interpretation of CA function. First, the rate-limiting step in $CO_2$ transport occurs at the site of the membrane, regardless of the complexity of the organism (e.g. unicells or metazoans). Second, CA localized in the boundary layer of the membrane is necessary for facilitated $CO_2$ diffusion. From this information it is apparent that the initial step in systemic $CO_2$ transport is the diffusion of $CO_2$ from the intracellular compartment of metabolically active tissue, across the plasma membrane, into the circulatory system. Furthermore, a combination of cytoplasmic and membrane-associated CA can be localized in such a way as to facilitate $CO_2$ transport across that membrane.

Although membrane-associated CA is believed to confer directionality on $CO_2$ transport from one biological compartment to another (e.g. see 70), cytoplasmic CA is believed to function simply in maintaining an instantaneous equilibrium between the chemical species of $CO_2$. Intracellular (including intraorganelle) CA has received attention recently for its potential role in carbon fixation for synthetic pathways of intermediary metabolism [e.g. gluconeogenesis and ureagenesis (16, 98); and photosynthesis in plants and symbiotic associations (2)].

What emerges from this initial discussion is an interesting concept that has not been given much consideration. The functions of CA in facilitated $CO_2$ transport across membranes and in supplying carbon for intermediary metabolism were already established when primitive unicellular and metazoan organisms were conducting gas exchange and ion transport across an undifferentiated integument. There was selective pressure for the evolution of CA function long before specialized respiratory and ion transporting epithelia evolved. Therefore, the primitive ancestral form of CA probably evolved to meet the $CO_2$ transport and metabolic demands on the cellular level. This review focuses on the multiple roles of CA in cellular transport and metabolism and on the influences those processes might have had on the evolution of CA function.

# CA AND CELLULAR CO2 TRANSPORT IN MUSCLE

## Subcellular Localization and Isozyme Distribution

It was originally postulated that muscle tissue would not contain CA because it was believed that the rapid hydration of $CO_2$ to $HCO_3^-$ would retard $CO_2$ transport into the blood (84). Perhaps for that reason, CA was not found in muscle until relatively recently (58, 108). Now it has been well established that CA is present in both skeletal and cardiac muscle (for recent reviews, see 5, 10, 17, 33, 38, 42, 89, 90). In mammalian skeletal muscle, the CA II and III (and possibly I) isozymes are present in the cytoplasm, with the distribution correlated to the specific metabolic classification of the muscle fiber. CA III is found predominantly in type I muscle fibers (slow twitch, red, oxidative), and CA II is present in type II fibers (fast-contracting, white, glycolytic or mixed glycolytic-oxidative). In addition, there is a CA that appears to be similar to the mammalian red blood cell Type II isozyme associated with the sarcolemma of all muscle fiber types. Furthermore, there is also CA associated with the sarcoplasmic reticulum of all muscle fiber types. In contrast, mammalian heart muscle appears to have CA associated with the sarcolemma and intracellular organelles only (6).

Although mammalian systems have been extensively studied during the last fifteen years, there has been only one report for lower vertebrates indicating that frog white muscle has a CA type II isozyme (87). Other comparative studies are lacking, but preliminary information (85, 86; R Henry, unpublished data) indicates that other lower vertebrate (i.e. fish) and invertebrate (crustaceans) muscles contain both cytoplasmic and microsomal CA.

## CA and Facilitated $CO_2$ Transport

Inhibition of CA in mammalian muscle is known to have a number of physiological consequences. Force of contraction is decreased for both twitch and tetany, and both contraction and relaxation times are increased. Inorganic phosphates are increased and intracellular pH (pHi) is decreased. From these and other results, muscle CA has been implicated as functioning in contraction, $Ca^{2+}/H^+$ transport by the sarcoplasmic reticulum (and therefore relaxation), neuromuscular transmission, metabolism and energetics, and facilitated $CO_2$ transport (34–37, 87). The latter role appears to have the most experimental support. Geers & Gros (37), using equations derived by Thews (94), calculated that there should be a reduction in pHi of about 0.13 units for cylindrically shaped muscle cells under conditions of CA inhibition. Their measured pHi depression of about 0.1 pH unit, after chlorzolamide treatment in isolated muscle fibers, was in close agreement. What is more interesting, however, is the fact that pHi was depressed in muscle fibers regardless of which CA isozyme was present; this strongly suggests that cellular $CO_2$ transport is a universal function of muscle CA, regardless of isozyme distribution.

Definitive evidence for the role of CA in cellular $CO_2$ transport outside of mammalian muscle is currently lacking, but circumstantial evidence appears to be supportive. Fish muscle is impermeable to $HCO_3^-$, and therefore $CO_2$ must diffuse across the sarcolemma in the gaseous molecular form (92). Furthermore, treatment of trout white muscle with the CA inhibitor acetazolamide appears to cause $CO_2$ retention in the intracellular fluid (Y Wang, R Henry & CM Wood, unpublished data).

Although the function of muscle CA in facilitated $CO_2$ transport is generally accepted, the specific role of cytoplasmic or sarcolemma CA and the quantitative contribution of each to the overall process have not been established. In mammalian muscle, CA on the extracellular surface of the sacrolemma is believed to facilitate $CO_2$ transport from the interstitial space, across the capillary membrane, into the blood (39, 101). A recently isolated, perfused trout tail muscle preparation (Y Wang & CM Wood, unpublished data) has been used to study $CO_2$ excretion in conjunction with CA function. Selective inhibition of extracellular sarcolemma CA by the membrane-impermeant CA inhibitor quaternary ammonium sulfanilamide (QAS; 49) resulted in reduced $CO_2$ excretion from muscle fibers, indicating that both cytoplasmic and membrane-associated CA pools may be important in cellular $CO_2$ transport (Y Wang, R Henry & CM Wood, unpublished data).

## CA AND CELLULAR NH₃ TRANSPORT

As with $CO_2$, ammonia transport and excretion has been most extensively studied on the systemic level. Because ammonia is the most abundant end product of nitrogen metabolism in aquatic animals, investigations into its excretion have focused on potential mechanisms of transport across the major epithelial surfaces (e.g. fish and invertebrate gills). The gills are also the organs of salt transport, thus early work centered on the relationship between ammonia and sodium transport. That work established the paradigm of $Na^+/NH_4^+$ exchange and implied that most of the ammonia excretion occurred in the ionized form by some mechanism of coupled transport (26, 68, 69). Two more recent advances, however, have changed the view of ammonia excretion: (a) Experimental evidence now supports the hypothesis that $Na^+$ transport at the gill occurs primarily by $Na^+/H^+$ exchange (27, 60, 62, 63), and more importantly, (b) the bulk of ammonia excretion appears to take place via $NH_3$ diffusion across the general epithelial membrane (1, 8, 9, 13, 28, 29, 64, 107).

In light of that information, our understanding of the behavior and transport of ammonia in solution becomes analogous to that of $CO_2$ (9). Ammonia exists both in gaseous ($NH_3$) and ionic ($NH_4^+$) forms. With a pK between 9 and 10, at physiological pH, about 97% of the total ammonia is in the protonated form in blood and intracellular fluid. Ammonia gas has both high water solubility and high permeability (values for $NH_3$ are between 10- and 100-fold higher than for $NH_4^+$) (9). The most abundant form does not appear to diffuse very readily, and the mobile (diffusable) form is present in very low amounts. The limiting step in ammonia transport occurs at the membrane, thus $NH_3$ diffusion down a small but significant $PNH_3$ gradient (40–50 μtorr) (8, 9) will depend on mobilization (dissociation) of $NH_3$ from the much larger $NH_4^+$ pool on the upstream side of the membrane. Furthermore, reprotonation of $NH_3$ to $NH_4^+$ on the downstream side of the membrane will facilitate $NH_3$ diffusion by maintaining a minimum downstream $PNH_3$, or in other words, maximizing the *trans*-membrane $PNH_3$ gradient.

Acidification of the external boundary layer of the gill has been shown to be important in ammonia excretion in fish (102, 105). Treatments that reduce either the production of protons or their availability to $NH_3$ in the external boundary layer reduce $NH_3$ diffusion by up to one third. Because $CO_2$ is excreted in its molecular form and can be hydrated to form protons, it has been suggested that $CO_2$ excretion and $NH_3$ excretion are linked and that the protons come directly from the catalyzed hydration of $CO_2$ by CA localized on the extracellular surface of the gill (82, 105). At this point it is still questionable whether extracellular CA on the apical surface of the gill is necessary for acidification and subsequent $NH_3$ trapping. Amiloride treatment alone reduces $NH_3$ excretion by 30% (105), indicating that a significant fraction of the protons come from apical $Na^+/H^+$ exchange. This reduction happens in spite of a concomitant 70% stimulation of $CO_2$ excretion caused by amiloride. These results cast doubt on the role of branchial CA in acidifying the extracelluar boundary layer water for $NH_3$ excretion. An increase in $CO_2$ excretion in the presence of external CA should provide adequate amounts of $H^+$ for $NH_3$ protonation and, therefore, excretion; yet $NH_3$ excretion is inhibited. Furthermore, the supply of protons from respiratory $CO_2$ can be short-circuited at a number of steps prior to reaching the apical surface. Acetazolamide treatment in the blood reduces $CO_2$ excretion at the initial step (mobilization of $HCO_3^-$ from blood) and reduces $NH_3$ excretion, while not having any effect on the apical membrane. The definitive experiments showing the presence and putative function of CA on the extracellular apical surface of the gill have not been performed.

CA may be more important in $NH_3$ excretion across the sarcolemma of muscle. In fish, one of the major metabolic sources of ammonia production, white muscle, contains high intracellular concentrations of total ammonia (6,000 μM). The $NH_4^+$ concentration gradient appears to be held in equilibrium by the *trans*-membrane potential, and there is also a very high $PNH_3$ gradient (400 μtorr) across the sarcolemma (106). For fish muscle at rest (low endogenous ammonia production), the bulk of ammonia excretion is believed to occur via diffusion of $NH_3$. In this case, CA on the sarcolemma, with an extracellular orientation, would facilitate $NH_3$ diffusion by acidifying the interstitial fluid boundary layer through the catalyzed hydration of $CO_2$. Again, definitive evidence for this function of CA is lacking, but preliminary results using QAS on an isolated, perfused trout muscle preparation indicate that inhibition of extracellular CA reduces ammonia excretion from muscle (Y Wang, R Henry & CM Wood, unpublished data).

## CA AND CELLULAR METABOLISM

Carbon dioxide and ammonia, the end products of carbohydrate and nitrogen catabolism, respectively, are primarily waste products that are eliminated from the animal by various routes of excretion. These chemical species are also used as substrates in a variety of metabolic pathways. CA can potentially play a role in metabolism in the specific steps that involve carbon fixation. Most of the catabolic reactions that produce carbon dioxide liberate $CO_2$ gas, and conversely, many of the carbon fixing reactions utilize $HCO_3^-$ (98). Intracellular (and intra-organelle) CA, by maintaining a virtually instantaneous chemical equilibrium between $CO_2$ and $HCO_3^-$, could allow for some of the metabolically produced $CO_2$ to be shunted into synthetic pathways. Indeed, CA has been shown to function in providing $HCO_3^-$ for the initial steps in glucose synthesis, fatty acid synthesis, general amino acid synthesis, and urea synthesis (16, 19, 20, 45, 46, 52, 54). Therefore, although CA is traditionally considered to be a transport enzyme, it is also an integral part of many biosynthetic pathways. CA is one of the few enzymes occupying a central role in both transport and metabolism, and as such it serves a molecular link between these two general processes (Figure 2). Most of the support for CA as a metabolic enzyme comes from work on mammalian systems, but two metabolic process have received considerable attention from a comparative standpoint: gluconeogenesis and ureagenesis.

### CA and Gluconeogenesis

In mammals, glucose is the major energy source of the brain and the exclusive substrate for erythrocytes. After periods of intense exercise, when glycogen reserves have been depleted, lactate recycling to glucose through the Cori cycle is important in maintaining a continuous supply of fuel to metabolically sensitive tissue (55). The mammalian liver is the primary site of gluconeogenesis, and one of the initial steps in the pathway, the carboxylation of pyruvate via pyruvate carboxylase (PC), occurs exclusively in the mitochondria (4).

Carbonic anhydrase (CA V) is known to be present in mammalian hepatocyte mitochondria (22, 95). Furthermore, when intact hepatocytes were incubated under conditions in which gluconeogenesis begins with $HCO_3^-$ fixation via PC (i.e. high lactate/pyruvate concentrations), treatment with CA inhibitors decreased glucose synthesis (20). Experiments on [14]C-labeled $NaHCO_3$ incorporation by PC showed a 65% reduction after CA inhibition (20). In contrast, under conditions in which gluconeogenesis begins independently of $HCO_3^-$

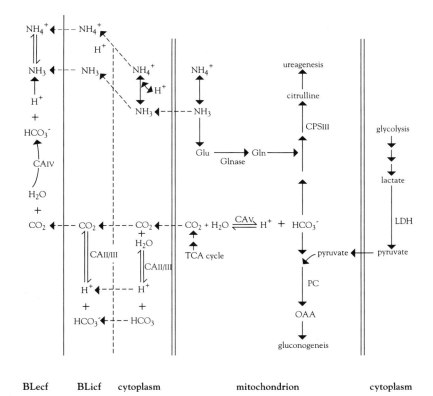

*Figure 2* Composite schematic diagram indicating the multiple physiological roles for the different CA isozymes in $CO_2$ and $NH_3$ transport and in gluconeogenesis and ureagenesis. BL, boundary layer; ecf, extracellular fluid; icf, intracellular fluid. See text for a complete explanation.

(i.e. high glutamine concentrations), CA inhibition had no effect on glucose synthesis.

The role of mitochondrial CA V in gluconeogenesis is supported by studies on other mammalian tissues as well. Rat kidney is a highly gluconeogenic tissue that contains high levels of CA activity; guinea pig kidney, which lacks mitochondrial CA, has only 10% of the gluconeogenic capability (based on relative rates of glucose synthesis in starved animals) (18, 103).

The situation in lower vertebrates is less clear. First, the liver is not a primary site of gluconeogenesis. In lower vertebrates (reptiles and amphibians), skeletal muscle appears to be responsible for lactate recycling (14, 31, 32, 40, 41, 104). In frogs, surgical removal of the liver does not affect lactate elimination or glycogen resynthesis (31). More specifically, in lizards, lactate produced by fast glycolytic fibers appears to be metabolized to glycogen preferentially in oxidative fiber types (41).

The liver of fish may also play a minor role in lactate-based gluconeogenesis. Elasmobranch (i.e. skate) hepatocytes do not utilize lactate to any significant degree in post-exercise gluconeogenesis (74), and teleost (i.e. toadfish) liver is responsible for clearing less than 2% of the post-exercise lactate load (96). At the very least, gluconeogenic capability appears to be spread among a variety of tissues, including liver, kidney, and muscle (73–76, 78, 97, 100).

There is very little known about the putative role of CA in gluconeogenesis in lower vertebrates. Even the most basic information on CA distribution among tissue types (e.g. muscle and liver) and its subcellular localization (e.g. mitochondrial or cytoplasmic) is lacking in all but one or two examples. Furthermore, even the metabolic pathways of glucose/glycogen resynthesis may not be consistant among species, as lower vertebrates have been shown to have very low levels of activity of two important gluconeogenic enzymes, pyruvate carboxylase (PC) and phosphoenol-pyruvate carboxykinase (PEPCK) (91, 98).

One study, in which the CA inhibitor acetazolamide was injected into intact chameleons and alligators, supports the role for CA in supplying $HCO_3^-$ for pyruvate carboxylation (53). Gluconeogenesis in frog muscle has also been shown to be bicarbonate-sensitive but for different reasons. The difficulty in documenting significant levels of PC activity, and the results of $^{14}C$ tracer and inhibitor studies, led Connett (14) to suggest that lactate recycling occurs exclusively in the cytoplasm, possibly by carboxylation of pyruvate through the reversal of malic enzyme. Recent studies in fish white muscle suggest that the initial steps of gluconeogenesis proceed by reversal of another enzyme, pyruvate kinase (PK) (88), a pathway that was ruled out for frog muscle (14).

There has been only one study on CA and gluconeogenesis in invertebrates (51). No evidence was found linking CA to post-exercise lactate recycling in aquatic and terrestrial crustaceans. Although significant levels of CA activity were found in both muscle and hepatopancreas, key gluconeogenic enzymes [e.g. PC, PEPCK, fructose bisphosphatase, and even lactate dehydrogenase (LDH) in the hepatopancreas] were not detected in any significant amount (51, 65, 66). Lactate turnover rates were low, the percent of lactate resynthesized to glycogen was small (<20%), and $^{14}C$ from labeled lactate appeared in a variety of end products, suggesting multiple metabolic fates for lactate (51). Crustacean tissues seem to be poised more toward the metabolism of amino acids over carbohydrates (97), and this could partially explain why classical gluconeogenesis (via the Cori cycle) is so hard to detect. The use of acetazolamide in intact animals did not provide any evidence supporting a role for CA in gluconeogenesis (51).

Despite this conflicting and somewhat confusing information, some general conclusions about the evolution of gluconeogenesis and the role of CA can be drawn. First, it appears that the rate of gluconeogenesis is proportional to the overall metabolic rate of the animal (i.e. mammals $\rightarrow$ reptiles $\rightarrow$ fish $\rightarrow$ invertebrates) (15). Second, two of the three proposed pathways of gluconeogenesis involve carbon fixation, and the rate of $CO_2$ consumption is much higher than can be accounted for by that produced through mitochondrial respiration (16). It has been suggested that the $CO_2$ deficit is made up by the decarboxylation reactions in the gluconeogenic pathway itself [i.e. oxaloacetate (OAA) to PEP via PEP carboxykinase]. That reaction produces molecular $CO_2$, which could be utilized directly by malic enzyme reversal or utilized as $HCO_3^-$ by PC after CA-catalyzed hydration. PK reversal, on the other hand, is independent of the $CO_2/HCO_3^-$ reactions and therefore not involved in the action of CA.

Lower vertebrates and invertebrates appear to have the same capacity for glycolysis as mammals, but gluconeogenesis proceeds at much slower rates (15). This would imply equal selective pressure across broad phylogenetic lines for the release of quick energy during burst exercise but not for the recycling of metabolic end products. The difference may lie in the fact that the mammalian central nervous tissue is very sensitive to glucose; rapid gluconeogenesis (especially in the liver) could have evolved to meet the metabolic demands of a well-developed central nervous system. If so, then rapid conversion of $CO_2$ to $HCO_3^-$ would have also been selected for, hence the importance of CA in ensuring that $HCO_3^-$ availability does not become limiting in the initial step of pyruvate carboxylation. Outside of mammalian systems, however, the comparative importance of gluconeogenesis and the putative role of CA are subjects that remain open to investigation.

## CA and Ureagenesis

The initial reaction of the urea cycle, the synthesis of carbamoyl phosphate from $HCO_3^-$ and $NH_3$, takes place in the mitochondria. In mammals, the enzyme catalyzing this reaction, carbamoyl phosphate synthetase (CPS I), is localized to the mitochondrial matrix (67). The bicarbonate is supplied by a specific CA isozyme (CA V), which is colocalized in the mitochondrial matrix. CA was first found in guinea pig liver mitochondria (22), and its distribution now appears to extend to mitochondria of both liver and muscle across a variety of mammalian species (90, 95).

The use of CA inhibitors (e.g. acetazolamide) on isolated, perfused rat liver, hepatocyte, and mitochondria preparations has shown CA V to be physiologically important in supplying $HCO_3^-$ for carbamoyl phosphate synthesis. Synthesis of citrulline in isolated mitochondria was reduced by 71% after treatment with acetazolamide (21), and urea synthesis in isolated hepatocytes was also reduced by another CA inhibitor, ethoxyzolamide (19). The concentrations of the inhibitors needed to inhibit citrulline/urea were also close to those needed to fully inhibit mitochondrial CA activity, and an excess of inhibitor did not further suppress metabolite production. In isolated perfused liver, acetazolamide also decreased citrulline production by about 70%, but inhibition of both citrulline and urea synthesis was overcome by increasing the concentration of $HCO_3^-$ to well above physiological levels (45–47). Furthermore, in intact rats in which CA was not inhibited, urea synthesis was dependent on $NH_3$ concentration only, unaffected by infusions of $HCO_3^-$ (12). CA V and CPS I have been suggested to exist in the mitochondrial matrix as a complex (21), and carbamoyl phosphate appears to exert product inhibition on both enzymes (11). Taken together, these data provide strong support for a metabolic role for mitochondrial CA.

Since relatively few lower vertebrates (especially aquatic species) and fewer invertebrates are ureagenic, comparative studies on the role of CA in urea metabolism are scarce. Recently Mommsen & Walsh (77) found that a species of toadfish synthesizes and excretes urea during periods of environmental stress. A multifactorial experimental approach showed that urea synthesis is sensitive to $HCO_3^-$ concentrations (99). Further study documented the presence of CA activity in both the cytoplasm and mitochondria of isolated toadfish hepatocytes, and treatment with acetazolamide resulted in a dose-dependent inhibition of urea synthesis (99). It was concluded that hepatocyte CA supplied $HCO_3^-$ for the initial synthesis of carbamoyl phosphate, although the relative contributions of cytoplasmic or mitochondrial CA could not be determined. Remarkably, for all that is known about urea metabolism in elasmobranchs, little or no information on CA distribution and potential metabolic function is available. A similar situation exists for invertebrates: Some species are known to produce urea, but the potential role of CA has never been investigated.

## THE EVOLUTION OF CA FUNCTION

Because CA was discovered in the mammalian red blood cell, it has been traditionally thought of as an enzyme of systemic $CO_2$ transport. As discussed above, however, multiple CA isozymes were in place and functioning at the cellular level long before the evolution of metazoans and integrated organ systems of transport. Recently, the argument has been made that CA can function as a true metabolic enzyme and that it may even have initially evolved to supply carbon for synthetic pathways (98). This is known to be the case in photosynthetic autotrophs (2), but for unicellular and more complexly organized heterotrophs (animals), it is not so simple. It is more probable that CA initially evolved as an enzyme whose function was in facilitated $CO_2$ transport on the cellular level. Evidence for this comes from both in vitro studies on

$CO_2$ diffusion in buffer solutions and across artificial membranes and from work on isolated muscle cells. In both cases, facilitated $CO_2$ diffusion occurs primarily at low $PCO_2$ (43, 59). In the presence of CA, and for $PCO_2$ values in the range of 5 torr, $CO_2$ diffusion is about five times higher than can be explained by the free diffusion of molecular $CO_2$. The rate increases exponentially as $PCO_2$ approaches zero, but it decreases toward the free diffusion rate of $CO_2$ as gas tension increases. The reason for this appears to be the dependence of facilitated $CO_2$ transport, not only on CA, but also on the concentration gradient of $HCO_3^-$ and on an adequate amount of protons that are supplied by mobile buffers (43). As $PCO_2$ increases, the concentration gradients of $HCO_3^-$ and mobile buffer decrease, and the transport of $CO_2$ is thus reduced, approaching the rate of free diffusion. It is possible that CA evolved as a result of selection pressure to maintain low intracellular $PCO_2$ in order to maximize facilitated $CO_2$ transport out of metabolically active tissue. Maintenance of an instantaneous equilibrium among $CO_2$ species via the catalytic action of CA at intracellular pH values of 7.0 and above (well above the pK' value of 6.1 for the $CO_2$ system) would result in low $PCO_2$ and a constant supply of $HCO_3^-$ for metabolic pathways.

If this was indeed the case in primitive organisms, then metabolism (and metabolic pathways of synthesis) would have evolved in a low $PCO_2$ environment. A number of key metabolic enzymes utilize $HCO_3^-$ (42, 98), and as metabolic rates increased with the higher complexity of metazoan organization (and the invasion of the terrestrial habitat), it is also plausible that CA became more important in meeting the higher demand for metabolic carbon fixation. Regardless, the comparative and evolutionary systemic and cellular functions of CA represent areas that remain fertile grounds for investigation.

## SUMMARY

The rate-limiting step in $CO_2$ transport for which CA is important occurs at the site of the membrane. Systemic $CO_2$ transport and excretion is comprised of a series of *trans*-membrane events strung together. CA appears to be just as important in facilitating $CO_2$ removal from metabolically active tissue into the ECF as it is in facilitating transport from the ECF across the respiratory epithelium. This is apparently accomplished by a combination of cytoplasmic (soluble) and membrane-associated CA. The function of CA in facilitated $CO_2$ transport from muscle also seems to play a related role in the removal of ammonia ($NH_3$) from tissues, and it may also function in facilitating systemic $NH_3$ excretion as well. Cytoplasmic and mitochondrial CA play an important role in supplying $HCO_3^-$ for the initial steps in gluconeogenesis and ureagenesis in mammals. The function of CA as a metabolic enzyme has been documented for ureagenesis in a select number of lower vertebrates but not invertebrates. The comparative importance of CA in gluconeogenesis is currently unclear.

## Literature Cited

1. Avella M, Bornancin M. 1989. A new analysis of ammonia and sodium transport through the gills of the freshwater rainbow trout (*Salmo gairdneri*). *J. Exp. Biol.* 142:155–75
2. Badger MR, Price GD. 1994. The role of carbonic anhydrase in photosynthesis. *Annu. Rev. Plant Physiol. Plant Mol. Biol.* 45:369–92
3. Bauer C, Gros G, Bartels H, eds. 1980. *Biophysics and Physiology of Carbon Dioxide.* New York: Springer-Verlag. 453 pp.
4. Bottger I, Wieland O. 1969. Intracellular localization of pyruvate carboxylase and phosphoenolpyruvate carboxykinase in rat liver. *Eur. J. Biochem.* 8:113–19
5. Bruns, W, Dermietzel R, Gros G. 1986. Carbonic anhydrase in the sarcoplasmic reticulum of rabbit skeletal muscle. *J. Physiol.* 371:351–64
6. Bruns W, Gros G. 1992. Membrane-bound carbonic anhydrase in the heart. *Am. J. Physiol.* 262:H577–84
7. Cameron JN. 1979. Excretion of $CO_2$ in water-breathing animals: a short review. *Marine Biol. Lett.* 1:3–13
8. Cameron JN, Heisler N. 1983. Studies of ammonia in the rainbow trout: physico-chemical parameters, acid-base behaviour and respiratory clearance. *J. Exp. Biol.* 105:107–25
9. Cameron JN, Heisler N. 1985. Ammonia transfer across fish gills: a review. In *Proceedings in Life Sciences: Circulation, Respiration, and Metabolism,* ed. R Gilles, pp.91–100. Heidelberg: Springer-Verlag
10. Carter ND. 1991. Hormonal and neuronal control of carbonic anhydrase III gene expression in skeletal muscle. See Ref. 23, pp. 247–56
11. Carter ND, Chegwidden WR, Hewett-Emmett D, Jeffrey S, Shiels A, Tashian RE. 1984. Novel inhibition of carbonic anhydrase isozymes I, II and III by carbamoyl phosphate. *FEBS Lett.* 165: 197–200
12. Cheema-Dhadli S, Jungas RL, Halperin ML. 1987. Regulation of urea synthesis by acid-base balance in vivo: role of $NH_3$ concentration. *Am. J. Physiol.* 252: F221–25
13. Claiborne JB, Evans DH. 1988. Ammonia and acid-base balance during high ammonia exposure in a marine teleost (*Myoxocephalus octodecimspinosus*). *J. Exp. Biol.* 140:89–105
14. Connett RJ. 1979. Glyconeogenesis from lactate in frog striated muscle. *Am. J. Physiol.* 6:C231–36
15. Coulson RA. 1987. Aerobic and anaerobic glycolysis in mammals and reptiles in vivo. *Comp. Biochem. Physiol.* 87B: 207–16
16. Coulson RA, Herbert JD. 1984. A role for carbonic anhydrase in intermediary metabolism. *Ann. NY Acad. Sci.* 429: 505–15
17. Dermietzel R, Leibstein A, Siffert W, Zamboglou N, Gros G. 1985. A fast screening method for histochemical localization of carbonic anhydrase. Application to kidney, skeletal muscle and thrombocytes. *J. Histochem. Cytochem.* 33:93–98
18. Dodgson SJ, Contino LC. 1988. Rat kidney mitochondrial carbonic anhydrase. *Arch. Biochem. Biophys.* 260: 334–41
19. Dodgson SJ, Forster RE. 1986. Carbonic anhydrase inhibition results in decreased urea production by hepatocytes. *J. Appl. Physiol.* 60:646–52
20. Dodgson SJ, Forster RE. 1986. Inhibition of CA V decreases glucose synthesis from pyruvate. *Arch. Biochem. Biophys.* 251:198–204
21. Dodgson SJ, Forster RE, Schwed DA, Storey BT. 1983. Contribution of matrix carbonic anhydrase to citrulline synthesis in isolated guinea pig liver mitochondria. *J. Biol. Chem.* 258:7696–701
22. Dodgson SJ, Forster RE, Storey BT, Mela L. 1980. Mitochondrial carbonic anhydrase. *Proc. Natl. Acad. Sci. USA* 77:5562–66
23. Dodgson SJ, Tashian RE, Gros G, Carter

ND, eds. 1991. *The Carbonic Anhydrases. Cellular Physiology and Molecular Genetics.* New York: Plenum. 379 pp.

24. Edsall JT. 1969. Carbon dioxide, carbonic acid and bicarbonate ion: physical properties and kinetics of interconversion. In $CO_2$: *Chemical, Biochemical and Physiological Aspects,* ed. RE Forster, JT Edsall, AB Otis, FJW Roughton Washington, DC: NASA SP #188

25. Effros RM, Mason G, Silverman P. 1981. Role of perfusion and diffusion in $^{14}CO_2$ exchange in the rabbit lung. *J. Appl. Physiol.* 51:1136–44

26. Evans DH. 1977. Further evidence for $Na/NH_4$ exchange in marine teleost fish. *J. Exp. Biol.* 70:213–20

27. Evans DH, Cameron JN. 1986. Gill ammonia transport. *J. Exp. Zool.* 239: 17–23

28. Evans DH, More KJ. 1988. Modes of ammonia transport across the gill epithelium of the dogfish pup (*Squalus acanthias*). *J. Exp. Biol.* 138:375–97

29. Evans DH, More KJ, Robbins SL. 1989. Modes of ammonia transport across the gill epithelium of the marine teleost fish *Opsanus beta. J. Exp. Biol.* 144:339–56

30. Forster RE, Nioka S, Henry RP, Dodgson SJ, Storey BT. 1986. Lung carbonic anhydrase. *Prog. Respir. Res.* 21:41–46

31. Fournier PA, Guderley H. 1992. Metabolic fate of lactate after vigorous activity in the leopard frog, *Rana pipiens. Am. J. Physiol.* 262:R245–54

32. Fournier PA, Guderley H. 1993. Muscle: the predominant glucose-producing organ in the leopard frog during exercise. *Am. J. Physiol.* 264:R239–43

33. Fremont P, Charest PM, Cote C, Rogers PA. 1991. Distribution and ultrastructural localization of carbonic anhydrase III in different skeletal muscle fiber types. See Ref. 23, pp. 241–46

34. Fremont P, Riverin H, Frenette J, Rogers PA, Cote C. 1991. Fatigue and recovery of rat soleus muscle are influenced by inhibition of an intracellular carbonic anhydrase isoform. *Am. J. Physiol.* 260: R615–21

35. Geers C, Gros G. 1984. Inhibition properties and inhibition kinetics of an extracellular carbonic anhydrase in perfused skeletal muscle. *Respir. Physiol.* 56:269–87

36. Geers C, Gros G. 1988. Carbonic anhydrase inhibition affects contraction of directly stimulated rat soleus. *Life Sci.* 42:37–45

37. Geers C, Gros G. 1990. Effects of carbonic anhydrase inhibitors on contraction, intracellular pH and energy-rich phosphates of rat skeletal muscle. *J. Physiol.* 423:279–97

38. Geers C, Gros G. 1991. Muscle carbonic anhydrase: function in muscle contraction and in the hemeostasis of muscle pH and $PCO_2$. See Ref. 23, pp. 227–39

39. Geers C, Gros G, Gartner A. 1985. Extracellular carbonic anhydrase of skeletal muscle associated with the sarcolemma. *J. Appl. Physiol.* 59:548–58

40. Gleeson TT, Dalessio PM. 1989. Lactate and glycogen metabolism in the lizard *Dipsosaurus dorsalis* following exhaustive exercise. *J. Exp. Biol.* 144:377–93

41. Gleeson TT, Dalessio PM. 1990. Lactate: a substrate for reptilian muscle gluconeogenesis following exhaustive exercise. *J. Comp. Physiol.* 160B:331–38

42. Gros G, Dodgson SJ. 1988. Velocity of $CO_2$ exchange in muscle and liver. *Annu. Rev. Physiol.* 50:669–94

43. Gros G, Moll W, Hoppe H, Gross H. 1976. Proton transport by phosphate diffusion—a mechanism for facilitated $CO_2$ diffusion. *J. Gen. Physiol.* 67:773–90

44. Gutknecht J, Bisson MA, Tosteson FC. 1977. Diffusion of carbon dioxide through lipid bilayer membranes: effects of carbonic anhydrase, bicarbonate and unstirred layers. *J. Gen. Physiol.* 69: 779–94

45. Haussinger D, Gerok W, Sies H. 1984. Hepatic role in pH regulation: role of intracellular glutamine cycle. *Trends Biochem. Sci.* 9:299–302

46. Haussinger D, Gerok W. 1985. Hepatic urea synthesis and pH regulation: role of $CO_2$, $HCO_3^-$, and the activity of carbonic anhydrase. *Eur. J. Biochem.* 152: 381–86

47. Haussinger D, Kaiser S, Stehle T, Gerok W. 1986. Liver carbonic anhydrase and urea synthesis: the effect of diuretics. *Biochem. Pharmacol.* 35:3317–22

48. Henry RP. 1984. The role of carbonic anhydrase in blood ion and acid-base regulation. *Am. Zool.* 24:241–53

49. Henry RP. 1987. Quaternary ammonium sulfanilamide: a membrane-impermeant carbonic anhydrase inhibitor. *Am. J. Physiol.* 252:R959–65

50. Henry RP. 1988. Multiple functions of crustacean gill carbonic anhydrase. *J. Exp. Zool.* 248:19–24

51. Henry RP, Booth CE, Lallier FH, Walsh PJ. 1994. Post exercise lactate production and metabolism in three species of aquatic and terrestrial decapod crustaceans. *J. Exp. Biol.* 186:215–34

52. Herbert JD, Coulson RA. 1984. A role for carbonic anhydrase in de novo fatty

acid synthesis. *Ann. NY Acad. Sci.* 429: 525–27

53. Herbert JD, Coulson RA, Hernandez T. 1983. Inhibition of pyruvate carboxylation in alligators and chameleons by carbonic anhydrase inhibitors. *Comp. Biochem. Physiol.* 75A:185–92

54. Herbert JD, Coulson RA, Hernandez T, Ehrensvard G. 1975. A carbonic anhydrase requirement for the synthesis of glutamine from pyruvate in the chameleon. *Biochem. Biophys. Res. Commun.* 65:1054–60

55. Hers HG, Hue L. 1983. Gluconeogenesis and related aspects of glycolysis. *Annu. Rev. Biochem.* 52:617–53

56. Hewett-Emmett D, Hopkins PJ, Tashian RE, Czelusniak J. 1984. Origins and molecular evolution of the carbonic anhydrase isozymes. *Ann. NY Acad. Sci.* 429:338–58

57. Hewett-Emmett D, Tashian RE. 1991. Structure and evolutionary origins of the carbonic anhydrase multigene family. See Ref. 23, pp. 15–32

58. Holmes RS. 1977. Purification, molecular properties, and ontogeny of carbonic anhydrase isozymes: evidence for A, B, and C isozymes in avian and mammalian tissues. *Eur. J. Biochem.* 78:511–20

59. Kawashiro T, Scheid P. 1976. Measurement of Krogh's diffusion constant of $CO_2$ in respiring muscle at various $CO_2$ levels: evidence for facilitated diffusion. *Pflügers Arch.* 362:127–33

60. Kerstetter TH, Kirschner LB, Rafuse DD. 1970. On the mechanism of sodium ion transport by the irrigated gills of rainbow trout (*Salmo gairdneri*). *J. Gen. Physiol.* 56:342–59

61. Kirshner LB. 1979. Control mechanisms in crustaceans and fishes. In *Mechanisms of Osmoregulation in Animals: Maintenance of Cell Volume,* ed. R Gilles, pp. 157–222. New York: Wiley

62. Kirschner LB, Greenwald L, Kerstetter T. 1973. Effect of amiloride on sodium transport across body surfaces of freshwater animals. *Am. J. Physiol.* 224:832–37

63. Kormanik GA, Cameron JN. 1981. Ammonia excretion in animals that breathe water: a review. *Marine Biol. Lett.* 2:11–23

64. Kormanik GA, Cameron JN. 1981. Ammonia excretion in the seawater blue crab (*Callinectes sapidus*) occurs by diffusion, and not $Na^+/NH_4^+$ exchange. *J. Comp. Physiol.* 141B:457–62

65. Lallier FH, Walsh PJ. 1991. Metabolic potential in tissues of the blue crab, *Callinectes sapidus. Bull. Marine Sci.* 48:665–69

66. Lallier FH, Walsh PJ. 1992. Metabolism of isolated hepatopancreas cells from the blue crab (*Callinectes sapidus*) under simulated postexercise and hypoxic conditions. *Physiol. Zool.* 65:712–23

67. Lusty CJ. 1979. Carbamoylphosphate synthetase I of rat liver mitochondria. *Eur. J. Biochem.* 85:373–83

68. Maetz J. 1973. $Na^+/NH_4^+$, $Na/H^+$ exchanges and $NH_3$ movement across the gills of *Carassius auratus. J. Exp. Biol.* 58:255–75

69. Maetz J, Garcia-Romeu F. 1964. The mechanisms of sodium and chloride uptake by the gills of a fresh water fish, *Carassius auratus.* II. Evidence for $NH_4^+/Na^+$ and $HCO_3^-/Cl^-$ exchanges. *J. Gen. Physiol.* 47:1209–27

70. Maren TH. 1967. Carbonic anhydrase: chemistry, physiology, and inhibition. *Physiol. Rev.* 47:595–781

71. Deleted in proof

72. Maren TH. 1980. Current status of membrane-bound carbonic anhydrase. *Ann. NY Acad. Sci.* 341:246–54

73. Milligan CL, Girard SS. 1993. Lactate metabolism in rainbow trout. *J. Exp. Biol.* 180:175–93

74. Mommsen TP, Moon TW. 1987. The metabolic potential of hepatocytes and kidney tissue in the little skate, *Raja erinacea. J. Exp. Zool.* 244:1–8

75. Mommsen TP, Suarez RK. 1984. Control of gluconeogenesis in rainbow trout hepatocytes: role of pyruvate branchpoint and phosphoenolpyruvate-pyruvate cycle. *Mol. Physiol.* 6:9–18

76. Mommsen TP, Walsh PJ, Moon TW. 1985. Gluconeogenesis in hepatocytes and kidney of Atlantic salmon. *Mol. Physiol.* 8:89–100

77. Mommsen TP, Walsh PJ. 1989. Evolution of urea synthesis in vertebrates: the piscine connection. *Science* 243:72–75

78. Moyes CD, Schulte PM, Hochachka PW. 1992. Recovery metabolism of trout white muscle: role of mitochondria. *Am. J. Physiol.* 262:R295–304

79. Nioka S, Forster RE. 1991. Lung carbonic anhydrase. See Ref. 23, pp. 333–40

80. Perry SF. 1986. Carbon dioxide excretion in fishes. *Can. J. Zool.* 64:565–72

81. Perry SF, Davie PS, Daxboeck C, Randall DJ. 1982. A comparison of $CO_2$ excretion in a spontaneously ventilating blood-perfused trout preparation and saline-perfused gill preparations: contribution of the branchial epithelium and red blood cell. *J. Exp. Biol.* 101:47–60

82. Rahim SM, Delaunoy JP, Laurent P. 1988. Identification and immunocytochemical localization of two different

carbonic anhydrase isoenzymes in teleostean fish erythrocytes and gill epithelia. *Histochemistry* 89:451–59

83. Randall DJ, Daxboeck C. 1984. Oxygen and carbon dioxide tranfer across fish gills. In *Fish Physiology*, ed. WS Hoar, DJ Randall, 10A:263–314. New York: Academic

84. Roughton FWJ. 1935. Recent work on carbon dioxide transport by the blood. *Physiol. Rev.* 15:241–96

85. Sanyal G, Swenson ER, Maren TH. 1982. The isolation of carbonic anhydrase from the muscle of *Squalus acanthias* and *Scomber scombrus*: inhibition studies. *Bull. Mt. Desert Island Biol. Lab.* 24:66–68

86. Sanyal G, Swenson ER, Pessah NI, Maren TH. 1982. The carbon dioxide hydration activity of skeletal muscle carbonic anhydrase. *Mol. Pharmacol.* 22:211–20

87. Scheid P, Siffert W. 1985. Effects of inhibiting carbonic anhydrase on isometric contraction of frog skeletal muscle. *J. Physiol.* 361:91–101

88. Schulte PM, Moyes CD, Hochachka PW. 1992. Integrating metabolic pathways in post-exercise recovery of white muscle. *J. Exp. Biol.* 166:181–95

89. Siffert W, Gros G. 1982. Carbonic anhydrase C in white skeletal muscle tissue. *Biochem. J.* 205:559–66

90. Storey BT. 1991. Skeletal muscle mitochondrial carbonic anhydrase. See Ref. 23, pp. 257–62

91. Suarez RK, Mommsen TP. 1987. Gluconeogenesis in teleost fishes. *Can. J. Zool.* 65:1869–82

92. Tang Y, Lin H, Randall DJ. 1992. Compartmental distributions of carbon dioxide and ammonia in rainbow trout at rest and following exercise, and the effect of bicarbonate infusion. *J. Exp. Biol.* 169:235–49

93. Tashian RE, Hewett-Emmett D, eds. 1984. *Biology and Chemistry of the Carbonic Anhydrases*. Vol. 429. New York: Ann. NY Acad. Sci. 640 pp.

94. Thews G. 1953. Uber die methematische Behandlung physiologischer Diffusionsprozesse in zylinderformigen Objekten. *Acta Biotheor.* 10:105–38

95. Vincent SH, Silverman DN. 1982. Carbonic anhydrase activity in mitochondria from rat liver. *J. Biol. Chem.* 257:6850–55

96. Walsh PJ. 1989. An in vitro model of post-exercise hepatic gluconeogenesis in the gulf toadfish *Opsanus beta*. *J. Exp. Biol.* 147:393–406

97. Walsh PJ, Henry RP. 1990. Enzyme activities in the golden crab, *Chaceon fenneri*, the red crab, *Chaceon quinquedens*, and the blue crab, *Callinectes sapidus*. *Marine Biol.* 106:343–46

98. Walsh PJ, Henry RP. 1991. Carbon dioxide and ammonia metabolism and exchange. In *Biochemistry and Molecular Biology of Fishes*, ed. PW Hochachka, TP Mommsen, 1:181–207. New York: Elsevier

99. Walsh PJ, Parent JJ, Henry RP. 1989. Carbonic anhydrase supplies bicarbonate for urea synthesis in toadfish (*Opsanus beta*) hepatocytes. *Physiol. Zool.* 62:1257–72

100. West TG, Schulte PM, Hochachka PW. 1994. Implications of hyperglycemia for post-exercise resynthesis of glycogen in trout skeletal muscle. *J. Exp. Biol.* 189:69–84

101. Wetzel P, Gros G. 1990. Sarcolemmal carbonic anhydrase in red and white rabbit skeletal muscle. *Arch. Biochem. Biophys.* 279:345–54

102. Wilson RW, Wright PM, Munger S, Wood CM. 1994. Ammonia excretion in freshwater rainbot trout (*Oncorhynchus mykiss*) and the importance of gill boundary layer acidification: lack of evidence for $Na^+/NH_4^+$ exchange. *J. Exp. Biol.* 191:37–58

103. Wirtherson G, Guder WG. 1986. Renal substrate metabolism. *Physiol. Rev.* 66:469–97

104. Withers PC, Lea M, Solberg TC, Baustian M, Hedrick M. 1988. Metabolic fates of lactate during recovery from activity in an anuran amphibian, *Bufo americanus*. *J. Exp. Zool.* 246:236–43

105. Wright PA, Randall DJ, Perry SF. 1989. Fish gill water boundary layer: a site of linkage between carbon dioxide and ammonia excretion. *J. Comp. Physiol.* 158B:627–35

106. Wright PA, Randall DJ, Wood CM. 1988. The distribution of ammonia and $H^+$ between tissue compartments in lemon sole (*Parophrys vetulus*) at rest, during hypercapnia, and following exercise. *J. Exp. Biol.* 136:149–75

107. Wright PA, Wood CM. 1985. An analysis of branchial ammonia excretion in the freshwater rainbow trout: effects of environmental pH change and sodium uptake blockade. *J. Exp. Biol.* 114:329–53

108. Zborowska-Sluis DT, L'Abbate A, Klassen GA. 1974. Evidence of carbonic anhydrase activity in skeletal muscle: a role for facilitative carbon dioxide transport. *Respir. Physiol.* 21:341–50

Annu. Rev. Physiol. 1996. 58:539–63
Copyright © 1996 by Annual Reviews Inc. All rights reserved

# DOWNREGULATION OF CELLULAR METABOLISM DURING ENVIRONMENTAL STRESS: Mechanisms and Implications

*Steven C. Hand*

Department of EPO Biology, University of Colorado, Boulder, Colorado 80309-0334

*Iris Hardewig*

Alfred-Wegener-Institute für Polar-und Meeresforschung, Columbusstrasse, 27515 Bremerhaven, Germany

KEY WORDS:     channel arrest, metabolic depression, protein synthesis, oxygen sensing, ubiquitin

---

### ABSTRACT

Survival time of organisms during exposure to environmental stresses that limit energy availability is, in general, directly related to the degree of metabolic depression achieved. The energetic cost savings realized by the organism is a consequence primarily of the ability to depress ion pumping activities of cells, macromolecular synthesis, and macromolecular turnover. Evidence supporting the concept of channel arrest—the reduction in ion leakage across cell membranes during hypometabolic states—has highlighted the energetic benefits of limiting ATP turnover related to cellular ion homeostasis. Depression of protein synthesis results in substantial bioenergetic savings. However, when protein synthesis is arrested, the preservation of macromolecules becomes increasingly important as the duration of quiescence is extended because the cellular capacity for replenishing these components is reduced. It is likely that the rate of macromolecular degradation is a key feature that sets the upper time limit for survival during chronic environmental stress.

---

## INTRODUCTION

Substantial progress has been made recently toward providing mechanistic explanations of how multiple facets of cellular energetics are depressed in

539

response to suboptimal environmental conditions. Bioenergetic constraints imposed by physical factors in the environment can be life threatening. When exposed to desiccating conditions in warm summer months, a land snail forms a mucus seal (epiphragm) for attachment to hard substrate, and as a result, its rate of tissue water loss to the air is reduced. However, under these conditions food intake is precluded. Energetic requirements of the snail must be met during these periods, which can extend for months and years, with internal energy stores such as glycogen and protein (7, 73, 84, 132). Molluscs and annelids that inhabit estuarine mud flats, encysted embryos of brine shrimp buried in sand and decaying algal mats, fish in stagnant pools, and turtles lying in the mud of a frozen lake during winter months can find the primary metabolic pathway for ATP production (oxidative phosphorylation) blocked by the limited availability of an electron acceptor (59, 65, 152, 155). Sediment cores from marine environments have uncovered viable copepod and rotifer embryos that have apparently withstood severe hypoxia/anoxia for 10–40 years, and these forms are now thought to serve as "egg banks" for future generations (105). Without metabolic energy conservation, survival during the above situations would be temporally compromised.

Tolerance to such environmental predicaments can have far-reaching ecological and evolutionary implications, including issues like predator avoidance, species survival, and species dissemination (44, 63, 89, 124). Equally interesting to metabolic and molecular physiologists are the mechanisms underlying the capacities for these organismic-level tolerances. As is emphasized in this review, studies of the coordinated responses to environmental insult have underscored the requirement for depressing both energy production (e.g. oxidative pathways) and energy consumption (e.g. ion pumping, protein synthesis, protein degradation). Otherwise, it is distinctly possible that cellular energy reserves would be depleted and organisms would reach an energetic state from which recovery was not possible (80). Although this concept is generally accepted (60, 65, 67, 68, 78, 145), the mechanisms underlying the downregulation of bioenergetic processes, particularly biosynthesis and macromolecular turnover, are only now becoming clear.

## THE PHENOMENON OF DOWNREGULATION

As noted above, metabolic downregulation is observed in many species in response to unfavorable environmental conditions such as cold, desiccation, anoxia, or starvation. The following overview is restricted to hypometabolic states that are induced by application of an exogenous environmental insult, as opposed to the state of diapause, where hypometabolism is controlled by endogenous factors. Diapausing organisms will remain hypometabolic even when exposed to physical conditions that would normally promote active metabolism and development (for review see 65). Although diapause is widespread biologically, the molecular and biochemical mechanisms controlling this form of dormancy are poorly understood (36, 65, 148).

## Degrees of Metabolic Depression

Hibernating mammals decrease body temperature during winter, which serves to reduce the metabolic costs of maintaining a large thermal gradient between the body and environment. The voluminous database on mammalian hibernation cannot be reviewed here (for reviews, see 22), but it is appropriate to note that hypothermia is accompanied by a marked drop in metabolic activity. Metabolic rate in hibernating marmots, for instance, is reduced to 8% of the basal energy requirement of active animals (52). During a bout of daily torpor in the deer mouse (*Peromyscus maniculatus*), with body temperature ($T_b$) 21.6°C at an ambient temperature of 10°C, the respiration rate is reduced to 26% of that measured under euthermic conditions ($T_b$ = 36.6°C) (113).

Oxygen consumption of the estivating frog *Neobatrachus wilsmorei* is reduced by 80 to 85% compared to the non-estivating rate (48). Similar values have been found in estivating land snails (6–8, 73, 84, 130). Both heat dissipation and oxygen consumption are decreased by 83% in the pulmonate snail *Oreohelix strigosa* during short-term estivation (130). The agreement between calorimetric and respirometric data indicates that the reduced energy provision by oxidative metabolism under these conditions is not compensated by anaerobic ATP production, at least during the first 48 h of estivation (130).

In response to dehydration, anhydrobiotic animals enter a state of cryptobiosis in which metabolism comes to a standstill in a reversible fashion (33, 66, 76); the organism at this point is reduced to nothing more than a morphological state (76). Various studies with anhydrobiotes have characterized the acute transitions in respiration accompanying dehydration and rehydration (27, 31, 34). Respiration rates of brine shrimp embryos from San Francisco Bay (*Artemia franciscana*) increase from undetectable levels to 1.0 $\mu$g $O_2 \cdot$mg dry mass$^{-1} \cdot$h$^{-1}$ within the first 45 min of hydration in the vapor phase of 0.5 M NaCl (27). Heat dissipation by these embryos from the Great Salt Lake (Utah) displays similar dependencies on hydration state as those for respiration (53).

Energy limitation due to lack of nutrients in the environment is often accompanied by a substantially decreased metabolic rate. In some bacterial strains, a reduction of the endogenous respiration by more than 90% has been observed upon starvation (110, 116). The marine *Vibrio* Ant-300, which can survive 2 years of starvation, reduces its respiration to only 0.007% of the rate observed under exponential growth (116). Similar depression of metabolism is seen during

**Table 1** Comparison of ATP turnover and survival time under anoxia for different facultative anerobes

| Species | ATP turnover (% aerobic rate) (°C) | $LT_{50}$[a] (°C) | Reference |
|---|---|---|---|
| *Carrasius auratus* | 26 (20) | 16 h (20) | 154, 155 |
| *Sipunculus nudus* | 27 (15) | ca 72 h (15) | 70, HO Pörtner, personal communication |
| *Cardium tuberculatum* | 6 (18) | 5 day (10) *(C. lamarcki, C. edule)* | 108, 149 |
| *Mytilus edulis* | 5 (13) | 35 day (10) (at 0.15 ml $O_2$/l) | 35, 150 |
| *Artica islanidica* | 1 (10) | 46 day (10) | 118, 149 |
| *Arstarte borealis* | 1 (10) | 80 day (10) | 118, 149 |
| *Artemia franciscana* | ≤0.5 (25) | ≥24 month (21–24) | 28, 64, 68a, 83 |

[a] $LT_{50}$ is the length of time under anoxia required for 50% mortality.

starvation in yeast cells, where maintenance metabolism during long-term starvation is very low and not measurable by conventional methods (61, 114).

In the absence of oxygen, an organism is dependent on anaerobic mechanisms of energy production, which provide less energy than oxidative phosphorylation in terms of ATP yield per mol substrate. To compensate for this low ATP yield, a large increase in the glycolytic rate is necessary to obtain the same amount of ATP per unit of time (Pasteur effect). This approach, however, leads to enormous expenditure of substrates and to high accumulation rates of metabolic waste products such as protons. In contrast to employing a Pasteur effect, a way to avoid such deleterious effects of anoxia is to minimize the ATP consumption under these conditions. Such a strategy is realized by most facultative anaerobes. In general, the key pattern emerging from facultative anaerobes is that the degree of metabolic depression observed under anoxia correlates with the duration of survival (Table 1).

Although anoxia-sensitive tissues such as rat hepatocytes do not decrease their ATP turnover and show a loss of viability within 2 h of anoxia (5), hepatocytes of the diving turtle *Chrysemys picta* display a 90% decrease of the ATP turnover and maintain viability for at least 10 h (17). These turtles show a remarkable tolerance to prolonged periods of anoxic submergence. They survive 2 weeks of anoxia at 18°C and 4–5 months at 3°C and reduce their metabolic heat dissipation to 85% of the normoxic value (86, 112, 152).

## ATP Coupling Vs Decoupling: Two Different Strategies

Most facultative anaerobes defend their ATP levels during anaerobiosis. In *Sipunculus nudus*, no significant change of the ATP concentration is observed after 24 h of anaerobiosis (70). In goldfish, ATP levels drop by only 14% after 3.5 h of anoxia (154). In *Mytilus edulis*, ATP concentrations decrease 20% during 24 h of anoxia, but do not fall below 60% of the normoxic level during 7 days of anoxic exposure (37).

In contrast, *Artemia franciscana* embryos show a sharp drop in ATP concentration (77%) within the first hour of anoxia, while metabolism is being severely depressed (2, 69). Similarly, there is a large depression of overall energy flow in locusts during bouts of anoxia, as measured with microcalorimetry (79, 160). Heat dissipation declines within about 1.5 h to 6–7% of normoxic values for *Schistocerca gregaria*, and whole body levels of ATP drop to 13% of control (aerobic) values (79). For small leeches, a large metabolic depression under severe hypoxia is associated with a 79% decline in ATP/ADP ratio (129).

These large net declines in tissue ATP level are predictably accompanied by downward shifts in intracellular pH because the net hydrolysis of ATP generates free protons, the stoichiometry of which depends on the $pH_i$ itself (123). Busa (18) suggests that the severe drop in $pH_i$ from 7.7 to 6.7 observed in *Artemia* embryos under anoxia (20, 94) is due substantially to proton formation during ATP hydrolysis. Indeed, animals that defend their ATP levels under anoxia show only minor changes in $pH_i$. In *Sipunculus*, where ATP levels remain constant, $pH_i$ decreases by only about 0.16 pH units (71). In *Mytilus edulis* (45) and goldfish (154), which both show a slight net decline in ATP, $pH_i$ drops about 0.26 and 0.48 units, respectively. However, Kwast et al (94) estimated that, at most, 27% of the protons responsible for the pH drop observed in *Artemia franciscana* are produced by ATP hydrolysis and that other factors contribute to the acidosis. As is discussed below, evidence from *Artemia* embryos suggests that large drops in $pH_i$ may serve as a cellular signal for downregulating various aspects of metabolism.

It is not fully clear at present why some organisms defend ATP levels under anoxia and some do not. The regulation of intracellular pH and ATP concentrations close to normoxic levels may be necessary for some species in order to maintain locomotory capacity. On the other hand, low pH and adenylate energy status are correlated with an extension of protein half-life during anoxia (see below), which suggests that a simultaneous decrease in these variables may be advantageous when locomotory performance is not critical.

# DOWNREGULATION OF ION PUMPING: CHANNEL ARREST

A considerable percent of the basal metabolic rate of a cell is attributed to ion pumping in order to maintain ion gradients across cell and mitochondrial membranes (11, 25). These gradients have various functions including propagation and amplification of signals in excitable membranes, facilitated diffusion or secondary active transport of metabolites, and mitochondrial ATP production. Furthermore, if ion gradients are severely compromised across the plasma membrane, voltage-gated calcium channels would open, resulting in large increases in intracellular $Ca^{2+}$ levels (77). The elevated calcium would then lead to abnormal activation of $Ca^{2+}$-activated phospholipases, thereby compromising the structural integrity of membranes and causing cell death (77).

## Metabolic Cost Estimates

The metabolic cost of ion transport is variable among tissues and is generally high in organs that are characterized by high ion fluxes or electrical activity. In human kidney, 70% of the total ATP turnover is attributed to $Na^+K^+$-ATPase activity. In human brain, this value amounts to about 50%, whereas it is considerably lower in muscle tissue (4–8%) (25). However, these and similar values must be viewed critically because the primary method for generating such results is the measurement of ouabain-inhibitable oxygen consumption. Nobes et al (115) have shown that long incubation of the tissue with ouabain (>10 min) can have secondary inhibitory effects on oxygen consumption, which can lead to an overestimation of the contribution of $Na^+K^+$-ATPase activity to total ATP turnover. Thus the metabolic cost for $Na^+K^+$ pumping might actually be lower than estimated in those studies where long incubation times have been employed.

An additional fraction of ATP turnover in cells is attributed to the maintenance of the proton gradient across the inner mitochondrial membrane. Dissipation of this gradient is not fully coupled with ATP production. Proton leakage through the membrane without ATP synthesis accounts for 20–40% of the respiration rate of isolated rat hepatocytes (12). A similarly high value of about 30% has been found in hepatocytes of a lizard (12).

If maintenance of ion balance consumes such a substantial fraction of the basal energy requirements, questions arise as to the fate of ion homeostasis under conditions of reduced energy provision. In the mammalian brain, which is highly sensitive to anoxia and ischemia, major perturbations of energy status and ion homeostasis are observed within a few minutes of anoxia. These events lead to loss of electrical activity and eventually to cell death (40, 142). The brain of the diving turtle *Chrysemys picta*, however, shows an extraordinary tolerance to prolonged anoxia. Turtle brain can survive 18 h of anoxia at 25°C, and during this time, ATP levels and ion gradients are preserved (40). This preservation of ion gradients is accomplished in the face of a severely depressed metabolic rate under anoxia (39, 102).

## *Mechanisms for Depression of Ion Leak and Ion Pumping*

The hypothesis of channel arrest predicts that the ion conductance of brain cells will be reduced under anoxia in order to spare ion transport and thus conserve energy (77). To evaluate this hypothesis, it is helpful to discriminate between voltage-gated channels and leakage channels. Voltage-gated channels allow for the rapid de- and repolarization of membranes and are necessary for the generation and propagation of action potentials. Leakage channels are responsible for low-rate ion diffusion along their gradients in resting cells.

A reduction in the number of voltage-gated $Na^+$ channels has been shown by selective labeling of the channels with $^3H$-brevetoxin, an inhibitor of voltage-gated $Na^+$ channels. In turtle brain, the number of channels is decreased by 58% within 15 min of anoxia (120, 121). The lower density of $Na^+$ channels is accompanied by a lower $Na^+$ conductivity of the membrane that leads to an elevation of the $Na^+$ spike threshold. This change in spike threshold may reduce spontaneous electrical activity of the brain. Evidence for reduced electrical activity under anoxia was obtained from the comparison of the degree of metabolic depression in anoxic brain slices and the whole brain in situ. Whereas an 80% drop in ATP turnover is observed in the brain in situ (102), electrically inactive cortical slices showed only a 30–42% decrease (39), indicating that about half of the reduction in ATP turnover observed in the working brain is due to a decrease of electrical activity. The metabolic depression that occurs in brain slices must be due to other mechanisms, one of which may be a decrease of passive ion leakage through the membrane in the resting state.

However, Doll and co-workers found that membrane resistance and ion conductance remain constant in the turtle brain during short-term and long-term anoxia (41, 42). Other studies, on the contrary, indicate that ion leakage may actually be reduced in the anoxic turtle brain because ion gradients are not dissipated under anoxia although energy provision is limited. The extracellular $K^+$ concentration, which rises abruptly in anoxic rat cortex, is almost constant during 48 h of anoxia in turtle brain (103). Bickler (9) showed that intracellular calcium concentration remains constant in anoxic cortical slices from turtle in contrast to rat cortex, where $Ca_i$ rises because of $Ca^{2+}$ influx from the extracellular space.

Data from other tissues and organisms also suggest a functional downregulation of ion channels during anoxia that prevents a rapid equilibration of ion gradients at decreased rates of $Na^+K^+$ pumping. In isolated hepatocytes from diving turtles, a 75% depression of the $Na^+K^+$-ATPase is observed under anoxia even though the membrane potential remained constant (16). The estivating frog *Neobatrachus wilsmorei* shows a decline of oxygen consumption to 20% of the non-estivating value, whereas transmembrane $Na^+K^+$ gradients are still maintained (48). It is unlikely that under conditions of substantially reduced ATP provision, the same amount of energy would be allocated to ion pumping. The maintenance of the $Na^+K^+$ gradients suggests a decreased dissipation that may be mediated by inhibition of the $Na^+$ symport and facilitated diffusion, or by reduction of membrane leakage through channel arrest (48).

Rat hepatocytes are able to preserve the proton motive force across the inner mitochondrial membrane in the absence of oxygen for at least 30 min (5). The authors suggest that the maintenance of this gradient is achieved by inhibition of passive ion flux through the membrane, and this phenomenon is considered to be a protective mechanism during short-term anoxia. Evidence for downregulation of proton leakage through the mitochondrial membrane has been obtained from comparisons of P:O ratios under normoxia and severe hypoxia in isolated mitochondria from rat liver and from embryos of the brine shrimp *Artemia franciscana* (54). Whereas phosphorylation efficiency drops during ADP limitation under normoxia, P:O ratios are conservatively fivefold higher under severe hypoxia when oxygen consumption is limited by oxygen supply. A reduction in proton leakage across the inner membrane under hypoxia could potentially explain this observation, which would decrease state 4 respiration.

The proton permeability of the inner mitochondrial membrane is dependent on the physical properties of the lipid bilayer and can be influenced by the degree of fatty acid saturation; a higher proportion of unsaturated fatty acids decreases the proton conductance of the membrane (13). However, changes of membrane composition in response to anoxia have not yet been reported. Shigenaga et al (141) showed that oxidative damage to mitochondria, which raises the levels of peroxidized lipids, increases the membrane permeability. Thus it is possible that reductions in free radical formation under severe hypoxia could translate into decreased membrane permeability.

Membrane conductance for ions through proteinaceous channels can be modulated either by changing the density of channels or by regulating the activity of the existing channels (120, 121). In addition to inhibition by $Ca^{2+}$ (98), changes in redox state (137), and shifts in pH (126), phosphorylation of channel proteins (99) appears to be the most widespread means of ion channel regulation. Interestingly, a direct effect of oxygen tension on $K^+$ channels has been observed in arterial chemoreceptor cells (51). The open probability of these channels is reversibly decreased by at least 50% on exposure to anoxia. Ganfornina & Lopez-Barneo suggest a direct effect of the oxygen tension via a heme-like prosthetic group bound to the channel molecule.

Finally, possible mechanisms for downregulating the $Na^+/K^+$-ATPase pump in response to anoxia include phosphorylation of the $\alpha$ subunit, reduction in catalytic activity due to lowered intracellular $Na^+$ concentrations, and removal of pumps from the membrane via endocytosis (16). These possibilities await experimental study.

# PROTEIN SYNTHESIS

Under resting conditions, the metabolic cost for protein synthesis ranges between 18 and 26% in various tissues and cell types (72). Even higher values are observed in tissues during growth or increased biosynthetic activity. In growing bacteria, between 40 and 60% of the ATP turnover is attributed to protein synthesis (146). During sexual maturation of turtles, large amounts of vittelogenin are produced in the liver. In this state, 28 to 36% of the ATP turnover of hepatocytes is from protein synthesis (96). Considering these high costs of protein synthesis, it is evident that this process could be one targeted for inhibition during metabolic depression.

Evidence from a number of organisms and tissues suggests that depression of protein synthesis is quite prevalent under environmental conditions that promote energy limitation. After 6 h of anoxia exposure in embryos of the brine shrimp *A. franciscana*, the synthesis rate of cytochrome c oxidase (COX) is reduced by 78% (80). Clegg & Jackson (29) have shown that incorporation of amino acids into the total protein fraction of these embryos under anoxia is also greatly depressed, which suggests that the results for COX are indicative of protein synthesis in general. Anoxic incubation of isolated turtle hepatocytes leads to a 92% decrease of incorporation of labeled leucine (96), which accounts for 33% of the total metabolic depression in these cells. Oxygen limitation has been demonstrated to depress protein synthesis in rat liver (50a, 143, 147). Similarly, by following incorporation of radiolabeled methionine into the protein fraction of livers isolated from active and hibernating ground squirrels, Whitten & Klain (161) demonstrated that a decrease in protein synthesis occurred in this tissue during hibernation; others have found similar trends in tissues of hibernating mammals (163, 164).

Protein synthesis is also arrested upon limited nutrient availability. In the ciliate *Tetrahymena*, protein synthesis is decreased by 70% during starvation (35). The rate of total protein synthesis in a strain of marine *Vibrio* sp. is decreased to 2.3% after 24 h of carbon starvation and to 0.7% after 3 days, when compared with the rate observed during exponential growth (49); polyribosomes could not be detected in these cells after 24 h of starvation. This phenomenon is part of a complex set of metabolic adjustments termed the stringent control response, which occurs in bacterial cells upon starvation (117).

As inferred from the above studies, downregulation of protein synthesis appears to be a general cost-saving response during energy limitation. In principle, mechanisms for this arrest could involve changes in the steady-state levels of messenger RNA and/or alterations that may occur in the capacity of the biosynthetic machinery (translational control).

## Alterations in Steady-State Levels of mRNA

Currently only limited data are available relating levels of mRNA to down-regulation of protein synthesis during metabolic depression. Hofmann & Hand (81) reported that a statistical decrease in the total pool of translatable mRNA in embryos of *A. franciscana* cannot be detected during the first 4 h of anoxia. This brief time interval was chosen because inhibited rates of protein synthesis under anoxia are already observable by this time (at least for COX). Similarly, no decrease in total translatable mRNA was observed under the condition of aerobic acidosis, an aerobic treatment that lowers intracellular pH with elevated $CO_2$ (19) and depresses protein synthesis to the same degree as anoxia (80, 82). Thus these data suggest that decreases in levels of total mRNA are not responsible for restricting the downregulation of protein synthesis. Recent data indicate that mRNA for subunit I of COX (COXI) does not change during 6 h of anoxia in these embryos (I Hardewig et al, unpublished observations), even though biosynthesis of this enzyme is substantially depressed after 6 h of anoxia (80).

Mitochondrial mRNA levels for NADH dehydrogenase subunits 3 and 4/4L, cytochrome c oxidase III, and $H^+$-ATPase subunits 6/6L do not show a measurable decline during the first 12 h of exposure to moderate hypoxia (15 torr) in HeLa cells (88). Only a slight decline in these mRNA species is seen after 24 h. However, a sharp fall (perhaps by as much as 95%) is observed after 48 h. The degradation rate of mRNAs was apparently not changed over a similar period of hypoxia in the presence of cordycepin (>50% degradation per 8 h). It would be helpful to directly compare this delayed fall in mitochondrial mRNA with the profile of biosynthetic rates for these proteins under hypoxia, but such data are currently lacking. After a 72 h hypoxic exposure (2% oxygen) of human myoblasts, a moderate decline in mRNA for ATP synthase subunit 6, NADH dehydrogenase subunit 1, and COX subunit III (all mitochondrially encoded) was noted, with selected glycolytic mRNAs (glyceraldehyde-3 phosphate dehydrogenase, pyruvate kinase, and triosephosphate isomerase) maintained at high levels (159).

Srere et al (144) provide evidence showing that alpha$_2$-macroglobulin is preferentially synthesized in ground squirrels (*Spermophilus richardsonii* and *S. columbianus*) during hibernation, in contrast to the pattern for plasma protein albumin. The upregulation of this species of mRNA is interesting in comparison with the overall depression of protein synthesis in liver during hibernation of ground squirrels (mentioned above).

Levels of polyadenylated mRNA were assessed in various tissues of turtles (*Trachemys scripta elegans*) that had been exposed to anoxic submergence for 16 h (43). With the exception of one tissue (white muscle; 30% decline), mRNA levels were unchanged over this period. However, the in vitro translatability of this phenol extracted, oligo(dT)-purified mRNA did not correlate well with the absolute amount of poly-A mRNA measured in a number of the tissues.

## Translational Control of Protein Synthesis

Thus in cases where precise time courses for changes in mRNA and protein synthesis have been compared during environmentally induced quiescence, the data point toward a substantial contribution of translational control to biosynthetic depression. A reduction in the number of polysomes in rat liver has been reported under anoxia (147). Similarly, a statistically significant decrease in the ratio of polysomes to monosomes has been seen after short-term (5 h) exposure of *Artemia* embryos to anoxia or aerobic acidosis (81). A slower disaggregation time has been reported by others (29). Diminished polysome levels were observed in liver extracts from hibernating ground squirrels relative to active animals (162). A rapid decrease in polysomes is consistent with an inhibition of initiation. In general, regulating the capacity of the translational machinery allows for rapid alteration of synthesis rates and for reversal of the inhibition or activation equally rapidly (74).

Evidence from a variety of systems suggests that a dominant mechanism for control of global protein synthesis (in terms of activity of the ribosome) is phosphorylation/dephosphorylation of translational components, primarily initiation and elongation factors (74). Studies using cell-free translation systems from *A. franciscana* embryos show that the arrest of protein synthesis during anoxia-induced quiescence is influenced by depression of translational capacity (82). Incorporation of [$^3$H]leucine by lysates prepared from 4-h anoxic embryos was 8% of that from aerobic (control) embryos, when measurements were performed at the respective pH values measured for each treatment in vivo. Similarly, lysates prepared from embryos exposed to 4 h of aerobic acidosis displayed incorporation rates that were 3% of control values. Because both anoxia and aerobic acidosis treatments depress $pH_i$ by approximately one pH unit (19, 20, 94) and promote metabolic arrest, lysates from each treatment were assayed over a range of physiologically relevant pH values (pH 6.4–8.0). The results support a role for intracellular pH as an initial signaling event in translational control during quiescence, yet at the same time indicate that a direct proton effect on the translational machinery is not the sole proximal agent for biosynthetic arrest in these embryos. One possibility consistent with these data is that the $pH_i$ transition serves to promote a covalent change in translational components (initiation factors, elongation factors). It is noteworthy that treatment of lysates from aerobic *Artemia* embryos with protein kinase C serves to depress translational capacity to that of lysates from anoxic embryos (I Hardewig & SC Hand, unpublished observations).

Precedence for such an influence of $pH_i$ on phosphorylation has been reported for starved *Tetrahymena thermophila,*, where a change of 0.8 pH unit was associated with reversible phosphorylation of a 40S ribosomal protein, which in turn altered protein synthesis (57). Similarly, in the absence of calcium mobilization, both serine/threonine phosphorylation and protein synthesis respond to change in $pH_i$ in hamster embryo cells (85). In contrast, protein synthesis in sea urchin eggs, long thought to be influenced predominantly by alkalinization of $pH_i$, can be activated in vivo to >50% of the rate observed during natural fertilization, even when $pH_i$ is held constant experimentally (134). The influence of changes in redox state, known to increase during fertilization (46), may have a substantial influence in controlling protein synthesis in this system (1), as well as $Ca^{2+}$ transience (e.g. 47).

## Coordination of Cytoplasmic and Mitochondrial Protein Synthesis

Another aspect of the downregulation of protein synthesis in quiescent cells is the manner in which biosynthesis within mitochondria is controlled. If protein synthesis is to be blocked universally during quiescence, then coordination of this process between cytoplasmic and mitochondrial compartments must be accomplished in some manner. Numerous nuclear genes required for mitochondrial DNA transcription and replication (26) and mitochondrial translation (32, 50, 125, 151, 165) have now been identified and cloned.

An excellent series of studies with *Saccharomyces cerevisiae* has documented the role of nuclearly encoded peptides in activating the translation of COX subunits I-III and cytochrome bc1 complex in the mitochondrion (32, 50, 90, 151). There often is more than one activator peptide per mitochondrial mRNA species. For yeast grown under anoxia, the expression of *PET494*, a nuclear gene coding for an activator of COXIII synthesis, was only 20% of that observed in yeast grown in aerobic conditions (106). It is proposed that expression of this type of activator protein controls the downregulation of COX I-III in response to anoxia and high glucose levels in these cells. Evidence suggests that the activator binds to the 5' leader sequence of the message, thereby fostering its translation. Thus if cytoplasmic translation is arrested, the availability of these activators becomes limited intramitochondrially, and the synthesis of gene products encoded by the mitochondrion is depressed.

This mechanism for coordination of protein synthesis of cytochrome subunits in the mitochondrial compartment as currently understood for yeast cells involves independent translational regulation of each gene, which seems on the surface to be unnecessarily complicated. It remains to be seen how widespread such a mechanism may be across eukaryotic cells in general. Evidence with *A. franciscana* embryos hints that other regulatory controls may be operative for downregulating mitochondrial protein synthesis during anaerobic quiescence. Preliminary results show that there is no statistical difference in total protein synthesis (assayed aerobically) between mitochondria isolated from aerobic embryos and embryos given 6 h of anoxia (T Anchordoguy et al, unpublished observations). This observation suggests that physiological factors (e.g. $pH_i$; oxygen limitation per se) may be involved in the downregulation of protein synthesis observed in vivo under anoxia, as opposed to the lack of nuclearly encoded activation factors.

Both $pH_i$ acidification (92) and oxygen deprivation (93) severely inhibit the capacity for protein synthesis in mitochondria isolated from A. franciscana embryos. When the extramitochondrial pH was lowered from 7.5 to 6.7, mitochondrial protein synthesis was reduced by 80%. This range of pH change mimics that seen in vivo during the transition into anoxia for Artemia embryos. At a constant pH of 7.5, exposure of mitochondria to anoxia reduced protein synthesis by 79%, compared with aerobic controls (93). When pH and oxygen deprivation were combined, a maximum of 89% inhibition was achieved. Thus oxygen deprivation and $pH_i$ both may contribute to downregulation of mitochondrial protein synthesis. The influence of extramitochondrial pH on protein synthesis appears to be mediated via changes in matrix pH and does not involve changes in matrix purine nucleotides (91). The strong influence of oxygen limitation cannot be explained by simply blocking the electron transport chain because cyanide titration under aerobic conditions does not inhibit protein synthesis as severely as does oxygen removal (91). Thus the effects of oxygen limitation apparently are multifaceted.

There appear to be multiple mechanisms that coordinate the depression of protein synthesis in cytoplasmic and mitochondrial compartments. It does not seem that the yeast paradigm is the only regulatory scheme applicable under all physiological conditions, particularly those characterized by acute changes in protein synthesis.

## PROTEIN TURNOVER

Another crucial problem that must be solved during hypometabolic states is how the integrity and viability of macromolecules are preserved. Considering that both energy-producing pathways and protein synthetic processes are arrested during quiescence, one would predict that protein turnover must also be depressed in order to avoid depletion of macromolecules. In terms of recovery from quiescence, insurmountable difficulties could arise if key metabolic enzymes have to be resynthesized de novo prior to resuming the energy flows characteristic of the active state. For example, Hofmann & Hand (80) have estimated that the apparent half-life of cytochrome c oxidase in A. franciscana is 31.5 h. Calculations indicate that if enzyme degradation rate is not depressed during quiescence, COX levels would drop below 5% of the control levels during a 6-day bout of anoxia. Yet these embryos show prompt recovery from anoxic periods of this length, as judged by increases in heat dissipation (64). As mentioned above, these embryos can survive anoxia-induced quiescence for 2 years (28), so clearly, protein half-life must be extended in order to avoid depletion of macromolecules.

## Extension of Macromolecular Half-Life

Consistent with this prediction, there is an increase in the half-life of COX during anoxia exposure on the order of 77-fold, relative to the value for aerobic controls (4). The estimated half-life under aerobic acidosis is increased 7.5-fold. Although degradation under aerobic acidosis is clearly slower than under control conditions of aerobic development, the rate is not depressed to the extent seen during anoxia. These results may reflect the marked difference in the adenylate pools in the embryo under aerobic acidosis or anoxia (see below).

Extended protein half-lives have been demonstrated more recently in isolated turtle hepatocytes under anoxia (97). Labile protein half-lives increased from 25 to 34 h, while the stable protein half-lives increased from 56 to 110 h. Land & Hochachka estimate that ATP-dependent proteolysis may account for 22% ($11 \ \mu mol \ ATP \bullet g^{-1} \bullet h^{-1}$) of the total cellular metabolism under aerobic conditions, but that under anoxia, this value is depressed by 93% to 0.73 $\mu mol$ $ATP \bullet g^{-1} \bullet h^{-1}$. Also, there is an apparent shift under anoxia to proteolysis that is largely energy independent (97).

An interesting set of observations has been made by Clegg et al (30) regarding an abundant 26-kDa protein that undergoes translocation to the nucleus during anoxia in embryos of *A. franciscana*. The reverse translocation occurs when anoxic embryos are returned to aerobic conditions. Furthermore, the 26-kDa protein appears to associate with an increased variety of soluble proteins under anoxia. Thus it is possible that the protein may serve as a protective molecular chaperone during prolonged anoxia and other forms of stress. This hypothesis is quite germane considering the extension of COX half-life in these embryos.

## Mechanisms for Depression of Protein Degradation

One implication from the extended half-lives of proteins is that protein degradation is markedly depressed under anoxia. Although multiple mechanisms are undoubtedly involved, the ATP dependence of the ubiquitin pathway for proteolysis (24), coupled with its inhibition at low pH (111, 127), makes the blockage of this pathway a likely candidate for increasing protein longevity during quiescence. In *A. franciscana* embryos, two hallmark features of anoxia-induced quiescence are a substantial rise in AMP at the expense of ATP (3) and a severe acidification of $pH_i$. The process of ubiquitination is known to be a key event in the degradation of short-lived proteins such as regulatory enzymes (24, 128, 135). The activation of the ubiquitin molecule by the E1 enzyme (ubiquitin-activating enzyme) allows ubiquitin to be covalently attached to a protein, thereby marking it for subsequent degradation. The E1 enzyme has an absolute requirement for ATP (24). The ubiquitinated proteins are subsequently degraded by a large (26S), ATP-dependent protease (55, 100, 139).

Anchordoguy & Hand (2) have reported a rapid decline in the level of ubiquitin-protein conjugates during entry into anoxia-induced quiescence in *A. franciscana* embryos. The levels of ubiquitin-conjugated proteins drop to 37% of control (aerobic) values during the first hour of anoxia and reach 7% in 24 h. The effect is rapidly reversed by returning embryos to control (aerobic) conditions (3). ATP falls to 5% of control values under anoxia and, importantly, AMP rises reciprocally. By comparison, when embryos are subjected to artificial acidosis under aerobic conditions ($pH_i$ drops sharply, but ATP does not change for hours), ubiquitin-conjugated proteins decline to 58% after 1 h.

Although the proximate mechanism for the depression of ubiquitination has not been proven, the decrease in $pH_i$ and the alterations in the adenylate pool both appear to contribute to the depression. However, the very low $K_{1/2}$ value for ATP (0.04 mM) (62) suggests that declining cellular ATP can only limit ubiquitination under the most severe conditions. Hershko et al (75) demonstrated a progressive inhibition of proteolysis in the presence of increasing AMP concentrations, from which an apparent $K_i$ for AMP of approximately 0.15 mM can be calculated. Consequently, inhibition of ubiquitination by AMP may explain why proteolysis in intact cells is depressed before ATP drops to levels sufficient to limit this process. What ever the proximal mechanism, arrest of ubiquitination in these embryos likely serves to depress ubiquitin-dependent degradation of protein (153) and helps preserve macromolecular integrity under anoxia. In regard to the extension of COX half-life documented above, it is noteworthy that ubiquitin conjugates and ubiquitin-conjugating enzymes are associated with mitochondria in rabbit brain (104). Therefore, it is plausible that control of mitochondrial protein turnover may involve the ubiquitin-dependent pathway.

Other factors that may be responsible for lowering protein degradation during anoxia include changes in 2,3-bisphosphoglycerate levels (inhibitor of ATP-dependent lysosomal proteolysis) (136) and increased synthesis of protease inhibitors like alpha$_2$-macroglobulin (144). Finally, it has been shown that phosphorylation can mediate changes in protein conformation that alter susceptibility to attack by $Ca^{2+}$-activated proteases (58).

## SENSING AND SIGNALING

From the foregoing information it is clear that many biochemical events are triggered in response to entry into quiescent states. Questions arise as to how these environmental perturbations are sensed and how these signals are transduced to initiate the downregulation processes reviewed above. At this point, the majority of information on this topic comes from studies of oxygen deprivation.

### Oxygen Sensing: Heme and Hemoproteins

Evidence indicates that in many cells, free heme and hemoproteins are intimately involved in oxygen sensing (56, 119, 140, 165). Heme is synthesized in the mitochondrion and then distributed to additional cellular locations (119). Due to its high, nonspecific affinity for proteins and membranes (165), the free exchangeable concentration of heme is difficult to measure, but it is thought to be in the range of 10–100 nM (119). There is an absolute requirement for molecular oxygen for heme biosynthesis at two steps catalyzed by coproporphyrinogen III oxidase and protoporphyrinogen IX oxidase; the former is the rate-limiting step in the process (95). Consequently, cellular levels of heme could be dependent on oxygen availability in the cell, although the affinity of coprophyrinogen III for oxygen is high, and the enzyme can be induced at low oxygen tensions (95, 165).

Heme is the prosthetic group in cytochromes and many oxygen-binding proteins, and evidence suggests that a hemoprotein serves as the oxygen sensor during the induction of erythropoietin (EPO) at low oxygen tensions in hepatoma cells (56, 140). The induction of EPO, a glycoprotein hormone responsible for altering erythrocyte levels, can be inhibited by carbon monoxide; reduced hemoproteins with accessible iron-binding sites are the only known targets for CO interactions in biological systems. The EPO induction is also blocked when heme synthesis is chemically inhibited (56).

### Signaling by DNA-Binding Proteins

Molecular evidence is rapidly accumulating supporting the widespread existence of control sequences that are regulated by DNA-binding proteins in response to oxygen levels. Transcription of numerous genes can be activated through the effect that heme has on heme-activation proteins (HAP). Binding of heme by HAP unmasks the DNA-binding domain of this protein and allows its binding to upstream activation sites for numerous genes (122). There are two distinct groupings of heme activation proteins (HAP1 and HAP2/3/4), and these are the only proteins thus far identified that mediate heme activation of transcription (for review see 165). Conversely, heme can serve to inhibit gene expression through the action of the repressor protein ROX1 (101). ROX1 binds to an operator sequence and is capable of repressing a variety of transcriptional activators (165). The expression of ROX1 is itself activated transcriptionally by heme via HAP1. There are also a number of oxygen-regulated genes whose expression is heme independent (165).

As mentioned above, expression of EPO is regulated by the influence of oxygen on transcription of its gene (140). An enhancer element located in the 3'-flanking region of the EPO gene activates the hypoxia-inducible transcription of the gene upon the binding of hypoxia-inducible factor 1 (HIF-1) to the enhancer sequence 5'-TACGTGCT-3' (see discussion in 107, 140). HIF-1 has recently been purified and characterized (158). The sensing of hypoxia by a hemoprotein has been proposed to somehow lead to the de novo synthesis of HIF-1. Subsequent to the elucidation of transcriptional activation of the EPO gene by HIF-1, additional HIF-1-binding sequences have been identified that flank various glycolytic enzymes and serve to modulate expression of these enzymes under hypoxia upon the binding of HIF-1 (140). Similarly, nuclear respiratory factor 1 (NRF-1) is a transcriptional activator involved in the coordinated regulation of nuclear genes encoding various respiratory chain enzymes (156, 157).

## Nontranscriptional Signaling

Regulation that is not directly based on transcriptional control may be equally important, if not more so, to the phenomenon of metabolic depression. Often the physiological response to environmental insult is rapid, occurring in minutes (69). Thus the influence of alterations in intracellular pH, phosphorylation, redox potential, nitric oxide levels, and even oxygen free radicals may be fundamentally linked to metabolic arrest.

Evidence indicates that the large $pH_i$ acidification measured in an *A. franciscana* embryo plays a regulatory role in the shutdown of metabolic and developmental activity during entry into anoxia (for review of mechanisms, see 65). Incubation under aerobic acidosis (which is not accompanied by reduction in ATP levels for at least several hours) (3) results in a quiescent embryo that displays many biochemical responses identical to those observed during anoxia. The latter observation provides compelling support for $pH_i$ as a key cellular signal in this metabolic switching. The possibilities for pH-induced changes in protein phosphorylation have been discussed above. Acidification of $pH_i$ may also contribute to metabolic depression in estivating land snails (6, 8, 130, 131, 133). However, evidence for a direct effect of $pH_i$ is equivocal in this case, and the influence of pH may be limited to providing an appropriate metabolic context for other effectors and hormones to function properly (21, 131, 138).

Phosphorylation of selected enzymes has been correlated with the down-regulation of metabolism in a number of organisms (145). These phosphorylation patterns (15) are associated with changes in levels of cyclic nucleotides. For example, Brooks & Storey (14) have provided evidence for the involvement of cGMP in the phosphorylation of pyruvate kinase in the anoxic whelk *Busycon canaliculatum*. The mechanisms for coupling changes in cyclic nucleotides to anoxic transitions are not well understood and, often, potential mechanisms for modulating activities of nucleotide cyclases in an oxygen-dependent manner appear to operate opposite to the direction required. For example, production of nitric oxide in hepatocytes has been linked to the stimulation of the soluble guanylate cyclase and an increase in cellular cGMP levels (10). Nitric oxide has been implicated in the signaling of a variety of cellular functions, and its synthesis from arginine by nitric oxide synthase requires molecular oxygen (109).

Protein synthesis in many cells is regulated by the phosphorylation of the $\alpha$-subunit of eukaryotic initiation factor 2 (eIF-$2\alpha$). One form of this factor is heme-regulated (HRI). Reductions in heme level activate HRI, and its activity is inhibited by high heme levels (23). This pattern suggests the possibility of oxygen-induced changes in initiation through the activity of HRI. NADPH: $NADP^+$ ratio also influences protein synthesis, an effect potentially mediated by protection of protein sulfhydryl groups by the thioredoxin system (87) or by direct inhibition of the guanine nucleotide exchange factor by $NADP^+$ (38).

## CONCLUSIONS

Survival time of organisms during exposure to environmental stresses that limit energy availability is, in general, directly related to the degree of metabolic depression achieved. The energetic cost savings realized by the organism is primarily a consequence of the ability to depress ion pumping activities of cells, macromolecular synthesis, and macromolecular turnover. It is likely that the rate of macromolecular degradation is a key feature that sets the upper time limit for survival during chronic anoxia.

Future studies that attempt to explain more precisely how environmental stresses are transduced into the required physiological responses should be meaningful in the context of integrative biology. In the area of oxygen sensing and signaling, for example, mechanisms for coupling changes in transcription and translation (both cytoplasmic and mitochondrial) to oxygen limitation remain to be fully elucidated. The potential involvement of new sensing mechanisms, beyond those events attributable to heme and hemoproteins, is apt to provide a clearer picture of how metabolic downregulation is coordinated. Nitric oxide is one cellular messenger receiving little attention from this perspective, and oxygen free radicals, primarily viewed as damaging by-products of electron transport systems, may actually have regulatory significance over short cellular distances. The selection pressures that establish for a given species whether advantage is gained by defending or not defending cellular adenylates during environmental insult deserve further consideration. One might speculate that certain organisms (including encysted or encapsulated stages for example), for which loss of locomotory performance is not a major concern, may benefit from macromolecular stabilization gained by allowing cellular ATP and intracellular pH to severely plummet (and AMP to rise) during chronic anoxia. At present, evidence for the potential role of protein phosphorylation in depressing catabolic pathways under anoxia in facultative anaerobes is limited essentially to data based on temporal correlations. Molecular genetics should aid in providing more compelling cases for roles of these regulatory events.

ACKNOWLEDGMENTS

Portions of the work discussed were supported by the National Science Foundation grants DCB-9018579 and IBN-9306652 to SCH. I Hardewig was supported by a Deutsche Forschungsgemeinshaft fellowship.

## Literature Cited

1. Akkaraju GR, Hansen LJ, Jagus R. 1991. Increase in eukaryotic initiation factor 2B activity following fertilization reflects changes in redox potential. *J. Biol. Chem.* 266:24451–59
2. Anchordoguy TJ, Hand SC. 1994. Acute blockage of the ubiquitin-mediated proteolytic pathway during invertebrate quiescence. *Am. J. Physiol.* 267:R895–900
3. Anchordoguy TJ, Hand SC. 1995. Reactivation of ubiquitination in *Artemia franciscana* embryos during recovery from anoxia-induced quiescence. *J. Exp. Biol.* 198:1299–1305
4. Anchordoguy TJ, Hofmann GH, Hand SC. 1993. Extension of enzyme half-life during quiescence in *Artemia* embryos. *Am. J. Physiol.* 264:R85–89
5. Andersson BS, Aw TY, Jones DP. 1987. Mitochondrial transmembrane potential and pH gradient during anoxia. *Am. J. Physiol.* 252:C349–55
6. Barnhart MC. 1986. Control of acid-base status in active and dormant land snails, *Otala lactea* (Pulmonata, Helicidae). *J. Comp. Physiol. B* 156:347–54
7. Barnhart MC, McMahon BR. 1987. Discontinuous carbon dioxide release and metabolic depression in dormant land snails. *J. Exp. Biol.* 128:123–38
8. Barnhart MC, McMahon BR. 1988. Depression of aerobic metabolism and intracellular pH by hypercapnia in land snails, Otala lactea. *J. Exp. Biol.* 138:289–99
9. Bickler PE. 1992. Cerebral anoxia in turtles: regulation of intracellular calcium and pH. *Am. J. Physiol.* 263:R1298–1302
10. Billiar TR, Curran RD, Harbrecht BG, Stadler J, Williams DL, et al. 1992. Association between synthesis and release of cGMP and nitric oxide biosynthesis by hepatocytes. *Am. J. Physiol.* 262:C1077–82
11. Brand MD. 1990. The contribution of the leak of protons across the mitochondrial inner membrane to standard metabolic rate. *J. Theor. Biol.* 145:267–86

12. Brand MD, Chien LF, Ainscow EK, Rolfe D, Porter RK. 1994. The causes and functions of mitochondrial proton leak. *Biochim. Biophys. Acta* 1187:132–39

13. Brand MD, Steverding D, Kadenbach B, Stevenson PM, Hafner RP. 1992. The mechanism of the increase in mitochondrial proton permeability induced by thyroid hormones. *Eur. J. Biochem.* 206:775–81

14. Brooks SPJ, Storey KB. 1990. cGMP-stimulated protein kinase phosphorylates pyruvate kinase in an anoxiatolerant marine mollusc. *J. Comp. Physiol. B* 160:309–16

15. Brooks SPJ, Storey KB. 1995. Protein phosphorylation patterns during aestivation in the land snail *Otala lactea. Mol. Cell. Biochem.* 143:7–13

16. Buck LT, Hochachka PW. 1993. Anoxic suppression of $Na^+$-$K^+$-ATPase and constant membrane potential in hepatocytes: support for channel arrest. *Am. J. Physiol.* 265:R1020–25

17. Buck LT, Land SC, Hochachka PW. 1993. Anoxia-tolerant hepatocytes: a model system for the study of reversible metabolic suppression. *Am. J. Physiol.* 265:R49–56

18. Busa WB. 1985. How to succeed at anaerobiosis without really dying. *Mol. Physiol.* 8:351–58

19. Busa WB, Crowe JH. 1983. Intracellular pH regulates transitions between dormancy and development of brine shrimp (*Artemia salina*) embryos. *Science* 221:366–68

20. Busa WB, Crowe JH, Matson GB. 1982. Intracellular pH and the metabolic status of dormant and developing *Artemia* embryos. *Arch. Biochem. Biophys.* 216:711–18

21. Busa WB, Nuccitelli R. 1984. Metabolic regulation via intracellular pH. *Am. J. Physiol.* 246:R409–38

22. Carey C, Florant GL, Wunder BA, Horowitz B, eds. 1993. *Life in the Cold III: Ecological, Physiological, and Molecular Mechanisms.* Boulder, CO: Westview Press, 575 pp.

23. Chen JJ, London IM. 1995. Regulation of protein synthesis by heme-regulated eIF-2α kinase. *Trends Biochem. Sci.* 20:105–8

24. Ciechanover A. 1994. The ubiquitin-proteolytic pathway. *Cell* 79:13–21

25. Clausen T, van Hardeveld C, Everts ME. 1991. Significance of cation transport in control of energy metabolism and thermogenesis. *Physiol. Rev.* 71:733–74

26. Clayton DA. 1991. Replication and transcription of vertebrate mitochondrial DNA. *Annu. Rev. Cell Biol.* 7:453–78

27. Clegg JS. 1976. Interrelationships between water and cellular metabolism in *Artemia* cysts. III. *Respir. Comp. Biochem. Physiol.* 53A:89–93

28. Clegg JS. 1994. Unusual response of *Artemia franciscana* embryos to prolonged anoxia. *J. Exp. Zool.* 270:332–34

29. Clegg JS, Jackson SA. 1989. Aspects of anaerobic metabolism of *Artemia* cysts. In *The Cellular and Molecular Biology of Artemia Development,* ed. AH Warner, J Bagshaw, T MacRae. pp. 1–15. New York: Plenum

30. Clegg JS, Jackson SA, Warner AH. 1994. Extensive intracellular translocations of a major protein accompany anoxia in embryos of *Artemia franciscana. Exp. Cell Res.* 212:77–83

31. Cooper AF Jr, Van Gundy SD. 1970. Metabolism of glycogen and neutral lipids by *Aphelenchus avenae* and *Caenorhabditis* sp. in aerobic, microaerobic, and anaerobic environments. *J. Nematol.* 2:305–15

32. Costanzo MC, Fox TD. 1990. Control of mitochondrial gene expression in *Saccharomyces cerevisiae. Annu. Rev. Genet.* 24:91–113

33. Crowe JH, Clegg JS, eds. 1978. *Dry Biological Systems.* New York/San Francisco/London: Academic. 357 pp.

34. Crowe JH, Madin KAC, Loomis SH. 1977. Anhydrobiosis in nematodes: metabolism during resumption of activity. *J. Exp. Zool.* 201:57–64

35. Cuny M, Sripati CE, Hayes DH. 1985. The specific phosphorylation of 40S ribosomal protein in growth-arrested *Tetrahymena* is induced by sodium. *J. Cell. Physiol.* 124:349–57

36. Danks HV. 1987. Insect dormancy: an ecological perspective. *Biol. Survey Can. Monogr. Ser. 1.* Gloucester, Ontario, Canada: Tyrell. 439 pp.

37. deZwaan A, Wijsmann TCM. 1976. Anaerobic metabolism in bivalvia (mollusca). Characteristics of anaerobic metabolism. *Comp. Biochem. Physiol.* 43A:53–58

38. Dholakia JN, Mueser TC, Woodley CL, Parkhurst LJ, Wahba AJ. 1986. The association of NADPH with guanine nucleotide exchange factor from rabbit reticulocytes: a role of pyridine dinucleotides in eukaryotic polypeptide chain initiation. *Proc. Natl. Acad. Sci. USA* 83:6746–50

39. Doll CJ, Hochachka PW, Hand SC. 1994. A microcalorimetric study of turtle cortical slices: insights into brain

metabolic depression. *J. Exp. Biol.* 191: 141–53

40. Doll CJ, Hochachka PW, Reiner PB. 1991. Effects of anoxia and metabolic arrest on turtle and rat cortical neurons. *Am. J. Physiol.* 260:R747–55

41. Doll CJ, Hochachka PW, Reiner PB. 1991. Channel arrest: implications from membrane resistance in turtle neurons. *Am. J. Physiol.* 261:R1321–24

42. Doll CJ, Hochachka PW, Reiner PB. 1993. Reduced ionic conductance in turtle brain. *Am. J. Physiol.* 265:R929–33

43. Douglas DN, Giband M, Altosaar I, Storey KB. 1994. Anoxia induces changes in translatable mRNA populations in turtle organs: a possible adaptive strategy for anaerobiosis. *J. Comp. Physiol. B* 164:405–14

44. Elgmork K. 1980. Evolutionary aspects of diapause in fresh-water copepods. In *Evolution and Ecology of Zooplankton Communities,* ed. WC Kerfoot, pp. 411–17. Hanover/London: Univ. Press New England

45. Ellington WR. 1983. The extent of intracellular acidification during anoxia in the catch muscle of two bivalve molluscs. *J. Exp. Zool.* 227:313–17

46. Epel D. 1964. A primary metabolic change of fertilization: interconversion of pyridine nucleotides. *Biochem. Biophys. Res. Commun.* 17:62–68

47. Epel D. 1990. The initiation of development at fertilization. *Cell Differ. Dev.* 29:1–12

48. Flanigan JE, Withers PC, Fuery CJ, Guppy M. 1993. Metabolic depression and $Na^+K^+$ gradients in the aestivating Australian goldfields frog, *Neobatrachus wilsmorei. J. Comp. Physiol. B* 163:587–93

49. Flärdh K, Cohen PS, Kjelleberg S. 1992. Ribosomes exist in large excess over the apparent demand for protein synthesis during carbon starvation in the marine *Vibrio* sp. strain CCUG 15956. *J. Bacteriol.* 174:6780–88

50. Fox TD, Shen Z. 1993. Positive control of translation in organellar genetic systems. In *Protein Synthesis and Targeting in Yeast,* ed. AJP Brown, MF Tuite, JEG McCarthy, pp. 157–66. Berlin: Springer-Verlag

50a. Frantz ID Jr, Loftfield RB, Miller WW. 1947. Incorporation of $C^{14}$ from carboxyl-labeled dl-alanine into the proteins of liver slices. *Science* 106:544–45

51. Ganfornina MD, Lopez-Barneo J. 1991. Single $K^+$ channels in membrane patches of arterial chemoreceptor cells are modulated by $O_2$ tension. *Proc. Natl. Acad. Sci. USA* 88:2927–30

52. Geiser F. 1988. Reduction of metabolism during hibernation and daily torpor in mammals and birds: temperature effect or physiological inhibition? *J. Comp. Physiol.* 158B:25–37

53. Glasheen JS, Hand SC. 1989. Metabolic heat dissipation and internal solute levels of *Artemia* embryos during changes in cell-associated water. *J. Exp. Biol.* 145:263–82

54. Gnaiger E, Mendez G, Hand SC. 1993. Mitochondrial efficiencies under microxic and normoxic conditions. *Biophys. J.* 64:489 (Abstr.)

55. Goldberg AL. 1995. Functions of the proteosome: the lysis at the end of the tunnel. *Science* 268:522–23

56. Goldberg MA, Dunning SP, Bunn HF. 1988. Regulation of the erythropoietin gene: evidence that the oxygen sensor is a heme protein. *Science* 242:1412–15

57. Goumard G, Cuny M, Sripati CE, Hayes DH. 1990. Monovalent cation-dependent reversible phosphorylation of a 40S ribosomal subunit protein in growth-arrested *Tetrahymena:* correlation with changes in intracellular pH. *FEBS Lett.* 262:335–38

58. Greenwood JA, Troncoso JC, Costello AC, Johnson GVW. 1993. Phosphorylation modulates calpain-mediated proteolysis and calmodulin binding of the 200-kDa and 160-kDA neurofilament proteins. *J. Neurochem.* 61:191–99

59. Grieshaber MK, Hardewig I, Kreutzer U, Pörtner HO. 1994. Physiological and metabolic responses to hypoxia in invertebrates. *Rev. Physiol. Biochem. Pharmacol.* 125:43–147

60. Guppy M, Fuery CJ, Flanigan JE. 1994. Biochemical principles of metabolic depression. *Comp. Biochem. Physiol.* 109B:175–89

61. Gustafsson L. 1991. Microbiological calorimetry. *Thermochim. Acta* 193: 145–71

62. Haas AL, Rose IA. 1982. The mechanism of ubiquitin activating enzyme. *J. Biol. Chem.* 257:10329–37

63. Hairston NG Jr. 1987. Diapause as a predator-avoidance adaptation. In *Predation. Direct and Indirect Impacts on Aquatic Communities,* ed. WC Kerfoot, A Sih, pp. 281–90. Hanover/London: Univ. Press New England

64. Hand SC. 1990. Heat dissipation during long-term anoxia in *Artemia franciscana* embryos: identification and fate of metabolic fuels. *J. Comp. Physiol. B* 160:357–63

65. Hand SC. 1991. Metabolic dormancy in aquatic invertebrates. *Adv. Comp. Environ. Physiol.* 8:1–50

66. Hand SC. 1992. Water content and metabolic organization in anhydrobiotic animals. In *Water and Life*, ed. GN Somero, CB Osmond, CL Bolis, pp. 104–27. Berlin: Springer-Verlag

67. Hand SC. 1993. pH$_i$ and anabolic arrest during anoxia in *Artemia franciscana* embryos. In *Surviving Hypoxia: Mechanisms of Control and Adaptation*, ed. PW Hochachka, PL Lutz, T Sick, M Rosenthal, G van den Thillart, pp. 171–85. Boca Raton, FL: CRC Press

68. Hand SC. 1993. Perspectives on molecular function in hibernators: insights from quiescent states of invertebrates. In *Life in the Cold III: Ecological, Physiological, and Molecular Mechanisms*, ed. C Carey, GL Florant, BA Wunder, B Horowitz, pp. 455–65. Boulder, CO: Westview Press

68a. Hand SC. 1995. Heat flow is measurable from *Artemia franciscana* embryos under anoxia. *J. Exp. Zool.* In press

69. Hand SC, Gnaiger E. 1988. Quantification of anaerobic dormancy in *Artemia* embryos: a calorimetric test of the control mechanism. *Science* 239:1425–27

70. Hardewig I, Addink ADF, Grieshaber MK, Pörtner HO, van den Thillert G. 1991. Metabolic rates at different oxygen levels determined by direct and indirect calorimetry in the oxyconformer *Sipunculus nudus*. *J. Exp. Biol.* 157:143–60

71. Hardewig I, Kreutzer U, Pörtner HO, Grieshaber MK. 1991. The role of phosphofructokinase in glycolytic control in the facultative anaerobe *Sipunculus nudus*. *J. Comp. Physiol. B* 161:581–89

72. Hawkins AJS. 1991. Protein turnover: a functional appraisal. *Funct. Ecol.* 5:222–33

73. Herreid CF. 1977. Metabolism of land snails (*Otala lactea*) during dormancy, arousal, and activity. *Comp. Biochem. Physiol.* 56A:211–15

74. Hershey JWB. 1991. Translational control in mammalian cells. *Annu. Rev. Biochem.* 60:717–55

75. Hershko A, Heller H, Ganoth D, Ciechanover A. 1978. Mode of degradation of abnormal globin chains in rabbit reticulocytes. In *Protein Turnover and Lysosome Function*, ed. HL Segal DJ Doyle, pp. 149–69. New York: Academic

76. Hinton HE. 1968. Reversible suspension of metabolism and the origin of life. *Proc. R. Soc. London Ser. B* 171:43–57

77. Hochachka PW. 1986. Defense strategies against hypoxia and hypothermia. *Science* 231:234–41

78. Hochachka PW, Guppy M. 1987. *Metabolic Arrest and the Control of Biological Time*. Cambridge, MA: Harvard Univ. Press. 227 pp.

79. Hochachka PW, Nener JC, Hoar J, Saurez RK, Hand SC. 1993. Disconnecting metabolism from adenylate control during extreme oxygen limitation. *Can. J. Zool.* 71:1267–70

80. Hofmann GE, Hand SC. 1990. Arrest of cytochrome c oxidase synthesis coordinated with catabolic arrest in dormant *Artemia* embryos. *Am. J. Physiol.* 258:R1184–91

81. Hofmann GH, Hand SC. 1992. Comparison of messenger RNA pools in *Artemia franciscana* embryos: evidence for translational control. *J. Exp. Biol.* 164:103–16

82. Hofmann GE, Hand SC. 1994. Global arrest of translation during invertebrate quiescence. *Proc. Natl. Acad. Sci. USA* 91:8492–96

83. Hontoria F, Crowe JH, Crowe LM, Amat F. 1993. Metabolic heat production by *Artemia* embryos under anoxic conditions. *J. Exp. Biol.* 178:149–59

84. Horne FR. 1973. The utilization of foodstuffs and urea production by a land snail during estivation. *Biol. Bull.* 144:321–30

85. Isfort RJ, Cody DB, Asquith TN, Ridder GM, Stuard GM, Leboeuf RA. 1993. Induction of protein phosphorylation, protein synthesis, immediate-early-gene expression and cellular proliferation by intracellular pH modulation. *Eur. J. Biochem.* 213:349–57

86. Jackson DC. 1968. Metabolic depression and oxygen depletion in the diving turtle. *J. Appl. Physiol.* 24:503–9

87. Jackson RJ, Herbert P, Campbell EA, Hunt T. 1983. The roles of sugar phosphates and thiol-reducing systems in the control of reticulocyte protein synthesis. *Eur. J. Biochem.* 131:313–24

88. Kadowaki T, Kitagawa Y. 1991. Hypoxic depression of mitochondrial mRNA levels in HeLa cell. *Exp. Cell Res.* 192:243–47

89. King CE. 1980. The genetic structure of zooplankton populations. In *Evolution and Ecology of Zooplankton Communities*, ed. WC Kerfoot, pp. 315–28. Hanover/London: Univ. Press New England

90. Kloekner-Gruissem B, McEwan JM, Poyton RO. 1987. Nuclear functions required for cytochrome c oxidase biogenesis in *Saccharomyces cerevisiae*: multiple *trans*-acting nuclear genes exert specific effects on expression of each of the cytochrome c oxidase subunits

encoded in mitochondrial DNA. *Curr. Genet.* 12:311–22

91. Kwast KE. 1995. *Mitochondrial protein synthesis and bioenergetics during transitions between aerobic development and anoxia-induced quiescence in Artemia franciscana embryos.* PhD thesis. Univ. Colorado, Boulder. 171 pp.

92. Kwast K, Hand SC. 1993. Regulatory features of protein synthesis in isolated mitochondria from *Artemia* embryos. *Am. J. Physiol.* 265:R1238–46

93. Kwast K, Hand SC. 1995. Oxygen and pH regulation of protein synthesis in mitochondria from *Artemia franciscana* embryos. *Biochem. J.* In press

94. Kwast KE, Shapiro JI, Rees BB, Hand SC. 1995. Oxidative phosphorylation and the realkalinization of intracellular pH during recovery from anoxia in *Artemia franciscana* embryos. *Biochim. Biophys. Acta.* In press

95. Labbe-Rois R, Labbe P. 1990. Tetrapyrrole and heme biosynthesis in the yeast *Saccharomyces cerevisiae.* In *Biosynthesis of Heme and Chlorophylls*, ed. HA Dailey, pp. 235–85. New York: McGraw-Hill

96. Land SC, Buck LT, Hochachka PW. 1993. Response of protein synthesis to anoxia and recovery in anoxia tolerant hepatocytes. *Am. J. Physiol.* 265:R41–48

97. Land SC, Hochachka PW. 1994. Protein turnover during metabolic arrest in turtle hepatocytes: role for energy dependence of proteolysis. *Am. J. Physiol.* 266: C1028–36

98. Latorre R, Oberhauser A, Labarca P, Alvarez O. 1989. Varieties of calcium-activated potassium channels. *Annu. Rev. Physiol.* 51:385–99

99. Levitan IB. 1994. Modulation of ion channels by protein phosphorylation and dephosphorylation. *Annu. Rev. Physiol.* 56:193–212

100. Löwe J, Stock D, Jap B, Zwickl P, Baumeister W, Huber R. 1995. Crystal structure of the 20S proteosome from the archaeon *T. acidophilum* at 3.4 resolution. *Science* 268:533–39

101. Lowry CV, Zitomer RS. 1988. *ROX1* encodes a heme-induced expression factor regulating *ANB1* and *CYC7* of *Saccharomyces cerevisiae. Mol. Cell. Biol.* 8:4651–58

102. Lutz PL, McMahon PM, Rosenthal M, Sick TJ. 1984. Relationship between aerobic and anaerobic energy production in turtle brain in situ. *Am. J. Physiol.* 265:R41–48

103. Lutz PL, Rosenthal M, Sick TJ. 1985. Living without oxygen: turtle brain as a model of anaerobic metabolism. *Mol. Physiol.* 8:411–25

104. Magnani M, Serafini G, Amtonelli A, Malatesta M, Gazzanelli G. 1991. Evidence for a particulate location of ubiquitin conjugates and ubiquitin-conjugating enzymes in rabbit brain. *J. Biol. Chem.* 266:21018–24

105. Marcus NH, Lutz R, Burnett W, Cable P. 1994. Age, viability, and vertical distribution of zooplankton resting eggs from an anoxic basin: evidence of an egg bank. *Limnol. Oceanogr.* 39:154–58

106. Marykwas DL, Fox TD. 1989. Control of the *Saccharomyces cerevisiae* regulatory gene *PET494*: transcriptional repression by glucose and translational induction by oxygen. *Mol. Cell. Biol.* 9:484–91

107. Maxwell PH, Pugh CW, Ratcliffe PJ. 1993. Inducible operator of the erythropoietin 3' enhancer in multiple cell lines: evidence for a widespread oxygen-sensing mechanism. *Proc. Natl. Acad. Sci. USA* 90:3423–27

108. Meinardus-Hager G, Gabbott PA, Gäde G. 1989. Regulatory steps of glycolysis during environmental anoxia and muscular work in the cockle *Cardium tuberculatum*: control of low and high glycolytic flux. *J. Comp. Physiol. B* 159:195–203

109. Moncada S, Palmer RMJ, Higgs EA. 1991. Nitric oxide: physiology, pathophysiology, and pharmacology. *Pharmacol. Rev.* 43:109–42

110. Morita RY. 1988. Bioavailability of energy and its relationship to growth and starvation survival in nature. *Can. J. Microbiol.* 34:437–41

111. Müller M, Dubiel W, Rathmann J, Rapoport S. 1980. Determination and characterization of energy-dependent proteolysis in rabbit reticulocytes. *Eur. J. Biochem.* 109:405–10

112. Musacchia XJ. 1959. The viability of *Chrysemys picta* submerged at various temperatures. *Physiol. Zool.* 32:47–50

113. Nestler JR. 1990. Relationships between respiratory quotient and metabolic rate during entry to and arousal from daily torpor in deer mice (*Peromyscus maniculatus*). *Physiol. Zool.* 63:504–15

114. Nilsson A, Larsson C, Gustafsson L. 1995. Catabolic capacity of *Saccharomyces cerevisiae* in relation to the physiological state and maintenance requirement. *Thermochim. Acta* 250:233–46

115. Nobes CD, Lakin-Thomas PL, Brand MD. 1989. The contribution of ATP turnover by the $Na^+K^+$ ATPase to the rate of respiration of hepatocytes.

Effects of thyroid status and fatty acids. *Biochim. Biophys. Acta* 976:241–45

116. Novitsky JA, Morita RY. 1977. Survival of the psychrophilic marine vibrio under long-term nutrient starvation. *Appl. Environ. Microbiol.* 33:635–41

117. Nyström T, Albertson NH, Flärdh K, Kjelleberg S. 1990. Physiological and molecular adaptation to starvation and recovery from starvation by the marine *Vibrio* sp. S14. *FEMS Microbiol. Ecol.* 74:129–40

118. Oeschger R. 1990. Long-term anaerobiosis in sublittoral marine invertebrates from Western Baltic Sea. *Mar. Ecol. Prog. Ser.* 59:133–43

119. Padmanaban G, Venkateswar V, Rangarajan PN. 1989. Haem as a multifunctional regulator. *Trends Biochem. Sci.* 14:492–96

120. Perez-Pinzon MA, Chan C, Rosenthal M, Sick TJ. 1992. Membrane and synaptic activity during anoxia in isolated turtle cerebellum. *Am. J. Physiol.* 262: R1057–63

121. Perez-Pinzon MA, Rosenthal M, Sick TJ, Lutz PL, Pablo J, Mash D. 1992. Downregulation of sodium channels during anoxia: a putative survival strategy of turtle brain. *Am. J. Physiol.* 262: R712–15

122. Pfeifer K, Kim K-S, Kogan S, Guarente L. 1989. Functional dissection and sequence of the yeast HAP1 activator. *Cell* 56:291–301

123. Pörtner HO. 1987. Contributions of anaerobic metabolism to pH regulation in animal tissues: theory. *J. Exp. Biol.* 131: 69–87

124. Pourriot R, Snell TW. 1983. Resting eggs in rotifers. *Hydrobiologia* 104: 213–24

125. Poyton RO, McEwen JE. 1996. Crosstalk between nuclear and mitochondrial genomes. *Annu. Rev. Biochem.* 65:In press

126. Prod'hom B, Peitrobon D, Hess P. 1987. Direct measurement of proton transfer rates to a group controlling the dihydropyridine-sensitive $Ca^{2+}$ channel. *Nature* 329:243–46

127. Rapoport S, Dubiel M, Müller M. 1985. Proteolysis of mitochondria in reticulocytes during maturation is ubiquitin-dependent and is accompanied by a high rate of ATP hydrolysis. *FEBS Lett.* 180: 249–52

128. Rechsteiner M. 1987. Ubiquitin-mediated pathways for intracellular proteolysis. *Annu. Rev. Cell Biol.* 3:1–30

129. Reddy DC, Davies RW. 1993. Metabolic adaptations by the leech *Nephelopsis*

*obscura* during long-term anoxia and recovery. *J. Exp. Zool.* 265:224–30

130. Rees BB, Hand SC. 1990. Heat dissipation, gas exchange and acid-base status in the land snail *Oreohelix strigosa* during short-term estivation. *J. Exp. Biol.* 152:77–92

131. Rees BB, Hand SC. 1991. Regulation of glycolysis in the land snail *Oreohelix* during estivation and artificial hypercapnia. *J. Comp. Physiol. B* 161:237–46

132. Rees B, Hand SC. 1993. Biochemical correlates of estivation tolerance in the mountain snail *Oreohelix* (Pulmonata: Oreohelicidae). *Biol. Bull.* 184:230–42

133. Rees B, Malhotra D, Shapiro J, Hand SC. 1991. Intracellular pH decreases during entry into estivation in the land snail *Oreohelix strigosa*. *J. Exp. Biol.* 159:525–30

134. Rees BB, Patton C, Grainger JL, Epel D. 1995. Protein synthesis increases after fertilization of sea urchin eggs in the absence of an increase in intracellular pH. *Dev. Biol.* 169:683–98

135. Rivett AJ. 1990. Eukaryotic protein degradation. *Curr. Opin. Cell Biol.* 2:1143–49

136. Roche E, Aniento F, Knecht E, Grisolia S. 1987. Bisphosphoglycerate inhibits ATP-stimulated proteolysis. *FEBS Lett.* 221:231–35

137. Ruppersberg JP, Stock M, Pongs O, Heinemann SH, Frank R, Koenen M. 1991. Regulation of fast inactivation of cloned mammalian Ik(A) channels by cysteine oxidation. *Nature* 352:711–14

138. Scholnick DA, Snyder GK, Spell AR. 1994. Acid-base status of a pulmonate land snail (*Helix aspersa*) and a prosobranch amphibious snail (*Pomacea bridgesi*) during dormancy. *J. Exp. Zool.* 268:293–98

139. Seemüller E, Lupas A, Stock D, Löwe J, Huber R, Baumeister W. 1995. Proteosome from *Thermoplasma acidophilum*: a threonine protease. *Science* 268: 579–82

140. Semenza GL, Roth PH, Fang HM, Wang GL. 1994. Transcriptional regulation of genes encoding glycolytic enzymes by hypoxia-inducible factor 1. *J. Biol. Chem.* 269:23757–63

141. Shigenaga MK, Hagen TM, Ames BN. 1994. Oxidative damage and mitochondrial decay in aging. *Proc. Natl. Acad. Sci. USA* 91:10771–78

142. Sick TS, Rosenthal M, LaManna JC, Lutz PL. 1982. Brain potassium homeostasis, anoxia, and metabolic inhibition in turtles and rats. *Am. J. Physiol.* 243: R281–88

143. Simpson MV, Tarver H. 1950. Studies

on protein synthesis in vitro. III. Further observations on the incorporation of methionine into liver protein. *Arch. Biochem.* 25:384–95

144. Srere HK, Wang LCH, Martin SL. 1992. Central role for differential gene expression in mammalian hibernation. *Proc. Natl. Acad. Sci. USA* 89:7119–23

145. Storey KB, Storey JM. 1990. Metabolic rate depression and biochemical adaptation in anaerobiosis, hibernation, and estivation. *Q. Rev. Biol.* 65:145–74

146. Stouthamer AH. 1977. Energetic aspects of the growth of micro-organisms. In *Microbial Energetics*, ed. BA Haddock, WA Hamilton, pp. 285–315. Cambridge: Cambridge Univ. Press

147. Surks MI, Berkowitz M. 1971. Rat hepatic polysome profiles and in vitro protein synthesis during hypoxia. *Am. J. Physiol.* 220:1606–9

148. Tauber MJ, Tauber CA, Masaki S. 1986. *Seasonal Adaptations of Insects.* New York/Oxford: Oxford Univ. Press. 414 pp.

149. Theede H. 1984. Physiological approaches to environmental problems of the Baltic. *Limnologica* 15:443–58

150. Theede H, Ponat A, Hiroki K, Schlieper C. 1969. Studies on the resistance of marine bottom invertebrates to oxygen-deficiency and hydrogen sulphide. *Mar. Biol.* 2:325–37

151. Tzagoloff A, Dieckmann CL. 1990. *PET* genes of *Saccharomyces cerevisiae.* *Microbiol. Rev.* 54:211–25

152. Ultsch G. 1985. The viability of nearctic freshwater turtles submerged in anoxia and normoxia at 3 and 10°C. *Comp. Biochem. Physiol.* 81A:607–11

153. van Breukelen F, Hand SC. 1994. ATP-dependent protein degradation in embryos of the brine shrimp, *Artemia franciscana. Physiologist* 37:A70 (Abst.)

154. van den Thillart G, van Waarde A, Muller HJ, Erkelens C, Addink A, Lugtenburg J. 1989. Fish muscle energy metabolism measured in vivo $^{31}$P-NMR during anoxia and recovery. *Am. J. Physiol.* 256:R922–29

155. van Waversveld J, Addink ADF, van den Thillart G. 1989. Simultaneous direct and indirect calorimetry on normoxic and anoxic goldfish. *J. Exp. Biol.* 142:325–35

156. Virbasius CA, Virbasius JV, Scarpulla RC. 1993. NRF-1, an activator involved in nuclear-mitochondrial interactions, utilizes a new DNA-binding domain conserved in a family of developmental regulators. *Genes Dev.* 7:243–45

157. Virbasius JV, Scarpulla RC. 1994. Activation of human mitochondrial transcription factor A gene by nuclear respiratory factors: a potential regulatory link between nuclear and mitochondrial gene expression in organelle biosynthesis. *Proc. Natl. Acad. Sci. USA* 91:1309–13

158. Wang GL, Semenza GL. 1995. Purification and characterization of hypoxia-inducible factor 1. *J. Biol. Chem.* 270:1230–38

159. Webster KA, Gunning P, Hardeman E, Wallace DC, Kedes L. 1990. Coordinate reciprocal trends in glycolytic and mitochondrial transcript accumulations during the in vitro differentiation of human myoblasts. *J. Cell. Physiol.* 142:566–73

160. Wegener G. 1993. Hypoxia and posthypoxic recovery in insects: physiological and metabolic aspects. In *Surviving Hypoxia: Mechanisms of Control and Adaptation*, ed. PW Hochachka, PL Lutz, T Sick, M Rosenthal, G. van den Thillart, pp. 417–34. Boca Raton, FL: CRC Press

161. Whitten BK, Klain GL. 1968. Protein metabolism in hepatic tissue of hibernating and arousing ground squirrels. *Am. J. Physiol.* 214: 1360–62

162. Whitten BK, Schrader LE, Huston RL, Honold RG. 1970. Hepatic polyribosomes and protein synthesis: seasonal changes in a hibernator. *Int. J. Biochem.* 1:406–8

163. Yacoe ME. 1983. Protein metabolism in the pectoralis muscle and liver of hibernating bats, *Eptesicus fuscus. J. Comp. Physiol.* 152:137–44

164. Zhegunov GF, Mikulinsky YE, Kudokotseva EV. 1988. Hyperactivation of protein synthesis in tissues of hibernating animals on arousal. *Cryo. Lett.* 9: 236–45

165. Zitomer RS, Lowry CV. 1992. Regulation of gene expression by oxygen in *Saccharomyces cerevisiae. Microbiol. Rev.* 56:1–11

*Annu. Rev. Physiol. 1996. 58:565–81*

# POST-EXERCISE LACTATE METABOLISM: A Comparative Review of Sites, Pathways, and Regulation

*Todd T. Gleeson*

Environmental, Population, and Organismic Biology, University of Colorado, Boulder, Colorado 80309–0334

KEY WORDS:  gluconeogenesis, glycogenesis, skeletal muscle, hepatic, fish, reptiles, amphibians, mammals, hormones

---

## ABSTRACT

Most vertebrates utilize supplemental lactate production to support the energetic demands of vigorous, brief exercise. Despite similar patterns of accumulation, there appears to be a trichotomy with regards to lactate processing post-exercise. Most fish retain most of their lactate intramuscularly, using it for in situ glycogen replenishment. Recent evaluation of fish muscle concludes that pyruvate kinase reversal is a probable gluconeogenic pathway. Amphibians and reptiles also utilize lactate as a muscle glyconeogenic substrate, but lactate is not sequestered post-exercise. None of these groups utilize hepatic gluconeogenesis to any significant extent post-exercise, and muscle glucose uptake is limited. Lactate oxidation plays a major role post-exercise in mammals, with hepatic and muscular gluco- and glyconeogenesis contributing to a lesser extent. Glucocorticoids may regulate lactate release from fish muscle, although catecholamines may influence glyconeogenesis in reptile muscle. Insulin affects lactate metabolism indirectly through its effects on muscle glucose metabolism.

---

## INTRODUCTION

Vigorous muscular exercise results in accumulation of l-lactate in most vertebrates and some invertebrates. Lactate accumulation has been the concern of exercise physiologists interested in the relationship of lactate accumulation to work intensity and capacity, the controversial relationship between lactate accumulation and ventilatory responses to exercise, and the correlation of lactate accumulation and muscular fatigue (13, 46). Physiological ecologists have used lactate accumulation to estimate maximal sustainable locomotor

565

speeds of animals and to estimate the metabolic and energetic consequences of behaviors in the field as diverse as egg laying, nest building, vocalization, diving, territorial defense, and prey capture (31, 33, 45, 81, 104).

This is not the first article to address the consequences of anaerobic energy production in animals. The general mammalian response to lactate accumulation has been reviewed in several articles (13, 14, 59, 92), and reviews of the exercise physiology of fishes (64, 73, 74) and amphibians and reptiles (7, 8, 31, 36) also have treated aspects of this subject. Studies of avian responses to exercise, however, have focused almost exclusively on respiratory and cardiovascular adjustments (86). In the sections that follow, an overview of lactate accumulation in vertebrates is provided, and the temporal variability in lactate removal is highlighted. Multiple fates of lactate carbon during recovery and the tissue sites in which lactate removal occurs are then discussed. Finally, physiological factors that affect regulation of lactate removal are reviewed. Wherever possible, the review focuses on data from experiments where animals have undergone supramaximal, non-sustainable exhaustive exercise of relatively brief duration (5 min or less). It is under these circumstances that lactate production has the most ecological and energetic importance to an animal and contributes most to expanding exercise performance. Lactate metabolism resulting from this type of activity occurs in a different metabolic and hormonal context relative to mechanisms of lactate turnover during or following exercise that is sustained for considerable periods of time.

## LACTATE ACCUMULATION AND TEMPORAL ASPECTS OF REMOVAL

### Magnitude of Lactate Accumulation

The initial metabolic response to brief, exhaustive exercise is similar in most vertebrates. This is readily apparent in similarly elevated blood lactate titers. Although Bennett & Seymour (11) report impressive blood lactate accumulations of 50–70 mmol/kg in crocodiles struggling to resist capture, post-exercise concentrations of 15–25 mmol/kg are more common in a variety of terrestrial vertebrates (Table 1).

Teleost fish generally sequester a greater fraction of their accumulated lactate intracellularly than do terrestrial vertebrates (64, 101), the result being that blood lactate accumulations are often lower in fish. Lactate sequestration is a unique and important component to the pattern of lactate removal in most members of this taxa (see below). Lower blood lactate concentrations in fish do not reflect a lower reliance on anaerobic metabolism, however, because peak muscle concentrations are comparable to other vertebrates. An exception

**Table 1**  Characteristics of blood and muscle lactate accumulation and removal in select animals following brief (2–10 min) exhaustive exercise[a]

| Species | Max(LA)$_{blood}$ | Max(LA)$_{muscle}$ | T$_{.67}$[b] | Lactate fate[c] | Reference |
|---|---|---|---|---|---|
| Mouse | 22.0 | 9.1 | 13 | O | 41, 43 |
| Rat | 24.0 | 20.0 | 24 | O | 15, 42 |
| Human | 15.2 | 28.1 | 37 | M | 2, 4, 52 |
| Rainbow trout | 19.7[d] | 48.0 | 435 | G | 64, 69 |
| Winter flounder | 1.3[d] | 15.0 | | G | 32 |
| Flathead sole | 1.8[d] | 15.0 | 882 | — | 97 |
| Sea raven | 0.6 | 11.4 | 810 | — | 65 |
| Skipjack tuna[e] | 42.0 | 108.0 | 140 | G | 1 |
| Shark[e] | 17.7[d] | — | 1050 | — | 80 |
| Leopard frog | 19.0 | 38.9 | 135 | G | 25 |
| Tiger salamander | 11.1 | — | 410 | G | 48, 103 |
| Bufonid toad | 17.7 | 33.0 | 155[f] | M | 82, 83, 105 |
| Green iguana | 14.9 | 31.6 | 120 | — | 70 |
| Desert iguana | 21.1 | 31.0 | 117 | G | 37 |

[a] Concentration units $\mu$mol/g or $\mu$mol/ml. [b] Recovery time (in min) required for 67% of the accumulated blood lactate to be removed. [c] Rate of lactate during quiet recovery: G, predominately glyconeogenic; O, predominately oxidative; M, mixed fate. [d] Peak lactate occurs 2–4 h after cessation of exercise. [e] 15 min exercise. [f] Estimated from whole body concentration.

to this generalization is the tuna. Following 15 min of vigorous exercise, skipjack tunas (1) increase white muscle lactate concentration in excess of 100 mM. Unlike salmonids and other teleosts, blood lactate in this scombrid quickly peaks at concentrations of approximately 40 mM in a pattern similar to that of most mammals.

## Rates of Lactate Accumulation

The available data suggest that the rates of lactate accumulation in fish and reptiles can exceed those of mammals and some amphibians by a factor of two (36). Rates of whole-body lactate accumulation in lizards during the first 30 s of activity average 8.7 mmol/g (8). If the same pattern of lactate accumulation (i.e. one half of the total accumulates in first 30 s) is assumed to be true in other vertebrates, as has been argued for small mammals (85), then the 30 s accumulation of reptiles and of fish (trout 8.6 mmol/g) (69) generally exceeds that of small mammals and humans (2.8–4.2 mmol/g) (2, 85). These differences in the rates of whole-body lactate accumulation are not explained by body mass or by body temperature because neither the rate of accumulation nor the capacity for lactate accumulation demonstrates strong allometric or thermal sensitivities (8, 21, 31).

## Time Course for Lactate Removal

If oxidative metabolism were the primary method of elimination of the post-exercise lactate pool in all vertebrates, similar whole-body accumulations of lactate in mammals and in ectotherms would predict that ectothermic vertebrates would retain lactate at elevated levels for many hours following activity, whereas lactate levels in mammals of similar size should return to resting levels shortly after exercise. Data on the time course of whole-body lactate removal are limited to a number of amphibians and small lizard species (see 36), but recovery in these animals is slower than in comparably sized mammals. Strictly comparable data for fish and for mammals are lacking. Using blood lactate levels as an index of whole-body lactate removal suggests that in general, lactate removal is more rapid in mammals than in other vertebrates. The time required to remove two thirds of the accumulated blood lactate in mammals following brief, vigorous activity ranges from 13 min in mice (41, 43) to 37 min in humans (2, 52). In comparison, removal of two thirds of the accumulated blood lactate load requires 2 to 17 h in a variety of ectothermic vertebrates (Table 1).

Based on the relationship between body mass and resting metabolic rate, one might also expect a relationship to exist between body mass and lactate removal. Evidence for such allometry is weak (36). There is a concomitant increase in body mass and recovery time in the mammals noted in Table 1, but the allometric relationship (b = 0.18 ± 0.033) is much less positive than the relationship between mass and metabolic rate (b = 0.75). Although Coulsen & Hernandez (19) hypothesized a positive allometric relationship between recovery time and body mass based on a comparison of 5 g anoles and 70 kg alligators, a more phylogenetically conservative comparison of lizards does not support that conclusion (9, 34, 37, 70), nor would a comparison within anuran amphibians (47). The determinants of the rate of lactate removal are multiple and interactive, involving both metabolic and hormonal factors, some of which are discussed below. It is clear, however, that no causal relationship exists between the rate of post-exercise oxygen consumption and lactate removal (10, 28, 29, 37, 68, 88, 100, 105).

A positive allometry for lactate removal would be more likely if there was a close relationship between the rate of oxidative metabolism post-exercise and lactate removal; that is, if the theory of oxygen debt was supported by the data. Gaesser & Brooks' review of the data (29), however, makes it clear that post-exercise oxygen consumption is not directly related to the magnitude of lactate accumulation. The unrelated time courses for lactate removal and for post-exercise oxygen consumption have been well documented in all vertebrate groups (except birds). Elevated lactate can persist long after rates of oxygen consumption have returned to normal (10, 29, 37, 68, 105), and the converse is also true (28). In trout, repeated exercise resulting in the same degree of lactate accumulation results in smaller elevations in oxygen consumption (88). Wagner & Gleeson (100) have recently shown that oxidative recovery and lactate removal exhibit different thermal sensitivities in lizards and that under conditions similar to those in the field, cooling the body temperature of a recovering animal can actually speed the rate at which oxygen consumption returns to resting levels while at the same time retarding the rate of lactate removal.

## PRINCIPAL FATES OF LACTATE AND SITES OF POST-EXERCISE LACTATE METABOLISM

The principal fates of the excess lactate that accumulates as a result of vigorous, brief exercise are oxidation to carbon dioxide and water and gluconeogenic production of glucose and tissue glycogen. Isotopic studies indicate that lactate carbon also finds its way into Krebs cycle intermediate, amino acid, and protein carbon pools (16, 37, 67, 105); however, these latter fates are more important for what they tell us about pathway kinetics and pool mixing than they are in the strict context of recovery energetics. In rats, lactate incorporation into the acid-insoluble protein fraction post-exercise can account for 6–9% of the labeled blood lactate carbon pool (16). Katz et al attribute some of the label appearance in glutamine and glutamate (16, 53) to the regional specialization of cells within the liver. Despite the shortcomings and complexities of isotopic studies (36, 59, 90), this technique has provided valuable insight into the nature of lactate removal in intact animals. Studies using isotopes, as well as studies relying on analysis of temporal and stoichiometric changes in metabolites, indicate that although the time course of lactate removal varies considerably among vertebrates, post-exercise lactate pools serve primarily as either a substrate for glycogen repletion, or a source of oxidizable substrate, or in support of some combination of those two functions.

### Lactate Removal in Intact Animals

Quantification of lactate removal has been investigated in a number of animals. Studies of post-exercise rats (15, 16, 28) indicate that lactate is largely oxidized during recovery, with labeled lactate carbon expired as $CO_2$. Estimates of lactate pool oxidation after 2 h of recovery range from 55 to 75%, depending upon the nature of the exercise and the position of the [14]C label on the lactate carbon skeleton (15, 28). Hatta reported that lactate oxidation following brief

(~100 s), strenuous exercise in rats accounted for 48% of the injected label after 2 h (41, 42), which increased to 74% if moderate treadmill exercise was continued during the recovery period (42). Gluconeogenic removal of lactate accounted for another 10–12% of the lactate pool after 2 h in rats (16). Brooks & Gaesser (16) estimated that after 4 h of recovery, approximately 18–25% of the injected label was incorporated into tissue glycogen (the actual estimate depends upon assumptions of the fraction of total muscle mass active in glycogen restitution). Hatta (41) reported that no significant lactate carbon was incorporated into muscle glycogen following intense exercise in rat. Both laboratories report that blood glucose plays a more significant role in muscle glycogen restitution following exercise in rats than does blood lactate. Mice are reported to oxidize approximately 28% of the labeled blood lactate pool after 30 min of recovery (43), and 40% after 60 min (41). Approximately 2% of the injected lactate label appeared in muscle glycogen 30 min after the cessation of exercise (43).

Reported patterns of lactate removal in intact humans are more varied than in rodents but seem to suggest that a larger fraction of the post-exercise lactate load is removed gluconeogenically under some circumstances. Hermansen & Vaage (44) reported that for human muscle, following three 60 s bouts of intense exercise, most of the accumulated muscle lactate in situ was removed by resynthesis of glycogen. Their calculations, which have been challenged (16), predicted that little lactate (<15%) was oxidized. Using stoichiometric accounting, Astrand et al (2) recently estimated a theoretical maximum of 40% for lactate oxidation following brief intense exercise, whereas replenishment of muscle glycogen was proposed as the fate of 50% of the post-exercise lactate pool. Lactate removal across the splanchnic bed was estimated as only 10% of the total. In contrast, Bangsbo et al (5) estimated that only 13–27% of the lactate removed in humans recovering from 3 min of intense leg exercise served as a glyconeogenic substrate. During continuous, heavy exercise, 80% of the lactate produced was reported to be oxidized (57), although this condition creates a much greater oxidative demand for substrate by the muscle than does quiet recovery as indicated in the cases above. Similarly, exercising dogs also utilize lactate as an important oxidative substrate (23), and it is generally regarded that lactate oxidation during exercise is a positive function of metabolic demand (92).

A handful of studies indicate that nonmammalian vertebrates utilize the post-exercise lactate pool as a more important source of glyconeogenic substrate. In many respects the most interesting pattern of lactate removal is that seen in several teleost fish, where the blood lactate pool and the muscle lactate pools are not in equilibrium. In rainbow trout, [14]C-lactate injected arterially post-exercise indicates that 20–30% of the blood lactate pool is reduced oxidatively (67) but that the turnover of blood lactate is insufficient to account for the removal of the muscle lactate pool (69). The evidence indicates that 80–85% of the lactate remains in muscle (64, 69, 98), that white muscle takes up some blood lactate (67), and that the intramuscular lactate pool is reduced as the muscle glycogen stores are replenished by in situ glyconeogenesis (67, 69). The pattern in salmon and in flounder appears qualitatively similar (68, 97, 98).

Indirect data from recovering leopard frogs (25) also indicate a glyconeogenic fate for lactate in these animals. A rate of muscle glycogen replenishment equal to the rate of lactate removal, coupled with no evidence for hepatic gluconeogenesis, argues strongly for muscle glyconeogenic removal of lactate. In the American toad *Bufo americanus*, U-$^{14}$C-lactate recovery following injection into the dorsal lymph sac indicated that the post-exercise fate of lactate in this anuran was 7% oxidative, 22–39% tissue glycogen, and another 24% as tissue protein (105). Two hours of recovery in the desert iguana resulted in lactate-fueled gluco- and glyconeogenesis sufficient to account for 50% of the lactate removed during that time period. Oxidation accounted for another 16% of the lactate, which represented approximately 40% of the post-exercise oxygen consumption (37).

## Tissue-Specific Lactate Removal

The patterns of in vivo lactate removal described above point to important roles for skeletal muscle in the metabolic utilization of lactate post-exercise. Meyerhof's results of the early 1920s (62, 63) first illustrated the ability of frog muscle to resynthesize glycogen from lactate. Decades later, his finding were confirmed by others (6, 18, 40) who also showed that muscle utilization of lactate to resynthesize glycogen was influenced by season, by lactate concentration, and by co-incubation with glucose. Fournier & Guderley (25) provided compelling evidence for the role of muscle in glycogen restitution when they showed in hepatectomized frogs that lactate is removed as quickly and muscle glycogen restored as completely as in control animals. Furthermore, they reported that perfused frog liver is incapable of glucose production from lactate (25, 79) and that glucose homeostasis during exercise is due to glucose production and export by skeletal muscle (26, 27). This is a very different scenario for lactate-glycogen metabolism than is generally described for mammals (14, 55), which involves a version of the Cori cycle (hepatic lactate uptake, hepatic gluconeogenesis and export, muscle glucose uptake, and glycogenesis). Arguing against such a role for the liver in nonmammalian vertebrates are the frequent reports that little $^{14}$C from labeled lactate appears as labeled plasma glucose post-exercise (37, 67, 68, 78), and more importantly, that glucose uptake by fish, amphibian, and lizard muscle is limited (39, 78, 102, 103).

Lizard skeletal muscle has a greater capacity for glycogen synthesis from lactate than from glucose, both in vivo (37, 38) and in vitro (39, 102), and it appears that muscle glycogen is restored via muscle gluconeogenesis. The oxidative fiber types of lizards are capable of greater rates of glycogen resynthesis than are the pale glycolytic fibers (38), but the threefold greater mass of white muscle (36) makes both fiber populations important in whole body lactate removal.

Although only 10–20% of the post-exercise lactate load is released into the blood of many fish, this pool serves as an important oxidative substrate, most notably for cardiac and red muscle (65–67, 69). White muscle, despite its low oxidative capacity for lactate, is also an important oxidative sink for lactate because of its large mass (32). White muscle is well known to retain much of its lactate intracellularly and to resynthesize glycogen directly (64, 101), a process estimated to require only 3.5% of the oxidative capacity of trout white muscle (72). Moyes et al (72, 75) suggest that fatty acid oxidation in fish white muscle provides both the metabolic energy and the inhibition of pyruvate oxidation during recovery. White muscle glycogen replenishment was shown to be facilitated by hepatectomy (67), which presumably makes more lactate available for white muscle utilization.

Skeletal muscle plays an important role in the oxidative removal of lactate in mammals. Brooks (14) describes a scenario in which at high levels of post-exercise oxygen consumption, lactate serves as a substrate for muscle oxidation. As metabolic rate declines, lactate can become a substrate for hepatic gluconeogenesis. The resulting glucose is exported to the muscle where it is deposited as glycogen. This mechanism appears to hold generally in rats and mice, and in humans during steady-state exercise (51, 57). During recovery from exercise, however, non-isotope data suggest that human muscle may retain roughly half of its lactate load for in situ resynthesis of glycogen (2, 44, but see 5), much as does muscle in nonmammalian vertebrates. Yet even under these conditions, muscle lactate oxidation is an important component. Baldwin, using rat muscle (3), was among the first to suggest that there was fiber-type specificity to lactate oxidation, a necessary condition for the "lactate shuttle," as proposed by Brooks (14), to occur. Fiber type-specific oxidation of lactate (slow-twitch >> fast-twitch glycolytic) has also been demonstrated in rabbit muscle (75, 76). Direct evidence of fiber-specific oxidation of lactate in humans is still lacking, however, and rates of lactate oxidation by mouse soleus and extensor digitorum longus (EDL) muscle differ very little (59). Fiber types also show specificity in their capacity for glyconeogenesis. The capacity for mammalian muscle glyconeogenesis has been demonstrated in rats, rabbits, and mice under a number of in situ and in vitro conditions (12, 59 and references therein; 75, 76, 94, 95), particularly those where lactate concentrations are elevated. In mice, fast-twitch EDL muscle exhibited nearly three times the rate for lactate-fueled glycogen resynthesis relative to the slow-twitch soleus (12, 96). However, these rates of glycogen synthesis were only a tenth that measured when glucose was the substrate, underscoring the importance of hepatic gluconeogenesis during recovery in rodents. Others have reported a similar relationship between fast-twitch fibers and glyconeogenesis in the perfused rat hindlimb (61) and in vivo (50), whereas slow-twitch fibers exhibited only a marginal capacity. In rabbit muscle, fast-twitch glycolytic fibers are predominately glyconeogenic in the presence of moderate (8 mM) lactate concentrations, whereas slow-twitch fibers metabolize lactate oxidatively under the same conditions (75). Rabbit slow-twitch fibers become lactate consumers at lower lactate concentrations (2.5 mM) than do fast-twitch fibers (4 mM), which probably reflects different functions of these fiber types in lactate metabolism at rest. In vivo, glycogen replenishment is also more rapid in human fast-twitch fibers than in slow-twitch fibers (99).

## Pathways for Muscle Glyconeogenesis

Lactate-supported muscle glyconeogenesis can occur by one of three biochemical pathways. The distinction between the three pathways is the mechanism by which pyruvate is converted back to phosphoenolpyruvate (PEP). The first pathway is the mechanism prevalent in hepatic and renal tissue (55), where pyruvate carboxylation/decarboxylation is catalyzed by pyruvate carboxylase (PC) and PEP carboxykinase (PEPCK) in association with malate dehydrogenase. This pathway is generally thought not to function in skeletal muscle because of the absence of PC activity in skeletal muscle (20). There is less consensus on the importance of the two remaining pathways: the reversal of pyruvate kinase (PK) and the pathway catalyzed by cytoplasmic malic enzyme (ME) and PEPCK. Data indicate that the former pathway may predominate in muscle of some ectothermic vertebrates with high glyconeogenic capacities, whereas the latter pathway exists in muscles of mammals. PK reversal was proposed by Dyson et al (24) as functional at a few percent of the forward rate of reaction. The best support for this pathway comes from the fish literature. Shulte et al (91) calculate that in trout white muscle, an approximate 200-fold increase in the [ATP]/free [ADP] ratio during recovery may bring the PK reaction close to equilibrium, making PK reversal realistic. Moyes & West (74) summarize data from several fish species indicating that the PK activity of white muscle is sufficiently high that reversal at only 0.05% of the maximal forward reaction rate could also account for the observed glyconeogenic flux in these animals. Fish muscle PK, unlike mammalian muscle PK, is also known to be affected by regulators (73). PK reversal is also indicated by the absence of PEPCK in white muscle of all fish studied, except marlin (73, 74, 94a). Amphibians and reptiles also possess high activities of muscle PK, a condition favoring PK reversal. PEPCK activity in lizard muscle is not detectable, although it exists in reptilian liver (RB Weinstein & T Gleeson, unpublished data). PEPCK activity is reportedly present in frog muscle, and Connett (18) reported that mercaptopicolinic acid (MPA) retards glyconeogenesis in frog muscle. MPA is a putative PEPCK inhibitor, although its specificity in amphibian tissues has not been demonstrated.

Mammalian muscle is reported to possess both ME and PEPCK activities (20). McLane & Holloszy (61) reported activities of both enzymes in rat fiber types that vary concordantly with the reported glyconeogenic capacities of those fiber types. Conflicting data exist as to whether this pathway is operative in vivo. Although Talmadge & Silverman (96) report MPA suppression of glyconeogenesis in mouse muscle, MPA did not affect glycogen replenishment in isolated muscle of rats (89) or rabbits (77). Although not dismissing the probable role of ME and PEPCK in skeletal muscle glyconeogenesis in some species, the strength of the fish data argues that PK reversal may be a competitive pathway for lactate carbon during recovery in other taxa as well. This aspect of recovery merits further investigation in all vertebrates.

## Adaptive Explanations for Glyconeogenic Removal of Lactate

Several authors have offered perspectives as to the advantages associated with muscle glyconeogenesis as a strategy for lactate removal post-exercise. Each proposal is predicated on the largely untested assumptions that rapid recovery and complete glycogen restitution are advantageous for the animal. None of the ideas is mutually exclusive. Utilizing glyconeogenic pathways for removal has been suggested to speed the rate of recovery in amphibians (105) relative to recovery that was dependent upon oxidative removal alone. This has some merit because estimated times for removal based upon the rate of oxidative metabolism alone suggest much longer periods of recovery than in fact occur. Rapid replenishment of muscle glycogen stores is thought to be another advantage of muscle glyconeogenic recovery in lizards and amphibians (25, 35, 105). Muscle glyconeogenesis may also allow for glycogen replenishment without having to forage or be exposed to predation while in a glycogen-depleted state (25, 37). The in situ lactate retention in fish muscle has been suggested as beneficial from the perspective of replenishment efficiency (64, 67). This argument posits that because release of lactate into the blood exposes the lactate pool to oxidation or utilization by other tissues, retention of lactate within recovering muscle serves to provide for more complete resynthesis of the glycogen stores. The observation that hepatectomy results in more complete muscle glycogen resynthesis in fish (67) supports this hypothesis. With the exception of hepatectomy, these ideas have not been tested and thus represent fertile ground for those interested in the interface of physiology and behavior.

# REGULATION OF POST-EXERCISE LACTATE METABOLISM

## *Hormonal Regulation*

In addition to variations in lactate concentration and muscle metabolic rate (12, 14, 57, 76, 77), there are several other factors influencing the rate and fate of post-exercise lactate metabolism. Catecholamines are potentially important regulators of post-exercise lactate metabolism because they are known to be elevated in all vertebrates as a result of vigorous activity (see references in 39, 56, 64). Epinephrine (E) and norepinephrine (NE) are known stimulators of hepatic glycogenolysis (55), and they also are known to stimulate hepatic gluconeogenesis both in mammals and in fish (22, 55, 71). Inhibiting hepatic pyruvate kinase function by phosphorylation is thought to be an important mechanism of regulation in both groups. Hepatic regulation of gluconeogenesis is a important aspect of lactate metabolism only in mammals, however, because the other vertebrate groups process their lactate load intramuscularly. Less is known about catecholamine effects on muscle lactate release or metabolism. Elevated E and NE are associated with enhanced lactate release and higher blood lactate levels in dogs (93), and inflections in plasma E and plasma lactate are correlated in humans (58). Adrenergic blockade has provided mixed responses on blood lactate dynamics in fish (64) and had no effect on lactate accumulation or rates of removal in *Anolis* lizards (T Gleeson, unpublished data). Muscle lactate metabolism in the lizard *Dipsosaurus dorsalis*, however, does exhibit E sensitivity. The rate of lactate carbon incorporation into glycogen by oxidative fibers is stimulated by E (39), although E has no effect on lactate or glucose oxidation. In contrast, McDermott & Bonen (59) report that E stimulates lactate oxidation in mammalian soleus muscle. No mechanism for catecholamine regulation of muscle lactate transport or metabolism has been proposed, but the observation that E stimulates muscle cAMP content (17) suggests a starting point.

Glucocorticoids are known to affect hepatic gluconeogenesis (55) and have recently been reported to dramatically affect lactate-glucose metabolism in muscle of some animals. Corticosteroid concentrations become elevated following strenuous exercise in lizards and fish and remain high for the period that encompasses lactate removal (39, 77). Post-exercise concentrations, however, have no impact on either lactate oxidation or glyconeogenesis in lizard muscle in vitro (39). In mouse muscle, cortisol inhibits glycogenesis (glucose to glycogen) in both red and white muscle but has no effect on glyconeogenesis from lactate unless glucose is also present (12). In trout, however, Pagnotta et al (77) recently reported that blocking the exercise-induced rise in plasma cortisol reduced peak blood lactate levels, accelerated blood and muscle lactate removal, and sped glycogen replenishment by many hours. They hypothesized that the increase in cortisol exerts a negative influence on metabolic recovery. Milligan's laboratory has confirmed this hypothesis in experiments where cortisol replacement in cortisol synthesis-blocked fish reestablished the long recovery period characteristic of trout (64).

In humans, insulin is expected to remain constant or fall slightly following exercise, depending upon the intensity and duration of exercise. Glucagon can be elevated twofold or more under the same conditions (30). Although insulin has a stimulatory effect on glucose incorporation into glycogen of mouse muscle (12), it has no effect on lactate incorporation when lactate is the sole substrate. Likewise, insulin has no direct effect on lactate uptake or incorporation in rat muscle, but in the presence of glucose, insulin inhibits lactate uptake and incorporation by 25 to 30% (61). Insulin increased the oxygen consumption of frog muscle and the oxidation of lactate (40). Glycogen synthesis from both lactate and glucose is stimulated in frog muscle by insulin, but when present together, lactate is preferentially oxidized, whereas glucose supports glycogenesis (40). The function of the lactate shuttle and Cori cycle in mammals means that insulin and glucagon effects on liver gluconeogenesis have a significant impact on lactate removal and glycogen restitution in mammals. These results are reviewed elsewhere (14, 55). There are no studies reporting effects of glucagon on lower vertebrate muscle. Glucagon and glucagon-like peptides do stimulate gluconeogenesis and glycogenolysis in hepatocytes of several species of fish (22), reptiles, and amphibians (49).

## pH and Body Temperature

Incubation pH has been shown to affect the rate of lactate metabolism in muscle, suggesting that the metabolic acidosis frequently accompanying exercise may affect the rate or fate of lactate removal. Frog muscle shows a depression in lactate-supported glyconeogenesis in acidotic conditions (6). Muscle from the green anole (*Anolis carolinensis*) demonstrates a pH optimum for glycogen resynthesis at pH 7.5 (T Gleeson, unpublished data), whereas mouse soleus and EDL demonstrate glycogenic optima at pH 6.5–7.0 (12). Recent characterization of mammalian skeletal muscle lactate transporters indicates that they often are pH sensitive (60, 84) and may provide a site for pH, $HCO_3^-$, or perhaps hormonal modification of lactate kinetics during recovery. Intracellular pH of trout muscle drops from pH 7.27 to 6.58 following exhaustive swimming (69, 91), which Schulte et al (91) have shown to be stimulatory to fish white muscle mitochondrial respiration under conditions similar to those during recovery. Experiments that would evaluate the effect of pH on the differential fate of lactate or differential glycogen replenishment in muscle tissues have yet to be designed.

Environmental temperature may also turn out to be an important regulator of post-exercise lactate metabolism, at least in ectothermic vertebrates. Numerous older studies have documented the effects of body temperature on the rate of lactate removal in ectotherms (see 21, 100). More recently, Kieffer et al (54) have shown that thermal acclimation in trout is accompanied by important changes in lactate kinetics post-exercise. Although muscle lactate accumulation and removal are thermally independent in trout, much more lactate is lost to the blood lactate pool at the cooler acclimation temperature. If the hypothesis that muscle lactate retention in fish is a feature that maximizes the efficiency of muscle glycogen replenishment (64, 67), then Kieffer et al's data should predict that cool fish would replenish muscle glycogen at higher efficiency than do warm fish. Wagner & Gleeson (100) recently attempted to model the field condition where a warm lizard once fatigued might choose to recover in either warm or cool microhabitats. They found that relative to constant warm conditions, the warm exercise-cool recovery condition resulted in slightly faster recovery to resting rates of oxygen consumption but prolonged lactate removal. Unpublished data (EL Wagner & T Gleeson) indicate that animals allowed to recover in a thermal gradient do select a cooler temperature at which to recover, and the effect of that behavior on glycogen replenish is now being investigated. Preliminary data indicate that body temperature may also influence the distribution of lactate carbon to oxidative vs glyconeogenic pathways.

## CONCLUDING REMARKS

Most vertebrates utilize supplemental lactate production to a similar degree to support the energetic demands of vigorous, brief exercise. This general pattern of vertebrate metabolism is surprising given the large differences in resting and maximal oxidative metabolism that exist among taxa, and the differences in behavior, body size, and body temperature of the animals discussed above. After about a decade of research, we are realizing that while similarities in accumulation exist, there appears to be a trichotomy with regard to lactate processing post-exercise. Most fish retain the bulk of their lactate intramuscularly, using it for in situ glycogen replenishment. Amphibians and reptiles also utilize lactate as a muscle glyconeogenic substrate, but lactate is more evenly distributed following exercise. None of these groups utilize hepatic gluconeogenesis to any significant extent post-exercise, and muscle glucose uptake is limited. Lactate oxidation plays the major role post-exercise in mammals, with hepatic and muscular gluco- and glyconeogenesis contributing to a lesser extent. The evolutionary history of these patterns would be interesting to elucidate. These distinctions suggest important differences in lactate transport mechanisms across the sarcolemma that have yet to be described and differences in hormonal regulation of muscle lactate metabolism that are just now being realized. Active research in these areas during the next few years should help reveal the physiological mechanisms underlying these differences.

ACKNOWLEDGMENTS

Thanks to Christopher Moyes and Louise Milligan for sharing manuscripts and preprints of their work. Support during the preparation of this article was provided by National Institutes of Health RO1 DK46408.

## Literature Cited

1. Arthur PG, West TG, Brill RW, Schulte PM, Hochachka PW. 1992. Recovery metabolism of skipjack tuna (*Katsuwonus pelamis*) white muscle: rapid and parallel changes in lactate and phosphocreatine after exercise. *Can. J. Zool.* 70:1230–39

2. Åstrand P-O, Hultman E, Juhlin-Dannfelt A, Reynolds G. 1986. Disposal of lactate during and after strenuous exercise in humans. *J. Appl. Physiol.* 61: 338–43

3. Baldwin KM, Hooker AM, Herrick RE. 1978. Lactate oxidative capacity in different types of muscle. *Biochem. Biophys. Res. Commun.* 83:151–57

4. Bangsbo J, Gollnick PD, Graham TE, Juel C, Kiens B, et al. 1990. Anaerobic energy production and $O_2$ deficit-debt relationship during exhaustive exercise in humans. *J. Physiol.* 422:539–59

5. Bangsbo J, Gollnick PD, Graham TE, Saltin B. 1991. Substrates for muscle glycogen synthesis in recovery from intense exercise in man. *J. Physiol.* 434: 423–40

6. Bendall JR, Taylor AA. 1970. The Meyerhof quotient and the synthesis of glycogen from lactate in frog and rabbit muscle. *Biochem. J.* 118:887–93

7. Bennett AF. 1978. Activity metabolism of the lower vertebrates. *Annu. Rev. Physiol.* 400:447–69

8. Bennett AF. 1982. The energetics of reptilian activity. In *Biology of the Reptilia*, ed. C Gans, FH Pough, 13:155–99. New York: Academic

9. Bennett AF, Licht P. 1972. Anaerobic metabolism during activity in lizards. *J. Comp. Physiol.* 81:277–88

10. Bennett AF, Licht P. 1973. Relative contributions of anaerobic and aerobic energy production during activity in Amphibia. *J. Comp. Physiol.* 87:351–60

11. Bennett AF, Seymour RS, Bradford DF, Webb GJW. 1985. Mass-dependence of anaerobic metabolism and acid-base disturbance during actuate in the salt-water crocodile, *Crocodylus porosus*. *J. Exp. Biol.* 118:161–71

12. Bonen A, McDermott JC, Tan MH. 1990. Glycogenesis and gluconeogenesis in skeletal muscle: effects of pH and hormones. *Am. J. Physiol.* 258:E693–700

13. Brooks GA. 1985. Anaerobic threshold: review of the concept and directions for future research. *Med. Sci. Sports Exerc.* 17:22–31

14. Brooks GA. 1986. The lactate shuttle during exercise and recovery. *Med. Sci. Sports Exerc.* 18:360–68

15. Brooks GA, Brauner KE, Cassens RG. 1973. Glycogen synthesis and metabolism of lactic acid after exercise. *Am. J. Physiol.* 224:1162–66

16. Brooks GA, Gaesser GA. 1980. End points of lactate and glucose metabolism after exhausting exercise. *J. Appl. Physiol.* 49:1057–69

17. Chasiotis D, Saltin B, Hultman E. 1983. Regulation of glycogenolysis in human muscle in response to epinephrine infusion. *J. Appl. Physiol.* 54:45–50

18. Connett RJ. 1979. Glyconeogenesis from lactate in frog striated muscle. *Am. J. Physiol.* 237:C231–36

19. Coulsen RA, Hernandez T. 1980. Oxygen debt in two reptiles: relationship between the time required for repayment

and metabolic rate. *Comp. Biochem. Physiol.* 65A:453–57

20. Crabtree B, Higgins SJ, Newsholme EA. 1972. The activities of pyruvate carboxylase, phosphoenolpyruvate carboxylase and fructose diphosphatase in muscles from vertebrates and invertebrates. *Biochem. J.* 130:391–96

21. Dalla Via J, Huber M, Wieser W, Lackner R. 1989. Temperature related responses of intermediary metabolism to forced exercise and recovery in juvenile *Rutilus rutilus* (L.)(Cyprinidae: Teleostei). *Physiol. Zool.* 62:964–76

22. Danulat E, Mommsen TP. 1990. Norepinephrine: a potent activator of glycogenolysis and gluconeogenesis in rockfish hepatocytes. *Gen. Comp. Endocrinol.* 78:12–22

23. Depocas F, Minaire Y, Chatonnet J. 1969. Rates of formation and oxidation of lactic acid in dogs at rest and during moderate exercise. *Can. J. Physiol. Pharmacol.* 47:603–10

24. Dyson RD, Cardenas JM, Barsotti RJ. 1975. The reversibility of skeletal muscle pyruvate kinase and an assessment of its capacity to support gluconeogenesis. *J. Biol. Chem.* 250:3316–21

25. Fournier PA, Guderley G. 1992. The metabolic fate of lactate following vigorous activity in the leopard frog, *Rana pipiens. Am. J. Physiol.* 262:R245–54

26. Fournier PA, Guderley G. 1993. Muscle: the predominant glucose-producing organ in the leopard frog during exercise. *Am. J. Physiol.* 264:R239–43

27. Fournier PA, Petrof EO, Guderley G. 1992. The glucosidic pathways and glucose production in frog muscle. *J. Biol. Chem.* 267:8234–37

28. Gaesser GA, Brooks GA. 1980. Glycogen repletion following continuous and intermittent exercise to exhaustion. *J. Appl. Physiol.* 49:722–28

29. Gaesser GA, Brooks GA. 1984. Metabolic bases of excess post-exercise oxygen consumption: a review. *Med. Sci. Sports Exerc.* 16:29–43

30. Galbo H, Holst JJ, Christensen NJ. 1975. Glucagon and plasma catecholamine responses to graded and prolonged exercise in man. *J. Appl. Physiol.* 38:70–76

31. Gatten RE Jr. 1985. The uses of anaerobiosis by amphibians and reptiles. *Am. Zool.* 25:945–54

32. Girard SS, Milligan, CL. 1992. The metabolic fate of blood-borne lactate in winter flounder (*Pseudopleuronectes americanus*) during recovery from strenuous exercise. *Physiol. Zool.* 65: 1114–34

33. Gleeson TT. 1979. Foraging and transport costs in the Galapagos marine iguana, *Amblyrhynchus cristatus. Physiol. Zool.* 52:549–57

34. Gleeson TT. 1982. Lactate and glycogen metabolism during and after exercise in the lizard *Sceloporus occidentalis. J. Comp. Physiol.* 147:79–84

35. Gleeson TT. 1985. Glycogen synthesis from lactate in skeletal muscle of the lizard *Dipsosaurus dorsalis. J. Comp. Physiol.* 156B:277–83

36. Gleeson TT. 1991. Patterns of metabolic recovery in reptiles and amphibians. *J. Exper. Biol.* 160:187–207

37. Gleeson TT, Dalessio PM. 1989. Lactate and glycogen metabolism in the lizard, *Dipsosaurus dorsalis,* following exhaustive exercise. *J. Exper. Biol.* 144:377–93

38. Gleeson TT, Dalessio PM. 1990. Lactate: a substrate for reptilian muscle gluconeogenesis following exhaustive exercise. *J. Comp. Physiol. B* 160:331–38

39. Gleeson TT, Dalessio PM, Carr JA, Wickler SJ, Mazzeo RS. 1993. Plasma catecholamine and corticosterone concentrations and their in vitro effects on lizard skeletal muscle lactate metabolism. *Am. J. Physiol.* 265:R632–39

40. Gourley DRH, Suh TK. 1969. Effects of insulin on oxidation and glycogenesis from glucose and glucose plus lactate in frog skeletal muscle. *Comp. Biochem. Physiol.* 29:137–48

41. Hatta H. 1990. Oxidative removal of lactate after strenuous exercise. *Ann. Physiol. Anthrop.* 9:213–18

42. Hatta H, Atomi Y, Yamamoto Y, Shinohara S, Yamada S. 1988. Oxidation of lactate in rats after short-term strenuous exercise. *Int. J. Sports Med.* 9:429–32

43. Hatta H, Soma R, Atomi Y. 1994. Effect of endurance training on oxidation of lactate in mice after supramaximal exercise. *Comp. Biochem. Physiol.* 107A: 27–30

44. Hermansen L, Vaage O. 1977. Lactate disappearance and glycogen synthesis in human muscle after maximal exercise. *Am. J. Physiol.* 233:E422–29

45. Hochachka PW 1986. Balancing conflicting metabolic demands of exercise and diving. *Fed. Proc.* 45(13):2948–52

46. Hogan MC, Gladden LB, Kurdak SS, Poole DC. 1994. Increase [lactate] in working muscle reduces tension development independent of pH. *Med. Sci. Sports Exerc.* 27:371–77

47. Hutchison VH, Miller K. 1979. Anaerobic capacity of amphibians. *Comp. Biochem. Physiol.* 63:213–16

48. Hutchison VH, Turney LD, Gratz RK.

1977. Aerobic and anaerobic metabolism during activity in the salamander *Ambystoma tigrinum*. *Physiol. Zool.* 50:189–202

49. Janssens PA, Giuliano M. 1989. Hormonal regulation of hepatic glycogenolysis in *Amphibolorus nuchalis*, the western netted dragon: an in vitro study. *J. Comp. Physiol.* 159:323–31

50. Johnson JL, Bagby GJ. 1988. Gluconeogenic pathway in liver and muscle glycogen synthesis after exercise. *J. Appl. Physiol.* 64:1591–99

51. Jorfeldt L. 1970. Metabolism of L-(+)-lactate in human skeletal muscle after exercise. *Acta Physiol. Scand. Suppl.* 338:1–72

52. Karlsson, J. 1971. Lactate and phosphagen concentrations in working muscle of man. *Acta Physiol. Scand. Suppl.* 358:1–72

53. Katz J, Wals P, Lee W-NP. 1993. Isotopomer studies of gluconeogenesis and the Krebs cycle with $^{13}C$-labeled lactate. *J. Biol. Chem.* 268:25509–21

54. Kieffer JD, Currie S, Tufts BL. 1994. Effects of environmental temperature on the metabolic and acid-base responses of rainbow trout to exhaustive exercise. *J. Exp. Biol.* 194:299–17

55. Kraus-Friedman N. 1984. Hormonal regulation of hepatic gluconeogenesis. *Physiol. Rev.* 64:170–769

56. Mazzeo RS. 1991. Catecholamine responses to acute and chronic exercise. *Med. Sci. Sports Med.* 23:839–45

57. Mazzeo RS, Brooks GA, Schoeller DA, Budinger TF. 1986. Disposal of [1–$^{13}C$]lactate in humans during rest and exercise. *J. Appl. Physiol.* 60:232–41

58. Mazzeo RS, Marshall P. 1989. Influence of plasma catecholamines on the lactate threshold during graded exercise. *J. Appl. Physiol.* 67:1319–22

59. McDermott JC, Bonen A. 1992. Glyconeogenic and oxidative lactate utilization in skeletal muscle. *Can. J. Physiol. Pharmacol.* 70:142–49

60. McDermott JC, Bonen A. 1993. Lactate transport in rat sarcolemmal vesicles and intact skeletal muscle, and after muscle contraction. *Acta Physiol. Scand.* 151:17–28

61. McLane JA, Holloszy JO. 1979. Glycogen synthesis from lactate in the three types of skeletal muscle. *J. Biol. Chem.* 254:6548–53

62. Meyerhof O. 1920. Die energieumwandlungen im muskel. I. Über die beziehungen der milchsaure zur warmebildung und arbeitsleistung des muskels in der anaerobiose. *Pflügers Arch.* 182: 238–83

63. Meyerhof O. 1920. Über die energieumwandlungen im muskel. II. Das schicksal der milchsaure in der erolunsperiode des muskels. *Pflügers Arch.* 182:284–17

64. Milligan CL. 1995. Metabolic recovery from exhaustive exercise in fish. *Comp. Biochem. Physiol. B.* In press

65. Milligan CL, Farrell TP. 1986. Extracellular and intracellular acid-base status following strenuous activity in the sea raven (Hemitripterus americanus). *J. Comp. Physiol.* 156:583–90

66. Milligan CL, Farrell TP. 1991. Lactate utilization by an in situ perfused trout heart: effects of workload and blockers of lactate transport. *J. Exp. Biol.* 155:357–73

67. Milligan CL, Girard SS. 1993. Lactate metabolism in rainbow trout. *J. Exp. Biol.* 180:175–93

68. Milligan CL, McDonald DG. 1988. In vivo lactate kinetics at rest and during recovery from exhaustive exercise in coho salmon (*Oncorhynchus kisutch*) and starry flounder (*Platichthys stellatus*). *J. Exp. Biol.* 135:119–31

69. Milligan CL, Wood CM. 1986. Tissue intracellular acid-base status and the fate of lactate after exhaustive exercise in the rainbow trout. *J Exp. Biol.* 123:123–44

70. Moberly WR. 1968. The metabolic responses of the common iguana, *Iguana iguana*, to activity under restraint. *Comp. Biochem. Physiol.* 27:1–20

71. Mommsen TP, Walsh PJ, Perry SF, Moon TW. 1988. Interactive effects of catecholamines and hypercapnia on glucose production in isolated trout hepatocytes. *Gen. Comp. Endocrinol.* 70:63–73

72. Moyes CD, Schulte PM, Hochachka PW. 1992. Recovery metabolism of trout white muscle: role of mitochondria. *Am. J. Physiol.* 262:R295–04

73. Moyes CD, Schulte PM, West TG. 1993. Burst exercise recovery metabolism in fish white muscle. In *Surviving Hypoxia: Mechanisms of Control and Adaptation*, ed. PW Hochachka, 35:528–37. Boca Raton, FL: CRC Press

74. Moyes CD, West TG. 1995. Exercise metabolism of fish. In *Biochemistry and Molecular Biology of Fishes*, ed. PW Hochachka, TP Mommsen, 4:367–92. New York: Elsevier

75. Pagliassotti MJ, Donovan CM. 1990. Role of cell type in net lactate removal by skeletal muscle. *Am. J. Physiol.* 258:E635–42

76. Pagliassotti MJ, Donovan CM. 1990. Glycogenesis from lactate in rabbit skeletal muscle fiber types. *Am. J. Physiol.* 258:R903–11

77. Pagnotta A, Brooks L, Milligan CL.

1995. The potential regulatory roles of cortisol in recovery from exhaustive exercise in rainbow trout. *Can. J. Zool.* 72:2136–46

78. Pagnotta A, Milligan CL. 1991. The role of blood glucose in the restoration of muscle glycogen during recovery from exhaustive exercise in rainbow trout (*Oncorhynchus mykiss*) and winter flounder (*Pseudopleuronectes americanus*). *J. Exp. Biol.* 161:489–508

79. Phillip JW, Hird FJR. 1977. Gluconeogenesis in vertebrate livers. *Comp. Biochem. Physiol.* 57B:127–31

80. Piiper J, Meyer M, Drees F. 1972. Hydrogen ion balance in the elasmobranch *Scyliorhinus stellaris* after exhausting activity. *Respir. Physiol.* 16: 290–03

81. Pough FH, Andrews RM. 1985. Use of anaerobic metabolism by free-ranging lizards. *Physiol. Zool.* 58:205–13

82. Putnam RW. 1979. The role of lactic acid accumulation in muscle fatigue of two species of anurans, *Xenopus laevis* and *Rana pipiens*. *J. Exp. Biol.* 82:35–51

83. Putnam RW. 1979. The basis for differences in lactic acid content after activity in different species of anuran amphibians. *Physiol. Zool.* 52:509–19

84. Roth DA. 1991. The sarcolemmal lactate transporter: transmembrane determinants of lactate flux. *Med. Sci. Sports Exerc.* 23:925–34

85. Ruben JA, Battalia DE. 1979. Aerobic and anaerobic metabolism during activity in small rodents. *J. Exp. Zool.* 208: 73–76

86. Saunders DK, Fedde MR. 1994. Exercise performance of birds. *Adv. Vet. Sci. Comp. Med.* 38B:139–90

87. Deleted in proof

88. Scarabello M, Heigenhauser GJ, Wood CM. 1992. Gas exchange, metabolite status and excess post-exercise oxygen consumption after repetitive bouts of exhaustive exercise in juvenile rainbow trout. *J. Exp. Biol.* 167:155–80

89. Shiota M, Golden S, Katz J. 1984. Lactate metabolism in the perfused rat hindlimb. *Biochem. J.* 222:281–92

90. Shulman GI, Landau BR. 1992. Pathways of glycogen repletion. *Physiol. Rev.* 72:1019–35

91. Shulte PM, Moyes CD, Hochachka PW. 1992. Integrating metabolic pathways in post-exercise recovery of white muscle. *J. Exp. Biol.* 166:181–96

92. Stainsby WN, Brooks, GA. 1990. Control of lactic acid metabolism in contracting muscles and during exercise. *Exerc. Sports Sci. Rev.* 18:29–63

93. Stainsby WN, Sumners C, Andrew GM.

1984. Plasma catecholamines and their effect on blood lactate and muscle lactate output. *J. Appl. Physiol.* 57:321–25

94. Stevenson RW, Mitchell DR, Hendrick GK, Rainey R, Cherrington AD, Frizzell RT. 1987. Lactate as substrate for glycogen resynthesis after exercise. *J. Appl. Physiol.* 62 2237–40

94a. Suarez RK, Mallet MD, Daxboek C, Hochachka PW. 1986. Enzymes of energy metabolism and gluconeogenesis in the Pacific blue marlin, *Makaira nigricans*. *Can. J. Zool.* 64:694–97

95. Talmadge RJ, Scheide JI, Silverman H. 1989. Glycogen synthesis from lactate in a chronically active muscle. *J. Appl. Physiol.* 66:2231–38

96. Talmadge RJ, Silverman H. 1992. Glyconeogenesis by skeletal muscle involvement of PEPCK. *FASEB J.* 6:A964

97. Turner JD, Wood CM. 1983. Physiological consequences of severe exercise in the inactive benthic flathead sole (*Hippoglossoides elassodon*): a comparison with the active pelagic rainbow trout (*Salmo gairdneri*). *J. Exp. Biol.* 104:269–88

98. Turner JD, Wood CM, Clark D. 1983. Lactate and proton dynamics in the rainbow trout (*Salmo gairdneri*). *J. Exp. Biol.* 104:247–68

99. Vollestad NK, Blom PCS, Gronnerod O. 1989. Resynthesis of glycogen in different muscle fibre types after prolonged exhaustive exercise in man. *Acta Physiol. Scand.* 137:15–21

100. Wagner EL, Gleeson TT. 1995. Low temperature and exercise recovery in desert iguanas. *Physiol. Zool.* In press

101. Wardle, CS. 1978. Non-release of lactic acid from anaerobic swimming muscle of plaice, *Pleuronectes platessa* L.: a stress reaction. *J. Exp. Biol.* 77:141–55

102. Wickler SJ, Gleeson TT. 1993. Lactate and glucose metabolism in mouse (*Mus musculus*) and reptile (*Anolis carolinenesis*) skeletal muscle. *Am. J. Physiol.* 264:R487–91

103. Wickler SJ, Wagner EL, Gleeson TT. 1995. Carbohydrate metabolism in larval and adult salamander (*Ambystoma tigrinum*) skeletal muscle. *Physiol. Zool.* In review

104. Wilson MA, Gatten RE Jr, Greenberg N. 1990. Glycolysis in *Anolis carolinenesis* during agonistic encounters. *Physiol. Behav.* 48:139–42

105. Withers PC, Lea M, Solberg TC, Baustain M, Hedrick M. 1988. Metabolic fates of lactate during recovery from activity in an anuran amphibian, *Bufo americanus*. *J. Exp. Zool.* 246:236–43

Annu. Rev. Physiol. 1996. 58:583–605

# UPPER LIMITS TO MASS-SPECIFIC METABOLIC RATES

*Raul K. Suarez*

Department of Biological Sciences, University of California, Santa Barbara, California 93106-9610

KEY WORDS: $V_{O_2\ max}$, exercise, glycolysis, enzyme activity, muscle, sustained metabolic rate

### ABSTRACT

An intriguing aspect of animal diversity is the wide range of maximal mass-specific metabolic rates attainable by various species. Metabolic ceilings vary with respect to whether hypermetabolic states involve relatively short bouts of burst or aerobic exercise, or long-term physical activity wherein time-averaged rates of dietary energy intake equal rates of energy expenditure. Design of metabolic flux capacities at the biochemical level can only be meaningfully considered in the context of design at higher levels of biological organization and maximum physiological requirements at the level of the whole organism. Studies of this nature have led to important insights concerning the rules that govern evolutionary design and the constraints that may set upper limits to mass-specific metabolic rates.

## INTRODUCTION

Various species achieve the highest rates of metabolism known in the Animal Kingdom as a consequence of factors that include size, lifestyle, and physical activity. Maximal metabolic rates achieved under various circumstances can be categorized into (*a*) those involving short bursts of exercise, as in sprints supported by phosphagen hydrolysis and/or glycolytic ATP production; (*b*) longer bouts at maximal aerobic capacity ($V_{O_2max}$) supported mainly by mitochondrial oxidative phosphorylation; and (*c*) activities sustainable for even longer durations, where energy input through the diet equals energy expenditure. These maximum metabolic rates at the level of the whole organism are the outcome of exquisitely matched rates of substrate and $O_2$ fluxes through multi-step pathways in various organs, tissues, and cell types. These maximal

583

rates, whether high or low, are made possible by structures and functional capacities that are the outcome of evolutionary processes. The factors that set proximate as well as ultimate upper metabolic limits would be expected to differ according to the nature of the activities involved.

A fruitful approach adopted in studies of the design of physiological systems involves assessment of the degree to which structures and functional capacities are matched to maximum physiological requirements or loads. In their pioneering studies of the pathway of $O_2$ through the mammalian respiratory and cardiovascular systems, Taylor, Weibel, and colleagues tested the hypothesis they call symmorphosis (131, 132, 141), which argues that animals are designed such that structures and functional capacities satisfy, but do not exceed, maximum physiological requirements or loads. Implicit in the hypothesis is the idea that functional capacities of the individual steps in multi-step pathways or processes are matched to each other. Diamond and colleagues have adopted this strategy of examining the degree to which capacities match loads in their studies of intestinal nutrient transport, incorporating into the analysis the idea that animals possess built-in safety margins (26–28). Although the concept of symmorphosis has provoked much debate (27, 28, 35, 48), it has been argued that it is a useful null hypothesis in studies of the relationships between functional design and maximum physiological performance (27).

This review concerns patterns of relationships between capacities and loads, as well as the costs and constraints that may set upper limits to capacities. Previous reviews adopting a similar approach have focused on higher levels of biological organization (69, 130). The present analysis differs from these reviews in its more extensive coverage of biochemical information, in its use of biochemical concepts, and in its attempt to better integrate biochemistry with organismal physiology.

## CAPACITIES AND LOADS AT THE BIOCHEMICAL LEVEL

Weiss, in 1947 (143), pointed out that physiology differs from biochemistry not in the kinds of techniques that are used, but in the kinds of questions that are asked. While biochemical studies have traditionally been purely mechanistic, physiological studies have also focused on questions relating to functional significance. Despite the great wealth of detailed information available from biochemistry and molecular biology, not much is known concerning how metabolic enzymes and mitochondria actually function in vivo. Even less is known concerning the rules that govern the design of functional capacities at the biochemical level.

Of great physiological relevance in considering evolutionary design at the level of multi-step biochemical pathways is the relationships between the capacities for flux ($V_{max}$) and maximum pathway flux rates ($J_{max}$) (91a). Because $V_{max}$ is a function of both enzyme concentration [E] and catalytic efficiency $k_{cat}$, i.e. $V_{max} = [E] \times k_{cat}$, it is appropriate to briefly consider whether high flux capacities are the outcome of high $k_{cat}$, high [E], or both.

## Metabolic Rates and Enzyme Catalytic Efficiencies

Do animals with high metabolic rates possess inherently faster enzymes? Among animals functioning at similar physiological temperatures, $k_{cat}$ values of homologous enzymes appear to be highly conserved and are independent of maximal metabolic rates. Differences in $k_{cat}$ appear to be correlated with differences in physiological temperature and the evolutionary trade-offs between catalytic efficiency, enzyme-ligand affinity, and thermal stability. Homeotherms with high body temperatures possess enzymes with more rigid, thermally stable structures and lower $k_{cat}$ values. Poikilotherms with low body temperatures possess enzymes that are not as rigid and thermally stable, but more efficient at catalysis. The picture becomes more complicated upon consideration of abyssal organisms, which generally display low metabolic rates, and whose enzymes function at low temperature and high pressure. In these organisms, the rigidity required for stability at high pressure has resulted in enzymes with low $k_{cat}$ values. However, the extremely low metabolic rates of these fishes are due largely to low concentrations of enzymes, not low $k_{cat}$ values (16, 62). The trade-offs between catalytic efficiency and stability are more fully discussed by Hochachka & Somero (62).

Because $k_{cat}$ values among animals with similar physiological temperatures are highly conserved, differences in $V_{max}$ values at the same enzyme-catalyzed step between species, between individuals in a species, or between cell types in an individual are generally considered to reflect differences in [E]. This implies that insights concerning the rules that govern the design of functional capacities at the biochemical level can be found by examining patterns of relationships between $V_{max}$ values, maximum rates of pathway flux, $J_{max}$, and fractional velocities at individual enzyme-catalyzed steps, $v/V_{max}$.

# ENERGY REQUIREMENTS OF MUSCLES

An established paradigm in metabolic biochemistry is that intracellular ATP concentrations are held relatively stable despite transitions between low and high rates of ATP hydrolysis (2). This is achieved through stoichiometric matching between rates of ATP hydrolysis and ATP synthesis. The mechanisms responsible for the matching of these rates have been the subject of biochemical research for most of this century. Mechanical work performed by muscles results in increased rates of ATP utilization, mainly by actomyosin

ATPase and, in many muscle types across species, by the $Ca^{2+}$-ATPase of the sarcoplasmic reticulum (63). Actomyosin ATPase activity accounts for 65–80% of the ATP hydrolyzed by contracting vertebrate skeletal muscles. The involvement of the ATP-dependent $Ca^{2+}$ pump of the sarcoplasmic reticulum in the process of excitation-contraction coupling results in 20–35% of overall rates of ATP hydrolysis, whereas $Na^+$-$K^+$-ATPase accounts for about 10%. The fractions of work-related rates of ATP-hydrolysis accounted for by these three major ATP-consuming processes in mammalian cardiac muscles are similar to those estimated in skeletal muscles (101). Asynchronous insect flight muscles lack a well-developed sarcoplasmic reticulum; the contribution of $Ca^{2+}$-ATPase to ATP turnover during flight is thought to be minimal (39, 77).

## BURST EXERCISE

The term burst exercise, as used here, includes the fast starts seen in fish that may involve just a few tail flips, the explosive leap of anuran amphibians as they lunge at prey or escape from predators, or exercise of short durations at intensities beyond those sustainable by aerobic ATP synthesis, e.g. cheetah chasing down prey or humans sprinting for Olympic medals. Because of their short durations or rates of ATP utilization surpassing mitochondrial capacities for ATP synthesis, such activities depend mainly, if not exclusively, upon substrate level ADP-phosphorylation reactions of two types. The first relies on phosphagens (e.g. creatine phosphate, CrP; arginine phosphate, ArgP) as phosphate donors in near-equilibrium reactions catalyzed by the corresponding phosphagen kinases (e.g. creatine phosphokinase, CPK; arginine phosphokinase, APK). The second involves ADP phosphorylation by substrate-level phosphorylation reactions in glycolysis.

### Phosphagen Kinases

The thermodynamics of phosphagen kinase reactions has recently been reviewed (40). Equilibrium constants ($K_{eq}$) of these reactions all favor ATP synthesis, although the exact values depend upon pH, free [$Mg^{2+}$], ionic strength, and temperature (40, 133). Phosphagen kinase reactions are generally thought to be close to equilibrium in vivo (40, 88), and there is considerable evidence for this in the case of the CPK reaction. Two functions are ascribed to phosphagen kinase reactions; both relate to the buffering of adenine nucleotide concentrations. The "temporal buffering" role was the one first recognized (12), and it is usually understood in terms of the maintenance of ATP concentrations (at the expense of phosphagen) under conditions of fluctuating (e.g. dramatically accelerated) rates of ATP hydrolysis. (The other role, called spatial buffering, is discussed below.) Ellington (40) has shown that the greater instability of CrP relative to other phosphagens, i.e. the higher $K_{eq}$ of the CPK reaction, makes this compound better suited as an ATP buffer at the high $[ATP]/[ADP]_f$ (where f refers to intracellular free concentration) ratios found in vertebrate muscles. Although discussion of the temporal buffering role of the CPK reaction has focused mainly on the buffering of [ATP], calculations by Funk et al (45) reveal that a single muscle twitch may result in only a 3% drop in [ATP] in the absence of the CPK reaction. Accompanying this relatively small change, however, are 4- and 16-fold increases in $[ADP]_f$ and $[AMP]_f$, respectively. Because ADP and AMP are important regulators of energy metabolism, it appears that buffering of the concentrations of all three adenine nucleotides is important.

Effective temporal buffering needs the maintenance of phosphagen hydrolysis reactions near equilibrium in vivo, which requires that $V_{max}$ values greatly exceed rates of ATP hydrolysis (92). This does not imply, however, that $V_{max}$ values have little or nothing to do with intracellular reaction rates. Saturation transfer NMR measurements in rats reveal that intracellular flux rates in both directions, i.e. CrP synthesis and hydrolysis, are directly related to enzyme content (7). This is despite the fact that $V_{max}$ values (in the direction of MgATP synthesis) exceed in vivo flux rates by an order of magnitude. Also, studies involving experimental manipulation of CPK levels using molecular techniques reveal that isolated muscle preparations from mutant mice deficient in the I-band associated isozyme of CPK are incapable of burst exercise (134). In these muscles, inversion transfer NMR measurements showed no transfer of labeled P nuclei between CrP and ATP, in contrast with controls. In the functionally opposite manipulation, transgenic mice with skeletal muscles expressing higher activities of CPK were found, by saturation transfer, to have flux rates greater than controls (11).

The comparative study of Newsholme et al (91) showed that fast-twitch glycolytic vertebrate and invertebrate (e.g. lobster and scallop) muscles possess greater phosphagen kinase activities than vertebrate red and cardiac muscles. In highly glycolytic muscles, such as the white muscles that make up most of the bulk of teleost fishes, fast starts and short sprints appear to be exclusively phosphagen based. For example, Dobson et al (31) showed that 10-s swimming bouts at about 5 body lengths/s in rainbow trout (*Oncorhynchus mykiss*) are accompanied by CrP depletion, but no glycogen depletion or lactate accumulation. This was despite estimated rates of muscle ATP turnover of between 188 and 598 $\mu$mol g$^{-1}$ min$^{-1}$ during the multiple 0.8-s bursts of swimming activity occurring during the 10-s periods. Other teleost species are capable of much faster sprint speeds, the highest of which may be around 25 body lengths/s (137). The relationship between CPK activity and maximal sprint speeds has not been examined. However, the power requirements for burst swimming increase with body mass (138, 146). Interestingly, Somero & Childress (113) find that CPK activities increase with size in two active swimmers, kelp bass (*Paralabrax clathratus*) and rainbow trout (*Oncorhynchus mykiss*) but not in a sedentary bottom dweller, the Dover sole (*Microstomus pacificus*). Pacific blue marlin (*Makaira nigricans*) possesses muscle CPK activities (127) higher than that of its smaller prey, skipjack tuna (*Euthynnus pelamis*) (52).

Among invertebrates, ArgP hydrolysis is found to supply most of the energy required for the shell-clapping escape responses of certain species of scallops, e.g. *Pecten maximus* (46), *Placopecten magellanicus* (24), and *Chlamys opercularis* (51). However, ATP is also depleted to various degrees in response to this type of exercise, down to 20% of resting levels in the case of *Chlamys opercularis* (51). It is important to note, however, that burst exercise is not universally anaerobic in molluscan species (4, 121).

## Glycolysis

Muscles that work at power outputs requiring rates of ATP hydrolysis in excess of mitochondrial capacities for oxidative phosphorylation will use glycolysis as an additional, if not main, source of ATP (59). Emmett & Hochachka, working on mammals (43), and Somero & Childress, working on pelagic species of fish (111), simultaneously and independently discovered that maximum glycolytic enzyme activities increase with body size in vertebrate skeletal muscles. It was also discovered that oxidative enzyme activities decrease with increasing body size. The latter finding by Emmett & Hochachka (43, 60) is consistent with information concerning the allometric scaling of mitochondrial volume densities (the fraction of fiber volume occupied by mitochondria, $Vv_{mt,f}$) (81) and oxidative capacities ($V_{O_2max}$) (130) in mammals. Somero & Childress (17, 111, 112) observed that lactate dehydrogenase (LDH) activities in pelagic species of fish scale against body length with an allometric exponent similar to that of power requirements of burst swimming. This, as well as the increases in both pyruvate kinase and CPK activities with body length, and the lack of this type of scaling in a bottom-dwelling species argues convincingly in favor of the adaptive significance of this scaling pattern.

Which $V_{max}$ value in glycolysis determines maximum glycolytic rate? In principle, the $V_{max}$ of the most rate-limiting step should be the value of interest (19, 91a, 92). However, $V_{max}$ values published over the years have tended to increase as extraction procedures have improved and as more knowledge has been gained concerning both the stabilization of the enzymes of interest and the optimization of assay conditions. For example, previous estimates of phosphofructokinase (PFK) activity in honeybee flight muscles were insufficient to account for glycolytic rates estimated during flight (19). Recently, it was found that hexose 6-phosphates are required to stabilize the enzyme (139). The development of metabolic control theory (58, 70) has resulted in the realization that all enzyme-catalyzed steps in pathways participate in the control of flux, that some steps may be more important (i.e. possess higher flux control coefficients) than others, and that the relative degree of control exerted by various steps may change with physiological circumstances.

Three decades ago, Danforth & Lyon (21) showed that glycolytic rates in tetanic mouse muscles are close to the maximum activities of glycogen phosphorylase (GP), most of which is converted to the "a" (active) form under these circumstances. This implies that maximum GP activity may set the upper limit to glycolytic flux rate. This is, of course, possible in muscle types where the $V_{max}$ values of steps downstream are not less than the $V_{max}$ for GP. However, in many types of muscles, maximum PFK activities are less than those of GP (e.g. 5). Danforth & Lyon (21) suggested that PFK may be more rate-limiting than GP at lower stimulation frequencies. The idea of dynamic shifts in the nature of glycolytic regulation was later recognized by Neely and colleagues in their studies of energy metabolism in rat hearts (73, 135). Although glucose transport and the hexokinase (HK) reaction were considered to be the most rate-limiting steps under normoxic conditions at low and moderate work rates (135), it was suggested that anoxia or maximum work rates under normoxic conditions resulted in flux limitation at the level of glyceraldehyde 3-phosphate dehydrogenase (73). More recently, Kashiwaya et al (71) applied control analysis to perfused, normoxic hearts and found that only 25% of control is accounted for by reactions downstream of phosphoglucoisomerase. This contrasts with the anoxic situation and is consistent with the conclusions of Neely and colleagues (73, 135).

Technical advances in the measurement of flux rates and the application of these to various systems, as well as discrimination between physiological and nonphysiological work rates, have made possible more critical evaluation of the relationships between enzyme $V_{max}$ values, $J_{max}$, and $v/V_{max}$. For example, although most GP activity is converted into the "a" form, and the enzyme in this form can function close to $V_{max}$ in tetanic muscles (21), this may not occur under physiological circumstances in vivo. In running rats, 24% of total GP activity is converted into the "a" form in red muscles and 23% in white muscles (50). Because rates of glycogenolysis were measured in the same study, and total GP activities (expressed in units of enzyme activity per g wet wt) in the red and white fiber types of the same muscles are known (5), it can be estimated that $v/V_{max}$ values in vivo correspond to only 7 and 3% of GP activity in the "a" form in red and white muscles, respectively. During burst exercise in rainbow trout, only 16% of total white muscle GP activity is converted to the "a" form (120). However, changes in modulator concentrations are such that the "b" form contributes to glycogen breakdown (86, 87), and rates of glycogenolysis (31) may be similar to total phosphorylase activities (120). It is noteworthy that during exercise, HK in trout red and white muscles functions at very low fractional velocities ($<1\%$ of $V_{max}$), and glucose does not contribute significantly as a metabolic fuel to energy production (145). An additional factor that must be taken into account is that $v/V_{max}$ is not constant when estimated for each of the reactions in glycolysis. Some of the reasons for this are well understood. Reactions maintained close to equilibrium in vivo require very high $V_{max}$ values, often orders of magnitude in excess of $J_{max}$, to maintain near-equilibium states at physiological flux rates (91a, 92). In contrast, reactions maintained far from equilibrium in vivo (e.g. HK and PFK) are catalyzed by enzymes that generally occur at lower $V_{max}$ values (19, 91a, 92) and, in various species, work over a wide range of $v/V_{max}$ values in vivo (R Suarez et al, unpublished data).

Therefore, contrary to earlier expectations, there are no simple, generally applicable ways to determine maximum glycolytic flux rates in vivo ($J_{max}$) on the basis of measurements of the $V_{max}$ values of key enzymes in vitro. This does not mean, however, that $V_{max}$ measurements are of no use. Newsholme et al (19, 91a, 92) are correct in pointing out that these values provide theoretical upper limits to flux rates. (However, whether $J_{max}$ values are ever equal to any of the $V_{max}$ values in a pathway is an important, often neglected, issue.) Such estimates continue to be of great value in studies where comparisons of relative flux capacities are of interest. Differences in maximum GP and PFK activities between fiber types or among muscles of different species do reflect demonstrable differences in capacities for gly-colytic flux (19). Even the maximal activities of enzymes catalyzing reactions maintained close to equilibrium provide useful insights into pathway design and enzyme function in vivo. The analysis of the triose-phosphate isomerase reaction in rat liver and muscle conducted by Veech et al (136) shows that a large excess in flux capacity is actually necessary to maintain a near-equi-librium relationship between products and substrates at physiological rates of net flux. Detailed studies of the phosphoglucoisomerase reaction in the flowering plant *Clarkia xantiana* (Onagraceae) reveal that the maximum activity of the enzyme is not greatly in excess of what is required to maintain the reaction (fructose 6-phosphate↔glucose 6-phosphate) close to equilib-rium at high rates of sucrose synthesis (75). A similar argument no doubt holds for other near-equilibrium steps. For example, LDH is found at maximal activities (in $\mu$mol min$^{-1}$ g$^{-1}$) in excess of 5000 in the white muscles of fast-swimming skipjack tunas (52), 500 in the less-athletic Amazon fish *Hoplias malabaricus* (61), and 5 (or less!) in several species of sluggish deep-sea fishes (16). The LDH-analogue octopine dehydrogenase occurs at much higher activities in fast-swimmming cephalopod molluscs than in more sluggish species (3). Clearly, there is much evidence indicating that the wide range in $V_{max}$ values observed inter- and intra-specifically is of functional significance.

# AEROBIC EXERCISE

The tremendous diversity in lifestyle, morphology, and physiology observed in the Animal Kingdom results in seldom-recognized differences between species in the kinds of activities that lead to maximal $O_2$ consumption rates. Calling in male frogs of certain species (e.g. *Hyla versicolor*) is accompanied by higher rates of $O_2$ consumption than maximal rates measured during loco- motion (129). This is made possible by highly aerobic trunk muscles that possess higher activities of oxidative enzymes, mitochondrial volumes, and capillary densities than locomotory muscles (80). Ingestion of prey by certain snake species, e.g. Burmese pythons (*Python molurus*), which adopt sit-and- wait prey capture strategies, results in post-feeding rates of $O_2$ consumption that also exceed those observed during locomotion (104, 105). In these snakes, it appears that hypertrophy of the gut, in preparation for digestion, is respon- sible for the increase in $V_{O_2}$ (104, 105). In the following sections, discussion of mitochondrial respiration in vivo is confined to $V_{O_2max}$ values attained during locomotory exercise.

## *Mitochondria and $V_{O2}$max*

Most of the $O_2$ taken up by animals exercising at (or close to) $V_{O_2max}$ is consumed by muscle mitochondria (130). In mammals, the $O_2$ transport ca- pacity of the cardiovascular system is thought to set the upper limit to $V_{O_2max}$ (72, 98). Because maximum mass-specific rates of aerobic metabolism, $V_{O_2max}/M_b$, scale inversely with body mass (130), much attention has been focused on the allometric scaling of structures and functional capacities in the pathway of $O_2$ from the external environment to the muscle mitochondria. The results of these studies have led to remarkable insights into the rules that govern structural and functional design in mammals; these have been the subject of previous reviews (130, 132).

Consistent with the discovery of the inverse relationship between the activi- ties of mitochondrial oxidative enzymes and body mass (43, 60), Mathieu et al (81) and Else & Hulbert (41, 42) found that small mammals possess higher $Vv_{mt,f}$ values than large mammals. The development of methods for estimation of total mitochondrial volume ($V_{mt}$) in skeletal muscles has made possible the calculation of maximal respiration rates per unit of mitochondrial volume, $V_{O_2max}/V_{mt}$. These values fall within the remarkably narrow range of 3–5 ml $O_2$ $cm^{-3}$ $min^{-1}$ (64, 130, 132). Mammalian skeletal muscle mitochondria possess mass-independent cristae surface densities (surface area per unit mi- tochondrial volume) between 20 and 40 $cm^2/cm^3$ (64). Comparisons of in vitro with in vivo rates of mitochondrial respiration (103) have led to the suggestion that skeletal muscle mitochondria in mammals exercising at $V_{O_2max}$ respire at their maximum capacities in vivo (103, 130, 132). All these data have led to the concept that mammalian skeletal muscle mitochondria constitute invariable functional units that are simply "added or subtracted" in Nature's experiments to produce mammalian species capable of a wide range of $V_{O_2max}/M_b$ values (130, 132).

It is instructive to compare what is known concerning the structural and functional correlates of $V_{O_2max}/M_b$ in other species with mammalian data. Mitochondrial morphometric parameters and respiration rates in vivo during exercise at (or close to) $V_{O_2max}$ in Cuban iguanas, rufous hummingbirds, Euglossine bees, and blowflies are listed in Table 1, along with data from the domestic cat. It is apparent from these data that $Vv_{mt,f}$ values increase with increasing $V_{O_2max}/M_b$, well beyond the highest values reported in mammalian skeletal muscles (122, 123). Cristae surface densities also vary between species in a manner consistent with $V_{O_2max}/M_b$. Skeletal muscles in Cuban iguanas (18) possess surface densities similar to the lowest values measured in mammals, whereas hummingbird and insect flight muscle mitochondria yield higher surface densities than mammals. Together, higher values of $Vv_{mt,f}$ and higher cristae surface densities allow flying hummingbirds and insects to achieve higher $V_{O_2}/M_b$ than reptiles and mammals (122, 123).

Although the respiratory and cardiovascular systems of mammals are designed to deliver $O_2$ to muscle mitochondria at mass-independent maximal rates of $3-5$ ml cm$^{-3}$ min$^{-1}$ (64, 130, 132), capacities for $O_2$ delivery in Cuban iguanas are lower (18), whereas those in hummingbirds and flying insects are higher. Hummingbirds, in particular, possess lung $O_2$ diffusing capacities 8.5-fold higher than mammals of similar body mass (33), hearts that are 2-fold larger than predicted on the basis of the allometric scaling of heart mass in birds (99), maximum cardiac outputs of about five times body mass per min (67), capillary volume densities two to six times greater than in mammalian hindlimb muscles (82, 125), and whole-body red cell circulation times estimated at about 1 s or less (67). Insects, with tracheal systems that branch within muscle fibers and lie in close proximity to the mitochondria, possess even higher capacities for $O_2$ transport (110, 144). As a consequence, $V_{O_2max}/V_{mt}$ values increase with increasing $V_{O_2max}/M_b$, from iguanas to mammals, hummingbirds, bees, and flies. However, values of $V_{O_2max}$ per m$^2$ of cristae surface area also increase with $V_{O_2max}/M_b$. This suggests, in addition to increasing capacities for $O_2$ delivery per m$^2$ of cristae, that densities of respiratory chain enzymes ($V_{max}$ values for electron transport and ATP synthesis) per cm$^2$ of cristae may increase as well (122, 123). Preliminary data are available suggesting that insect flight muscle mitochondria possess inherently higher respiratory capacities than mitochondria from vertebrate skeletal muscles (128). It seems clear that muscle mitochondria are not created equal because some contain more cristae (and, presumably, greater activities of respiratory chain enzymes) than others. However, studies of

**Table 1**   Mitochondrial morphometry and respiration rates in locomotory muscles. Volume densities represent percent of fiber volume occupied by mitochondria. Cristae surface densities represent surface areas per unit mitochondrial volume

| | Volume density (%) | Cristae surface density $(m^2/cm^3)$ | ml $O_2/(cm^3 \times min)$ | $\mu l$ $O_2/(m^2 \times min)$ |
|---|---|---|---|---|
| Cuban iguana[a] | 3 | 25 | 1 | 40 |
| Cat[b] | 4 – 6 | 35 | 3 – 5 | 86 – 143 |
| Humming-bird[c] | 35 | 58 | 7 – 10 | 121 – 172 |
| Euglossine bee[d] | 43 | 50 | 16 | 320 |
| Blowfly[e] | 40 | 53 | 23 | 434 |

[a] *Cyclura nubila*. (Data from 18.)
[b] Morphometric data from soleus and gracilis (103). Respiration rates represent mammalian range of $V_{O_2max}$ values (130).
[c] *Selasphorus rufus*. (Data from 125.)
[d] *Euglossa cagnata*. (Data from 13,14.)
[e] Morphometric data from *Calliphora erythrocephala* (109). $V_{O_2}$ during flight from *Lucilia sericata* (22).

the sort pioneered by Schwerzmann et al (103) that combine morphometric with biochemical measurements need to be conducted using a variety of species capable of a wide range of $V_{O_2max}/M_b$ values.

## Biochemical Implications of Mitochondrial Volume Densities and Distributions

The highest $Vv_{mt,f}$ values observed in locomotory muscles (~45%) are about as high as those found in mammalian cardiac muscles (65, 140). Muscles with high $Vv_{mt,f}$ values have a greater fraction of their mitochondria localized under the sarcolemma (e.g. 125). Mainwood & Rakusan (78) proposed that this enhances capacities for intracellular $O_2$ transport because diffusion distances between the sarcolemma and these mitochondria would be less than if mitochondrial distributions were random and mostly interfibrillar. In hummingbird flight muscles, where rates of $O_2$ consumption are about 2 ml $g^{-1}$ $min^{-1}$ (125, 126), subsarcolemmal mitochondria account for 40% of total mitochondrial volume (125). Whether such subsarcolemmal distributions do facilitate $O_2$ flux is debated. On the basis of measurements of the oxygenation state of myoglobin in fast-frozen exercised dog muscles, Honig and colleagues (49) proposed that intracellular $pO_2$ gradients are shallow and that $pO_2$ values are high enough to saturate cytochrome a,$a_3$ oxidase, even during exercise at $V_{O_2max}$. Spectro-photometric measurements of the redox state of cytochrome a,$a_3$ in exercising muscles have yielded conflicting results. Stainsby et al (118) report increased oxidation of cytochrome a,$a_3$ during twitch and tetanic contractions, whereas

Duhaylongsod et al (36) find near-complete reduction, "not significantly different from that observed at death," at $V_{O_2max}$.

Mitochondrial distributions in the muscles of animal taxa besides birds and mammals provide further food for thought. Highly active squids (e.g. *Symplectoteuthis oualaniensis*) possess muscles used for their jetting mode of locomotion that contain mitochondria localized exclusively in the central core of the fibers (89). Continuously active gill bailer muscles in the green crab *Carcinus maenas* contain a band of mitochondria localized exclusively at the periphery of each fiber (119). It has been suggested that localization of sites of ATP synthesis some distance away from the sites of ATP hydrolysis may result, at high rates of ATP turnover, in diffusion limitation of aerobic metabolism. Jacobus (66) estimates that intracellular free ADP gradients are not large enough to drive diffusion at rates sufficient to account for high rates of ATP turnover, such as those measured in mammalian cardiac muscle. Therefore, it was proposed that spatial buffering of adenine nucleotides may be the other functional role of the CPK reaction. Several proponents of this idea have advocated the existence of a creatine phosphate shuttle (6). However, NMR data obtained from intact, exercising muscles do not support the shuttle hypothesis (106, 107). Furthermore, Meyer et al (88) have shown mathematically that both temporal and spatial buffering are simply consequences of the near-equilibium nature of the reaction catalyzed by CPK. Thus in the same manner that high concentrations of myoglobin enhance intracellular $O_2$ fluxes (because $O_2$ can diffuse "as" oxymyoglobin), adenine nucleotide fluxes are enhanced because high-energy phosphate can diffuse as PCr, whereas phosphate acceptor can diffuse mainly in the form of Cr between mitochondria and myofibrils. The importance of maintaining near-equilibrium between the substrates and products of phosphagen kinase reactions despite changing and, at times, extremely high rates of ATP hydrolysis in highly aerobic muscles is reflected in the high enzymatic capacities measured in hummingbird (124) and locust (100) flight muscles ($\sim$2800 and $\sim$2200 $\mu$mol g$^{-1}$ min$^{-1}$ of CPK and APK, respectively).

Differences in mitochondrial content may, along with other factors, result in differences in mechanisms of regulation of oxidative metabolism as well. Dudley et al (34) showed, through experimental alteration of the mitochondrial content of rat skeletal muscles, that increased mitochondrial content resulted in increased sensitivity of respiration to control by [ADP]$_f$. Kushmerick et al (76) found that changes in [ADP]$_f$ are enough to account for respiratory control in cat fast-twitch muscles but not in slow-twitch muscles where $Vv_{mt,f}$ is higher (103).

## SUSTAINED METABOLIC RATES

Peterson et al (95) defined sustained metabolic rate (SusMR) as the highest time-averaged metabolic rate sustainable for prolonged periods (days or weeks) during which energy balance is maintained via food intake. The ratio of SusMR and RMR (resting metabolic rate) yields sustained metabolic scope (SusMS). In their survey of SusMR and RMR data from 37 species, including humans, eutherian and marsupial mammals, birds, and lizards, Peterson et al (95) showed that most SusMS values ranged between 1.5 and 5, and the highest values approached 7. SusMR and SusMS values are considered to be of great biological significance (142). As a consequence of the metabolic costs of thermoregulation, they may be involved in establishing the low-temperature tolerance limits of vertebrate homeotherms, thus influencing their biogeographic distribution patterns (10, 23, 142). SusMR may influence reproductive strategies by establishing the upper limits to the number of nestlings that birds are able to provision (32) and the number of babies that mother mammals are able to nurse (54–56). There is considerable interest in the factors that establish SusMR values. Hypotheses have considered whether upper limits might be established by central (energy-providing) capacities, peripheral (energy-consuming or waste-disposal) capacities, or whether central and peripheral capacities are matched to each other (as might be predicted by symmorphosis) such that no specific bottlenecks exist.

Numerous investigations have involved testing the hypothesis that digestive capacities determine SusMR values. Diamond and colleagues have demonstrated that digestive enzyme activities and nutrient transport capacities in small intestines exceed nutritional requirements by certain measurable safety margins and that digestive capacities are up-regulated in response to increased metabolic demands (26, 28, 29). When the litter size of mother mice was artificially increased, milk production rates increased such that SusMR (measured by time-averaged rates of food ingestion) exceeded basal metabolic rates (BMR) by a maximum of 7.2-fold (55). However, mice exposed to low temperature increased SusMR (to thermoregulate) to a maximum of only 4.7 times BMR (74), and lactating mice at low temperature showed higher rates of food intake (SusMR) than lactating mice at room temperature or virgin mice at low temperature (56). In agreement with Diamond and colleagues, McDevitt & Speakman (84, 85) also conclude that digestive capacity does not determine SusMR in their study of voles (*Microtus agrestis*) exposed to low temperature. Adding increasing numbers of chicks to house wren (*Troglodytes aedon*) nests resulted in increased field metabolic rates (FMR, measured with doubly-labeled water) in the parents (38). However, FMR values under these conditions were only 65% of SusMR achieved by wrens subjected to both exercise and low temperature in the laboratory (37). Thus although SusMR values obviously cannot exceed the capacities of digestive systems to process the fuels required for energy metabolism, the central and/or peripheral processes that actually determine species-specific SusMR values remain the subject of active investigation.

## COSTS AND CONSTRAINTS

### The Cost of Being Macho or Motherly

The idea that animals are designed economically, such that excess capacities beyond necessary safety margins are eliminated by natural selection, has been both influential (27, 28) and controversial (35, 48). Biological structures (and associated functional capacities) occupy space and require resources, energy, and time to build and maintain. It is, therefore, reasonable to hypothesize that the extra costs incurred in building excess capacities, as well as other constraining factors, may impose upper limits to the enhancement of capacities beyond those required. Whether such costs and constraints have, through natural selection, resulted in optimal design is the subject of debate.

At the level of the whole organism, much evidence indicates that enhanced physiological capacities are accompanied by increased maintenance costs. Among male dragonflies competing for females with which to mate, macho individuals (possessing greater masses of flight muscle relative to body mass) are more successful than those not as well endowed (79). However, the higher metabolic costs associated with being macho are such that these individuals store less fat and are more at risk of starving during periods when foraging flights are energetically unprofitable. Comparisons between species of birds and among individuals within species reveal that high BMR values are associated with large fractions of body mass accounted for by metabolically active organs, such as the heart, liver, and kidney (20). Abilities to sustain high FMR (e.g. during periods of maximal foraging effort associated with feeding of nestlings) also increase with BMR (20). Temperate birds and mammals possess greater masses of metabolically active organs (96) and display higher BMR (23) or summit metabolic rates ($V_{O_2sum}$) during thermogenesis (114) than tropical species. The physiological literature abounds with examples of organ hypertrophy or atrophy resulting from increased use or disuse. Such phenomena are interpreted in terms of the benefits of building extra capacities in times of extra need and the costs of maintaining high capacities when periods of extra need have passed.

### The Cost of the Metabolic Machinery

The energetic cost of protein turnover has recently been reviewed (57). It is assumed that protein synthesis costs 5 ATP molecules per peptide bond (4 ATP equivalents per peptide bond plus 1 ATP for active transport). The cost of protein turnover (synthesis + degradation) is more difficult to ascertain because there are different proteolytic pathways, requiring different amounts of ATP, possible for each protein molecule degraded. In mammals, at least 77% of protein synthesis is thought to be involved in turnover (i.e. replacement of degraded protein), rather than net deposition. It is estimated that at least 20% of BMR represents the metabolic cost of protein synthesis.

Because turning over protein is energetically expensive, it is reasonable to propose (in the context of biochemical capacities) that cells should synthesize and maintain, in Diamond's words (26), "enough, but not too much" enzyme. It is certainly possible to maintain higher [E] simply by slowing down rates of degradation and increasing half-life. The cost of accumulating more enzyme can be illustrated by using the enzyme GP in the pectoral muscles of chickens as a specific example (44). Broilers and layers have, through artificial selection, evolved high rates of muscle growth or egg-laying abilities, respectively. Broilers gain pectoral muscle mass, accumulate muscle protein, and synthesize GP at greater rates than layers. Data published by Flannery et al (44) illustrate the importance of taking both synthesis and degradation rates into account in attempting to explain differences in absolute amounts, as well as rates of accumulation of specific proteins. Young broilers (3 weeks) accumulate GP at higher rates than young layers, but these higher rates of accumulation result from lower rates of degradation, rather than higher rates of synthesis per gram of pectoral muscle. In contrast, at 8 weeks of age, GP synthesis rates in broilers exceed those of layers. It can be calculated that at this age, GP synthesis in broilers costs the equivalent of 1.7 nmol ATP g muscle$^{-1}$ min$^{-1}$. This may seem to be a low rate of ATP utilization in comparison with estimated rates of ATP turnover in resting muscle [e.g. ~480 μmol g$^{-1}$ min$^{-1}$ in humans (8)]. However, muscles contain thousands of kinds of enzymes and structural proteins, and GP turns over more slowly than the average protein (44). In addition, while the cost of synthesizing GP at higher rates per gram of muscle in broilers exceeds that in layers by 2.6-fold, the energetic cost for the whole animal (because broilers possess 4-fold more flight muscle than layers) is greater by about 10-fold. The implications of this difference in cost are intriguing, especially when considered in the context of natural selection in the wild perhaps favoring the rapid development of burst (escape) exercise abilities in early life.

## UPPER LIMITS

Because maximum physiological performance is based on the design of functional capacities, the upper limits to the design of such capacities are of great biological significance. At various levels of organization, upper limits to design have been suggested.

Among vertebrate homeotherms, $V_{O_2,max}$ values are set by the $O_2$ transport capacities of cardiovascular systems (72, 98). Nature's smallest and, presumably, most metabolically active vertebrate homeotherms all weigh about 2 g as adults (Thai bumblebee bats *Craseonycteris thonglongyai*, Etruscan shrews *Suncus etruscus*, and Cuban bee hummingbirds *Mellisuga helenae*). Schmidt-Nielsen (99) has suggested that the lower limit to vertebrate homeotherm size, as well as the upper limit to $V_{O_2max}/M_b$, may be set by the $O_2$-transport capacities of the cardiovascular system. Cardiac physiology may preclude heart rates greater than 1300 beats per min. Heart mass/body mass ratios greater than those in the smallest birds and bats may not be possible, at least partly because of incurred costs (reflected in high BMR values).

In locomotory and cardiac muscles, it has been proposed that there might be an upper limit to mitochondrial volume densities ($Vv_{mt,f}$) (60, 122, 125, 140). The highest values of $Vv_{mt,f}$ known in cardiac (Etruscan shrews, 140) and locomotory (blowfly, 109; Euglossine bee, 13, 14; and anchovy, 68) muscles are about 45%. Although muscle power outputs increase with $Vv_{mt,f}$ (94), mitochondrial volume densities beyond a certain point would result in diminished capacities for mechanical work and large, underused capacities for mitochondrial ATP synthesis (60, 122, 125, 140). The occurrence of higher $Vv_{mt,f}$ values (~63%) in billfish eye and brain heater organs (9), highly aerobic muscles that do no mechanical work, supports the suggestion that trade-offs between capacities for mechanical work and oxidative ATP synthesis have resulted in the upper limit to $Vv_{mt,f}$ of about 45% in locomotory and cardiac muscles.

Pathways of muscle energy metabolism are unique in terms of the high concentrations of enzymes catalyzing the reactions involved. Albe et al (1) conducted a survey of substrate/enzyme active site concentration ratios in various pathways in yeast, *E. coli, D. discoideum*, human RBC, rat liver, pig heart, and rat and rabbit skeletal muscles. Glycolytic reactions in muscles yield virtually all ratios that are less than 1.0 (active site concentrations in excess of substrate concentrations). An even more convincing case for crowded conditions in the cell is made by Srere (115, 116), who estimates that the matrix of liver mitochondria consists of more than 50% protein. Hackenbrock (53) observed that stimulation of respiration results in reduction of the matrix volume of liver mitochondria. This transition from the orthodox to condensed conformation must involve expulsion of bulk water from the matrix. Various lines of evidence have led to the proposal that the Krebs cycle enzymes function as a channeled multi-enzyme complex that Srere (97) calls the metabolon.

Given a constant mitochondrial volume, greater cristae surface areas (i.e. greater surface area for respiratory chain enzymes) result in less space available for matrix enzymes. Model calculations by Srere (116) predict that cristae surface densities of about 50 $m^2/cm^3$ result in just enough room between the inner surfaces of the cristae for three to four average-sized Krebs cycle enzymes. This is within the range found in insect and hummingbird flight muscles

(Table 1). The highest recorded cristae surface densities, $70 \ m^2/cm^3$ in skipjack tuna (*Katsuwonus pelamis*) red muscles (90), may leave room for only two to three average-size Krebs cycle enzymes between the inner surfaces of the cristae. Another upper limit that requires consideration concerns the number of enzyme molecules per unit cristae surface area that can be accommodated. There is some uncertainty concerning the fraction of cristae surface area occupied by electron transport chain components, adenine nucleotide translocator, and ATP synthase molecules (108). One of the few existing estimates puts this figure at about 42% (102). Whatever this value may be, protein packing densities are probably higher in the cristae of muscle mitochondria (103). Evolutionary up-regulation of mitochondrial oxidative capacities may therefore be limited by the availability of space for both cristae and matrix enzymes (122, 123). Theoretical calculations and empirical data therefore support the "standing-room only" (25) image of the intracellular environment, as well as the suggestion that availability of space may set upper limits to [E] (60, 122, 123). Along with other factors, upper limits to [E] may contribute to the establishment of upper limits to mass-specific metabolic rates.

What other evolutionary options might there be for up-regulation of flux capacities through pathways of energy metabolism? One possibility, considering how crowded cells are and how expensive it is to synthesize enzymes, is to increase the fractional velocities ($v/V_{max}$) at which enzymes function in vivo. As discussed previously, $v/V_{max}$ values for enzymes catalyzing reactions maintained close to equilibrium are necessarily very low. However, it may be that species able to sustain high maximal flux rates may do so by increasing $v/V_{max}$ at steps far from equilibrium (and potentially rate-limiting) in vivo. Thus although HK and PFK work at extremely low fractional velocities (<1%) in trout cardiac and red muscles during exercise (145), these enzymes may function at maximal and half-maximal velocities, respectively, in flying honeybees (R Suarez et al, unpublished data).

Another factor that may be involved in setting the upper limit to aerobic metabolic rate (and lower limit to body size) among vertebrate homeotherms may be the thermodynamic efficiency of mitochondrial oxidative phosphorylation. In an NMR study of the scaling of cardiac bioenergetics in mammals, Dobson & Headrick (30) observe that the thermodynamic efficiency of mitochondrial oxidative phosphorylation is inversely related to body mass. Extrapolation to the hearts of 2 g vertebrate homeotherms suggests thermodynamic efficiencies approaching 100%, leading to the provocative suggestion of a thermodynamic limit to homeotherm body mass.

## CONCLUDING REMARKS

The further development of our understanding of how physiological systems and metabolic enzymes work in vivo (117), and the constraints and limits to their design, will greatly influence the manner in which optimality hypotheses are proposed and tested. Perhaps it will be realized that the ultimate goal is really not to prove or disprove symmorphosis once and for all, but in agreement with Diamond (27) and Parker & Maynard Smith (93), to use optimality hypotheses as starting points and as analytical tools. The field of comparative physiology and biochemistry has entered into a fascinating and exciting historical phase in which there can be much productive interaction between those who study mechanisms and those who study their evolution (47).

ACKNOWLEDGMENTS

In developing the ideas presented here, I benefited greatly from discussions with PW Hochachka, ER Weibel, CR Taylor, JM Diamond, and RK Josephson. I also thank GP Dobson, S Secor, and K Hammond for useful discussions and for making available unpublished information. I gratefully acknowledge past financial support of my research from the Natural Sciences and Engineering Research Council (Canada), and current support from the National Science Foundation (USA).

## Literature Cited

1. Albe KR, Butler MH, Wright BE. 1990. Cellular concentration of enzymes and their substrates. *J. Theor. Biol.* 143:163–95

2. Atkinson DE. 1977. *Cellular Energy Metabolism and Its Regulation.* New York: Academic. 293 pp.

3. Baldwin J. 1982. Correlations between enzyme profiles in cephalopod muscle and swimming behavior. *Pac. Sci.* 36:349–56

4. Baldwin J, Lee AK. 1979. Contributions of aerobic and anaerobic energy production during swimming in the bivalve mollusc *Limaria fragilis* (Family Limidae). *J. Comp. Physiol.* 129:361–64

5. Baldwin KM, Winder WW, Terjung RL, Holloszy JO. 1973. Glycolytic enzymes in different types of skeletal muscle: adaptation to exercise. *Am. J. Physiol.* 225:962–66

6. Bessman SP, Geiger PJ. 1981. Transport of energy in muscle: the phosphoryl-creatine shuttle. *Science* 211:448–52

7. Bittl JA, DeLayre J, Ingwall JS. 1987. Rate equation for creatine kinase predicts the in vivo reaction velocity: $^{31}P$ NMR surface coil studies in brain, heart, and skeletal muscle of the living rat. *Biochemistry* 26:6083–90

8. Blei ML, Conley KE, Kushmerick MJ. 1993. Separate measures of ATP utilization and recovery in human skeletal muscle. *J. Physiol.* 465:203–22

9. Bloch BA. 1991. Endothermy in fish: thermogenesis, ecology and evolution. In *Biochemistry and Molecular Biology of Fishes,* ed. PW Hochachka, TP Mommsen, 1:269–311. Elsevier

10. Bozinovic F, Rosenmann M. 1989. Maximum metabolic rate of rodents: physiological and ecological consequences on distributional limits. *Func. Ecol.* 3:173–81

11. Brosnan MJ, Raman SP, Chen L, Koretsky AP. 1993. Altering creatine kinase isoenzymes in transgenic mouse muscle by overexpression of the B subunit. *Am. J. Physiol.* 264:C151–60

12. Cain DF, Davies RE. 1963. Breakdown of adenosine triphosphate during a single contraction of working muscle. *Biochem. Biophys. Res. Commun.* 8:361–66

13. Casey TM, Ellington CP. 1990. Ener-

getics of insect flight. In *Energy Transformations in Cells and Organisms*, ed. W Wieser, E Gnaiger, pp. 200–10. Stuttgart/New York: Georg Thieme Verlag

14. Casey TM, Ellington CP, Gabriel JM. 1992. Allometric scaling of muscle performance and metabolism. In *Hypoxia and Mountain Medicine*, ed. JR Sutton, G Coates, CS Houston, pp. 152–162. Burlington, VT: Queen City Printers

15. Deleted in proof

16. Childress JJ, Somero GN. 1979. Depth-related enzymic activities in muscle, brain and heart of deep-living pelagic marine teleosts. *Mar. Biol.* 52:273–83

17. Childress JJ, Somero GN. 1990. Metabolic scaling: a new perspective based on scaling of glycolytic enzyme activities. *Am. Zool.* 30:161–73

18. Conley KE, Christian KA, Hoppeler H, Weibel ER. 1989. Capillary and mitochondrial unit in muscles of a large lizard. *Am. J. Physiol.* 256:R982–89

19. Crabtree B, Newsholme EA. 1972. The activities of phosphorylase, hexokinase, phosphofructokinase, lactate dehydrogenase and the glycerol 3-phosphate dehydrogenases in muscles from vertebrates and invertebrates. *Biochem. J.* 126:49–58

20. Daan S, Masman D, Groenewold A. 1990. Avian basal metabolic rates: their association with body composition and energy expenditure in nature. *Am. J. Physiol.* 259:R333–40

21. Danforth WH, Lyon JB Jr. 1964. Glycogenolysis during tetanic contraction of isolated mouse muscles in the presence and absence of phosphorylase a. *J. Biol. Chem.* 239:4047–50

22. Davis RA, Fraenkel G. 1940. The oxygen consumption of flies during flight. *J. Exp. Biol.* 17:402–7

23. Dawson WR, Marsh RL, Yacoe ME. 1983. Metabolic adjustments of small passerine birds for migration and cold. *Am. J. Physiol.* 245:R755–67

24. de Zwaan A, Thompson RJ, Livingstone DR. 1980. Physiological and biochemical aspects of the valve snap and valve closure responses in the giant scallop *Placopecten magellanicus* II. IJ. *Biochem. J. Comp. Physiol.* 137:105–14

25. Diamond JM. 1990. How to fuel a hummingbird. *Nature* 348:392

26. Diamond J. 1991. Evolutionary design of intestinal nutrient absorption: enough but not too much. *News Physiol. Sci.* 6:92–96

27. Diamond JM. 1992. The red flag of optimality. *Nature* 355:204–6

28. Diamond J, Hammond K. 1992. The matches, achieved by natural selection,

between biological capacities and their natural loads. *Experientia* 48:551–57

29. Diamond JM, Hammond KA. 1992. Intestinal determinants of muscle performance. In *Hypoxia and Mountain Medicine*, ed. JR Sutton, G Coates, CS Houston, pp. 163–70. Burlington, VT: Queen City Printers

30. Dobson GP, Headrick JP. 1995. Bioenergetic scaling: metabolic design and body size constraints in mammals. *Proc. Natl. Acad. Sci. USA* 92:7317–21

31. Dobson GP, Parkhouse WS, Hochachka PW. 1987. Regulation of ATP-generating pathways in trout fast-twitch skeletal muscle. *Am. J. Physiol.* 253:R186–94

32. Drent RH, Daan S. 1980. The prudent parent: energetic adjustments in avian breeding. *Ardea* 68:225–52

33. Dubach M. 1981. Quantitative analysis of the respiratory system of the house sparrow, budgerigar, and violet-eared hummingbird. *Respir. Physiol.* 46:43–60

34. Dudley GA, Tullson PC, Terjung RL. The influence of mitochondrial content on the sensitivity of respiratory control. *J. Biol. Chem.* 262:9109–14

35. Dudley R, Gans C. 1991. A critique of symmorphosis and optimality models in physiology. *Physiol. Zool.* 64:627–37

36. Duhaylongsod FG, Griebel JA, Bacon DS, Wolfe WG, Piantadosi CA. 1993. Effects of muscle contraction on cytochrome aa3 redox state. *J. Appl. Physiol.* 75:790–97

37. Dykstra CR, Karasov WH. 1992. Changes in gut structure and function of house wrens (*Troglodytes aedon*) in response to increased energy demands. *Physiol. Zool.* 65:422–42

38. Dykstra CR, Karasov WH. 1993. Nesting energetics of house wrens. *Auk* 110:481–91

39. Ellington CP. 1985. Power and efficiency of insect flight muscle. *J. Exp. Biol.* 115:293–304

40. Ellington WR. 1989. Phosphocreatine represents a thermodynamic and functional improvement over other muscle phosphagens. *J. Exp. Biol.* 143:177–94

41. Else PL, Hulbert AJ. 1985. Mammals: an allometric study of metabolism at tissue and mitochondrial level. *Am. J. Physiol.* 248:R415–21

42. Else PL, Hulbert AJ. 1985. An allometric comparison of the mitochondria of mammalian and reptilian tissues: the implications for the evolution of endothermy. *J. Comp. Physiol.* 156:3–11

43. Emmett B, Hochachka PW. 1981. Scaling of oxidative and glycolytic enzymes in mammals. *Respir. Physiol.* 45:261–72

44. Flannery AV, Easterby JS, Beynon RJ. 1992. Turnover of glycogen phosphorylase in the pectoralis muscle of broiler and layer chickens. *Biochem. J.* 286: 915–22

45. Funk C, Clark A Jr, Connett RJ. 1989. How phosphocreatine buffers cyclic changes in ATP demand in working muscle. In *Oxygen Transport to Tissue*, ed. K Rakusan, GP Biro, TK Goldstick, Z Turek, 11:687–92. New York/London: Plenum

46. Gade G, Weeda E, Gabbott PA. 1978. Changes in the level of octopine during the escape responses of the scallop, *Pecten maximus* (L.). *J. Comp. Physiol.* 124:121–27

47. Garland T Jr, Carter PA. 1994. Evolutionary physiology. *Annu. Rev. Physiol.* 56:579–621

48. Garland T Jr, Huey RB. 1987. Testing symmorphosis: does structure match functional requirements? *Evolution* 41: 1404–9

49. Gayeski TEJ, Connett RJ, Honig CR. 1987. Minimum intracellular $pO_2$ for maximum cytochrome turnover in red muscle in situ. *Am. J. Physiol.* 252: H906–15

50. Goldfarb AH, Bruno JF, Buckenmeyer PJ. 1989. Intensity and duration of exercise effects on skeletal muscle cAMP, phosphorylase, and glycogen. *J. Appl. Physiol.* 66:190–94

51. Grieshaber M. 1978. Breakdown and formation of high-energy phosphates and octopine in the adductor muscle of the scallop, *Chlamys opercularis* (L.). *J. Comp. Physiol.* 126:269–76

52. Guppy M, Hulbert WC, Hochachka PW. 1979. Metabolic sources of heat and power in tuna muscles. II. Enzyme and metabolite profiles. *J. Exp. Biol.* 82: 303–20

53. Hackenbrock CR. 1966. Ultrastructural bases for metabolically linked mechanical activity in mitochondria. *J. Cell Biol.* 30:269–97

54. Hammond K, Diamond J. 1992. An experimental test for a ceiling on sustained metabolic rate in lactating mice. *Physiol. Zool.* 65:952–77

55. Hammond K, Diamond J. 1994. Limits to dietary nutrient intake and intestinal nutrient uptake in lactating mice. *Physiol. Zool.* 67:282–303

56. Hammond K, Konarzewski M, Torres RM, Diamond J. 1994. Metabolic ceilings under a combination of peak energy demands. *Physiol. Zool.* 67:1479–506

57. Hawkins AJS. 1991. Protein turnover: a functional appraisal. *Func. Ecol.* 5: 222–33

58. Heinrich R, Rapoport TA. 1974. A linear steady-state treatment of enzymatic chains. General properties, control and effector strength. *Eur. J. Biochem.* 42: 89–95

59. Hochachka PW. 1985. Fuels and pathways as designed systems for support of muscle work. *J. Exp. Biol.* 115:149–64

60. Hochachka PW, Emmett B, Suarez RK. 1988. Limits and constraints in the scaling of oxidative and glycolytic enzymes in homeotherms. *Can. J. Zool.* 66:1128–38

61. Hochachka PW, Guppy M, Guderley HE, Storey KB, Hulbert WC. 1978. Metabolic biochemistry of water- vs air-breathing fishes: muscle enzymes and ultrastructure. *Can. J. Zool.* 56:736–50

62. Hochachka PW, Somero GN. 1984. *Biochemical Adaptation.* Princeton, NJ: Princeton Univ. Press. 538 pp.

63. Homsher E. 1987. Muscle enthalpy production and its relationship to actomyosin ATPase. *Annu. Rev. Physiol.* 49: 673–90

64. Hoppeler H, Lindstedt SL. 1985. Malleability of skeletal muscle in overcoming limitations: structural elements. *J. Exp. Biol.* 115:355–64

65. Hoppeler H, Lindstedt SL, Claassen H, Taylor CR, Mathieu O, Weibel ER. 1984. Scaling mitochondrial volume in heart to body mass. *Respir. Physiol.* 55:131–37

66. Jacobus WE. 1985. Theoretical support for the heart phosphocreatine energy transport shuttle based on the intracellular diffusion limited mobility of ADP. *Biochem. Biophys. Res. Commun.* 133: 1035–41

67. Johansen K. 1987. The world as a laboratory: physiological insights from Nature's experiments. In *Advances in Physiological Research*, ed. H. McLennan, JR Ledsome, CHS McIntosh, DR Jones, pp. 377–96. New York: Plenum

68. Johnston IA, Moon TW. 1981. Fine structure and metabolism of multiple innervated fast muscle fibers in teleost fish. *Cell Tissue Res.* 219:92–109

69. Jones JH, Lindstedt SL. 1993. Limits to maximal performance. *Annu. Rev. Physiol.* 55:547–69

70. Kacser H, Burns JA. 1973. The control of flux. *Symp. Soc. Exp. Biol.* 27:65–104

71. Kashiwaya Y, Sato K, Tsuchiya N, Thomas S, Fell DA, et al. 1994. Control of glucose utilization in working perfused rat heart. *J. Biol. Chem.* 269: 25502–14

72. Knight DR, Schaffartzik W, Poole DC,

Hogan MC, Bebout DE, Wagner PD. 1993. Effects of hyperoxia on maximal leg $O_2$ supply and utilization in men. *J. Appl. Physiol.* 75:2586–94

73. Kobayashi K, Neely JR. 1979. Control of maximum rates of glycolysis in rat cardiac muscle. *Circ. Res.* 44:166–75

74. Konarzewski M, Diamond J. 1994. Peak sustained metabolic rate and its individual variation in cold-stressed mice. *Physiol. Zool.* 67:1186–212

75. Kruckeberg AL, Neuhaus HE, Feil R, Gottlieb LD, Stitt M. 1989. Decreased-activity mutants of phosphoglucose isomerase in the cytosol and chloroplast of *Clarkia xantiana*. Impact on mass-action ratios and fluxes to sucrose and starch, and estimation of flux control coefficients and elasticity coefficients. *Biochem. J.* 261:457–67

76. Kushmerick MJ, Meyer RA, Brown TR. 1992. Regulation of oxygen consumption in fast- and slow-twitch muscle. *Am. J. Physiol.* 263:C598–606

77. Lund J, Webb MR, White DCS. 1987. Changes in the ATPase activity of insect fibrillar flight muscle during calcium strain activation probed by phosphate-water oxygen exchange. *J. Biol. Chem.* 262:8584–90

78. Mainwood GW, Rakusan K. 1982. A model for intracellular energy transport. *Can. J. Physiol. Pharmacol.* 60:98–102

79. Marden JH. 1989. Bodybuilding dragonflies: costs and benefits of maximizing flight muscle. *Physiol. Zool.* 62:505–21

80. Marsh RL, Taigen TL. 1987. Properties enhancing aerobic capacity of calling muscles in gray tree frogs *Hyla versicolor*. *Am. J. Physiol.* 252:R786–93

81. Mathieu O, Krauer R, Hoppeler H, Gehr P, Lindstedt, et al. 1981. Design of the mammalian respiratory system. VII. Scaling mitochondrial volume in skeletal muscle to body mass. *Respir. Physiol.* 44:113–28

82. Mathieu-Costello O, Suarez RK, Hochachka PW. 1992. Capillary-to-fiber geometry and mitochondrial density in hummingbird flight muscle. *Respir. Physiol.* 89:113–32

83. McAllister RM, Ogilvie RW, Terjung RL. 1990. Impact of reduced cytochrome oxidase activity on peak oxygen consumption of muscle. *J. Appl. Physiol.* 69:384–89

84. McDevitt RM, Speakman JR. 1994. Limits to sustainable metabolic rate during transient exposure to low temperatures in short-tailed field voles (*Microtus agrestis*). *Physiol. Zool.* 67:1103–16

85. McDevitt RM, Speakman JR. 1994. Central limits to sustainable metabolic rate have no role in cold acclimation of the short-tailed field vole (*Microtus agrestis*). *Physiol. Zool.* 67:1117–39

86. Mehrani H, Storey KB. 1993. Control of glycogenolysis and effects of exercise on phosphorylase kinase and cAMP-dependent protein kinase in rainbow trout organs. *Biochem. Cell Biol.* 71:501–6

87. Mehrani H, Storey KB. 1993. Purification and molecular properties of glycogen phosphorylase b from trout muscle. *Biochem. Cell Biol.* 71:308–12

88. Meyer RA, Sweeney HL, Kushmerick MJ. 1984. A simple analysis of the phosphocreatine shuttle. *Am. J. Physiol.* 24766:C365–77

89. Moon TW, Hulbert WC. 1975. The ultrastructure of the mantle musculature of the squid *Symplectoteuthis oualaniensis*. *Comp. Biochem. Physiol.* 52B: 145–49

90. Moyes CD, Mathieu-Costello OA, Brill RW, Hochachka PW. 1992. Mitochondrial metabolism of cardiac and skeletal muscles from a fast (*Katsuwonus pelamis*) and a slow (*Cyprinus carpio*) fish. *Can. J. Zool.* 70:1246–53

91. Newsholme EA, Beis I, Leech AR, Zammit VA. 1978. The role of creatine kinase and arginine kinase in muscle. *Biochem. J.* 172:533–37

91a. Newholme EA, Crabtree B. 1986. Maximum catalytic activity of some key enzymes in provision of physiologically useful information about metabolic fluxes. *J. Exp. Zool.* 239:159–67

92. Newsholme, EA, Crabtree B, Zammit VA. 1980. Use of enzyme activities as indices of maximum rates of fuel utilization. *Ciba Found. Symp.* 73:245–58

93. Parker GA, Maynard Smith J. 1990. Optimality theory in evolutionary biology. *Nature* 348:27–33

94. Pennycuick CJ, Rezende MA. 1984. The specific power output of aerobic muscle, related to the power density of mitochondria. *J. Exp. Biol.* 108:377–92

95. Peterson CC, Nagy KA, Diamond J. 1990. Sustained metabolic scope. *Proc. Natl. Acad. Sci. USA* 87:2324–28

96. Rensch I, Rensch B. 1956. Relative Organmasse bei tropischen Warmbluetern. *Zool. Anz.* 156:106–24

97. Robinson JB Jr, Inman L, Sumegi B, Srere PA. 1987. Further characterization of the Krebs tricarboxylic acid cycle metabolon. *J. Biol. Chem.* 262:1786–90

98. Schaffartzik W, Barton ED, Poole DC, Tsukimoto K, Hogan MC, et al. 1993. Effect of reduced hemoglobin on leg oxygen uptake during maximal exercise in humans. *J. Appl. Physiol.* 75:491–98

604    SUAREZ

99. Schmidt-Nielsen K. 1984. *Scaling. Why is Animal Size So Important?* Cambridge: Cambridge Univ. Press. 241 pp.
100. Schneider A, Wiesner RJ, Grieshaber MK. 1989. On the role of arginine kinase in insect flight muscle. *Insect Biochem.* 19:471–80
101. Schramm M, Kleiber H-G, Daut J. 1994. The energy expenditure of actomyosin ATPase, $Ca^{2+}$-ATPase and $Na^+,K^+$-ATPase in guinea pig cardiac ventricular muscle. *J. Physiol.* 481:647–62
102. Schwerzmann K, Cruz-Orive LM, Eggman R, Sanger A, Weibel ER. 1986. Molecular architecture of the inner membrane of mitochondria from rat liver: a combined biochemical and stereological study. *J. Cell Biol.* 102:97–103
103. Schwerzmann K, Hoppeler H, Kayar SR, Weibel ER. 1989. Oxidative capacity of muscle mitochondria: correlation of physiological, biochemical, and morphometric characteristics. *Proc. Natl. Acad. Sci. USA* 86:1583–87
104. Secor SM, Diamond J. 1995. Adaptive responses to feeding in Burmese pythons: pay before pumping. *J. Exp. Biol.* 198:1313–25
105. Secor SM, Stein ED, Diamond J. 1994. Rapid upregulation of snake intestine in response to feeding: a new model of intestinal adaptation. *Am. J. Physiol.* 266:G695–705
106. Shoubridge EA, Radda GK. 1984. A $^{31}$P-nuclear magnetic resonance study of skeletal muscle metabolism in rats depleted of creatine with the analogue B-guanidinopropionic acid. *Biochim. Biophys. Acta* 805:79–88
107. Shoubridge EA, Radda GK. 1987. A gated $^{31}$P NMR study of tetanic contraction in rat muscle depleted of phosphocreatine. *Am. J. Physiol.* 252: C532–42
108. Slater EC. 1987. The mechanism of the conservation of energy of biological oxidations. *Eur. J. Biochem.* 166:489–504
109. Smith DS. 1963. The structure of flight muscle sarcosomes in the blowfly *Calliphora erythrocephala* (Diptera). *J. Cell Biol.* 19:114–38
110. Snyder GK, Sheafor B, Scholnick D, Farrelly C. 1995. Gas exchange in the insect tracheal system. *J. Theor. Biol.* 172:199–207
111. Somero GN, Childress JJ. 1980. A violation of the metabolism-size scaling paradigm: activities of glycolytic enzymes in muscle increase in larger-size fish. *Physiol. Zool.* 53:322–37
112. Somero GN, Childress JJ. 1985. Scaling of oxidative and glycolytic enzyme activities in fish muscle. In *Circulation, Respiration, and Metabolism*, ed. R

Gilles, pp. 250–62. Berlin/Heidelberg: Springer-Verlag
113. Somero GN, Childress JJ. 1990. Scaling of ATP-supplying enzymes, myofibrillar proteins and buffering capacities in fish muscle: relationship to locomotory habit. *J. Exp. Biol.* 149:319–33
114. Sparti A. 1992. Thermogenic capacity of shrews (Mammalia Soricidea) and its relationship with basal rate of metabolism. *Physiol. Zool.* 65:77–96
115. Srere PA. 1980. The infrastructure of the mitochondrial matrix. *Trends Biochem. Sci.* 5:120–21
116. Srere PA. 1985. Organization of proteins within the mitochondrion. In *Organized Multienzyme Systems. Catalytic Properties*, ed. G Rickey Welch, pp. 1–61. New York/London: Academic
117. Srere P. 1994. Complexities of metabolic regulation. *Trends Biochem. Sci.* 19: 519–20
118. Stainsby WN, Brechue WF, O'Drobinak DM, Barclay JK. 1989. Oxidation/reduction state of cytochrome oxidase during repetitive contractions. *J. Appl. Physiol.* 67:2158–62
119. Stokes DR, Josephson RK. 1992. Structural organization of two fast, rhythmically active crustacean muscles. *Cell Tissue Res.* 267:571–82
120. Storey KB. 1991. Metabolic consequence of exercise in organs of rainbow trout. *J. Exp. Zool.* 260:157–64
121. Storey KB, Storey JM. 1978. Energy metabolism in the mantle muscle of the squid, *Loligo pealeii*. *J. Comp. Physiol.* 123:169–75
122. Suarez RK. 1992. Oxygen and $VO_{2max}$: Are muscle mitochondria created equal? In *Hypoxia and Mountain Medicine*, ed. JR Sutton G Coates, CS Houston, pp. 136–142. Burlington, VT: Queen City Printers
123. Suarez RK. 1992. Hummingbird flight: sustaining the highest mass-specific metabolic rates among vertebrates. *Experientia* 48:565–70
124. Suarez RK, Brown GS, Hochachka PW. 1986. Metabolic sources of energy for hummingbird flight. *Am. J. Physiol.* 251: R537–42
125. Suarez RK, Lighton JRB, Brown GS, Mathieu-Costello O. 1991. Mitochondrial respiration in hummingbird flight muscles. *Proc. Natl. Acad. Sci. USA* 88:4870–73
126. Suarez RK, Lighton JRB, Moyes CD, Brown GS, Gass CL, Hochachka PW. 1990. Fuel selection in rufous hummingbirds: ecological implications of metabolic biochemistry. *Proc. Natl. Acad. Sci. USA* 87:9207–10

127. Suarez RK, Mallet MD, Daxboeck C, Hochachka PW. 1986. Enzymes of energy metabolism and gluconeogenesis in the Pacific blue marlin *Makaira nigricans*. *Can. J. Zool.* 64:694–97

128. Suarez RK, Moyes CD. Mitochondrial respiration in locust flight muscles. *J. Exp. Zool.* 263:351–55

129. Taigen TL, Wells KD. 1985. Energetics of vocalization by an anuran amphibian (*Hyla versicolor*). *J. Comp. Physiol.* 155:163–70

130. Taylor CR. 1987. Structural and functional limits to oxidative metabolism: insights from scaling. *Annu. Rev. Physiol.* 49:135–46

131. Taylor CR, Weibel ER. 1981. Design of the mammalian respiratory system. I. Problem and strategy. *Respir. Physiol.* 44:1–10

132. Taylor CR, Weibel ER, Karas RH, Hoppeler H. 1989. Matching structures and functions in the respiratory system. Allometric and adaptive variations in energy demand. In *Comparative Pulmonary Physiology. Current Concepts*, ed. SC Wood, pp. 27–65. New York/Basel: Dekker

133. Teague WE Jr, Dobson GP. 1992. Effect of temperature on the creatine kinase equilibrium. *J. Biol. Chem.* 267:14084–93

134. van Deursen J, Heerschap A, Oerlemans F, Ruitenbeek W, Jap P, et al. 1993. Skeletal muscles of mice deficient in muscle creatine kinase lack burst activity. *Cell* 74:621–31

135. Vary TC, Reibel DK, Neely JR. 1981. Control of energy metabolism of heart muscle. *Annu. Rev. Physiol.* 43:419–30

136. Veech RL, Raijman L, Dalziel K, Krebs HA. 1969. Disequilibrium in the triosephosphate isomerase system in rat liver. *Biochem. J.* 115:837–42

137. Wardle CS. 1975. Limit of fish swimming speed. *Nature* 255:725–27

138. Webb PW. 1977. Effects of size on performance and energetics of fish. In *Scale Effects in Animal Locomotion*, ed. TJ Pedley, pp. 315–32. New York: Academic

139. Wegener G, Schmidt H, Leech AR, Newsholme EA. 1986. Antagonistic effects of hexose 1,6-bisphosphates and fructose 2,6-bisphosphate on the activity of 6-phosphofructokinase purified from honey-bee flight muscle. *Biochem. J.* 236:925–28

140. Weibel ER. Design and performance of muscular systems: an overview. *J. Exp. Biol.* 115:405–12

141. Weibel ER, Taylor CR, Hoppeler H. 1991. The concept of symmorphosis: a testable hypothesis of structure-function relationship. *Proc. Natl. Acad. Sci. USA* 88:10357–61

142. Weiner J. 1992. Physiological limits to sustainable energy budgets in birds and mammals: ecological implications. *Trends Ecol. Evol.* 7:384–88

143. Weiss P. 1947. The place of physiology in the biological sciences. *Fed. Proc.* 6:523–25

144. Weis-Fogh T. 1964. Diffusion in insect wing muscle, the most active tissue known. *J. Exp. Biol.* 41:229–56

145. West TG, Arthur PG, Suarez RK, Doll CJ, Hochachka PW. 1993. In vivo utilization of glucose by heart and locomotory muscles of exercising rainbow trout (*Oncorhynchus mykiss*). *J. Exp. Biol.* 177:63–79

146. Wu TY. 1977. Introduction to the scaling of aquatic animal locomotion. In *Scale Effects in Animal Locomotion*, ed. TJ Pedley, pp. 203–32. New York: Academic

*Annu. Rev. Physiol. 1996. 58:607–18*

# MOLECULAR MECHANISMS OF RENAL APICAL Na/PHOSPHATE COTRANSPORT

## *H. Murer and J. Biber*

Institute of Physiology, University Zürich; 8057 Zürich, Switzerland

KEY WORDS:   kidney, proximal tubule, Na/P$_i$-cotransport

### ABSTRACT

In the proximal tubule, sodium-dependent transport of phosphate (P$_i$) through the brush-border membrane represents the inital step in P$_i$ reabsorption. cDNAs encoding several renal proximal tubule apical Na/P$_i$ cotransport systems have been identified. These Na/P$_i$ cotransporters are subdivided into type I (NaP$_i$-1) and a type II (NaP$_i$-2). Electrophysiological studies reveal that P$_i$ transport by Na/P$_i$ cotransporters is electrogenic. Regulation of proximal P$_i$ reabsorption by dietary P$_i$ intake and parathyroid hormone is primarily due to an alteration of apical type II Na/P$_i$ cotransport; a rapid change of brush-border Na/P$_i$ cotransport most likely occurs via an endo/exocytic mechanism. No evidence for physiological control of type I cotransporters has been obtained. Altered P$_i$ reabsorption as observed in X-linked hypophosphatemia is largely via the type II Na/P$_i$ cotransporter.

## INTRODUCTION

Reabsorption of phosphate by proximal tubule cells is a major determinant of the plasma level of inorganic phosphate (P$_i$). Transepithelial P$_i$ transport occurs via P$_i$ transport systems located in the apical and basolateral membrane of the proximal tubule cell. Uptake of P$_i$ at the apical cell surface requires sodium (Na/P$_i$ cotransport) and represents the rate-limiting step of P$_i$ reabsorption. The rate of proximal P$_i$ reabsorption is adjusted by the homeostatic needs of the body. Several hormonal and nonhormonal factors influence P$_i$ reabsorption via a change of apical Na/P$_i$ cotransport activity.

In recent years, several cDNAs encoding for renal Na/P$_i$ cotransport systems have been identified. In this review we discuss the progress made in elucidating the physiology of proximal tubule P$_i$ reabsorption.

607

0066–4278/96/0315–0607$08.00

## PROXIMAL TUBULE APICAL Na/P$_i$ COTRANSPORT SYSTEMS

### Identification of Two Types

Originally, a Na/P$_i$ cotransport system of rabbit kidney cortex was identified by expression cloning using oocytes of *Xenopus laevis* and tracer flux studies using $^{32}$P$_i$ (NaP$_i$-1; 47). With use of a NaP$_i$-1 cDNA probe, homologous proteins have subsequently been identified in mouse and human kidney cortex (10, 11, 38). After extraction of brush-border membranes of rabbit kidney cortex with organic solvents, a protein was purified, which upon reconstitution into liposomes, exhibited Na/P$_i$ cotransport (16). Based on its molecular weight, this protein likely represents a cotransporter similar to NaP$_i$-1. A new round of expression cloning, starting from rat and human kidney cortex cDNA libraries, identified additional Na/P$_i$ cotransporters: NaP$_i$-2 and NaP$_i$-3 (35). Amino acid comparison revealed that the Na/P$_i$ cotransport systems NaP$_i$-1 and NaP$_i$-2/3 share weak overall homology (20% identity). Therefore, the identified renal Na/P$_i$ cotransporters have been classified as type I (NaP$_i$-1-related) and type II (NaP$_i$-2-related) systems (39). Additional type II Na/P$_i$ cotransporters were identified by homology screening using a NaP$_i$-2 cDNA probe: NaP$_i$-4 from opossum kidney (OK) cells (42), NaP$_i$-5 from flounder kidney (48), NaP$_i$-6 from rabbit kidney cortex (45), and NaP$_i$-7 from mouse kidney cortex (12, 23). A type II Na/P$_i$ cotransport system has also been reported to be expressed in bovine renal NBL-1 cells (26).

Based on sequence comparison, similarity of type I cotransporters to a hypothetical protein (C38C10) of *Caenorhabditis elegans* was noted. Because the hydropathy profile of the *C. elegans* protein is almost identical to the profile of type I cotransporters, it seems likely that this protein exhibits transport functions similar to the NaP$_i$-1 Na/P$_i$ cotransporter. Cloning of a Na/P$_i$ cotransport system from cerebellar granule cells has recently been described (41). This protein has 30% identity to the type I Na/P$_i$ cotransporter, and hydropathy analysis suggests that this brain-specific Na/P$_i$ cotransporter may belong to the type I cotransporter group. Thus far sequence comparison of the type II Na/P$_i$ cotransporter with current protein sequence databases reveals no significant homologies.

### Structural Aspects

Type I Na/P$_i$ cotransporters are ~465-amino acids in length, and type II cotransporters are ~635-amino acids in length with predicted unglycosylated masses of 55 and 68 kDa, respectively (39). On western blots using brush-border membranes isolated from kidney cortex, the type I cotransporter appears as a 60–65-kDa protein (6, 17), and the type II cotransporter as a 80–90-kDa protein

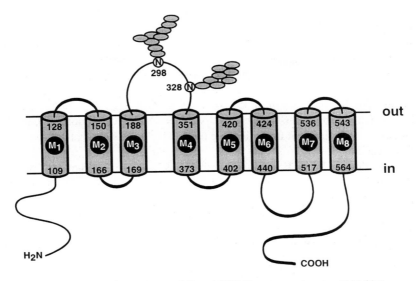

*Figure 1*  Predicted secondary structure of the type II Na/P$_i$ cotransport system NaP$_i$-2/rat.

(14). Amino acid sequences for both types of Na/P$_i$ cotransporters contain several potential sites for *N*-glycosylation (35, 42, 45, 47). For the type II cotransporter (NaP$_i$-2), two sites of *N*-glycosylation have been demonstrated by site-directed mutagenesis (25). *N*-glycosylation of the NaP$_i$-2 protein at positions $N_{298}$ and $N_{328}$ is not required for normal transport activity. Thus far there is no direct evidence of *N*-glycosylation of the type I cotransport system nor of *O*-linked glycosylation of either type of Na/P$_i$ cotransport system.

A model for the orientation of the type II cotransporter (NaP$_i$-2) within the membrane is depicted in Figure 1. Hydropathy analysis predicts eight transmembrane-spanning regions with a *N*-glycosylated extracellular loop of approximately 150 amino acids between the transmembrane segments M$_3$ and M$_4$. Binding studies using antibodies directed against the N-terminus of the type II cotransporter (NaP$_i$-2) and isolated membranes of kidney cortex reveal that the N-terminus of type II cotransporters is oriented toward the cytoplasmic surface (T Hammond, personal communication). Type I cotransporters are predicted to span the membrane seven to nine times (39), although no further structural information on the orientation of type I cotransporters is available.

Amino acid sequences of cloned renal Na/P$_i$ cotransport systems contain several potential phosphorylation sites for protein kinase C. By addition of $^{32}$P-ATP to isolated renal brush-border membranes, phosphorylation of the type II cotransporter (NaP$_i$-2) has recently been demonstrated (24). A direct relationship between phosphorylation of type II cotransporters and hormonal regulation by parathyroid hormone, for example, has not been established. In oocytes of *X. laevis* injected with type II cotransporter(NaP$_i$-2) cDNA, activation of protein kinase C by phorbol esters decreased type II related Na/P$_i$ cotransport activity (24). However, site-directed mutagenesis of predicted consensus sites for protein kinase C (positions S$_5$, S$_{91}$, S$_{462}$, T$_{508}$, and S$_{625}$) did not prevent phorbol ester-induced inactivation of Na/P$_i$ cotransport (24), which suggests involvement of unpredictable phosphorylation sites that remain to be determined.

Irradiation of brush-border membrane vesicles gave a target size of 230 kDa for Na/P$_i$ cotransport activity (18). Assuming that in vesicle studies, the type II Na/P$_i$ cotransport system contributes largely to the transport of P$_i$ (see below), the target size suggests that the functional unit of proximal apical Na/P$_i$ cotransport consists of a homodimer of type II cotransporters. This issue has to be explored further by cross-linking and immunoprecipitation experiments.

## Tissue Localization

Northern blot analysis demonstrates expression of type I cotransporter-related mRNA in kidney cortex and also in the liver (21, 47). Expression of type II-related mRNA was found exclusively in kidney cortex; mRNA related to the human type II cotransporter NaP$_i$-3 was also observed in lung tissue (35). Further northern blot analysis showed no cross-reaction with mRNA isolated from small intestine.

Detailed analysis with single microdissected nephron segments and amplification of mRNA after reverse transcription (RT-PCR) and in situ hybridization demonstrated uniform expression of mRNA of both types of Na/P$_i$ cotransporters in the proximal tubules (10, 14, 15). A small amount of type II-related mRNA was also detected in collecting ducts which, by immunohistochemistry, was not associated with expression of the type II protein (14).

Immunohistochemical studies reveal that both types of renal Na/P$_i$ cotransport systems are expressed at the brush-border membrane of proximal tubule cells; no immunoreactivity was detected at the basolateral membrane surface. Under normal physiological conditions, the type I cotransporter is expressed uniformly in apical membranes of all proximal nephron segments of superficial and deep nephrons (6), whereas expression of the type II cotransporter (NaP$_i$-2) is more heterogeneous. Strongest immunoreactivity of anti-(NaP$_i$-2) antibodies was observed in S$_1$ segments of deep nephrons (14). Immunoelectron microscopy reveals a uniform distribution of the type II cotransporter along the microvilli (M Lötscher, personal communication).

## Chromosomal Localization

The type II cotransporter gene has been mapped to human chromosome 5q35 (32), and the type I cotransporter gene has been mapped to human chromosome 6p21.3-p23 (11) and to chromosome 13 of mouse (10).

## Specificity, Kinetics, and Electrogenicity

Renal proximal Na/$P_i$ cotransport has been extensively characterized by tracer flux studies using isolated proximal brush-border membrane vesicles (for review see 4, 19, 22, 40). The availability of renal Na/$P_i$ cotransporter cDNAs opened new possibilities for study of the transport mechanisms under defined conditions such as by electrophysiological methods and using oocytes of *X. laevis* as an expression system.

The type II Na/$P_i$ cotransporter (NaP$_i$-2, expressed in oocytes) transports primarily inorganic phosphate and does not interact with sulfate (35, 37). Other results demonstrate that arsenate, a competitve inhibitor of Na/$P_i$ cotransport (27), is also transported by the type II cotransporter NaP$_i$-7 (23). Electrophysiological studies using arsenate as a substrate suggest a $K_m$ for arsenate about tenfold higher than for $P_i$. Phosphonocarboxylic acids, originally developed as antiviral agents, inhibit brush-border membrane Na/$P_i$ cotransport (29). Kinetic studies reveal that phosphonoformic acid (PFA), one of the most effective of this group of compounds, competitively inhibits cotransport with a $K_i$ around 1 mM (28). Type II cotransport activity, as expressed in oocytes, is also inhibited by PFA in a competitive manner, without transport of PFA (A Busch, unpublished data).

In contrast to the type II Na/$P_i$ cotransporter, the type I cotransporter (NaP$_i$-1) exibits a broader substrate specificity and, in addition to $P_i$, transports other anions as well (A Busch, personal communication). Further studies are needed to elucidate this new aspect of type I Na/$P_i$ cotransporters and to clarify the exact physiological role of type I Na/$P_i$ cotransporters.

In voltage-clamped oocytes of *X. laevis* injected with type II cRNA (NaP$_i$-2), superfusion with phosphate in a sodium-containing medium elicited an inwardly directed current (Ip), indicating the movement of a positive charge during the transport process (7, 23). At a given concentration of $P_i$, Ip was a function of extracellular sodium ($K_m$ ~50 mM), whereas at constant sodium, variation of the $P_i$ concentration did not affect the interaction with sodium. The calculated Hill coefficients of these interactions suggest a 3:1 coupling ratio of Na vs $P_i$. The discrepancy of the coupling ratio of 2:1, as derived from $P_i$ transport studies in brush-border membrane vesicles (40), may be explained by factors such as heterogeneity and electrical properties of the vesicle population.

The $K_m$ for $P_i$ transport of type II cotransporters is a function of the Na concentration. At a holding potential of $-50$ mV, the $K_m$ ranged from 0.1 to 0.5 mM as the external Na concentration dropped from 100 to 50 mM (7). These observations are in agreement with an ordered interaction of cosubstrate and substrate (Na first, $P_i$ second) with the transporter at the extracellular surface.

Electrogenic transport of $P_i$ is decreased by a depolarization of the membrane potential from $-80$ to $+10$ mV (7). This potential dependence may explain inhibition of proximal tubule $P_i$ transport by other Na-coupled transport processes as a result of decrease in the driving force (3, 40).

## pH-Dependence

In most species, proximal tubule $P_i$ reabsorption and brush-border membrane Na/$P_i$ cotransport are increased by increasing intratubular/extravesicular pH. Early tracer flux studies provided evidence that the pH dependence might be due to pH effects on Na interaction and related to some preferential transport of divalent $P_i$ (1, 40). In studies using oocytes of *X. laevis* injected with cRNA of type II transporter (NaP$_i$-2), evidence showed that pH dependence is not primarily a consequence of preferential transport of divalent $P_i$ (the carrier likely interacts with both mono- and divalent $P_i$) but also includes an altered affinity of the transporter for Na ions at different pH values (7, 23). In contrast to Na/$P_i$ cotransport by the type II cotransporters, the type I cotransporter exhibits no pH dependence (oocyte expression studies; A Busch, personal communication).

## RELEVANCE OF IDENTIFIED Na/$P_i$ COTRANSPORTERS TO THE CONTROL OF $P_i$ HOMEOSTASIS

The rate of proximal tubule reabsorption of phosphate is controlled by several hormonal and nonhormonal factors (4). Early studies revealed evidence that most of the described phosphaturic active factors influence the rate of proximal tubule apical Na/$P_i$ cotransport (40). In the following, we discuss briefly the progress made in elucidating the molecular mechanisms of two physiologically important regulators of proximal $P_i$ reabsorption; dietary $P_i$ intake and parathyroid hormone. Also, the availability of molecular probes (such as for the type II cotransport system) allowed the genetic disease X-linked hypophosphatemia to be investigated in more detail.

## Regulation by Dietary $P_i$ Intake

Dietary restriction of $P_i$ is associated with an adaptive increase of the overall proximal tubule capacity to reabsorb $P_i$. Part of this phenomenon is independent of extrarenal factors such as PTH, vitamin D, plasma calcium, and growth hormone (4, 19). In vivo or in vitro restriction of $P_i$ demonstrates that an increase of apical proximal Na/$P_i$ cotransport is mediated by an increase of maximal transport activity, $V_{max}$, which in in vivo conditions is observed within 2 h after dietary $P_i$ restriction (acute adaptation) and which lasts for several days (chronic adaptation) (8, 9, 34). Using antibodies and cDNA probes of type I and II Na/$P_i$ cotransporters, it was demonstrated by western and northern blots and by immunohistochemistry that the type II Na/$P_i$ cotransporter at both mRNA and protein levels represents a target for altered $P_i$ intake (33, 45, 46), whereas the type I cotransport system is not affected by $P_i$ restriction (5, 45). In acute adaptation (2 h), an increase of apical Na/$P_i$ cotransport is paralled by an increase in type II cotransporter protein (NaP$_i$-2) within the apical membrane of all proximal deep and superficial tubular segments; after 4 h there is also an increase of type II mRNA (33). Up-regulated Na/$P_i$ cotransport is reversible by a $P_i$-rich diet given to chronically adapted rats (9). In brush-border membranes of adapted rats fed with a $P_i$-rich diet, the abundance of the type II cotransporter in the apical membrane decreases within 2 to 4 h with no decrease of the corresponding mRNA (33). These data suggest that in response to acute alterations of dietary $P_i$ content, the number of type II Na/$P_i$ cotransporters (NaP$_i$-2) in the proximal apical membrane can be changed rapidly by mechanisms independent of de novo protein synthesis. In addition to the brush-border membrane, immunoreactivity of anti-(NaP$_i$-2) antibodies in fixed rat kidney cortex slices obtained from animals treated with low or high phosphate diet was also observed in intracellular vesicular structures, and staining intensity associated with these structures varied depending on $P_i$ diet (33). This suggests the existence of an endo/exocytic apparatus (13) by which type II Na/$P_i$ cotransporters can be rapidly inserted into or retrieved from the apical membrane. In agreement with these findings, the presence of type II cotransporters has been demonstrated in isolated proximal tubule endosomal membrane fractions (T Hammond, personal communication).

## Hormonal Regulation

Parathyroid hormone (PTH) produces a decrease in urinary $P_i$ excretion by inhibition of brush-border Na/$P_i$ cotransport (4, 19). In vitro studies demonstrate the importance of a signaling pathway involving protein kinases type A and/or C (40). Furthermore, these studies provide evidence that the inhibitory effect of PTH may involve an endocytic retrieval of Na/$P_i$ cotransport systems from the apical membrane (28, 30, 36). With antibodies directed against the type II cotransporter (NaP$_i$-2), it has been demonstrated by immunohistochemistry that PTH given to parathyroidectomized rats provokes a decrease of type II cotransporters within the apical membrane that is paralleled by a change of brush-border membrane Na/$P_i$ cotransport (31) and increased immunoreactivity of anti-($NaP_i$-2) antibodies in a subapical region (M Lötscher, personal communication). In the same study, no changes of the cellular localization of gamma-glutamyl transpeptidase were observed, which suggests that PTH activates an endocytic mechanism resulting in a rather specific internalization of type II $Na/P_i$ cotransporters ($NaP_i$-2). It is not known if PTH also regulates the abundance of type I cotransporters within the proximal apical membrane.

In OK cells, epidermal growth factor (EGF) inhibits type II-related $Na/P_i$ cotransport (2). Using a cDNA probe against the type II cotransporter of OK cells ($NaP_i$-4), EGF was shown to cause a decrease of $NaP_i$-4 mRNA abundance, which precedes the decrease of $Na/P_i$ cotransport. This effect of EGF was inhibited by actinomycin D which inhibits transcription (2).

## X-Linked Hypophosphatemia

In X-linked hypophosphatemia, the renal defect in $P_i$ reabsorption is localized to the brush borders of proximal tubule cells. In brush-border membranes isolated from *Hyp* mice, a murine homologue of human X-linked hypophosphatemia, kinetic studies demonstrate that $Na/P_i$ cotransport has half the maximal transport rate with no change in the apparent affinity for $P_i$ (43). A decrease of $P_i$ reabsorption in *Hyp*-mice has been correlated with a lower abundance of the type II cotransporter ($NaP_i$-2) in immunohistochemical studies, with parallel reduction of type II mRNA expression (12, 44). Because the type II cotransporter gene has been mapped to human chromosome 5q35 (32), it seems likely that the candidacy of the type II gene for X-linked hypophosphatemia can be excluded. Rather, these data suggest that the gene at the *Hyp* locus may be involved in the regulation of the type II $Na/P_i$ cotransporter gene transcription or may influence the turnover of type II mRNA.

## SUMMARY AND PERSPECTIVES

By expression cloning, two types of proximal tubule apical $Na/P_i$ cotransport systems (type I and type II) have been identified (Figure 2). It has become clear that the type II $Na/P_i$ cotransporter represents a target for the physiological and pathophysiological regulation of proximal reabsorption of phosphate. This fact, together with the kinetic characteristics of type II cotransporter, demonstrate that the type II $Na/P_i$ cotransport system is most relevant for proximal tubule $P_i$ reabsorption. The exact role of the type I $Na/P_i$ cotransporter in proximal $P_i$ reabsorption and in the transport of other substrates is currently less clear and needs further investigation.

It will be important to understand more about the signaling mechanisms underlying the postulated endo/exocytic movement of type II $Na/P_i$ cotransporters that lead to acute changes of brush-border membrane $Na/P_i$ cotransport. In particular, it will be necessary to elucidate if and how phosphorylation reactions are involved and to define the intracellular structures of the endo/exo-

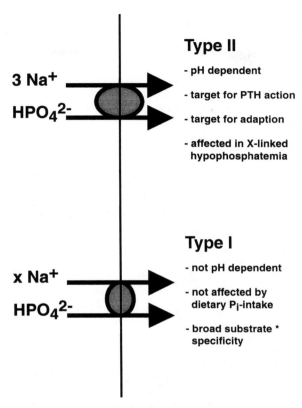

$3 Na^+$

$HPO_4^{2-}$

**Type II**

- pH dependent

- target for PTH action

- target for adaption

- affected in X-linked
  hypophosphatemia

$x Na^+$

$HPO_4^{2-}$

**Type I**

- not pH dependent

- not affected by
  dietary $P_i$-intake

- broad substrate *
  specificity

*Figure 2*   Characteristics of identified renal proximal Na/P$_i$ cotransporters type I and type II.

cytic apparatus involved. At the gene level, it will be necessary to elucidate its organization in order to understand the mechanisms involved in chronic regulations of Na/P$_i$ cotransport related to the type II Na/P$_i$ cotransporter. Furthermore, sufficient quantities of these integral membrane proteins have to be isolated to allow for structural investigations. Thus far the type II cotransporter (NaP$_i$-2) has been expressed in Sf9 insect cells (20), which may eventually allow a purification of this protein.

ACKNOWLEDGMENTS

The authors would like to thank all co-workers who participated in discussions and contributed experimental data to this work. Also we thank the Swiss

National Funds for the continuous financial support (Grant No. 32.30785 to HM and Grant No. 32.28664 to JB).

## Literature Cited

1. Amstutz M, Mohrmann M, Gmaj P, Murer H. 1985. Effect of pH on phosphate transport in rat renal brush border membrane vesicles. *Am. J. Physiol.* 248: F705–10

2. Arar M, Baum M, Biber J, Murer H, Levi M. 1995. Epidermal growth factor inhibits Na-P$_i$ cotransport and mRNA in OK-cells. *Am. J. Physiol.* 268:F309–14

3. Barett PQ, Aronson PS. 1982. Glucose and alanine inhibition of phosphate transport in renal microvillus membrane vesicles. *Am. J. Physiol.* 242:F126–31

4. Berndt TJ, Knox FG. 1992. Renal regulation of phosphate excretion. In *The Kidney, Physiology and Pathophysiology*, ed. GW Seldin, G Giebisch. New York: Raven. 2511 pp.

5. Biber J, Caderas G, Stange G, Werner A, Murer H. 1993. Effect of low phosphate diet on sodium/phosphate cotransport mRNA and protein content and on oocyte expression of phosphate transport. *Pediatr. Nephrol.* 7:823–26

6. Biber J, Custer M, Werner A, Kaissling B, Murer H. 1993. Localization of NaP$_i$-1, a Na/P$_i$ cotransporter, in rabbit kidney proximal tubules. II. Localization by immunohistochemistry. *Pflügers Arch.* 424:210–15

7. Busch A, Waldegger S, Herzer T, Biber J, Markovich D, et al. 1994. Electrophysiological analysis of Na/P$_i$-cotransport mediated by a transporter cloned from rat kidney and expressed in *Xenopus* oocytes. *Proc. Natl. Acad. Sci. USA* 91:8205–8

8. Caverzasio J, Bonjour J-P. 1985. Mechanism of rapid phosphate transport adaptation to a single low P$_i$ meal in rat renal brush border membranes. *Pflügers Arch.* 404:227-31

9. Cheng L, Liang CT, Sacktor B. 1983. Phosphate uptake by renal membrane vesicles of rabbits adapted to high and low phosphorous diet. *Am. J. Physiol.* 245:F175–80

10. Chong SS, Kozak CA, Liu L, Kristjanson K, Dunn ST, et al. 1994. Molecular cloning, chromosome localization and characterization of the cDNA encoding a murine sodium-dependent phosphate cotransporter. *Am. J. Physiol.* 268: F1038–45

11. Chong SS, Kristjansson K, Zoghbi HY, Hughes MR. 1993. Molecular cloning of the cDNA encoding a human renal sodium phosphate transport protein and its assignment to chromosome 6p21.3-p23. *Genomics* 18:355–59

12. Collins JF, Ghishan FK. 1994. Molecular cloning, functional expression, tissue distribution and in situ hybridization of the renal sodium phosphate transporter in the control and hypophosphatemic mouse. *FASEB J.* 8:862–68

13. Cui S, Christensen EI. 1993. Three-dimensional organization of the vacuolar apparatus involved in endocytosis and membrane recycling of rat kidney proximal tubule cells. *Exp. Nephrol.* 1:175–84

14. Custer M, Lötscher M, Biber J, Murer H, Kaissling B. 1994. Expression of Na/P$_i$-cotransport (NaP$_i$-2) in rat kidney: localization by RT-PCR and immunohistochemistry. *Am. J. Physiol.* 266: F767–74

15. Custer M, Meier F, Schlatter E, Greger R, Garcia-Perez A, et al. 1993. Localization of NaP$_i$-1, a Na-P$_i$ cotransporter in rabbit kidney proximal tubules. I. mRNA localization by reverse transcription/polymerase chain reaction. *Pflügers Arch.* 424:203–9

16. Debiec H, Ronco PM. 1993. Identification and epitope analysis of the renal Na/P$_i$ cotransport protein using monoclonal antibodies. *J. Biol. Chem.* 268: 13356–63

17. Delisle M-C, Boyer C, Vachon V, Giroux S, Beliveau R. 1994. Immunodetection and characterization of proteins implicated in renal sodium/phosphate cotransport. *Biochim. Biophys. Acta* 1190:289–96

18. Delisle MC, Vachon V, Giroux S, Potier M, Laprade R, et al. 1992. Molecular

size of the renal sodium/phosphate symporter in native and reconstituted systems. *Biochim. Biophys. Acta* 1104: 132–36

19. Dennis V. 1992. Phosphate homeostasis. In *Handbook of Physiology*, ed. EE Windhager. New York: Oxford Univ. Press. 1785 pp.

20. Fucentese M, Winterhalter K, Murer H, Biber J. 1995. Functional expression of rat renal Na/$P_i$-cotransport (Na$P_i$-2) in Sf9 cells by the baculovirus system. *J. Memb. Biol.* 144:43–48

21. Gishan FK, Rebeitz R, Honda T, Nakagawa N. 1993. Characterization and expression of a novel Na-inorganic phosphate transporter at the liver plasma membrane of the rat. *Gastroenterology* 105:519–26

22. Hammerman MR. 1986. Phosphate transport across renal proximal tubular cell membranes. *Am. J. Physiol.* 251: F385–98

23. Hartmann C, Wagner CA, Busch AE, Markovich D, Biber J, et al. 1995. Transport characteristics of a murine renal Na/$P_i$-cotransporter. *Pflügers Arch.* 430:830–36

24. Hayes G, Busch A, Lang F, Biber J, Murer H. 1995. Protein kinase C consensus sites and the regulation of renal Na$P_i$-cotransport (Na$P_i$-2) expressed in *Xenopus laevis* oocytes. *Pflügers Arch.* 430:819–24

25. Hayes G, Busch A, Lötscher M, Waldegger S, Lang F, et al. 1994. Role of N-linked glycosylation in rat renal Na/$P_i$-cotransport. *J. Biol. Chem.* 269: 24143–49

26. Helps C, Murer H, McGivan J. 1995. Cloning and sequence analysis of the cDNA encoding a putative sodium dependent phosphate transporter from the bovine renal epithelial cell line NBL-1. *Eur. J. Biochem.* 228:927–30

27. Hoffmann N, Thees M, Kinne R. 1976. Phosphate transport by isolated renal brush border vesicles. *Pflügers Arch.* 362:147–56

28. Hoppe A, Lin JT, Onsgard M, Knox FG, Dousa TP. 1991. Quantitation of the Na-$P_i$ cotransporter in renal cortical brush border membranes. *J. Biol. Chem.* 266:11528–36

29. Kempson SA. 1988. Novel specific inhibitors of epithelial phosphate transport. *News Physiol. Sci.* 3:154–57

30. Kempson SA, Helme-Kolb C, Abraham MI, Murer H. 1990. Parathyroid hormone action on phosphate transport is inhibited by high osmolality. *Am. J. Physiol.* 258:F1336–44

31. Kempson SA, Lötscher M, Kaissling B, Biber J, Murer H, et al. 1995. Parathyroid hormone action on phosphate transporter mRNA and protein in rat renal proximal tubules. *J. Am. Physiol.* 268: F784–91

32. Kos CH, Tihy F, Econs MJ, Murer H, Lemieux N, Tenenhouse HS. 1994. Localization of a renal sodium-phosphate cotransporter gene to human chromosome 5q35. *Genomics* 19:176–77

33. Levi M, Lötscher M, Sorribas V, Custer M, Arar M, et al. 1994. Cellular mechanisms of acute and chronic adaptation of rat renal $P_i$ transporter to alterations in dietary $P_i$. *Am. J. Physiol.* 267:F900–8

34. Levine BS, Ho K, Hodsman A, Kurokawa K, Coburn JW. 1984. Early renal brush border membrane adaptation to dietary phosphorous. *Miner. Electrolyte Metab.* 10:222–27

35. Magagnin S, Werner A, Markovich D, Sorribas V, Stange G, et al. 1993. Expression cloning of human and rat renal cortex Na/$P_i$ cotransport. *Proc. Natl. Acad. Sci. USA* 90:5979–83

36. Malmstrom K, Murer H. 1987. Parathyroid hormone regulates phosphate transport in OK-cells via an irreversible inactivation of a membrane protein. *FEBS Lett.* 216:257–60

37. Markovich D, Forgo J, Stange G, Biber J, Murer H. 1993. Expression cloning of rat renal Na/$SO_4$ cotransport. *Proc. Natl. Acad. Sci. USA* 90:8073–77

38. Miyamoto K, Tatsumi S, Sonoda T, Yamamoto H, Minami H, et al. 1995. Cloning and functional expression of a Na-dependent phosphate cotransporter from human kidney: cDNA cloning and functional expression. *Biochem. J.* 305: 81–85

39. Murer H, Biber J. 1994. Renal sodium-phosphate cotransport. *Curr. Opin. Nephrol.* 3:504–10

40. Murer H, Werner A, Reshkin S, Wuarin F, Biber J. 1991. Cellular mechanisms in proximal tubular reabsorption of inorganic phosphate. *Am. J. Physiol.* 260: C885–99

41. Ni B, Rosteck PR, Nadi NS, Paul SM. 1994. Cloning and expression of a cDNA encoding a brain-specific Na-dependent inorganic phosphate cotransporter. *Proc. Natl. Acad. Sci. USA* 91: 5607–11

42. Sorribas V, Markovich D, Hayes G, Stange G, Forgo J, et al. 1994. Cloning of a Na/$P_i$-cotransporter from opossum kidney cells. *J. Biol. Chem.* 269:6615–21

43. Tenenhouse HS, Martel J. 1993. Renal adaptation to phosphate deprivation: les-

sons from the X-linked Hyp mouse. *Pediatr. Nephrol.* 7:312–18

44. Tenenhouse HS, Werner A, Biber J, Ma S, Roy S, Murer H. 1994. Renal Na-phosphate cotransport in murine X-linked hypophosphatemic rickets. Molecular characterization. *J. Clin. Invest.* 93:671–73

45. Verri T, Markovich D, Perego C, Norbis F, Stange G, et al. 1995. Cloning and regulation of a rabbit renal Na/P$_i$-cotransporter. *Am. J. Physiol.* 268: F626–33

46. Werner A, Kempson SA, Biber J, Murer H. 1994. Increase of Na/P$_i$-cotransport encoding mRNA in response to low P$_i$ diet in rat kidney cortex. *J. Biol. Chem.* 269:6637–39

47. Werner A, Moore ML, Mantei N, Biber J, Semenza G, et al. 1991. Cloning and expression of cDNA for a Na/P$_i$ cotransport system of kidney cortex. *Proc. Natl. Acad. Sci. USA* 88:9608–12

48. Werner A, Murer H, Kinne R. 1994. Cloning and expression of a renal Na/P$_i$-cotransport system from flounder. *Am. J. Physiol.* 267:F311–17

*Annu. Rev. Physiol. 1996. 58:619–48*

# PATHOPHYSIOLOGY OF THE AQUAPORIN WATER CHANNELS

*Landon S. King*[1,2] *and Peter Agre*[1,3]

Department of Medicine[1], Division of Pulmonary and Critical Care Medicine[2], and Department of Biological Chemistry[3], Johns Hopkins University School of Medicine, Baltimore, Maryland 21205

KEY WORDS:  edema, brain, lung, diabetes insipidus, water permeability

### ABSTRACT

Discovery of aquaporin water channel proteins has provided insight into the molecular mechanism of membrane water permeability. The distribution of known mammalian aquaporins predicts roles in physiology and disease. Aquaporin-1 mediates proximal tubule fluid reabsorption, secretion of aqueous humor and cerebrospinal fluid, and lung water homeostasis. Aquaporin-2 mediates vasopressin-dependent renal collecting duct water permeability; mutations or downregulation can cause nephrogenic diabetes insipidus. Aquaporin-3 in the basolateral membrane of the collecting duct provides an exit pathway for reabsorbed water. Aquaporin-4 is abundant in brain and probably participates in reabsorption of cerebrospinal fluid, osmoregulation, and regulation of brain edema. Aquaporin-5 mediates fluid secretion in salivary and lacrimal glands and is abundant in alveolar epithelium of the lung. Specific regulation of membrane water permeability will likely prove important to understanding edema formation and fluid balance in both normal physiology and disease.

## INTRODUCTION

Water is a critical component of all biological systems; however, the mechanisms by which water traverses cell membranes remained enigmatic until recently. Certain epithelia exhibit membrane water permeability far too great to be explained by diffusion through a lipid bilayer, which led to speculation about the existence of water-specific channels or pores in some tissues. The discovery of Aquaporin-1 (AQP1; CHIP) and the subsequent identification of homologous water channel proteins has advanced the phenomenon of membrane water permeability to a molecular level. In this review we present information on the basic biology of aquaporins and concentrate on Aquaporin-

619

1, about which the most is known. Additionally, however, we discuss roles for the aquaporins in a number of physiologic and pathophysiologic processes.

## THE SEARCH FOR WATER CHANNELS

### The Case for Water Channels

Water can cross plasma membranes by two basic pathways: diffusion through the lipid bilayer or transit through water-selective channels. Diffusional water permeability ($P_d$) is temperature dependent, constrained by membrane lipid organization and fluidity, and therefore has a high Arrhenius activation energy ($E_a$ >10 kcal/mol). Osmotic water permeability ($P_f$) reflects membrane water permeability under conditions of an osmotic gradient across the membrane. In many tissues, $P_f/P_d$ is ≈1, which suggests that water crosses the membrane strictly by diffusion (41).

The existence of water channels was strongly suggested by observations made over several decades (reviewed in 3): (a) Osmotically driven water movement across red blood cell membranes and renal proximal tubular epithelium was too rapid to be explained by diffusion through the membrane, with a $P_f/P_d$ >>1 (41); (b) mercurial compounds could reversibly inhibit the high osmotic permeability across red cell (79) and proximal tubule (149) membranes; and (c) radiation inactivation studies in both renal brush-border membrane vesicles (141) and red cell membranes (142) implicated a membrane protein of 30 ± 3 kDa as the mediator of high water permeability in those tissues. Multiple candidate proteins, including the band 3 anion exchanger (132), the sodium-independent glucose transporter GLUT1 (42), and CFTR (54), were proposed as the molecular water channel over the past decade, but all were found to be lacking in some requisite characteristic (3, 144). As described here, the identity of molecular water channels was recently shown to be a new family of membrane proteins termed aquaporins (4).

### Discovery of Aquaporin-1

Aquaporin-1 (AQP1), the archetypal water channel protein, was serendipitously discovered during studies of the human red cell Rh protein. A 28-kDa protein, thought to be a proteolytic breakdown product of the 32-kDa Rh polypeptide (121), proved to be a discrete integral membrane protein, abundant in red cells and renal proximal convoluted tubules (34, 129). Partial sequencing of the amino terminus suggested homology with the major intrinsic protein of lens (MIP) (129), and cloning of the full-length cDNA from a human bone marrow library (110) confirmed the homology. Kyte & Doolittle hydropathy analysis of the full-length cDNA suggested six bilayer-spanning domains, which coupled with homology to the presumed membrane channel proteins of the MIP family, led to the name CHIP28, for channel-forming integral protein of 28 kDa. Subsequent to its demonstration as the first water channel (111), CHIP was designated Aquaporin-1 (abbreviated AQP1) by the Human Genome Committee; that nomenclature is used through the remainder of this review.

A number of clues suggested that this newly discovered membrane channel could be the long-sought water channel. The number of copies of AQP1 protein in red cells, ~2 × $10^5$/cell (34, 129), was similar to the predicted number of water channels in red cells (132); radiation inactivation studies of native water channels predicted a protein similar in size to AQP1 (141, 142); and the distribution in red cells and renal proximal tubules (34) was the same as the physiologically defined, mercury-inhibitable water channel (41).

Expression of AQP1 cRNA in *Xenopus laevis* oocytes, known to have low water permeability at baseline, provided the evidence that indeed AQP1 was a water-specific channel (111). Transfer of AQP1-injected oocytes to hypotonic solution led to swelling and rupture, with little change in control-injected oocytes. The $P_f$ of AQP1-injected oocytes ($200 \times 10^{-4}$ cm/s) was 8-fold greater than control oocytes at 22°C, and 30-fold greater at 10°C. The calculated $E_a$ for the AQP1-injected oocytes was ~3 kcal/mol, consistent with channel-mediated water movement (78), whereas the $E_a$ for control oocytes was >10 kcal/mol. The $P_f$ and $E_a$ for AQP1-injected oocytes were similar to those demonstrated for the putative water channels in red cell membranes (78). Additionally, AQP1-mediated water movement was inhibited by $HgCl_2$ (111), as had been shown for both red cells (79) and renal proximal tubule (149). Patch-clamp studies revealed no new ionic currents in AQP1-injected oocytes until the point of rupture, providing evidence that the channel was water specific (111).

Reconstitution of purified AQP1 into proteoliposomes proved that AQP1 does not require accessory proteins to exhibit full function as a water channel and further confirmed the specificity for water because urea, protons, hydroxyl ions, ammonium ions, and salts were not transported (155). The unit water permeability of AQP1 in reconstituted liposomes was calculated (~3 × $10^9$ $H_2O$ molecules per subunit per second) (155) and, when extrapolated to the intact red cell, indicated that AQP1-mediated water permeability was sufficient to explain the known water permeability of the red cell (41).

## The Expanding Family of Aquaporins

AQP1 has sequence homology to the MIP family of proteins, an ancient family of proteins thought to form membrane transporters (117, 144). AQP1 and MIP are 42% identical, with identity between AQP1 and other family members ranging from 20 to 40% (110, 117). All of the family members, including AQP1, have a three amino acid motif of Asn-Pro-Ala at points corresponding

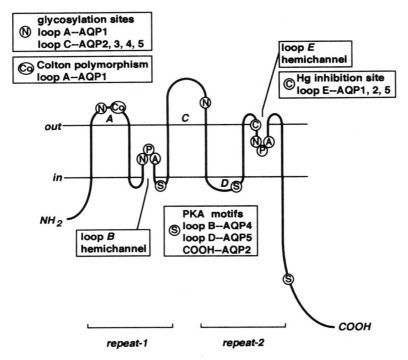

*Figure 1* Proposed topology of aquaporins based on aquaporin-1, showing potential sites for glycosylation, phosphorylation, and mercury inhibition for all known mammalian aquaporins.

to loops B and E of AQP1 (Figure 1; see below). Additionally, amino acids surrounding both Asn-Pro-Ala motifs were highly conserved in all family members. Degenerate primers to the highly conserved regions have been used in conjunction with reverse transcription polymerase chain reaction (PCR) to identify potential aquaporins in tissues of interest. At present, at least four other mammalian aquaporins have been identified: AQP2, AQP3, AQP4, and AQP5 (37, 48, 53, 58, 62, 77, 116). There is little doubt that additional mammalian homologues will soon follow, and the existence of several plant homologues has been established (27).

## Structure and Function of the Aquaporins

MIP26 was noted to have internal homology between the first and second halves of the molecule (105), which is presumed to represent an ancient gene duplication (117). A similar observation was made for AQP1 (110) and all other members of the MIP family (117). In support of the gene duplication theory is the similarity in gene organization between MIP, AQP1, and AQP2, each having a large first exon that includes the amino-terminal half of the molecule, with smaller exons 2 through 4 encoding the carboxy-terminal half (30, 87, 109).

The highest degree of internal homology in AQP1 is between the regions of the Asn-Pro-Ala motifs found in loops B and E (Figure 1) (110). Interestingly, loop B and loop E are proposed to be oriented at 180° to each other on opposite sides of the membrane, a unique biological orientation. Additionally, within the MIP family, the amino-terminal half of each protein is more closely related to the amino-terminal half of other family members than are the carboxy-terminal halves related (117). This led to the proposal that the amino-terminal half of the molecule subserves functions more common to all family members, whereas the carboxy-terminal half provides each protein with its unique functional specificity (117).

Hydrophobicity analysis of both MIP (50) and AQP1 (110) suggested six bilayer-spanning domains, and that remains the consensus view (144). Antibody labeling of the amino and carboxy termini demonstrated both to be intracellular (129, 98). Preston et al performed vectorial proteolysis in functional AQP1 molecules using the E1 epitope of avian coronavirus and demonstrated that loops C and E are extracellular, whereas loops B and D are intracellular (Figure 1) (113). The N-glycosylation site for AQP1 is in loop A, proving its extracellular location, whereas AQP2, 3, 4, and 5 have an N-glycosylation consensus in loop C (37, 48, 53, 58, 62, 77, 116), further suggesting the extracellular location of that region.

Protein immunoblots of red cell membranes with affinity-purified anti-AQP1 antibodies demonstrated a discrete band of 28-kDa, the AQP1 core protein, and a more diffuse band from 40 to 60 kDa, the core protein plus an Asn-linked complex carbohydrate (129). The appearance and abundance of the upper band varies in different tissues (97). Biochemical analysis of highly purified AQP1 revealed that only one of the four subunits forming the functional tetramer was glycosylated (129). Elimination of the N-glycosylation site in AQP1 did not alter its trafficking or function in the X. laevis expression system, although the role of glycosylation in mammalian cells is most likely related to membrane trafficking (113).

Native water channels in red cells (79) and renal proximal tubule (149) are inhibitable by mercurial agents. This may explain the actions of calomel ($HgCl_2$), a drug previously used as a diuretic. Cysteine-scanning mutagenesis with systematic substitution of serine for each of the four cysteines of AQP1 revealed Cys189 to be the mercury-sensitive site in the molecule (112) (Figure 1), an observation confirmed by other investigators (159). Insertion of larger amino acids into position 189 greatly reduced osmotic water movement and raised the possibility that Cys189 might be located near the aqueous pore. However, protein immunoblots of C189 mutants with diminished water permeability revealed incompletely formed glycans, suggesting altered protein folding or trafficking as the cause of decreased water permeability (63). Position 73 in loop B is analogous to Cys189 but located on the cytoplasmic face of the membrane. Introduction of a cysteine into position 73 returned mercury sensitivity to AQP1 mutants that had been rendered mercury-insensitive by substitution for Cys189; substitution of larger residues into position 73 again reduced osmotic water permeability (63). These results suggested that both position 189 and position 73 of AQP1 were near the presumed mouth of the water channel and led to the proposal of the "hourglass" model of AQP1, with loops B and E extending into the bilayer, and the front and back half of the molecule folding together to form the narrow aqueous pore (63). Definitive proof of this model awaits high resolution structural analysis.

AQP1 assembles in the membrane as a homotetramer, as demonstrated by hydrodynamic studies (129), freeze fracture of proteoliposomes (145, 156) and renal proximal tubule cells (145), and electron microscopic analyses of two-dimensional crystals from purified functional AQP1 protein (147). Complementation studies by Jung and colleagues using dimeric AQP1 mutants with and without mercury-sensitive sites suggested that the tetramer is comprised of four independent functional units (63); details of the aqueous pathway through the molecule remain to be elucidated. The requirement for tetrameric assembly is as yet unexplained, although it may reflect instability of the monomer in the lipid bilayer (39).

## Regulation of the Aquaporins

Regulation of each of the aquaporins will probably be unique, although common or shared features will likely emerge. AQP1 appears to be constitutively expressed and active in those tissues in which it is found (3). Several lines of evidence, however, suggest a more dynamic regulation. Lanahan and colleagues demonstrated that AQP1 was a delayed early-response gene, induced in mouse 3T3 fibroblasts by serum or growth factors (71). The functional role of AQP1 in this setting is unknown, but some have postulated a requirement for transient water channel expression prior to cell division (144).

Developmental expression of AQP1 occurs in three patterns (14): (a) high-level expression during fetal life with downregulation after birth (corneal endothelium, mesenchyme around growing bone, endocardium); (b) high-level expression early in fetal life persisting through adulthood (choroid plexus); and (c) initiation of expression in late gestation or early postnatal life, persisting through adulthood (RBC, kidney, lung) (65, 130). This complex pattern of expression predicts multiple, tissue-specific regulatory mechanisms. Recent studies have demonstrated tissue-specific induction of AQP1 in fetal and adult lung following administration of corticosteroids (65), suggesting that endogenous hormones may regulate expression.

AQP2, 4, and 5 contain a protein kinase A (PKA) phosphorylation consensus sequence in the positions noted in Figure 1 (48, 53, 62, 116). Phosphorylation is thought to regulate both trafficking and gating of AQP2, although definitive studies have yet to be done. Phosphorylation of AQP2 in *X. laevis* oocytes increased water permeability (70), whereas direct phosphorylation of AQP2 in collecting duct vesicles had no effect on water permeability (72). Phosphorylation of AQP2, 4, and 5 provides an appealing mechanism for rapid regulation of membrane water permeability but at present is only conjecture.

# PATHOPHYSIOLOGY OF THE AQUAPORINS

Each of the mammalian aquaporins has a unique tissue distribution, with only rare overlap between homologues. We present information on the distribution, and in some cases regulation, of each the aquaporins, which lends itself to speculation on their function in normal physiology and disease. Moreover, since the list of known aquaporins is certainly not complete, the reader is cautioned that the involvement of these proteins in human disease states is a new area of investigation that is rapidly emerging.

## *Aquaporin-1*

DISTRIBUTION    *Red cell*    Red cells are thought to need water permeability to survive transit through the renal medulla, where the interstitial osmolality is above 1 M. Red cells also require urea channels for rapid loading and unloading of solute as they pass through the hypertonic renal medulla (78, 80). It was initially proposed that water and urea permeated the red cell membrane through the same channel (78), but the discovery of AQP1 (34, 111) and cloning of urea transporters from kidney (153) and erythrocytes (101) confirmed the existence of distinct pathways. It is presumed that the high membrane water permeability imparted to the red cell by AQP1 facilitates red cell survival under changing osmotic conditions, but the specific requirement for red cell water channels is not obvious. That genetically AQP1-deficient humans are not anemic and have little evidence of hemolysis begs the question of water channel function in red cells (114) (see below).

Identification of the human AQP1 gene at chromosome 7p14 (87) allowed recognition of the coincident location of little-known blood group antigens, the Colton antigens, at 7p (157). Immunoprecipitation with anti-Colton antisera demonstrated that Colton antigens were on AQP1, and DNA sequencing of Colton-typed individuals revealed that a known Colton polymorphism resulted from an alanine to valine change at residue 45 in extracellular loop A of AQP1 (Figure 1) (131). Demonstration of Colton antigens on AQP1 made possible subsequent identification of extremely rare AQP1-deficient individuals (see below).

*Kidney* The nephron, the individual functioning unit of the kidney, consists of a series of specialized segments manifesting unique absorption properties. Of the 180 liters of glomerular filtrate formed each day, 80 to 90% is reabsorbed in the proximal tubule and descending thin limb of Henle's loop (DTL), segments known to have constitutively high water permeability. The ascending thin and thick limbs of Henle's loop, distal convoluted tubule, and connecting tubule are known to be largely impermeable to water. The remaining 10–20% of the glomerular filtrate is reabsorbed in a vasopressin-dependent fashion in the collecting duct (see AQP2 below) (67).

Immunolocalization studies demonstrated abundant AQP1 throughout the proximal tubule and the DTL, with no expression at other sites in the nephron (96, 98). AQP1 constituted approximately 4% of proximal tubule brush border protein, with less expression on the basolateral membrane (96, 98); there was no intracellular pool of AQP1 (96). Recent quantitation of AQP1 in the renal tubule by ELISA revealed greater expression in the DTL than the proximal tubule (81). Calculations based on AQP1 density and the unit water conductance of a single AQP1 molecule (155) suggest that AQP1-mediated osmotic water permeability in both the proximal tubule and the descending thin limb is sufficient to account for the known water permeabilities of those segments (81).

The vasa recta are the vascular supply of the renal medulla and are critical to generation and maintenance of an axial osmotic gradient through the medulla (67). Nielsen et al recently demonstrated that AQP1 was present on both the apical and basolateral membrane of endothelial cells of the descending vasa recta; the ascending vasa recta could not be assessed (96). Perfusion studies revealed mercury-inhibitable water permeability in the descending vasa recta, thereby providing both anatomic and functional evidence that AQP1 mediates vasa recta water transport (96).

The ontogeny of AQP1 expression in kidney parallels development of renal concentrating mechanisms (8). The rat develops the ability to concentrate urine postnatally; AQP1 is present in the rat proximal tubule from 2 days before birth and increases rapidly after delivery (130). In human fetal kidney, AQP1 was present in the proximal tubule at 14-weeks gestation, consistent with the advanced in utero development of the human kidney compared to the rat (5).

*Eye* Fluid management is critical to normal function of the eye. The cornea consists of an outer epithelial layer, a well-hydrated stroma, and an endothelial layer covering the internal surface. Histologically, corneal endothelial cells appear to be secretory cells, with large nuclei, many mitochondria, and a well-developed endoplasmic reticulum and Golgi. The endothelium removes fluid from the overlying stroma and secretes it into the aqueous humor (107).

Aqueous humor is secreted by the nonpigmented epithelium of the anterior ciliary body. It is estimated that each ciliary epithelial cell secretes one third of its own volume per minute against an oncotic pressure gradient to generate aqueous humor (20). Following formation, aqueous humor travels through the pupil to the lateral margins of the anterior chamber, where it is reabsorbed through the trabecular meshwork into the canals of Schlemm (24, 52).

AQP1 was abundant in both the anterior ciliary epithelium (97, 133) and canals of Schlemm (133), which suggests a role in secretion and uptake of aqueous humor. The iris, which has high water permeability thought to facilitate rapid shape changes occurring with pupillary constriction, also labeled strongly for AQP1 (97, 133). AQP1 was present only in the endothelial layer of the cornea (97), where it likely participates in regulation of corneal hydration, critical to corneal transparency (107). Of note, the corneal endothelium is amitotic after initial development (107). The ontogeny of AQP1 in corneal endothelium was similar, message expression occurring only in fetal life (14) with persistence of AQP1 protein into maturity (97).

*Brain*    Cerebrospinal fluid (CSF) supports and protects the brain. The physical constraints of the bony skull mandate tight regulation of CSF volume, which in humans is approximately 140 ml and turns over four to five times per day. CSF is made by the choroid plexus, a specialized structure located in the walls of the lateral, third, and fourth ventricles that consists of a vascular core covered by a secretory epithelium. The choroid plexus of the lateral ventricle is the predominant site of CSF formation (76, 123).

Immunolocalization studies demonstrated that AQP1 was abundant in apical membrane microvilli of the choroid epithelium but was not found elsewhere in the brain (97). Colocalization of AQP1 with a Na/K ATPase (40) in the apical membrane strongly suggests a role in CSF production.

*Lung*    The fluid requirements of the lung are complex. In development, the lung fills with fluid, a process necessary for normal lung growth and airway branching (102). At birth, fluid is rapidly reabsorbed as the lung assumes responsibility for gas exchange from the placenta (12). The mature lung must maintain appropriate hydration of the airways and parenchyma in order to optimize oxygenation and lung defense mechanisms (90).

In rat lung, AQP1 is abundant in the peribronchial vasculature and visceral pleura, minimally present in alveolar capillaries and epithelium, and not present in airway epithelium (65). AQP1 was reported in rat alveolar epithelium by in situ hybridization (55) and was weakly expressed in cultured rat alveolar type II cells (44). AQP1 distribution in human lung is similar to that in the rat, but with increased expression in alveolar capillaries and abundant expression on both apical and basolateral membranes of cells adjacent to alveolar type II cells, called aquaporin-1 expressing pneumocytes. Human alveolar type I and type II cells do not express AQP1 (65a). The distribution of AQP1 in the lung suggests participation in regulation of interstitial fluid, airway hydration, and at least in the human, clearance of alveolar liquid.

AQP1 was expressed in fetal rat lung late in gestation and increased dramatically from the last prenatal day to the first postnatal day (65). AQP1 expression in fetal rat lung was both accelerated and increased by corticosteroids (65), consistent with known effects of corticosteroids on fetal lung maturation (33, 75). Lung water accumulates in the peribronchial space prior to its reabsorption after birth (12). AQP1 was abundant in the peribronchial vasculature of one-day-old rat lung and may facilitate reabsorption of lung water into the lymphatics and circulation (65). The timing of expression, response to steroids, and distribution of AQP1 strongly suggest a role in perinatal lung water clearance.

*Other tissues*    AQP1 has been localized to several other tissues by immunohistochemical analysis. AQP1 was present in biliary epithelium (97) and cultured cholangiocytes (118), suggesting a role in secretion and modulation of bile (6). Although intestinal lymphatic vessels (lacteals) express AQP1, it was not present in the epithelium or fenestrated capillaries of the small intestine or colon (97); in situ hybridization data suggesting the presence of AQP1 in colonic crypt epithelial cells (55) have not been confirmed by immunohistochemistry (97). AQP1 was present in nonfenestrated capillary endothelium of the lacrimal and salivary glands, pancreas, and lactating mammary gland, but was not present in glandular epithelium in any of those tissues. Additionally, AQP1 was found in nonfenestrated endothelium of skeletal, cardiac, and smooth muscle (97). These vascular distributions suggest a role for AQP1 in interstitial fluid formation, as well as regulation of fluid available to glandular epithelia, but demonstrate that AQP1 does not mediate glandular secretion. Recently, AQP1 has been localized to additional sites including the inner ear (134) and smooth muscle of the male epididymis (19).

AQP1 AND DISEASE    Although no primary AQP1-related diseases have thus far been identified, the distribution of this protein suggests potential roles in several clinical disorders.

*Genetic deficiency*    Discovery of Colton blood group antigens on AQP1 (131), coupled with the review of worldwide blood bank referencing, led to identification of five Colton-null kindreds. Protein immunoblots of red cell membranes from probands in three Colton-null kindreds showed that each had either a complete absence or profound deficiency of AQP1 (114). DNA sequencing demonstrated that each was homozygous for a different mutation in the AQP1 gene, and biophysical studies of their red cells revealed an absence of functional water channels. Surprisingly, all three probands appeared clinically normal (114).

A number of interesting issues were raised by discovery of individuals lacking AQP1. The Colton (AQP1) null frequency is extremely low, as only five kindreds were identified from worldwide blood bank referencing, a screen of tens or even hundreds of millions of blood donors and transfusion recipients. The heterozygote frequency would be highly informative but is difficult to determine. Were the heterozygote frequency higher than predicted based on the apparent homozygote frequency, it might suggest that AQP1 mutations are indeed lethal, or at least severe, and lend credance to the idea that AQP1-deficient individuals have some form of compensation facilitating survival. This has been shown to occur in other biological systems. For example, germline EGF receptor mutations were lethal in mice of some genetic backgrounds but not others, although it should be noted that all had abnormalities (125, 139). Sickle cell disease provides another example; in certain populations, expression of fetal hemoglobin into adulthood ameliorates the symptoms of the disease (108). AQP1 mutation could be a generally severe genetic mutation tolerated only in the context of a genetic background conferring some survival advantage.

How could compensation for AQP1 deficiency occur? As AQP1 is but one of a family of water channels, increased expression of a different aquaporin in select sites could perhaps compensate for a loss of AQP1-mediated water permeability. Undiscovered aquaporins with distributions overlapping AQP1 could also compensate, although in the AQP1-deficient individuals studied, it is clear that additional water channels were not present in red cell membranes (114). Alternatively, these individuals could have enhanced salt transport mechanisms, thereby overcoming the diminished water permeability of membranes lacking AQP1.

Although the Colton-null individuals do not manifest overt phenotypic abnormalities, it is not yet clear what subtle functional abnormalities exist. Recent analysis has revealed a minor degree of shortened red cell survival in two of the homozygotes, although neither had reduced hemoglobin levels (84a). Water deprivation might uncover a defect in maximal urinary concentrating ability because of diminished proximal tubule reabsorption and loss of medullary gradient. Exercise testing might provoke abnormalities of gas exchange or lung mechanics secondary to inadequate clearance of interstial fluid. All of the known Colton-null individuals are female; does AQP1 deficiency have a more severe phenotype in males? Each of these issues is of interest; the answer awaits further understanding of the biology of AQP1.

*Secondary dysfunction or deficiency*   Despite the apparent normalcy of humans with disruption of the *AQP-1* gene, the distribution of AQP1 protein predicts associated pathophysiology. Although the absence of anemia in the Colton-null individuals calls into question the significance of water channels in red cells (114), a patient with significant anemia was recently identified who had ~90% deficiency of AQP1 and total absence of CD44 on her red cell membranes (5). This patient expressed fetal and embryonic globin into adolescence which, in combination with the AQP1 and CD44 abnormalities, constituted a novel form of congenital dyserythropoiesis. The red cell membrane water permeability was dramatically reduced in this patient, but it is not clear to what extent absence of water channels contributed to her anemia (5).

Although anti-Colton antibodies are rarely encountered, they are clinically significant and have been shown to accelerate the destruction of red blood cells carrying the corresponding Colton antigens (68). Anti-Colton antibodies have been implicated in hemolytic transfusion reactions (68), as well as in hemolytic disease of the newborn (128), since Colton antigens (AQP1) are well developed on human red cells at birth (5).

AQP1 dysfunction could play a role in other red cell disorders. In sickle cell disease, sickled erythrocytes are dehydrated compared to normal red cells (61), with decreased diffusional water permeability (47). Therapies designed to increase fetal hemoblobin synthesis to combat the disease have also been demonstrated to increase mean corpuscular volume of red cells (103). As AQP1 is the principle determinant of red cell membrane water permeability, dehydration of sickled cells could reflect a change in AQP1 expression or function that can be favorably altered by hydroxyurea or other agents.

The distribution of AQP1 in the eye predicts a role in several diseases. Visual field loss or blindness results from glaucoma, a disease of elevated intraocular pressure, thought to result from diminished reabsorption of aqueous humor (52). AQP1 in the anterior ciliary epithelium and canals of Schlemm (97, 133) may mediate both secretion and reabsorption of aqueous humor and thereby participate in the pathogenesis of glaucoma. AQP1 likely provides the pathway for secretion of water from the corneal stroma to the aqueous humor, helping maintain corneal transparency. Downregulation of AQP1 mRNA synthesis soon after birth (14) and the concomitant inability to produce new AQP1 protein may partially explain the observation that trauma to the corneal endothelium leads to corneal edema (107).

The distribution of AQP1 in the choroid plexus (97) strongly suggests participation in CSF formation. Increased CSF production has been implicated as the etiology of only a single disease—choroid plexus papilloma. However, technical considerations limit measurement of CSF formation so that the true incidence of overproduction of CSF may be underestimated (115).

The ontogeny and distribution (65) of AQP1 in lung strongly suggest a role in lung development and, by inference, in the pathology of the premature lung. Lung AQP1 exhibits a developmental program and response to corticosteroids similar to that of Na channels (99) and surfactant (33, 75), which have been implicated in the pathophysiology of the premature lung. We propose that AQP1 plays a significant role in lung development, and that disorders of AQP1 expression or function will contribute to the spectrum of neonatal lung disease.

The abundance of AQP1 in the peribronchial vasculature (65) predicts involvement in a number of pulmonary diseases. As pulmonary edema develops, fluid first accumulates in the peribronchial space before extending through the interstitium and into the alveolar space (31, 136). In an isolated sheep lung, water transport into the alveolar space was inhibited by mercury, which suggests functional water channels at an undefined anatomic level in the pathway from blood to alveolus (44). In recent studies of oxygen toxicity in rats, lung AQP1 was downregulated as edema developed (L King, unpublished observations). It is tantalizing to speculate that AQP1 in the peribronchial vasculature mediates clearance of lung water from that space; reductions in AQP1 expression would therefore lead to fluid accumulation.

Experimental evidence suggests that in both hydrostatic and increased permeability models of pulmonary edema the visceral pleura may unload excess lung water into the pleural space (150). Abundant AQP1 in the visceral pleura of the rat lung (65) may mediate transport of fluid from the lung into the pleural space.

Although asthma is principally an inflammatory disease (21), there is growing recognition of the role that lung water can play in modulating airway obstruction (17, 152). Fluid in the airway or peribronchial space can alter airway geometry, uncouple the airway from the elastic forces of the surrounding parenchyma, or amplify the effects of any degree of bronchial smooth muscle constriction, all of which can increase airway obstruction (152). Asthmatics given intravenous fluid boluses experience a decrement in their forced expiratory volume, similar in magnitude to that induced by hyperventilation of dry air (49). Patients with left ventricular failure have airway hyperresponsiveness to methacholine challenge and improvement in exertional performance with vasoconstrictors (22, 23), which suggests that alterations in lung perfusion and lung water can contribute to airway obstruction. Alternatively, changes in airway hydration may produce osmotic changes in the airway lumen, leading to mediator release (7) or changes in membrane potential (151). In short, accumulating evidence suggests that dysregulation of lung water can modulate airway obstruction, (17, 152). Individual susceptibility to diseases like exercise-induced asthma (7) or high-altitude pulmonary edema (122) may reflect variations in expression and regulation of AQP1.

Finally, future studies may demonstrate that specific alterations in membrane water permeability are conceptually important in understanding formation of edema in the lung and other tissues. The filtration coefficient of the Starling equation describes membrane water permeability, but in thought and practice is generally assessed in the context of hydrostatic changes or coupled to permeability changes for solutes (90). Recent observations of AQP1 induction by corticosteroids (65) and downregulation during oxygen toxicity (L King, unpublished observation) provide evidence that AQP1 expression may be dynamically regulated. The renal collecting duct is rapidly tranformed from being water impermeable to being highly water permeable by translocation of AQP2 to the apical membrane (see below). Insight into function and regulation of water channels in the lung and elsewhere may lead to changes in the way we conceptualize regulation of water movement.

AQP1 may prove to be integral to numerous other pathophysiologic processes. Carlsson et al recently demonstrated that AQP1 in peritoneal capillary endothelium mediated uptake of peritoneal dialysate (25). Autosomal dominant polycystic kidney disease (ADPKD) results from expansion of renal tubules into multiple fluid-filled cysts and progresses to renal failure in a high percentage of people. AQP1 and AQP2 (see below) have been localized to tubular epithelium of ADPKD cysts in a mutually exclusive distribution (10, 35). Although primary disorders of AQP1 and AQP2 are not likely to be the cause of ADPKD, these aquaporins probably facilitate secretion of fluid into the dilated cysts and contribute to development of the disease.

## MIP (Aquaporin-0)

DISTRIBUTION AND FUNCTION.    The lens of the eye consists of two types of cells; epithelial cells on the anterior surface and fiber cells formed on the lateral margins of the lens by differentiation of epithelial cells. Continuous formation of new fiber cells laterally leads to compression of old fiber cells to form the lens nucleus. As fiber cells differentiate from epithelial cells and migrate centrally, the nucleus and organelles are lost; the cells accumulate crystallin proteins, elongate, and increase in size severalfold; and protein-synthesis stops (50, 32). Fiber cells form a functional syncytium with closely connected membranes; the interstitial space is <5% of lens volume (106). Because the lens is avascular, nutrients must come from the surrounding bathing fluids (32, 38).

MIP constitutes over 60% of the membrane protein of lens fiber cells. While MIP has been intensively studied for the past decade, no predominant function has emerged. MIP was initially thought to be a gap junction protein (50), but Ehring et al suggested it was a voltage-gated ion channel that helped to minimize the extracellular fluid in the lens and maintain lens transparency (38).

Recently, several investigators demonstrated that MIP-injected X. laevis oocytes had increased osmotic water permeability with low Arrhenius activation energy similar to the other aquaporins, although the magnitude of water transport was severalfold lower than AQP1 (26, 69, 89). No ion channel activity was noted.

MIP AND DISEASE    MIP is likely to help maintain fluid balance in the lens, as proposed by Ehring et al (38). Although water channel properties could be the mechanism by which MIP regulates lens water, additional functions may be defined in the future. Maintenance of lens transparency requires tight control of the extracellular fluid in the lens (38). Lens nuclear water content increases with age (126), and lens edema is observed in the early stages of cataract formation (106). Alterations in MIP function would be predicted to lead to lens edema and development of cataracts.

A mouse strain developing fetal cataracts was identified several years ago (88) and was recently shown to have undetectable levels of MIP in the lens (124). Both the *cat* mutation (88) and MIP (51) have been mapped to the distal end of chromosome 10. Detailed analysis of cataract formation in the *cat* mouse may lead to definitive assignment of function to MIP (A Shiels, personal communication).

Interestingly, Zampighi et al demonstrated that MIP existed as a 26-kDa protein in calves but was partially degraded to a 22-kDa fragment in adult cattle (154), which raises the possibility that age-related changes in MIP may contribute to development of both cataracts and presbyopia.

## Aquaporin-2

DISTRIBUTION AND REGULATION    The renal collecting duct is the final arbiter of urinary excretion, increasing its membrane water permeability in the presence of arginine vasopressin (AVP) to reabsorb the 10–20% of glomerular filtrate not reabsorbed by the proximal nephron (67). Histologic studies of collecting duct epithelium demonstrated AVP-induced translocation of cytoplasmic vesicles to the apical membrane coincident with increased membrane water permeability. Thus the "shuttle hypothesis" was proposed to explain the reversible water permeability of collecting principal cells (146).

It is now clear that AQP2, previously referred to as AQP-CD (48), is the predominant AVP-sensitive water channel in the collecting duct. AQP2 is located in the principal cells of the collecting duct (48, 94), where it is found primarily in intracellular vesicles and at the apical membrane; reduced amounts of AQP2 are present at the basolateral membrane (94). The presumed link between AQP2 and AVP was strengthened by studies demonstrating that Brattleboro rats, deficient in AVP, had low-level baseline AQP2 expression that was increased by AVP administration (36). Recent studies demonstrated AVP-induced translocation of AQP2-containing vesicles to the apical membrane, with a simultaneous increase in membrane water permeability (93, 120), thereby confirming both the shuttle hypothesis (146) and the initial speculation that AQP2 mediates AVP-regulated collecting duct water permeability (48).

The mechanisms by which AVP stimulates AQP2 synthesis and redistribution are unknown, although components of the pathway include binding of AVP to the $V_2$ receptor (56), generation of intracellular cAMP, and participation of synaptobrevin in vesicle translocation (60). Regulation of AQP2 will likely prove to be complex because synthesis, translocation, and gating have been identified as targets for regulation (2). Dehydration increased expression of AQP2 protein (83, 94) and mRNA (77, 121a) in rats. Recent studies demonstrating that AVP and dehydration have different effects on AQP2 synthesis and redistribution suggest another level of control (83). Additional factors regulating AQP2 expression and function are certain to be identified.

AQP2 AND DISEASE    *Genetic deficiency*    In contrast to genetically AQP1-deficient humans (114), AQP2 deficiency produces a dramatic clinical phenotype. Nephrogenic diabetes insipidus (NDI) is a disease whose etiology is renal resistance to AVP and whose clinical hallmark is excretion of large volumes of dilute urine (57). The cause of X-linked recessive NDI was recently shown to be mutations of the AVP *V2-receptor* gene (104, 119). Other forms of inheritance have been identified, however, leading to speculation about additional mechanisms. Deen et al described a single patient with autosomal recessive NDI who was a compound heterozygote for mutations in the *aquaporin-2* gene (30), and additional patients have recently been described (143). Mutant AQP2 proteins expressed in *X. laevis* oocytes did not form functional water channels (30, 143) due to a defect in trafficking to the oocyte plasma membrane (29). It is anticipated that patients with congenital NDI will be identified who have normal *V2-receptor* and *aquaporin-2* genes but who have defects in AQP2 translocation pathways (64).

It was recently shown that AQP2 protein is present in normal urine but is markedly reduced in urine from patients with both nephrogenic and central diabetes insipidus (CDI) (64). AVP administration increased urinary excretion of AQP2 in patients with CDI but had no effect in NDI. Urine assays for AQP2 could ultimately prove valuable, but at present they offer little advantage over currently available tests.

*Acquired dysfunction*   Acquired nephrogenic diabetes insipidus is not infrequently encountered in clinical practice. Lithium is a known cause of NDI; 50% of patients taking lithium have defective urine concentration mechanisms, with 20% manifesting overt polyuria (15). Lithium is thought to antagonize AVP action on the collecting duct by inhibition of cAMP generation in principal cells (28), although the mechanism is not completely established. Marples et al recently demonstrated that chronic lithium administration in rats dramatically reduced expression of AQP2 (83). Exogenous AVP partially corrected the lithium-induced AQP2 reduction, whereas thirsting increased AQP2 synthesis but with little redistribution to the apical membrane, a mechanistically interesting observation suggesting uncoupling of AQP2 synthesis and translocation. AQP2 expression increased slowly after cessation of lithium, consistent with human data demonstrating slow recovery after NDI (57).

The list of acquired causes of NDI is long (57), and it is likely many will ultimately be linked with alterations in AQP2 expression. Frøkieor et al recently demonstrated that bilateral ureteral obstruction downregulates AQP2 expression (46), and Marples et al made similar observations for chronic hypokalemia (84); both are well-recognized causes of NDI. As we gain insight into its regulation, targeted induction of AQP2 may provide a strategy for treating NDI.

Impaired water excretion contributes to the clinical presentation of a number of pathologic states, including congestive heart failure, cirrhosis, and the syndrome of inappropriate antidiuretic hormone (SIADH) (11). Upregulation of AQP2 expression may be found to mediate the increase in distal nephron water reabsorption in many of those conditions. Indeed, it was recently reported that renal medullary AQP2 mRNA and protein levels were mildly increased in a rat model of cirrhosis (9). Considerable evidence suggests that in most cases of impaired water excretion, increased AQP2 expression would be secondary to increased circulating AVP (11). However, cases of primary dysregulation of AQP2 expression may be uncovered as our understanding of AQP2 regulation increases. Fourteen percent of a series of patients with SIADH had normal AVP levels (158), and it is not unlikely that among the myriad of drugs reported to cause SIADH (11) are some that act on AQP2 synthesis or redistribution independent of AVP. Whether increased AQP2 expression is a primary or secondary event, it may ultimately prove to be a therapeutic target when water excretion is impaired.

## Aquaporin-3

Aquaporin-3 was identified by three separate groups looking for renal aquaporins (37, 58, 77). A major functional discrepancy currently exists; two groups reported that AQP3 transports water and a small amount of transport of other molecules (glycerol and urea) (37, 58); a third reported only glycerol transport (77). AQP3 is located in the basolateral membrane of principal cells throughout the collecting duct (37, 45, 58, 77). Additionally, AQP3 has been found in the basolateral membrane of tracheal epithelium; in meningeal cells at the surface of the brain; in the conjunctival epithelium of the eye; and on the basolateral membrane of villous epithelial cells of the distal colon (45).

The significance of the difference in channel selectivity of AQP3 compared with the other aquaporins is unknown. Likewise, its function in the basolateral distribution is unknown, although one can easily postulate tissue-specific entry (trachea) or exit (kidney) pathways for transcellular water movement.

## Aquaporin-4

DISTRIBUTION    AQP4 was cloned from lung (53) and brain cDNA libraries (62), although brain appears to be its predominant distribution. AQP4 is distinct from the other aquaporins in that water transport is not inhibitable by mercury compounds (53, 62), thus its initial name was "Mercury-insensitive water channel" (MIWC) (53).

*Brain*    Cerebrospinal fluid (CSF) is formed in the choroid plexus of the lateral ventricles; interestingly, some investigators have reported that ventricular ependymal cells may also contribute to CSF production (76). From the lateral ventricle, CSF courses through the ventricular and aqueductal system into the basal cisterns and subarachnoid space, from which it travels down the spinal cord or over the convexity of the brain (1, 76). CSF is reabsorbed through the arachnoid villi, vascular outpouchings of arachnoid membrane that have been reported to function as valves (1, 76, 123). Arachnoid villi, or granulations, as groups of villi are called, are found at the base and over the convexity of the brain.

Both in situ hybridization (53, 62) and immunohistochemistry (45; S Nielsen, unpublished observations) revealed labeling of AQP4 on the ependymal cells of the cerebral ventricles and the pial surface on the convexity of the brain. Labeling was also seen in the ependymal lining of the aqueductal system and at the base of the brain (62). This distribution strikingly coincides with known areas of CSF reabsorption and modulation (1, 76), and implicates AQP4 in regulation of CSF outflow.

Additionally, AQP4 was localized to the Purkinje layer of the cerebellum, as well as to the supraoptic and paraventricular nuclei of the hypothalamus (62; S Nielsen, unpublished observations). It is difficult to speculate on the role AQP4 might play in cerebellar function. The finding of localization of AQP4 to the supraoptic and paraventricular nuclei is extremely provocative because magnocellular cells in those nuclei synthesize and release AVP in response to osmotic changes of ~1% (18). Although the exact site of osmosensation is subject to debate, it was recently shown that volume changes in magnocellular cells are tightly coupled to membrane conductance changes, perhaps through stretch-sensitive ionic channels (100). AQP4 in the hypothalamus may mediate osmoregulation by facilitating rapid and sensitive stretch responses to small osmotic changes.

As early as the turn of the century, cerebral capillaries were recognized as being less permeable to both small and large molecules than systemic vessels, which led to the concept of the blood-brain barrier (59). Endothelial cells of cerebral capillaries are nonfenestrated, with higher resistance tight junctions and lower rates of transcytosis than peripheral capillaries (59). They contain mitochondria and Na/K ATPase, suggestive of secretory cells (123). Astrocyte foot processes surround 80–95% of the circumference of cerebral capillaries, and have been implicated in the generation and maintenance of the blood-brain barrier endothelial cell phenotype, although the mechanisms underlying that influence are not known (59). As with CSF volume, extracellular fluid volume in the brain must be tightly controlled because of the noncompliance of the encapsulating bony skull (123).

Immunolocalization studies demonstrated AQP4 in astrocyte foot processes surrounding capillaries throughout the brain parenchyma (S Nielsen, unpublished data). Astrocytes induce blood-brain barrier endothelial cell characteristics in transplantation studies (59), but little is currently known about astrocyte function in regulation of brain water. AQP4 may facilitate astrocyte removal of water secreted into the extracellular space by endothelial cells. Other investigators have localized AQP4 to glial cells (45); its function there is not known.

*Kidney*  AQP4 was found in the basolateral membrane of collecting duct principal cells (45), believed to have constitutively high water permeability (135). Presumably, AQP4 provides an exit pathway for water entering the principal cell, although colocalization with AQP2 (94) and AQP3 (37, 45, 58) in the basolateral membrane complicates assignment of a unique function to any of the three in that distribution. Future studies may demonstrate a more specific segment and cell type location for each. Of interest, Nielsen identified AQP4 in the most distal collecting duct in the inner medulla (S Nielsen, unpublished observations), a site known to have constitutively high, vasopressin-insensitive water permeability (67).

*Lung*  AQP4 was described in the basolateral membrane of tracheal and bronchial epithelium (45). No AQP4 was seen in alveolar epithelium. Airway hydration is necessary for maintenance of mucociliary clearance, and changes in hydration may participate in the pathogenesis of exercise- or cold-induced asthma (7). Specific localization to the basolateral membrane of lung airway epithelium predicts the existence of other water channels in the apical membrane.

*Other locations*    AQP4 was reported to be in the basolateral membrane of nonpigmented epithelial cells of the ciliary body; pigmented cells of the iris; and several layers of the retina, including the inner and outer nuclear layers, and the ganglion cell layer. AQP4 was also reported to be weakly present in the basolateral membrane of villous epithelial cells of distal colon (45).

AQP4 AND DISEASE    Although questions regarding distribution await resolution, available data strongly suggest a role for AQP4 in a number of physiologic and pathologic processes.

Pseudotumor cerebri (benign intracranial hypertension) and normal pressure hydrocephalus (NPH) are believed to result from abnormalities of CSF reabsorption (82, 85, 115). Pseudotumor cerebri is most frequently found in overweight females, often in the setting of exogenous vitamin or hormone use, or endogenous hormonal abnormalities (85). It is particularly appealing to implicate AQP4 in that disease, not only because AQP4 has been localized to sites of CSF reabsorption (45, 53, 62; S Nielsen, unpublished observations), but because the example of hormonal modulation of aquaporins determined for AQP1 (65) and AQP2 (93) may extend to AQP4.

Cerebral edema is generally categorized as cytotoxic or vasogenic, although the two frequently overlap (66, 85). Cytotoxic edema is thought to represent disordered cell osmoregulation; increased brain water is secondary to cell swelling. Cytotoxic edema is seen in cerebral hypoxia, acute plasma hypoosmolality, or osmotic disequilibrium syndromes, such as renal failure and hemodialysis, or diabetic hyperosmolar states (43, 85). Vasogenic edema results from alterations in the permeability characteristics of the blood-brain barrier and is the presumed mechanism of cerebral edema associated with tumors, ischemia and infarction, or infection (43, 85). The molecular basis for cerebral edema in all of these conditions is unknown.

The abundance of AQP4 on astrocyte foot processes of the blood-brain barrier suggests a role in regulation of extracellular fluid volume. Conditions known to produce cerebral edema may do so by altering expression of AQP4 on astrocytes or perhaps by inducing expression of AQP4 or another aquaporin on endothelial cells not normally expressing water channels, thereby dramatically altering membrane water permeability. Understanding the function and regulation of aquaporins in the brain should provide insight into the mechanisms of cerebral edema.

One could easily speculate that AQP4 forms part of the sensor or transduction mechanism of osmoregulation in the supraoptic and paraventricular nuclei.

SIADH is manifest as hyponatremia with an inappropriately concentrated urine; the cause in many cases is thought to be an alteration in the set point for AVP release (57). Central diabetes insipidus (CDI) (11) is at the other end of the spectrum, with hypernatremia and an inability to concentrate urine resulting from absent or insufficient release of AVP; 25 to 50% of cases of CDI are idiopathic. Changes in AQP4 expression or regulation may alter the mechanosensor properties of magnocellular neurons in the supraoptic and paraventricular nuclei (100) and result in dysregulation of AVP release.

## Aquaporin-5

DISTRIBUTION   The absence of AQP1 in glandular epithelia predicted the existence of other aquaporins in that distribution. Raina et al cloned AQP5 from a salivary gland library specifically in pursuit of glandular epithelial water channels (116). AQP5 is similar to the other aquaporins in water transport properties and has a protein kinase A (PKA) consensus in a cytoplasmic loop similar to that of AQP2 (48). The tissues that express AQP5 are noted for dynamic regulation of fluid secretion. PKA-mediated phosphorylation may produce rapid changes in trafficking or gating of AQP5 similar to those seen with AQP2 (2).

Lacrimal gland secretions provide the bulk of the aqueous tear film (73) and are regulated by a variety of neural and hormonal (73, 86, 148) factors. Tear production diminishes with sleep, reflecting the notion that tear formation is an active process requiring specific stimulation (73). Salivary glands consist of secretory lobules with serous- and mucus-secreting cells and excretory ducts lined with a distinct epithelium that modifies the basal cell secretions. Neural and hormonal stimuli, including a variety of secretagogues, induce large and rapid reductions in the cell volume of salivary acinar cells (92). AQP5 was abundant in the secretory epithelium of rat lacrimal and submandibular gland but not in other glandular structures (116; S Nielsen, unpublished observation). AQP5 likely provides the pathway for water secretion in those glands.

The corneal epithelium is known to exhibit apical chloride and water secretion in the presence of catecholamines or stimulators of cAMP (107). AQP5 is present in the corneal epithelium and may participate in corneal desiccation and maintenance of corneal transparency (116).

As noted previously, localization studies of AQP1 in lung revealed minimal labeling of alveolar epithelium in the rat (65). AQP5 was strongly present on Northern analysis of rat lung RNA (116), and recent immunolocalization studies suggest abundant expression on alveolar type I cells (65a).

AQP5 AND DISEASE   Distribution of AQP5 in glandular epithelia of lacrimal and submandibular glands suggests that alterations in its expression or function would lead to insufficiency of those organs. Non-immune-mediated lacrimal insufficiency is a prevalent problem, with a strong gender bias (more females than males) (148). Circulating androgens are required for normal gland growth and function, but the molecular basis of the inability to secrete water is unknown. Likewise, the mechanism of glandular insufficiency after radiation for head and neck cancer is unknown. We believe that changes in AQP5 will provide an explanation in some of these conditions.

Some models of lung airway fluid regulation propose secretion of fluid in the alveolus and distal airway with reabsorption occurring as fluid is swept proximally by the mucociliary elevator (16). The abundance of AQP5 in the alveolar epithelium of the rat (S Nielsen, unpublished observations) may provide insight into the location and regulation of lung fluid secretion. The distribution of AQP5 in human lung is not yet known; if found in bronchioles or larger airways, AQP5 may contribute directly to airway hydration or water reabsorption at those levels. In cystic fibrosis (CF), airway secretions become increasingly viscous and difficult to clear, predisposing to infection and airway damage. No direct measurements of airway surface liquids have been made in CF (13). Although it is not likely that primary changes in AQP5 (or other AQPs) contribute to the pathogenesis of CF, the cystic fibrosis transmembrane conductance regulator (CFTR) may in some fashion interact with an aquaporin to regulate water secretion, as has recently been shown for CFTR regulation of sodium channels (137).

Drowning victims have often been noted to have "dry but atelectatic" lungs; the inhaled water is rapidly reabsorbed, but disruption of surfactant produces alveolar collapse and gas exchange abnormalities. Hemolysis has been noted, particularly in fresh-water drownings, but the clinical significance is often unclear (91). We suspect that fluid in the airway, particularly hypotonic solutions, is provided rapid access to the circulation by passage through AQP5.

Preliminary data suggest that changes in AQP5 expression might be involved in edema formation in acute lung injury. Oxygen-toxic rats have marked up- and downregulation of AQP5 expression at different times during edema formation (L King, unpublished observations), raising the possibility that alterations in AQP5 ultimately dictate progression to alveolar flooding.

Curiously, the distribution of AQP5 coincides almost exactly with the organ involvement of Sjören's disease, an immunologically mediated process causing dry eyes and dry mouth, with a variety of pulmonary manifestations (138). The antigen(s) driving immune destruction of the involved organs are unknown, but the coincidence of distribution with AQP5 is provocative.

## Undiscovered Aquaporins

Several tissues in which aquaporins have not been found are strongly suspected of harboring unidentified aquaporins. The retinal pigment epithelium is a highly metabolically active cell layer that appears to actively control the interstitial osmolality between it and the retinal rods and cones (74). As such, it is a likely source of additional aquaporins.

AQP5 probably mediates secretion in submandibular and lacrimal glands, but parotid, pancreas, and sweat glands are similarly designed secretory organs in which no aquaporins have been identified. The thyroid, although having structured secretory elements that are different from the other glands mentioned, is nonetheless also a likely site for identification of new aquaporins.

Joints may well incorporate aquaporins into their normal structure and function. Articular cartilage is more than 70% water, with sparsely located chondrocytes that oversee remodeling (127) and presumably hydration. Arthritis, traumatic and inflammatory, is accompanied by an increase in joint fluid. Clearly, numerous mechanisms are involved, but altered expression of an already identified or unidentified aquaporin is an appealing hypothesis.

## SUMMARY

The discovery of aquaporin water channels brings the promise that we will soon understand the molecular basis of water movement across biological membranes in the setting of both normal physiology and disease. The specific distribution of each of the known mammalian aquaporins strongly predicts a unique functional role. While our understanding of the physiology of aquaporins is at present only rudimentary, and specific disease associations await further experimentation, the example of nephrogenic diabetes insipidus resulting from mutations or downregulation of AQP2 is highly instructive. Specific alterations in membrane water permeability may prove to be as relevant to understanding water movement across membranes as ion channels and oncotic pressure.

ACKNOWLEDGMENTS

Support for this work was provided by National Institutes of Health grants HL33991 and HL48268 (PA), and NRSA F32 HL09119-02 (LK).

## Literature Cited

1. Adams RD, Victor M. 1989. Disturbances of cerebrospinal fluid circulation, including hydrocephalus and meningeal reactions. In *Principles of Neurology*, pp. 501–15. New York: McGraw-Hill

2. Agre P, Brown D, Nielsen S. 1995. Aquaporin water channels: unanswered questions and unresolved controversies. *Curr. Opin. Cell Biol.* 7:472–83

3. Agre P, Preston GM, Smith BL, Jung JS, Raina S, et al. 1993. Aquaporin

CHIP, the archetypal molecular water channel. *Am. J. Physiol.* 265:F463–76

4. Agre P, Sasaki S, Chrispeels MJ. 1993. Aquaporins: a family of water channel proteins. *Am. J. Physiol.* 265:F461

5. Agre P, Smith BL, Baumgarten R, Preston GM, Pressman E, et al. 1994. Human red cell aquaporin CHIP: II. Expression during normal fetal development and in a novel congenital dyserythropoietic anemia. *J. Clin. Invest.* 94:1050–58

6. Alpini G, Phillips JO, LaRusso NF. 1994. The biology of biliary epithelia. In *The Liver: Biology and Pathobiology*, ed. IM Arias, JL Boyer, N Fausto, WB Jakoby, DA Schachter, DA Shafritz. pp. 623–53, New York: Raven. 3rd ed.

7. Anderson SD, Togias AG. 1994. Dry air and hyperosmolar challenge in asthma and rhinitis. In *Asthma and Rhinitis*, ed. WW Busse, ST Holgate. pp. 1178–95. Boston: Blackwell

8. Aperia A, Celsi G. 1992. Ontogenic processes in nephron epithelia: structure, enzymes, and function. See Ref. 123a, pp. 803–28

9. Asahina Y, Izumi N, Enomoto N, Sasaki S, Fushimi K, et al. 1995. Increased gene expression of water channel in cirrhotic rat kidneys. *Hepatology* 21: 169–73

10. Bachinsky DR, Sabolic I, Emmanouel DS, Jefferson DM, Carone FA, et al. 1995. Water channel expression in human ADPKD kidneys. *Am. J. Physiol.* 268:F398–403

11. Bichet DG, Kluge R, Howard RL, Schrier RW. 1992. Hyponatremic states. See Ref. 123a, pp. 1727–51

12. Bland RD, Chapman DL. 1994. Absorption of liquid from the lungs at birth. In *Fluid and Solute Transport in the Airspaces of the Lungs*, ed. RM Effros, HK Chang. pp. 303–22. New York: Dekker

13. Boat TF, Boucher RC. 1994. Cystic fibrosis. See Ref. 90a, pp. 1418–50

14. Bondy C, Chin E, Smith BL, Preston GM, Agre P. 1993. Developmental gene expression and tissue distribution of the CHIP28 water channel protein. *Proc. Natl. Acad. Sci. USA* 90:4500–4

15. Boton R, Gaviria M, Battle DC. 1987. Prevalence, pathogenesis, and treatment of renal dysfunction associated with chronic lithium therapy. *Am. J. Kidney Dis.* 10:329–45

16. Boucher RC. 1994. Human airway ion transport: part one. *Am. J. Respir. Crit. Care Med.* 150:271–81

17. Boucher RC, Gilbert IA, Hogg JC, King M, Knowles MR, Nadel J. 1995. Non-muscular airway obstruction and asthma. *Am. J. Respir. Crit. Care Med.* 152:408–10

18. Bourque CW, Oliet SHR, Richard D. 1994. Osmoreceptors, osmoreception, and osmoregulation. *Frontiers Neuroendocrinol.* 15:231–74

19. Brown D, Verbavatz JM, Valenti B, Lui B, Sabolic I. 1993. Localization of the CHIP28 water channel in reabsorptive segments of the rat male reproductive tract. *Eur. J. Cell Biol.* 61:264–73

20. Brubaker RF. 1991. Flow of aqueous humor in humans. *Invest. Ophthalmol. Vis. Sci.* 32:3145–66

21. Busse WW, Coffman RL, Gelfand EW, Kay AB, Rosenwasser LJ. 1995. Mechanisms of persistent airway inflammation in asthma. *Am. J. Respir. Crit. Care Med.* 152:388–93

22. Cabanes L, Costes F, Weber S, Regnard J, Benvenuti C, et al. 1992. Improvement in exercise performance by inhalation of methoxamine in patients with impaired left ventricular function. *New Engl. J. Med.* 326:1661–65

23. Cabanes LR, Weber SN, Matran R, Regnard J, Richard MO, et al. 1989. Bronchial hyperresponsiveness to methacholine in patients with impaired left ventricular function. *New Engl. J. Med.* 320:1317–22

24. Caprioli J. 1992. The ciliary epithelium and aqueous humor. See Ref. 52, pp. 228–47

25. Carlsson O, Nielsen S, Zakaria ER, Rippe B. 1995. In vivo inhibition of transcellular water channels (Aquaporin-1) during acute peritoneal dialysis in rats. *Am. J. Physiol.* In press

26. Chandy G, Kreman M, Laidlaw DL, Zampighi GA, Hall JE. 1995. The water permeability per molecule of MIP is less than that of CHIP. *Biophys. J.* 68: 353 (Abstr.)

27. Chrispeels MJ, Agre P. 1994. Aquaporins: water channel proteins of plant and animal cells. *Trends Biochem. Sci.* 19: 421–25

28. Christensen S, Kusano E, Yusufi AN, Murayama N, Dousa TP. 1985. Pathogenesis of nephrogenic diabetes insipidus due to chronic administration of lithium in rats. *J. Clin. Invest.* 75:1869–79

29. Deen PMT, Croes H, van Aubel RAMH, Ginsel LA, van Os CH. 1995. Water channels encoded by mutant aquaporin-2 genes in nephrogenic diabetes insipidus are impaired in their cellular routing. *J. Clin. Invest.* 95:2291–96

30. Deen PMT, Verdijk MAJ, Knoers NVAM, Wieringa B, Monnens LAH, et

al. 1994. Requirement of human renal water channel aquaporin-2 for vasopressin-dependent concentration of urine. *Science* 264:92–95

31. Deffebach ME, Charan NB, Lakshminarayan S, Butler J. 1987. The bronchial circulation. *Am. Rev. Resp. Dis.* 135: 463–81

32. De Jong WW, Hendriks W, Mulders JWM, Bloemendal H. 1989. Evolution of eye lens crystallins: the stress connection. *Trends Biochem. Sci.* 14:365–68

33. DeLemos RA, Shermata DW, Knelson JH, Kotas R, Avery ME. 1970. Acceleration of appearance of pulmonary surfactant in the fetal lamb by administration of corticosteroids. *Am. Rev. Resp. Dis.* 102:459–61

34. Denker BM, Smith BL, Kuhajda FP, Agre P. 1988. Identification, purification, and characterization of a novel $M_r$ 28,000 integral membrane protein from erythrocytes and renal tubules. *J. Biol. Chem.* 263:15634–42

35. Devuyst O, Agre P, Smith BL, Knepper MA, Wilson PD. 1995. Expression of AQP-CHIP and AQP-CD during kidney development and in polycystic kidney diseases. Presented at *XIII Int. Cong. Nephrology, Madrid.* p. 25

36. DiGiovanni SR, Nielsen S, Christensen EI, Knepper MA. 1994. Regulation of collecting duct water channel expression by vasopressin in Brattleboro rat. *Proc. Natl. Acad. Sci. USA* 91:8984–88

37. Echevarria M, Windhager EE, Tate SS, Frindt G. 1994. Cloning and expression of AQP3, a water channel from the medullary collecting duct of rat kidney. *Proc. Natl. Acad. Sci. USA* 91:10997–1001

38. Ehring GR, Zampighi G, Horwitz J, Bok D, Hall JE. 1990. Properties of channels reconstituted from the major intrinsic protein of lens fiber membranes. *J. Gen. Physiol.* 96:631–64

39. Engel A, Walz T, Agre P. 1994. The aquaporin family of membrane water channels. *Curr. Opin. Struct. Biol.* 4: 545–53

40. Ernst SA, Palacios JR, Siegel GJ. 1986. Immunocytochemical localisation of $Na^+$, $K^+$ ATPase catalytic polypeptide in mouse choroid plexus. *J. Histochem. Cytochem.* 34:189–95

41. Finkelstein A. 1987. *Water Movement Through Lipid Bilayers, Pores, and Plasma Membranes,* pp. 166–84. New York: Wiley

42. Fischbarg J, Kuang K, Hirsch J, Lecuona S, Rogozinski L, et al. 1989. Evidence that the glucose transporter

serves as a water channel in J774 macrophages. *Proc. Natl. Acad. Sci. USA* 86: 8397–401

43. Fishman RA. 1995. Brain edema and disorders of intracranial pressure. See Ref. 119a, pp. 302–10

44. Folkesson HG, Matthay MA, Hasegawa H, Kheradmand F, Verkman AS. 1994. Transcellular water transport in lung alveolar epithelium through mercury-sensitive water channels. *Proc. Natl. Acad. Sci. USA* 91:4970–74

45. Frigeri A, Gropper MA, Turck CW, Verkman AS. 1995. Immunolocalization of the mercurial-insensitive water channel and glycerol intrinsic protein in epithelial plasma membranes. *Proc. Natl. Acad. Sci. USA* 92:4328–31

46. Frøkioer J, Marples D, Knepper MA, Nielsen S. 1995. Bilateral ureteral obstruction downregulates expression of the vasopressin sensitive aquaporin-2 water channel in rat kidney. *Am. J. Physiol.* In press

47. Fung LWM, Narasimhan C, Lu HZ, Westerman MP. 1989. Reduced water exchange in sickle cell anemia red cells: a membrane abnormality. *Biochim. Biophys. Acta* 982:167–72

48. Fushimi K, Shinichi U, Hara Y, Hiratya Y, Marumo F, Sasaki S. 1993. Cloning and expression of apical membrane water channel of rat kidney collecting tubule. *Nature* 361:549–52

49. Gilbert IA, Winslow CJ, Lenner KA, Nelson JA, McFadden ER. 1993. Vascular volume expansion and thermally induced asthma. *Eur. Respir. J.* 6:189–97

50. Gorin NB, Yancey SB, Cline J, Revel JP, Horwitz J. 1984. The major intrinsic protein (MIP) of the bovine lens fiber membrane. *Cell* 39:49–59

51. Griffin CS, Shiels A. 1992. Localisation of the gene for the major intrinsic protein of eye lens-fibre cell membranes to mouse chromosome 10 by in situ hybridisation. *Cytogenet. Cell. Genet.* 59: 300–2

52. Hart WM Jr, ed. 1992. Intraocular pressure. In *Adler's Physiology of the Eye,* pp. 248–67. St. Louis, MO: Mosby

53. Hasegawa H, Ma T, Skach W, Matthay MA, Verkman AS. 1994. Molecular cloning of a mercurial-insensitive water channel expressed in selected water-transporting tissues. *J. Biol. Chem.* 269: 5497–500

54. Hasegawa H, Skach W, Baker O, Calayag MC, Lingappa V, Verkman AS. 1992. A multifunctional aqueous channel formed by CFTR. *Science* 258: 1477–79

55. Hasegawa H, Zhang R, Dohrman A, Verkman AS. 1993. Tissue specific expression of mRNA encoding rat kidney water channel CHIP28k by in situ hybridization. *Am. J. Physiol.* 264:C237–45

56. Hayashi M, Sasaki S, Tsuganezawa H, Monkawa T, Kitajima W, et al. 1994. Expression and distribution of aquaporin of collecting duct are regulated by vasopressin V2 receptor in rat kidney. *J. Clin. Invest.* 94:1778–86

57. Howard RL, Bichet DG, Schrier RW. 1992. Hypernatremic and polyuric states. See Ref. 123a, pp. 1753–77

58. Ishibashi K, Sasaki S, Fushimi K, Uchida S, Kuwahara M, et al. 1994. Molecular cloning and expression of a member of the aquaporin family with permeability to glycerol and urea in addition to water expressed at the basolateral membrane of kidney collecting duct cells. *Proc. Natl. Acad. Sci. USA* 91:6269–73

59. Janzer RC. 1993. The blood-brain barrier: cellular basis. *J. Inher. Metab. Dis.* 16:639–47

60. Jo I, Harris WH, Amendt-Raduege AM, Majewski RR, Hammond TG. 1995. Rat kidney papilla contains abundant synaptobrevin protein that participates in the fusion of antidiuretic hormone-regulated water channel-containing endosomes in vitro. *Proc. Natl. Acad. Sci. USA* 92: 1876–80

61. Joiner CH. 1993. Cation transport and volume regulation in sickle red blood cells. *Am. J. Physiol.* 264:C251–70

62. Jung JS, Bhat RV, Preston GM, Baraban JM, Agre P. 1994. Molecular characterization of an aquaporin cDNA from brain: a candidate osmoreceptor and regulator of water balance. *Proc. Natl. Acad. Sci. USA* 91:13052–56

63. Jung JS, Preston GM, Smith BL, Guggino WB, Agre P. 1994. Molecular structure of the water channel through Aquaporin CHIP: the hourglass model. *J. Biol. Chem.* 269:14648–54

64. Kanno K, Sasaki S, Hirata Y, Ishikawa S, Fushimi K, et al. 1995. Urinary excretion of aquaporin-2 in patients with diabetes insipidus. *New Engl. J. Med.* 332:1540–45

65. King LS, Nielsen S, Agre P. 1995. Aquaporin-1 water channel protein in lung: developmental patterns and steroid-induced expression in fetal rat. *J. Clin. Invest.* In press

65a. King LS, Nielsen S, Agre P. 1995. Aquaporin-5 is expressed in rat type I pneumocytes. *Am. J. Respir. Crit. Care Med.* In press

66. Klatzo I. 1994. Evolution of brain edema concepts. *Acta Neurochir. Suppl.* 60:3–6

67. Knepper MA, Rector FC Jr. 1991. Urinary concentration and dilution. In *The Kidney*, ed. BM Brenner, FC Rector. pp. 445–82. Philadelphia: Saunders. 4th ed.

68. Kurtz SR, Kuszaj T, Ouellet R, Valeri CR. 1982. Survival of homozygous Coa (Colton) in a patient with anti-Coa1. *Vox Sang.* 43:28–30

69. Kushmerick C, Rice SJ, Baldo GH, Haspel HC, Mathias RT. 1994. Cloning, expression, and functional studies of frog lens MIP. *Biophys. J.* 66:215 (Abstr.)

70. Kuwahara M, Fushimi K, Terada Y, Bai L, Marumo F, Sasaki S. 1995. cAMP-dependent phosphorylation stimulates water permeability of aquaporin-collecting duct water channel protein expressed in *Xenopus* oocytes. *J. Biol. Chem.* 270: 10384–87

71. Lanahan A, Williams JB, Sanders LK, Nathans D. 1992. Growth factor-induced delayed early response genes. *Mol. Cell. Biol.* 12:3919–29

72. Lande MB, Jo I, Zeidel ML, Somers M, Harris HW. 1995. Phosphorylation of Aquaporin-2 does not alter the membrane water permeability of rat papillary water channel-containing vesicles. *J. Biol. Chem.* In press

73. Lemp MA, Wolfley DE. 1992. The lacrimal apparatus. See Ref. 52, pp. 18–28

74. Li JD, Govardovskii VI, Steinberg RH. 1994. Light dependent hydration of the space surrounding photoreceptors in the cat retina. *Vis. Neurosci.* 11:743–52

75. Liggins GC, Howie RN. 1972. A controlled trial of antepartum glucocorticoid treatment for prevention of the respiratory distress syndrome in premature infants. *Pediatrics* 50:515–25

76. Lyons MK, Meyer FB. 1990. Cerebrospinal fluid physiology and the management of increased intracranial pressure. *Mayo Clin. Proc.* 65:684–707

77. Ma T, Frigeri A, Hasegawa H, Verkman AS. 1994. Cloning of a water channel homolog expressed in brain meningeal cells and kidney collecting duct that functions as a stilbene-sensitive glycerol transporter. *J. Biol. Chem.* 269:21845–49

78. Macey RI. 1984. Transport of water and urea in red blood cells. *Am. J. Physiol.* 246:C195–203

79. Macey RI, Farmer REL. 1970. Inhibition of water and solute permeability in human red cells. *Biochim. Biophys. Acta* 211:104–6

80. Macey RI, Yousef LW. 1988. Osmotic

stability of red cells in renal circulation requires rapid urea transport. *Am. J. Physiol.* 23:C669–74

81. Maeda Y, Smith BL, Agre P, Knepper MA. 1995. Quantification of aquaporin-CHIP water channel protein in microdissected renal tubules by fluorescence-based ELISA. *J. Clin. Invest.* 95:422–28

82. Mann JD, Johnson RN, Butler AB, Bass NH. 1979. Impairment of cerebrospinal fluid circulatory dynamics in pseudotumor cerebri and response to steroid treatment. *Neurology* 29:550 (Abstr.)

83. Marples D, Christensen S, Christensen EI, Ottosen PD, Nielsen S. 1995. Lithium-induced downregulation of aquaporin-2 water channel expression in rat kidney medulla. *J. Clin. Invest.* 95:1838–45

84a. Mathai JC, Muri S, Smith BL, Preston GM, Mohandas N, et al. 1995. Functional analysis of aquaporin-1-deficient red cells: the Colton-null phenotype. *J. Biol. Chem.* In press

84. Marples D, Dørup J, Knepper MA, Nielsen S. 1995. Hypokalemia-induced downregulation of aquaporin-2 water channel expression in rat kidney medulla and cortex. *J. Clin. Invest.* In press

85. Milhorat TH. 1992. Classification of the cerebral edemas with reference to hydrocephalus and pseudotumor cerebri. *Child's Nerv. Syst.* 8:301–6

86. Mircheff AK. 1989. Lacrimal fluid and electrolyte secretion: a review. *Curr. Eye Res.* 8:607–16

87. Moon C, Preston GM, Griffin CA, Jabs EW, Agre P. 1993. The Aquaporin-CHIP28 gene: structure, organization and chromosomal localization. *J. Biol. Chem.* 268:15772–78

88. Muggleton-Harris AL, Festing MFW, Hall M. 1987. A gene location for the inheritance of the Cataract Fraser (*Cat^Fr*) mouse congenital cataract. *Genet. Res.* 49:235–38

89. Mulders SM, Preston GM, Deen PMT, Guggino WB, van Os CH, Agre P. 1995. Water channel properties of major intrinsic protein of lens. *J. Biol. Chem.* 270:9010–16

90. Murray, JF. 1986. *The Normal Lung*, pp. 283–312. Philadelphia: Saunders

90a. Murray JF, Nadel JA, eds. 1994. *Textbook of Respiratory Medicine*. Philadelphia: Saunders. 2nd ed.

91. Nadel JA, Denison D. 1994. Disorders associated with diving. See Ref. 90a, pp. 2099–16

92. Nauntofte B. 1992. Regulation of electrolyte and fluid secretion in salivary acinar cells: review. *Am. J. Physiol.* 263:G823–37

93. Nielsen S, Chou CL, Marples D, Christensen EI, Kishore BK, Knepper MA. 1995. Vasopressin increases water permeability of kidney collecting duct by inducing translocation of Aquaporin-CD water channels to plasma membrane. *Proc. Natl. Acad. Sci. USA* 92:1013–17

94. Nielsen S, DiGiovanni SR, Christensen EI, Knepper MA, Harris HW. 1993. Cellular and subcellular immunolocalization of vasopressin-regulated water channel in rat kidney. *Proc. Natl. Acad. Sci. USA* 90:11663–67

95. Deleted in proof

96. Nielsen S, Pallone T, Smith BL, Christensen EI, Agre P, Maunsbach AB. 1995. Aquaporin-1 water channels in short and long loop descending thin limbs and in descending vasa recta in rat kidney. *Am. J. Physiol.* 268:F1023–37

97. Nielsen S, Smith BL, Christensen EI, Agre P. 1993. Distribution of the aquaporin CHIP in secretory and resorptive epithelia and capillary endothelia. *Proc. Natl. Acad. Sci. USA* 90:7275–79

98. Nielsen S, Smith BL, Christensen EI, Knepper MA, Agre P. 1993. CHIP28 water channels are localized in constitutively water-permeable segments of nephron. *J. Cell Biol.* 120:371–83

99. O'Brodovich H, Canessa C, Ueda J, Rafii B, Rossier BC, Edelson J. 1993. Expression of the epithelial Na+ channel in the developing rat lung. *Am. J. Physiol.* 265:C491–96

100. Oliet SHR, Bourque CW. 1993. Mechanosensitive channels transduce osmosensitivity in supraoptic neurons. *Nature* 364:341–43

101. Olives B, Neau N, Bailly P, Hediger MA, Rousselet G, et al. 1994. Cloning and functional expression of a urea transporter from human bone marrow cells. *J. Biol. Chem.* 269:31649–52

102. Olver RE. 1994. Fluid secretion and absorption in the fetus. In *Fluid and Solute Transport in the Airspaces of the Lungs.* ed. RM Effros, HK Chang. pp. 281–302. New York: Dekker

103. Orringer EP, Blythe DSB, Johnson AE, Phillips G Jr, Dover GJ, Parker JC. 1991. Effects of hydroxyurea on hemoglobin F and water content in the red blood cells of dogs and patients with sickle cell anemia. *Blood* 78:212–16

104. Pan Y, Metzenberg A, Das S, Jing B, Gitschier J. 1992. Mutations in the V2 vasopressin receptor gene are associated with X-linked nephrogenic diabetes insipidus. *Nat. Genet.* 2:103–6

105. Pao, GM, Wu LF, Johnson KD, Höfte

H, Chrispeels MJ, et al. 1991. Evolution of the MIP family of integral membrane transport proteins. *Mol. Microbiol.* 5: 33–37

106. Paterson CA, Delamere NA. 1992. The lens. See Ref. 52, pp. 348–90

107. Pepose J, Ubels JL. 1992. The cornea. See Ref. 52, pp. 29–70

108. Perrine RP, Pembrey ME, John P, Perrine S, Shoup F. 1978. Natural history of sickle cell anemia in Saudi Arabs. *Ann. Int. Med.* 88:1–6

109. Pisano MM, Chepelinsky AB. 1991. Genomic cloning, complete nucleotide sequence, and structure of the human gene encoding the major intrinsic protein (MIP) of lens. *Genomics* 11:981–90

110. Preston GM, Agre P. 1991. Molecular cloning of the red cell integral protein of $M_r$ 28,000: a member of an ancient channel family. *Proc. Natl. Acad. Sci. USA* 88:11110–14

111. Preston GM, Carroll TP, Guggino WB, Agre P. 1992. Appearance of water channels in *Xenopus* oocytes expressing red cell CHIP28 protein. *Science* 256: 385–87

112. Preston GM, Jung JS, Guggino WB, Agre P. 1993. The mercury-sensitive residue at cysteine-189 in the CHIP28 water channel. *J. Biol. Chem.* 268:17–20

113. Preston GM, Jung JS, Guggino WB, Agre P. 1994. Membrane topology of Aquaporin CHIP: analysis of functional epitope scanning mutants by vectorial proteolysis. *J. Biol. Chem.* 269:1668–73

114. Preston GM, Smith BL, Zeidel ML, Moulds JJ, Agre P. 1994. Mutations in Aquaporin-1 in phenotypically normal humans without functional CHIP water channels. *Science* 265:1585–87

115. Prockop LD. 1995. Hydrocephalus. See Ref. 119a, pp. 294–302

116. Raina S, Preston GM, Guggino WB, Agre P. 1995. Molecular cloning and characterization of an aquaporin cDNA from salivary, lacrimal, and respiratory tissues. *J. Biol. Chem.* 270:1908–12

117. Reizer J, Reizer A, Saier MH. 1993. The MIP family of integral membrane channel proteins: sequence comparisons, evolutionary relationships, reconstructed pathways of evolution, and proposed functional differentiation of the two repeated halves of the proteins. *Crit. Rev. Biochem. Mol. Biol.* 28:235–57

118. Roberts SK, Yano M, Ueno Y, Pham L, Alpini G, et al. 1994. Cholangiocytes express the aquaporin CHIP and transport water via a channel-mediated mechanism. *Proc. Natl. Acad. Sci. USA* 91:13009–13

119. Rosenthal W, Seibold A, Antaramian A, Lonergan M, Arthus M, et al. 1992. Molecular identification of the gene responsible for congenital nephrogenic diabetes insipidus. *Nature* 359:233–35

119a. Rowland LP, ed. 1995. *Merrit's Textbook of Neurology*. Malvern, PA: Williams & Wilkins

120. Sabolic I, Katsura T, Verbavatz JM, Brown D. 1995. The AQP2 water channel: effect of vasopressin treatment, microtubule disruption, and distribution in neonatal rats. *J. Membr. Biol.* 143:165–75

121. Saboori AM, Smith BL, Agre P. 1988. Polymorphism in the $M_r$ 32,000 Rh protein purified from Rh(D)- positive and -negative erythrocytes. *Proc. Natl. Acad. Sci. USA* 85:4042–45

121a. Sasaki S, Fushimi K, Uchida S, Marumo F. 1992. Regulation and localization of two types of water channels in the rat kidney. *J. Am. Soc. Nephrol.* 3:798 (Abstr.)

122. Schoene RB, Hackett PH, Hornbein TF. 1994. High altitude. See Ref. 90a, pp. 2062–98

123. Segal MB. 1993. Extracellular and cerebrospinal fluids. *J. Inher. Metab. Dis.* 16:617–38

123a. Seldin DW, Giebisch G, eds. 1992. *The Kidney: Physiology and Pathophysiology*. New York: Raven

124. Shiels A, Griffin CS. 1993. Aberrant expression of the gene for lens major intrinsic protein in the CAT mouse. *Curr. Eye Res.* 12:913–21

125. Sibilia M, Wagner EF. 1995. Strain-dependent epithelial defects in mice lacking the EGF receptor. *Science* 269: 234–38

126. Siebinga I, Vrensen GFJM, de Mul FFM, Greve J. 1991. Age-related changes in local water and protein content of human eye lenses measured by Raman microspectroscopy. *Exp. Eye Res.* 53:233–39

127. Simkin PA. 1988. Joints: structure and function. In *Primer on the Rheumatic Diseases*, ed. HR Schumacher, Jr. pp. 18–23. Atlanta: Arthritis Found. 9th ed.

128. Simpson WKH. 1973. Anti-Coa and severe haemolytic disease of the newborn. *S. Afr. Med. J.* 47:1302–4

129. Smith BL, Agre P. 1991. Erythrocyte $M_r$ 28,000 transmembrane protein exists as a multi-subunit oligomer similar to channel proteins. *J. Biol. Chem.* 266: 6407–15

130. Smith BL, Baumgarten R, Nielsen S, Raben DM, Zeidel ML, Agre P. 1993. Concurrent expression of erythroid and renal Aquaporin CHIP and appearance

of water channel activity in perinatal rats. *J. Clin. Invest.* 92:2035–41

131. Smith BL, Preston GM, Spring FA, Anstee DJ, Agre P. 1994. Human red cell Aquaporin CHIP: I. Molecular characterization of ABH and Colton blood group antigens. *J. Clin. Invest.* 94:1043–49

132. Solomon AK, Chasan B, Dix JA, Lukacovic MF, Toon MR, Verkman AS. 1983. The aqueous pore in the red cell membrane. *Ann. NY Acad. Sci.* 414:97–124

133. Stamer WD, Snyder RW, Smith BL, Agre P, Regan JW. 1994. Localization of Aquaporin CHIP in the human eye: implications in the pathogenesis of glaucoma and other disorders of ocular fluid balance. *Inves. Ophthal. Vis. Sci.* 35: 3867–72

134. Stankovic KM, Adams JC, Brown D. 1995. Immunolocalization of aquaporin CHIP in the guinea pig inner ear. *Am. J. Physiol.* In press

135. Strange K, Spring KR. 1987. Cell membrane water permeability of rabbit cortical collecting duct. *J. Membr. Biol.* 96:27–43

136. Staub NC, Nagano H, Pearce ML. 1967. Pulmonary edema in dogs, especially the sequence of fluid accumulation in lungs. *J. Appl. Physiol.* 22:227–40

137. Stutts MJ, Canessa CM, Olsen JC, Hamrick M, Cohn JA, et al. 1995. CFTR as a cAMP-dependent regulator of sodium channels. *Science* 269:847–50

138. Talal N. 1988. Sjögren's syndrome. In *Primer on the Rheumatic Diseases*, ed. HR Schumacher, Jr., pp. 136–38. Atlanta: Arthritis Found. 9th ed.

139. Threadgill DW, Dlugosz AA, Hansen LA, Tennenbaum T, Lichti U, et al. 1995. Targeted disruption of mouse EGF receptor: effect of genetic background on mutant phenotype. *Science* 269:230–34

140. Deleted in proof

141. Van Hoek AN, Hom ML, Luthjens LH, de Jong MD, Dempster JA, van Os CH. 1991. Functional unit of 30 kDa for proximal tubule water channels as revealed by radiation inactivation. *J. Biol. Chem.* 266:16633–35

142. Van Hoek AN, Luthjens LH, Hom ML, van Os CH, Dempster JA. 1992. A 30 kDa functional size for the erythrocyte water channel determined by in situ radiation inactivation. *Biochem. Biophys. Res. Comm.* 184:1331–38

143. Van Lieburg AF, Verdijk MAJ, Knoers VVAM, van Essen AJ, Proesmans W, et al. 1994. Patients with autosomal nephrogenic diabetes insipidus homozy-

gous for mutations in the aquaporin-2 water-channel gene. *Am. J. Hum. Genet.* 55:648–52

144. Van Os CH, Deen PMT, Dempster JA. 1994. Aquaporins: water selective channels in biological membranes. *Biochim. Biophys. Acta* 1197:291–309

145. Verbavatz JM, Brown D, Sabolic I, Valenti G, Ausiello DA, et al. 1993. Tetrameric assembly of CHIP28 water channels in liposomes and cell membranes: a freeze-fracture study. *J. Cell. Biol.* 123:605–18

146. Wade JB, Stetson DL, Lewis SA. 1981. ADH action: evidence for a membrane shuttle hypothesis. *Ann. NY Acad. Sci.* 372:106–17

147. Walz T, Smith BL, Zeidel ML, Engel A, Agre P. 1994. Biologically active two-dimensional crystals of Aquaporin CHIP. *J. Biol. Chem.* 269: 1583–86

148. Warren DW. 1994. Hormonal influences on the lacrimal gland. *Int. Ophthalmol. Clin.* 34:19–25

149. Whittembury G, Carpi-Medina P, Gonzalez E, Linares H. 1984. Effect of para-chloromercuribenzenesulfonic acid and temperature on cell water osmotic permeability of proximal straight tubules. *Biochim. Biophys. Acta* 775:365–73

150. Wiener-Kronish JP, Broaddus VC. 1993. Interrelationship of pleural and pulmonary interstitial liquid. *Annu. Rev. Physiol.* 55:209–26

151. Willumsen NJ, Davis CW, Boucher RC. 1994. Selective response of human airway epithelia to luminal but not serosal solution hypertonicity. *J. Clin. Invest.* 94:779–87

152. Yager D, Kamm RD, Drazen JM. 1995. Airway wall liquid: sources and role as an amplifier of bronchoconstriction. *Chest* 107:105S–10

153. You G, Smith CP, Kanal Y, Lee W, Steizner M, Hediger MA. 1993. Cloning and characterization of the vasopressin-regulated urea transporter. *Nature* 365: 844–47

154. Zampighi GA, Hall JE, Ehring GR, Simon SA. 1989. The structural organization and protein composition of lens fiber junctions. *J. Cell Biol.* 108:2255–75

155. Zeidel ML, Ambudkar SV, Smith BL, Agre P. 1992. Reconstitution of functional water channels in liposomes containing purified red cell CHIP28 protein. *Biochemistry* 31:7436–40

156. Zeidel ML, Nielsen S, Smith BL, Ambudkar SV, Maunsbach AB, Agre P. 1994. Ultrastructure, pharmacologic in-

hibition, and transport-selectivity of Aquaporin CHIP in proteoliposomes. *Biochemistry* 33:1606–15

157. Zelinski T, Kaita H, Gilson T, Coghlan G, Philips S, Lewis M. 1990. Linkage between the Colton blood group locus and ASSP11 on chromosome 7. *Genomics* 6:623–25

158. Zerbe R, Stropes L, Robertson G. 1980.

Vasopressin function in the syndrome of inappropriate antidiuresis. *Annu. Rev. Med.* 31:315–27

159. Zhang R, van Hoek AN, Biwersi J, Verkman AS. 1993. Mutation at cysteine 189 blocks the water permeability of rat kidney water channel CHIP28k. *Biochemistry* 32:2938–41

Annu. Rev. Physiol. 1996. 58:649–68

# MOLECULAR MECHANISMS OF NaCl COTRANSPORT

*Mark R. Kaplan, David B. Mount, and Eric Delpire*

Laboratory of Molecular Physiology and Biophysics, Renal Division, Department of Medicine, Brigham & Women's Hospital and Harvard Medical School, Boston, Massachusetts 02115

*Gerardo Gamba*

Department of Nephrology, Instituto Nacional de la Nutricion Salvador Zubiran, Vasco de Quiroga No. 15, Tlalpan 14000, Mexico, DF, Mexico

*Steven C. Hebert*

Laboratory of Molecular Physiology and Biophysics, Renal Division, Department of Medicine, Brigham & Women's Hospital and Harvard Medical School, Boston, Massachusetts 02115

KEY WORDS:    cloning, electroneutral, ion transport, regulation, diuretic sensitivity

## ABSTRACT

Electroneutral Na-(K)-Cl cotransporters are present in most cell types, where they play an important role in both sodium-chloride absorption and secretion and cell volume regulation. Recent advances in the molecular identification of these cotransporters have provided a new level of insight into the mechanisms of sodium-chloride-coupled cotransport and its regulation. Here we review what is known about the Na-(K)-Cl cotransporters cloned to date and what can be deduced about their structure and function and summarize recent physiological investigations of the regulation of Na-(K)-Cl cotransport. These studies represent the beginning of an exciting and rapidly expanding field examining the molecular mechanisms of sodium-chloride-coupled cotransport.

## INTRODUCTION

Major advances have been made over the past few years in the molecular identification of the major electroneutral sodium-chloride-coupled entry mechanisms expressed in epithelial and other cells. This information is already advancing our understanding of the evolution, structure, and function of these

649

transporters. In this review, we discuss these new developments with particular emphasis on describing the molecular structure and localization of the bumetanide-sensitive $Na^+$-$K^+$-$2Cl^-$ and thiazide-sensitive $Na^+$-$Cl^-$ cotransporters. These sodium-(potassium)-chloride cotransporters represent the major target sites for clinically useful diuretics including the "loop" diuretics [furosemide (Lasix®) and bumetanide (Bumex®)] and the benzothiadiazines [or thiazides like chlorothiazide (Diuril®)]. Armed with probes (nucleotide, antibodies, etc) generated from these newly discovered molecules, we anticipate that future studies will significantly expand our understanding of the regulation and localization of these cotransporters in both renal and nonrenal epithelia as well as in non-epithelial cells.

## The Electroneutral Sodium-(Potassium)-Chloride Cotransporters: General Types and Functions

Three groups of electroneutral sodium-chloride transport systems have been identified and can be grouped according to whether $K^+$ accompanies $Na^+$ and $Cl^-$ in the transport process and to their sensitivities to specific classes of inhibitors (Figure 1): (a) the benzothiadiazine (or thiazide)-sensitive $Na^+$:$Cl^-$ cotransporter (TSC) (13, 21, 48, 84); (b) the sulfamoylbenzoic acid (or bumetanide)-sensitive $Na^+$:$K^+$:$2Cl^-$ and $Na^+$:$Cl^-$ symporters (BSC,NKCC) (28, 34, 77); and (c) the synchronous operation of the amiloride-sensitive $Na^+$:$H^+$ antiporter and the stilbene-sensitive $Cl^-$:$HCO_3^-$ exchanger (47, 82). The latter electroneutral mechanism requires the synchronous function of two distinct and unrelated membrane proteins, the $Na^+$:$H^+$ antiporter and the $Cl^-$:$HCO_3^-$ exchanger (11, 41, 72, 80, 81), and thus is not a true coupled sodium-chloride cotransporter. This double exchanger system, however, can be inhibited by thiazides via their action on carbonic anhydrase (24) (see Figure 1). This has led to some confusion in the literature because inhibition of NaCl transport by thiazides cannot be used, by itself, to distinguish between true $Na^+$-$Cl^-$ cotransport and synchronous operation of $Na^+$:$H^+$ and $Cl^-$:$HCO_3^-$ exchangers.

The electroneutral $Na^+$-$(K^+)$-$Cl^-$ cotransporters are nearly ubiquitously expressed and function in the maintenance and regulation of cell volume during hypertonic challenges, during cell growth, and with other cell volume perturbations (27, 37) (see Figure 2). In addition, these cotransporters provide the major chloride entry mechanisms present in most chloride absorptive (e.g. in distal renal tubules) and secretory (e.g. in salivary glands) epithelia (Figure 2). Both electroneutral $Na^+$-$(K^+)$-$Cl^-$ cotransporters are expressed in the mammalian kidney where they function in NaCl reabsorption, providing critical components of the mechanisms responsible for divalent mineral ion ($Ca^{2+}$ and $Mg^{2+}$) reabsorption, in urine dilution, and in the countercurrent multiplication mechanism required for urine concentration (38). In the mammalian kidney,

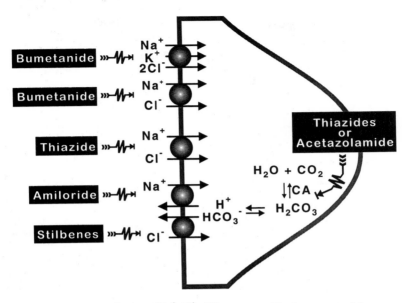

*Figure 1*  Functional classification of $Na^+$-$(K^+)$-$Cl^-$ cotransport. The three groups of electroneutral $Na^+$-$(K^+)$-$Cl^-$ cotransporters are distinguished by their $K^+$ dependence and diuretic sensitivity. Only bumetanide-inhibitable cotransport, which is ubiquitous, is dependent on potassium, although some bumetanide-inhibitable cotransport is not potassium dependent. Thiazides inhibit a simple $Na^+$-$Cl^-$ cotransporter, studied mostly in the distal convoluted tubule of the nephron. The $Na^+$-$H^+$ antiporter that operates in parallel to the $Cl^-$-$HCO_3^-$ exchanger is inhibited directly by amiloride or stilbenes and indirectly by acetazolamide or thiazides, which inhibit carbonic anhydrase.

the bumetanide-sensitive $Na^+$-$K^+$-$2Cl^-$ and thiazide-sensitive $Na^+$-$Cl^-$ cotransporters are located on apical membranes of thick ascending limbs (TALs) (7, 29, 74–76, 88) and distal convoluted tubules, respectively. The molecular cloning of these renal $Na^+$-$(K^+)$-$Cl^-$ cotransporters should provide new and important insights into the pharmacological and hormonal regulation of $Na^+$-$(K^+)$-$Cl^-$ cotransport. These latter issues are briefly discussed herein, although a clear understanding will require future studies.

## MOLECULAR ASPECTS OF THE $Na^+$-$(K^+)$-$Cl^-$ COTRANSPORTERS

### *Cloning of the $Na^+$-$(K^+)$-$Cl^-$ Cotransporters*

Molecular identification of the electroneutral $Na^+$-$(K^+)$-$Cl^-$ cotransporters began with the cloning of molecules from different marine species, harkening

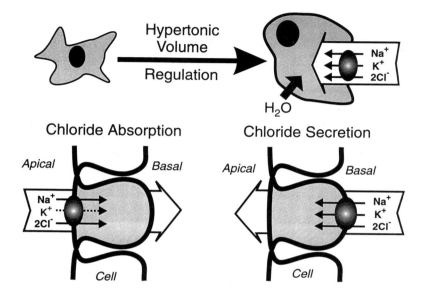

*Figure 2*   Electroneutral Na$^+$-K$^+$-2Cl$^-$ cotransport in volume regulation, absorption, and secretion. In the upper part of the figure a Na$^+$-K$^+$-2Cl$^-$ cotransporter is depicted on a cell membrane where it is important in cell volume regulation. Under conditions of hypertonic cell shrinkage, the Na$^+$-K$^+$-2Cl$^-$ cotransporter can rapidly increase intracellular tonicity, drive H$_2$O into the cell, and return cell volume to normal. Also depicted are two epithelial cells with transmembrane Na$^+$-K$^+$-2Cl$^-$ cotransporters. Apical cotransporters are responsible for NaCl and fluid reabsorption in the distal nephron, whereas basolateral cotransporters provide Cl$^-$ for apical secretion through Cl$^-$ channels in secretory epithelia.

back to the elegant studies in fish by HW Smith. These fish cDNAs were then used to isolate similar molecules from mammalian cells. Gamba and coworkers used an expression cloning strategy in *Xenopus laevis* oocytes to isolate a 3.7-kb cDNA (flTSC) (26) encoding an electroneutral thiazide-sensitive co-transporter from the urinary bladder of the winter flounder *Pseudopleuronectes americanus*. The winter flounder urinary bladder is anatomically and function-ally an extension of the teleost mesonephric kidney and, like the mammalian renal distal tubule, absorbs NaCl via a thiazide-sensitive Na$^+$-Cl$^-$ cotransport mechanism. The extensive similarities in the functional and pharmacological characteristics of the NaCl absorption processes in the rat distal convoluted tubule and the flounder urinary bladder suggested that Na$^+$-Cl$^-$ cotransport expressed in these epithelia may be similar (74). Thus the flounder TSC cDNA obtained by expression cloning was used in an homology-based screening strategy to isolate an ~4.4.-kb cDNA encoding the apical thiazide-sensitive Na$^+$-Cl$^-$ cotransporter from rat kidney cortex (rTSC1) (25) and the ~4.7-kb cDNAs encoding the apical bumetanide-sensitive Na$^+$-K$^+$-2Cl$^-$ cotransporters from rat (rBSC1) (25) and mouse (mBSC1) (2) kidney outer medullas. Moreover, degenerate PCR primers designed from regions of high homology between flTSC, rTSC1, and rBSC1 were more recently used to amplify a product from a mouse IMCD cell line, and this DNA fragment was then used to isolate a basolateral (secretory) form of the Na$^+$-K$^+$-2Cl$^-$ cotransporter (mBSC2) (17).

A different cloning approach was employed by Forbush and coworkers (92). They first isolated and purified an ~195-kDa benzmetanide-binding protein from the Cl$^-$ secretory epithelium of the rectal gland of the dogfish shark *Squalus acanthias* and then raised antibodies against the isolated protein and used these antibodies to screen an expression library. Using this strategy, these investigators isolated an ~4.8-kb cDNA (NKCC1) (92) encoding a basolateral or secretory-type Na$^+$-K$^+$-2Cl$^-$ cotransporter from the shark rectal gland. NKCC1 cDNA was then used to clone, by homology, a cDNA (NKCC2) (66) believed to encode a renal absorptive Na$^+$-K$^+$-2Cl$^-$ cotransporter from rabbit kidney cortex and medulla. Subsequently, the latter cDNA was used to clone a similar molecule from mouse kidney (42).

## The Na$^+$-(K$^+$)-Cl$^-$ Cotransporter Family

These electroneutral Na$^+$-(K$^+$)-Cl$^-$ cotransporters establish a new family of transport proteins that share a remarkable degree of similarity in amino acid sequence and proposed topology despite their differences in number and types of ions transported and sensitivities to inhibitors (see Table 1 and Figures 3 and 4). All these proteins have predicted molecular weights for the unglycosylated core protein of between 110–130, and each contains at least one, and up to nine, potential N-linked glycosylation sites, consistent with the higher molecular weight found on Western blots using cotransporter isoform-specific antibodies (see below). The basic topology of these cotransporters deduced from hydropathy analyses (see Figure 3) consists of a central hydrophobic core region containing possibly 12 membrane-spanning segments between large hydrophilic (and putatively intracellular) amino and carboxyl termini. The overall sequence identity among the cotransporter proteins is approximately 45–50%; greatest in the hydrophobic core and the carboxy-terminus and lowest in the amino terminus (Figure 3).

An homology tree of the deduced Na$^+$-(K$^+$)-Cl$^-$ cotransporter proteins is depicted in Figure 4 and shows that the vertebrate cotransporters form three distinct subgroups (also, see Figure 5). We propose to name these subgroups ENCC1, ENCC2, and ENCC3 (Electroneutral Sodium-Chloride Cotransporters). Table 1 provides the basic description of these subgroups and the original names used for these cDNAs (and proteins). The ENCC1 subgroup is formed by the mammalian renal and teleost thiazide-sensitive Na$^+$-Cl$^-$ cotransporters,

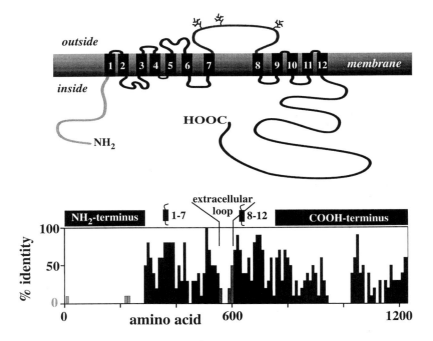

*Figure 3* Molecular structure of Na$^+$-(K$^+$)-Cl$^-$ cotransporters. Membrane topology of the Na$^+$-(K$^+$)-Cl$^-$ cotransporters by hydropathy analysis of the amino acid sequence shows 12 hydrophobic membrane-spanning segments and long hydrophilic, intracellular amino and carboxyl termini. Three N-linked glycosylation sites are depicted on the large extracellular loop between the seventh and eighth membrane-spanning segments. The identity bar graph comparing amino acid sequences of the thiazide-sensitive Na$^+$-Cl$^-$ cotransporter from flounder bladder (flTSC), the thiazide-sensitive Na$^+$-Cl$^-$ cotransporter from rat kidney (rTSC1), and the bumetanide-sensitive Na$^+$-K$^+$-2Cl$^-$ cotransporter from rat kidney (rBSC1) shows that the membrane-spanning segments and the carboxyl termini share the greatest homology, whereas the amino termini and the M7-M8 extracellular loop are the least homologous.

which share 62% overall amino acid identity. The ENCC2 subgroup consists of the absorptive Na$^+$-K$^+$-2Cl$^-$ cotransporters from rat, rabbit, and mouse kidney and exhibit >90% identity. The two Na$^+$-K$^+$-2Cl$^-$ cotransporters found in secretory epithelia and in certain non-epithelial cells share 72% identity and form the ENCC3 subgroup. Although the highest degrees of identity are exhibited between members within a specific ENCC subgroup, significant homology is maintained even when comparing molecules that cross vertebrate ENCC subgroups: ENCC1 vs ENCC2 (46–52%); ENCC1 vs ENCC3 (47–50%); ENCC2 vs ENCC3 (59–61%). This similarity among ENCC subgroups is obtained whether the comparisons involve fish (teleost or elasmobranch) or mammalian isoforms.

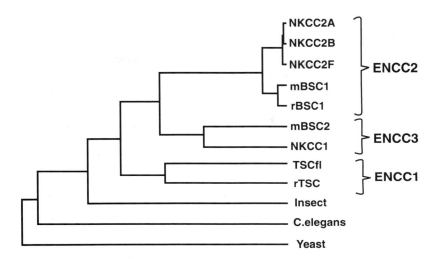

*Figure 4*  The electroneutral sodium-chloride cotransporter (ENCC) family. A homology tree of the cloned $Na^+$-$(K^+)$-$Cl^-$ cotransporters based on amino acid sequences shows that the vertebrate $Na^+$-$(K^+)$-$Cl^-$ cotransporters cloned thus far can be divided into three major groups: ENCC1, ENCC2, and ENCC3. For homology comparisons and further explanation, see Figure 5 and text. More distant family members include certain insect, *C. elegans*, and yeast genes, yet to be functionally characterized.

In addition to the vertebrate members of the electroneutral $Na^+$-$(K^+)$-$Cl^-$ cotransporter family, Figure 4 shows a more distant homology to genes of uncertain functional significance from the Malphigian tubule of *Manduca sexta* (an insect), *Caenorhabditis elegans* (a nematode), and *Saccharomyces cerevisiae* (baker's yeast). These invertebrate proteins share 37%, 17%, and 16% identity, respectively, with ENCC2 (rBSC1). The amino-terminal region and first three membrane-spanning segments of flTSC (ENCC1) also have significant homology with a 128-amino acid hypothetical protein from cyanobacterium *Synechococcus* sp. (8). Thus the vertebrate ENCCs appear to have evolved from an ancient ancestral gene expressed in primitive eukaryotes.

The BSC1 and BSC2 cotransporter transcripts clearly arise from different genes and not splice variants of a single gene because the ENCC2 and ENCC3 genes in mouse have been localized to different chromosomes (2 and 18, respectively) (17). Molecular diversity of $Na^+$-$(K^+)$-$Cl^-$ cotransporters in mammals is, however, increased by alternative splicing. Payne & Forbush (66) reported splice variations in the $Na^+$-$K^+$-$2Cl^-$ cotransporter from rabbit kidney, where they found three variable cassette exons (NKCC2A, NKCC2B, and NKCC2F exhibiting 69% identity; Figure 4; Table 1) for a 96-base pair region

**Table 1**   The electroneutral sodium chloride cotransporter (ENCC) gene family

| Proposed gene name | Primary functions | Diuretic sensitivity | Original name | Source of cDNA | Amino acid number, predicted $M_r$ | References |
|---|---|---|---|---|---|---|
| ENCC1 | NaCl cotransport in absorptive epithelia | Thiazides | TSCfl | Flounder urinary bladder | 1023 112-kDa | 25 |
| | | | rTSC | Rat kidney | 1002 110-kDa | 26 |
| ENCC2 | NaKCl cotransport in absorptive epithelia | Bumetanide | BSC1 | Rat kidney (mouse kidney) | 1095 120-kDa | 26 |
| | | | NKCC2 | Rabbit kidney | 1099 121 kDa | 66 |
| ENCC3 | NaKCl cotransport in secretory epithelia or volume regulation during cell shrinkage | Bumetanide | BSC2 | Mouse IMCD3 cells | 1205 130-kDa | 17 |
| | | | NKCC1 | Shark rectal gland | 1192 130-kDa | 92 |

including the second membrane-spanning segment (see Figure 3). Northern blot analysis of the A, B, and F isoforms shows differential transcript expression in the kidney, with NKCC2F found principally in the outer medulla, NKCC2B found only in the cortex, and NKCC2A found in both cortex and outer medulla (66). Ellison and coworkers have recently reported a splice variation in the mouse thiazide-sensitive cotransporter involving an in-frame deletion of 105-base pairs spanning the putative fourth membrane-spanning segment (49), and we have reported finding two fully functional but different-sized rTSC1 clones (rTSC1a ~4.4 kb and rTSC1b ~3.3 kb) differing only by a truncated 3' untranslated region of 231-base pairs (25). In cloning rTSC1, A Miyanoshita and coworkers (unpublished data) also found three additional cDNAs of 3.9 kb, 5.4 kb, and 5.6 kb. The functional significance of these splice isoforms of the ENCC1 and ENCC2 subgroup members remains to be established.

## Na-(K)-Cl Cotransporter Transcript and Protein Localization

The ENCC3-type $Na^+-K^+-2Cl^-$ cotransporters appear to be widely expressed in shark (92) and mammals (17). In the dogfish shark, the rectal gland and many other shark tissues (brain, gill, intestine, heart, kidney, liver, and testis)

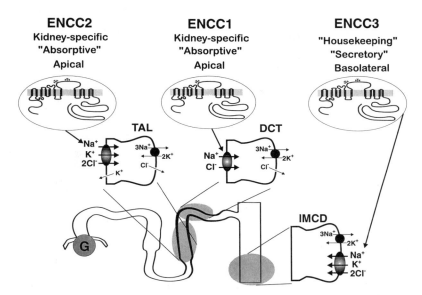

*Figure 5*  Electroneutral sodium-(potassium)-chloride cotransporters in the mammalian kidney. The diagram shows renal localization of the ENCC family members: the thiazide-sensitive $Na^+$-$Cl^-$ cotransporter (electroneutral sodium-chloride cotransporter 1, ENCC1) found in the flounder bladder or the distal convoluted tubule of the mammalian nephron; the apical, absorptive bumetanide-sensitive $Na^+$-$K^+$-$2Cl^-$ cotransporter (ENCC2) found in the TAL of the loop of Henle; and the ubiquitous, basolateral, secretory bumetanide-sensitive $Na^+$-$K^+$-$2Cl^-$ cotransporter (ENCC3). ENCC3 member mBSC2 was cloned from a mouse IMCD cell line but is found in many other tissues.

expressed a 7.4-kb NKCC1 transcript; a smaller ~5.2-kb transcript was only found in kidney (92). The mammalian ENCC3 (mBSC2) $Na^+$-$K^+$-$2Cl^-$ cotransporter cloned from a mouse IMCD cell line was found in mouse kidney (strongest in inner medulla, presumably in the IMCD; M Kaplan et al, unpublished observations), salivary gland, stomach, colon, heart, lung, testis, brain, and skeletal muscle, as well as in several cell lines known to express $Na^+$-$K^+$-$2Cl^-$ cotransport activity (e.g. MEL, T84, and MDCK) (17). In contrast, the ENCC2-type $Na^+$-$K^+$-$2Cl^-$ cotransporters were found only in the kidney (25). By in situ hybridization, we showed that the rBSC1 (ENCC2) transcript is expressed in the outer medulla and extends into the cortex along medullary-cortical rays in a pattern consistent with expression in the medullary and cortical thick ascending limbs (see Figure 6*B*) (25). The wide tissue distribution of ENCC3 compared with the unique location of ENCC2 in the TAL suggests that these two cotransporters are under regulation by different promoters and possess different physiological functions. Polyclonal antibodies generated

**A**    **B**

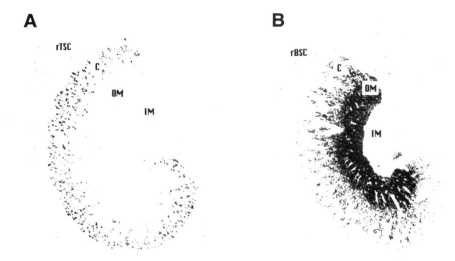

*Figure 6* Cotransporter transcript localization in the kidney. In situ hybridization in rat kidneys shows mRNA of rTSC localized to the cortex (*A*), whereas mRNA from rBSC localizes to the outer medulla and extends along medullary-cortical rays into the cortex (*B*), consistent with expression in distal convoluted tubule and thick ascending limbs, respectively. C, cortex; OM, outer medulla; IM, inner medulla.

against one of the ENCC2-type $Na^+$-$K^+$-$2Cl^-$ cotransporter proteins (rBSC1) (45) showed that this cotransporter is located along the apical aspect of epithelial cells of the medullary (MTAL) and cortical (CTAL) thick ascending limbs, in a pattern very similar to the transcript localization by in situ hybridization. In addition, a major band of ~150 kDa was found on western blots of rat kidney using this anti-rBSC1 antibody, a size in agreement with that of the major [$^3$H]BSTBA-binding protein found in dog and mouse kidney (33, 35). These localization studies, together with the functional expression studies of ENCC2 in *X. laevis* oocytes (25), strongly suggest that ENCC2 (or rBSC1) encodes the well-characterized apical, absorptive $Na^+$-$K^+$-$2Cl^-$ cotransporter in the TAL, whereas the ENCC3 (mBSC2) isoforms are apparently expressed on basolateral membranes of certain epithelia where they likely participate in salt and/or fluid secretion. In nonpolarized cells such as muscle and red cells, the basolateral ENCC3 isoform may play a role in cell volume regulation. Further localization studies of the ENCC3 $Na^+$-$K^+$-$2Cl^-$ cotransporters will be needed to define the specific tissue distribution and to verify the membrane location in epithelial cells.

In the winter flounder, a 3.7-kb mRNA encoding the ENCC1-type $Na^+$-$Cl^-$ cotransporter (flTSC) was found only in the urinary bladder (functionally analogous to the mammalian distal tubule); however, a smaller 3.0-kb transcript (identical to the 3.7-kb transcript except for a truncated amino terminus) that does not exhibit $Na^+$ uptake when expressed in *X. laevis* oocytes was found in ovary, skeletal muscle, eye, brain, and kidney (26). In contrast, on northern blots of rat tissues, the mammalian ENCC1-type $Na^+$-$Cl^-$ cotransporter mRNA was identified only in kidney. The pattern of rTSC mRNA distribution in rat kidney was consistent with expression in the distal convoluted tubule (DCT; see Figure 6A) (25), and using a ENCC1-specific polyclonal antibody, we have recently shown that the cotransporter protein is present exclusively on apical membranes of these nephron segments (67). Thus the rTSC1-type $Na^+$-$Cl^-$ cotransporter mRNA and protein localization combined with functional data in *X. laevis* oocytes indicate that the ENCC1 gene encodes the absorptive $Na^+$-$Cl^-$ cotransporter in the DCT. Although these results suggest that the ENCC1-type $Na^+$-$Cl^-$ cotransporter may be kidney specific, there is evidence for expression of a thiazide-sensitive $Na^+$-$Cl^-$ cotransporter in certain bone cells (5) and other (possibly vascular) cells (1, 12). Further studies will be needed to determine if this cotransporter is the rTSC1-type or a new member of the ENCC1 subgroup.

# REGULATION

## *General Regulation of $Na^+$-$(K^+)$-$Cl^-$ Cotransport*

On considering the existence of at least two distinct genes encoding the $Na^+$-$K^+$-$2Cl^-$ cotransporter, the expression of numerous splice variants, and the ubiquitous distribution of the ENCC3-type $Na^+$-$K^+$-$2Cl^-$ cotransporter, it seems clear, at the outset, that this cotransporter will be regulated via a wide array of different pathways. The study of both acute and chronic regulation of the cotransporter is essential in defining the physiological significance of a particular pathway in the various tissues where it is expressed. Most of the literature has focused on cotransporter regulation in acute settings. The recent cloning of the cotransporter now provides the tools (genetic, nucleotide, and antibody) to investigate its regulation at the transcriptional level and to define the pathways of regulation during chronic adaptation to changes in the cell environment. For instance, one recent study has explored the role of the basolateral isoform of the cotransporter in *Necturus maculosus* stomach and demonstrated its important role in acid secretion (73). Physiological changes occuring during meals (e.g. stomach distension, gastrin production) have been shown to up-regulate the level of mRNA encoding the cotransporter.

$Na^+$-$(K^+)$-$Cl^-$ cotransport is a passive process, consuming no energy directly, although ATP is consumed in phosphorylation processes that are required for transport (27, 32, 57), and it is generally agreed that acute regulation of

$Na^+$-$K^+$-$2Cl^-$ cotransport occurs mainly through phosphorylation/dephosphorylation mechanisms. In this regard, several potential phosphorylation sites for serine-threonine kinases [protein kinase C and cAMP-dependent protein kinase (protein kinase A (PKA)] can be identified on the ENCC2- and ENCC3-type $Na^+$-$K^+$-$2Cl^-$ cotransporters, mostly in the putative carboxyl terminus. The molecular details of phosphorylation remain to be worked out, although Forbush and coworkers have identified a peptide that becomes phosphorylated during cAMP-dependent activation of the cotransporter in shark rectal gland (54). Interestingly, this latter site is not identified using standard PKA phosphorylation motifs.

Table 2 lists various pathways of regulation found in different cell types. It is clear that diverse stimuli affect the activity of the cotransporter: volume changes, fatty acids (prostaglandin E2), growth factors (epidermal and nerve growth factors), and hormones (norepinephrine, calcitonin, parathyroid hormone, angiotensin II, vasopressin, atrial natriuretic peptide, intestinal peptide). With the exception of cell volume, all other stimuli modulate the activity of the cotransporter through receptor-mediated changes in intracellular messengers which alter the activity of a variety of kinases that affect the phosphorylation state of the cotransport protein. Although exceptions exist, a consensus can be drawn for the ubiquitous ENCC3-type isoform: Phosphorylation through protein kinase A stimulates the cotransporter, whereas phosphorylation through protein kinase C inhibits it. In some systems, cGMP has been implicated as a regulator and can lead to both inhibition and activation, depending on the cell type. Calcium has also been suggested as a potential second messenger; however, as discussed below, part of its effect may be through other transport mechanisms. Although it was known that shrinkage activated $Na^+$, $K^+$, $Cl^-$ influx before the cotransporter was identified (for review see 27), the mechanisms by which the activation take place are still not known. Whereas dephosphorylation of the cotransport protein is believed to be involved in the shrinkage activation, no consensus exists concerning the identity of the phosphatase and the pathway of action. In Ehrlich ascites tumor cells, phosphorylation through protein kinase C has been reported to be involved in transducing the volume perturbation. As also indicated in Table 2, the cytoskeleton may play an essential role in regulating the activity of the cotransporter and possibly could be part of the transduction mechanism during shrinkage activation.

Aside from metabolic pathways directly pointing to phosphorylation/dephosphorylation mechanisms as a way of regulation, there is the additional evidence that the intracellular $Cl^-$ concentration may directly modulate the activity of the $Na^+$-$K^+$-$2Cl^-$ cotransporter (36, 70). This sensitivity to internal $Cl^-$ is thought not to be the direct result of an alteration in the electrochemical driving force for turnover of the cotransporter. It is, however, difficult to determine if this modulation is due to kinetic effects such as differential

**Table 2**  Regulation of Na-(K)-Cl cotransport

| Stimulus | Messenger | Effect | Cell type | Reference |
|---|---|---|---|---|
| Volume | PKC | Activation | Ehrlich | |
| | ? | Activation | Rat brain endoth cells | 85 |
| | ? | Activation | PC12 cells | 52 |
| PGE2 | cAMP-PKA | Activation | Osteoblast | 89 |
| ? | cAMP-PKA | Activation | Shark rectal gland | 55 |
| Norepinephrine | cAMP-PKA | Activation | Parotid acinar cells | 64 |
| Carbachol | cAMP-PKA | Activation | Human labial gland ac | 83 |
| ? | cAMP-PKA | Activation | Avian salt gland | 79 |
| ? | cAMP-PKA | Activation | Rat mesangial | 40 |
| Calcitonin | cAMP-PKA | Activation | TAL | 87 |
| | cAMP-PKA | Activation | Fetal human NPCE | 15 |
| — | PKC | Activation | Rat mesangial cells | 40 |
| — | PKC | Inhibition | Bovine endothelial cells | 61 |
| — | PKC | Inhibition | Osteoblasts | 89 |
| — | PKC | Inhibition | Ocular ciliary NPEC | 14 |
| — | PKC | Inhibition | Fetal human PCEC | 86 |
| — | PKC | Inhibition | T84 cells | 59 |
| | cGMP | Activation | Rat mesangial | 40 |
| ANP | cGMP | Inhibition | Rabbit ventricular Myocytes | 9,10 |
| NGF | ? | Activation | PC12 cells | 52 |
| Endothelin | ? | Activation | Rat brain endothelial cells | 85 |
| Angiotensin | Ca | Activation | Rat mesangial cells | 40 |
| Vasopressin | Ca | Activation | Bovine endoth cells | 61 |
| Bradykinin | PhoC/Ca | Activation | Bovine endoth cells | 61 |
| Bradykinin | PhoC/Ca | Activation | Ehrlich cells | 44 |
| — | PP1 | Activation | Rat parotid acinar cells | 65 |
| — | PP1 | Activation | Avian erythrocytes | 63 |
| — | PP1 | Activation | PC12 cells | 52 |
| — | PP1 | Activation | Rat brain endoth cells | 85 |
| VIP | — | Activation | Rat colon crypt cells | 19 |
| Oxidant stress | — | Inhibition | Pulmonary VEC | 20 |
| ? | F-actin | T84 | 58 | |

affinities and selectivity of the two anion-binding sites as demonstrated by Hedge & Palfrey (39), to differential order of ion binding at the two aspects of the membrane as demonstrated for $K^+$-$Cl^-$ cotransport by Delpire & Lauf (16), or to binding of $Cl^-$ to an internal modifier site on the cotransporter protein itself of some associated subunit molecule. In $Cl^-$ secretory epithelia, mechanisms that tightly couple apical and basolateral systems must be in place, and $Cl^-$ itself may play an essential role in this coupling (70). It would be of considerable interest to determine if the apical isoform, which mediates $Na^+$-$(K^+)$-$Cl^-$ reabsorption in the distal nephron with the $Cl^-$ moving through $Cl^-$ channels on the basolateral membrane, also exhibits such a sensitivity to internal $Cl^-$. Intracellular $Cl^-$ levels have also been invoked for the differential volume regulatory responses by primary and secondary regulatory volume increases (RVIs). Indeed, the vast majority of cells, when submitted to hypertonic solution shrink, do not undergo RVI. However, when the cells are submitted to a hypotonic medium and are allowed to volume regulate (RVD) prior to a return to isosmotic saline, they first shrink and then undergo RVI. In both cases, the conditions can be set to induce identical volume reductions, and still they behave differently. A major difference between the cells in both situations is the much lower intracellular $Cl^-$ concentration in cells that undergo RVD. It would be interesting to demonstrate that the activity of the $Na^+$-$K^+$-$2Cl^-$ cotransporter is significantly increased in cells exposed to hypotonicity followed by a return to isosmotic conditions.

It is of importance to note that regulation of cotransport activity can also occur indirectly via another transport mechanism located within either the same or opposite membrane. Thus the apical $Na^+$-$K^+$-$2Cl^-$ cotransporter in the TAL is closely modulated by the activity of the apical $K^+$ channel (38). In this system, it is believed that recycling of $K^+$ through the channel provides both external $K^+$ as substrate for the cotransporter and generation of an electropositive lumen, which provide a driving force for additional $Na^+$ reabsorption through the paracellular pathway. In endothelial cells, bradykinin or ATP up-regulates the $Na^+$-$K^+$-$2Cl^-$ cotransporter through activation of $Ca^{2+}$-dependent $K^+$ channels and decrease in internal $K^+$ (62).

## $Na^+$-$(K^+)$-$Cl^-$ Cotransport in the Mammalian Kidney: Types and Regulation

In addition to the well-studied $Na^+$-$K^+$-$2Cl^-$ cotransporter (ENCC2-type) present in TALs, a similar cotransport activity has been identified in several other renal cell types, including proximal tubule (68), macula densa (43, 50, 51, 53), IMCD (17, 31), and mesangial cells (40). The molecular identification of these latter cotransporters, however, is not known with certainty. Loop diuretics have long been known to affect both tubuloglomerular feedback and renin secretion,

**Table 3**  Control of Na-(K)-Cl transport in thick ascending limb

| Stimulatory | | Inhibitory | |
| --- | --- | --- | --- |
| Hormone | Species, reference | Hormone or factor | Species, reference |
| ADH | Mouse, rat (18, 77) | $PGE_2$ | Mouse (78) |
| $\beta$-adrenergic | Mouse (8) | ANF | Rat (60) |
| Calcitonin | Mouse (18) | Platelet-activating factor | Mouse (3) |
| PTH | Mouse (18) | TNF | Rat (23) |
| Insulin | Mouse, rat (46,56) | Cytochrome P450 -AA metabolites | Rabbit (22) |
| Mineralocorticoid | Mouse (30) | ? $Ca^{2+}$ | Mouse (78) |
| | | Acidosis | Rabbit (91) |
| | | Adenosine | Rat (6) |

and a direct functional role for $Na^+$-$K^+$-$2Cl^-$ cotransport in both of these processes has been demonstrated (43, 53). In addition, using both direct (cell impalement; 50) and indirect (measurement of intracellular pH; 51) techniques, bumetanide-sensitive $Na^+$-$K^+$-$2Cl^-$ cotransport has been detected in macula densa cells. The molecular identity of the macula densa cotransporter is unknown. The "basolateral-type" $Na^+$-$K^+$-$2Cl^-$ cotransporter (see Figure 5) (ENCC3-type; mBSC2) activity has been described in suspensions of rat IMCD cells (31); however, the contribution of this cotransporter to salt handling by the IMCD is as yet unclear, although its activation may be involved in the natriuresis induced by ANP (71). There is preliminary evidence for the stimulation of basolateral loop diuretic-sensitive $Na^+$-$K^+$-$2Cl^-$ cotransport in the proximal tubule in hyperosmotic conditions (90), and primary cultures of proximal tubular cells exhibit an osmotically sensitive $Na^+$-$K^+$-$2Cl^-$ cotransporter (68). In primary culture, rat mesangial cells have bumetanide-sensitive $Na^+$-$K^+$-$2Cl^-$ cotransport, which can be activated by vasopressin and angiotensin II, but the physiological role of this cotransporter is unknown (40).

Sodium chloride reabsorption by the TAL is regulated by a number of factors (see Table 3). Those hormones that activate cAMP-dependent pathways are stimulatory, and other factors such as $PGE_2$ and extracellular $Ca^{2+}$ can abrogate this stimulation via activation of $G_i$ (78). The recently cloned receptor for extracellular $Ca^{2+}$ (69) is expressed in the TAL (D Riccardi & SC Hebert, unpublished results), where it could potentially activate PKC via $G_q$ or inactivate PKA via $G_i$; both effects would be expected to decrease NaCl transport. Any component of the salt transport machinery within the TAL is a potential target for regulation. For example, pharmacological doses of mineralocorticoid can activate MTAL sodium transport via an effect on the MTAL $Na^+/K^+$-ATPase (30). In contrast, the negative influence of tumor necrosis factor (TNF) may be mediated by inhibition of $Na^+/K^+$-ATPase (23). Vasopressin has been shown to directly activate MTAL $Na^+$-$K^+$-$2Cl^-$ cotransport (90), and at least in the mouse MTAL, $Na^+$-$Cl^-$ cotransport is converted to the more energy efficient $Na^+$-$K^+$-$2Cl^-$ cotransport under the influence of vasopressin. Conversely, cytochrome P450-dependent metabolites of arachidonic acid appear to inhibit $Na^+$-$K^+$-$2Cl^-$ cotransport (22).

## SUMMARY

Electroneutral $Na^+$-$(K^+)$-$Cl^-$ cotransport has been well-characterized over the past fifteen years ever since it was first described by Geck and coworkers in 1980 (28). The molecular identification and isolation of specific cDNAs encoding the cotransport proteins should provide a wealth of new insights into the mechanisms of $Na^+$-$(K^+)$-$Cl^-$ cotransport and its complicated regulation. This review summarizes very early knowledge regarding the molecular aspects of NaCl cotransport in what promises to be a fast-growing field exploring NaCl handling by epithelial and non-epithelial cells and the interplay between $Na^+$-$(K^+)$-$Cl^-$ cotransport and other ion transport and regulatory systems.

ACKNOWLEDGMENTS

This work was supported by grants from the National Institutes of Health to SCH (DK45792 and DK36803), to MRK (DK08898), to DBM (DK02328), and to ED (HL45291), and by a grant from CONACYT (2036-M and 3840-M) to GG. We are grateful to the members of the Laboratory of Molecular Physiology and Biophysics, Renal Division, Brigham and Women's Hospital for valuable discussions and input.

*Literature Cited*

1. Aleksandro D, Wysznacka W, Gajewski J. 1959. Influence of chlorothiazide upon arterial responsiveness to nor-epinephrine in hypertensive subjects. *New Engl. J. Med.* 261:1052–55
2. Baekgard A, Lombardi M, Hebert SC. 1994. Cloning and characterization of the bumetanide-sensitive Na-(K)-Cl cotransporter from mouse kidney outer medulla. *J. Am. Soc. Nephrol.* 5:282 (Abstr.)
3. Bailly C, Barlet-Bas C, Amiel C. 1992. Platelet activating factor inhibits Cl and K transport in the medullary thick ascending limb. *Kidney Int.* 41:269–74
4. Bailly C, Imbert-Teboul M, Roinel N, Amiel C. 1990. Isoproterenol increases Ca, Mg, and NaCl reabsorption in mouse thick ascending limb. *Am. J. Physiol.* 258-27:F1224–31
5. Barry ELR, Gesek FA, Friedman PA. 1994. Expression of the thiazide-sensi-

tive Na:Cl cotransporter in osteoblast-like cells. *J. Am. Soc. Nephrol.* 5:282 (Abstr.)

6. Beach RE, Good DW. 1992. Effects of adenosine on ion transport in rat medullary thick ascending limb. *Am. J. Physiol.* 263–32:F482–87

7. Burg MB. 1982. Thick ascending limb of Henle's loop. *Kidney Int.* 22:454–64

8. Cantrell A, Bryant DA. 1987. Molecular cloning and nucleotide sequence of the psaA and psaB genes for the cyanobacterium *Synechoccus* sp. PCC. 7002. *Plant Mol. Biol.* 9:453–68

9. Clemo HF, Baumgarten CM. 1991. Atrial natriuretic factor decreases cell volume of rabbit atrial and ventricular myocytes. *Am. J. Physiol.* 260:C681–90

10. Clemo HF, Feher JJ, Baumgarten CM. 1992. Modulation of rabbit ventricular cell volume and $Na^+/K^+/2Cl^-$ cotransport by cGMP and atrial natriuretic factor. *J. Gen. Physiol.* 100:89–114

11. Collins JF, Honda T, Knobel S, Bulus NM, Conary J, et al. 1993. Molecular cloning, sequencing, tissue distribution, and functional expression of a $Na^+/H^+$ exchanger (NHE2). *Proc. Natl. Acad. Sci. USA* 90:3938–42

12. Conway J, Palermo H. 1963. The vascular effect of the thiazide diuretics. *Arch. Int. Med.* 111:203–7

13. Costanzo LS. 1985. Localization of diuretic action in microperfused rat distal tubules: Ca and Na transport. *Am. J. Physiol.* 248:F527–35

14. Crook RB, Polansky JR. 1994. Stimulation of $Na^+,K^+,Cl^-$ cotransport by forskolin-activated adenylyl cyclase in fetal human nonpigmented epithelial cells. *Invest. Ophthalmol. Vis. Sci.* 35: 3374–83

15. Crook RB, von Brauchitsch DK, Polansky JR. 1992. Potassium transport in nonpigmented epithelial cells of ocular ciliary body: inhibition of a $Na^+$, $K^+$, $Cl^-$ cotransporter by protein kinase C. *J. Cell. Physiol.* 153:214–20

16. Delpire E, Lauf PK. 1991. Kinetics of Cl-dependent K fluxes in hypotonically swollen low K sheep erythrocytes. *J. Gen. Physiol.* 97:173–93

17. Delpire E, Rauchman MI, Beier DR, Hebert SC, Gullans SR. 1994. Molecular cloning and chromosomal localization of a putative basolateral $Na^+$-$K^+$-$2Cl^-$ cotransporter from mouse inner medullary collecting duct (mIMCD-3) cells. *J. Biol. Chem.* 269:25677–83

18. De Rouffignac C, Di Stefano A, Wittner M, Roinel N, Elalouf JM. 1991. Consequences of differential effects of ADH and other peptide hormones on thick

ascending limb of mammalian kidney. *Am. J. Physiol.* 260–29:R1023–35

19. Diener M. 1994. Segmental differences along the crypt axis in the response of cell volume to secretagogues or hypotonic medium in the rat colon. *Pflügers Arch.* 426:462–64

20. Elliott SJ, Schilling WP. 1992. Oxidant stress alters $Na^+$ pump and $Na(+)$-$K(+)$-$Cl$- cotransporter activities in vascular endothelial cells. *Am. J. Physiol.* 263: H96–102

21. Ellison DH, Valazquez H, Wright FS. 1987. Thiazide-sensitive sodium chloride cotransport in early distal tubule. *Am. J. Physiol.* 253–22:F546–54

22. Escalante B, Erlij D, Falck JR, McGiff JC. 1994. Cytochrome P-450 arachidonate metabolites affect ion fluxes in rabbit medullary thick ascending limb. *Am. J. Physiol.* 266–35:C1775–82

23. Escalante BA, Ferreri NR, Dunn CE, McGiff JC. 1994. Cytokines affect ion transport in primary cultured thick ascending limb of Henle's loop cells. *Am. J. Physiol.* 266–35:C1568–76

24. Fried TA, Kunau RT. 1986. Thiazide diuretics. In *Diuretics: Physiology, Pharmacology, and Clinical Use,* ed. JH Dirks, RAL Sutton, pp. 66–85. Philadelphia: Saunders

25. Gamba G, Miyanoshita A, Lombardi M, Lytton J, Lee W-S, et al. 1994. Molecular cloning, primary structure and characterization of two members of the mammalian electroneutral sodium-(potassium)-chloride cotransporter family expressed in kidney. *J. Biol. Chem.* 269: 17713–22

26. Gamba G, Saltzberg SN, Lombardi M, Miyanoshita A, Lytton J, et al. 1993. Primary structure and functional expression of a cDNA encoding the thiazide-sensitive, electroneutral sodium-chloride cotransporter. *Proc. Natl. Acad. Sci. USA* 90:2749–53

27. Geck P, Heinz E. 1986. The Na-K-2Cl cotransport system. *J. Membr. Biol.* 91: 97–105

28. Geck P, Pietrzyk C, Burckhardt B-C, Pfeiffer B, Heinz E. 1980. Electrically silent cotransport of Na, K and Cl in Ehrlich cells. *Biochim. Biophys. Acta* 600:432–47

29. Greger R. 1985. Ion transport mechanisms in thick ascending limb of Henle's loop of mammalian nephron. *Physiol. Rev.* 65:760–97

30. Grossman EB, Hebert SC. 1988. Modulation of Na-K-ATPase activity in the mouse medullary thick ascending limb of Henle. Effects of mineralocorticoids and sodium. *J. Clin. Invest.* 81:885–92

31. Grupp C, Pavenstadt-Grupp I, Grunewald RW, Bevan C, Stokes JB, Kinne RKH. 1989. A Na-K-Cl cotransporter in isolated rat papillary collecting duct cells. *Kidney Int.* 36:201–9

32. Haas M. 1989. Properties and diversity of (Na-K-Cl) cotransporters. *Annu. Rev. Physiol.* 51:443–57

33. Haas M, Dunham PB, Forbush B III. 1991. [$^3$H]Bumetanide binding to mouse kidney membranes: identification of corresponding membrane proteins. *Am. J. Physiol.* 260–29:C791–804

34. Haas M, Forbush B III. 1987. Na,K,Cl-cotransport system: characterization by bumetanide binding and photolabelling. *Kidney Int.* 32:S134–40

35. Haas M, Forbush B III. 1987. Photolabeling of a 150-kDa (Na+K+Cl) cotransport protein from dog kidney with a bumetanide analogue. *Am. J. Physiol.* 253–22:C243–50

36. Haas M, McBrayer DG. 1994. Na-K-Cl cotransport in nystatin-treated tracheal cells: regulation by isoproterenol, apical UTP, and [Cl]$_i$. *Am. J. Physiol.* 266:C1440–52

37. Hebert SC. 1987. Volume regulation in renal epithelial cells. *Semin. Nephrol.* 7:48–60

38. Hebert SC, Andreoli TE. 1984. Control of NaCl transport in the thick ascending limb. *Am. J. Physiol.* 246:F745–56

39. Hegde RS, Palfrey HC. 1992. Ionic effects on bumetanide binding to the activated Na/K/2Cl cotransporter: selectivity and kinetic properties of ion binding sites. *J. Membr. Biol.* 126:27–37

40. Homma T, Harris RC. 1991. Time-dependent biphasic regulation of Na+/K+/Cl− cotransport in rat glomerular mesangial cells. *J. Biol. Chem.* 266:13553–59

41. Igarashi P, Reilly RF, Hildebrandt F, Biemesderfer D, Reboucas NA, et al. 1991. Molecular biology of renal Na+-H+ exchangers. *Kidney Int.* 40:S84–89

42. Igarashi P, Vanden Heuvel GB, Quaggin SE, Payne JA, Forbush B III. 1994. Cloning, embryonic expression, and chromosomal localization of murine renal Na-K-Cl cotransporter (NKCC2). *J. Am. Soc. Nephrol.* 5:288 (Abstr.)

43. Ito S, Carretero OA. 1990. An in vitro approach to the study of macula densa-mediated glomerular hemodynamics. *Kidney Int.* 38:1206–10

44. Jensen BS, Jessen F, Hoffmann EK. 1993. Na+, K+, Cl− cotransport and its regulation in Ehrlich ascites tumor cells. Ca$^{2+}$/calmodulin and protein kinase C dependent pathways. *J. Membr. Biol.* 131:161–78

45. Kaplan MR, Plotkin MD, Lee W-S, Xu Z-C, Lytton J, Hebert SC. 1995. Apical localization of the Na-K-Cl cotransporter, rBSC1, on rat thick ascending limbs. *Kidney Int.* In press

46. Kirchner KA. 1988. Insulin increases loop segment chloride reabsorption in the euglycemic rat. *Am. J. Physiol.* 255–24:F1206–13

47. Kleyman TR, Cragoe EJ Jr. 1988. Amiloride and its analogs as tools in the study of ion transport. *J. Membr. Biol.* 105:1–21

48. Kunau RT, Weller DR, Webb HL. 1987. Clarification of the site of action of chlorothiazide in the rat nephron. *J. Clin. Invest.* 56:407–10

49. Kunchaparty S, Bernstein PL, Bartiss A, Desir GV, Reilly R, Ellison DH. 1995. Evidence for alternative splicing of the thiazide-sensitive Na-Cl transporter in mouse kidney. *FASEB J.* 9: A586 (Abstr.)

50. Lapointe J-Y, Bell PD, Cardinal J. 1990. Direct evidence for apical Na+:2Cl−:K+ cotransport in macula densa cells. *Am. J. Physiol.* 258–27:F1466–69

51. Lapointe J-Y, Laamarti A, Hurst AM, Fowler BC, Bell PD. 1995. Activation of Na:2Cl:K cotransport by luminal chloride in macula densa cells. *Kidney Int.* 47:752–57

52. Leung S, O'Donnell ME, Martinez A, Palfrey HC. 1994. Regulation by nerve growth factor and protein phosphorylation of Na/K/2Cl cotransport and cell volume in PC12 cells. *J. Biol. Chem.* 269:10581–89

53. Lorenz JN, Weihprecht H, Schnermann J, Skott O, Briggs JP. 1991. Renin release from isolated juxtaglomerular apparatus depends on macula densa chloride transport. *Am. J. Physiol.* 260–29:F486–93

54. Lytle C, Forbush B III. 1992. The Na-K-Cl cotransport protein of shark rectal gland. II. Regulation by direct phosphorylation. *J. Biol. Chem.* 267:25438–43

55. Lytle C, Forbush B III. 1987. Na-K-Cl cotransport in the shark rectal gland II. Regulation in isolated tubules. *Am. J. Physiol.* 62:C1009–17

56. Mandon B, Siga E, Chabardes D, Firsov D, Roinel N, De Rouffignac C. 1993. Insulin stimulates Na+, Cl−, Ca$^{2+}$, and Mg$^{2+}$ transports in TAL of mouse nephron: cross-potentiation with AVP. *Am. J. Physiol.* 265–34:F361–69

57. Martinez-Maldonado M, Cordova HR. 1990. Cellular and molecular aspects of the renal effects of diuretic agents. *Kidney Int.* 38:632–41

58. Matthews JB, Awtrey CS, Hecht G,

Tally KJ, Thompson RS, Madara JL. 1993. Phorbol ester sequentially downregulates cAMP-regulated basolateral and apical Cl⁻ transport pathways in T84 cells. *Am. J. Physiol.* 265:C1109–17

59. Matthews JB, Awtrey CS, Madara JL. 1992. Microfilament-dependent activation of Na⁺/K⁺/2Cl⁻ cotransport by cAMP in intestinal epithelial monolayers. *J. Clin. Invest.* 90:1608–13

60. Nonoguchi H, Tomita K, Marumo F. 1992. Effects of atrial natriuretic peptide and vasopressin on chloride transport in long- and short-looped medullary thick ascending limbs. *J. Clin. Invest.* 90:349–57

61. O'Donnell ME. 1991. Endothelial cell sodium-potassium-chloride cotransport. Evidence of regulation by $Ca^{2+}$ and protein kinase C. *J. Biol. Chem.* 266: 11559–66

62. O'Neill WC, Steinberg D. 1995. Intracellular $Ca^{2+}$ regulates Na-K-2Cl cotransport in endothelial cells via $Ca^{2+}$-dependent K⁺ channels. *FASEB J.* 9: A260 (Abstr.)

63. Palfrey HC, Pewitt B. 1993. The ATP and $Mg^{2+}$ dependence of Na⁺-K⁺-2Cl⁻ cotransport reflects a requirement for protein phosphorylation: studies using calyculin A. *Pflügers Arch.* 425:321–28

64. Paulais M, Turner RJ. 1992. Beta-adrenergic upregulation of the Na(+)-K(+)-2Cl⁻ cotransporter in rat parotid acinar cells. *J. Clin. Invest.* 89:1142–47

65. Paulais M, Turner RJ. 1992. Activation of the Na(+)-K(+)-2Cl⁻ cotransporter in rat parotid acinar cells by aluminum fluoride and phosphatase inhibitors. *J. Biol. Chem.* 267:21558–63

66. Payne JA, Forbush B III. 1994. Alternatively spliced isoforms of the putative renal Na-K-Cl cotransporter are differentially distributed within the rabbit kidney. *Proc. Natl. Acad. Sci. USA* 91: 4544–48

67. Plotkin MD, Kaplan MR, Verlander JW, Gullans SR, Hebert SC. 1995. Localization of the thiazide-sensitive NA-CL cotransporter (TSC) in the mammalian kidney. *J. Am. Soc. Nephrol.* 6:342 (Abstr.)

68. Raat NJH, Hartog A, van Os CH, Bindels RJM. 1994. Regulation of Na⁺-K⁺-2Cl⁻ cotransport activity in rabbit proximal tubule in primary culture. *Am. J. Physiol.* 267–36:F63–69

69. Riccardi D, Park J, Lee W-S, Gamba G, Brown EM, Hebert SC. 1995. Cloning and functional expression of a rat kidney extracellular calcium/polyvalent cation-sensing receptor. *Proc. Natl. Acad. Sci. USA* 92:131–35

70. Robertson MA, Foskett JK. 1994. Na⁺ transport pathways in secretory acinar cells: membrane cross talk mediated by $[Cl]_i$. *Am. J. Physiol.* 267:C146–56

71. Rocha AS, Kudo LH. 1990. Atrial peptide and cGMP effects on NaCl transport in inner medullary collecting duct. *Am. J. Physiol.* 259–28:F258–68

72. Sardet C, Franchi A, Pouysségur J. 1989. Molecular cloning, primary structure, and expression of the human growth factor-activatable Na⁺/H⁺ antiporter. *Cell* 56:271–80

73. Soybel DI, Gullans SR, Maxwell F, Delpire E. 1995. Role of basolateral Na-K-Cl cotransport in HCl secretion by amphibian gastric mucosa. *Am. J. Physiol.* 269–38:C242–49

74. Stokes JB. 1984. Sodium chloride absorption by the urinary bladder of the winter flounder. A thiazide-sensitive, electrically neutral transport system. *J. Clin. Invest.* 74:7–16

75. Stokes JB. 1989. Electroneutral NaCl transport in the distal tubule. *Kidney Int.* 36:427–33

76. Stokes JB. 1990. Sodium and potassium transport by the collecting duct. *Kidney Int.* 38:679–86

77. Sun A, Grossman EB, Lombardi M, Hebert SC. 1991. Vasopressin alters the mechanism of apical Cl⁻entry from Na⁺:Cl⁻ to Na⁺:K⁺:2Cl⁻ cotransport in mouse medullary thick ascending limb. *J. Membr. Biol.* 120:83–94

78. Takaichi K, Kurokawa K. 1988. Inhibitory guanosine triphosphate-binding protein-mediated regulation of vasopressin action in isolated single medullary tubules of mouse kidney. *J. Clin. Invest.* 82:1437–44

79. Torchia JC, Lytle C, Pon DJ, Forbush B III, Sen AK. 1992. The Na-K-Cl cotransporter of avian salt gland. Phosphorylation in response to cAMP-dependent and calcium-dependent secretagogues. *J. Biol. Chem.* 267: 25444–50

80. Tse C-M, Brant SR, Walker MS, Pouysségur J, Donowitz M. 1992. Cloning and sequencing of a rabbit cDNA encoding an intestinal and kidney-specific Na⁺/H⁺ exchanger isoform (NHE-3). *J. Biol. Chem.* 267:9340–46

81. Tse C-M, Ma AI, Yang VW, Watson AJM, Levine S, et al. 1991. Molecular cloning and expression of a cDNA encoding the rabbit ileal villus cell basolateral membrane Na⁺/H⁺ exchanger. *EMBO J.* 10:1957–67

82. Turnberg LA, Bieberdorf FA, Morawski SG, Fordtran JS. 1970. Interrelationships of chloride, bicarbonate, sodium,

and hydrogen transport in the human ileum. *J. Clin. Invest.* 49:557–67

83. Valdez IH, Paulais M, Fox PC, Turner RJ. 1994. Microfluorometric studies of intracellular $Ca^{2+}$ and $Na^+$ concentrations in normal human labial gland acini. *Am. J. Physiol.* 267:G601–7

84. Velazquez H, Good DW, Wright FS. 1984. Mutual dependence of sodium and chloride absorption by renal distal tubule. *Am. J. Physiol.* 247:F904–11

85. Vigne P, Lopez Farre A, Frelin C. 1994. Na(+)-K(+)-Cl⁻ cotransporter of brain capillary endothelial cells. Properties and regulation by endothelins, hyperosmolar solutions, calyculin A, and interleukin-1. *J. Biol. Chem.* 269:19925–30

86. von Brauchitsch DK, Crook RB. 1993. Protein kinase C regulation of a $Na^+$, $K^+$, Cl⁻ cotransporter in fetal human pigmented ciliary epithelial cells. *Exp. Eye Res.* 57:699–708

87. Vuillemin T, Teulon J, Geniteau-Legendre M, Baudouin B, Estrade S, et al. 1992. Regulation by calcitonin of $Na^+$-$K^+$-Cl⁻ cotransport in rabbit thick ascending limb cell line. *Am. J. Physiol.* 263–32:C563–72

88. Warnock DG, Eveloff JL. 1982. NaCl entry mechanisms in the luminal membrane of the renal tubule. *Am. J. Physiol.* 242:F561–74

89. Whisenant N, Zhang B-X, Khademazad M, Loessberg P, Muallem S. 1991. Regulation of Na-K-2Cl cotransport in osteoblasts. *Am. J. Physiol.* 261:C433–40

90. Whittembury G, Gutierrez A, Gonzalez E, Geibel J, Giebisch G. 1992. Hyperosmotic (30mM) urea shocks uncover a $Na^+Cl^{2+}K$ cotransport in the proximal straight tubule. *J. Am. Soc. Nephrol.* 3:801 (Abstr.)

91. Wingo CS. 1986. Effect of acidosis on chloride transport in the cortical thick ascending limb of Henle perfused in vitro. *J. Clin. Invest.* 78:1324–30

92. Xu J-C, Lytle C, Zhu TT, Payne JA, Benz E Jr, Forbush B III. 1994. Molecular cloning and functional expression of the bumetanide-sensitive Na-K-Cl cotransporter. *Proc. Natl. Acad. Sci. USA* 91:2201–5

# SPECIAL TOPIC: MOLECULAR
# MOTORS OF EUKARYOTIC CELLS

*Introduction,* H. Lee Sweeney, *Special Topic Editor*

Two of the cytoskeletal filament systems of eukaryotic cells (microtubules and microfilaments) provide the intracellular scaffolding for the directed movement and force generation of molecular motor proteins. Based on the cytoskeletal system with which they interact, two broad categories of eukaryotic molecular motors thus exist. Actin-based (microfilament) motility relies on the myosin superfamily of motor proteins, whereas tubulin-based (microtubule) motility is derived from two superfamilies of motor proteins; kinesin and dynein. All the molecular motors utilize ATP breakdown to produce strain, which results in force production and movement along either an actin filament or a microtubule.

The first described motor protein, myosin II, was naturally that of the tissue specialized for movement and force generation, muscle (2, 3, 9, 10, 14). It proved easy to isolate and study because of its high concentration and specialized organization in muscle cells. Recently, the crystal structure of the myosin II motor domain was solved (11, 12), which has allowed the wealth of biochemical data on myosin to be interpreted within the framework of a protein structure. This has led to a situation where much of our thinking about how a motor protein functions is based on myosin II and its cyclic interaction with actin in muscle.

Examination of a microtubular structure specialized for movement, the ciliary apparatus, led to the discovery of dynein, the first described microtubule-associated molecular motor (4). The large size and isoform and subunit complexity of dynein have made it difficult to produce and characterize, and thus it remains the least understood of the three classes of motors. Kinesin was the last of the three superfamilies of motor proteins to be discovered. It first was isolated as the anterograde motor of axonal transport (15). Kinesin is the smallest of the three motors and the easiest motor to produce using heterologous expression. Solution of its crystal structure is imminent, and thus understanding of its motor activity is likely to progress rapidly.

There has been an explosion in the rate of discovery of molecular motors based on the ability to use polymerase chain reaction (PCR) to amplify sequences that are homologous to the conserved regions within each of the three classes of motor proteins. In the case of myosin, the superfamily is now known to consist of at least nine distinct classes of myosin-like proteins (1, 6, 13). The cellular function of these proteins and, indeed, whether they all function as motors, has yet to be established. The situation is comparable for both the kinesin (5, 8) and dynein (7) superfamilies.

This section devoted to the molecular motors of eukaryotic cells includes a chapter that provides a synthesis of the structure of the active site of myosin II with its known biochemistry. Another presents an overview of the biophysical properties of kinesin movements on microtubules. A comparison of the enzyme kinetic properties of myosin, kinesin, and dynein is the subject of a third chapter. The last chapter summarizes studies that have utilized mutational analysis of the motor proteins to delineate aspects of their function.

## *Literature Cited*

1. Cheney RE, Riley MA, Mooseker MS. 1993. Phylogenetic analysis of the myosin superfamily. *Cell Motil. Cytoskelet.* 24:215–23
2. Engelhardt VA, Lyubimova MN. 1939. Myosin and adenosinetriphosphatase. *Nature* 144:668–70
3. Endelhardt VA, Lyubimova MN. 1942. On the mechanochemistry of muscle. *Biokhimiya* 7:205–17
4. Gibbons IR. 1963. Studies on the protein components of cilia from *Tetrahymena pyriformis*. *Proc. Natl. Acad. Sci. USA* 50:1002–10
5. Goldstein LS. 1993. With apologies to Scheherazade: tails of 1001 kinesin motors. *Annu. Rev. Genet.* 27:319–51
6. Goodson HV, Spudich JA. 1993. Molecular evolution of the myosin family: relationships derived from comparisons of amino acid sequences. *Proc. Natl. Acad. Sci. USA* 90:659–63
7. Holzbaur ELF, Vallee RB. 1994. Dyneins: molecular structure and cellular function. *Annu. Rev. Cell Biol.* 10:339–72
8. Hoyt MA. 1994. Cellular roles of kinesin and related proteins. *Curr. Opin. Cell Biol.* 6:63–68

9. Needham DM. 1942. The adenosinetriphosphatase activity of myosin preparations. *Biochem J.* 36:113–20
10. Needham DM. 1950. Myosin and adenosinetriphosphate in relation to muscle contraction. *Biochim. Biophys. Acta* 4:42–49
11. Rayment I, Holden HM, Whittaker M, Yohn CB, Lorenz M, et al. 1993. Structure of the actin-myosin complex and its implications for muscle contraction. *Science* 261:58–65
12. Rayment I, Rypniewski WR, Schmidt-Bède K, Smith R, Tomchick DR, et al. 1993. Three-dimensional structure of myosin subfragment-1: a molecular motor. *Science* 261:50–58
13. Reinhard J, Scheel AA, Diekmann D, Hall A, Ruppert C, Bèhler M. 1995. A novel type of myosin implicated in signalling by rho family GTPases. *EMBO J.* 14:697–704
14. Szent-Gyorgyi A. 1943. The contraction of myosin threads. *Stud. Inst. Med. Chem. Univ. Szeged* 1:17–28
15. Vale RD, Reese TS, Sheetz MP. 1985. Identification of a novel force-generating protein, kinesin, involved in microtubule-based motility. *Cell* 42:39–50

Annu. Rev. Physiol. 1996. 58:671–702

# THE ACTIVE SITE OF MYOSIN

*Ivan Rayment and Clyde Smith*[1]

Institute for Enzyme Research and Department of Biochemistry, University of Wisconsin, Madison, Wisconsin 53705

*Ralph G. Yount*

Department of Biochemistry and Biophysics, and Department of Chemistry, Washington State University, Pullman, Washington 99164-4660

KEY WORDS:    myosin, protein structure, chemical modification, muscle contraction

ABSTRACT

The significance of myosin has been expanded recently with the realization that it is found in every eukaryotic cell, where it has a role in cytokinesis, cell division, and vesicle transport. Advances in molecular genetics and expression systems related to myosin and actin have helped to reveal the extent of the myosin superfamily. New motility assays and techniques have provided information about the residues involved in ATP hydrolysis and the conformational change induced by nucleotide binding. The results of these techniques revealing structural and functional information combined with previous studies of the active site of myosin should provide future direction for studying this exciting and rapidly moving area of biochemistry.

## INTRODUCTION

The molecular mechanism by which myosin transduces chemical energy into directed movement has been a subject of compelling interest for many years due to its obvious role in muscle contraction. Its significance has been expanded in recent years by the realization that this molecular motor has been found in every eukaryotic cell, where it functions in such diverse roles as cytokinesis, cell division, and vesicle transport. The appreciation of the abundance of this molecular motif has been accompanied by an improvement in the tools to study it and by a vast increase in the fundamental understanding of its structure and function. Three advances have made particularly important contributions: (*a*) The application of molecular genetics and the development

[1]Present address, Department of Chemistry and Biochemistry, Massey University, Palmerston North, New Zealand.

671

0066-4278/96/0315-0671$08.00

of expression systems to myosin and actin have revealed the extent of the myosin super family and provided the tools to manipulate its function (12, 45, 59, 74, 117, 127). (b) The development of motility assays and techniques to observe the physical properties of a single or small group of molecules has provided the tools to determine the fundamental properties of this molecular motor in terms of the distance traveled per ATP hydrolyzed and the work performed (25, 44, 52, 122, 126, 144). (c) The determination of the molecular structures of both actin and myosin has provided a structural framework with which to interpret the previous biochemical and chemical studies of actomyosin (26, 27, 55, 103).

The rapid progress in recent years in our understanding of the myosin-based motility was made possible by many years of physiological, chemical and kinetic investigation. Although there is a rush to abandon earlier approaches with the availability of new techniques, the information from the previous studies, when combined with the recent findings, provides an opportunity to learn more about the molecular mechanism of muscle contraction. This review reexamines the earlier studies of the active site of myosin and combines them with the more recent structural results and proposes future directions of study for this rapidly moving area of biochemistry.

The review is organized in the following way: First the structures of the myosin head are summarized, with an emphasis on the mechanism of ATP hydrolysis and the conformational changes induced by nucleotide binding. Then the chemical studies that have provided definitive information about residues involved in the catalytic mechanism are discussed in the context of the structural information.

## STRUCTURE OF CHICKEN SKELETAL MYOSIN SUBFRAGMENT-1

The myosin molecule is highly asymmetric, consisting of two globular heads attached to a long tail. It has a molecular mass of approximately 500 kDa and is built from six polypeptide chains; two heavy chains for a total molecular mass of 400 kDa and two sets of light chains with each light chain species having a molecular mass of approximately 20 kDa. Each globular head is composed of approximately 850-amino acid residues that have one of the respective heavy chains and are associated with two of the light chains. The remaining portions of the two heavy chains assemble to form an extended coiled-coil that is nearly 1500 Å in length. The globular heads contain the nucleotide-binding sites and the actin-binding regions, whereas the long rod-like portion of myosin forms the backbone of the thick filament. The myosin heads can be readily cleaved from the rest of the molecule by mild proteolysis to yield the so-called subfragments-1, which are very soluble components.

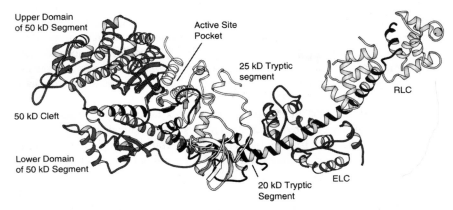

*Figure 1* Ribbon representation of chicken skeletal muscle myosin subfragment-1 looking into the narrow cleft that splits the central segment of the heavy chain. The heavy chain is displayed in different shades of gray to delineate the NH2-terminal, central, and COOH-terminal fragments that extend from residues Asp 4 Glu 204, Gly 216 Tyr 626, and Gln 647 Lys 843, respectively. These segments are separated by disordered loops in the X-ray structure and were previously identified by mild tryptic cleavage of the myosin head as the 25-, 50-, and 20-kDa fragments, respectively (4, 84). These tryptic fragments are not independent folding domains; however, they are convenient for identifying large segments of the structure. The regulatory and essential light chains are labeled RLC and ELC, respectively. Figures 1, 3, 4, and 6–9 were prepared with the molecular graphics program MOLSCRIPT (64).

These subfragments, first identified in 1962 (87), contain all the necessary elements to generate movement of actin during ATP hydrolysis (122).

The structure of skeletal muscle myosin subfragment-1 (S1) revealed that the myosin head itself is highly asymmetric (Figure 1). It has a length of over 165 Å, is approximately 65 Å wide and 40 Å deep at its thickest end (103). This molecular fragment may be divided into two parts: a globular component that is formed exclusively from the myosin heavy chain and an extended motif that contains the last 60 amino acids of the heavy chain of S1 that form an α-helix around which the essential and regulatory light chains bind. The light chains themselves share structural and sequence similarity with calmodulin and troponin-C (17), although the way in which the myosin light chains interact with the heavy chain differs from that observed for calmodulin (51, 77). The structure of this part of the head from scallop myosin has been determined independently and has been referred to as the regulatory domain (143). These structures suggest that one of the roles of the light chains is to stabilize the conformation of this helix, which is consistent with earlier observations by electron microscopy (28). In addition, these light chains may serve to transduce and amplify the effects of conformational changes associated with the binding and release of nucleotide at the thick portion of the head (103).

The globular fragment of the myosin head contains both the nucleotide- and actin-binding sites and, as shown by studies on an engineered truncated myosin heavy chain, is capable of causing movement of actin in an in vitro motility assay, although at a much reduced rate (53, 68). This part of the molecule has been referred to as the myosin motor domain, although this is somewhat misleading because this part of the myosin head contains at least three distinct structural domains.

The myosin motor domain exhibits a complex arrangement of secondary structural elements centered around a large, seven-stranded, mostly parallel β-sheet. This motif is formed by components from all three major tryptic fragments; 25, 50, and 20 kDa from the $NH_2$-terminus of the S1 heavy chain (4, 84). The nucleotide-binding pocket is located at the end of the central β-strand of this sheet and is abutted on one side by the 25-kDa segment of the heavy chain and on the other by the 50-kDa segment. The location of this nucleotide-binding pocket was determined by the positions of amino acid residues originally identified from affinity photolabeling studies to be active site residues (145) and by the position of the consensus sequence for phosphate-binding loops previously observed in adenylate kinase, the ras protein, and other nucleoside triphosphate-dependent enzymes (86, 91, 128).

In addition to the nucleotide-binding pocket, the myosin head contains several other prominent clefts and grooves that define structural domains. The most obvious cleft splits the 50-kDa region into an upper and a lower domain (Figure 1). This narrow cleft runs from directly under the nucleotide-binding pocket toward the end of the molecule. These two parts of the molecule seen in the X-ray structure are not in Van der Waals contact with one another. It has been suggested that this cleft plays a central role in the functioning of myosin as a molecular motor (102).

## Structural Models of the Contractile Cycle

In order to use the X-ray structure to propose a structural model for muscle contraction, it is necessary to know how myosin interacts with actin. An approximate molecular model for the actomyosin complex was attained through a combination of the structure of chicken skeletal muscle myosin subfragment-1 with the earlier structure of actin (48, 55) and an image reconstruction of the actomyosin complex obtained by electron microscopy (79, 80). This structure was used as the basis of a structural hypothesis for how myosin converts chemical energy into directed movement (102). The major tenet of this hypothesis was that domain movements in myosin, induced by the binding of ATP to the actin-bound state, generate a cyclical series of conformational changes that reduce the affinity of myosin for actin and place the myosin in a state in which it can hydrolyze the nucleotide. Movement of myosin relative to actin was suggested to occur through reversal of the induced conformational changes as myosin rebinds to actin and releases the reaction products. Central to this hypothesis was the suggestion that myosin interacts with actin in a stereo-specific manner such that the onset of binding requires the molecules to be in a unique orientation before the power stroke is initiated. Furthermore, it was suggested that the narrow cleft that splits the central 50-kDa segment of the heavy chain was the communication route between the nucleotide- and actin-binding site. It was envisaged that when ATP binds to the actomyosin complex, it causes the narrow cleft to open, which serves to disrupt the actin-binding site and reduce the affinity of myosin for actin (102). Thereafter, it was envisaged that the nucleotide-binding pocket closed around ATP and reconfigured the active site for hydrolysis.

Several questions were raised by the structure of chicken skeletal muscle myosin subfragment-1 and the molecular model for muscle contraction that was derived from it. For example, what is the structure of the myosin head with ATP bound? Questions also arose from the strategy adopted to obtain crystals of chicken skeletal myosin S1 (103). In that study it was found necessary to reductively methylate lysine residues in S1 in order to grow crystals suitable for structural analysis (69, 78). Myosin retains its enzymatic activity after this modification even though many of the rate constants associated with the steps in the hydrolytic process are altered (141). Control studies, in which the structure of hen egg white lysozyme was determined after chemical modification, revealed that reductive methylation had minimal effect on its tertiary structure (107). It remained to be determined whether the reductive alkylation had significantly altered the relative arrangement of domains within myosin. Some concern has been expressed because of the altered kinetic properties of methylated S1; that its structure might be unsuitable as the foundation for a structural model of myosin-based motility (7, 95). These concerns and other questions have been addressed by the recent determination of the structure of a truncated myosin head from *Dictyostelium discoideum* (S1Dc) (53) in the presence of MgADP and either beryllium fluoride or aluminum fluoride at 2.0 and 2.6 Å resolution, respectively (26, 27). The structure of the Mg pyrophosphate (MgPPi) complex of the same molecule has also been determined (114). These nonmethylated structures show only minor topological differences from the earlier methylated S1 structure.

## STRUCTURAL STUDIES OF MYOSIN NUCLEOTIDE COMPLEXES

Chemical studies have shown that it is possible to trap ADP in the active site of myosin in a variety of ways including cross-linking the two reactive sulphydryl groups in the myosin heavy chain (50, 135, 136) and through the

```
Chicken    4 DAEMAAFGEAAPYLRKSEKERIEAQNKPFDAKSSVFVVHPKE..SFVKGT  51
             ::    ::  .||:  .: :.    . ..  |  :    : ..||| |: |.
S1Dc       2 NPIHDRTSDYHKYLKVKQGDSDLFKLTVSDKRYIWYNPDPKERDSYECGE  51

Chicken   52 IQSKEGGKVTVKTEGGETLTVKEDQVFSMNPPKYDKIEDMAMMTHLHEPA 101
             | |..::..|.|| :|:.  ||.|:.  .|| |:| :||. :..|:|||
S1Dc      52 IVSETSDSFTFKTVDGQDRQVKKDDANQRNPIKFDGVEDMSELSYLNEPA 101

Chicken  102 VLYNLKERYAAWMIYTYSGLFCVTVNPYKWLPVYNPEVVLAYRGKKRQEA 151
             |:.||: ||.. :|||||||| |.|||:|::|:|..|:|  ::|::|.|.
S1Dc     102 VFHNLRVRYNQDLIYTYSGLFLVAVNPFKRIPIYTQEMVDIFKGRRRNEV 151

Chicken  152 PPHIFSISDNAYQFMLTDRENQSILITGESGAGKTVNTKRVIQYFATIAA 201
             :||||.||| ||. ||.||:|||:||||||||||| |||:||||:|.:|:
S1Dc     152 APHIFAISDVAYRSMLDDRQNQSLLITGESGAGKTENTKKVIQYLASVAG 201

Chicken  202 SGEKKKEEQSGKMQGTLEDQIISANPLLEAFGNAKTVRNDNSSRFGKFIR 251
             ..:        :.  |.||:||: |||:|||||||||.||:||||||||
S1Dc     202 RNQ.......ANGSGVLEQQILQANPILEAFGNAKTTRNNNSSRFGKFIE 244

Chicken  252 IHFGATGKLASADIETYLLEKSRVTFQLPAERSYHIFYQIMSNKKPELID 301
             |:|...| :.:.|.|:.||||||||.|| ..||.|||||::. .:|  .
S1Dc     245 IQFNNAGFISGASIQSYLLEKSRVVFQSETERNYHIFYQLLAGATAEEKK 294

Chicken  302 MLLITTNPYDYHYVSQGE.ITVPSIDDQEELMATDSAIDILGFSADEKTA 350
             |  : ..| .::|:.|:: :.:.:.:.| ||:. | |:||:|||.:|. .
S1Dc     295 ALHL.AGPESFNYLNQSGYVDIKGVSDSEEFKITRQAMDIVGFSQEEQMS 343

Chicken  351 IYKLTGAVMHYGNLKFKQKQREEQAEPDGTEVADKAAYLMGLNSAELLKA 400
             |:|:..:::|.||:|| :|. :|.| :|..  | |..:|:|.. | ||
S1Dc     344 IFKIIAGILHLGNIKF.EKGAGEGAVLKDKTALNAASTVFGVNPSVLEKA 392

Chicken  401 LCYPRVKVGNEFVTKGQTVSQVHNSVGALAKAVYEKMFLWMVIRINQQLD 450
             |  ||: .|.::|..  .|..  .| :||.||:|:::|||:| :||. |
S1Dc     393 LMEPRILAGRDLVAQHLNVEKSSSSRDALVKALYGRLFLWLVKKINNVL. 441

Chicken  451 TKQPRQYFIGVLDIAGFEIFDFNSFEQLCINFTNEKLQQFFNHHMFVLEQ 500
             ..:.:.||||||||.|||||..||||||||||:|||||||||||||| |||
S1Dc     442 CQERKAYFIGVLDISGFEIFKVNSFEQLCINYTNEKLQQFFNHHMFKLEQ 491

Chicken  501 EEYKKEGIEWEFIDFGMDLAACIELIE..KPMGIFSILEEECMFPKATDT 548
             ||| || |:|.|||||:| .|.|:||  .| ||:.:|:|:::||.|||.
S1Dc     492 EEYLKEKINWTFIDFGLDSQATIDLIDGRQPPGILALLDEQSVFPNATDN 541
```

formation of stable complexes of ADP with phosphate analogues such as vanadate (36–38) and more recently beryllium fluoride and aluminum fluoride (96, 97, 138). It has been suggested that these complexes are analogues of the metastable ADP•Pi state that occurs after hydrolysis of ATP (75, 96). The ability to trap ADP and nucleotide analogues in the active site was essential for photochemical mapping of the nucleotide-binding site, because it allowed

```
Chicken 501 EEYKKEGIEWEFIDFGMDLAACIELIE..KPMGIFSILEEECMFPKATDT 548
            ||| || |:|.|||||:| .|.|:|| .| ||:..|:|:::||.|||.
S1Dc    492 EEYLKEKINWTFIDFGLDSQATIDLIDGRQPPGILALLDEQSVFPNATDN 541

Chicken 549 SFKNKLYDQHLGKSNNFQKPKPAKGKAEAHFSLVHYAGTVDYNISGWLEK 598
            .: .||..: |...::.|: .| ..|::.|||| | |:| :||||
S1Dc    542 TLITKLHSHFSKKNAKYEEPRFSK....TEFGVTHYAGQVMYEIQDWLEK 587

Chicken 599 NKDPLNETVIGLYQKSSVKTLALLFATYGGEAEGGGGKKGGKKKGSSFQT 648
            |||||.:.: :..|| ..:. || .:.. : |||..| |
S1Dc    588 NKDPLQQDLELCFKDSSDNVVTKLF........NDPNIASRAKKGANFIT 629

Chicken 649 VSALFRENLNKLMANLRSTHPHFVRCIIPNETKTPGAMEHELVLHQLRCN 698
            |.| ::|.|..|||.| .|:||||||||||:.. |: :|..:||.|||||
S1Dc    630 VAAQYKEQLASLMATLETTNPHFVRCIIPNNKQLPAKLEDKVVLDQLRCN 679

Chicken 699 GVLEGIRICRKGFPSRVLYADFKQRYRVLNASAIPEGQFMDSKKASEKLL 748
            |||||||||.|||||.|::|||| .|| :|.:.. .::: ||.||.: :|
S1Dc    680 GVLEGIRITRKGFPNRIIYADFVKRYYLLAPNVPRDAE..DSQKATDAVL 727

Chicken 749 GSIDVDHTQYRFGHTKVFFKAGLLGLLEEMRDD 748
            :::|..||||| ||:||:|| |: :|| |::
S1Dc    728 KHLNIDPEQYRFGITKIFFRAGQLARIEEAREQ 727
```

*Figure 2*  Sequence alignment of the motor segments of chicken skeletal muscle and *Dictyostelium discoideum* myosin II. The residues that are noted by solid boxes have been implicated by chemical studies to be associated with the active site.

high specificity of photomodification for otherwise very low specificity reagents (145). The results of these studies are addressed below.

A truncated myosin head was expressed in *Dictyostelium discoideum* in order to obtain a smaller molecular fragment more amenable for structural studies. This was generated genetically by terminating the myosin heavy chain in the long α-helix that forms the back bone of the light chain-binding motif (53). The molecular fragment contains 761-amino acid residues in *Dictyostelium discoideum*, which is shorter than in chicken S1 due to shorter loops that connect the major tryptic fragments. An alignment of the chicken and *Dictyostelium discoideum* myosin sequences is shown in Figure 2. This truncated myosin head retains a limited ability to move (53) and crystallizes readily without the need for chemical modification (26, 27, 114).

## Tertiary Structure of MgADP•BeFx•S1Dc

The tertiary structure of the beryllium fluoride complex is exceedingly similar to that of chicken skeletal muscle myosin subfragment-1. A comparison of the chicken and *Dictyostelium* myosin heads is shown in Figure 3a. The rms

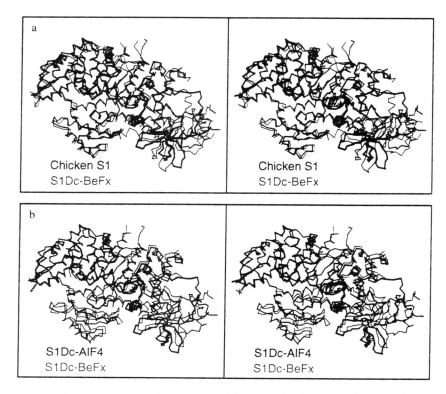

*Figure 3*    Stereo α carbon plots of the alignment of the motor units of (*upper panel*) chicken skeletal muscle myosin and MgADP•BeF$_x$•S1Dc complex of *Dictyostelium* myosin and (*lower panel*) MgADP•BeF$_x$•S1Dc and MgADP•AlF$_4$•S1Dc complexes of *Dictyostelium* myosin. The MgADP•BeF$_x$•S1Dc structure is shown in gray thick lines. In both panels, the structures of chicken skeletal muscle myosin S1 and MgADP•AlF$_4$•S1Dc are shown in black.

difference between 554 equivalent α-carbons in chicken and *Dictyostelium* myosin is 1.25 Å, which is close to the expected difference of 1.1 Å for two proteins that share the same function and exhibit 47% sequence identity (13, 130). The structural similarity between these two proteins convincingly establishes that reductive methylation does not grossly change the domain structure of chicken S1 (103). However, it was surprising to observe that the narrow cleft that splits the 50-kDa segment of the heavy chain is equally open in both chicken and MgADP•BeF$_x$•S1Dc structures and that the nucleotide-binding pocket has only closed about 1 Å relative to that observed in the chicken skeletal myosin S1.

## Tertiary Structure of MgADP•AlF₄•S1Dc

The individual tertiary structural domains in the MgADP•AlF₄•S1Dc complex are very similar to those of the MgADP•BeF$_x$•S1Dc complex. However, the relationship between the domains has changed (Figure 3b). The most obvious difference is the partial closure of the cleft that splits the central segment of the myosin heavy chain. This results in a significant rearrangement of the COOH-terminal segment of the polypeptide chain and a modification of the region associated with the reactive cysteine residues (Cys 697 and 707) in skeletal muscle. This conformational change is due to differences in the hydrogen bond for the BeF$_x$ and AlF₄ moieties in the active site and is discussed below. However, the binding of MgADP is very similar in both complexes.

## Structure of Adenine- and Ribose-Binding Pockets

The nucleotide-binding site lies at the base of a pocket formed on one side by residues from the NH₂-terminal segment of the myosin heavy chain and on the other by residues from the central section (Figure 4). In both complexes, the purine ring is in the anti conformation relative to the ribose, which exhibits a C3′-endo ring pucker. Almost all the residues involved in the binding of the nucleotide lie above the plane of the β-sheet that forms the major tertiary structural motif in the myosin head. However, the pocket extends down into the opening between the cleft that splits the upper and lower domains of the central 50-kDa segment. A schematic drawing of the myosin-nucleotide interactions in the MgADP•BeF$_x$•S1Dc complex is shown in Figure 5. The binding site for the purine ring in both complexes is formed almost exclusively from residues in the NH₂-terminal segment of the chain and involves residues Gly 184, Glu 187, and Asn 188. It also includes contributions from Asn 127, Pro 128, Arg 131, and Tyr 135, which form the top edge of the nucleotide-binding pocket. Arg 131 folds over the purine ring, protecting it from external solvent, and forms a salt bridge with Glu 187. There is a hydrogen bond between the 6-amino group of adenine and Oa of Tyr 135, which is a highly conserved residue. Although there are several buried water molecules that form hydrogen bonds between the purine and protein, there are few other specific contacts between the purine ring and the protein. This is consistent with the observation that myosin will hydrolyze a wide range of nucleotides and organic triphosphates (93, 140). The lack of specificity contrasts with the G proteins or other ATP-dependent enzymes that utilize a phosphate-binding loop (86, 91). However, this is consistent with the primary function of the myosin motor domain to convert the energy from hydrolysis of a phosphate bond into mechanical work.

The ribose moiety of ADP forms few specific interactions with the protein or water molecules. However, Asn 127, which is highly conserved, does form a hydrogen bond to the ring oxygen, O4′. The lack of specific interactions

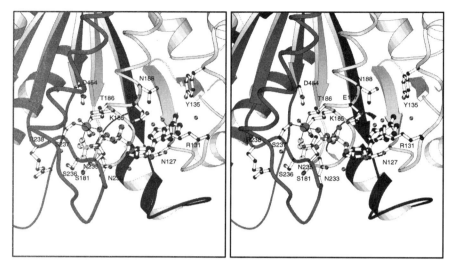

*Figure 4* Stereo ribbon representation view of the nucleotide-binding region of the MgADP•BeF$_x$•S1Dc complex. The tertiary structure is shown in shades of gray to distinguish the NH$_2$-terminal, central, and COOH-terminal segments of the myosin heavy chain. This reveals the orientation of the nucleotide and its associated magnesium ion. The phosphate-binding site is located in the middle of the large β-sheet that forms the major structural motif in the myosin head and lies at the COOH-terminal end of the central β-strand. (Modified with permission from Reference 27.)

explains why myosin can utilize organotriphosphates that replace the ribose ring with an aminoethyl group and the purine ring with derivatives of nitrobenzene and still generate force in muscle fibers (129). The 2′ and 3′ hydroxyl groups are both exposed to solvent, which allows for the attachment of a wide variety of functional groups including spin-labels, fluorophores, and photo-labels to the ribose ring in these positions without affecting function (14, 20, 21).

## Structure of the Triphosphate-Binding Pocket

The coordination of the α- and β-phosphates is similar in both MgADP•BeF$_x$•S1Dc and MgADP•AlF$_4$•S1Dc. However, there are significant differences between the coordination and structure of the beryllium and aluminum fluoride moieties. The α- and β-phosphate groups and both metallofluoride moieties extend down into a narrow tunnel formed by the phosphate-binding loop Gly 179 to Val 187 on one side and residues Asn 233 to Gly 240 on the other. This tunnel opens into the apex of the cleft that splits the upper and lower domains of the central 50-kDa segment of the heavy chain. The mag-

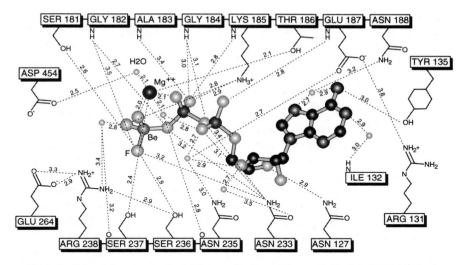

*Figure 5* Schematic representation of the coordination of the metallofluoride-ADP complex in MgADP•BeF$_x$•S1Dc. Hydrogen bonds less than 3.5 Å and ionic interactions less than 3.7 Å are shown as dashed lines with the corresponding distances. Only those interactions with the appropriate stereochemistry to participate in these interactions are included. (Modified with permission from Reference 27.)

nesium ion is located at the top of the tunnel (Figure 4) and is surrounded by six ligands in an approximately octahedral arrangement and plays a central role in chelating the nucleotide complex, where it interacts with the β-phosphate and the metallofluoride moieties. The Mg$^{2+}$ ion is also coordinated to two protein ligands, Oγ1 of Thr 186 and Oγ of Ser 237 and two water molecules. These two water molecules are an integral part of the coordination scheme of the nucleotide. One of these water molecules interacts with the carboxyl side chain of Asp 454. The second interacts with the main chain carbonyl oxygen of Asn 235 and one of the β-phosphate oxygen atoms.

There is an extensive series of specific interactions between the α- and β-phosphate groups and metallofluoride moieties with the protein (Figures 4 and 5). Every oxygen and fluorine atom of the pseudo-triphosphate moieties is involved in a hydrogen-bonding interaction. However, there are more interactions with the β-phosphate and metallofluoride moieties than the α-phosphate group. Many of these interactions are provided by the amide-hydrogens of the phosphate-binding loop on one side and by residues Asn 233 to Gly 240 on the other, either directly or via a buried water molecule.

The bottom of the nucleotide-binding pocket abuts the apex of the narrow cleft that splits the 50-kDa segment of the heavy chain. The region around the metallofluoride moiety is referred to as the γ-phosphate pocket. This pocket contains several well-ordered water molecules in both structures. The presence of water in the γ-phosphate pocket is important because hydrolysis is known to occur via nucleophilic attack of a water on the terminal phosphate (132).

## Structure of BeF$_X$ and AlF4$^-$ in the Active Site

In the MgADP•BeF$_x$•S1Dc complex the electron density is consistent with three fluorine atoms bonded to a central beryllium atom that is coordinated by a terminal oxygen of the β-phosphate. There is little electron density for the beryllium atom; however, the geometry of the bridging oxygen and the three fluorine ligands is consistent with a tetrahedral BeF$_3$O adduct. NMR studies of the beryllium fluoride-ADP adduct with smooth muscle myosin suggest that this complex is a mixture of fluoroberyllates (46). The calculated bond distances for the BeF$_3$O adduct are similar to those expected for ATP. Thus the MgADP•BeF$_x$ complex is an analogue of ATP in the active site.

In contrast, the aluminum atom exhibits octahedral coordination in MgADP•AlF$_4$•S1Dc. One of the ligands is contributed by an oxygen atom of the β-phosphate. Four of the remaining ligands lie in a plane and are most likely fluorine atoms, which is consistent with NMR spectroscopic studies of this complex in smooth muscle myosin (75). The sixth ligand, which was not well defined, is a water molecule axial to the pseudo-bridging oxygen atom. The stereochemistry observed for the AlF4$^-$ moiety is similar to that seen in the structures of the G protein G$_{i\alpha1}$ and transducin α complexes with guanosine diphosphate (GDP) and aluminum fluoride (16, 115).

## Comparison of the Metallofluoride Complexes

The bond distance to the pseudo-bridging oxygen is distinctly longer (2.0 Å) in the MgADP•AlF$_4$•S1Dc complex, than in the MgADP•BeF$_x$•S1Dc (1.57 Å) complex. This change allows one of the fluorine ligands to the aluminum to form a short hydrogen bond to the amide hydrogen of Gly 457, which stabilizes a movement of 4.4 Å by the main chain. Gly 457 is completely conserved in the myosin superfamily. In the MgADP•BeF$_x$•S1Dc complex, the respective fluorine is too far away to form this interaction. Because of the longer bond distance to the pseudo-bridging oxygen observed in the MgADP•AlF$_4$•S1Dc complex, it appears that this complex is an analogue of the transition state for hydrolysis. The MgGDP•AlF$_4$ structures of the G protein G$_{i\alpha1}$ and transducin α complexes were also interpreted as transition state analogues (16, 115).

Superposition of the major domains of MgADP•BeF$_x$•S1Dc, MgADP•AlF$_4$•S1Dc, and chicken myosin S1 indicates that the overall fold of these parts of the S1 molecule is essentially identical in all of these structures. The

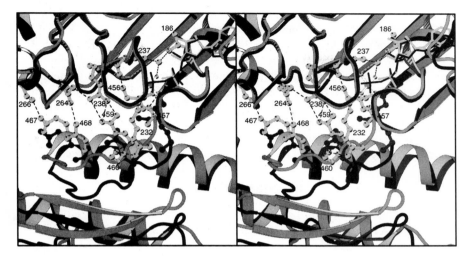

*Figure 6* Structural differences in the γ-phosphate pockets of the BeF$_x$-S1Dc and MgADP•
AlF$_4$•S1Dc complexes. The additional interactions between the upper and lower domains of the
central segment of the myosin heavy chain prompted by the AlF4$^-$ ion are included. Side chain and
nucleotide positions in MgADP•AlF$_4$•S1Dc are shown in light gray and their corresponding
orientation in MgADP•BeF$_x$•S1Dc in dark gray. (Modified with permission from Reference 27.)

rms difference between the MgADP•AlF$_4$•S1Dc and MgADP•BeF$_x$•S1Dc
structures is 1.5 Å, which results from the partial closure of the narrow cleft
in the central 50-kDa segment (Figure 3b, Figure 6). The cleft closure results
from a concerted rigid-body rotation of the lower domain, Gly 457 to Ser 619,
by about 5°. The outer edge of the cleft moves by more than 5 Å. The
movement is accomplished by a change in the main chain torsion angles at
residues Ile 455 and Gly 457, located at the end of a β-strand that drops from
the upper part of the central domain into the lower. The conformational torsion
angles in residues on either side of this hinge region remain virtually unchanged.

The flexing at Ile 455 and Gly 457 brings the loop from Ser 456 to Ser 465
and the NH$_2$-terminal region of the following helix (Phe 466 to Cys 470) into
close proximity to a region in the upper central domain near the active site.
Five new interdomain contacts are introduced, including several water-medi-
ated interactions (Figure 6). It is noteworthy that the segment that follows the
conserved glycine residue is one of the most highly conserved sections of the
myosin sequence across all known functional myosin motors (131). Although
less obvious, the residues in the upper domain that are in contact with the
lower domain are also highly conserved. The structural and functional role of

this part of the myosin molecule was not fully appreciated prior to the solution of the structure of the aluminum fluoride complex.

Movement of the lower domain relative to the upper domain of the central segment of the heavy chain in the MgADP•AlF$_4$•S1Dc complex is coupled to a structural change in the COOH-terminal domains. The current model for the MgADP•AlF$_4$•S1Dc complex suggests that the COOH-terminal domain of the myosin heavy chain might rotate by as much as 20°. Unfortunately, the polypeptide chain beyond Lys 690 in the MgADP•AlF$_4$•S1Dc complex appears to adopt multiple conformations in the crystal. This lack of conformational stability is most likely due to the absence of the essential light chain.

## STRUCTURAL MECHANISM OF HYDROLYSIS

Kinetic studies on myosin have provided a chemical description for the hydrolysis of ATP and established the relationship between nucleotide hydrolysis and the generation of directed movement (24, 32, 33, 35, 120). Early kinetic studies revealed that the contractile cycle contains an unexpected feature in that the hydrolysis step occurs when myosin is not tightly bound to actin. Lymn & Taylor, in their classic study, demonstrated that hydrolysis occurs rapidly after ATP promotes the dissociation of actin from the actomyosin complex (71). This results in a metastable state in the absence of actin, where the equilibrium constant between ATP and ADP•Pi in the active site is in the range of 1 to 10 (2, 3, 71, 124). There is rapid interconversion between substrate and products (2, 112, 123, 133). The metastable state has a considerably higher affinity for actin. Rebinding of myosin to actin reduces the stability of the metastable state and enhances the rate of product release. Subsequent fiber studies have revealed that the power stroke is triggered by phosphate release (reviewed in 35).

It is well established that hydrolysis of ATP occurs by attack of a water molecule on the γ-phosphorous (22, 112, 133). However, very little is known about the role of the protein in ATP hydrolysis. It has commonly been assumed that catalysis would require a general base, although its identity has not been defined. Examination of the γ-phosphate pocket in both MgADP•BeF$_x$•S1Dc and MgADP•AlF$_4$•S1Dc does not reveal any amino acid side chain within 5 Å of the beryllium or aluminum that might function as a catalytic base. The lack of an obvious amino acid that can function as a base suggests that γ-phosphate water might function as its own base and might accept the proton from the nucleophilic water directly. A similar mechanism has been suggested for transducin α (115) and p21[ras] (108) Alternatively, one of the conserved serine residues associated with the γ-phosphate pocket might serve as an intermediate in the transfer of the proton from the nucleophilic water molecule to the γ-phosphate by hydrogen exchange. This would proceed with better stereochemistry than direct transfer to the γ-phosphate. Proton exchange for serine residues, as measured by NMR at 4°C (67), is $<30\ s^{-1}$ and is faster than ATP hydrolysis by myosin ($\sim$5 $s^{-1}$ at 3°C) (119). A possible candidate for this type of proton transfer is Ser 236, which is also an absolutely conserved amino acid residue.

## Is Myosin a Back-Door Enzyme?

Fiber studies have revealed that the power stroke is associated with the release of inorganic phosphate (reviewed in 35). ADP release occurs after the initiation of the power stroke. The structures of the myosin:nucleotide complexes show that the phosphate must leave the active site by a route different from the one it entered because its exit is blocked by ADP. The same conclusion was reached by modeling ATP in the active site of myosin (146). There are very few examples of this behavior in enzymes, although it has been suggested from computational studies of acetylcholine esterase (34). Departure of the phosphate via a different route from which it enters the active site, coupled with the conformational change implicated in the transition state, provides an explanation for the puzzling metastable myosin•ADP•Pi state that is central to the kinetic mechanism of contraction.

In the absence of actin, product release from the metastable state is slow. There is no proton release until phosphate leaves the active site (2). Furthermore, $^{18}$O exchange studies have suggested that the phosphate group of the product is tumbling rapidly in the active site because all the non-bridge phosphate oxygen atoms are equivalent (8, 123). The partial closure of the cleft in the 50-kDa segment of the heavy chain observed in MgADP•AlF$_4$•S1Dc complex, which mimics the transition state for hydrolysis, results in reduced access of solvent to the γ-phosphate pocket. This conformational change, which is suggested to be essential for hydrolysis, would prevent loss of phosphate from the enzyme.

## Revised Contractile Model

The original model for the contractile cycle derived from the structure of chicken skeletal muscle myosin S1 suggested that the nucleotide pocket closed when ATP bound to generate a bent molecule (102). This suggestion arose from the apparent openness of the nucleotide-binding pocket, from photolabeling studies (discussed below), and from the very high binding affinity of myosin for ATP (39). The structures of the nucleotide complexes of S1Dc show that this hypothesis was incorrect. It would appear that closure of the nucleotide pocket is not the source of the major conformational change that is responsible for the molecular basis of muscle contraction. This is consistent with recent fluorescence quenching measurements, showing that the purine base of $\varepsilon$ATP experiences a similar environment at the beginning and end of the contractile cycle (29). It is also consistent with studies of myosin in which a fluorescent nucleotide has been photo-cross-linked to the active site (70). The structures of the beryllium and aluminum fluoride complexes suggest that movements in the myosin heavy chain associated with the lower domain of the central 50-kDa segment coupled to movements in the COOH-terminal segment are the primary source of this conformational change. These observations have formed the basis of a revised structural model for the contractile cycle (26).

## CHEMICAL STUDIES OF THE CATALYTIC MECHANISM

There have been an exceedingly large number of chemical studies on myosin directed toward identifying the role of individual amino acids. It is probably true that every conceivable chemical strategy for defining the catalytic function of a protein has been applied to this molecule. Herein we focus on those studies that have identified the location of a specific amino acid residue rather than a general location within a peptide fragment. There are three general approaches that have proven to be of great value: site-specific photolabeling, chemical modification, and proteolytic modification. The most illuminating examples of each of these strategies, as applied to myosin, are discussed in the context of its structure.

### Photolabeling Studies

Photolabeling has proven to be an invaluable tool for identifying residues in the active site. This has been made possible because of the ability to trap photoreactive nucleotide analogues in the active site, which eliminates most of the problems of nonspecific labeling. Table 1 lists the location of amino acid residues that have been identified by photolabeling, whereas Figure 7 shows the position of the equivalent residues in S1Dc. The photolabeling sites fall into three classes: (a) those that reside in the $\gamma$-phosphate pocket; (b) those that lie close to the adenine ring; and (c) those that are adjacent to the 2′ and 3′ hydroxyl oxygen atoms of the ribose.

LABELING CLOSE TO THE ADENINE POCKET TRYPTOPHAN OR ARGININE    The residues identified in Figure 7 line the active site pocket and come from both the 25- and 50-kDa tryptic fragments. As shown by the MgADP•BeF$_x$•S1Dc structure, the adenine-binding site is provided almost entirely by residues from the 25-kDa fragment. Consistent with this finding, all photolabeling experiments with purine analogues of ATP (Table 1) label only 25-kDa residues. Evidence that 8-N$_3$ATP also photolabels the 20-kDa fragment (76) is likely

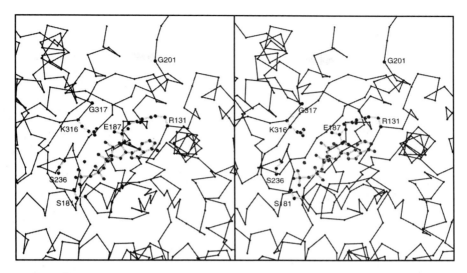

*Figure 7* Location of the amino acid residues that have been implicated in the active site from photolabeling studies mapped onto the structure of MgADP•BeF$_x$•S1Dc. The sequence numbering is given relative to the equivalent amino acid in *Dictyostelium*.

the result of nonspecific labeling, because the photoprobe was used without any trapping procedure. Inspection of the nucleotide S1Dc structures show that the closest residues in the 20-kDa fragment are at least 5.5 Å away from ATP. Likewise, the earlier indication that the essential light chain of gizzard myosin was part of the active site (89) has been shown to be an artifact of the labeling procedure (43).

Both tryptophan (90) and arginine (57) in the same location (Trp 130 in rabbit skeletal and Arg 131 in scallop) are photolabeled by azido ATP analogues (Table 1). These residues are on one side of the active site pocket, and in the MgADP•BeF$_x$•S1Dc structure, the Arg lies over the adenine ring forming a salt-link with Glu 187. The analogous Glu in gizzard myosin (Glu 185) is directly photolabeled by reaction with UDP (30) or ADP (31). Skeletal myosin is not photolabeled this way because the less reactive Val replaces Glu. Interestingly, several myosins with Val in this position are paired with Trp, suggesting these residues may bind over the adenine ring in a manner analogous to the Arg-Glu pair observed in S1Dc.

Regardless, the above type of binding to the adenine ring does not appear to be critical because Trp 130 in rabbit skeletal myosin can be modified chemically (94) or photochemically (70) with little or no effect on the kinetics of actin-activated MgATPase activity. In addition, myosin photolabeled at Trp

**Table 1** Summary of active site residues identified by photolabeling

| Myosin | Analogue | Trapping method | Residues photolabeled in heavy chain | Equivalent residue in chicken | Equivalent residue in S1Dc | References |
|---|---|---|---|---|---|---|
| Rabbit skeletal | NANDP | SH1-SH2 | Trp 130 | Trp 131 | Arg 131 | (90) |
|  | 2-N$_3$ADP | SH1-SH2 | Trp 130 | Trp 131 | Arg 131 | (41) |
|  | Bz$_2$ADP | SH1-SH2 | Ser 324 | Ser 324 | Gly 317 | (72) |
|  | MgADP·Vi | Vanadate | Ser 180 | Ser 181 | Ser 181 | (19) |
| Photomodified skeletal S1 | MgADP·Vi | Vanadate | Ser 243 | Ser 243 | Ser 236 | (42) |
| Cardiac | NANDP | SH1-SH2 or vanadate | Trp 129 | Trp 131 | Arg 313 | b |
| Smooth (gizzard) | Bz$_2$ADP | Co$^{2+}$·Vanadate | Pro 324 | Pro 323 | Lys 316 | (14) |
|  | UDP | Co$^{2+}$·vanadate | Glu 185 | Val 187 | Glu 187 | (31) |
|  | ADP | Co$^{2+}$·vanadate | Glu 185 | Val 187 | Glu 187 | (30) |
|  | Mg·ADP·Vi | Fanadate or 10S conformation | Ser 179 | Ser 181 | Ser 181 | (15) |
| Scallop (Aquepectin) | NANDP | Mn$^{2+}$·Vanadate (no Ca$^{2+}$) | Arg 128 | Trp 131 | Arg 131 | (57) |
|  | NANDP | Mn$^{2+}$·vanadate (plus additional Ca$^{2+}$/Mg$^{2+}$) | Cys 198 / Arg 128 | Ala 201 / Trp 131 | Gly 201 / Arg 131 | (58) |
| Acanthamoeba Myosin II | UTP | None | Glu 190 | Val 187 | Glu 187 | (1) |

a Modified with permission from Reference 145.
b Y. Okamoto and R. G. Yount unpublished results

130 in fibers behaves normally in all the standard measurements of mechanical function (70). This photolabeled Trp must swing out of the way of MgATP to allow normal ATP binding, cleavage, and cross-bridge motion. As such, Trp is an attractive location to place spectroscopic probes by use of appropriate new photoaffinity labels.

LABELING WITH PROBES ATTACHED TO THE 2' AND 3' RIBOSE HYDROXYL GROUPS The heavy chain region near the ribose ring binding site is photolabeled by 3'(2')-$O$-(4-benzoyl)benzoyl ATP at Ser 324 in rabbit skeletal myosin (Table 1). As noted above, myosin photolabeled here in fibers behaves in a manner identical to its behavior in unmodified fibers (70) and represents a second site to place spectroscopic probes. Because Ser 324 in the 50-kDa fragment is opposite Trp 130 and is 13–15 Å distant in the chicken S1 structure (103), it was believed these residues would move closer together on binding to ATP (102). However, modeling of ATP into the chicken S1 active site (D Lawson, unpublished results) shows that the photoreactive carbonyl of Bz$_2$ATP can lie next to Ser 324 without movement of any residues. This result agrees with the observation that the chicken S1 structure and that of S1Dc with bound nucleotide are essentially the same (27). The S1Dc structure also shows that there are no specific interactions between the protein and the 2'(3') hydroxyls, which are exposed to solvent. This finding had been predicted by the fact that a large number of ribose-modified ATP analogues function normally with myosin. These include the bulky Bz$_2$ATP and 3'[2']-dansyl- and $N$-methyl anthraniloyl derivatives of ATP (20, 142).

LABELING OF GROUPS IN THE γ-PHOSPHATE POCKET   Vanadate has proven to be a valuable tool for mapping the active site of myosin. In combination with MgADP, it constitutes a powerful inhibitor of the ATPase activity through the formation of a long-lived complex that was believed to mimic either the metastable ADP•Pi state or the transition state for hydrolysis. The ability to trap nucleotide analogues in the active site was the key step in achieving highly specific photolabeling described above. In addition to the trapping phenomena, vanadate exhibits an intrinsic photochemical reactivity that results in modification of either Ser 181 or Ser 243 (Ser 236 in *Dictyostelium*) (18, 19, 42). This is followed by photo-induced cleavage of the myosin heavy chain (40). The X-ray structures reveal that the side chains of both residues are involved in coordination of the metallofluoride moiety that mimics the γ-phosphate. In retrospect, the paucity of groups labeled in the γ-phosphate pocket is consistent with the apparent lack of a catalytic base because it is expected that such a group would be a prime target for chemical modification. Likewise, the photo-modification of Ser 243 (rabbit skeletal myosin) by vanadate is consistent with the suggestion that the analogous residue in *Dictyostelium* myosin (Ser 236) functions as a proton shuttle (27).

## Intrinsic Fluorescence Measurements on Myosin

The changes in the intrinsic fluorescence of myosin have proven to be a sensitive probe for the development of the kinetic model for the contractile cycle (83, 123, 139) and critical for demonstrating that binding of ATP to the active site is a multistep process that consists of several distinct conformational states (71, 124). It has suggested that only one or two tryptophan residues experience an altered environment (92, 139) and that these residues are located in the 50-kDa tryptic fragment (137). Even so, it has been difficult to identify exactly which tryptophan(s) and hence component(s) of the protein are responsible for these phenomena. In skeletal muscle myosin, Trp 510 has been proposed as the residue responsible for the fluorescence changes based on fluorescence energy transfer measurements, proximity arguments from cross-linking between SH1 and SH2 to cysteines in the 50-kDa segment of the heavy chain, and sequence conservation (47, 54, 131).

The tryptophan residues present in chicken skeletal myosin S1 are shown on Figure 8. Of these, only Trp 510 is almost completely conserved across the myosin superfamily. The section of random coil that contains this residue in S1Dc exhibits different conformations in the beryllium and aluminum fluoride complexes. This is consistent with earlier suggestions that this is the likely candidate for the fluorescence change. There are four other tryptophan residues in the globular segment of chicken skeletal myosin S1. Two, Trp 113 and Trp 131, are located close to the outer edge of the nucleotide-binding pocket and both are exposed to solvent. It is unlikely that Trp 113 is responsible because this residue is an aspartate residue in *Dictyostelium* myosin II, which exhibits a fluorescence enhancement even in the absence of Trp 113 (105) (although at a reduced level). Conversely, chemical studies have shown that Trp 131 is not the one responsible for the fluorescence change (94, 137). Trp 440 is located in the actin interface in the upper domain of the 50-kDa tryptic fragment and is most distant from the nucleotide-binding site. There is no evidence for any conformational change at this location during nucleotide hydrolysis, although when myosin binds to actin, a change in the environment of Trp 440 might occur. Finally, Trp 595 is located in the lower domain of the 50-kDa tryptic fragment under the highly conserved segment that lines the cleft separating the upper and lower domains. This tryptophan also might change its environment when myosin binds to actin.

It has been suggested that the fluorescence enhancement is due to an interaction between an ionizable side chain and the indole ring (6). In chicken skeletal myosin, Trp 510 lies under the pocket that contains the reactive

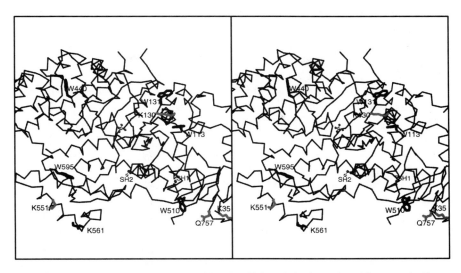

*Figure 8* Location of the tryptophan residues in chicken skeletal myosin subfragment-1. Also shown is the location of the posttranslationally modified amino acids and the reactive cysteine residues. The β-barrel in the $NH_2$-terminal tryptic segment (residues 36–75) has been omitted for clarity.

cysteine residue (Cys 707) and is surrounded by the hydrophobic residues, Tyr 503, Phe 512, Phe 711, and a highly conserved Gly 710. Trp 510 is exposed on one edge to the solvent. The exact reason for the fluorescence enhancement cannot be explained by the present structures because it is likely that the exact nature of the conformational change that occurs around Trp 510 is influenced by the essential light chain, which is missing from the structures of S1Dc. Even so, this region appears responsive to the state of the active site and is probably of greater importance than first imagined. It would be a good target for mutagenesis.

## Reactive Cysteine Residues

The myosin heavy chain in skeletal muscle contains two reactive cysteine residues that have been the subject of extensive investigation over many years (5, 104, 109, 113). At one time these residues were believed to be critical for enzymatic function because large modifying agents have a profound effect on ATPase activity. However, careful modification with small blocking groups revealed that the most reactive cysteines are not directly involved in catalysis (134). Even so, probes attached to the reactive cysteines have proven to be invaluable tools for sensing conformational changes in the active site and in myosin-actin interactions (23, 50, 56, 60, 100, 104, 135, 136). Indeed, it is possible to cross-link these reactive cysteine residues with a variety of reagents that all result in trapping MgADP in the active site (9, 50, 104, 135, 136). This evidence suggested that the reactive cysteine residues reside in a flexible loop. Thus it was great surprise to find that in the structure of chicken S1 these amino acids were at least 17 Å apart and separated by an α-helix (103). This was interpreted as further evidence that the region associated with the reactive cysteine residues in skeletal muscle undergoes a substantial conformational change during the contractile cycle (50). It should be noted that the sequence between the reactive cysteine residues includes two conserved glycine residues, one of which is in the α-helix, which would certainly facilitate a conformational change.

In MgADP•BeF$_x$•S1Dc, the polypeptide chain between the residues equivalent to SH1 and SH2 adopts a conformation similar to that seen in chicken S1. However, in MgADP•AlF$_4$•S1Dc, the helix separating these residues rotates by at least 20° but does not bring the equivalent residues in proximity close enough to allow formation of a disulfide bond. This most likely arises because the essential light chain is missing from the MgADP•AlF$_4$•S1Dc complex. It has been suggested that the domains adjacent to the reactive cysteines serve to transmit a conformational change to the essential light chain that is fundamental to the conversion of chemical energy into directed movement (26). In the absence of the light chain, the conformational change observed in S1Dc does not represent the true change. The nature of this change cannot be predicted based on the current X-ray structures. Consequently, the present structures cannot explain the cross-linking of the reactive cysteine residues in skeletal muscle in the presence of ATP or the enormous literature associated with the chemical and physiological behavior induced by modification of these amino acids.

## Reactive Lysine Residue

Early studies revealed that the myosin head of skeletal muscle contains a reactive lysine residue (Lys 84 chicken skeletal) (65, 66) that is located in the NH$_2$-terminal tryptic fragment of the heavy chain (49, 82, 85) and lies at the interface with the 20-kDa tryptic fragment in a crevice that extends to the reactive cysteine residue (Figure 9). Modification of this residue with 2,4,6-trinitrobenzene sulfonate (TNBS) enhances the intrinsic MgATPase activity sevenfold, whereas the actin-activated MgATPase activity is reduced to that of the now enhanced intrinsic activity. Interestingly the rate of chemical modification is reduced in the presence of MgATP (85).

There is an unusual aspect to modification of the reactive lysine residue. In

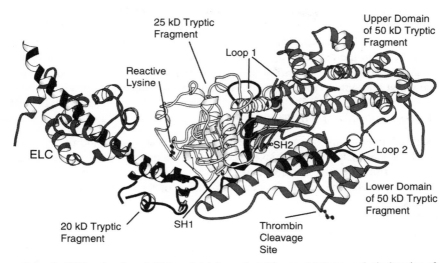

*Figure 9*  Ribbon drawing of chicken skeletal myosin subfragment-1 that reveals the location of the major trypsin cleavage sites (loop 1 and 2). These loops are disordered in chicken skeletal S1. Also shown is the location of the thrombin cleavage site, reactive cysteine residues (SH1 and SH2), and the reactive lysine residue.

the presence of MgPPi or MgADP, only half the molecules are trinitrophenylated (81). This appears to be true not only for myosin but also for subfragment-1 (61). At one time it was thought that this difference was due to microheterogeneity in the amino acid sequence close to the reactive lysine (82); however, more recent investigations have shown that this is not true (62, 63). Based on these observations, it has been suggested that the myosin heads exist in two conformations when complexed with MgPPi or MgADP and that these interconvert slowly in the presence of TNBS (61). It is difficult to explain the observation of half-site reactivity for myosin subfragment-1 (61) in terms of the currently available X-ray structures or models (kinetic and structural) for muscle contraction.

Examination of the chicken and *Dictyostelium* structures does not lead to any obvious reason for the reactivity except that this lysine does not form a salt-bridge with any of its surrounding side chains. It would appear that the reactive lysine lies at a domain interface that influences both the nucleotide- and actin-binding sites that are 35 and 50 Å, respectively, from the lysine residue. Because the rate of reaction of the lysine residue is sensitive to the contents of the active site, there must be a conformational change in the proximity of this side chain that is influenced by actin and the contents of the nucleotide-binding site. Interestingly, a substantial number of mutations in β-cardiac myosin that have been implicated in familial hypertrophic cardio-myopathy map to the interface between the essential light chain and the heavy chain (101). There is also evidence from chemical cross-linking that the interface between the essential light chain and heavy chain changes during ATP hydrolysis (98, 99). This part of the myosin molecule deserves more attention now that the tools to investigate its function are available.

## Posttranslational Modifications

Skeletal muscle myosin contains several posttranslationally modified amino acid residues including, for chicken skeletal muscle myosin, a monomethylated Lys 35, trimethylated Lys 130 and Lys 551, and a 3-$N$-methylated His 757 (73) (Figure 8). The reason for the modification of these amino acid residues is unknown.

Lys 130 is close but external to the adenine-binding pocket in chicken skeletal muscle myosin S1 (103). In many other myosins the equivalent residue is an arginine. Because both trimethylated lysine and arginine would be expected to carry a constitutive positive charge, it suggested that they might be involved in salt links to the phosphate groups of the nucleotide (121).

In *Dictyostelium* myosin, Lys 130 is not involved in any aspect of nucleotide binding. This residue forms a salt bridge with Asp 113, which also lies outside the nucleotide-binding pocket. The latter residue is not highly conserved across the myosin superfamily, which suggests that the salt bridge is not a conserved feature of the myosin molecule. In the structure of chicken skeletal muscle myosin, this residue is clearly trimethylated (103), whereas in *Dictyostelium* myosin, no density for the three additional methyl groups is evident. It is not clear what role this residue plays in the contractile mechanism. Site-directed mutagenesis of *Dictyostelium* myosin shows that conversion of this residue to a leucine generates a molecule with an increased $K_m$ for ATP but unchanged maximal actin-activated ATPase activity or motility (106). The resulting mutant protein is less stable than the wild type presumably because of the introduction of a hydrophobic residue at the surface of the protein and the loss of a salt bridge. Given its location, it is possible that Lys 130 might play an indirect role in stabilizing the conformation of the neighboring residues that form the purine-binding site.

## Proteolytic Cleavage

Limited proteolysis of the myosin head has proved to be invaluable for defining functional segments of this large complex molecule. Much attention has been focused on the three major tryptic fragments (4, 84). The X-ray structural studies have shown that the tryptic fragments arise from cleavage at two flexible loops (Figure 9) rather than between distinct domains (103). These loops are disordered in chicken S1. In *Dictyostelium* myosin these loops are considerably shorter but still exhibit some disorder and evidence of flexibility. The loop between the 25- and 50-kDa tryptic fragment has been called loop 1, whereas the loop between the 50- and 20-kDa tryptic fragment has been given the name loop 2 (116). These loops exhibit considerable sequence variability (131). It appears that the composition of these loops influences the kinetic behavior of myosin. Early proteolytic studies demonstrated that cleavage of loop 2 abolished the actin-activated ATPase activity, whereas other ATPase activities were not eliminated (84). Replacement of loop 2 in *Dictyostelium* myosin with the equivalent sequence from skeletal and smooth muscle causes a change in the $V_{max}$ for actin activation that reflects the activity of the parent. However, the changes in motility did not exhibit the same trend (125). Thus it is clear that the composition and state of loop 2 influences the nucleotide-binding site most likely by modifying the transition from the weakly to strongly bound state of actin and hence altering the probability of the phosphate release. It is possible that one of the functions of loop 2 is to maintain myosin in close proximity to the actin filament when it is the weakly bound state and thereby improve the efficiency of the contractile apparatus. This is important because myosin spends a small proportion of its duty cycle bound to actin, and diffusion of the myosin head away from the actin filament would reduce the effectiveness of myosin-based motility.

The function of loop 1 is less clearly defined. Proteolysis of this loop does not eliminate the actin-activated ATPase activity (84). Kinetic studies have shown that the rate of release of ADP might be a fundamental constraint on the maximum rate of shortening or motility (110, 111). Subsequently, it has been suggested that the composition of loop 1 influences the release of ADP from the nucleotide-binding site and that this is responsible in part for the differences in motility between different myosins (116).

Although most studies have focused on the major tryptic fragments, other sites have been defined that, when combined with the three-dimensional structure, provide further functional insight. Normal skeletal muscle myosin is insensitive to cleavage by thrombin. However, if the reactive cysteine residues are oxidatively cross-linked, it becomes possible to clip the heavy chain between Lys 561 and Ser 562 (chicken sequence) (10, 11), which abolishes the ATPase activity even when the disulfide bond is reduced. Lys 561 and Ser 562 are located in a loop in the lower domain of the 50-kDa segment, at a considerable distance from the phosphate-binding loop (Figure 9). Furthermore, the loop lies close to the actin-binding surface on the face of the molecule opposite from the 50-kDa cleft. The effect of this cleavage is difficult to explain. It appears that the integrity of this part of the molecule is essential for complete function. It is conceivable that the lower domain of the 50-kDa segment fulfills a role in communication between the nucleotide- and actin-binding sites. It is noteworthy that the cleavage loop is adjacent to the segment that carries Trp 510 and exhibits a conformational change in the MgADP•AlF$_4$ complex. This area of the molecule deserves more attention from mutagenesis and chemical studies.

Complementary studies on scallop striated muscle myosin reveal that proteolysis of the actomyosin complex with trypsin also abolishes the high salt (KEDTA and CaATP) ATPase activity (118). The cleavage site is in the general vicinity of that recognized by thrombin, although the exact site has not been determined (88, 118). In principle, there are two loops that might be recognized by trypsin: one centered on Lys 562 and one between Ala 571 and Ala 575 (chicken). The latter loop, although disordered in the structure of chicken skeletal S1, has been implicated in a second binding site to actin (80, 102) and should be less sensitive to proteolysis by trypsin in the actomyosin complex. Because the scallop cleavage site is available in the actomyosin complex, the trypsin site is most likely that at Lys 562 and is therefore equivalent to the thrombin site.

## CONCLUSIONS

Reexamination of the chemical literature for myosin in the context of the recent structural studies reveals that the region associated with the reactive cysteine residues plays a central role in the contractile mechanism. It appears that the major conformational changes in the myosin head are associated with movement of the lower domain of the central 50-kDa segment of the heavy chain, which in turn alters the arrangement of the domains that interface with the reactive cysteine residues. The chemical literature also suggests that there are changes in the interface between the essential light chain and heavy chain during energy transduction. These conclusions were not obvious during the initial examination of the X-ray structure (102, 103) and reveal the importance of attempting to correlate the vast chemical and physiological literature for myosin with the X-ray structures. It is also clear that these structures cannot account for all the chemical literature, which suggests that other states of the myosin molecule during the contractile cycle are yet to be observed. Together these studies suggest future directions for the investigation of myosin-based motility.

ACKNOWLEDGMENT

This research was supported in part by National Institutes of Health grant AR35186 to IR and DK05195 to RGY. CAS was supported by grant number TW05194 from the Fogarty International Center of the National Institutes of Health.

## Literature Cited

1. Atkinson MAL, Robinson EA, Appella E, Korn ED. 1985. Amino acid sequence of the active site of *Acanthamoeba* myosin II. *J. Biol. Chem.* 261:1844–48
2. Bagshaw CR, Trentham DR. 1973. The reversibility of adenosine triphosphate cleavage by myosin. *Biochem. J.* 133:323–28
3. Bagshaw CR, Trentham DR. 1974. The characterization of myosin-product complexes and of product-release steps during the magnesium ion-dependent adenosine triphosphatase reaction. *Biochem. J.* 141:331–49
4. Balint M, Sreter FA, Wolf I, Nagy B, Gergley J. 1975. The substructure of heavy meromyosin, the effect of Ca and $Mg^{2+}$ on the tryptic fragmentation of heavy meromyosin. *J. Biol. Chem.* 250:6168–77
5. Barany M, Barany K. 1959. Studies on "active centers" of l-myosin. *Biochim. Biophys. Acta* 35:293–309
6. Bivin DB, Kubota S, Pearlstein R, Morales MF. 1993. On how a myosin tryptophan may be perturbed. *Proc. Natl. Acad. Sci. USA* 90:6791–95
7. Bivin DB, Ue K, Khoroshev M, Morales MF. 1994. Effect of lysine methylation and other ATPase modulators on the active site of myosin subfragment-1. *Proc. Natl. Acad. Sci. USA* 91:8665–69
8. Bowater R, Zimmerman RW, Webb MR. 1990. Kinetics of ATP and inorganic phosphate release during hydrolysis of ATP by rabbit skeletal actomyosin subfragment-1. Oxygen exchange between ATP or phosphate. *J. Biol. Chem.* 265:171–76
9. Chalovich JM, Greene LE, Eisenberg E. 1983. Crosslinked myosin subfragment 1: a stable analogue of the subfragment-1.ATP complex. *Proc. Natl. Acad. Sci. USA* 80:4909–13
10. Chaussepied P, Mornet D, Audemard E, Derancourt J, Kassab R. 1986. Abolition of ATPase activities of skeletal myosin subfragment-1 by a new selective cleavage within the 50-Kilodalton heavy chain segment. *Biochemistry* 25:1134–40
11. Chaussepied P, Mornet D, Barman TE, Travers F, Kassab R. 1986. Alteration of the ATP hydrolysis and actin binding

12. Cheney RE, Mooseker MS. 1992. Unconventional myosins. *Curr. Opin. Cell Biol.* 4:27–35
13. Chothia C, Lesk AM. 1986. The relationship between the divergence of sequence and structure in proteins. *EMBO J.* 5:823–26
14. Cole D, Yount RG. 1990. Photolabeling of the 6 and 10 S conformations of gizzard myosin with 3′(2′)-O-(4-benzoyl)benzoyl-ATP proline 324 is near the active site. *J. Biol. Chem.* 265:22547–56
15. Cole DG, Yount RG. 1992. Stability and photochemical properties of vanadate-trapped nucleotide complexes of gizzard myosin in the 6S and 10S conformations: identification of an active-site serine. *Biochemistry* 31:6186–92
16. Coleman DE, Berghuis AM, Lee E, Linder ME, Gilman AG, Sprang SR. 1994. Structures of active conformations of Giα1 and the mechanism of GTP hydrolysis. *Science* 265:1405–12
17. Collins JH. 1991. Myosin light chains and troponin C: structural and evolutionary relationships revealed by amino acid sequence comparisons. *J. Muscle Res. Cell Motil.* 12:3–25
18. Cremo CR, Grammer JC, Yount RG. 1988. UV-induced vanadate-dependent modification and cleavage of skeletal myosin subfragment-1 heavy chain. 2. Oxidation of serine in the 23 kDa. $NH_2$-terminal tryptic peptide. *Biochemistry* 27:8415–20
19. Cremo CR, Grammer JC, Yount RG. 1989. Direct chemical evidence that serine 180 of the glycine-rich loop in myosin binds to ATP. *J. Biol. Chem.* 264:6608–11
20. Cremo CR, Neuron JM, Yount RG. 1990. Interaction of myosin subfragment 1 with fluorescent ribose-modified nucleotides. A comparison of vandate trapping and $SH_1$-$SH_2$ cross-linking. *Biochemistry* 29:3309–19
21. Crowder MC, Cooke R. 1987. The orientation of spin-labelled nucleotides bound to myosin in glycerinated muscle fibers. *Biophys. J.* 51:323–33
22. Dale MP, Hackney DD. 1987. Analysis

of positional isotope exchange in ATP by cleavage of the βP-OγP bond. Demonstration of negligible positional isotope exchange by myosin. *Biochemistry* 26:8365–72

23. Dos Remedios CG, Cooke R. 1984. Fluorescence energy transfer between probes on actin and probes on myosin. *Biochim. Biophys. Acta* 788: 193–205

24. Eisenberg E, Greene LE. 1980. The relation of muscle biochemistry to muscle physiology. *Annu. Rev. Physiol.* 42: 293–309

25. Finer JT, Simmons RM, Spudich JA. 1994. Single myosin molecule mechanics: piconewton forces and nanometre steps. *Nature* 368:113–19

26. Fisher AJ, Smith CA, Thoden J, Smith R, Sutoh K, et al. 1995. Structural studies of myosin:nucleotide complexes: a revised model for the molecular basis of muscle contraction. *Biophys. J.* 68: 19s–28s

27. Fisher AJ, Smith CA, Thoden J, Smith R, Sutoh K, et al. 1995. X-ray structures of the myosin motor domain of *Dictyostelium discoideum* complexed with MgADP•BeF$_x$ and MgA•DAlF$_4$⁻. *Biochemistry*. In press

28. Flicker PF, Wallimann T, Vibert P. 1983. Electron microscopy of scallop myosin, location of the regulatory light chains. *J. Mol. Biol.* 169:723–41

29. Franks-Skiba K, Hwang T, Cooke R. 1994. Quenching of fluorescent nucleotides bound to myosin: a probe of the active-site conformation. *Biochemistry* 33:12720–28

30. Garabedian T, Yount RG. 1990. Direct photolabeling of gizzard myosin with UDP and vanadate places Glu-185 at the active site. *J. Biol. Chem.* 265: 22547–33

31. Garabedian T, Yount RG. 1991. Direct photoaffinity labeling of gizzard myosin with vanadate-trapped ADP. *Biochemistry* 30:10126–32

32. Geeves MA. 1991. The dynamics of actin and myosin association and the crossbridge model of muscle contraction. *Biochem. J.* 274:1–14

33. Geeves MA, Goody RS, Gutfreund H. 1984. Kinetics of the acto-S1 interaction as a guide to a model for the crossbridge cycle. *J. Muscle Res. Cell Motil.* 5:351–61

34. Gilson MK, Strautsma JP, McCammon JA, Ripoli DR, Faerman CH, et al. 1994. Open "back door" in a molecular dynamics simulation of acetylcholinesterase. *Science* 263:1276–78

35. Goldman YE. 1987. Kinetics of the

actomyosin ATPase in muscle fibers. *Annu. Rev. Physiol.* 49:637–54

36. Goodno CC. 1979. Inhibition of myosin ATPase by vanadate ion. *Proc. Natl. Acad. Sci. USA* 76:2620–24

37. Goodno CC. 1982. Myosin active-site trapping with vanadate ion. In *Methods in Enzymology*, ed. D Frederiksen, L Cunningham, 85:116–23. New York: Academic

38. Goodno CC, Taylor EW. 1982. Inhibition of actomyosin ATPase by vanadate. *Proc. Natl. Acad. Sci. USA* 79:21–25

39. Goody RS, Hofmann W, Mannherz HG. 1977. The binding constant of ATP to myosin S1 fragment. *Eur. J. Biochem.* 78:317–24

40. Grammer JC, Cremo CR, Yount RG. 1988. UV-induced vanadate-dependent modification and cleavage of skeletal myosin subfragment-1 heavy chain. 1. Evidence for active site modification. *Biochemistry* 27:8408–15

41. Grammer JC, Kuwayama H, Yount RG. 1993. Photoaffinity labeling of skeletal myosin with 2-azidoadenosine triphosphate. *Biochemistry* 32:5725–32

42. Grammer JC, Yount RG. 1991. Photochemical evidence that Ser-243 of myosin's heavy chain is near the phosphate binding site for ATP. *Biophys. J.* 59: 226a

43. Grammer JC, Yount RG. 1993. Is the essential light chain (LC$_{17}$) at the active site of gizzard myosin? A reinvestigation. *Biophys. J.* 64:A143

44. Harada Y, Noguchi A, Kishino A, Yanagida T. 1987. Sliding movement of single actin filaments on one-headed myosin filaments. *Nature* 326:805–8

45. Hennessey ES, Drummond DR, Sparrow JC. 1993. Molecular genetics of actin function. *Biochem. J.* 282:657–71

46. Henry GD, Maruta S, Ikebe M, Sykes BD. 1993. Observation of multiple myosin subfragment 1-ADP-fluoroberyllate complexes by ¹⁹F NMR spectrocopy. *Biochemistry* 32:10451–56

47. Hiratsuka T. 1992. Spatial proximity of ATPase-sensitive tryptophanyl residue(s) and Cys-697 in myosin ATPase. *J. Biol. Chem.* 267:14949–54

48. Holmes KC, Popp D, Gebhard W, Kabsch W. 1990. Atomic model of the actin filament. *Nature* 347:44–49

49. Hozumi T, Muhlrad A. 1981. Reactive lysyl of myosin subfragment 1: location on the 27K fragment and labeling properties. *Biochemistry* 20:2945–50

50. Huston EE, Grammer JC, Yount RG. 1988. The flexibility of the myosin heavy chain: direct evidence that the region containing SH1 and SH2 can

move 10 Å under the influence of nucleotide binding. *Biochemistry* 27: 8945–52

51. Ikura M, Clore MG, Gronenborn AM, Zhu G, Klee CB, Bax A. 1992. Solution structure of a calmodulin-target peptide complex by multidimensional NMR. *Science* 256:632–38

52. Ishijima A, Harada Y, Kojima H, Funatsu T, Higuchi H, Yanagida T. 1994. Single-molecule analysis of the actomyosin motor using nano-manipulation. *Biochem. Biophys. Res. Commun.* 199: 1057–63

53. Itakura S, Yamakawa H, Toyoshima YY, Ishijima A, Kojima T, et al. 1993. Force-generating domain of myosin motor. *Biochem. Biophys. Res. Commun.* 196:1504–10

54. Johnson WC, Bivin DB, Ue K, Morales MF. 1991. A search for protein structural changes accompanying the contractile interaction. *Proc. Natl. Acad. Sci. USA* 88:9748–50

55. Kabsch W, Mannherz HG, Suck D, Pai EF, Holmes KC. 1990. Atomic structure of the actin:DNase I complex. *Nature* 347:37–44

56. Kasprzak AA, Chaussepied P, Morales MF. 1989. Localization of a contact site between actin and myosin in the three-dimensional structure of the acto-S1 complex. *Biochemistry* 28:9230–38

57. Kerwin BA, Yount RG. 1992. Photoaffinity labeling of scallop myosin with 2-[(4-azido-2-nitrophenyl)amino]ethyl diphosphate. Identification of an active site arginine analogous to tryptophan-130 in skeletal muscle myosin. *Bioconjugate Chem.* 3:328–36

58. Kerwin BA, Yount RG. 1993. Photolabelling evidence for calcium-induced conformational changes at the ATP binding site of scallop myosin. *Proc. Natl. Acad. Sci. USA* 90:9035–39

59. Kiehart DP. 1990. Molecular dissection of myosin heavy chain function. *Cell* 60:347–50

60. Kirshenbaumm K, Papp S, Highsmith S. 1993. Cross-linking myosin subfragment-1 Cys-697 and Cys-707 modifies ATP and actin binding site interactions. *Biophys. J.* 65:1121–29

61. Komatsu H, Emoto K, Tawada K. 1993. Half-stoichiometric trinitrophenylation of myosin subfragment 1 in the presence of pyrophosphate or adenosine diphosphate. *J. Biol. Chem.* 268:7799–808

62. Komatsu H, Tawada K. 1993. Microheterogeneity around the reactive lysine residue in the myosin heavy chain from rabbit skeletal muscle. *J. Biol. Chem.* 268:16974–78

63. Komatsu H, Tawada K. 1994. Trinitrophenylation of the reactive lysine residue in double-headed myosin in the presence of PP$_i$. *J. Biochem.* 115:1190–96

64. Kraulis PJ. 1991. MOLSCRIPT: a Program to produce both detailed and schematic plots of protein structures. *J. Appl. Crystallogr.* 24:946–50

65. Kubo S, Tokura S, Tonomura Y. 1960. On the active site of myosin a-adenosine triphosphatase I. Reaction of the enzyme with trinitrobenzenesulphonate. *J. Biol. Chem.* 235:2835–39

66. Kubo S, Tokuyama H, Tonomura Y. 1965. On the active site of myosin a-adenosine triphosphatase v. partial solution of the chemical structure around the binding site of trinitrobenzenesulphonate. *Biochim. Biophys. Acta* 100: 459–70

67. Liepinsh E, Otting G, Wüthrich K. 1992. NMR Spectrocopy of hydroxyl protons in aqueous solutions of peptides and proteins. *J. Biomol. NMR* 2:447–65

68. Lowey S, Trybus KM. 1995. Role of skeletal muscle myosin light chains. *Biophys. J.* 68:120s–7s

69. Lundblad RL. 1991. *Chemical Reagents for Protein Modification.* Boca Raton, FL: CRC. 2nd ed.

70. Luo Y, Wang D, Cremo CR, Pate E, Cooke R, Yount RG. 1995. Photoaffinity ADP analogs as covalently attached reporter groups of the active site of myosin subfragment-1. *Biochemistry* 34:1978–87

71. Lymn RW, Taylor EW. 1971. Mechanism of adenosine triphosphate hydrolysis of actomyosin. *Biochemistry* 10: 4617–24

72. Mahmood R, Elzinga M, Yount RG. 1989. Serine-324 of myosin's heavy chain is photoaffinity-labeled by 3'(2')-O-(4-benzoyl)-benzoyladenosine triphosphate. *Biochemistry* 28:3989–95

73. Maita T, Yajima E, Nagata S, Miyanishi T, Nakayama S, Matsuda G. 1991. The primary structure of skeletal muscle myosin heavy chain: IV. Sequence of the rod and the complete 1,938-residue sequence of the heavy chain. *J. Biochem.* 110:75–87

74. Manstein DJ, Ruppel KM, Kubalek L, Spudich JA. 1991. Manipulation and expression of molecular motors in *Dictyostelium discoideum. J. Cell Sci. Suppl.* 14:63–66

75. Maruta S, Henry GD, Sykes BD, Ikebe M. 1993. Formation of stable myosin-ADP-alumium fluoride and myosin-ADP-beryllium fluoride complexes and

their analysis using [19]F NMR. *J. Biol. Chem.* 268:7093–100

76. Maruta S, Miyanishi T, Matsuda G. 1989. Localization of the ATP binding site in the 23 kDa and 20 kDa regions of the heavy chain of the skeletal muscle myosin head. *Eur. J. Biochem.* 184:213–21

77. Meador WE, Means AR, Quiocho FA. 1992. Target enzyme recognition by calmodulin: 2.4 Å structure of a calmodulin-peptide complex. *Science* 257:1251–55

78. Means GE, Feeney RE. 1968. Reductive alkylation of amino groups in proteins. *Biochemistry* 7:2192–201

79. Milligan RA, Flicker PF. 1987. Structural relationships of actin, myosin, and tropomyosin revealed by cryo-electron microscopy. *J. Cell Biol.* 105:29–39

80. Milligan RA, Whitaker M, Safer D. 1990. Molecular structure of F-actin and location of surface binding sites. *Nature* 348(348):217–21

81. Miyanashi T, Inoue A, Tonomura Y. 1979. Differential modification of specific lysine residues in the two kinds of subfragment-1 of myosin with 2,4,6-trinitrobenzenesulfonate. *J. Biochem.* 85:747–53

82. Miyanishi T, Maita T, Matsuda G, Tonomura Y. 1982. Differences in chemical structure around the reactive lysine residues in the burst and the nonburst heads of skeletal muscle myosin. *J. Biochem.* 91:1845–53

83. Morita F. 1967. Interaction of heavy meromyosin with substrate; difference in ultraviolet absorption spectrum between heavy meromyosin and its Michaelis-Menten complex. *J. Biol. Chem.* 242:4501–6

84. Mornet D, Pantel P, Audemard E, Kassab R. 1979. The limited tryptic cleavage of chymotryptic S1: an approach to the characterisation of the actin site in myosin heads. *Biochem. Biophys. Res. Commun.* 89:925–32

85. Mornet D, Pantel P, Bertrand R, Audemard E, Kassab R. 1980. Localization of the reactive trinitrophenylated lysyl residue of myosin ATPase site in the NH$_2$-terminal (27k domain of S1 heavy chain. *FEBS Lett.* 117:183–88

86. Muller CW, Schulz GE. 1992. Structure of the complex between adenylate kinase from *Escherichia coli* and the inhibitor Ap5A refined at 1.9 Å resolution. *J. Mol. Biol.* 224:159–77

87. Muller H, Perry SV. 1962. The degradation of heavy meromyosin by trypsin. *Biochem. J.* 85:431–39

88. Nyitray L, Goodwin EB, Szent-Gyorgyi AG. 1991. Complete primary structure of a scallop muscle myosin heavy chain. *J. Biol. Chem.* 266:18469–76

89. Okamoto Y, Sekine T, Grammer JC, Yount RG. 1986. Photochemical evidence that the essential light chain is at the active site of smooth muscle myosin. *Nature* 324:78–80

90. Okamoto Y, Yount RG. 1985. Identification of an active site peptide of skeletal myosin after photoaffinity labeling with N-(4-azido-2-nitrophenyl)-2-aminoethyl diphosphate. *Proc. Natl. Acad. Sci. USA.* 82:1575–79

91. Pai EF, Krengel U, Petsko GA, Goody RS, Kabsch W, Wittinghofer A. 1990. Refined structure of the triphosphate conformation of H-ras-p21 at 1.35 Å resolution: implications for the mechanism of GTP hydrolysis. *EMBO J.* 9:2351–59

92. Papp SJ, Highsmith S. 1993. The ATP-induced myosin subfragment-1 fluorescence is due to one tryptophan. *Biochim. Biophys. Acta* 1202:169–72

93. Pate E, Franks-Skiba K, White H, Cooke R. 1993. The use of differing nucleotides to investigate cross-bridge kinetics. *J. Biol. Chem.* 268:10046–53

94. Peyser YM, Muhlrad A, Werber MM. 1990. Tryptophan-130 is the most reactive tryptophan residue in rabbit skeletal myosin subfragment-1. *FEBS Lett.* 259:346–48

95. Phan BC, Cheung P, Reisler E, Muhlrad A. 1994. Extensively methylated myosin subfragment-1: examination of local structure, interactions with nucleotides and actin, and ligand-induced conformational changes. *Biochemistry* 33:1286–95

96. Phan BC, Faller LD, Reisler E. 1993. Kinetic and equilibrium analysis of the interactions of actomyosin subfragment-1.ADP with beryllium fluoride. *Biochemistry* 32:7712–19

97. Phan BC, Reisler E. 1992. Inhibition of myosin ATPase by beryllium fluoride. *Biochemistry* 31:4787–93

98. Pliszka B. 1990. Influence of nucleotide on chemical crosslinking between alkali light chains and the heavy chain of myosin subfragment-1. *Biochim. Biophys. Acta* 1040:89–94

99. Pliszka B. 1993. Mapping of the region of the heavy chain of myosin subfragment-1 that can be crosslinked to the alkali light chains. *Biochem. Mol. Biol. Int.* 31:381–88

100. Rajasekharan KN, Sivaramakrishnan M, Burke M. 1987. Proximity and ligand-induced movement of interdomain residues in myosin subfragment-1 con-

taining trapped MgADP and MgPPi probed by multifunctional cross-linking. *J. Biol. Chem.* 262:11207–14

101. Rayment I, Holden HM, Sellers JR, Fananapazir L, Epstein ND. 1995. Structural interpretation of the mutations in the β-cardiac myosin that have been implicated in familial hypertrophic cardiomyopathy. *Proc. Natl. Acad. Sci. USA* 92:3864–68

102. Rayment I, Holden HM, Whittaker M, Yohn CB, Lorenz M, Holmes KC, et al. 1993. Structure of the actin-myosin complex and its implications for muscle contraction. *Science* 261:58–65

103. Rayment I, Rypniewski WR, Schmidt-Bäse K, Smith R, Tomchick DR, et al. 1993. Three-dimensional structure of myosin subfragment-1: a molecular motor. *Science* 261:50–58

104. Reisler E, Burke M, Himmelfarb S, Harrington WF. 1974. Spatial proximity of the two essential sulfhydryl groups of myosin. *Biochemistry* 13:3837–40

105. Ritchie MD, Geeves MA, Woodward SKA, Manstein DJ. 1993. Kinetic characterization of a cytoplasmic motor domain expressed in *Dictyostelium discoideum*. *Proc. Natl. Acad. Sci. USA* 90:8619–23

106. Ruppel KM, Uyeda TQP, Spudich JA. 1994. Role of highly conserved lysine 130 of myosin motor domain. *J. Biol. Chem.* 269:18773–80

107. Rypniewski WR, Holden HM, Rayment I. 1993. Structural consequences of reductive methylation of lysine residues in hen egg white lysozyme: an X-ray analysis at 1.8 Å resolution. *Biochemistry* 32:9851–58

108. Schweins T, Geyer M, Scheffzek K, Warshel A, Kalbitzer HR, Wittinghofer A. 1995. Substrate-assisted catalysis as a mechanism for GTP hydrolysis of p21ras and other GTP-binding proteins. *Struct. Biol.* 2:36–44

109. Sekine T, Kielley WW. 1964. The enzymatic properties of N-ethylmaleimide modified myosin. *Biochim. Biophys. Acta* 81:336–45

110. Siemankowski RF, White HD. 1984. Kinetics of the interaction between actin, ADP, and cardiac myosin-S1. *J. Biol. Chem.* 259:5045–53

111. Siemankowski RF, Wiseman MO, White HD. 1985. ADP dissociation from actomyosin subfragment-1 is sufficiently slow to limit the unloaded shortening velocity in vertebrate muscle. *Proc. Natl. Acad. Sci. USA* 82:658–62

112. Sleep JA, Hackney DD, Boyer PD. 1980. The equivalence of phosphate oxygens for exchange and the hydrolysis

characteristics revealed by the distribution of [18O]Pi species formed by myosin and actomyosin ATPase. *J. Biol. Chem.* 255:4094–99

113. Sleep JA, Trybus KM, Johnson KA, Taylor EW. 1981. Kinetic studies of normal and modified heavy meromyosin and subfragment-1. *J. Muscle Res. Cell Motil.* 2:373–99

114. Smith CA, Rayment I. 1995. X-ray structure of the magnesium(II)-pyrophosphate complex of the truncated head of *Dictyostelium discoideum* myosin to 2.7 Å resolution. *Biochemistry*. In press

115. Sondek J, Lambright DG, Noel JP, Hamm HE, Sigler PB. 1994. GTPase mechanism of G proteins from the 1.7-Å crystal structure of transducin α-GDP-AlF4−. *Nature* 372:276–79

116. Spudich JA. 1994. How molecular motors work. *Nature* 372:515–18

117. Sweeney HL, Straceski AJ, Leinwand LA, Tikunov BA, Faust L. 1994. Heterologous expression of a cardiomyopathic myosin that is defective in its actin interaction. *J. Biol. Chem.* 269:1603–6

118. Szentkiralyi EM. 1987. An intact heavy chain at the actin-subfragment 1 interface is required for ATPase activity in scallop myosin. *J. Muscle Res. Cell Motil.* 8:349–57

119. Taylor EW. 1977. Transient phase of adenosine triphosphate hydrolysis by myosin, heavy meromyosin, and subfragment 1. *Biochemistry* 16:732–40

120. Taylor EW. 1979. Mechanism of actomyosin ATPase and the problem of muscle contraction. *CRC Crit. Rev. Biochem.* 6:103–64

121. Tong SW, Elzinga M. 1983. The sequence of the NH2-terminal 204-residue fragment of the heavy chain of rabbit skeletal muscle myosin. *J. Biol. Chem.* 258:13100–10

122. Toyoshima YY, Kron SJ, McNally EM, Niebling KR, Toyoshima C, Spudich JA. 1987. Myosin subfragment-1 is sufficient to move actin filaments in vitro. *Nature* 328:536–39

123. Trentham DR, Eccleston JF, Bagshaw CR. 1976. Kinetic analysis of ATPase mechanisms. *Q. Rev. Biophys.* 9:217–81

124. Trybus KM, Taylor EW. 1982. Transient kinetics of adenosine 5′-diphosphate and adenosine 5′-(β,γ,-imidotriphosphate) binding to subfragment-1 and actosubfragment-1. *Biochemistry* 21:1284–94

125. Uyeda TQP, Ruppel KM, Spudich JA. 1994. Enzymatic activities correlate with chimaeric substitutions at the ac-

tin-binding face of myosin. *Nature* 368: 567–69

126. Vale RD. 1994. Getting a grip on myosin. *Cell* 78:733–37

127. Vale RD, Goldstein LSB. 1990. One motor, many tails: an expanding repertoire of force-generating enzymes. *Cell* 60:883–85

128. Walker JE, Saraste M, Runswick MJ, Gay NJ. 1982. Distantly related sequences in the α- and β-subunits of ATP synthase, myosin, kinases, and other ATP-requiring enzymes and a common nucleotide binding fold. *EMBO J.* 1: 945–51

129. Wang D, Pate E, Cooke R, Yount R. 1993. Synthesis of non-nucleotide ATP analogues and characterization of their chemomechanical interaction with muscle fibres. *J. Muscle Res. Cell Motil.* 14:484–97

130. Warrick HM, De Lozanne A, Leinwand LA, Spudich JA. 1986. Conserved protein domains in a myosin heavy chain gene from *Dictyostelium dicoideum*. *Proc. Natl. Acad. Sc. USA* 83:9433–37

131. Warrick HM, Spudich JA. 1987. Myosin structure and function in cell motility. *Annu. Rev. Cell Biol.* 3:379–421

132. Webb MR, Trentham DR. 1980. The stereochemical course of phosphoric residue transfer during the myosin ATPase reaction. *J. Biol. Chem.* 255:8629–32

133. Webb MR, Trentham DR. 1981. The mechanism of ATP hydrolysis catalyzed by myosin and actomyosin, using rapid reaction techniques to study oxygen exchange. *J. Biol. Chem.* 256: 10910–16

134. Weidner H, Wetzel R, Eckstein F. 1978. The nonessential nature of sulfhydryl groups for ATPase activity in myosin. *J. Biol. Chem.* 253:2763–68

135. Wells JA, Yount RG. 1979. Active site trapping of nucleotides by crosslinking of two sulphydryls in myosin subfragment-1. *Proc. Natl. Acad. Sci. USA* 76: 4966–70

136. Wells JA, Yount RG. 1980. Reaction of 5,5′-dithiobis(2-nitrobenzoic acid) with myosin subfragment-1: evidence

for formation of a single protein disulfide with trapping of metal nucleotide at the active site. *Biochemistry* 19:1711–17

137. Werber MM, Peyser YM, Muhlrad A. 1987. Modification of myosin subfragment-1 tryptophans by dimethyl (2-hydroxy-5-nitrobenzyl)sulphonium bromide. *Biochemistry* 26:2903–9

138. Werber MM, Peyser M, Muhlrad A. 1992. Characterization of stable beryllium fluoride, aluminum fluoride, and vanadate containing myosin subfragment 1-nucleotide complexes. *Biochemistry* 31:7190–97

139. Werber MM, Szent-Gyorgyi AG, Fasman GD. 1972. Fluorescence studies on heavy meromyosin-substrate interaction. *Biochemistry* 11:2872–83

140. White HD, Belknap B, Jiang W. 1993. Kinetics of binding and hydrolysis of a series of nucleoside triphophates by actomyosin-S1. *J. Biol. Chem.* 268:10039–45

141. White HW, Rayment I. 1993. Kinetic characterization of reductively methylated myosin subfragment-1. *Biochemistry* 32:9859–65

142. Woodward SK, Eccleston JF, Geeves MA. 1991. Kinetics of the interaction of 2′(3′)-O-(N-methylanthraniloyl) ATP with myosin subfragment 1 and actomyosin subfragment 1: characterization of two acto-s1.ADP complexes. *Biochemistry* 30:422–30

143. Xie X, Harrison DH, Schlichting I, Sweet RM, Kalabokis VN, et al. 1994. Structure of the regulatory domain of scallop myosin at 2.8 Å resolution. *Nature* 368:306–12

144. Yanagida T, Harada Y, Ishijima A. 1993. Nano-manipulation of actomyosin molecular motors in vitro: a new working principle. *Trends Biochem. Sci.* 18: 319–24

145. Yount RG, Cremo CR, Grammer JC, Kerwin BA. 1992. Photochemical mapping of the active site of myosin. *Philos. Trans. R. Soc. London* B336: 55–61

146. Yount RG, Lawson D, Rayment I. 1995. Is myosin a "back door" enzyme? *Biophys. J.* 68:44s–9s

Annu. Rev. Physiol. 1996. 58:703–29

# THE MOVEMENT OF KINESIN ALONG MICROTUBULES

*Jonathon Howard*

Department of Physiology & Biophysics, University of Washington, Box 357290, Seattle, Washington 98195-7290

KEY WORDS: molecular motor, motor protein, cell motility, chemomechanical transduction

## ABSTRACT

The molecular motor kinesin is a homodimer containing two heads—globular domains each of which has an ATP- and a microtubule-binding site. It is argued by analogy to other proteins with coiled-coil dimerization domains that the kinesin dimer has an approximate axis of rotational symmetry. The path kinesin follows along the surface of the microtubule is parallel to the protofilaments, and the steps are likely separated by 8 nm, the length of the tubulin dimer. Micromechanical recordings from single kinesin molecules indicate that one motor can exert a force as great as 5 pN. The efficiency of kinesin probably is in the order of 50%, considering the free energy available from ATP hydrolysis. Structural, mechanical, and biochemical experiments suggest that in order not to let go of a microtubule, the two heads of kinesin might move in a coordinated manner, perhaps undergoing a rotary motion.

## INTRODUCTION

Motor proteins are enzymes that convert the chemical energy derived from the hydrolysis of ATP into mechanical work used to power cellular motility. In addition to specialized motile cells like muscle fibers and processes like cilia, all eukaryotic cells have motor proteins. The reason is that eukaryotic cells are large and their cytosols crowded with filaments and organelles; as a result, diffusion is too slow to efficiently move material from one part of a cell to another (53). Instead, the intracellular transport of organelles such as vesicles, mitochondria, and chromosomes is mediated by motor proteins that include myosins and dyneins, relatives of the proteins found in the specialized muscle and ciliated cells. In addition, there is a third family of motor proteins, the kinesins, which are the subject of this review.

How do these motor proteins work? The answer requires an approach analogous to that of an engineer who wishes to understand how a machine

703

like an internal combustion engine or an electrical motor works. How much force does the motor generate? How fast does it move? What path along its associated cytoskeletal filament does it follow? How much fuel does it consume and with what efficiency? What makes these questions especially fascinating is that motor proteins are very unusual machines that do what no manmade machines do—they convert chemical energy to mechanical energy directly rather than via an intermediate such as heat or electrical energy.

The motor protein kinesin (8, 72), which transports organelles along microtubules, serves as an excellent model for understanding the molecular mechanism of force generation. Studying kinesin has a number of advantages over studying myosin and dynein. First, the motile machinery subserving organelle transport is biochemically and geometrically simpler than that driving cilial and muscle motility. A corollary of this simplicity is that a single molecule of kinesin can move a large distance along a microtubule without falling off (6, 39; see below), whereas myosin (and probably dynein) require several motors for continuous movement (71). Second, kinesin's motor domain is small, only about one third that of myosin's and one tenth that of dynein's. Thus the small size of kinesin, together with the ability to assay single motors, has facilitated structural and functional analysis of this motor. By comparing the structural, chemical, and mechanical properties of kinesin to myosin, it is hoped that the essential features of the biological motor reaction will be revealed.

## STRUCTURE OF KINESIN

Native kinesin, for example the protein purified from bovine brain, consists of two heavy chains and two light chains (7) (Figure 1). The motor resides in the heavy chains: If the light chains (13) are lost during purification (32) or if the heavy chain gene of *Drosophila* kinesin is expressed in bacteria without the light chain gene (77), the resulting protein, a dimer (5, 41), moves at the same speed as native kinesin. Thus the light chains, which may be involved in the binding of kinesin to organelles, are not essential for motility and will not be further considered.

### Seven Domains

Kinesin's heavy chain contains seven functional domains based on the most recent evidence from electron microscopy, protein chemistry, and sequence analysis (Figure 1). All sequence numbers refer to the *Drosophila* kinesin heavy chain (DKH) (76). The proposed domain boundaries may differ by several amino acids from the actual boundaries.

DOMAIN 1    The motor domain (aa 1–344), which is also called a head, is sufficient for motility. Recombinant proteins with the complementary carboxy-

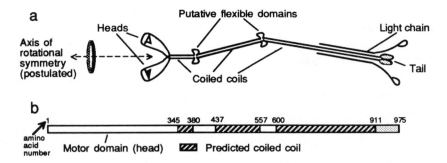

*Figure 1* Proposed structural domains of kinesin. (*a*) Structural model of native kinesin showing the location of the heads, the three coiled coils interrupted by two flexible domains, the tail domain, and the light chains. Each head has longest dimension ~9 nm, and the whole molecule is ~75 nm long. The half arrows in each head denote the postulated symmetry relation between the heads. (*b*) *Drosophila* kinesin heavy chain amino acid sequence (76) showing the proposed seven domains.

terminal sequences deleted still move, although less well than the full-length protein (5, 67, 77). The globular motor domain is ~9 nm by ~3 × 3 nm based on electron microscopy (65, 36) and hydrodynamic measurements (41).

DOMAIN 2    The dimerization domain (aa 345–380) is predicted to form a parallel coiled-coil dimer (54, 67). In accordance with this prediction, the sedimentation coefficient for DKH(1–392) is approximately twice that of DKH(1–340), as expected if the former protein were a dimer and the latter a monomer (41).

DOMAIN 3    The link domain (aa 381–436), containing proline 399, corresponds to a break in the predicted coiled coil. This domain likely includes a flexible region because it is susceptible to proteolysis (45, 49).

DOMAINS 4–6    Coil 1 (aa 437–556) and coil 2 (aa 600–910), predicted coiled coils, have high α-helix content as assayed by circular dichroism, and electron microscopy suggests that they form parallel dimers (15). Cross-linking studies indicate that the peptide chains of coil 2 are in register (15). Coil 1 and coil 2 are separated by the kink domain (aa 557–599) in which the coiled coil is expected to be broken by proline 587. The thin stalk seen by electron microscopy to protrude from the head domain has a length of ~50 nm (36, 65), consistent with the total predicted length of coil 1 and coil 2, and is bent near the middle at a location consistent with the kink. Coil 2's predicted coiled coil is disrupted three times. Coil 2 probably binds to the light chains (22), perhaps via a tetrameric coiled coil.

DOMAIN 7   The tail (aa 911–975) is positively charged and may bind to organelles and to the glass and plastic surfaces used in motility assays.

## Kinesin-Related Proteins

Since the original discovery of kinesin, a large family of proteins with homology to kinesin's motor domain has been discovered (reviewed in 27, 28). For example, *Drosophila* may have more than 30 genes related to the kinesin gene (18). The sequence identity in the motor domains of these proteins is ≥30%, sufficiently high to suggest that the protein folds are similar. Yet, remarkably, these proteins display a wide range of motor phenotypes. For example, the *Drosophila* ncd protein has 40–45% sequence identity to kinesin in the motor domain and forms a similar-shaped complex with microtubules as assessed by negative-stain electron microscopy (36a), but the ncd protein moves along microtubules in the opposite direction to kinesin (55, 74). The structural basis for this switch in directionality is a major unanswered question.

The nonmotor domains of the kinesin-related proteins are dissimilar. It is likely that the different tail domains hook the motors to their different cargoes.

## The Symmetry of Kinesin

Because each of kinesin's head domains is identical, the two-headed kinesin molecule depicted in Figure 1a does not have bilateral symmetry. Thus it is wrong to think of a kinesin molecule as having a right foot and a left foot. Instead, it has two left feet! The gait of kinesin is therefore fundamentally different to that of a walking animal whose alternating legs make mirror motions.

What is the spatial relationship between kinesin's two heads? In principle, the two protein monomers of a homodimer may be related spatially by rotation and translation. In this general case, the dimer has a polarity and the two monomers are not equivalent. For example, it would be possible to distinguish a front and a back (or a left and a right) monomer. However, in practice, homodimers are found to be related approximately by an axis of twofold rotational symmetry (i.e. there is little or no translation). The reason is that if the association is through the same complementary surfaces on each monomer (via what is termed an isologous interaction; 11), then nonequivalent association of the two surfaces to form a nonsymmetrical dimer is disfavored because some of the complementary sites would not be paired. Thus we might expect the kinesin homodimer (with both heads in the same nucleotide state) to possess an approximate axis of rotational symmetry. This expectation is bolstered by the finding that kinesin dimerizes via a coiled coil (see above) because those coiled-coil homodimers and dimers whose structures are known, the catabolite-activating protein (CAP) (75) and the

GCN4 leucine zipper (61), both have approximate axes of rotational symmetry. The near symmetry of these coiled-coil dimers is a consequence of the hydrophobic residues from one monomer being adjacent to the identical residues in the other [they lie side by side according to the "knobs-in-holes" packing postulated by Crick (12)]. Such registration is favored energetically because misregistration would give rise to unpaired hydrophobic residues that protrude from each end of the coiled coil.

Thus, although the structure of the kinesin dimer is not known, there is good reason to hypothesize that kinesin (with both heads in the same nucleotide state) has approximate twofold rotational symmetry and, therefore, that the two heads are spatially equivalent. The natural extrapolation of this reasoning is that the two heads might be functionally equivalent; they have the same hydrolysis cycles and make the same motions. We refer to this supposition as the equivalence hypothesis. It should be stressed that twofold rotational symmetry does not necessarily imply equivalence. For example, the binding of one head to a microtubule could induce a symmetry-breaking conformational change that persists throughout the encounter of the dimer with the microtubule. Thus the equivalence hypothesis presupposes that the protein has no such "memory."

The equivalence hypothesis has several consequences that can be appreciated by comparing kinesin to the two coiled-coil dimers mentioned above. Both CAP and GCN4 are transcription factors that bind nearly palindromic, double-stranded DNA. Such DNA also has approximate rotational symmetry; the dual symmetry of protein and substrate facilitates simultaneous association of the two DNA-binding $\alpha$-helices into successive major grooves of the DNA (56). In contrast, the polar microtubule is not rotationally symmetric. Thus kinesin's symmetric heads could not bind simultaneously to a microtubule without severe distortion; i.e. the rotational symmetry would have to be broken as the heads assume the translational symmetry necessary for simultaneous binding. The implications of such symmetry breaking on the motor mechanism are discussed below.

## DISTANCES THAT CHARACTERIZE A MOTOR REACTION

A motor protein may move several micrometers or even millimeters along a filament. This distance is much larger than the motor's dimension. Thus the motor reaction must be a cyclic one in which the motor repetitively binds to and unbinds from the filament. There are a number of distinct distances that characterize this reaction. Because these distances have not been clearly distinguished in the literature, the following definitions are offered (Figure 2).

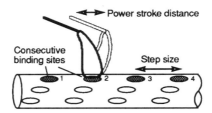

*Figure 2* Cartoon of a hypothetical motor protein and its associated filament illustrating the distinction between the power stroke, which is a property of the motor, and the step size, which is a property of the filament. In particular, the power-stroke distance need not equal the step size.

The step size (*d*) is the distance between consecutive motor-binding sites on the surface of the filament: If we follow one motor over time and mark the places on the filament that the motor binds, then the distances between these marks are the step-size distances (62). In this definition, one motor means one motor molecule, so that a dimer containing two heads is considered to be one motor. The step size depends on the structure of the filament. Because the actin and tubulin monomers that respectively make up actin filaments and microtubules do not have repeated sequences of amino acids, it is unlikely that there is more than one motor-binding site per monomer. Thus the step size must be equal to the distance between the consecutive subunits onto which the motor touches down. The step size could be highly variable: The motor may switch randomly between protofilaments or it could maintain a direction but skip over a variable number of subunits. Alternatively, the step could be highly stereotyped as the motor follows a precise path across the filament's surface lattice. The step size could depend on the load and on the number of motors participating in the motion.

In order to reach the next binding site, it is necessary for the motor to undergo a conformational change. We define the power-stroke distance (δ) as the magnitude of this conformational change (Figure 2). The power-stroke distance is a property of the motor itself. The power-stroke distance is defined more precisely when we consider models of force generation. Here we stress that the step size and power-stroke distances need not be equal. For example, in muscle, there are numerous motors driving the sliding of the thin filament over the thick filament. After a particular motor has moved through its power stroke and detached from the filament, the other motors may move the thin filament so as to bring the next binding site to the motor in question. Thus the step size could be much larger than the power stroke and need not be an integral multiple of it. For kinesin, which as a single motor can move processively along microtubules, we expect the step size and the power stroke to be of similar magnitudes. But they need not be equal, because any mismatch between the power stroke and the step size could be compensated for by (*a*) diffusion of the kinesin-coated organelle to bring kinesin's head to another binding site on the microtubule or (*b*) thermally induced strain in an elastic element within kinesin's head domain.

The distance moved per ATP hydrolyzed could be less than, equal to, or greater than either the step size or the power stroke. For example, if there is slippage or if not all ATP hydrolysis events lead to motion (futile hydrolysis events), the hydrolysis distance could be smaller. On the other hand, if there is more than one mechanical cycle per hydrolysis cycle, the hydrolysis distance could be larger than either the step size or the power stroke. In this case the motor would be analogous to a wind-up toy soldier that takes several steps while winding.

## KINESIN'S STEP SIZE

Kinesin's step size is most likely 8 nm, the distance between the tubulin dimers along each of the 13 protofilaments that make up the microtubule. Myosin's step size is probably ~40 nm, the period of the actin filament. The evidence for these conclusions is summarized below.

### *Structural Evidence*

MICROTUBULE STRUCTURE   A microtubule is a hollow cylinder whose surface is made up of tubulin dimers (2). The dimers, which are composed of two different but homologous subunits ($\alpha$ and $\beta$), bind head-to-tail to form a protofilament whose axis roughly parallels that of the microtubule. Several protofilaments then associate laterally to form a sheet whose closure defines the wall of the microtubule. Because the protofilaments are parallel, the microtubule is a polar structure.

KINESIN FOLLOWS THE PROTOFILAMENT AXIS   It makes sense that a motor like kinesin, which transports organelles along microtubules, would move parallel to the protofilament axis because this is the shortest path between the ends of a microtubule. To test whether this is indeed the case, we performed the following experiment (Figure 3; 62). By altering the buffer conditions, we polymerized microtubules with either 12, 13, or 14 protofilaments (12-, 13-, and 14-mers). The protofilaments of a 13-mer run almost exactly parallel to the axis of the microtubule. (13-mers are the most common microtubule found inside cells.) But the protofilaments of a 14-mer follow a shallow, left-handed helical path around the surface of the microtubule. The pitch of this so-called supertwist can be measured by cryoelectron microscopy and is found to be

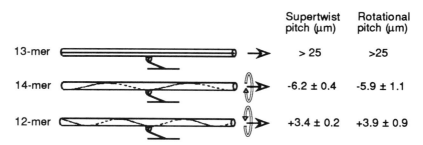

| | Supertwist pitch (μm) | Rotational pitch (μm) |
|---|---|---|
| 13-mer | > 25 | >25 |
| 14-mer | -6.2 ± 0.4 | -5.9 ± 1.1 |
| 12-mer | +3.4 ± 0.2 | +3.9 ± 0.9 |

*Figure 3* Experiment showing that kinesin moves parallel to the microtubule's protofilaments. Microtubules with different numbers of protofilaments have different supertwists. The protofilaments of 13-mers run parallel to the microtubule's axis, whereas those of 14-mers follow a shallow left-handed helix around the surface of the microtubule (note that the width of the microtubule is greatly exaggerated). The table at the right gives the supertwist pitch measured by cryoelectron microscopy and the pitch of the rotation of the microtubules as they move in a gliding assay across a kinesin-coated surface (62).

approximately 6 μm. The protofilaments of the 12-mer follow a right-handed helix (of opposite handedness to the 14-mer) with a pitch of about 4 μm. The various supertwists arise from rotations of the microtubules' surface lattices to permit closure with the various numbers of protofilaments (73).

We then asked whether these microtubules rotated as they glided over a surface coated with kinesin. If kinesin follows the protofilament axis, we do not expect the 13-mers to rotate, but we expect the 14-mers and 12-mers to rotate with the appropriate pitches and handednesses. The experimental results closely matched the predictions (Figure 3). Therefore, these results rule out the possibility that kinesin follows a path that is angled with respect to the protofilament axis. The experiments on the 13-mers were then repeated using very low kinesin density on the surface—conditions in which the microtubules are moved by single motors (39). Because there was no detectable random rotation of the microtubule, we were able to rule out the possibility that the motor switches randomly from protofilament to protofilament. If random switches do take place, they are rare; less than 2% of the steps result in sideways movements.

These rotation experiments show that kinesin moves parallel to the protofilaments. Because the intersubunit spacing along the protofilament is 4 nm, and there are no repeat sequences within the individual tubulin subunits, the most likely prediction is that the step size is a multiple of 4 nm if the kinesin head can bind to either of the tubulin subunits, or 8 nm if one kinesin head can bind per dimer.

ONE KINESIN-BINDING SITE PER DIMER    Two groups (33, 40) have decorated microtubules with bacterially expressed kinesin head domains in order to measure the stoichiometry of kinesin's binding to tubulin. There is only one strongly bound, monomeric 340-amino acid head domain per tubulin dimer (40, 41).

THE SYMMETRY OF KINESIN ARGUES AGAINST STEPS THAT ALTERNATE BETWEEN ADJACENT PROTOFILAMENTS   The simplest synthesis of the two results—that kinesin follows the protofilament axis and that there is only one kinesin-binding site per dimer—is that the step size is either 8 nm [Figure 4(i) and (ii)], or a multiple of 8 nm. However, because kinesin has two heads, it is formally possible that kinesin alternates between two protofilaments [e.g. Figure 4(iii)]. If this were the case, the step size would depend on the lattice type. For the B lattice (2) shown in Figure 4, where the offset between neighboring protofilaments is ~1 nm, the components of the step sizes in a direction parallel to the microtubule's long axis would be 1 and 7 nm [Figure 4(iii)]. Alternatively, if the microtubule adopts an A lattice, the steps might be 3 and 5 nm.

The structure of kinesin provides an important clue to the step size. The equivalence hypothesis developed above implies that kinesin cannot switch back and forth between protofilaments as shown in Figure 4(iii). The reason is that if head 1, attached to a protofilament we call a, were to undergo a conformational change and subsequent motion to bring head 2 to the neighboring protofilament called b, then the equivalent conformational change by head 2 would bring head 1 to the next protofilament called c, not back to the original protofilament a. But the procession a→b→c etc would lead to a rotation of a 13-mer and is therefore excluded by the rotation experiments of Ray et al (62). Thus the steps must be colinear. By a similar argument, the steps must be equally spaced: The mark left by one head must fall exactly half way between the marks left by the other because both heads must make identical steps. Thus equivalence implies steps that are a multiple of 8 nm.

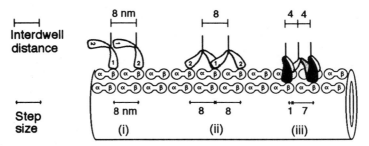

*Figure 4*  Possible stepping patterns for kinesin as it moves along a microtubule. Two protofilaments in the B lattice are drawn. In (i), only one head is usually bound while in (ii) both heads are usually bound. In (iii), kinesin is shown straddling two protofilaments—such motion requires the heads to be nonequivalent.

The step size has been defined differently by other workers. As the ATP concentration is reduced, and the motor spends most of its time bound to the filament (all motors studied so far bind strongly to their respective filaments in the absence of ATP), the heads are expected to dwell at their binding sites for longer and longer times as they wait for ATP molecules to arrive. The cargo is also expected to dwell at particular locations. The step size was defined by Svoboda et al (70) as the cargo's interdwell distance. But the step size (as we have defined it) need not be equal to interdwell distance. For example, in Figure 4(iii), the interdwell distance is 4 nm (because both heads are bound), whereas the steps are 1 nm and 7 nm. Because equivalence of the heads rules out this pattern of motion, the equivalence hypothesis also implies that the step size equals the interdwell distance; thus the two definitions are the same.

## High-Resolution Mechanical Measurements

The structural evidence just reviewed favors a step that is 8 nm or a multiple of 8 nm. Given that single molecules of kinesin can move processively along microtubules and that the longest dimension of the kinesin head is only ~9 nm, it is hard to imagine how the step could be 16 nm or more. Thus an 8-nm step is expected. It would be highly desirable to test these structural predictions by directly monitoring the motion of a single kinesin molecule as it moves along a microtubule. Are the steps 8 nm, or is the pattern more complex? Several laboratories (20, 46, 57, 70) have constructed apparatuses capable of making high-resolution measurements from motor proteins. The first published report is from Svoboda et al (70). These workers tracked the motion of kinesin-coated silica beads along microtubules fixed to a glass surface—an optical trap exerted a force on the bead whose position was monitored with an interferometer. The kinesin density on the beads was so low that the motion was likely driven by single motors (see below).

The data of Svoboda et al (70) rule out a step of ≥16 nm, although this hypothesis was not specifically tested. At low ATP or at high force, when the speed is low, the motion is clearly not smooth but proceeds via jumps at irregular intervals. The amplitude of the jumps is highly variable—jumps as small as 4 nm (which is the approximate noise level at the filtering frequency used) and as large as 20 nm were discerned. The important observation is that the fraction of steps of apparent amplitude ≥16 nm is only 6/49 (figures 5 and 6 in Reference 70). Thus the overwhelming majority of steps are <16 nm. Indeed, probably all the underlying steps are <16 nm because the larger steps can probably be accounted for by either the recording noise or the rapid succession of two or more smaller steps. Thus kinesin step size is most likely 8nm.

## Myosin's Step Size

An ingenious experiment by Molloy et al (60) demonstrates that myosin's step size is ~40 nm. An actin filament connecting two glass beads was pulled taut and "bowed" back and forth through a few hundred nanometers across a raised surface coated with myosin S1 head fragment. Two optical traps independently manipulated the two beads. The image of one bead was projected onto a sensitive photodiode so that the displacement of the filament by the myosin could be detected. Molloy et al found that myosin only interacted with the filament at ~40 nm intervals. This result has a simple structural interpretation: Myosin can only bind to actin monomers on the filaments that have the correct radial orientation. This occurs every 38 nm, the pitch of each of the shallow (two-start) helices that make up the actin filament. How could a myosin molecule in a muscle span this large distance? Presumably, the other myosins in the highly ordered sarcomere move the actin filament to bring the next binding site on the filament to the molecule in question, just as the optical tweezers did in the Molloy et al experiment.

## POWER-STROKE VS RATCHET MODELS FOR FORCE GENERATION

Kinesin's power-stroke distance is not known but is expected to be similar to the step size because single kinesin molecules can move processively along microtubules. Myosin's power-stroke distance is probably ~5 nm (59), a distance compatible with a large swinging motion of myosin's regulatory domain (63, 64). But a question more fundamental than the amplitude of the power stroke is whether the power-stroke model is even correct. In this section, we consider the power-stroke model in more detail and discuss how this and other models have been tested by recent mechanical recordings from single motor proteins.

## Power-Stroke Model

The standard model (Figure 5a) assumes that the motor contains an elastic element (of stiffness $\kappa$) which, while attached to the filament, suddenly shortens through a distance $\delta$ (the power stroke distance defined above) and becomes strained. This initially strained state is denoted A2 by Leibler & Huse (51) and has also been referred to as the strongly bound state (e.g. 37). Directed motion results when this strain is relieved as the motor relaxes. The motor then returns to the initial conformation—the recovery stroke—so that it can rebind to the filament at a different site on the surface. A rigorous mathematical formulation of the model can be found in Leibler & Huse (51). Evidence

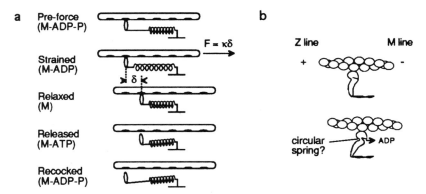

*Figure 5* (a) Power-stroke model in which it is hypothesized that the motor binds prior to undergoing a conformational change that strains an internal elastic element. Nucleotide states for myosin are indicated in parentheses. (b) Possible realization of the power stroke of myosin interacting with actin.

identifying the nucleotide states associated with each of the proposed mechanical states of myosin is summarized in Bagshaw (4).

## Structure of Myosin

The X-ray-derived structure of the myosin head (63, 64) is consistent with this model (as well as other models such as the motor-diffusion model below) if we assume that the elastic element is not a linear spring like that shown in Figure 5a but a spiral or leaf spring located near the interface between the motor and regulatory domains. For example, if such a circular spring were located near the phosphate-binding site where the actin cleft and nucleotide pocket meet, then rotation through 45° would move the distal end of the 8-nm-long α-helical light chain domain through ~5 nm (Figure 5b). An attractive idea raised in the original paper (61, but see 21) is that the power stroke could correspond to the opening of the nucleotide-binding pocket. Such motion would have a large component parallel to the axis of the actin filament and would be directed toward the filament's plus or barbed end, i.e. in the direction of myosin's motion.

## Motor-Diffusion Model

A key feature of the power-stroke model is that there is an attached, prestrained state (Figure 5a top). There is, however, no strong experimental support for this state. An alternative is that the motor develops strain before it binds (Figure 6a). According to this idea, which goes back to the theory of Huxley (44), the elastic element within the motor undergoes thermal fluctuations and only when

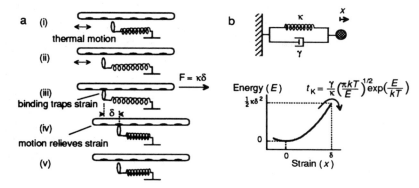

*Figure 6*  (*a*) Motor-diffusion model in which it is hypothesized that an internal elastic element undergoes thermal motion and binds to the filament in a strained state. (*b*) Kramers (48) equation for the rate at which a particle on a damped spring can diffuse over a potential energy barrier of height $E$. In the case of kinesin with $E = 1/2\kappa\delta^2 = 10\,kT$ (using $\delta = 8$ nm and $\kappa = 1$ pN/nm) and $\gamma = 6\pi\eta r = 10^{-10}$ N·s/m (using viscosity $\eta = 10^{-3}$ N·s/m$^2$ and radius $r = 5$ nm), the Kramers time, $t_K$, to diffuse over the barrier is 1.2 ms. For myosin to cross the same barrier would take about twice as long because its dimension is about twice that of kinesin.

a large strain energy has been acquired does the motor bind to the filament. This idea forms the basis for some ratchet models (e.g. 10). The crucial question is whether such a diffusive mechanism would be fast enough given that the motion will be damped by the viscosity of the surrounding fluid and possibly by the protein itself. This general diffusion problem was solved by Kramers (48) (Figure 6*b*). Application of his rate theory using reasonable values for the stiffness and hydrodynamic damping (see Figure 6 legend) gives times of 1 and 2 ms, respectively, for kinesin and myosin to pick up $40 \times 10^{-21}$ J of energy (corresponding to an efficiency of ~40%; see below). Because such times are short compared with the hydrolysis times of these motors, tens of milliseconds, this diffusive mechanism is quite plausible. The counter argument made by Eisenberg & Hill (17) assumed an unrealistically high work per myosin head of $70 \times 10^{-21}$ J (see 42).

## Organelle- or Filament-Diffusion Model

For an organelle motor like kinesin, a quite different motor mechanism can be envisaged. According to this ratchet diffusion model (9), the motor rectifies the diffusion of the organelle to which it is attached (Figure 7). If a motor is fixed, as in a filament gliding assay, then it is the filament's diffusion that is rectified. In order to get directed movement, one thinks of the motor molecule as a pawl (19) that permits movement relative to the filament (the ratchet) only

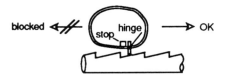

*Figure 7*  A ratchet model in which the motor is hypothesized to rectify the undirected Brownian motion of an organelle to which it is attached.

in the preferred direction. In the original discussion of the pawl and ratchet by Feynman et al (19), it was noted that if the pawl and ratchet were at different temperatures, then such a machine could be used to do work without violating the second law of thermodynamics. However, such a temperature difference between a motor and its filament is not possible: As pointed out by Leibler & Huse (51), molecular motors are not heat engines because the diffusion of heat is so rapid over the dimensions of a protein that the necessary thermal gradients will dissipate within picoseconds, a time scale much faster than the microsecond to millisecond time scales of the transitions between the different chemical states of the motor. Even though the model does not specify how ATP hydrolysis could lead to rectified motion, the model is appealing because it takes only a very short time for an organelle to diffuse a distance equal to the size of a protein subunit: For example a 200-nm diameter sphere will diffuse 8 nm in water in only 16 μs.[1] Despite the appeal, the model is ruled out by the high viscosity experiments described below.

## FORCE MEASUREMENTS FROM SINGLE KINESIN MOLECULES

How much force do we expect a motor protein to be able to generate? The maximum work (= force × working distance) that a motor can perform is bounded by the free energy decrease associated with the hydrolysis of a molecule of ATP, ~25 $kT$ or ~$100 \times 10^{-21}$ J.[2] In the case of kinesin, for which we expect the power stroke to be comparable to the step size of 8 nm, the force must be ≤12 pN. The force generated by single molecules of kinesin has been measured using several different techniques. The most reliable methods indicate that a single kinesin molecule is able to generate a force of 4 to 6 pN.

---

[1]The average time, $t$, to diffuse a distance, $x$, is $x^2/2D$, where $D = kT/\gamma$ is the diffusion coefficient and $\gamma$ is the damping coefficient. For a sphere of radius $r$ in a fluid of viscosity $\eta$, $\gamma = 6\pi\eta r$.

[2]$\Delta G_{ATP \rightarrow ADP + P_i} \cong 110 \times 10^{-21}$ J at pH = 7.1, 2 mM Mg, 25°C, 0.2 M ionic strength, [ATP] = 4 mM, [ADP] = 0.02 mM, [P$_i$] = 2 mM, 37°C (4, 14). Note that an erroneous value of $84 \times 10^{-21}$ J was used in (42) and (38).

Thus, provided that each step is associated with the hydrolysis of just one molecule of ATP, the efficiency of kinesin is approximately 40%, comparable to the optimal efficiency of myosin in muscle (4), and similar to that of other biological energy transducing processes such as ion pumping, electron transport, and ATP synthesis (68).

## Forces Exerted Against Viscous and Elastic Loads

A number of different experimental techniques have been used to put single kinesin molecules under known loads. In one method, a hydrodynamic load was applied by increasing the viscosity ($\eta$) of the solution through which kinesin moves a microtubule up to 200-fold by adding chemically inert macromolecules to the buffer (42). At high viscosity and at a low density of kinesin on the surface, the longer microtubules moved more slowly than the shorter ones. This slowing is expected if the damping on the longer microtubules is significantly loading the motors because the drag force is proportional to microtubule length ($L$) according to $F_{drag} = C^{\parallel} \eta \cdot v \cdot L$. $v$ is the gliding speed and $C^{\parallel}(= 7 \pm 1)$ is a constant that depends on the microtubule's diameter and height above the surface. As an example, the drag on a 16-µm-long microtubule being moved at 250 nm/s through a solution of viscosity 120 mN·s·m$^{-2}$ (~100 times that of water) is 3.4 pN. It was found that the speed decreased linearly as the viscous force increased, and extrapolating to zero speed gave a maximum time-average force of 4 to 5 pN.

In two other approaches, an elastic load was applied to the motor using either optical tweezers (69) or flexible glass fibers as force transducers (Figure 8; 57). With both approaches, as the elastic restoring force increased, the speed of movement decreased proportionally, and the motors stopped when the load reached ~5 pN. The consistency between these two approaches is remarkable because the geometries of the two techniques are quite different. In the optical

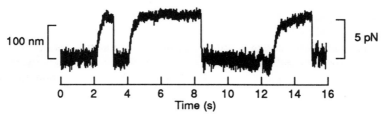

*Figure 8*  A single kinesin molecule pulling a microtubule attached to a force transducer (57). Initially the motor is disengaged so the microtubule and the glass fiber to which it is attached are free to undergo thermal motion. After 2 s, the motor engages and pulls the microtubule through 120 nm, exerting a maximum force of 5.2 pN ([ATP] = 0.67 mM), and disengaging ~1 s later. Three such encounters are shown.

tweezers setup, the microtubule is fixed to the substrate and kinesin is attached to a small glass bead (diameter ~0.5 μm) upon which the optical force acts. The force-fiber geometry is upside down: The motor is fixed to the substrate, and the microtubule is attached to the force transducer.

A similar maximum force was obtained by Gittes et al (23, 24) in which kinesin was challenged to buckle microtubules of calibrated flexural rigidity (25).

## Implications of the Force Measurements

LINEAR FORCE-VELOCITY CURVES ARE CONSISTENT WITH MANY MODELS  The linear decrease in kinesin's speed as the viscous or elastic load is increased is predicted by many models (42, 51). Where does the nonlinear force-velocity curve of whole muscle fibers (35) come from? The answer is that as the load on a muscle decreases, the stiffness of the muscle also decreases, indicating that the number of attached myosin heads probably also decreases; the corrected relationship between velocity and force per attached head is therefore more nearly linear (34). Thus there is no evidence that myosin's molecular force-velocity curve is nonlinear.

THE ORGANELLE-DIFFUSION MODEL CAN BE REJECTED  The viscosity experiments provide a test for diffusional models for force generation because the high viscosity of the solution will greatly slow down steps in the cycle that are diffusive in nature. The organelle- or filament-diffusion model can be ruled out because it can produce only small forces, $\leq 2kT/d \cong 1$ pN (using the step size $d = 8$ nm; 42). Observations that kinesin can buckle microtubules (23, 25) and that the detached time is short (57, 70, see below) are also inconsistent with organelle-diffusion models.

THE FORCE EXERTED AGAINST A VISCOUS LOAD IS CONSISTENT WITH THE MOTOR-DIFFUSION AND POWER-STOKE MODELS  Both models predict that the maximum force, $F_{max}$, exerted against a viscous load is (42, 51)

$$F_{max}^{viscous} \approx \kappa \cdot \delta. \qquad 1.$$

Thus a maximum force of $\approx 4$pN is consistent with a stiffness ($\kappa$) of $\approx 0.5$ pN/nm (0.5 mN/m) and a power-stroke distance ($\delta$) of 8 nm. Such a stiffness is compatible with the lower bound of 0.15 pN/nm deduced by Meyhöfer and Howard (57).

KINESIN'S DETACHED TIME IS VERY BRIEF  In the simplest models (e.g. 51), the maximum force exerted by a motor protein against an elastic load is

$$F_{max}^{elastic} = \frac{\kappa \cdot \delta}{1 + t_D \cdot \kappa / \gamma} \qquad 2.$$

where $t_D$ is the time per hydrolysis cycle that the motor is detached (i.e. the detached time) and $\gamma$ is the damping (in the tweezers assay the damping acts on the bead, and in the force-fiber assay, it acts on the microtubule and glass fiber). The reasoning is that the distance slipped backwards while the motor is detached is $t_D F/\gamma$ ($F$ is the external elastic force), whereas the distance moved forward during the attached part of the cycle, the working stroke[3], is $\delta$-$F/\kappa$ (assuming that the motor does not detach prematurely). The equation follows by noting that the speed drops to zero (the condition of maximum force) when the forward and backward (slippage) distances are equal.

Because it is observed that $F_{max}^{viscous} \approx F_{max}^{elastic}$, a comparison of Equations 1 and 2 indicates that the detached time must be small. The intuitive reason for this is that slippage, which occurs while the motor is detached, will tend to reduce the force exerted against a sustained elastic load but not against a viscous load. A quantitative bound on the detached time was obtained by Meyhöfer & Howard (57) who found that the maximum force exerted against an elastic load was independent of the damping ($\gamma$): Equation 2, therefore, implies that $t_D \ll \gamma/\kappa = \gamma \, \delta \, /F_{max} = 8$ µs, using $\delta = 8$ nm, $\gamma = 0.005$ µN·s/m (69), and $F_{max} = 5.4$ pN. Thus the detached time is very brief. Such a short detached time poses a serious problem for the models that we have discussed, especially for the motor diffusion model, which requires ~1 ms to diffuse over its activation barrier. The resolution of this problem probably requires the interaction of kinesin's two heads (see below).

WHY DOES THE MOTOR SLOW DOWN AT HIGH LOADS?   There are two quite different reasons why a motor might slow down at high force. First, its rate of stepping could decrease, e.g. its hydrolysis cycle could be slowed down by the opposing force. Second, the stepping rate could be maintained, but the distance slipped during each cycle may increase (51).

Increased slippage cannot explain kinesin's reduction in speed at high force. Although some slips of amplitude ~8 nm are seen at high load (57, 69), the infrequency of such slips (<1/s) argues against slippage as the main reason for the reduction in speed because the frequency of slips at high load would have to equal the frequency of forward steps at low load (~100/s corresponding to an unloaded speed of ~0.5 to 1 µm/s). Thus the stepping rate must decrease.

The simplest possibility is that the ATP hydrolysis cycle slows in response to an applied force. This slowing would be analogous to the Fenn effect of muscle (4), in which the hydrolysis rate decreases as the load increases. A load-depend-

---

[3]The reason that the working stroke is less than the power stroke is that if there is an external force ($F$), then the strain at the cessation of movement is not zero but will be some $x$ ($>0$) that is needed to oppose the external force ($x = F/\kappa$, where $\kappa$ is the spring constant of the motor). In other words, the working stroke is ($\delta$-$x$). If the motor detaches prematurely, then the working stroke will be even smaller (51)

ent hydrolysis rate implies that a rate-limiting chemical transition (taking place while the motor is attached to the filament) has a displacement component in the direction opposite to the applied force. We recently obtained stronger evidence for a force-dependent step in the hydrolysis cycle. When a kinesin molecule buckles a microtubule that has been clamped at its minus end (the slow-growing end), the load on the motor develops a component that is perpendicular to the axis of the microtubule. This component tends to pull the motor away from the microtubule's surface. If there is significant detached time during which the motor slips backwards, we would expect the perpendicular component of the load to augment the detachment and subsequent slippage, and therefore result in a slowing of the motion. But, on the contrary, the speed increases. This means that the perpendicular load actually catalyzes the forward reaction. Such behavior is consistent with kinesin's hydrolysis cycle having a rate-limiting transition that is sensitive to external load. Such sensitivity would arise naturally if the transition were associated with a conformational change that had a component toward the plus end of the microtubule (which would be opposed by the parallel load), as well as a component away from the surface (which would be augmented by a perpendicular load) (24).

## THE ROLE OF KINESIN'S TWO HEADS

There are several reasons to think that kinesin's two-headed structure is crucial to its motility. The most important is that kinesin is a processive motor—it can move a large distance along a microtubule without falling off (see below). Kinesin spends very little time detached, and two heads would give the motor a surer grip. The question is how independently the two heads move and whether they undergo similar or different motions. One thing is clear; the two heads of a two-headed motor cannot work completely independently because they are connected and therefore cannot move along the filament at different speeds. Two degrees of coordination between the heads can be envisaged: (a) an uncoordinated interaction in which the two heads bind quasi-independently, each spending most of the time attached so that together they are likely to spend only a very short time detached [16; e.g. Figure 4(ii)]; and (b) a coordinated interaction in which the two heads alternate, with one unbinding only after the other has bound [30; e.g. Figure 4(i)]. The evidence summarized below favors the latter so-called hand-over-hand mechanism. A plausible model for how the two heads might move in this manner is presented.

### Reasons for Believing that Kinesin's Two Heads Move in a Coordinated Manner

Kinesin can move processively along microtubules. Dilution experiments first indicated that single kinesin molecules are capable of moving along microtubules for considerable distances (several micrometers corresponding to several hundred steps) without detaching (6, 39). The initial evidence was that motion could be observed at a very low density of kinesin on the surface, that the moving microtubules swiveled about a single point on the surface (at which the motor was presumed to be located), and that the rate at which microtubules bound to and moved across a kinesin-coated surface was proportional to the density of motors on the surface. The recent force measurements (42, 57, 69) establish this processivity almost beyond doubt by showing that there is an indivisible force-generating unit that produces ~5 pN of force. The only remaining possibility that this motor unit is a small, constant-sized aggregate of kinesins is unlikely because the formation of such an aggregate is likely to be too slow at the concentration of kinesin used to coat the surfaces (39).

The high ATPase of kinesin, ~50 per head per second (41, 49), is consistent with motility of single kinesin molecules: One 8-nm step per ATP hydrolyzed gives a speed of ~800 nm/s, similar to the observed unloaded speed. The very low concentration of microtubules needed to activate dimeric kinesin's ATPase is consistent with individual dimers taking several steps for each diffusive encounter with a microtubule (31).

The processivity of kinesin mandates that this motor spends little time detached from the filament. The initial experiments done in the absence of external loads suggested detached times of ≤1 ms. The more recent force measurements indicate detachment times of ≤1 μs. Evidently, some type of role for two heads is required, either coordinated or uncoordinated, to maintain contact between motor and filament.

SINGLE-HEADED CONSTRUCTS MOVE LESS WELL    First, kinesin's motor domain, with dimerization and coil domains deleted, moves more slowly than the full-length dimeric protein (5, 67). Even the fastest single-headed kinesin, K340BIO (5), moves at only 20% of the dimer's speed. This protein may not even be monomeric in the motility assay as its biotinylated fusion domain could dimerize on the multivalent streptavidin used to coat the beads in these experiments. Second, the isolated motor domain does not move in low density assays. Although this result may be due to technical problems involved in coupling the motor to the surface, it may indicate that the single-headed motor is not processive. Finally, the single-headed motor switches randomly between adjacent protofilaments with a frequency about ten times greater than that of native two-headed kinesin (5). Taken together, these observations suggest that there is some kind of interaction, coordinated or uncoordinated, between kinesin's two heads.

CHEMICAL COOPERATIVITY BETWEEN THE HEADS    Recently Hackney (30) directly demonstrated a remarkable negative cooperativity between dimeric kinesin's two nucleotide-binding sites. Kinesin binds ADP strongly in the absence of microtubules (the off time is ~100 s). Hackney bound ADP to each of the heads of a dimer, then added microtubules (in the absence of nucleotides). Only 50% of the ADP was released immediately (within 1 s), while the other half came off with a similar low rate observed in the absence of microtubules (off time ~100 s). Repeating the experiment in the presence of ATP gave 100% release within a few seconds, showing that the substoichiometric release was not due to inactive protein. Repeating the experiment with single-headed kinesin also gave 100% ADP release. The interpretations are clear: (*a*) When one head in the dimer is in a rigor state (attached to a microtubule in the absence of nucleotide), the other head cannot attach (in a conformation that promotes ADP release); and (*b*) ATP binding to the attached head promotes ADP release from the other head. Furthermore, ATP-induced detachment of the first head is not necessary for ADP release from the second because the nonhydrolyzable ATP analogue AMP-PNP, which promotes a strong attachment between kinesin and microtubules, also gives rapid 100% release of ADP (54a). This negative cooperativity shows that the two heads do not bind independently but instead strongly suggests a coordinated mechanism.

IMPLICATIONS OF THE EQUIVALENCE HYPOTHESIS    As argued above, if kinesin has an axis of twofold rotational symmetry, considerable flexibility between the heads would be necessary for the two heads to bind to one microtubule; i.e. the symmetry must be broken for the two heads to adopt the translational symmetry needed for simultaneous attachment to the polar microtubule. However, there is no evidence that kinesin has such flexibility. Unlike myosin, whose limited proteolysis reveals flexible regions between its heads, kinesin is proteolytically cleaved not between its heads as originally thought (45, 49), but distal to the heads in the linker domain (41). Therefore, it seems unlikely that kinesin's two heads, if they are in the same nucleotide state, could bind simultaneously to one microtubule. This structural picture derives some experimental support from the observation that in the presence of AMP-PNP, one kinesin dimer binds per tubulin dimer (i.e. only one of the heads is bound; 41, but see 33). This picture also agrees with the ADP release experiments described above if the dimer with only one ADP bound still has approximate rotational symmetry.

The symmetry of the heads suggests a structural mechanism by which the hydrolysis cycles of the two heads could be coordinated—uncoordinated cycles are not allowed because they would lead to simultaneous binding. According to this picture, steric hindranace induces coordination. Coordination between the heads arises from the requirement that the heads be in different nucleotide states to simultaneously attach to the one microtubule. It is nucleotide binding that breaks the symmetry of the heads. Implicit within such an idea is that kinesin is like a rotary engine: The motion of a head will have a handedness, and the handedness will be the same for both heads by the equivalence hypothesis. There is an analogy to the $F_1$-ATP synthase. The threefold rotational symmetry of this molecule is broken in a spectacular way—each member of the triad is in a different nucleotide state in the crystal (1)! This suggests a phase lag between the three catalytic subunits, as expected if they rotate relative to the central subunit as the enzyme couples proton transport to ATP synthesis. Such a motion evokes the rotation of the bacterial motor (66).

## A Plausible Alternating Head Model—A Rotary Engine

A rotary, hand-over-hand model, Figure 9, accounts for several features of kinesin-driven motility. First, it can explain how kinesin might span the 8 nm between adjacent dimers with a head only slightly longer (~9 nm). This is accomplished by postulating a rotation within the attached head to bring the trailing head, which has an incorrect orientation to bind the microtubule (due to the symmetry), to the front and into the correct orientation for binding (transition (i)→(ii) in Figure 9). Thus the second head acts as a long lever, analogous to the long $\alpha$-helix within myosin's regulatory domain, which amplifies the smaller rotation of the attached head [a similar idea has been proposed by Hackney (30) for a nonrotary model].

The model of Figure 9 incorporates the Hackney (30) result by postulating that in state (i) only one head is bound and that ATP binding breaks the symmetry by inducing the rotation (i)→(ii). Consistent with the observation that AMP-PNP induces strong binding between kinesin and microtubules (50), the ATP state is shown as an attached one. It is envisaged that a diffusive process like that described for the motor-diffusion model (above) would lead to the transition

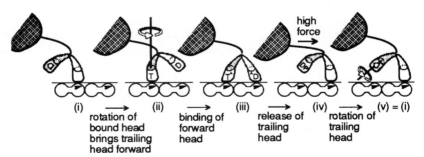

*Figure 9* A rotary engine model for movement of kinesin along a microtubule. The basis of the model is that the two heads are related by an axis of rotational symmetry and undergo identical, sequential motions. In (i) the trailing head is shown stippled to indicate that it is incorrectly oriented to bind to the microtubule (the symmetry axis bisects the heads). The transition (i)→(ii) is hypothesized to entail a rotation of the distal part of the attached head to bring the trailing head forward. The symmetry breaking transition rotates this head so that it can now bind to the microtubule (iii). The unbinding of the now trailing head pulls the load forward (iv). Hypothetical nucleotide states are indicated. D = ADP, T = ATD, DP = ADP · $P_i$.

(ii)→(iii). As shown, state (iii) is force generating, but because both heads are attached, it is highly strained and therefore expected to be short-lived. The unbinding of the rear head would relieve the internal strain and transfer it to the load, making state (iv) the main force-generating state. At the same time, the trailing head would quickly rotate back to its initial conformation, perhaps associated with phosphate release. The power-stroke distance would equal the step size as in the motor-diffusion model. The elasticity could reside in the neck region.

A bonus of this model is that it can simply explain how structurally similar motors could move in opposite directions. Because the location of the axis of rotational symmetry is arbitrary, one can easily envisage a motor whose unattached head is located toward the plus end of the microtubule [rather than toward the minus end as drawn for kinesin in Figure 9(i)]. Then exactly the same rotary motion within the attached head would swing the unattached head toward the minus end of the microtubule, and lead to movement in the opposite direction to kinesin. Thus the reason that ncd moves in the opposite direction to kinesin might be that ncd's dimerization domain (which is amino terminal to the motor domain, rather than carboxy terminal as found for kinesin; see Figure 1*b*) shifts the axis of symmetry so that the unbound head is closer to the plus end of the microtubule.

The model makes an unusual and seemingly unthinkable prediction. Every step is accompanied by a 180° rotation. The rotation will always be in the same direction because of the assumed equivalence of the heads [state (v) is identical to state (i)]. Thus the tail (and organelle) will tend to wind up like the rubber band of a toy airplane. How could this torsion be relieved? Perhaps the reason that kinesin has such torsional flexibility—it costs <1 $kT$ of energy to twist kinesin through 360° (43)—is to accommodate some torsion. Torsion could be relieved completely either within the motor, for example through swiveling of a peptide bond, or outside of the motor, for example by a free rotation of the motor's tail in the fluid membrane of an organelle.

If this rotary mechanism is correct—and it should be stressed that the equivalence hypothesis upon which the mechanism rests, while reasonable, has not been critically tested—then the gait of the molecular motor kinesin is more machine-like than animal-like: Although proteins could have axles, animals with their nerves and blood vessels cannot (29).

## FUNCTIONAL IMPLICATIONS: RELATING MOLECULAR PHYSIOLOGY TO THE BIOLOGY OF KINESIN

This review has focused on the mechanism of force generation. Little regard has been given to the biology of kinesin. How does kinesin's structure and mechanism relate to its function as an organelle transporter?

The movement of organelles along filaments is very different from the sliding of filaments, which forms the basis of muscle and sperm motility. Although large arrays of myosins and dyneins drive filament sliding in these specialized cells, only a limited number of kinesin molecules can drive the movement of one organelle because the contact area between an organelle and a microtubule is very limited. Indeed, for small organelles, at most a handful of motors could mediate the interaction (3, 58). Thus kinesin's processivity makes it well adapted as an organelle transporter because if kinesin were to let go, the organelle would diffuse away from the microtubule, and transport would be delayed until the organelle rebound. On the other hand, if one myosin or dynein were to let go, the structure of the sarcomere or axoneme would not be compromised.

Another difference between filament and organelle motors is that the former are bound in precisely aligned arrays, whereas the latter are likely to be randomly oriented on the surfaces of organelles. Random orientation poses a number of problems. First, the rate at which an organelle can latch onto a filament might be prohibitively low if the organelle as a whole must rotate for the motor and its binding site on the filament to become stereospecifically aligned. Second, if each motor can interact with a filament over only a restricted range of angles, then only a small fraction of randomly oriented motors will be able to work simultaneously to move the organelle along the filament. The finding that kinesin has a region of high torsional flexibility between its organelle-binding domain and its filament-binding domain (43) solves both these problems: Binding of the head to the filament can be achieved quickly by torsion of the motor rather than rotation of the organelle, and two or more unaligned motors can contribute additively to the force.

The ability of kinesin to generate high force, perhaps even higher than that generated by myosin in muscle, is likely to be an adaptation for the intracellular transport of vesicles. The cytoplasm is so crowded by protein filaments that the mobility of organelles is greatly impeded. Using fluorescent tracer molecules of various sizes, Luby-Phelps et al (53) estimated that the pores between the structural barriers in the cytoplasm are about 50 nm wide. Therefore, to drag larger-diameter vesicles through this matrix, it is necessary that kinesin generate sufficient force to push these structural barriers out of the way. Because organelles are moved by a relatively small number of motors, it makes sense that each motor can generate a large force. The deformation of the cytoplasmic matrix is likely to be slow, on the order of milliseconds to seconds (such a time-dependence is referred to as viscoelasticity) (e.g. 52). It seems reasonable that the association times of ~1 s over which kinesin exerts maximum force before letting go completely (Figure 8) might be matched to the relaxation time of the viscoelastic cytoplasm. If the organelle becomes stuck for more than a second or so, it might mean that there is an impenetrable barrier. A strategy to solve this problem might be to detach after a few seconds and wait for diffusion to allow a circuitous way around.

Thus the unique properties of kinesin, those that distinguish kinesin from myosin and dynein, are seen as adaptations of kinesin to its unique cellular role.

ACKNOWLEDGMENTS

I thank my collaborators over the past five years—David Coy, Fred Gittes, Alan Hunt, Edgar Meyhöfer, Brian Mickey, Ron Milligan, and Mitra Ray— who contributed tremendously to the data and ideas presented here. I also thank the current members of the lab, especially Will Hancock, as well as Bryant Chase, Karla Neugebauer, and Linda Wordeman for comments on an earlier manuscript. Special thanks go to Lubert Stryer—our yearly afternoon discussions are an inspiration. This work was supported by the National Institutes of Health (AR40593), the Pew Charitable Trusts, and the Human Frontier Science Program.

> Any *Annual Review* chapter, as well as any article cited in an *Annual Review* chapter, may be purchased from the Annual Reviews Preprints and Reprints service. 1-800-347-8007; 415-259-5017; email: arpr@class.org

## Literature Cited

1. Abrahams JP, Leslie AGW, Lutter R, Walker JE. 1994. Structure at 2.8 Å of $F_1$-ATPase from bovine heart mitochondria. *Nature* 370:621–28
2. Amos LA, Klug A. 1974. Arrangement of subunits in flagellar microtubules. *J. Cell. Sci.* 14:523–49
3. Ashkin A, Schütze K, Dziedzic JM, Euteneuer U, Schliwa M. 1990. Force generation of organelle transport measured in vivo by an infrared laser trap. *Nature* 348:346–48
4. Bagshaw CR. 1993. *Muscle Contraction.* New York: Chapman Hill. 2nd ed.
5. Berliner E, Young EC, Anderson K, Mahtani HK, Gelles J. 1995. Failure of single-headed kinesin to track parallel to protofilaments. *Nature* 373:718–21
6. Block SM, Goldstein LSB, Schnapp BJ. 1990. Bead movement by single kinesin molecules studied with optical tweezers. *Nature* 348:348–52
7. Bloom GS, Wagner MC, Pfister KK, Brady ST. 1988. Native structure and physical properties of bovine brain kinesin and identification of the ATP-binding subunit polypeptide. *Biochemistry* 27:3409–16

8. Brady ST. 1985. A novel brain ATPase with properties expected for the fast axonal transport motor. *Nature* 317:73–75
9. Braxton S, Yount RG. 1989. A ratchet diffusion model for directed motion in muscle. *Biophys J.* 55:A12 (Abstr.)
10. Cordova NJ, Ermentrout B, Oster GF. 1992. Dynamics of single-motor molecules: the thermal ratchet model. *Proc. Natl. Acad. Sci. USA* 89:339–43
11. Creighton TE. 1993. *Proteins.* New York: Freeman. 2nd ed.
12. Crick FHC. 1953. The packing of α-helices: simple coiled coils. *Acta Cryst.* 6:689–97
13. Cyr JL, Pfister KK, Bloom GS, Slaughter CA, Brady ST. 1991. Molecular genetics of kinesin light chains: generation of isoforms by alternative splicing. *Proc. Natl. Acad. Sci. USA* 88:10114–18
14. Daniels F, Alberty RA. 1975. *Physical Chemistry.* New York: Wiley & Sons. 4th ed.
15. de Cuevas M, Tao T, Goldstein LSB. 1992. Evidence that the stalk of *Drosophila* kinesin heavy chain is an α-helical coiled coil. *J. Cell Biol.* 116:957–65

16. Duke T, Leibler S. 1995. Minimal strain-dependent model for motor proteins. *Biophys. J.* Submitted
17. Eisenberg E, Hill TL. 1978. A cross-bridge model of muscle contraction. *Prog. Biophys. Mol. Biol.* 33:55–82
18. Endow SA, Hatsumi M. 1991. A multimember kinesin gene family in *Drosophila*. *Proc. Natl. Acad. Sci. USA* 88: 4424–27
19. Feynman RP, Leighton RB, Sands M. 1963. *The Feynman Lectures on Physics*, Vol. 1. Reading, MA: Addison-Wesley
20. Finer JT, Simmons RM, Spudich JA. 1994. Single myosin molecule mechanics: piconewton forces and nanometer steps. *Nature* 368:113–19
21. Fisher AJ, Smith CA, Thoden J, Smith R, Sutoh K, et al. 1995. Structural studies of myosin: nucleotide complexes: a revised model for the molecular basis of muscle contraction. *Biophys. J.* 68: S19–S28
22. Gauger AK, Goldstein LSB. 1993. The *Drosophila* kinesin light chain. *J. Biol. Chem.* 268:13657–66
23. Gittes F, Meyhöfer E, Baek S, Howard J. 1994. A simple piconewton-scale in vitro force assay for kinesin. *Biophys. J.* 66:A312 (Abstr.)
24. Gittes F, Meyhöfer E, Baek S, Howard J. 1996. Directional loading of the kinesin motor molecule as it buckles a microtubule. *Biophys. J.* 70:In press
25. Gittes F, Mickey B, Nettleton J, Howard J. 1993. Flexural rigidity of microtubules and actin filaments measured from thermal fluctuations in shape. *J. Cell Biol.* 120:923–34
26. Goldman YE, Huxley AF. 1994. Actin compliance: are you pulling my chain. *Biophys. J.* 67:2131–36
27. Goldstein LSB. 1993. With apologies to Scheherazade: tails of 1001 kinesin motors. *Annu. Rev. Genet.* 27:319–51
28. Goodson HV, Kang SJ, Endow SA. 1994. Molecular phylogeny of the kinesin family of microtubule motor proteins. *J. Cell Sci.* 107:1875–84
29. Gray J. 1959. *How Animals Move*. Cambridge: At the Univ. Press
30. Hackney DD. 1994. Evidence for alternating head catalysis by kinesin during microtubule-stimulated ATP hydrolysis. *Proc. Natl. Acad. Sci. USA* 91:6865–69
31. Hackney DD. 1995. Implications of diffusion-controlled limit for processivity of dimeric kinesin head domains. *Biophys. J.* 68:S267–70
32. Hackney DD, Levitt JD, Wagner DD. 1991. Characterization of $\alpha_2\beta_2$ and $\alpha_2$ forms of kinesin. *Biochem. Biophys. Res. Commun.* 174:810–15
33. Harrison BC, Marchese-Ragona SP, Gilbert SP, Cheng N, Steven AC, Johnson KA. 1993. Kinesin decoration of the microtubule surface: one kinesin head per tubulin heterodimer. *Nature* 362:73–75
34. Haugen P. 1988. The stiffness under isotonic releases during a twitch of a frog muscle fiber. In *Molecular Mechanism of Muscle Contraction*, ed. H Sugi, GH Pollack, pp. 461–69. New York: Plenum
35. Hill AV. 1938. The heat of shortening and the dynamic constants of muscle. *Proc. R. Soc. London* 126:136–95
36. Hirokawa N, Pfister KK, Yorifuji H, Wagner MC, Brady ST, Bloom GS. 1989. Submolecular domains of bovine brain kinesin identified by electron microscopy and monoclonal antibody decoration. *Cell* 56:867–78
36a. Hirose K, Lockhart A, Cross RA, Amos LA. 1995. Nucleotide-dependent angular change in kinesin motor domain bound to kinesin. *Nature* 376:277–79
37. Holmes KC. 1995. The actomyosin interaction and its control by tropomyosin. *Biophys. J.* 68:S2–S7
38. Howard J. 1995. The mechanics of force generation by kinesin. *Biophys. J.* 68: S245–S55
39. Howard J, Hudspeth AJ, Vale RD. 1989. Movement of microtubules by single kinesin molecules. *Nature* 342:154–58
40. Huang T-G, Hackney DD. 1994. *Drosophila* kinesin minimal motor domain expressed in *Escherichia coli*. *J. Biol. Chem.* 269:16493–501
41. Huang T-G, Suhan J, Hackney DD. 1994. *Drosophila* kinesin motor domain extending to amino acid position 392 is dimeric when expressed in *Escherichia coli*. *J. Biol. Chem.* 269:16502–7
42. Hunt AJ, Gittes F, Howard J. 1994. The force exerted by a single kinesin molecule against a viscous load. *Biophys. J.* 67:766–81
43. Hunt AJ, Howard J. 1993. Kinesin swivels to permit microtubule movement in any direction. *Proc. Natl. Acad. Sci. USA* 90:11653–57
44. Huxley AF. 1957. Muscle structure and theories of contraction. *Prog. Biophys. Biophys. Chem.* 7:255–318
45. Ingold AL, Cohn SA, Scholey JM. 1988. Monoclonal antibodies to kinesin heavy chains. *J. Cell Biol.* 107:2657–67
46. Ishijima A, Harada Y, Kojima H, Funatsu T, Higuchi H, Yanagida T. 1994. Single-molecule analysis of the actomyosin motor using nano-manipulation.

*Biochem. Biophys. Res. Commun.* 199: 1057–63

47. Kojima H, Ishijima A, Yanagida T. 1994. Direct measurement of the stiffness of single actin filaments with and without tropomyosin by in vitro nanomanipulation. *Proc. Natl. Acad. Sci. USA* 91:12962–66

48. Kramers HA. 1940. Brownian motion in a field of force and the diffusion model of chemical reactions. *Physica* 7:284–304

49. Kuznetsov SA, Vaisberg YA, Rothwell SW, Murphy DB, Gelfand VI. 1989. Isolation of a 45-kDa fragment from the kinesin heavy chain with enhanced ATPase and microtubule-binding activities. *J. Biol. Chem.* 264:589–95

50. Lasek RJ, Brady ST. 1985. Attachment of transported vesicles to microtubules in axoplasm is facilitated by AMP-PNP. *Nature* 316:645–47

51. Leibler S, Huse D. 1993. Porters versus rowers: a unified stochastic model of motor proteins. *J. Cell Biol.* 121:1357–68

52. Luby-Phelps K. 1994. Physical properties of cytoplasm. *Curr. Opin. Cell Biol.* 6:3–9

53. Luby-Phelps K, Castle PE, Taylor DL, Lanni F. 1987. Hindered diffusion of inert tracer particles in the cytoplasm of mouse 3T3 cells. *Proc. Natl. Acad. Sci. USA* 84:4910–13

54. Lupas A, van Dyke M, Stock J. 1991. Predicting coiled coils from protein sequence. *Science* 252:1162–64

54a. Ma YZ, Taylor EW. 1995. Kinetic mechanism of microtubule-kinesin ATPase motor domain K560. *Biophys. J.* 68:A28 (Abstr.)

55. McDonald HB, Stewart RJ, Goldstein LSB. 1990. The kinesin-like ncd protein of Drosophila is a minus end-directed microtubule motor. *Cell* 63:1159–65

56. McKay DB, Steitz TA. 1981. Structure of catabolite gene activator protein at 2.9 Å resolution suggests binding to left-handed B-DNA. *Nature* 290:744–49

57. Meyhöfer E, Howard J. 1995. The force generated by a single molecule of kinesin against an elastic load. *Proc. Natl. Acad. Sci. USA* 92:574–78

58. Miller RH, Lasek RJ. 1985. Crossbridges mediate anterograde and retrograde vesicle transport along microtubules in squid axoplasm. *J. Cell Biol.* 101:2181–93

59. Molloy JE, Burns JE, Kendrick-Jones J, Tregear RT, White DCS. 1995. Force and movement produced by a single myosin head. *Nature.* 378:209–12

60. Molloy JE, Burns JE, Sparrow JC, Tregear RT, Kendrick-Jones J, White DCS. 1995. Single-molecule mechanics of heavy meromyosin and S1 interacting with rabbit or Drosophila actins using optical tweezers. *Biophys. J.* 68:S298–305

61. O'Shea EK, Klemm JD, Kim PS, Alber T. 1991. X-ray structure of the GCN4 leucine zipper, a two-stranded, parallel coiled coil. *Science* 254:539–44

62. Ray S, Meyhöfer E, Milligan RA, Howard J. 1993. Kinesin follows the microtubule's protofilament axis. *J. Cell Biol.* 121:1083–93

63. Rayment I, Holden HM, Whittaker M, Yohn CB, Lorenz M, et al. 1993. Structure of the actin-myosin complex and its implications for muscle contraction. *Science* 261:58–65

64. Rayment I, Rypniewski WR, Schmidt-Bäse K, Smith R, Tomchick DR, et al. 1993. Three-dimensional structure of myosin subfragment-1: a molecular motor. *Science* 261:50–58

65. Scholey JM, Heuser J, Yang JT, Goldstein LSB. 1989. Identification of globular mechanochemical heads of kinesin. *Nature* 338:355–57

66. Silverman M, Simon M. 1974. Flagellar rotation and the mechanism of bacterial motility. *Nature* 249:73–74

67. Stewart RJ, Thaler JP, Goldstein LSB. 1993. Direction of microtubule movement is an intrinsic property of the motor domains of kinesin heavy chain and Drosophila ncd protein. *Proc. Natl. Acad. Sci. USA* 90:5209–13

68. Stryer L. 1995. *Biochemistry.* New York: Freeman. 4th ed.

69. Svoboda K, Block SM. 1994. Force and velocity measured for single kinesin molecules. *Cell* 77:773–84

70. Svoboda K, Schmidt CF, Schnapp BJ, Block SM. 1993. Direct observation of kinesin stepping by optical trapping interferometry. *Nature* 256:721–27

71. Uyeda TQP, Kron SJ, Spudich JA. 1990. Myosin step size. Estimation from slow gliding movement of actin over low densities of heavy meromyosin. *J. Mol. Biol.* 214:699–710

72. Vale RD, Reese TS, Sheetz MP. 1985. Identification of a novel force-generating protein, kinesin, involved in microtubule-based motility. *Cell* 42:39–50

73. Wade RH, Chrétien D. 1993. Cryoelectron microscopy of microtubules. *J. Struct. Biol.* 110:1–27

74. Walker RA, Salmon ED, Endow SA. 1990. The Drosophila claret segregation protein is a minus-end directed motor molecule. *Nature* 347:780–82

75. Weber IT, Steitz TA. 1987. Structure of a complex of catabolite gene activator protein and cyclic AMP refined at 2.5 Å resolution. *J. Mol. Biol.* 198:311–26

76. Yang JT, Laymon RA, Goldstein LSB. 1989. A three-domain structure of kinesin heavy chain revealed by DNA sequence and microtubule binding analysis. *Cell* 56:879–89

77. Yang JT, Saxton WM, Stewart RJ, Raff EC, Goldstein LSB. 1990. Evidence that the head of kinesin is sufficient for force generation and motility in vitro. *Science* 249:42–47

*Annu. Rev. Physiol. 1996. 58:731–50*

# THE KINETIC CYCLES OF MYOSIN, KINESIN, AND DYNEIN

*David D. Hackney*

Department of Biological Sciences, Carnegie Mellon University, 4400 Fifth Avenue, Pittsburgh, Pennsylvania 15213

KEY WORDS:    adenosine triphosphatase, actin, microtubule, motility, mechanism

## ABSTRACT

The ATPase cycles of the molecular motors myosin, kinesin, and dynein are reviewed, with emphasis on their similarities and differences. Myosin generates motility along actin filaments and functions in muscle contraction, organelle movement, and cytokinesis. Dynein and kinesin produce movement along microtubules. All the motors exhibit burst kinetics with rate-limiting product release. Binding of the products-complex to the filament accelerates product release and completes the ATPase cycle. Kinesin is able to generate processive movement, and the possibilities for how this could be generated by coupling to ATP hydrolysis are discussed.

## INTRODUCTION

Myosin has been the object of intense investigation for many years, and its mechanism of actin-stimulated ATP hydrolysis is understood at a detailed, if incomplete, level. The other major molecular motors, dynein and kinesin, are less well known. This review focuses on the ATPase mechanisms of these enzymes, with emphasis on their similarities and differences. Because of the great breadth of these topics, it is only possible to reference a small fraction of the original work. Most of the citations are of review articles, recent lead references, or those of particular relevance.

### Comparative Structure

All three classes of motors have a similar three-domain organization, with a globular head or motor domain that possesses an actin- or microtubule- (MT) stimulated ATPase activity; a linker region that is usually highly elongated, but is short in myosin I; and a terminal domain that attaches the motor to the

731

load that will be moved (see 7, 13, 31, 36, 58, 73, 76, 79, 83, 94, 122 for reviews). The three classes of motors, however, share no homology at the amino acid sequence level beyond their common possession of a consensus P-loop for nucleotide binding (85, 116). Both myosin II and kinesin have two heads joined onto a long $\alpha$-helical coiled-coil domain that produces dimerization. Subfragment 1 (S1) and heavy meromyosin (HMM) are single- and double-headed truncated myosins that remain soluble at low ionic strength. Kinesin has the experimental advantage that it is comparatively small and simple. Thus the head domain of kinesin consists of only a single chain of ~38 kDa (see 53) that is equivalent in size to the two myosin light chains alone. Dynein is much larger and more complex. The molecule has two or three heads connected to a common base by stalks. There are two or three heavy chains of ~500 kDa that contain multiple consensus ATP-binding domains (26, 70), although only one is believed to be catalytic because loss of ATPase activity correlates with photocleavage at the V1 site (27). The roles of the other ATP-binding domains are unknown. There are also a number of intermediate and light chains.

Myosin and kinesin are members of large superfamilies of related proteins that share the motor domain but differ in other regions (11, 31, 32, 108, 112). Although many of these family members have been characterized only at the sequence level, it is presumed that they are also motors that move different cargoes specified by their unique regions (113). The dynein family does not appear to be as diverse, and there are only two closely related major members, cytoplasmic and axonemal dynein, although numerous isoforms are known (2, 77). This review concentrates on the mechanisms of the founding members of these families.

Both myosin II (104, 110) and kinesin (41, 48) are present in folded conformations under physiological conditions. In myosin from nonmuscle and smooth muscle cells, the folded 10 S form is inhibited (15, 55). Kinesin is also folded into a 9 S conformation (41) that is produced by interaction of the neck region with a region close to the C-terminal (44). The influence of the binding of the tail domains on the kinetics of the head is not known in detail but appears to produce an inhibited form (52).

## Comparative Motility

Myosin, kinesin, and dynein exhibit major differences in their motility properties, and it is hoped that these differences will be meaningfully reflected in their ATPase properties as measured in solution. Myosin in muscle must be able to produce rapid shortening as well as develop considerable isometric force. This is accomplished, in part, by myosin operating in a supramolecular framework that allows many myosin molecules to work in concert. Axonemal dynein is similar in that the supramolecular structure of the axoneme holds the dynein heads near the MTs, and many dyneins operate together to produce sliding. In both cases, the affinity of the heads for actin or MTs is low in the presence of ATP. Kinesin moves small membrane vesicles along MTs, and there is room for only one or a limited number of kinesin molecules in the interface region between the vesicle and the MT (69). If kinesin were detached from the MT during most of its ATPase cycle, the vesicle would be free to diffuse away and motility would be lost. Sustained association of a single kinesin with a MT during ATP-driven motility is in fact observed in vitro and this "single motor" motility indicates that kinesin can remain attached to a MT while simultaneously undergoing sequential movement along the MT (6, 51). This sustained contact with the MT could be produced, in part, by kinesin spending most of its ATPase cycle attached to the MT, with only a brief period during which it jumps to the next tubulin subunit. An additional factor is that only two-headed dimeric species have been shown to drive single-motor motility and to track along a single-protofilament track (5, 23, 78). An attractive explanation for this action is that the two head domains could alternate attachment such that the dimer remains associated while the individual heads can release and reattach to different sites.

Classical kinesin has its motor domain at the N-terminal of the heavy chain and moves toward the (+) end of the MT, whereas ncd has its motor domain at the C-terminal and moves toward the (−) end (68). To date, all of the N- and C-terminal family members have followed this pattern for direction of motion, but it is not simply a function of positional attachment because work with chimeric motors has indicated that the direction of movement is an intrinsic property of the head domain itself (103). The limited data on the kinetics of C-terminal motors indicate that the fundamental ATPase scheme is the same (64) and thus the origin of the reversal remains a challenge. Another intriguing finding is interaction between the actin- and MT-based motility systems in vivo (62).

The use of laser traps has allowed the investigation of the properties of single kinesin molecules working against a load. With this technique it has been possible to demonstrate that kinesin takes discreet steps of ~8 nm (105) corresponding to the spacing between tubulin dimers along a protofilament. It has not yet been possible to demonstrate comparable single-motor motility with myosin or dynein, which is consistent with their weak attachment to actin or MTs during ATP hydrolysis. It is possible, however, to observe single ATPase cycle events with myosin (21, 56) by confining an actin filament close to single myosins. This type of experiment allows investigation of the kinetics from a stochastic view of single elementary processes and is an area of great future interest.

## MYOSIN

The mechanism of myosin has been thoroughly reviewed (3, 22, 33, 47, 100, 106), and this review focuses on general properties for comparison with the other motors and on more recent results. A minimal scheme for all motor proteins is

$$E + ATP \underset{k_{-1}}{\overset{k_1}{\rightleftarrows}} E \cdot ATP \underset{k_{-2}}{\overset{k_2}{\rightleftarrows}} E^* \cdot ATP \underset{k_{-3}}{\overset{\overset{HOH}{\downarrow}k_3}{\rightleftarrows}} E^* \cdot ADP \cdot Pi \underset{k_{-4}}{\overset{k_4}{\rightleftarrows}} E^{*\,\prime} \cdot ADP \cdot P \underset{k_{-5}}{\overset{k_5}{\rightleftarrows}} E^* \cdot ADP + Pi \underset{k_{-6}}{\overset{k_6}{\rightleftarrows}} E + ADP.$$

In the absence of actin, ATP binds rapidly and essentially irreversibly ($k_{-2} = \sim0$), followed by rapid hydrolysis. Release of the products ADP and Pi is slow because it follows a conformational change that is the rate-limiting step ($k_4$) of the ATPase cycle. Following this conformational change, release of Pi and ADP is rapid. Pi release occurs first and is followed by slower ADP release. The binding of both ATP and ADP is at least a two-step process, with initial formation of a loosely bound complex that isomerizes to a more strongly bound complex. The powerful technique of $^{18}O$ oxygen exchange indicates that the hydrolysis step is highly reversible ($k_4 << k_{-3}$), with incorporation of multiple water-derived oxygens into the bound Pi before slow release via steps 4 and 5 (4, 120). In spite of the extensive incorporation of water-derived oxygens into the Pi that is released, myosin does not catalyze positional isotope exchange at the β-phosphoryl to a significant degree (16). Hydrolysis proceeds with inversion about the γ-phosphoryl group for both myosin (119) and dynein (91).

Actin activates net ATP hydrolysis by acceleration of the release of Pi and ADP. The central result of Lymn & Taylor (65) was that there is an antagonism between binding of actin and nucleotide to myosin. Thus myosin binds tightly to actin in the absence of nucleotides (rigor), but binding of ATP greatly reduces the affinity of myosin for actin and results in the rapid ($>1000$ s$^{-1}$) release of myosin•ATP (M•ATP) complex. Correspondingly, the affinity of myosin for ATP is very high in the absence of actin, as discussed above, but binding of myosin•nucleotide complexes to actin stimulates release of the nucleotide—both for release of Pi and ADP as part of the normal catalytic cycle and for release of ATP (98). Thus the major pathway for flux during hydrolysis is ATP binding to the rigor complex, followed by rapid dissociation to generate free myosin with bound ATP. Subsequently, ATP is hydrolyzed and the M•ADP•Pi complex can bind back to actin with stimulation of Pi release to form the actin•myosin•ADP complex (A•M•ADP). The transition to the force-producing state is believed to occur as a consequence of this rebinding, and the resulting A•M•ADP intermediate is believed to be initially in a strained state due to extension of an elastic element. Subsequent release of ADP completes the cycle and returns the system to the strongly bound rigor state. In this scheme, actin accelerates net ATP hydrolysis by accelerating the release of products (ADP, Pi) from myosin. This is particularly evident from the pattern of $^{18}O$ exchange. At low actin, exchange is extensive because $k_4 << k_{-3}$ and the hydrolysis step reverses many times before slow release of Pi. Higher actin concentrations accelerate the release of Pi and thus decrease the lifetime of the M•ADP•Pi state and decrease the average incorporation of water (95, 97).

The steps in the ATPase cycle are coupled to the series of conformational changes that result in generation of movement. Numerous ideas have been proposed for the structural basis of this change. The recent solution of the structure of S1 (81) and the regulatory domain (123) indicates that the back portion of S1 is elongated, with the light chains wrapped around a long central alpha helix. This light chain–binding helix could act as lever arm so that small changes in the orientation of the main catalytic domains could be amplified into large displacements at the end of the arm where it attaches to the rod (80). Much future structural and mutational analysis will be required to definitively determine the source of the motion, but for analysis of motility, it is only necessary to assume that motion of some type relative to the attachment point occurs. Analysis of mutant myosin and actins should be particularly helpful in clarifying these issues (24, 83).

One complexity of the myosin ATPase cycle is that the physical binding of S1 heads to actin is weaker than the apparent stimulation of ATPase activity under some circumstances, but physical binding can still be saturated without inhibition (102). This requires that hydrolysis must also occur while S1 is bound to actin. The hydrolysis of ATP by myosin while bound to actin is usually referred to as a nondissociating pathway, but it should be emphasized that rapid dissociation is still occurring at $>1000 \ s^{-1}$. The key result is that the rate of ATP hydrolysis is largely insensitive to whether the M•ATP complex is free or bound to actin. These considerations and other experimental results have led to the general idea that there are two major types of S1 complexes with actin and that it is the transition between them that drives the power stroke (19). Furthermore, it has been proposed that association of all myosin•nucleotide complexes with actin proceeds through weakly bound species (22).

There is now considerable evidence for formation of high-energy states that only occur during ATP hydrolysis. One early result from Sleep & Hutton (99) showed, by analysis of the exchange of $^{32}P$ between Pi and ATP, that the A•M'•ADP intermediate that is formed directly by Pi release following ATP hydrolysis is not the same as the A•M•ADP intermediate that is formed by binding ADP from the medium. Exchange between ATP and Pi is stimulated even more in muscle fibers (8). In this case, the A•M'•ADP state is further constrained by the fact that its energy can be stored temporarily as strain. With free acto-S1, this energy is likely to be rapidly dissipated, but in a fiber, the cross bridge will be able to maintain strain and thus the rebinding of Pi becomes more favorable. A related stimulation of exchange between water oxygens and Pi of the medium is also observed (118).

Detailed discussion is beyond the scope of this review, but several important observations are relevant to how the catalytic cycle relates to the mechanical properties of muscle. [See Ma & Taylor and references therein for a recent analysis of myofibril ATPase (66).] The introduction of caged nucleotides has allowed the observation of the initial rapid stages of ATP hydrolysis in fibers without the limitations caused by diffusion (20). One area of controversy has been the distance moved per ATP hydrolyzed (the step size). Values have ranged from >100 (45) to 5 nm (111). These results have been reviewed (10, 54; see 21, 56, 72, 121, 124 and references therein for more recent treatments).

# KINESIN

Kinesin was discovered comparatively recently (9, 114) as the motor responsible for movement of some membranous organelles along MTs. A key discovery was that AMP-PNP inhibited motility by inducing the tight binding of the organelles to MTs (63). This enabled the facile purification of kinesin from crude brain extracts by affinity purification involving sequential binding of kinesin to MTs in the presence of AMP-PNP, followed by the selective release by excess ATP (114). The tight binding that is induced by a nonhydrolyzable ATP analogue suggests that the ternary complex of ATP with kinesin and MTs would not dissociate rapidly. With actomyosin, AMP-PNP produces dissociation, although not as effectively as ATP (34).

## Native Kinesin

Initial preparations of neuronal kinesin had variable low rates of MT-stimulated ATPase but could drive sliding of MTs at high rates when adsorbed to a glass surface in an in vitro motility assay. This was likely due to a number of factors including the fact that sliding was still observed even when active motors were only a small percent of the protein adsorbed on the glass (51). Kuznetsov & Gelfand (60) reported the first preparation of kinesin with high rates of MT-stimulated ATPase. Subsequent analysis (35, 43) of the mechanism of this preparation from bovine brain demonstrated that it shared many of the features of the myosin ATPase. In the absence of actin, burst kinetics were observed in which ATP was bound and rapidly hydrolyzed, but product release was slow. The predominant steady-state intermediate had one ADP bound per site, and the release rate of this bound ADP equaled the steady-state turnover rate. Furthermore, MTs stimulated the release of this bound ADP in a manner that is similar to the stimulation by actin of product release from myosin. However, two significant differences from myosin were noted. One was that Pi release was much faster than steady-state turnover so that the predominate kinesin•products complex contained only ADP and not ADP•Pi. This rapid release of Pi could be demonstrated by gel filtration and $^{18}O$ exchange. Essentially no incorporation of water-derived oxygens into Pi was observed during MT-stimulated hydrolysis by kinesin (35). The most direct explanation is that $k_4 >> k_{-3}$, which is the exact opposite of the situation with myosin. This result is consistent with rapid release of Pi, which greatly reduces the lifetime of the E•ADP•Pi intermediate and provides no opportunity for reformation of E•ATP. The kinetics of the burst phase were determined by Sadhu & Taylor (84) who demonstrated by rapid kinetic approaches that the rate of the hydrolytic step was $6-10 s^{-1}$ in the absence of MTs and that this was faster than the maximum steady-state rate of $3 s^{-1}$ with saturating MTs. Using fluorescent 2'(3")-[O-(N-methylanthraniloyl]ATP (mant-ATP), they were further able to show that ATP binding was at least a two-step process with an isomerization.

The other significant difference from myosin is that ADP binding to kinesin is much stronger. ADP binds much more weakly than ATP to myosin, but ADP binds to kinesin as strongly as ATP and causes severe product inhibition of ATPase activity (35) and motility (82). In fact, ADP binding was so strong that the enzyme, as isolated, contained close to a stoichiometric level of ADP that was retained thorough chromatography in the absence of added ATP or ADP. Observation of the burst phase was only possible because nucleotide-free kinesin could be obtained by chromatography in the presence of excess EDTA.

These results with kinesin isolated from bovine brain must be viewed with caution, however, because there are a number of indications that the kinetics of native kinesin in solution do not correspond to the kinetics of the motors that drive active sliding. One problem is that the maximum rates of MT-stimulated ATPase are variable and too low to readily produce the observed sliding velocity. Native $\alpha_2\beta_2$ kinesin has a maximum MT-stimulated rate of only ~1 $s^{-1}$ (42, 115), and this requires a step size per ATP of >200 nM (52). The variations observed in ATPase rates are in part the result of limited proteolyis, which greatly increases activity (42, 61). A second problem is that the binding of native kinesin to MTs is too weak in the presence of ATP to maintain the sustained contact required for processive motion. Binding of native kinesin to MTs is so weak in the presence of ATP that over 90% of the kinesin remains unbound even at concentrations of MTs that are fivefold in excess of the $K_{0.5}^{MT}$ value for stimulation of ATPase activity (DD Hackney, unpublished observations). This is analogous experimentally to the refractory state in actomyosin (102), but the magnitude of the discrepancy is much greater for kinesin and the mechanism may differ. It is likely that these properties of kinesin in solution are related to the interaction with the tail domains in the 9 S configuration.

## Expressed Head Domains

The use of isolated head domains provides a means to evaluate the activity of heads in the absence of tails. Head domains can be obtained from native kinesin by limited proteolyis (61, 87), but the yield of native kinesin is so low that obtaining an amount sufficient for extensive rapid kinetic analysis would be problematic. Rather, domain fragments and various chimeric constructs can be readily obtained from the cloned gene, and the properties of a number of these constructs have been investigated (5, 103, 126). Gilbert & Johnson (28) provided the first detailed mechanistic study on K401, which contains amino acids 5–401 of *Drosophila* kinesin heavy chain with a modified N-terminus. This construct has a low ATPase rate in the absence of MTs and a high ATPase rate in the presence of saturating levels of MTs (0.01 to 10-20 s$^{-1}$, respectively). The concentration of MTs required for half saturation, $K_{0.5}^{MT}$, is 0.9 μM. This preparation was originally reported to be monomeric based on STEM analysis (29), but DKH392 (53), which contains amino acids 1–392, was shown to be dimeric. Sequence analysis predicts that the region between 340 and 400 has a high probability for formation of coiled-coil (103), and the fact that the shorter DKH340 (and also DKH357) were shown to be monomeric (53) suggests that constructs of 392 amino acids and larger are dimeric due to the presence of a coiled-coil neck region before an apparent flexible hinge in the proline 399 region (53, 125). Subsequent hydrodynamic investigation of K401 and other constructs has confirmed this pattern (5, 14, 44). Estimates of the axial ratio of the 38-kDa head domain have varied from a moderately asymmetric value of 2.7 for DKH340 (53) to a highly asymmetric value of 7.07 for K341 (14).

DKH392 is also highly activated by MTs (0.005 to ~40 s$^{-1}$ or almost a 10,000-fold activation) (38). In addition to the two to fourfold higher ATPase rate of DKH392 vs K401, these preparations also differ in $K_{0.5}^{MT}$ values, with DKH392 having a much lower value of 30–50 nM when assayed at low head concentration in buffer containing 25 mM KCl. Analysis is complicated by the fact that the observed $K_{0.5}^{MT}$ value increases steeply with increasing concentration of dimeric kinesin in the assay (38) and with increasing ionic strength. The $K_{0.5}^{MT}$ value for K401 was determined at high concentration of K401, which likely accounts for most of its high reported value. This concentration dependence is reasonable in light of the processive and tight interaction of dimeric kinesin with MTs. At high occupancy of the MT lattice with kinesin heads, rebinding of a released head will be disfavored because potential binding sites are occupied. Also, there may be direct steric interference between head domains attached to neighboring tubulins that prevents normal processive movement and leads to premature release of the heads from the MT. Thus the high observed $K_{0.5}^{MT}$ values at high head concentration are a reflection of the ratio of heads to MTs in addition to the intrinsic affinity of dimeric kinesin for an unoccupied MT lattice.

These kinetic properties of DKH392 are consistent with the requirements for single-motor motility and indicate that isolated dimeric kinesin heads in the absence of tail domains are capable of processive motion. Thus the $k_{cat}$ value of ~40 $s^{-1}$ (80 $s^{-1}$ per dimer) at saturating MTs corresponds to a sliding rate of 640 nm/s for a step size of 8 nm per ATP, and this is close to the observed sliding rate of 900 nm/s for *Drosophila* kinesin (86). The $k_{cat}/K_{0.5}^{MT}$ value of >1000 $\mu M^{-1}s^{-1}$ per dimer is in excess of the diffusional controlled limit for rebinding to the MT (39), indicating that many ATP molecules are hydrolyzed during each diffusional encounter with a MT as required for processive movement. The ATPase kinetics and diffusional rebinding rate have also been determined in higher salt buffers more characteristic of physiological conditions (160 mM ionic strength), and it was found that DKH392 still hydrolyzed 120 ATP molecules per diffusional encounter (39a). This corresponds to a detachment rate of 0.7 $s^{-1}$ and an average persistence time on the MT of ~1 s, consistent with the extent of processivity observed by motility (6).

## Rapid Kinetic Analysis

Analysis of the burst kinetics of expressed head domains of kinesin is difficult because they are unstable in the absence of nucleotide and switch into an inactive conformation that can only slowly rebind ATP (52). This instability is also shared by ncd (64). Consequently, most of the rapid kinetic data have been obtained starting from the rigor-like complex of the head and MT in the absence of bound nucleotide. This complex binds ATP rapidly and exhibits burst kinetics with a maximum hydrolysis rate of 75–120 $s^{-1}$ at saturating ATP (29). The burst size is substoichiometric, which is attributed to rapid release of ATP before hydrolysis, although this observation requires reinvestigation because a tethered dimer would also have a substoichiometric burst amplitude without the need for invoking rapid ATP release (see below). More recent work (30) using a newly developed method for monitoring released Pi has confirmed that Pi release is rapid. The observed rate of 13 $s^{-1}$ for the burst phase of Pi release is slower than hydrolysis and is similar to both the steady-state rate (10–20 $s^{-1}$) and the rate of ATP-induced release of kinesin from the MT, as determined by light scattering (13 $s^{-1}$). Interpretation of the Pi release experiments is complicated by a number of factors, however. One is that a substoichiometric burst was observed by formation of ADP in either 0 or 100 mM KCl (29, 30), but a stoichiometric burst was observed by Pi release (30) at 100 mM KCl, and the basis for this discrepancy is unclear. Furthermore, the steady-state ATPase rate of ~5 s$^{-1}$ observed by Pi release with 0.075 μM MTs at 0 mM KCl is significantly larger than the value of 0.8–1.5 s$^{-1}$ expected for $k_{cat}$ and $K_{0.5}^{MT}$ values of 10–20 s$^{-1}$ and 0.9 μM, respectively. This discrepancy is much larger at 100 mM KCl because the $K_{0.5}^{MT}$ value is much higher and the predicted steady-state rate correspondingly smaller, yet the observed rate by Pi release is still 4.2 s$^{-1}$. These discrepancies may be due to the low concentration of heads that was used in the Pi release experiments and the strong dependence of the observed $K_{0.5}^{MT}$ value on the concentration of heads as discussed above. In this context, the observation that the burst size at 0 mM KCl was fivefold larger than the concentration of heads (30) is difficult to interpret. The suggestion that this represents the hydrolysis of multiple ATP molecules before diffusional escape of K401 from the MT would be consistent with the processive hydrolysis exhibited by DKH392 (38, 39).

The maximum rate of MT-induced release of ADP from E•ADP for K401 was 300 s$^{-1}$, as determined with fluorescent mant-ADP (30). Ma & Taylor, however, have reported that MT-stimulated ADP release is much slower with their human kinesin constructs and that ADP release is the rate-limiting step (67). Changes in intrinsic fluorescence on nucleotide binding greatly aided in evaluation of the rapid kinetics of myosin, but this technique is not applicable to kinesin because the 38-kDa head domain lacks tryptophan.

The value of 13 s$^{-1}$ for detachment of K401 as measured by light scattering (30) appears in conflict with the 0.7 s$^{-1}$ value measured with DKH392 based on its ATPase kinetics as discussed above, but this may relate to differences in how the experiments were conducted. One consideration is that the lattice of MT-binding sites is usually filled at the beginning of a light scattering or fluorescence experiment so that the magnitude of the signal change is maximized. In the case of actomyosin, this is not as serious a concern because the S1 usually diffusionally separates from the actin filament, even when vacant actin sites are available (see 1, 107, however, for reports of the influence of lattice saturation on acto-S1). In the case of a processive and tightly binding motor like kinesin, the extent of lattice occupancy is a major factor because the first heads to be released from a full lattice are not able to readily rebind due to lack of vacant sites. After a significant fraction of the sites become vacant, heads can rebind to these sites before diffusional escape. The observed release rate of 13 s$^{-1}$ for K401 at high lattice occupancy needs to be reevaluated in this context and may not be indicative of either the low release rate of a dimeric construct from a largely unoccupied lattice or the higher release rate of monomeric heads. Determination of the kinetic cycle for individual head domains remains a major goal for future work.

## Stoichiometry of MT Binding

It is clear that both monomeric and dimeric head constructs bind with a striking 8-nm periodicity along the MT (46, 53, 59, 101). This distance corresponds to the spacing of tubulin heterodimers along the protofilament. Initial cross-linking experiments indicated that the binding site was exclusively on the β subunit of tubulin (101), but more recent cross-linking results (117) have detected contact with both α and β subunits. The stoichiometry of binding was originally reported for K401 as one head per tubulin dimer (46), which corresponds to half of a kinesin dimer per tubulin dimer. Work with DKH340 and DKH392 has indicated, however, that a stoichiometry of one head per tubulin dimer is only observed with monomeric species and that dimeric species such DKH392, and by inference K401, have a higher stoichiometry of one kinesin dimer per tubulin dimer (53). There are differences in experimental procedures and in the methods used to estimate the equivalence point that likely account for this discrepancy. In particular, the binding of monomeric DKH340 is essentially stoichiometric at low to moderate ionic strength, with a sharp break in the binding curve at the equivalence point; whereas it is more difficult to saturate the MT lattice with dimeric DKH392, and an excess of DKH392 is usually required in order to approach saturation with one DKH392 dimer per tubulin dimer.

The second head of a bound dimer is not likely to be attached to the MT because all of the sites are already filled with the first head that is already bound. The existence of such a tethered dimer is strongly supported by the observation of half-site reactivity of dimeric kinesin during ATP hydrolysis (37). It was found that monomeric kinesin•ADP complexes release all of their ADP on binding to the MT with formation of a tight rigor complex, but dimeric kinesin heads only loose half of their bound ADP on binding to the MT. This is consistent with formation of a tethered species with one head attached to the MT in a rigor-like linkage without bound nucleotide, whereas the other head is held off the MT by the steric constraints of the dimer and retains its bound ADP. Furthermore, the ADP on the tethered head is turning over at a rate that is consistent with it being an intermediate on the main pathway of steady-state ATP hydrolysis.

# DYNEIN

The ATPase mechanism of dynein has been most thoroughly studied with the three-headed 22S (30S) form *Tetrahymena* axonemes, and this discussion focuses on that preparation. (See 12, 58, 76, 88, 122 for previous reviews of its structure and mechanism.) Dynein also binds and hydrolyzes ATP rapidly with burst kinetics indicative of rate-limiting product release (57). ATP hydrolysis during the burst phase is fast at 55 s$^{-1}$ (57), and more recent work has revised that number upward to 150 s⁻¹ (92). As is the case with kinesin, Pi release is rapid, but the release of ADP is also fast at 2–8 s⁻¹, and net ADP binding is weak ($K_i$ = 0.4 mM) (50). The hydrolysis is reversible, although much less so than for myosin, with an average of 0.4 reversals ($k_3$:$k_4$ = 0.4) as determined by the extent of $^{18}O$ exchange during hydrolysis (50). Pi readily rebinds to E•ADP and can regenerate E•ATP, as indicated by a rapid medium Pi⇄HOH exchange (50) that results in a loss of $^{18}O$ from labeled Pi in the medium. This medium exchange has the same partitioning coefficient as intermediate exchange during net hydrolysis of free ATP, indicating that medium exchange likely results from a subset of the reaction occurring during net hydrolysis. As with kinesin, no structural probes such as changes in intrinsic fluorescence have been discovered that would allow investigation of conformational changes that occur. This may be because of the large size of dynein and the possibility that major conformational changes will be confined to only one consensus ATP-binding domain.

The physiological role of the high, variable basal rate of ATP hydrolysis by dynein in the absence of MTs is unclear. One possibility is that it represents loss of the normal control present on dynein in situ. The higher observed basal rates of 8 s⁻¹ approach the maximum actin-stimulated rates for skeletal S1 and even exceed the maximum rates for smooth muscle myosin. With myosin, it is discouragingly easy to generate preparations that have lost the tight control on product release that results in low basal rates characteristic of the native state. This is especially true with nonskeletal myosin (15, 17). A high basal rate may be of less concern for dynein because cilia and flagella normally are constantly beating and thus always undergoing more rapid MT-activated hydrolysis. However, it is interesting to note that the basal rate of cytoplasmic dynein is significantly lower at ~0.1 s⁻¹ (93).

One result of the high basal ATPase rate is that dynein preparations exhibit low fractional stimulation by MTs. This is particularly a problem because microtubule-associated proteins (MAPs) strongly inhibit activation by MTs, and significant activation is only observed with MAP-free MTs (71) or when dynein is reintroduced into the axonemal lattice (25). Even for a favorable case with a low basal rate of 1.5 s⁻¹, it required 500 μM MTs (>50 mg/ml) to increase the ATPase rate by fivefold (71). It was not possible to estimate the $K_{0.5}{}^{MT}$ value for axonemal dynein because the interaction is too weak. The second order rate constant for stimulation of ATPase by MTs was 0.012 $\mu M^{-1}s^{-1}$, and this is low compared with values for myosin and kinesin. Crosslinking of dynein to MTs increases the local tubulin concentration and produces a 30-fold stimulation to 150 s⁻¹ (92), which corresponds to an effective molarity for tubulin of >10 mM. Activation by MTs was easier to establish with cytoplasmic dynein because of a lower basal rate and the fact that the ATPase rate saturated at a much lower concentration of MTs (93).

As does kinesin, dynein binds strongly to MTs in a rigor-like state in the absence of nucleotide at its active site. Binding of ATP to the dynein-MT complex results in the rapid dissociation of dynein•ATP from the MT at a rate of >1000 s$^{-1}$ (75). This dissociation rate exceeds the hydrolysis rate of 55–150 s$^{-1}$ and thus hydrolysis occurs after dissociation from the MT. The rate-limiting step is likely to be rebinding of dynein•ADP back to the MT with stimulation of ADP release (49), at least at subsaturating MTs levels where Pi release is more rapid than MT-stimulated ADP release. This may not necessarily be the case at MTs levels close to saturation, and it would be of interest to determine if the extent of $^{18}$O exchange by cross-linked dynein-MTs was lower. One striking result is that the second order rate for MT stimulation of ADP release is 100-fold less than that for bimolecular recombination of dynein•ADP with MTs and associated ADP release. This has led to the suggestion (49) that the dynein•ADP species in each case are different, with dynein* •ADP used to designate a high energy state produced by ATP hydrolysis and dynein•ADP used to designate a low energy state produced by binding of medium ADP to dynein. In spite of the large difference in their kinetics of interaction with MTs, both dynein*•ADP and dynein•ADP have essentially the same kinetics for binding of Pi and reformation of bound ATP, as indicated by identical $^{18}$O exchange patterns for both species (50).

## COMPARISON

All three motors share an underlying antagonism between nucleotide binding and filament binding. All produce strongly bound rigor-like states that are dissociated following binding of ATP that likely forces cyclic dissociation and reassociation during hydrolysis of each ATP. ATP-induced dissociation is rapid for both myosin and dynein at >1000 s$^{-1}$. ATP-induced dissociation of kinesin from MTs is likely to be considerably slower, but the reported rates with dimeric constructs do not provide information about the kinetics of individual head domains.

The reversibility of ATP hydrolysis differs dramatically: Myosin undergoes an average of ~200 reversals, dynein 0.4, and kinesin <0.04. This is in part due to more rapid release of Pi by dynein and kinesin. Interesting, dynein is the only species to exhibit a rapid exchange of oxygens atoms between water and Pi (medium Pi$\rightleftarrows$ HOH oxygen exchange), which indicates that bound ATP is readily accessible from medium ADP and Pi for dynein only. This is reflected in the rate for Pi rebinding determined from oxygen exchange, which is 8000 M$^{-1}$s$^{-1}$ for dynein (50), but only 3.9 M$^{-1}$s$^{-1}$ for myosin at pH 7 (96). Medium exchange has not been determined for kinesin in the absence of MTs, but exchange is very slow even in the presence of MTs (DD Hackney, unpublished observations). The facile rebinding of Pi and reversal to bound ATP by dynein is consistent with the particularily strong inhibition of dynein by vanadate. This inhibition is believed to result from vanadate mimicking Pi and binding to an ADP state.

There are a number of differences between these motors in addition to the selectivity of vanadate. Shimizu and coworkers (89) have made an extensive comparison of the substrate specificity and inhibition patterns and have determined characteristic profiles for each motor type. One major difference is that AMP-PNP induces tight binding of kinesin to MTs, which was the basis for the initial discovery of kinesin. Alternative nucleotides are also useful in probing different parts of a mechanistic scheme and have proven useful for profiling myosin (121).

Another significant difference between the motors is in their affinity for ADP. Both myosin and dynein have low affinity for ADP, and ADP is ineffective in dissociation of the actomyosin and dynein-MT complexes. In contrast, kinesin has high affinity for ADP with a $K_d$ of ~1 nM. Thus the E•ADP complex is of low energy, and most of the energy of ATP hydrolysis has been expended before it is generated. One consequence is that ADP is nearly as effective as ATP in dissociation of monomeric kinesin heads with MTs (W Jiang & DD Hackney, unpublished observation) and causes premature release of kinesin from MTs in motility assays (82). More detailed comparison between the three classes of enzymes, particularily for kinesin, will require considerably more kinetic and mechanistic information.

## MULTIPLE HEADS

Myosin is able to bind to actin with both heads, but the actin-activated kinetics of single-headed S1 and double-headed HMM are essentially identical at saturating levels of ATP, as discussed by Taylor (106). Cooperation between heads results in tighter binding of HMM to actin as opposed to S1, but only if binding is strong (18, 33). In this case, binding of one head of HMM to actin allows the other tethered head to bind without additional loss of translational entropy. If the binding is weak, however, then the second head is unlikely to bind before the first head releases and any advantage is lost. Kinetic consequences of tethering acto-HMM can be observed at low ATP levels. If both heads are initially attached to actin in the absence of nucleotide, then ATP binding to one head will cause it to be released from the actin, but it is not free to diffuse away because it is held near the actin by the other head, which is still attached. At low ATP concentrations, hydrolysis and reattachment of the tethered head will occur before ATP can bind to the rigor head and produce net release of the dimer. Just such rapid cycling of one head without net dissociation of the dimer has been observed in an elevated rate of ATPase for HMM vs S1 at low ATP and in the pattern of [18]O oxygen exchange (40). Most of the flux of Pi produced by acto-HMM at low ATP has the oxygen exchange pattern characteristic of acto-S1 at high, but not fully saturated, actin concentration. At high ATP level, ATP binding to the rigor head of the tethered dimer is fast and produces net dissociation of the dimer from actin with a return to the oxygen exchange pattern characteristic of acto-S1 at low actin concentration. Caution is necessary, however, in drawing detailed conclusions because proteolytically derived HMM has partially degraded light chains. The light chains are in the neck region, and their modification could influence the flexibility of the heads and allow modes of simultaneous interaction of both heads with actin that would not be possible with native myosin. Also, HMM can cross-link actin filaments into rafts under some circumstances (109).

Dynein also can bind to a MT with its heads in rigor linkage (74, 75) and appears to generate tethered species if partially released. Omoto & Johnson (71) demonstrated that MTs produce a larger stimulation of ATPase at lower ATP than at higher ATP, consistent with cycling of tethered heads on and off of the MT while the trimer remained attached through other heads (as discussed for HMM). In addition, lags are seen under some conditions in the light-scattering signal produced by release of dynein from MTs induced by ATP plus vanadate (90). These complex kinetics are consistent with the need to simultaneously release all three heads of dynein before the trimer undergoes net dissociation from the MT. Lags are only observed at low ATP, yet this simple model should produce lags in both high and low ATP. It has been suggested that the absence of lag may represent different, perhaps cooperative, binding at high ATP (90). In light of the discovery that dynein heavy chains contain multiple consensus nucleotide-binding sites, it may also reflect changes in mechanism produced by the occupancy of these other sites.

The situation with dimeric kinesin is more complex. Both heads do not bind simultaneously to the same MT during steady-state ATP hydrolysis (37) or in the presence of AMP-PNP (53), and the predominant binding mode is likely to be the tethered species even at saturating ATP. Although the tethered species appear to be similar for HMM and kinesin, they have very different kinetics for interaction with actin or MTs. Because the tethered heads of HMM or dynein can rebind to the filament with stimulation of product release while the other head is still attached in rigor, an acceleration of ATP hydrolysis is produced. With kinesin, the two heads of the dimer are not connected to the neck by a highly flexible hinge (53), and the steric constraints imposed on the tethered head by this linkage are the likely cause of its inability to bind to the MT with release of ADP (37). Release of the rigor linkage by ATP binding would allow the tethered head the freedom to rapidly bind to the MT with ADP release. Such flip-flop mechanisms readily lead to models that account for the processive behavior of kinesin and allow for many cycles of ATP hydrolysis without net dissociation of the dimer from the MT (37). It should be emphasized that the observation of half-site reaction of dimeric kinesin with MTs only indicates that the tethered species is the predominant steady-state intermediate. A large number of different detailed models are consistent with this basic property and produce processive behavior. In particular, the existence of the tethered species does not preclude that kinesin can transiently go through species with both heads attached to the MT. The only constraint is that such species cannot predominate at steady state. The observation that kinesin remains attached to a MT even under levels of force that would cause its separation if the dimer released for >72 μs (105) indicates that the rigor head may not need to fully dissociate from the MT before the tethered head can attach and the events could even be concerted.

## Literature Cited

1. Andreev OA, Andreeva AL, Borejdo J. 1993. Polarization of fluorescently labeled myosin subfragment-1 fully or partially decorating muscle fibers and myofibrils. *Biophys. J.* 65:1027–38
2. Asai DJ, Beckwith SM, Kandl KA, Keating HH, Tjandra H, Forney JD. 1994. The dynein genes of *Paramecium tetraurelia.* Sequences adjacent to the catalytic P-loop identify cytoplasmic and axonemal heavy chain isoforms. *J. Cell Sci.* 107:839–47
3. Bagshaw CR, 1993. *Muscle Contraction. London: Chapman & Hall. 155 pp.*
4. Bagshaw CR, Trentham DR, Wolcott RG, Boyer PD. 1975. Oxygen exchange in the γ-phosphoryl group of protein-bound ATP during Mg$^{2+}$-dependent adenosine triphosphatase activity of myosin. *Proc. Natl. Acad. Sci. USA* 72:2592–96
5. Berliner E, Young EC, Anderson K, Mahtani HK, Gelles J. 1995. Failure of a single-headed kinesin to track parallel to microtubule protofilaments. *Nature* 373:718–21
6. Block SM, Goldstein LSB, Schnapp BJ. 1990. Bead movement by single kinesin molecules studied with optical tweezers. *Nature* 348:348–52
7. Bloom GS, Endow SA. 1994. Motor proteins 1: kinesins. *Protein Profile* 1:1059–1116
8. Bowater R, Sleep JA. 1988. Demembranated muscle fibers catalyze a more rapid exchange between phosphate and

adenosine triphosphate than actomyosin subfragment 1. *Biochemistry* 27:5314–23
9. Brady ST. 1985. A novel brain ATPase with properties expected for the fast axonal transport motor. *Nature* 317:73–75
10. Burton K. 1992. Myosin step size: estimates from motility assays and shortening muscle. *J. Mus. Res. Cell Motil.* 13:590–607
11. Cheney RE, Riley MA, Mooseker MS. 1993. Phylogenetic analysis of the myosin superfamily. *Cell Motil. Cytoskelet.* 24:215–23
12. Chilcote TJ, Johnson KA. 1989. Microtubule-dynein cross-bridge cycle and the kinetics of 5′-adenylyl imidodiphosphate (AMP-PNP). See Ref. 117a, pp. 235–43
13. Cooke R. 1989. Structure of the myosin head. *Cell Motil. Cytoskelet.* 14:183–86
14. Correia JJ, Gilbert SP, Moyer ML, Johnson KA. 1995. Sedimentation studies on the kinesin motor domain constructs K401, K366, and K341. *Biochemistry* 34:4898–907
15. Cross RA, Jackson AP, Citi S, Kendrick-Jones J, Bagshaw CR. 1988. Active site trapping of nucleotide by smooth and non-muscle myosins. *J. Mol. Biol.* 203:173–81
16. Dale MP, Hackney DD. 1987. Analysis of positional isotope exchange in ATP by cleavage of the β P-O γ P bond. Demonstration of negligible positional

isotope exchange by myosin. *Biochemistry* 26:8365–72
17. Dash PK, Hackney DD. 1991. The mechanism of the ATP hydrolysis by smooth muscle myosin and subfragments using steady state titration and $^{18}O$ exchange. *Biochem. Int.* 25:1013–22
18. Duong AM, Reisler E. 1989. Nucleotide-induced states of myosin subfragment 1 cross-linked to actin. *Biochemistry* 28:3502–9
19. Eisenberg E, Hill TL. 1985. Muscle contraction and free energy transduction in biological systems. *Science* 227:999–1006
20. Ferenczi MA, Homsher E, Trentham DR. 1984. The kinetics of magnesium adenosine triphosphate cleavage in skinned muscle fibres of the rabbit. *J. Physiol.* 352:575–99
21. Finer JT, Simmons RM, Spudich JA. 1994. Single myosin molecule mechanics: piconewton forces and nanometre steps. *Nature* 368:113–19
22. Geeves MA. 1991. The dynamics of actin and myosin association and the crossbridge model of muscle contraction. *Biochem. J.* 274:1–14
23. Gelles J, Schnapp BJ, Sheetz MP. 1988. Tracking kinesin-driven movements with nanometer-scale precision. *Nature* 331:450–53
24. Gerisch G, Noegel AA, Schleicher M. 1991. Genetic alteration of proteins in actin-based motility systems. *Annu. Rev. Physiol.* 53:607–28
25. Gibbons IR, Fronk E. 1979. A latent adenosine triphosphatase form of dynein 1 from sea urchin sperm flagella. *J. Biol. Chem.* 254:187–96
26. Gibbons IR, Gibbons BH, Mocz G, Asai DJ. 1991. Multiple nucleotide-binding sites in the sequence of dynein β heavy chain. *Nature* 352:640–43
27. Gibbons IR, Lee-Eiford A, Mocz G, Phillipson CA, Tang WY, Gibbons BH. 1987. Photosensitized cleavage of dynein heavy chains. Cleavage at the "V1 site" by irradiation at 365 nm in the presence of ATP and vanadate. *J. Biol. Chem.* 262:2780–86
28. Gilbert SP, Johnson KA. 1993. Expression, purification, and characterization of the *Drosophila* kinesin motor domain produced in *Echerichia coli*. *Biochemistry* 32:4677–84
29. Gilbert SP, Johnson KA. 1994. Presteady-state kinetics of the microtubule-kinesin ATPase. *Biochemistry* 33:1951–60
30. Gilbert SP, Webb MR, Brune M, Johnson KA. 1995. Pathway of processive ATP hydrolysis by kinesin. *Nature* 373:671–76
31. Goldstein LSB. 1993. With apologies to Scheherazade: tails of 1001 kinesin motors. *Annu. Rev. Genet.* 27:319–51
32. Goodson HV, Kang SJ, Endow SA. 1994. Molecular phylogeny of the kinesin family of microtubule motor proteins. *J. Cell Sci.* 107:1875–84
33. Goody RS, Holmes KC. 1983. Crossbridges and the mechanism of muscle contraction. *Biochim. Biophys. Acta* 726:13–39
34. Greene LE, Eisenberg E. 1980. Dissociation of the actin-subfragment 1 complex by adenyl-5′-yl imidodiphosphate, ADP, and PPi. *J. Biol. Chem.* 255:543–48
35. Hackney DD. 1988. Kinesin ATPase: rate-limiting ADP release. *Proc. Natl. Acad. Sci. USA* 85:6314–18
36. Hackney DD. 1992. Kinesin and myosin ATPases: variations on a theme. *Philos. Trans. R. Soc. London Biol.* 336:13–18
37. Hackney DD. 1994. Evidence for alternating head catalysis by kinesin during microtubule-stimulated ATP hydrolysis. *Proc. Natl. Acad. Sci. USA* 91:6865–69
38. Hackney DD. 1994. The rate limiting step in microtubule-stimulated ATP hydrolysis by dimeric kinesin head domains occurs while bound to the microtubule. *J. Biol. Chem.* 269:16508–11
39. Hackney DD. 1995. Implications of diffusion-controlled limit for processivity of dimeric kinesin head domains. *Biophys. J.* 68:267s–70s
39a. Hackney DD. 1995. Highly processive microtubule-stimulated ATP hydrolysis by dimeric kinesin head domains. *Nature*. In press
40. Hackney DD, Clark PK. 1984. Catalytic consequences of oligomeric organization: kinetic evidence for 'tethered' acto-heavy meromyosin at low ATP concentration. *Proc. Natl. Acad. Sci. USA* 81:5345–49
41. Hackney DD, Levitt JD, Suhan J. 1992. Kinesin undergoes a 9 S to 6 S conformational transition. *J. Biol. Chem.* 267:8696–701
42. Hackney DD, Levitt JD, Wagner DD. 1991. Characterization of α2β2 and α2 forms of kinesin. *Biochem. Biophys. Res. Commun.* 174:810–15
43. Hackney DD, Malik A, Wright KW. 1989. Nucleotide-free kinesin hydrolyzes ATP with burst kinetics. *J. Biol. Chem.* 264:15943–48
44. Hackney DD, Nagy JM. 1995. Minimum size of kinesin head domains for

dimerization and interaction with tail domains. *Biophys. J.* 68:286a

45. Harada Y, Sakurada TA, Thomas DD, Yanagida T. 1990. Mechanochemical coupling in actomyosin energy transduction studied by in vitro movement assay. *J. Mol. Biol.* 216:49–68

46. Harrison BC, Marchese-Ragona SP, Gilbert SP, Cheng N, Steven AC, Johnson KA. 1993. Decoration of the microtubule surface by one kinesin head per tubulin heterodimer. *Nature* 362:73–75

47. Hibberd MG, Trentham DR. 1986. Relationship between chemical and mechanical events during muscular contraction. *Annu. Rev. Biophys. Chem.* 15:119–61

48. Hisanaga S, Murofushi H, Okuhara K, Sato R, Masuda Y, et al. 1989. The molecular structure of adrenal medulla kinesin. *Cell Motil. Cytoskelet.* 12:264–72

49. Holzbaur EL, Johnson KA. 1989. Microtubules accelerate ADP release by dynein. *Biochemistry* 28:7010–16

50. Holzbaur EL, Johnson KA. 1989. ADP release is rate limiting in steady-state turnover by dynein adenosinetriphsophatase. *Biochemistry* 28:5577–85

51. Howard J, Hudspeth AJ, Vale RD. 1989. Movement of microtubules by single kinesin molecules. *Nature* 342:154–58

52. Huang T-G, Hackney DD. 1994. *Drosophila* kinesin minimal motor domain expressed in *Escherichia coli*. Purification and kinetic characterization. *J. Biol. Chem.* 269:16493–501

53. Huang T-G, Suhan J, Hackney DD. 1994. *Drosophila* kinesin motor domain extending to amino acid position 392 is dimeric when expressed in *Escherichia coli*. *J. Biol. Chem.* 269:16502–7

54. Huxley HE. 1990. Sliding filaments and molecular motile systems. *J. Biol. Chem.* 265:8347–50

55. Ikebe M, Hinkins S, Hartshorne DJ. 1983. Correlation of enzymatic properties and conformation of smooth muscle myosin. *Biochemistry* 22:4580–87

56. Ishijima A, Harada Y, Kojima H, Funatsu T, Higuchi H, Yanagida Y. 1994. Single-molecule analysis of the actomyosin motor using nano-manipulation. *Biochem. Biophys. Res. Commun.* 199:1057–63

57. Johnson KA. 1983. The pathway of ATP hydrolysis by dynein. Kinetics of a presteady state phosphate burst. *J. Biol. Chem.* 258:13825–32

58. Johnson KA. 1985. Pathway of the microtubule-dynein ATPase and the structure of dynein: a comparison with acto-

myosin. *Annu. Rev. Biophys. Chem.* 14:161–88

59. Kikkawa M, Ishikawa T, Nakata T, Wakabayashi T, Hirokawa, N. 1994. Direct visualisation of the microtubule lattice seam in vitro and in vivo. *J. Cell. Biol.* 127:1965–71

60. Kuznetsov SA, Gelfand VI. 1986. Bovine brain kinesin is a microtubule-activated ATPase. *Proc. Natl. Acad. Sci. USA* 83:8530–34

61. Kuznetsov SA, Vaisberg EA, Rothwell SW, Murphy DB, Gelfand VI. 1989. Isolation of a 45-kDa fragment from the kinesin heavy chain with enhanced ATPase and microtubule-binding activities. *J. Biol. Chem.* 264:589–95

62. Langford GM. 1995. Actin- and microtubule-dependent organelle motors: interrelationships between the two motility systems. *Curr. Opin. Cell Biol.* 7:82–88

63. Lasek RJ, Brady ST. 1985. Attachment of transported vesicles to microtubules in axoplasm is facilitated by AMP-PNP. *Nature* 316:645–47

64. Lockhart A, Cross RA. 1994. Origins of reversed directionality in the ncd molecular motor. *EMBO J.* 13:751–57

65. Lymn RW, Taylor EW. 1971. Mechanism of adenosine triphosphate hydrolysis by actomyosin. *Biochemistry* 10:4617–24

66. Ma YZ, Taylor EW. 1994. Kinetic mechanism of myofibril ATPase. *Biophys. J.* 66:1542–53

67. Ma YZ, Taylor EW. 1995. Kinetic mechanism of microtubule-kinesin ATPase motor domain K560. *Biophys. J.* 68:A28

68. McDonald HB, Stewart RJ, Goldstein LS. 1990. The kinesin-like ncd protein of Drosophila is a minus end-directed microtubule motor. *Cell* 63:1159–65

69. Miller RH, Lasek RJ. 1985. Crossbridges mediate anterograde and retrograde vesicle transport along microtubules in squid axoplasm. *J. Cell Biol.* 101:2181–93

70. Ogawa K. 1991. Four ATP-binding sites in the midregion of the $\beta$ heavy chain of dynein. *Nature* 352:643–45

71. Omoto CK, Johnson KA. 1986. Activation of the dynein adenosinetriphosphatase by microtubules. *Biochemistry* 25:419–27

72. Pate E, Franks-Skiba K, White H, Cooke R. 1993. The use of differing nucleotides to investigate cross-bridge kinetics. *J. Biol. Chem.* 268:10046–53

73. Pollard TD, Doberstein SK, Zot HG.

1991. Myosin-I. *Annu. Rev. Physiol.* 53: 653–81

74. Porter ME, Johnson KA. 1983. Characterization of the ATP-sensitive binding of *Tetrahymena* 30 S dynein to bovine brain microtubules. *J. Biol. Chem.* 258: 6575–81

75. Porter ME, Johnson KA. 1983. Transient state kinetic analysis of the ATP-induced dissociation of the dynein-microtubule complex. *J. Biol. Chem.* 258:6582–87

76. Porter ME, Johnson KA. 1989. Dynein structure and function. *Annu. Rev. Cell Biol.* 5:119–51

77. Rasmusson K, Serr M, Gepner J, Gibbons I, Hays TS. 1994. A family of dynein genes in *Drosophila melanogaster*. *Mol. Biol. Cell* 5:45–55

78. Ray S, Meyhofer E, Milligan RA, Howard J. 1993. Kinesin follows the microtubule's protofilament axis. *J. Cell Biol.* 121:1083–93

79. Rayment I, Holden HM. 1994. The three-dimensional structure of a molecular motor. *Trends. Biochem. Sci.* 19: 129–134

80. Rayment I, Holden HM, Whittaker M, Yohn CB, Lorenz M, et al. 1993. Structure of the actin-myosin complex and its implications for muscle contraction. *Science* 261:58–65

81. Rayment I, Rypniewski WR, Schmidt-Base K, Smith R, Tomchick DR, et al. 1993. Three-dimensional structure of myosin subfragment-1: a molecular motor. *Science* 261:50–58

82. Romberg L, Vale RD. 1993. Chemomechanical cycle of kinesin differs from that of myosin. *Nature* 361:168–70

83. Ruppel KM, Spudich JA. 1995. Myosin motor function: structural and mutagentic approaches. *Curr. Biol.* 7:89–93

84. Sadhu A, Taylor EW. 1992. A kinetic study of the kinesin ATPase. *J. Biol. Chem.* 267:11352–59

85. Saraste M, Sibbald PR, Wittinghofer A. 1990. The P-loop—a common motif in ATP- and GTP-binding proteins. *Trends Biochem. Sci.* 15:430–34

86. Saxton WM, Porter ME, Cohn SA, Scholey JM, Raff EC, McIntosh JR. 1988. *Drosophila* kinesin: characterization of microtubule motility and ATPase. *Proc. Natl. Acad. Sci. USA* 85: 1109–13

87. Scholey JM, Heuser J, Yang JT, Goldstein LSB. 1989. Identification of globular mechanochemical heads of kinesin. *Nature* 338:355–57

88. Schroer TA, Sheetz MP. 1991. Functions of microtubule-based motors. *Annu. Rev. Physiol.* 53:629–52

89. Shimizu T, Furusawa K, Ohashi S, Toyoshima YY, Okuno M, et al. 1991. Nucleotide specificity of the enzymatic and motile activities of dynein, kinesin and heavy meromyosin. *J. Cell Biol.* 112:1189–97

90. Shimizu T, Johnson KA. 1983. Kinetic evidence for multiple dynein ATPase sites. *J. Biol. Chem.* 258:13841–46

91. Shimizu T, Katsura T, Domainico PL, Marchese-Ragona SP, Johnson KA. 1989. Adenosine 5'-O-(3-thiotriphosphate) hydrolysis by dynein. *Biochemistry* 28:7022–27

92. Shimizu T, Marchese-Ragona SP, Johnson KA. 1989. Activation of the dynein adenosinetriphosphatase by cross-linking to microtubules. *Biochemistry* 28:7016–21

93. Shpetner HS, Paschal BM, Vallee RB. 1988. Characterization of the microtubule-activated ATPase of brain cytoplasmic dynein (MAP 1C). *J. Cell Biol.* 107:1001–9

94. Skoufias DA, Scholey JM. 1993. Cytoplasmic microtubule-based motor proteins. *Curr. Opin. Cell Biol.* 5:95–104

95. Sleep JA, Boyer PD. 1978. Effect of actin concentration on the intermediate oxygen exchange of myosin; relation to the refractory state and the mechanism of exchange. *Biochemistry* 17:5417–22

96. Sleep JA, Hackney DD, Boyer PD. 1978. Characterization of phosphate oxygen exchange reactions catalyzed by myosin through measurement of the distribution of $^{18}$O-labeled species. *J. Biol. Chem.* 253:5235–38

97. Sleep JA, Hackney DD, Boyer PD. 1980. The equivalence of phosphate oxygens for exchange and the hydrolysis characteristics revealed by distribution of [$^{18}$O]Pi species formed by myosin and actomyosin ATPase. *J. Biol. Chem.* 255:4097–99

98. Sleep JA, Hutton RL. 1978. Actin mediated release of ATP from a myosin-ATP complex. *Biochemistry* 17: 5423–30

99. Sleep JA, Hutton RL. 1980. Exchange between inorganic phosphate and adenosine 5'-triphosphate in the medium by actomyosin subfragment 1. *Biochemistry* 19:1276–83

100. Sleep JA, Smith SJ. 1981. Actomyosin ATPase and muscle contraction. *Curr. Top. Bioeng.* 11:239–86

101. Song YH, Mandelkow E. 1993. Recombinant kinesin motor domain binds to beta-tubulin and decorates microtubules with a B surface lattice. *Proc. Natl. Acad. Sci. USA* 90:1671–75

102. Stein LA, Chock PB, Eisenberg E. 1984.

The rate-limiting step in the actomyosin adenosinetriphosphatase cycle. *Biochemistry* 23:1555–63

103. Stewart RJ, Tahler JP, Goldstein LSB. 1993. Direction of microtubule movement is an intrinsic property of the ncd and kinesin heavy chain motor domains. *Proc. Natl. Acad. Sci. USA* 90:5209–13

104. Suzuki H, Kamata T, Ohnishi H, Watanabe S. 1982. Adenosine triphosphate-induced reversible change in the conformation of chicken gizzard mysoin and heavy meromyosin. *J. Biochem.* 91: 1699–705

105. Svoboda K, Schmidt CF, Schnapp BJ, Block SM. 1993. Direct observation of kinesin stepping by optical trapping interferometry. *Nature* 365:721–27

106. Taylor EW. 1979. Mechanism of actomyosin ATPase and the problem of muscle contraction. *CRC Crit. Rev. Biochem.* 6:103–164

107. Tesi C, Travers F, Barman T. 1990. Cryoenzymic studies on actomyosin ATPase. Evidence that the degree of saturation of actin with myosin subfragment 1 affects the kinetics of the binding of ATP. *Biochemistry* 29:1846–52

108. Titus MA. 1993. Myosins. *Curr. Opin. Cell Biol.* 5:77–81

109. Trinick J, Offer G. 1979. Cross-linking of actin filaments by heavy meromyosin. *J. Mol. Biol.* 133:549–56

110. Trybus DM, Huiatt TW, Lowey S. 1982. A bent monomeric conformation of myosin from smooth muscle. *Proc. Natl. Acad. Sci. USA* 79:6151–55

111. Uyeda TQ, Warrick HM, Kron SJ, Spudich JA. 1991. Quantized velocities at low myosin densities in an in vitro motility assay. *Nature* 353:307–11

112. Vale RD. 1992. Microtubule motors: many new models of the assembly line. *Trends. Biochem. Sci.* 17:300–4

113. Vale RD, Goldstein LSB. 1990. One motor, many tails: an expanding repertoire of force-generating enzymes. *Cell* 60:883–885

114. Vale RD, Reese TS, Sheetz MP. 1985. Identification of a novel force-generating protein, kinesin, involved in microtubule-based motility. *Cell* 42:39–50

115. Wagner MC, Pfister KK, Bloom GS, Brady ST. 1989. Copurification of kinesin polypeptides with microtubule-stimulated magnesium ATPase activity and kinetic analysis of enzymic properties. *Cell Motil. Cytoskelet.* 12:195–215

116. Walker JE, Saraste M, Runswick MJ, Gay NJ. 1982. Distantly related sequences in the α- and β-subunits of the ATP synthase, myosin, kinases and other ATP-requiring enzymes and a common nucleotide binding fold. *EMBO. J.* 1:945–51

117. Walker RA. 1995. NCD and kinesin motor domains interact with both α and β tubulin. *Proc. Natl. Acad. Sci. USA* 92:5960–64

117a. Warner FD, Satir P, Gibbons IR, eds. 1989. *Cell Movement. The Dynein ATPases.* New York: Liss. 337 pp.

118. Webb MR, Hibberd MG, Goldman YE, Trentham DR. 1986. Oxygen exchange between Pi in the medium and water during ATP hydrolysis mediated by skinned fibers from rabbit skeletal muscle. Evidence for Pi binding to a force-generating state. *J. Biol. Chem.* 261: 15557–64

119. Webb MR, Trentham DR. 1980. The stereochemical course of phosphoric residue transfer during the myosin ATPase reaction. *J. Biol. Chem.* 255:8629–32

120. Webb MR, Trentham DR. 1981. The mechanism of ATP hydrolysis catalyzed by myosin and actomyosin, using rapid reaction techniques to study oxygen exchange. *J. Biol. Chem.* 256:10910–16

121. White HD, Belknap B, Jiang W 1993. Kinetics of binding and hydrolysis of a series of nucleoside triphosphates by actomyosin-S1. *J. Biol. Chem.* 268: 10039–45

122. Witman GB. 1989. Composition and molecular organization of the dyneins. See Ref. 117a, pp. 25–35

123. Xie X, Harrison DH, Schlichting I, Sweet RM, Kalabokis VN, et al. 1994. Structure of the regulatory domain of scallop myosin at 2.8 Å resolution. *Nature* 368:306–12

124. Yanagida T, Harada Y, Ishijima A. 1993. Nano-manipulation of actomyosin molecular motors in vitro: a new working principle. *Trends. Biochem. Sci.* 18: 319–23

125. Yang JT, Laymon RA, Goldstein LSB. 1989. A three-domain structure of kinesin heavy chain revealed by DNA sequence and microtubule binding analyses. *Cell* 56:879–89

126. Yang JT, Saxton WM, Stewart RJ, Raff EC, Goldstein LSB. 1990. Evidence that the head of kinesin is sufficient for force generation and motility in vitro. *Science* 249:42–47

Annu. Rev. Physiol. 1996. 58:751–92

# MUTATIONAL ANALYSIS OF MOTOR PROTEINS

## H. Lee Sweeney

Department of Physiology, University of Pennsylvania School of Medicine, 3700 Hamilton Walk, Philadelphia, Pennsylvania 19104-6085

## Erika L. F. Holzbaur

Department of Animal Biology, University of Pennsylvania School of Veterinary Medicine, 3800 Spruce Street, Philadelphia, Pennsylvania 19104-6044

KEY WORDS:    molecular motor, myosin, kinesin, dynein, mutation

### ABSTRACT

Mutations in motor proteins, which can arise by design or randomly, provide powerful insights into the normal function of the protein. This review organizes the available data on mutations of members of the myosin, kinesin, and dynein superfamilies of motor proteins. These data contribute to an understanding of the cellular role of the motor proteins as well as provide insights into the fundamental mechanisms of motor function.

## INTRODUCTION

Studies of mutant motor proteins can be broadly divided into two groups: those concerned with delineation of the cellular function of motor proteins and those that are focused on the structure/function relationships of the motor proteins themselves. Cellular function studies have been restricted to organisms in which molecular genetic studies are tractable, including *Saccharomyces cerevisiae, Dictyostelium discoideum, Chlamydomonas, Caenorhabditis elegans,* and *Drosophila melanogaster.* Recently, transgenic mice have been used to study myosin function, as have muscles from humans with myosin heavy chain mutations (hypertrophic cardiomyopathy patients).

Detailed structure/function studies of the motor proteins are only possible given either a homologous or heterologous expression system that is capable of producing amounts of protein that are suitable for biochemical studies. For the light chains of myosin II, considerable work has been accomplished using *E. coli* as an expression system. For the coexpression of the heavy chain and

751

light chains of myosin II, both *Dictyostelium* myosin nulls (homologous expression) and the SF9 cell/baculovirus expression system (heterologous expression) have been utilized (132, 211). Additionally, COS cells have been reported as a heterologous expression system for myosin (187). Most kinesin structure/function studies have exploited *E. coli* as an expression system. In the case of dynein, heterologous expression has not been reported.

# MUTATIONAL ANALYSIS OF MYOSIN

## Myosin and Myosin-Related Proteins

Almost 30 years passed between the postulation of myosin II as the enzyme driving muscle contraction (43) and the recognition that it additionally was involved in motility in nonmuscle cells (1, 73, 74). It was another seven years before the discovery of myosin I, the second member of the myosin superfamily (170). However, the significance of that discovery did not become clear until the late 1980s (31, 101). Now the myosin superfamily is known to contain a minimum of nine classes of motor proteins (18, 63, 185) that are likely involved in a number of distinct cellular functions.

## Mutations That Provide Insight Into Cellular Function

MYOSIN I    The heavy chain of myosin I does not form dimers (as does that of myosin II) but instead has a truncated tail that contains lipid-binding domains, and in some isoforms, an actin-binding domain (35). Myosin I that is localized at the leading edge in motile cells is primarily responsible for cell locomotion (24, 31, 96). Accordingly, gene disruption studies targeting myosin I have been performed in *Dictyostelium* (100, 215, 240). These studies conclude that there is some redundancy in myosin I isoform function in terms of gross cellular motility. However, there is likely to be specialization of myosin I functional roles, but delineation of subtle functional alterations in mutant cells will require detailed phenotypic analysis (34).

MYOSIN II    Myosin II is necessary for cytokinesis as definitively proven by the creation of a *Dictyostelium* myosin II null through the use of homologous recombination (31). In dividing cells, myosin II assembles into filaments in the contractile ring during anaphase, and these filaments disassemble once cell division is complete. Interestingly, this study not only demonstrated that myosin II is necessary for cytokinesis, it demonstrated that myosin II is not necessary for cell locomotion, in spite of the fact that myosin II is associated with cortical actin in eukaryotic cells (24), where it is necessary for capping. However, in *Dictyostelium* myosin II nulls, the quality of cell movement is affected (97), and myosin II is required for normal progression through the *Dictyostelium* developmental cycle (39, 204). Morphogenesis in *Drosophila*, a higher organism, is dependent upon the presence of the nonmuscle isoform of myosin II (249). *Dictyostelium* mutants lacking either the myosin II essential light chains (ELCs) or regulatory light chains (RLCs) are also defective in cytokinesis and development (17, 157, 171). The nonmuscle myosin II RLC of *Drosophila* has also been shown to be necessary for cytokinesis (105).

Myosin II thick filament formation has been the subject of a number of studies using *Drosophila*. Myosin heavy chain gene dosage appears to be critical for myofibril formation, with more than three copies of the gene leading to loss of muscle function (6, 28). A myosin II heavy chain mutant with a single amino acid change in the motor domain blocked filament formation in vivo (111). Thus, as may be the case with some of the human cardiac myosin mutations described below, defective actin-myosin interactions may inhibit normal thick filament formation. In a study on the myosin II RLC of *Drosophila* muscle, diminished expression of the light chain resulted in myofilament disarray and loss of muscle function (235).

A number of mutations have been described for the myosin II heavy chain (*unc-54* gene product) of *C. elegans* (32, 45, 131, 148). Generally, these mutations disrupt the function of the body wall muscles. Many mutations, including nulls, truncated heavy chains, and some missense mutations, result in the inability of *unc54* myosin to form thick filaments. Other missense mutations (including a mutation in a conserved active site residue; G118) alter enzymatic activity but do not interfer with thick filament formation (32). Interestingly, one group of missense mutations that results in normal structure but with a slowing of the myosin activity was isolated as suppressors of *unc-22* (twitchin) mutations (148).

Mutations in the myosin II heavy chain isoform expressed in the human heart and slow skeletal muscles give rise to an inherited human disease, hypertrophic cardiomyopathy (HCM) (3, 4, 36, 46, 48, 49, 52, 70, 133, 134, 152, 153, 165, 202, 230, 238, 250). To date, more than thirty distinct missense mutations have been described within the human population. The positions of many of these mutations have been mapped within the crystal structure of the myosin II head (181). Myosin isolated from the muscles of hypertrophic cardiomyopathic patients with myosin heavy chain mutations moves actin filaments with decreased velocity in an in vitro motility assay (29). Muscle fibers isolated from human slow skeletal muscle of patients with myosin heavy chain mutations display slower than normal shortening velocities and markedly diminished power output (114). By altering the actin-myosin cross-bridge kinetics, these mutations alter the force-velocity (and pressure-velocity) relationship of cardiac muscle. Thus at a given pressure, a heart containing mutant myosin produces less power (power = force • velocity) than a normal heart of the same size. The physiological and ultimately pathophysiological response is compensatory hypertrophy. However, myosin mutations do not account for all patients with this disease. Recently, mutations in other sarcomeric proteins have also been linked to HCM(214).

MYOSIN III    The gene products of the *Drosophila ninaC* gene are two members of the myosin superfamily that have been categorized as myosin III (18). The gene products are essentially a myosin I with a regulatory kinase domain fused at the N-terminal (149). Mutant analysis has shown that the ninaC proteins have differential distributions within photoreceptor cells in *Drosophila* (77, 172). The smaller of the two proteins is cytoplasmic, whereas the larger is associated with microvillar structures (rhabdomeres) that are essential for phototransduction. Loss of the larger protein results in loss of phototransduction and retinal degeneration. Further studies reveal that the myosin motor domain is necessary for localization and structural integrity of the rhabdomeres, whereas the kinase domain is required for phototransduction (173). Calmodulin is associated with the ninaC myosin III and likely is an associated light chain (174).

OTHER MEMBERS OF THE MYOSIN SUPERFAMILY    Mutational analysis has established that myosin V is a two-headed myosin involved in vesicle transport (64, 99, 142). Additionally, it has also demonstrated that calmodulin is at least one type of light chain associated with the myosin V heavy chain (11). Intriguingly, the yeast myosin V null phenotype can be suppressed by overexpression of a member of the kinesin superfamily (124). Thus vesicle transport in a cell may utilize both actin and microtubular pathways.

Mutations in a myosin VII heavy chain gene in mice and in humans leads to deafness (58, 239). The role of myosin VII in the process of auditory transduction is currently a matter of speculation (239).

## Mutations That Provide Insight Into Molecular Structure/Function

HEAVY CHAIN OF MYOSIN II    The ability to perform detailed structural and biochemical studies of mutant myosin was dependent on the development of expression systems capable of producing milligram quantities of active protein. To date, only two systems have fulfilled this role for myosin II: *Dictyostelium* myosin nulls and the baculovirus/SF9 cell system. *Dictyostelium* myosin II nulls can be used for expression of mutant *Dictyostelium* myosin II (132), and a number of studies have used this system for expression of mutations in the *Dictyostelium* myosin II heavy chain (see below). When the expressed myosin is full length, the *Dictyostelium* system offers the additional advantage of assessing the cellular impact of the mutation as well as the effect on the isolated protein.

Although the majority of studies involving the mutational analysis of the myosin II heavy chain have been done with *Dictyostelium*, it has proven useful primarily as a homologous expression system. The first reported use of heterologous expression of myosin II utilized the baculovirus/SF9 expression system (211) to express a truncated wild-type and mutant cardiac myosin (rat α cardiac myosin II heavy chain, coexpressed with the rat cardiac essential and regulatory light chains). Subsequently, the baculovirus system was utilized for expression of chicken smooth muscle myosin II (220). There are unpublished reports of successful expression of other myosin II isoforms using this expression system, as well as success with other members of the myosin superfamily. Thus the baculovirus/SF9 expression system eventually may play a major role in elucidating myosin structure/function relationships.

Following the publication of the myosin II crystal structure (182, 183; see figure 1 in I Rayment et al, this volume), it became apparent that the region of the myosin II heavy chain that binds the essential and regulatory light chains might act as a "lever arm." This lever arm would amplify structural rearrangements in the catalytic domain of the myosin head and thus provide movement on the order of nanometers at the end of the lever arm. The first test of this hypothesis was a study that involved removal of the regulatory light chain binding region from the *Dictyostelium* myosin II heavy chain (224). The resulting myosin moved at a velocity that was approximately one half of that of wild-type myosin. A more severe truncation, in which both light chain-binding sites were removed from the *Dictyostelium* myosin II heavy chain, resulted in a myosin that moved with a smaller step size (94). (This study provided the important first demonstration that the globular myosin head, exclusive of the light chain-binding domain, constitutes a molecular motor.) However, a definitive validation of the lever arm concept will require the construction of an extended lever arm (i.e. additional light chain-binding sites) and measureable increases in the velocity of movement and/or step size of the motor. Unpublished studies (JA Spudich et al) indicate that such data are forthcoming. Recently, three-dimensional image reconstructions of actin decorated with baculovirus-expressed myosin S1 fragments, in the presence or absence of ADP, provide direct evidence for the lever arm hypothesis (241).

The actin binding interface of myosin has been examined using mutagenesis. An unstructured loop, the 50-kDa/20-kDa junctional loop (loop 2 in figure 9 of I Rayment et al, this volume), known to be at the actin interface, has been the subject of chimeric myosin II construction in two studies (189, 223). The initial study substituted putative actin-binding loops from rabbit skeletal, chicken smooth, rat cardiac α and rat cardiac β myosin II heavy chains into the *Dictyostelium* myosin II heavy chain (223). A range of actin-activated ATPase activities was measured among the wild-type and chimeric myosins, with the order of activity magnitude corresponding to that of the maximal ATPase activities of the myosins from which the loops were derived. Because the ATPase assays were performed at a single actin concentration, it is not possible to ascertain if differences in ATPase activity reflect differences only in $V_{max}$, or in $K_{ATPase}$ as well. A more recent study, which substituted the skeletal and $\beta$ cardiac loops into a chicken smooth muscle myosin II heavy chain, did not demonstrate a difference in the $V_{max}$ of the actin-activated ATPase activity with loop substitutions, but differences in $K_{ATPase}$ were noted (189). The apparent actin affinity was highest for the skeletal loop, intermediate for the cardiac loop, and lowest for the wild-type smooth loop. These data support a model in which this loop provides weak electrostatic binding to actin, which positions the myosin head on the actin surface so that strong interactions leading to force generation can proceed.

Physiologically, this loop may be important in regulating the rate of force development, which is a significant variable in muscle contraction, and which likely is matched to the speed of shortening of the muscle. A perusal of all nonmuscle and smooth muscle myosin II sequences in the database reveals that they all have less net positive charge in loop 2 than is found in the loops of vertebrate striated muscle myosin IIs. This may relate to the faster speed of contraction of vertebrate striated muscles, which in turn necessitates a higher weak binding affinity for actin to support a higher rate of force development. Interestingly, this loop is extremely large and highly charged in myosin VI (72), where it could provide an electrostatic tether to keep the myosin VI close to the actin surface. Such a tether would be essential if myosin VI were designed to carry cargo on actin filaments at low motor densities, and if myosin VI were to display the short duty cycle (in contrast to kinesin) that is characteristic of myosin II.

The notion of loop 2 functioning as an electrostatic tether could explain another feature of the studies on loop chimeras (189, 223). In these studies, the myosin loops that conferred the highest ATPase activities and/or the lowest $K_{ATPase}$ values gave rise to the lowest in vitro motility values, which suggests that with increased affinity (due to increased net positive charge in the loop) for the actin filament comes a drag on the unloaded shortening velocity. Related to this is the finding in smooth muscle myosin chimera experiments (189) that the loop substitutions from striated muscle myosin IIs lead not only to lower $K_{ATPase}$ values but also to activation of smooth muscle heavy meromyosin (HMM) (a truncated, dimeric myosin II that does not form filaments) in the absence of RLC phosphorylation. This finding suggests that if the weak binding of myosin to actin is sufficiently enhanced, it can overcome the inhibition of enzymatic activity placed on the truncated (HMM) myosin II structure in the absence of RLC phosphorylation. Whether the substitution of a striated myosin loop 2 could overcome the additional structural constraints conferred upon dephosphorylated full-length smooth muscle myosin by folding is an interesting and unresolved question.

Another loop at the actin-binding interface has been the focus of a number of studies. This loop (the HCM loop) contains the arginine that is converted to glutamine in patients with HCM (52). A mixture of wild-type and mutant β-cardiac myosin from the soleus muscles of patients with this mutation was isolated for characterization in an in vitro motility assay (29). The myosin mixture containing the mutant heavy chain translocated actin filaments at a slower than normal rate. In a later study, this mutation was created in rat α-cardiac HMM (211). To assess whether the effect of the mutation was dominant over wild-type myosin, mixtures of wild-type and mutant myosin were assayed for in vitro motility. The results demonstrated that the mutant myosin disproportionately slows the movement. Additionally, the mutation resulted in a small increase in the $K_{app}$ ($K_{ATPase}$) for actin and a threefold decrease in the ATPase $V_{max}$ of the actin-activated ATPase activity. Altogether, the results suggest that the major consequence of the mutation is the slowing of progression through the steps of the actin-myosin cross-bridge cycle. Intriguingly, the phosphorylatable serine, which is involved in control of actin-activated ATPase of *Acanthamoeba* myosin I, is in the region of myosin I that corresponds to the position of Arg-403 in conventional myosin (13). This phosphorylation has a small effect on the $K_{app}$ of myosin I for actin, and a large effect (increase) on the actin-activated ATPase activity. Actin interactions in this region of all myosins may be a determinant of ATPase activity.

A mutation near the active site of myosin II was the conversion of highly conserved Leu-130 to leucine using *Dictyostelium* myosin null cells (191). The mutant protein was able to rescue myosin II function in the cells and had relatively normal activity. The myosin was, however, less stable and had a lowered ATP affinity, compared with the wild-type protein. (See I Rayment et al, this volume, for detailed discussion.)

A number of studies have used mutagenesis to investigate the regulation and functional significance of filament assembly/disassembly of the myosin II rod, in particular in *Dictyostelium*. The first mutant myosin II heavy chains expressed in *Dictyostelium* involved mutations in the myosin rod (37, 38). Ultimately, phosphorylation sites in the *Dictyostelium* myosin II heavy chain were identified and shown, by mutagenesis, to regulate filament disassembly in vivo. Another study on the *Dictyostelium* myosin II rod involved a 58-kDa deletion of the proximal part of the rod, including the HMM-LMM junction (112). Although the resulting mutant myosin gave normal in vitro motility, cellular cytokinesis was impaired, in spite of the fact that the mutant myosin could form filaments. A series of C-terminal truncations in the *Dictyostelium* myosin II heavy chain were used to define a 35-amino acid region of the myosin II rod that is necessary for filament formation (116). Lastly, chimeric myosin II heavy chains, with the *Dictyostelium* myosin II head and the rat cardiac myosin II rod, were constructed and expressed in *Dictyostelium* myosin II null cells (115). These chimeric myosins were able to rescue a number of myosin II functions. Furthermore, a 29-amino acid region in the cardiac rod was confirmed as necessary for myosin II filament formation in vivo.

The role of the nonhelical tailpiece of the vertebrate nonmuscle myosin II rod was investigated using *E. coli* to express rod fragments (81). The presence of the tailpiece greatly facilitated assembly. Analysis suggested that the nature of the effect was not via specific site interaction with the tailpiece but more likely involved the tailpiece sterically blocking aggregations that were not productive for filament assembly. A more detailed mutagenesis study focused on the assembly properties of *Acanthamoeba* myosin II, and delineated regions necessary for the formation of antiparallel dimers, for the formation of antiparallel tetramers, and for the association of two antiparallel tetramers into an octameric minifilament (199). Additionally, tight packing of filaments required a region of the rod near the head-rod junction.

COS cells were used to express rat $\alpha$-cardiac myosin II heavy chains that were either wild type or contained one of the seven distinct single amino acid mutations associated with HCM in either the myosin S1 (head) or S2 domain (206). All the HCM mutations resulted in impaired filament assembly, as compared with the wild type. Thus mutations in the catalytic domain of myosin can exert influence on filament structure. Whether this observation has direct relevance to the pathophysiology of HCM is not resolved.

Baculovirus expression has been used in two studies (136, 220) to demonstrate that if the smooth muscle myosin II heavy chain is truncated so that stable dimerization of the two heavy chains is lost, then regulation is lost (the actin-activated ATPase activity is high in the absence of RLC phosphorylation). These results agree with proteolytic studies (27) demonstrating that for smooth muscle myosin to be regulated, it must exist as a two-headed dimer. Unpublished studies (KM Trybus & HL Sweeney) show that myosin II rod also plays an essential role in regulation, beyond causing dimerization per se.

## Mutations That Provide Insight Into Molecular Structure/Function

ESSENTIAL LIGHT CHAIN OF MYOSIN II    Recent experiments reveal that both C-terminal and N-terminal domains of the ELC are important for binding to the myosin heavy chain (80). Studies have revealed that removal of either the ELC or RLC of myosin decreases the speed of shortening in motility assays

(128), and removal of the ELC also decreases force generation (228). Although this could be expected considering that the neck region may collapse upon light chain removal, thus effectively shortening the lever arm of the myosin II motor, the effect is greater for the ELC than for the RLC, which might indicate that the extent of neck collapse is not equivalent in both cases. However, the crystal structures of chicken myosin II S1 and *Dictyostelium* myosin II motor domain suggest another possibility (200). The C-terminus of the ELC likely forms an extensive interface with the myosin motor domain that is critical in transmitting rearrangements following phosphate and ADP release into movement of the lever arm. In this view, the ELC is not merely a passive structural reinforcement of the lever arm but serves a critical transduction role in the process of movement. Unpublished experiments (RL Chisholm) involving mutations in this region of the ELC support this view.

A comparison of sequences of ELC isoforms reveals that other than one isoform (LC3-f) all vertebrate striated muscle ELC isoforms have an extended N-terminus that is missing in nonmuscle and invertebrate ELC isoforms. A number of experimental approaches have led to the conclusion that some part of this N-terminal extension interacts with actin (16, 76, 113, 121, 144, 176, 207, 217); several lines of evidence (144, 207, 217) indicate that the interaction is with the C-terminus of actin. Other studies suggest that this putative interaction between the N-terminal domains of all the striated muscle ELCs, except LC-3f and the C-terminus of actin, could be a mechanism for altering the maximal velocity of shortening (9, 128, 186, 210). This hypothesis was directly tested in a study focusing on four lysine residues that are invariant in all ELCs with N-terminal extensions (208). Fibers reconstituted with ELCs in which there was replacement of lysines with alanines (i.e. removal of the positive charge) shortened with increased $V_{max}$ compared with fibers reconstituted with wild-type ELCs (208). Thus charge interactions between the N-terminus of the ELC and actin (presumably at the C-terminus of actin) may slow filament sliding. An unexplored role for this light chain extension is suggested by the tethering concept discussed for the actin-binding loop (loop 2) of myosin II (see above). The N-terminal extension may serve to keep the myosin head near the filament surface, which could increase the probability of actin interaction.

REGULATORY LIGHT CHAIN OF MYOSIN II    To date, the majority of mutagenesis experiments performed on myosin II have been on its RLC subunit. This is due to the fact that RLCs can be expressed in *E. coli* and the expressed light chains can be exchanged for the native RLCs either on purified myosin or within a permeabilized muscle cell preparation. Furthermore, the RLC plays a central role in the regulation of activity of smooth and nonmuscle myosin II.

The RLCs from skeletal muscle and smooth muscle are highly homologous (71% similarity and 53% identity in sequence). Both RLCs contain a high-affinity divalent cation-binding site near the N-terminus that mutational analysis has demonstrated is necessary for proper binding of the light chain to the myosin II heavy chain (184). Unlike striated muscle contraction, the initiation of smooth muscle contraction must be preceded by serine phosphorylation of the myosin RLC (219). Although the RLC is also reversibly phosphorylated in vertebrate striated muscle (at a homologous serine), this phosphorylation simply modulates contractile activity (209). The loss of myosin regulation in striated muscle is the result of undetermined alterations in the myosin heavy chain. Additionally, the smooth muscle and skeletal muscle RLCs are not functionally equivalent. The RLC from skeletal muscle myosin (skRLC) is unable to confer regulation to smooth muscle myosin (a phosphorylation-regulated myosin) and locks the myosin in the off state when substituted for the endogenous smooth muscle RLC (smRLC) (221). Also, the smRLC can confer calcium sensitivity to scallop muscle myosin (a $Ca^{2+}$-regulated myosin), whereas the skRLC fails to do so (15). However, no RLC can inhibit the activity of vertebrate skeletal muscle myosin (177).

Phosphorylation of the myosin II RLC promotes unfolding of the myosin (transition from 6S to 10S conformation; 156) as well as turning on the ATPase activity. Mutagenesis studies that have removed and reversed positively charged residues immediately N-terminal of the phosphorylatable serine of the smooth muscle myosin II RLC demonstrate that the interactions regulating the folded-to-extended conformational transition in smooth muscle myosin are distinct from those controlling ATPase activity (90, 102, 212). Myosin that is kept unfolded and assembled into filaments by charge substitutions in the RLC is inactive (or with some charge substitutions slightly activated) unless the mutant RLC chain is phosphorylated. This observation is consistent with previous studies that showed phosphorylation-dependent activation of myosin was locked in the filamentous state by virtue of monoclonal antibodies (218) or by incorporation of a chimeric N-terminal skeletal/C-terminal smooth muscle RLC, which prevented folding but maintained phosphorylation-dependent regulation of ATPase activity (221). Thus phosphorylation must exert an effect on ATPase activity of the molecule, which is not tightly coupled to myosin's ability to undergo the folded-to-extended transition, in contrast to the mechanism proposed based on studies with monomeric myosin (89). This activation of ATPase activity and motility, unlike folding, does not depend solely on alteration of net charge at the N-terminus, but also has spatial constraints that are completely satisfied only by a phosphate moiety.

Studies of chimeric RLCs comprised of the N- or C- terminal half of each skeletal muscle myosin RLC (skRLC) and smooth muscle myosin RLC (smRLC) indicate that it is the C-terminal half of skRLC that lacks structural elements necessary for phosphorylation-mediated regulation (221). C-terminal truncation studies on the smooth RLC indicate that this region of the light chain must be present for tight binding (92, 222), normal coupling between ATPase activity, and motility (222) and that it contains a region that is necessary to confer regulation (92, 222). Based on phosphorylation-mediated regulation of glycogen phosphorylase (203), a recent study examined the possibility of residues in the C-terminus providing coordination of the phosphoryl serine in the N-terminal domain of the RLC (247). Substitution of four arginine residues present in the C-terminal half of the smRLC (conserved in all regulated myosin RLCs), but missing in nonregulated myosin RLCs, restored regulation to the skRLC (247). [Although skeletal muscle RLC has maintained the ability to inhibit the activity of smooth muscle myosin, regulation (i.e. activation) of activity via phosphorylation of the RLC has been lost.] The four arginines are located in four domains (the E, F, G, and H helices), using calmodulin nomenclature for the helices, as revealed in the crystal structures of chicken skeletal myosin S1 (183) and the scallop myosin regulatory domain (244). A functional role in regulation for a subset of the missing arginine residues was postulated by analogy to the case of glycogen phosphorylase, wherein arginines residing in different helices coordinate the phosphoserine (203). Global rearrangement of helices is associated with the coordination of the phosphoserine. Based on the orientation of the corresponding residues in chicken skeletal structure (183), only the arginines found in helices E and H appear to be positioned appropriately to coordinate the phosphate of the phosphoserine by hydrogen bonds. The coordination of the phosphoserine may cause conformational changes that lead to regulation of myosin through altered interactions involving the two RLCs and the myosin heavy chain.

Based on this model, one could predict that loss of the conserved arginines in the E and H helices of the smooth muscle RLC would result in loss of regulation. Indeed, in a study (92) where a region of the skRLC H helix was substituted into the smRLC H helix, the H helix arginine was lost and so was regulation. Furthermore, based on regulation of glycogen phosphorylase, the N-terminal basic residues may be involved in stabilizing the interaction of the phosphoserine with its coordination sites. Such a mechanism would explain the results of a study wherein cleavage of the smooth RLC removed Arg-13 and Arg-16 and generated a RLC that could not activate smooth muscle myosin (HMM), even when Ser-19 was phosphorylated (91). This hypothetical regulatory scheme also is supported by NMR results (119). The N-terminal region of the RLC exhibits segmental mobility independently of the rest of the molecule. When the RLC is phosphorylated, mobility of the N-terminal segment is diminished, and the serine phosphate is influenced by neighboring positively charged side chains.

Another type of myosin II regulation involving the regulatory light chain is found in myosin II of scallop striated muscle (107). This regulation involves direct $Ca^{2+}$ binding to the neck region of myosin. The location of the $Ca^{2+}$-binding site was revealed in the crystal structure of scallop myosin II neck (244). Coordination of $Ca^{2+}$ binding requires contributions from the ELC (primarily), the myosin heavy chain, and the RLC. The RLC contribution involves a glycine residue in the loop between the F and G helices, which is absolutely conserved in regulated myosin RLCs. Removal of this glycine results in loss of regulation, trapping the myosin in the off state (94), which explains earlier results indicating that some conserved elements of the C-terminal region of the RLC are necessary for $Ca^{2+}$ binding (190).

In the striated muscles of vertebrates, phosphorylation of myosin II RLC modulates the rate of force production and the steady-state force at submaximal levels of thin filament activation (209). This action may be explained either by movement of myosin heads away from the thick filament backbone (143) or by a disordering of the heads, which may indicate increased mobility (26, 120). The mechanism for this effect involves a simple charge alteration via phosphorylation that is mimicked by altering the fixed charge adjacent to the phosphorylatable serine (212). This may be analogous to the electrostatic mechanism (discussed above) that accounts for the ability of smRLC phosphorylation to unfold the bent smooth muscle myosin monomer to the extended conformation (212).

In the indirect flight muscle (IFM) of *Drosophila*, the RLC appears to provide a tether (via a long N-terminal extension that is homologous to the vertebrate striated muscle ELC) and contains a positively charged region N-terminal to the phosphorylatable serine, as is found in the vertebrate RLCs (23). Thus this light chain probably contains structural elements capable of pulling heads either toward the thick filament and away from the thin filament, when the serine is dephosphorylated, or toward the thin filament, when the RLC is phosphorylated. Although this action still is not well established, it appears that the RLC is constitutively phosphorylated in the IFM (216). When the putative phosphorylation site(s) of the *Drosophila* RLC were removed (replaced by alanines) and the mutant light chain was expressed in *Drosophila* muscles, flight ability was lost (216). Interestingly, maximal steady-state force was not altered, but the ability of the muscles to perform oscillatory work was greatly diminished. Additionally, the mutant RLC, which was expressed in all striated muscles, did not prevent the functioning of other muscles. Based on experiments with RLC phosphorylation in vertebrate muscles, one would expect the mutant RLC to give rise to less force at submaximal levels of calcium activation (but normal force at saturating calcium) and diminished rates of force generation. For the performance of oscillatory work, *Drosophila* IFM is designed to work at a fixed frequency and relies on stretch activation and shortening deactivation to turn contraction on and off. One can postulate how altered RLC phosphorylation could interfere with stretch activation of muscle. If the rate of force development is slowed (by removing the phosphorylation sites of a normally phosphorylated RLC), then cross-bridges would not be able to attach and generate force during the time window of thin filament activation. In *Drosophila* IFM, this would result in diminished oscillatory work. However, slowing of the rate of force development would not affect maximal steady-state force. To understand how slowing of cross-bridge attachment rate to the thin filament would affect the force at submaximal levels of thin filament activation, imagine regulated units of the thin filament going on and off as calcium associates and dissociates from troponin C. Again, a time window for cross-bridge attachment would exist and thus the probability of attachment (and force production) increases as the rate of attachment increases (i.e. as the level of RLC phosphorylation increases).

# MUTATIONAL ANALYSIS OF KINESIN

Several recent papers have reviewed the molecular biology and genetics of the kinesin superfamily (61, 62, 85). Herein the focus is on mutational analysis as a probe for structure/function relationships.

## Kinesin and Kinesin-Related Proteins

Kinesin, initially discovered as an anterograde microtubule-based motor involved in the transport of vesicles and organelles, is now known to be a representative member of a superfamily of related proteins. These proteins share sequence homology within a limited domain of ~340 amino acids, identified as the force-producing domain of kinesin, which includes binding sites for both nucleotide and the microtubule. Outside this motor domain, the polypeptides in the kinesin superfamily diverge significantly. These divergent sequences are thought to be responsible for the targeting of the kinesin-related proteins to different cellular functions. Although genetic deletion studies suggest that the activities of many of the kinesin-related proteins are similar, or that these motors may often partially overlap in function, it is likely that most of the kinesin-related proteins are relatively specialized in their cellular roles.

## Mutations That Provide Insight Into Cellular Function

MEMBRANE TRANSPORT    Kinesin was initially identified as a motor for vesicular trafficking along the axon (226), and this function was supported by analysis of kinesin heavy chain (*khc*) mutations (196). The gene encoding the kinesin heavy chain was determined to be essential for viability in *Drosophila*;

flies carrying the null mutation died by the third instar stage of larval development. Disruption of the *khc* gene resulted in slowed larval growth as well as a significant loss of motility relative to wild-type larvae. The phenotypes displayed by the kinesin mutants were judged to be most consistent with a neuronal defect. Neurons from *khc* mutant larvae exhibited impaired action potential propagation as well as inhibited function at presynaptic terminals, with an observed correlation between the axonal length and the severity of the defect exhibited by that neuron (54). Because no significant decrease in the concentration of synaptic vesicles at the terminals of the *khc* larvae was detected, it was concluded that the defect was not likely to be due to impaired transport of synaptic vesicles, but rather to impaired transport of vesicles bearing ion channels to the presynaptic terminal.

The specificity of kinesin and the kinesin-related proteins for transporting particular types of cellular organelles and vesicles along the axon is apparent in the contrast of two genes characterized in *C. elegans. unc-116* encodes the probable *khc* homologue in *C. elegans* (164). Alleles of *unc-116* were found to be maternal effect-lethal, with progressive loss of mobility observed throughout the larval stages. For the *unc-116* mutants of *C. elegans*, as was observed for *khc* mutants in *Drosophila*, the progressive paralysis did not result from the impaired transport of synaptic vesicles (164). In contrast, characterization of mutants at the *unc-104* locus of *C. elegans*, which encodes a kinesin-related protein, revealed that severe alleles led to the loss of neuronal synapses (69). The basis for the *unc-104* defect is thought to be a specific failure in the transport of synaptic vesicles. The synaptic vesicles were observed to accumulate within the neuronal cell bodies rather than undergoing transport along the axon. Thus, *unc-116*, the probable kinesin homologue in *C. elegans*, and the kinesin-related protein product of the *C. elegans unc-104* gene both appear to be anterograde axonal motors with markedly different specificities for the types of organelles transported.

Polymerase chain reaction (PCR) screens for kinesin-related proteins in the murine nervous system have revealed at least five distinct polypeptides, several of which were shown to have brain-specific expression (2). Taken together, the observations in *C. elegans* and mouse suggest that there may be a family of anterograde transporter proteins that are specialized for specific classes of organelles or vesicles. For example, a newly characterized member of the murine kinesin superfamily, KIF1B, has been shown to be localized to mitochondria and functions in vitro to transport mitochondria along microtubules (151).

MITOSIS AND MEIOSIS    One of the first kinesin-related proteins identified, the product of the *bimC* gene from *Aspergillus nidulans,* was observed to exhibit a mitotic defect due to a temperature-sensitive allele. The *bimC4* mutation in

*A. nidulans* was found to interfere with the separation of spindle pole bodies, resulting in the development of abnormal spindles (44). The bimC polypeptide is now thought to be the prototype member of a bimC family, which includes cut7 (*Schizosaccharomyces pombe;* 68), KIP1 and CIN8 (*Saccharomyces cerevisiae;* 85, 188), KLP61F (*Drosophila;* 75), and Eg5 (*Xenopus laevis;* 118). Disruption of the essential *KLP61F* gene in *Drosophila* results in the arrest of dividing diploid cells in metaphase, probably because the duplicated centrosomes failed to separate (75). An apparently related protein from *Drosophila*, KRP130, has been shown to be a homotetramer (21). Other members of this family may also form oligomers capable of binding to anti-parallel microtubules emanating from opposite poles, which could then push apart the spindle poles.

Disruption of the *S. cerevisiae* gene, *KAR3*, which also encodes a kinesin-related protein, was found to block karyogamy, the fusion of haploid nuclei during conjugation. Expression of the *kar3-1* mutant polypeptide apparently disrupts the movement of the two nuclei along cytoplasmic microtubules. Although disruption of *KAR3* function did not block mitosis, deletion and mutation strains were observed to grow more slowly, with an increase in the number of nonviable cells produced, which suggests partial mitotic arrest due to a defect in spindle elongation (141).

Two mutations in *Drosophila* have been associated with meiotic defects. Mutations in the *nod* gene result in meiotic defects, as well as defects in the separation of chromosomes during mitosis early in embryogenesis (40, 41, 138). The kinesin-like protein encoded by the *nod* gene was determined to be essential for the distributive segregation of nonexchange chromosomes during meiosis (25).

In contrast to the apparent specificity observed for kinesin and some kinesin homologues in organelle transport, there is evidence for functional redundancy among the kinesin-related proteins involved in cell division in *S. cerevisiae*. Roof et al (188) and Hoyt et al (85) have characterized genes encoding two kinesin-related proteins in *S. cerevisiae, KIP1* and *CIN8*. *CIN8* was initially identified as a gene required for normal fidelity of chromosome transmission (85). *KIP1*, which was cloned in a PCR screen for kinesin-related proteins, displayed no obvious defects in mitosis, meiosis, or karyogamy in mutant strains (188). The predicted products of the *KIP1* and *CIN8* genes share sequence homology in the common and defining kinesin motor domain, but the tail sequences diverge significantly (85).

Although deletion mutants for either of these genes were viable, a double *kip1-cin8* mutant exhibited a lethal phenotype due to a failure in spindle pole separation during cell division (85, 188). Careful phenotypic analysis with a temperature-sensitive allele of *cin8* in a *kip1* deletion strain indicated that the products of these genes were also required for the maintenance of a bipolar spindle; upon shift to the restrictive temperature, the bipolar spindle in pre-anaphase cells collapsed, leaving the duplicated spindle pole bodies side-by-side (194). However, anaphase spindles were found to be resistant to the collapse induced by the shift to the restrictive temperature. The genetic data therefore suggest that these two polypeptides overlap in function but are not completely interchangeable; nor is it clear if they act via similar mechanisms within the cell.

OTHER CELLULAR FUNCTIONS    Several recent observations have identified novel and perhaps unexpected functions for kinesin-related proteins. Lillie & Brown (124) performed a screen for multicopy suppressors (i.e. genes that can suppress a defect in a heterologous gene when over-expressed) of *MYO2*, a myosin superfamily member involved in polarized secretion in yeast. They identified a novel gene, *SMY1*, that encodes a kinesin-related protein. That a kinesin-related protein may partially compensate for a defect in an actin-based motor is of particular interest. Although the *SMY1* gene is not essential in yeast, simultaneous disruption of both the *SMY1* and *MYO2* genes was lethal (124, 125).

Kinesin-related proteins have also been localized to eukaryotic flagella. The analysis of *fla10*, a temperature-sensitive mutation in *Chlamydomonas* that results in defective flagellar assembly, revealed that this gene encodes a kinesin-related protein termed KHP1. The KHP1 polypeptide was demonstrated to be a flagellar component (234) and is postulated to be involved in the transport of axonemal components to the tips of elongating flagella. A distinct kinesin-related protein, Klp1, was also identified in PCR screens in *Chlamydomonas*,. The Klp1 polypeptide has been localized exclusively within flagella to the C2 microtubule of the central pair (8). Klp1 is not required for flagellar assembly but appears to be involved in the mediation of the rotation or twisting of the central pair microtubules. Immunological analysis of axonemal proteins suggests that there are multiple distinct kinesin-related proteins found within *Chlamydomonas* flagella (50); thus genetic and mutational analyses should prove key in the characterization of the function of these genes either in flagellar assembly or in the generation of force within the axoneme.

## Mutations That Provide Insight Into Molecular Structure

STRUCTURE OF KINESIN    Native kinesin forms a heterotetramer, with two heavy chains of ~120 kDa and two light chains of ~60 kDa (226). Based on the predicted amino acid sequence of the heavy chain, a three-domain structure was proposed: a globular head that includes the motor domain, an extended segment predicted to form an α-helical coiled-coil between the two kinesin heavy chains, and a globular tail domain (245). Structural analysis of native kinesin by electron microscopy supports this model—the native enzyme was observed to be a ~80-nm-long rod, with a pair of globular heads at one end, and a fan-shaped tail at the other end (78). Antibody decoration experiments have localized the light chains to the tail region of the molecule. The kinesin rod domain has been shown to form a bend or kink under some conditions (30, 78), and it has been suggested that a change in the conformation of kinesin may correlate with changes in the enzymatic or motor activity of the molecule (67). In this way, the regulation of kinesin motor activity might resemble that of nonmuscle myosin II.

KINESIN MOTOR DOMAIN   The mapping of the kinesin motor domain to the amino-terminal globular head observed by electron microscopy was confirmed in experiments examining the properties of various constructs of kinesin expressed in *E. coli*. The amino-terminal 339 residues of kinesin have been demonstrated to be sufficient to drive microtubule gliding in vitro if fused to a spectrin tail (205, 246).

NUCLEOTIDE-BINDING SITE   The nucleotide-binding site of kinesin was originally identified by its similarity to motifs in other proteins that had been shown to be involved in the binding of ATP. Residues 92–106 of kinesin match the consensus sequence ($GX_4GKTX_6I/V$; 232). Yang et al (245) found that a construct expressed in vitro that lacked this consensus motif bound to microtubules in a nucleotide-insensitive manner. Analysis of the *kar3-1* allele of the kinesin-related protein Kar3p has confirmed the identity of this site (141). *kar3-1* has a semidominant phenotype suggesting that the expression of the mutant protein poisons nuclear fusion. The molecular basis of the mutation was mapped to a single amino acid substitution of Glu for Gly-479, which results in an alteration of the nucleotide-binding consensus motif from ($GX_4GKT$) to ($GX_4EKT$) (141). This mutation apparently reduces or prevents nucleotide-dependent dissociation of the polypeptide from the microtubule. The mutant polypeptide, unlike the wild-type, was found to decorate cytoplasmic microtubules (141).

A similar conclusion comes from the analysis of the mutant allele of nod, $nod^{DTW}$. The dominant phenotype of disrupted distributive chromosome segregation in heterozygous females is specifically due to a point mutation within the consensus ATP-binding motif, in which Asn is substituted for Ser, so that the motif GQTGTGKS encoded by $nod^+$ becomes GQTGTGKN in the $nod^{DTW}$ allele (179). This suggests that for $nod^{DTW}$, as was observed for *kar3-1,* the altered polypeptide remains rigor-bound to the microtubule, rather than dissociating upon nucleotide binding and hydrolysis, and that this rigor binding is the basis of the dominant nature of the phenotype. This hypothesis is strengthened by the observation that two intragenic suppressors of the dominant phenotype of $nod^{DTW}$ map to the predicted microtubule-binding domain (179), which suggests that the predicted rigor binding of the dominant mutant might be overcome by a second mutation that weakens the affinity of the polypeptide for microtubules. This has not yet been tested directly.

MICROTUBULE-BINDING MOTIFS    The nucleotide-sensitive microtubule-binding site of the kinesin motor domain has not yet been well defined. Using deletion constructs of kinesin expressed in an vitro transcription/translation system, Yang et al (245) mapped the microtubule-binding domain to the carboxy-terminal end of the motor domain, corresponding to amino acids 320 through 390. For most kinesin-related proteins, the microtubule-binding domain has been identified based only on homology to the kinesin sequence.

Although kinesin is thought to be a vesicle motor, as described above, many of the kinesin-related proteins have been either proposed to, or shown to, function in mitosis and meiosis. In many postulated mechanisms for the roles of motor molecules in these processes, a microtubule-cross-bridging function is proposed that would allow the motor to mediate the sliding of adjacent microtubules. CENP-E, the largest kinesin-related polypeptide identified, has been shown to encode both a kinesin-like motor domain and a secondary, nucleotide-insensitive microtubule-binding domain. This 312-kDa CEN-P polypeptide is predicted to form an extended α-helical rod nearly four times longer than that of kinesin (248). Studies on deletion constructs expressed in an in vitro transcription/translation system have revealed a second microtubule-binding domain within the carboxy-terminal 99 amino acids of the polypeptide. The binding of this carboxy-terminal motif to microtubules was determined to be insensitive to nucleotide. The predicted sequence in this region is proline rich (13% of the encoded amino acids are proline) and basic, thus showing similarity to previously characterized microtubule-binding motifs in MAP2 and tau. The affinity of this region of the polypeptide for microtubules was abolished by phosphorylation either in vivo, or in vitro when phosphorylated with purified MPF. These results demonstrate that the microtubule-cross-bridging activity of CENP-E may be closely regulated in vivo (123).

The Kar3p polypeptide from *S. cerevisiae* is also thought to encode a second microtubule-binding motif, which may also mediate nucleotide-insensitive binding. The tail region of the *KAR3*-encoded polypeptide is predicted to be basic and proline rich (8%; 141), properties it shares with the microtubule-binding motif in CENP-E described above. The *ncd* gene product has been shown to cross-link and bundle microtubules in vitro (14, 138). Other kinesin-related proteins lacking a second microtubule-binding site may still dimerize or assemble to form higher order structures in vivo, which would then allow them to cross-bridge microtubules in a nucleotide-dependent manner, as has been proposed for the products of the *CIN8* and *KIP1* genes (194).

DIMERIZATION DOMAIN    Initial models of *Drosophila* kinesin suggested that the central rod domain with its predicted α-helical coiled-coil mediates the dimerization of two kinesin heavy chains and focused attention on Pro-399 as part of a flexible hinge that would link each of the two globular heads to the entwined stalk (88, 245). However, it has now been demonstrated that the expression in *E. coli* of a construct including residues 1 through 340 of *Drosophila* kinesin results in a monomer, whereas a slightly longer construct—residues 1 through 392—forms a dimer in solution (88). Berliner et al (7) also report that a construct encoding the first 340 amino acids of kinesin is monomeric but that constructs extending to amino acids 401 or 448 are dimeric. These results map the dimerization domain of the two kinesin heads to residues 340 through 392, a region predicted to form a coiled-coil (88, 205) and suggest a structural model in which the two kinesin head domains form a tightly coupled unit that is connected to the stalk by a flexible hinge centered about Pro-399 (88). This tight coupling of the head domains would then allow kinetic cooperativity for ATPase activity and force production (59, 65, 66; reviewed by D Hackney, this volume).

STRUCTURE OF THE KINESIN-RELATED PROTEINS    Neither the tertiary nor quaternary structure of kinesin is apparently conserved among the kinesin-related proteins. Although these proteins share homology in the motor domain, it is not necessarily localized to the amino terminus of the polypeptide as in kinesin. For example, Kar3p (a minus end-directed motor; 42) and ncd (also a minus-end directed motor; 139, 233) have their motor domains localized to the C-terminal end. However, Stewart et al (205) have clearly demonstrated that the orientation of force production is an intrinsic property of the motor domain and is not affected by the localization of the motor domain within the polypeptide, at either the amino-terminal or carboxy-terminal end.

Although Kar3p and the ncd polypeptide both resemble kinesin, e.g. they are predicted to fold to form a three-domain structure with two globular domains separated by an extended α-helical domain with a heptad repeat structure predicted to form a coiled-coil interaction, other kinesin-related proteins differ markedly in their predicted secondary structure. For example, KIP2 from *S. cerevisiae,* MCAK cloned from CHO cells, and the murine kinesin-related protein kif2 were all found to encode a kinesin-related domain near the center of the predicted polypeptide sequences (2, 188, 242).

The role of secondary structure in mediating motor function is now under examination for the minus-end directed motor ncd. Endow et al (40) have described an allele of ncd, *MC2,* which was generated by injecting *Drosophila* with a construct in which approximately one third of the predicted α-helical coiled-coil central stalk of ncd was deleted. The resulting transformant was then transferred into a *ncd* null background. Although the MC2 construct expressed in vitro had near wild-type microtubule motor activity and was also able to bundle microtubules and generate torque, the transformant flies showed a phenotype consistent with a partial loss of ncd function. MC2 partially rescued the null mutant, with dosage-dependent effects on the rescue of X-chromosome missegregation. It is unclear if the incomplete nature of the rescue was due to lower expression levels, or if these results illustrate the role of the stalk in ncd function. Potentially, the truncated ncd may not interact effectively with other cellular proteins, perhaps because binding epitopes are missing or because the shorter form of the enzyme may not extend sufficiently in vivo to fulfill its cellular role.

## Mutations That Provide Insight Into Molecular Mechanisms

The kinesin-related proteins Kar3p, ncd, and nod are to date the best charac-terized in terms of mutational analysis. The *kar3-1* allele described by Meluh & Rose (141) (discussed above) encodes a point mutation in the nucleotide-binding site that results in a semi-dominant phenotype in which the rigor-bound Kar3p poisons karogamy. The mutant polypeptide might interfere with func-tion in the diploid strain simply by blocking the binding of the wild-type active motor or potentially may form a quaternary structure in which the mutant polypeptide associates with wild-type subunits. Evidence for polypeptide in-teractions of Kar3p comes from the analysis of the *S. cerevisiae CIK1* gene. Phenotypic analyses of *CIK1* deletion mutants revealed a striking similarity to the effects induced by deletion of *KAR3* (159). The products of *CIK1* and *KAR3* were determined to interact using the yeast two-hybrid system and were also observed to coimmunoprecipitate (158), thus suggesting that the two polypeptides are part of the same protein complex within the cell. *CIK1* and *KAR3* are predicted to encode polypeptides with extended α-helical structure, and thus the interaction may be mediated by the formation of a heteroduplex coiled-coil.

CIN8 and KIP1 were found to overlap in function in *S. cerevisiae*, because single mutants were viable but the double mutation was lethal. Saunders & Hoyt (194) determined that extragenic suppressor alleles of the lethal defect in the double mutant mapped to the *KAR3* gene. Deletion of *KAR3* was also found to partially suppress the lethality of the *kip1-cin8* phenotype, by partially mitigating the collapse of pre-anaphase bipolar spindles observed in the *kip1-cin8* double-deletion strain. These results suggest a model for the separation of spindle poles in which either or both Kip1p and Cin8p provide the outward force, and Kar3p provides an inward-directed or compressive force. In a further screen for suppressor mutations of a *cin8* temperature-sensitive-*kip1* deletion strain, molecular analysis of seven suppressor mutations indicated that each had a point mutation within the *KAR3* gene sequence (86). The seven alleles had seven different amino acid alterations, but all were localized within the motor domain of KAR3. Two of the mutations, Glu to Asp, and Asn to Lys, involve residues that are highly conserved among the kinesin superfamily members (86). Although the first change, a substitution of one acidic residue for another, was observed to have little phenotypic effect on karyogamy or meiosis, the second change, in which a charged basic residue was substituted for an uncharged residue, had more dramatic effects on karyogamy and meiosis. Overall these data suggest that the specific site mutations may have differing effects on the ability of the Kar3 protein to function in its three distinct roles in mitosis, meiosis, and karyogamy.

O'Connell et al (154) recently identified a kinesin-related polypeptide in *A. nidulans,* KLPA, that is most closely related to KAR3 and ncd but shares no sequence similarity outside of the carboxyl-terminus motor domain. Although a null mutation in KLPA had no observable phenotype, over-expression of the protein was found to result in a block in nuclear division. Deletion of KLPA was found to partially suppress the spindle pole separation defect of a bimC mutant (described above). This observation also supports models for mitosis in which microtubule-based motor proteins provide carefully balanced forces. Loss of one motor may potentially disrupt the balance, but this loss can be counterbalanced by loss of a second motor, which generates opposing force. However, this model does not address the question of why some motors, for example Cin8p and Kip1p, apparently overlap in function, while others are essential, such as the bimC gene product.

Rasooly et al (180) performed a detailed structure/function analysis on *NOD*, which is required for the accurate segregation of nonexchange chromosomes in meiosis in female *Drosophila*, apparently by mediating the retention of the nonexchange chromosomes at the metaphase plate (213). As described above, the $nod^{DTW}$ allele has a dominant meiotic phenotype due to a point mutation within the ATP-binding domain. In a screen for revertants of the dominant phenotype, two extragenic suppressors were isolated and characterized. These alleles, $nod^{DR2}$ and $nod^{DR3}$, each encode point mutations, which result in the alteration of Asp (151) to Asn, and Arg(194) to His, respectively (179, 180). Both second site intragenic suppressor mutations are predicted to occur within the putative microtubule-binding site of the nod polypeptide, suggesting that the dominant affect of rigor binding of the $nod^{DTW}$ allele is overcome by a weakening in the affinity of nod for microtubules. A third allele, $nod^{DR5}$, encodes a partial revertant with a Ser substituted for Gly in a sequence strongly conserved among kinesin-related proteins that is localized between the predicted ATP- and microtubule-binding motifs. Analysis of truncation mutants of nod suggests that the last 12 to 20 amino acids are critical for either the function or the stability of the nod polypeptide.

Analysis of ncd in *Drosophila* suggests that the polypeptide product of this gene is involved in chromosome segregation in mitosis and meiosis. Komma et al (110) have characterized a dominant mutation at this locus, $ncd^D$, in which females are essential wild-type for the maternal effect of ncd on mitosis in the embryo, but exhibit high frequencies of meiotic chromosome nondisjunction. Two alterations in the predicted amino acid sequence of $ncd^D$ were identified, one of which maps to the putative microtubule-binding domain, changing an amino acid residue that is highly conserved among the kinesin-related proteins, Val-556 to Phe. The second alteration in sequence relative to wild-type is the substitution of Ser for Asn-696, which is four residues from the C-terminal end of the polypeptide. Although it is more likely that the alteration in the microtubule-binding site, rather than the point mutation at the carboxy-terminus, is responsible for the phenotype, the observations of Rasooly et al (180) on the effects of truncation mutations of ncd suggest that the carboxy-terminal sequences of these polypeptides may also be critical. Therefore, a clear distinction between the effects of the two amino acid substitutions cannot be made. The difficulty in making predictions about the importance of amino acid changes outside the motor domains is further highlighted by the observation that *klpA* from *A. nidulans* is able to complement the karogamy defect in *S. cerevisiae*, which results from a null mutation in *KAR3*, even though the sequences of the two kinesin-related proteins lack any apparent homology outside the motor domain (154).

## MUTATIONAL ANALYSIS OF CYTOPLASMIC AND AXONEMAL DYNEINS

Recent genetic studies in a wide range of organisms have greatly clarified the nature and extent of the dynein gene family. Thus far only a single gene encoding the heavy chain of cytoplasmic dynein has been found to be expressed in many organisms. Therefore, unlike the observed functional specificity demonstrated by many members of the kinesin superfamily, a single intracellular dynein motor may be adapted to many distinct cellular functions. In contrast, there is a family of related genes that encodes the axonemal dynein heavy chains. Comparisons of axonemal dynein genes from sea urchin and *Drosophila* have led to the suggestion that these genes arose by duplication and divergence early on and are now maintained as a required set of genes for the assembly and function of the complex structure of the eukaryotic axoneme (55, 178). The number of genes that encode dynein-associated polypeptides such as intermediate and light chains is currently unknown. The structure and sequence analysis of axonemal and cytoplasmic dyneins have been recently reviewed (83).

## Mutations That Provide Insight Into Cellular Function

CYTOPLASMIC DYNEIN    Cytoplasmic dynein was initially identified biochemically as a microtubule-activated ATPase isolated from mammalian brain and from the nematode *C. elegans* (130, 162). Analysis of the brain enzyme indicated that cytoplasmic dynein was a minus end-directed motor, which led to the suggestion that its primary function in neurons might be to move organelles and vesicles from the synapse back to the cell body (163), a hypothesis supported by studies of retrograde axonal transport (79, 198). However, the identification of cytoplasmic dynein in nonneuronal cells and tissues clearly indicated that the enzyme had an additional cellular role or roles. Recent research suggests that dynein also functions in mitosis (225), Golgi localization (25), and transport of lysosomes and endosomes (5, 126).

Genetic evidence for the cellular functions of cytoplasmic dynein is now accumulating. The effects of mutations in the gene encoding cytoplasmic dynein heavy chain was assayed by targeted gene disruption in yeast. Both Li et al (122) and Eshel et al (47) have isolated the yeast dynein heavy chain gene and constructed strains of *S. cerevisiae* with gross deletions at this locus. Analysis of these mutant strains indicated that expression of cytoplasmic dynein is not essential for vegetative growth in yeast, although Li et al (122) did note a slowing of the cell cycle in the mutant strains. Spindle assembly, spindle elongation, and chromosome segregation were not disrupted by the deletion of the dynein gene. However, both Li et al (122) and Eshel et al (47) noted that mutations in the yeast dynein gene caused the disruption of segregation of the duplicated nuclei between mother and bud. Because of a disruption in the alignment of the mitotic spindle with the neck, there was a large increase in the frequency of improper segregation of nuclei. Thus expression of cytoplasmic dynein is apparently critical for normal nuclear migration in *S. cerevisiae*.

Dynein may play a further, partially degenerate, role in yeast. A double-mutant strain carrying deletions in *dyn1*, the cytoplasmic dynein heavy chain gene, and in *cin8*, which encodes a kinesin-related protein (described above), was found to be inviable. Analysis of triple-mutant strains carrying mutations in *kip1* (also a kinesin-related protein, see above), *dyn1,* and *cin8* indicated that all three motors were involved in the segregation of chromosomes during anaphase in yeast (195). These data indicate that a single cellular process involves the partially overlapping function of both dynein and kinesin-related motor proteins. However, models for the roles of the different motors suggest that they function by distinct mechanisms, in that dynein is thought to provide outward pulling force on the spindle poles, and the kinesin-related proteins cin8 and kip1 may push on the poles from within (84, 194).

Similar phenotypes of disrupted nuclear migration were also observed to result from mutations in the dynein gene in the filamentous fungi *A. nidulans* and *Neurospora crassa.* Cloning of the *nudA* gene in *A. nidulans* (243) and the *ro-1* gene in *N. crassa* (168) led to the identification and characterization of cytoplasmic dynein heavy chain genes. In neither organism was the dynein gene found to be essential. However, in both of these organisms, dynein expression was required for the normal migration of nuclei along the hyphae.

In higher eukaryotes, however, the disruption of the gene encoding for cytoplasmic dynein heavy chain has a more profound effect. McGrail et al (140) analyzed mutations in the *Drosophila* gene *Dhc64C* and found that some alleles result in late embryonic lethality, indicating that dynein expression is essential, and that dynein function is not redundant with other motors, such as the minus-end directed kinesin-related proteins described above. Some alleles generated by McGrail et al (140) were observed to produce a rough-eye phenotype, similar to that observed for the *Glued* mutation (169; discussed below).

AXONEMAL DYNEINS    Many laboratories have contributed to a detailed mutational analysis of axonemal dyneins, primarily in the genetically and biochemically tractable species *Chlamydomonas.* Although the overall role of axonemal dynein clearly is to drive ciliary and flagellar beating, the detailed study of many mutations has led to insights into the nature of force production, generation of flagellar waveform, and coordinate regulation of motility. These studies have also highlighted the complexity of the axoneme in terms of structure and assembly.

Axonemal dynein heavy chains are encoded by perhaps 13 genes (55). The products of these genes are specifically localized within the axoneme. In *Chlamydomonas,* outer arm dyneins, which cross-bridge the perimeter of the outer doublet microtubules, are formed from three distinct heavy chains, the product of the $\alpha$, $\beta$, and $\gamma$ dynein heavy chain genes. The inner arm dyneins are much more complex, with at least three distinct species formed from eight distinct heavy chains (102, 135, 167).

Many of the characterized flagellar mutants have been correlated with specific structural defects, such as the loss of either outer or inner dynein arms (10). However, for many of these mutations, it has been difficult to correlate precisely a gene defect with a single lost or defective polypeptide. This is due to the complex interactions involved in the assembly of the macromolecular structures of the axoneme. For example, the expression of a truncated form of one dynein polypeptide can lead to the failure to assemble the entire dynein arm in the axoneme (see below). Because flagellar localization and stability of the unassembled dynein polypeptides may be variable, it is difficult to correlate the defective gene with its gene product unless other information is considered.

The comparative analysis of outer arm-less and inner arm-less mutants has led to the conclusion that the outer and inner arm dyneins contribute in distinct ways to force production. Defects in outer arm dyneins lead to decreased flagellar beat frequency, slowing flagellar motility but not altering the characteristics of the waveform. In contrast, inner arm dynein defects are correlated with alterations in the characteristics of the flagellar waveform (12). Studies of paralyzed mutants of *Chlamydomonas* also have pointed to key roles for the central pair of microtubules and the radial spokes in the generation of the flagellar waveform, as mutants lacking either of these structures display a paralyzed flagellar phenotype. Analysis of suppressors of these mutations has led to a better understanding of the regulation of dynein activity and flagellar function, as described below.

AXONEMAL DYNEIN MUTATIONS IN HIGHER EUKARYOTES    An obvious function for dynein is to mediate the motility of sperm, and Gepner & Hays (53) have localized a gene encoding a *Drosophila* dynein heavy chain gene to the *kl-5* locus of the Y chromosome. The *kl-5* locus was previously identified as a region on the Y chromosome, which is required for male fertility. Thus in *Drosophila,* at least one gene required for spermatogenesis is localized to the Y chromosome, but because multiple dynein and non-dynein genes are required for the correct assembly of a functional flagellar axoneme, the evolutionary advantage of this localization is unclear.

## Mutations That Provide Insight Into Molecular Structure

DYNEIN STRUCTURE    Both cytoplasmic and axonemal outer arm dyneins share a basic structure in which two or three globular heads are connected by apparently flexible strands to a common base (98, 227). Each head and its stalk is formed from a single dynein heavy chain, which ranges in size from 470 to 540 kDa. The heads interact with the microtubule in a nucleotide-dependent manner and are the site of force production. For axonemal dyneins, the intermediate chains have been mapped to the base of the complex and may mediate the structural binding of the dynein to the A-tubule of the axoneme (108, 109). By analogy, the intermediate chains of cytoplasmic dynein are thought to mediate the binding of the intracellular enzyme to its vesicular cargo (161). The localization of the light-intermediate and light chains within the dynein structure is not yet known (see 83 for a recent review of dynein structure).

CYTOPLASMIC DYNEIN ASSEMBLY    Comparisons of cytoplasmic and axonemal dynein intermediate chain sequences have revealed that the carboxy-terminal halves of these polypeptides are related, but the amino-terminal sequences

diverge significantly (161). This observation suggests that the carboxy-terminal half of the intermediate chain is involved in a function common to both
axonemal and cytoplasmic dyneins, such as assembly of the macromolecular
complex. In recent studies in *Dictyostelium,* constructs over-expressing full-
length cytoplasmic dynein intermediate chain, or either the amino- or carboxy-
terminal halves of this polypeptide, were used to transform wild-type cells.
Both the full-length and carboxy-terminal constructs associated with the native
dynein heavy chain expressed in these cells. In contrast, the amino-terminal
construct was not found in association with the dynein heavy chain, thus
indicating that the determinants required for association of the intermediate
chain with the heavy chain are encoded in the carboxy-terminal half of the
polypeptide, which is conserved among axonemal and cytoplasmic dyneins (L
Trivinos-Lagos, C Collins & RL Chisholm, manuscript submitted). The amino-
terminal domain of the intermediate chain may encode determinants that target
the holoenzyme within the cell, specifying localization to either the A subfiber
of the outer double microtubule for axonemal dynein, or to a vesicle or
organelle for cytoplasmic dynein. In support of this hypothesis, analysis of the
*Dictyostelium* strains over-expressing the carboxy-terminal half of the cytoplasmic dynein intermediate chain also revealed a striking growth defect due
to a mitotic block (L Trivinos-Lagos, C Collins & RL Chisholm, manuscript
submitted). This block occurs because the truncated intermediate chain apparently is able to bind to dynein, but not to target the enzyme appropriately
within the cell. Thus in *Dictyostelium,* as well as in *Drosophila,* dynein appears
to be essential for normal cell division.

AXONEMAL DYNEIN ASSEMBLY    *Chlamydomonas* mutants have been identified with defects in either the α or the β heavy chains of outer arm dynein.
The *oda-11* mutant was identified by RFLP analysis as genetically linked to
the gene encoding the α heavy chain (192). Outer arm dynein isolated from
this mutant had only the β and γ heavy chains, and there was a corresponding
loss of the outermost appendage of the outer arm dynein axoneme cross-sections observed by electron micrographs. The *oda-11* mutant is motile, swimming with a speed of 119 μm/s, which is less than the wild-type rate of 194
μm/s, but considerably faster than the speed of *oda-1,* a mutant completely
lacking in outer arm dyneins, which swims at 62 μm/s. Beat frequencies were
observed to follow a similar pattern (192).

In contrast, *oda4,* a mutant with a defect in the β heavy chain (104, 129),
completely lacks outer arm dyneins (104). This difference suggests that an
intact β chain is essential for the correct assembly or localization of outer arm
dynein within the axoneme. To further test this hypothesis, Sakakibara et al
(193) analyzed a mutant *Chlamydomonas* strain that produces a truncated β
heavy chain. The mutant allele *oda4-s7* encodes a β heavy chain of ~160 kDa,

rather than the full-length polypeptide of predicted molecular mass of 520 kDa (145). Observation of the mutant axonemes by electron microscopy revealed that while the ability of the *oda4-s7* mutant to assemble outer arms was somewhat impaired, the α and γ chains continued to assemble within the axoneme with the truncated β form. Therefore, the mutational analysis of Sakakibara et al (193) has mapped the site of interaction of the α and γ chains with the β chain and the necessary determinants for correct localization of the outer arms within the axoneme to the amino-terminal domain of the β chain. Mocz & Gibbons (147) have shown that the amino-terminal region of the β heavy chain interacts with microtubules in an ATP-insensitive manner. Together, the genetic and biochemical evidence suggest that the amino-terminal domain of the β dynein heavy chain, along with the intermediate chains, forms the base of the outer arm dynein, which mediates its structural binding to the A-tubule.

Because the truncated β chain is predicted to lack its catalytic domain, it is expected that this would have an effect on the function of the outer arm dynein. The mutant strain was observed to swim at 65 μm/s, similar to the swimming rate of the allele *oda4*, which completely lacks outer dynein arms and swims at 62 μm/s. Although the expression of a truncated β heavy chain allows the correct assembly of the outer arm dynein complex, loss of the β dynein head almost completely blocked activity of this dynein, which is in contrast to the effects of the loss of the α dynein head. Thus mutational analysis has revealed both structural determinants for assembly and a significant difference in the in vivo role of the three heads of axonemal outer arm dynein.

The axonemal dynein 70-kDa intermediate chain (IC70) has also been demonstrated to be key in the assembly of outer arm dyneins. *oda6* mutants in *Chlamydomonas* lack outer dynein arms, and this locus has been shown to encode the IC70 polypeptide (146). King et al (108) have demonstrated a direct interaction between the IC70 polypeptide and the microtubule in cross-linking studies. However, it is not yet known if outer arm dyneins are assembled in the cytoplasm and the intact intermediate chain is required for accurate localization of the complex to the axoneme, or if the dynein is assembled in situ and the binding of IC70 to the microtubule is a required step in the assembly of the holoenzyme.

## Mutations That Provide Insight Into Molecular Mechanism

The initial molecular characterization of the β heavy chain of axonemal dynein from sea urchin (56, 155) revealed the striking and unexpected result of the identification of four consensus P-loop elements within the central region of the polypeptide. The finding of four possible nucleotide-binding sites rather than the expected one site per dynein head (57, 97) has since been observed within all reported dynein heavy chain sequences. The four P-loops are, therefore, a characteristic of both axonemal and cytoplasmic dyneins, although some of these motifs are more tightly conserved than others (83). By comparing vanadate photocleavage data with the predicted polypeptide sequence, Gibbons et al (56) identified the first P-loop element as the probable catalytic site for the enzyme. The function or functions of the remaining motifs remain speculative and are obvious targets for further mutational analysis. The recent demonstration that active cytoplasmic dynein heavy chain can be expressed in baculovirus (137) should allow these studies to proceed rapidly.

An excellent example of the power of mutational analyses to provide otherwise elusive insight into structure/function relationships of axonemal dyneins comes from the work of Porter and her colleagues who have performed a detailed analysis of the structural basis for the suppressor activity of the *sup-pf* mutation. As noted above, many *Chlamydomonas* mutants exhibit a paralyzed flagellar phenotype due to defects in the structure or assembly of the central pair of axonemal microtubules or the radial spokes, which project centrally from the outer doublet microtubules toward the central pair. Results from reconstitution experiments by Smith & Sale (201) suggest that for some mutants the mechanism of this paralysis is the inappropriate posttranslational modification of the dynein in the axoneme, which is mediated by the radial spokes. Huang et al (87) isolated extragenic suppressor mutants of both radial spoke and central pair mutants that were capable of restoring flagellar motility. When expressed in a wild-type background, one of these mutant alleles, *sup-pf-1,* was itself observed to result in a significant reduction in flagellar beat frequency (87).

The *sup-pf* locus has been shown to be tightly linked to the *ODA4* locus (129), which in turn has been shown by RFLP analysis to encode the β dynein heavy chain gene (175). Porter et al (175) have now characterized two suppressor alleles of *sup-pf-1* in molecular detail and have shown that in each case extragenic suppression resulted from a distinct small in-frame deletion within the coding sequence of the β dynein heavy chain gene. *sup-pf-1-1* has a 21-bp in-frame deletion, resulting in a loss of 7 amino acids (3190–3196), and *sup-pf-1-2* has a 30-bp in-frame deletion, resulting in the loss of 10 amino acids (3158–3167). Although these two alterations in coding sequence are distinct, they both occur within a region that is highly conserved among the dynein heavy chain sequences characterized to date. While no known or well-characterized motifs are disrupted by these deletions, it is notable that each results in the disruption of sequence predicted to form an α-helical coiled-coil.

The observed appearance of both axonemal and cytoplasmic dyneins by scanning transmission microscopy clearly indicates relatively extended protein structure in the stalks connecting the dynein heads to a common base (98, 227). However, the predicted amino acids sequences for dynein heavy chains do not suggest a high probability of formation of extended α-helical coiled-coil structure, as is seen in the rod domains of other motors such as kinesin and myosin. The two small deletions observed in the *sup-pf-1* suppressor mutants occur within the relatively short stretches of coiled-coil predicted for the dynein heavy chain. There is very little information available on the overall folding of the dynein heavy chain to form its characteristic head and neck structure, but most likely the short region of predicted coiled-coil sequence forms the neck region. The observation of Porter et al (175) that short deletions within this predicted neck lead to dramatic effects on the overall rates of flagellar motility led them to propose, by analogy with observations on myosin, kinesin, and kinesin-related proteins, that altering the length of the dynein neck would alter the effective coupling of ATP hydrolysis and force production. For example, constructs encoding progressively increasing truncations of the tail domains of either kinesin heavy chain or ncd truncation constructs produced proteins that exhibited decreasing translocation frequencies in vitro (205).

Alternatively, an hypothesis that would address both the observed effect of the *sup-pf-1-1* allele on flagellar motility when expressed in a wild-type background, as well as its ability to suppress the paralyzed phenotype of a central pair mutant, is that the deleted regions have a regulatory role, perhaps in modulating or coordinating the activities of multiple dynein motors within the axoneme. Thus suppression of paralysis may occur by overriding a normal inhibitory signal that is not recognized by the mutant alleles of the β heavy chain. While the specific mechanism of suppression has yet to be determined, it is clear that the molecular characterization of these alleles points to specific sequences that otherwise would not have been targeted for investigation.

## Mutations That Provide Insight Into Regulatory Mechanisms

The activities of the biological motor enzymes are likely to be tightly regulated, although little is known about the specific mechanisms for the regulation of either cytoplasmic or axonemal dyneins. Accumulating evidence suggests that reversible phosphorylation is involved in regulating the activity of the motors or their association with their cellular cargo (33, 127; see 231 for a recent review of the role of phosphorylation in regulating axonemal dyneins). For both cytoplasmic and axonemal dyneins there is also genetic and biochemical evidence suggesting that interacting oligomeric protein complexes are involved in the regulation of their cellular activity. Cytoplasmic dynein activity appears to be modulated by the dynactin complex, and axonemal dynein appears to be regulated by its interaction with the dynein regulatory complex.

THE DYNACTIN COMPLEX    Initial biochemical characterization of cytoplasmic dynein from rat tissues such as liver and testis indicated that additional polypeptides of 150 and 45 kDa copurified with the dynein through the final step of the preparation, which was cosedimentation at 20S on a sucrose density gradient (22). The 150- and 45-kDa polypeptides have since been characterized as members of a distinct 20S complex, dynactin, which also includes polypeptides of 24, 27, 32, 37, 42, 50, 62, 136, and 135 kDa (197). The 45-kDa polypeptide, the most abundant polypeptide in the complex, has been identified as a novel actin-related protein, centractin or Arp1 (19, 117, 160), and the 42-kDa polypeptide is conventional actin (197). The 37- and 32-kDa polypeptides have been identified as the $\alpha$ and $\beta$ subunits of the capping protein CapZ (197). The 150-kDa polypeptide p150$^{Glued}$ was identified by characterization of cDNAs as homologous to the product of the *Glued* locus in *Drosophila* (82).

The first identified allele of the *Glued* locus, $Gl^1$, was isolated as a dominant mutation that disrupted compound eye and optic lobe formation in *Drosophila* (169). The null mutation is lethal, and genetic mosaic analysis revealed a cell-lethal phenotype (71). The recent characterization of cytoplasmic dynein mutants in *Drosophila* has suggested a very similar phenotype of late embryonic lethality, with less severe alleles producing a rough-eyed phenotype (140). Some alleles of the dynein gene were found to act as dominant enhancers or suppressors of the $Gl^1$ mutation, evidence for a genetic interaction between the dynein heavy chain and Glued polypeptide in vivo. This genetic evidence is supported by biochemical evidence for a direct interaction (236).

The data of Plamman et al (168) also provide genetic evidence for a common function for dynein and dynactin in vivo. The analysis of two *ropy* mutations in *Neurospora crassa,* both of which exhibit the identical phenotype of curled hyphae with abnormal nuclear distribution, revealed that *ro-1* encodes cytoplasmic dynein heavy chain and *ro-4* encodes Arp1 or centractin, the major component of the dynactin complex. Although neither of these genes is essential in *N. crassa,* both were found to be required to maintain the normal uniform distribution of nuclei throughout fungal hyphae.

In *S. cerevisiae* there is also evidence for an interaction between cytoplasmic dynein and components of the dynactin complex. Both Clark & Meyer (20) and Muhua et al (150) isolated the putative Arp1 homologue from yeast and found that mutations in this gene resulted in defects in spindle orientation and nuclear migration that were very similar to those previously observed for dynein mutants. However, as discussed by Clark & Meyer (20) it is not yet clear if the gene identified (referred to as either *ACT3* or *ACT5*) is indeed the true functional homologue of vertebrate Arp1. Analysis of the sequences of the known actin-related proteins suggests that the recently identified yeast protein may be representative of a unique class of these polypeptides.

Recent biochemical evidence supports the genetic evidence for the interaction of the dynein and dynactin complexes. Using affinity chromatography we have determined that cytoplasmic dynein is specifically retained from total brain cytosol on an affinity matrix with bound p150$^{Glued}$ (106). A similar result has been reported by Vaughan et al (229) who mapped a direct interaction between the dynein intermediate chain and the p150$^{Glued}$ polypeptide by blot overlay interactions.

The mechanism by which dynactin may modulate dynein function in vivo remains speculative. Gill et al (60) have shown that in the absence of dynactin, dynein is incapable of mediating vesicular transport along microtubules in an in vitro assay, although microtubule gliding was observed. We have determined that p150$^{Glued}$ is capable of a direct binding to microtubules (237) and to cytoplasmin dynein (106). Dynactin may serve as a vesicle-bound receptor for dynein, or it may mediate the initial formation of a ternary complex among microtubule, vesicle, and motor, as has been proposed for the related polypeptide CLIP-170. Alternatively, dynactin may play a more active role in vesicular transport, perhaps preventing the diffusion of the vesicle away from the microtubule during the detached stage of the cross-bridge cycle (237).

THE DYNEIN REGULATORY COMPLEX   For axonemal dynein there is also evidence that a large macromolecular complex, the dynein regulatory complex, is involved in the control of motor function. The dynein regulatory complex has an apparent molecular weight of at least 500 and is composed of at least seven polypeptides, most of which have been identified by the analysis of flagellar mutants (166). Mutations that disrupt the regulatory complex suppress the paralyzed flagellar phenotype resulting from mutations altering either the radial spokes or central pair microtubules. This suppression is similar to the extragenic suppression exhibited by mutant alleles of the β dynein heavy chain locus, described above.

The mechanism by which the dynein regulatory complex affects the activity of the axonemal dynein arms is not yet clear. Part of the function of the complex apparently is to localize subsets of the inner dynein arms, perhaps by forming part of the A-tubule-binding site for these dyneins (166). The dynein regulatory complex has been localized within the axoneme to the junction between the radial spokes and the inner dynein arms (51), which has led to the hypothesis that this complex is part of a signaling pathway that transmits signals from the central pair or radial spokes to the dynein. In the absence of central pair or radial spokes, there may be no positive induction, which thus allows constitutive negative regulation to induce a paralyzed phenotype. The removal of the inhibitory signal by disruption of the dynein regulatory complex may then allow the unregulated activation of flagellar dyneins, leading to the suppression of the paralyzed phenotype.

# CONCLUDING REMARKS

Mutational analysis of the motor proteins has provided numerous insights into their cellular roles as well as structure/function insights into motor function and the regulation of motor activity. Yet this is only the beginning of the systematic molecular dissections that promise to delineate the roles that molecular motors play and the mechanisms underlying their functions. The resolution of the crystal structure of the myosin II motor domain and the existence of myosin expression systems have created an opportunity for studies on myosin structure/function relationships to proceed rapidly. Given that kinesin expression is relatively straightforward, a rapid growth in kinesin structure/function studies will undoubtedly follow the publication of the crystal structures of ncd and kinesin. Thus this is an exciting time for the field of molecular motors, and one can expect a rapid expansion of our knowledge during the next decade.

ACKNOWLEDGMENTS

The authors gratefully acknowledge the critical insight of Elizabeth Holleran, David Roof, Frederick Holzbaur, Kathleen Trybus, and Clare Waterman-Storer.

*Literature Cited*

1. Adelman MR, Taylor EW. 1969. Further purification and characterization of slime mold myosin and slime mold actin. *Biochemistry* 8:4976–88
2. Aizawa H, Sekine Y, Takemura R, Zhang Z, Nangaku M, Hirokawa N. 1992. Kinesin family in murine central nervous system. *J. Cell Biol.* 119:1287–96
3. Al-Mahdawi S, Chamberlain LS, Cleland J, Nihoyannopoulos P, Gilligan D, et al. 1993. Identification of a mutation in the β cardiac myosin heavy chain gene in a family with hypertrophic cardiomyopathy. *Br. Heart J.* 69:136–41
4. Anan R, Greve G, Thierfelder L, Watkins H, McKenna WJ, et al. 1994. Prognostic implications of novel β cardiac myosin heavy chain gene mutations that cause familial hypertrophic cardiomyopathy. *J. Clin. Invest.* 93:280–85
5. Aniento F, Emans N, Griffiths G, Gruenberg J. 1993. Cytoplasmic dynein-dependent vesicular transport from early to late endosomes. *J. Cell Biol.* 123:1373–87
6. Beall CJ, Sepanski MA, Fyrberg EA. 1989. Genetic dissection of *Drosophila* myofibril formation: effects of actin and myosin heavy chain null alleles. *Genes Dev.* 3:131–40
7. Berliner E, Young EC, Anderson K, Mahtani HK, Gelles J. 1995. Failure of a single-headed kinesin to track parallel to microtubule protofilaments. *Nature* 373:718–21
8. Bernstein M, Beech PL, Katz SG, Rosenbaum JL. 1994. A new kinesin-like protein (Klp1) localized to a single microtubule of the *Chlamydomonas* flagellum. *J. Cell Biol.* 125:1313–26
9. Bottinelli R, Betto R, Schiaffino S, Reggiani C. 1994. Maximum shortening velocity and coexistence of myosin heavy

chain isoforms in single skinned fast fibres of rat skeletal muscle. *J. Muscle Res. Cell Motil.* 15:413–19

10. Blair DF, Dutcher SK. 1992. Flagella in prokaryotes and lower eukaryotes. *Curr. Opin. Genet. Dev.* 2:756–67

11. Brockerhoff SE, Stevens RC, Davis TN. 1994. The unconventional myosin, Myo2p, is a calmodulin target at sites of cell growth in *Saccharomyces cerevisiae. J. Cell Biol.* 124:315–23

12. Brokaw CJ, Kamiya R. 1987. Bending patterns of *Chlamydomonas* flagella: IV. Mutants with defects in inner and outer dynein arms indicate differences in dynein arm function. *Cell Motil. Cytoskelet.* 8:68–75

13. Brzeska H, Lynch TJ, Martin B, Korn ED. 1989. The localization and sequence of the phosphorylation sites of *Acanthamoeba* myosin I. An improved method for locating the phosphorylated amino acid. *J. Biol. Chem.* 264:19340–48

14. Chandra R, Salmon ED, Erickson HP, Lockhart A, Endow SA. 1993. Structural and functional domains of the *Drosophila* ncd microtubule motor protein. *J. Biol. Chem.* 268:9005–13

15. Chantler PD, Szent-Gyorgyi AG. 1980. Regulatory light-chains and scallop myosin, full dissociation, reversibility and co-operative effects. *J. Mol. Biol.* 138:473–92

16. Chaussepied P, Kasprzak AA. 1989. Isolation and characterization of the G-actin-myosin head complex. *Nature* 342:950–53

17. Chen P, Ostrow BD, Tafuri SR, Chisholm RL. 1994. Targeted disruption of the *Dictyostelium RMLC* gene produces cells defective in cytokinesis and development. *J. Cell Biol.* 127:1933–44

18. Cheney RE, Riley MA, Mooseker MS. 1993. Phylogenetic analysis of the myosin superfamily. *Cell Motil. Cytoskelet.* 24:215–23

19. Clark SW, Meyer DI. 1992. Centractin is an actin homologue associated with the centrosome. *Nature* 359:246–50

20. Clark SW, Meyer DI. 1994. ACT3: a putative centractin homologue in *S. cerevisiae* is required for proper orientation of the mitotic spindle. *J. Cell Biol.* 127:129–38

21. Cole DG, Saxton WM, Sheehan KB, Scholey JM. 1994. A "slow" homotetrameric kinesin-related motor protein purified from *Drosophila* embryos. *J. Biol. Chem.* 269:22913–16

22. Collins CA, Vallee RB. 1989. Preparation of microtubules from rat liver and testis: cytoplasmic dynein is a major microtubule-associated protein. *Cell Motil. Cytoskelet.* 14:491–500

23. Collins JH. 1991. Myosin light chains and troponin-C: structural and evolutionary relationships revealed by amino acid sequence comparisons. *J. Muscle Res. Cell Motil.* 12:3–25

24. Conrad PA, Giuliano KA, Fisher G, Collins K, Matsudaira PT, Taylor DL. 1993. Relative distribution of actin, myosin I and myosin II during the wound healing response of fibroblasts. *J. Cell Biol.* 120:1381–91

25. Corthesy-Theulaz I, Pauloin A, Pfeffer SR. 1992. Cytoplasmic dynein participates in the centrosomal localization of the Golgi complex. *J. Cell Biol.* 118:1333–45

26. Craig R, Padron R, Kendrick-Jones J. 1987. Structural changes accompanying phosphorylation of tarantula muscle myosin filaments. *J. Cell Biol.* 105:1319–27

27. Cremo CR, Sellers JR, Facemyer KC. 1995. Two heads are required for phosphorylation-dependent regulation of smooth muscle myosin. *J. Biol. Chem.* 270:2171–75

28. Cripps RM, Becker KD, Mardahl M, Kronert WA, Hodges D, Bernstein SI. 1994. Transformation of *Drosophila melanogaster* with the wild-type myosin heavy-chain gene: rescue of mutant phenotypes and analysis of defects caused by overexpression. *J. Cell Biol.* 126:689–99

29. Cuda G, Fananapazir L, Zhu W-S, Sellers JR, Epstein ND. 1993. Skeletal muscle expression and abnormal function of β-myosin in hypertrophic cardiomyopathy. *J. Clin. Invest.* 91:2861–65

30. de Cuevas M, Tao T, Goldstein LSB. 1992. Evidence that the stalk of *Drosophila* kinesin heavy chain is an α-helical coiled coil. *J. Cell Biol.* 166:957–65

31. De Lozanne A, Spudich JA. 1987. Disruption of the *Dictyostelium* myosin heavy chain gene by homologous recombination. *Science* 236:1086–91

32. Dibb NJ, Brown DM, Karn J, Moerman DG, Bolten SL, Waterston RH. 1985. Sequence analysis of mutations that affect the synthesis, assembly and enzymatic activity of the *unc-54* myosin heavy chain of *Caenorhabditis elegans. J. Mol. Biol.* 183:543–51

33. Dillman JF, Pfister KK. 1994. Differential phosphorylation in vivo of cytoplasmic dynein associated with anterogradely moving organelles. *J. Cell Biol.* 127:1671–81

34. Doberstein SK, Baines IC, Wiegand G, Korn ED, Pollard TD. 1993. Inhibition

of contractile vacuole function in vivo by antibodies against myosin-I. *Nature* 365:841–43

35. Doberstein SK, Pollard TD. 1992. Localization and specificity of the phospholipid and actin binding sites on the tail of *Acanthamoeba* myosin IC. *J. Cell Biol.* 117:1241–49

36. Dufour C, Dausse E, Fetler L, Dubourg O, Bouhour J-B, et al. 1994. Identification of a mutation near a functional site of the β cardiac myosin heavy chain gene in a family with hypertrophic cardiomyopathy. *J. Mol. Cell Cardiol.* 26:1241–47

37. Egeloff TT, Brown SS, Spudich JA. 1991. Spatial and temporal control of nonmuscle myosin localization: identification of a domain that is necessary for myosin filament disassembly in vivo. *J. Cell Biol.* 112:667–88

38. Egeloff TT, Lee RJ, Spudich JA. 1993. *Dictyostelium* myosin heavy chain phosphorylation sites regulate myosin filament assembly and localization in vivo. *Cell* 75:363–71

39. Eliott S, Joss GH, Spudich A, Williams KL. 1993. Patterns in *Dictyostelium discoideum:* the role of myosin II in the transition from the unicellular to the multicellular. *J. Cell Sci.* 104:457–66

40. Endow SA, Chandra R, Komma DJ, Yamamoto AH, Salmon ED. 1994. Mutants of the *Drosophila* ncd microtubule motor protein cause centrosomal and spindle pole defects in mitosis. *J. Cell Sci.* 107:859–67

41. Endow SA, Hanikoff S, Soler-Niedziela L. 1990. Mediation of meioitic and early mitotic chromosome segregation in *Drosophila* by a protein related to kinesin. *Nature* 345:81–83

42. Endow SA, Kang SJ, Satterwhite LL, Rose MD, Skeen VP, Salmon ED. 1994. Yeast Kar3 is a minus-end microtubule motor protein that destabilizes microtubules preferentially at the minus ends. *EMBO J.* 13:2708–13

43. Engelhardt VA, Lyubimova MN. 1939. Myosin and adenosinetriphosphatase. *Nature* 144:668–70

44. Enos AP, Morris NR. 1990. Mutation of a gene that encodes a kinesin-like protein blocks nuclear division in A. nidulans. *Cell* 60:1019–27

45. Epstein HF, Waterston RH, Brenner S. 1974. A mutant affecting the heavy chain of myosin in *Caenorhabditis elegans. J. Mol. Biol.* 90:291–300

46. Epstein ND, Cohn GM, Cyran F, Fananapazir L. 1992. Differences in clinical expression of hypertrophic cardiomyopathy associated with two distinct mutations in the β-myosin heavy chain gene. *Circulation* 86:345–52

47. Eshel D, Urrestarauzu LA, Vissers S, Jauniaux JC, van Vliet-Reedijk JC, et al. 1993. Cytoplasmic dynein is required for normal nuclear segregation in yeast. *Proc. Natl. Acad. Sci. USA* 90:11172–76

48. Fananapazir L, Dalakas MC, Cyran LF, Cohn G, Epstein ND. 1993. Missense mutations in the β-myosin heavy-chain gene cause central core disease in hypertrophic cardiomyopathy. *Proc. Natl. Acad. Sci. USA* 90:3993–97

49. Fananapazir L, Epstein ND. 1994. Genotype-phenotype correlations in hypertrophic cardiomyopathy. Insights provided by comparisons of kindreds with distinct and identical β-myosin heavy chain gene mutations. *Circulation* 89:22–32

50. Fox LA, Sawin KE, Sale WS. 1994. Kinesin-related proteins in eukaryotic flagella. *J. Cell Sci.* 107:1545–50

51. Gardner LC, O'Toole E, Perrone CA, Giddings T, Porter ME. 1994. Components of a "dynein regulatory complex" are located at the junction between the radial spokes and the dynein arms in *Chlamydomonas* flagella. *J. Cell Biol.* 127:1311–25

52. Geisterfer-Lowrance AAT, Kass S, Tanigawa G, Vosberg H-P, McKenna W, et al. 1990. A molecular basis for familial hypertrophic cardiomyopathy: a β cardiac myosin heavy chain missense mutation. *Cell* 62:999–1006

53. Gepner J, Hays TS. 1993. A fertility region on the Y chromosome of *Drosophila melanogaster* encodes a dynein microtubule motor. *Proc. Natl. Acad. Sci. USA* 90:11132–36

54. Gho M, McDonald K, Ganetzky B, Saxton WM. 1992. Effects of kinesin mutations on neuronal functions. *Science* 258:313–16

55. Gibbons BH, Asai DJ, Tang WJY, Hays TS, Gibbons IR. 1994. Phylogeny and expression of axonemal and cytoplasmic dynein genes in sea urchins. *Mol. Biol. Cell* 5:57–70

56. Gibbons IR, Gibbons BH, Mocz G, Asai DJ. 1991. Multiple nucleotide-binding sites in the sequence of dynein β heavy chain. *Nature* 352:640–43

57. Gibbons IR, Lee-Eiford A, Mocz G, Phillipson CA, Tang WJY, Gibbons BH. 1987. Photosensitized cleavage of dynein heavy chains. *J. Biol. Chem.* 262:2780–86

58. Gibson F, Walsh J, Mburu P, Varela A, Brown KA, et al. 1995. A type VII myosin encoded by the mouse deafness gene *shaker-1. Nature* 374:62–64

59. Gilbert SP, Webb WR, Brune M, Johnson, KA. 1995. Pathway of processive ATP hydrolysis by kinesin. *Nature* 373:671–76

60. Gill SR, Schroer A, Szilak I, Steuer ER, Sheetz MP, Cleveland DW. 1991. Dynactin, a conserved, ubiquitously expressed component of an activator of vesicle motility mediated by cytoplasmic dynein. *J. Cell Biol.* 115:1639–50

61. Goldstein LS. 1993. With apologies to Scheherazade: tails of 1001 kinesin motors. *Annu. Rev. Genet.* 27:319–51

62. Goodson HV, Kang SJ, Endow SA. 1994. Molecular phlogeny of the kinesin family of microtubule motor proteins. *J. Cell Sci.* 107:1875–84

63. Goodson HV, Spudich JA. 1993. Molecular evolution of the myosin family: relationships derived from comparisons of amino acid sequences. *Proc. Natl. Acad. Sci. USA* 90:659–63

64. Govindan B, Bowser R, Novick P. 1995. The role of Myo2, a yeast class V myosin, in vesicular transport. *J. Cell Biol.* 128:1055–67

65. Hackney DD. 1994. The rate-limiting step in microtubule-stimulate ATP hydrolysis by dimeric kinesin head domains occurs while bound to the microtubule. *J. Biol. Chem.* 269:16508–11

66. Hackney DD. 1994. Evidence for alternating head catalysis by kinesin during microtubule-stimulated ATP hydrolysis. *Proc. Natl. Acad. Sci. USA* 91:6865–69

67. Hackney DD, Levitt JD, Suhan J. 1992. Kinesin undergoes a 9 S to 6 S conformational transition. *J. Biol. Chem.* 267:8696–701

68. Hagan I, Yanagida M. 1990. Novel potential mitotic motor protein encoded by the fission yeast *cut7+* gene. *Nature* 347:563–66

69. Hall DH, Hedgecock EM. 1991. Kinesin-related gene unc-104 is required for axonal transport of synaptic vesicles in C. elegans. *Cell* 65:837–47

70. Harada H, Kimura A, Nishi H, Sasazuki T, Toshima H. 1993. A missense mutation of cardiac β-myosin heavy chain gene linked to a familial hypertrophic cardiomyopathy in affected Japanese families. *Biochem. Biophys. Res. Commun.* 194:791–98

71. Harte PJ, Kankel DR. 1982. Genetic analysis of mutations at the *Glued* locus and interacting loci in *Drosophila melanogaster*. *Genetics* 101:477–501

72. Hasson TB, Mooseker MS. 1994. Porcine myosin-VI: characterization of a new mammalian unconventional myosin. *J. Cell Biol.* 127:425–40

73. Hatano S, Oosawa F. 1966. Isolation and characterization of *Plasmodium* actin. *Biochim. Biophys. Acta* 127:488–98

74. Hatano S, Tazawa M. 1968. Isolation, purification and characterization of myosin B from *Myxomycele plasmodium*. *Biochim. Biophys. Acta* 154:507–19

75. Heck MMS, Pereira A, Pesavento P, Yannoni Y, Spradling AC, Goldstein LSB. 1993. The kinesin-like protein KLP61F is essential for mitosis in *Drosophila*. *J. Cell Biol.* 123:665–79

76. Henry GD, Winstanley MA, Dalgarno DC, Marcus G, Scott M, et al. 1985. Characterization of the actin-binding site on the alkali light chain of myosin. *Biochim. Biophys. Acta* 830:233–43

77. Hicks JL, Williams DS. 1992. Distribution of the myosin I-like *ninaC* proteins in the *Drosophila* retina and ultrastructural analysis of mutant phenotypes. *J. Cell Sci.* 101:247–54

78. Hirokawa N, Pfister KK, Yorifuji H, Wagner MC, Brady ST, Bloom GS. 1989. Submolecular domains of bovine brain kinesin identified by electron microscopy and monoclonal antibody decoration. *Cell* 56:867–78

79. Hirokawa N, Sato-Yoshitake R, Yoshida T, Kawashima T. 1990. Brain dynein (MAP1C) localizes on both anterogradely and retrogradely transported membranous organelles in vivo. *J. Cell Biol.* 111:1027–37

80. Ho G, Chen T-L, Chisholm RL. 1995. Both the amino and carboxyl termini of *Dictyostelium* myosin essential light chain are required for binding to myosin heavy chain. *J. Biol. Chem.* In press

81. Hodge TP, Cross R, Kendrick-Jones J. 1992. Role of the COOH-terminal nonhelical tailpiece in the assembly of a vertebrate nonmuscle myosin rod. *J. Cell Biol.* 118:1085–95

82. Holzbaur ELF, Hammarback JA, Paschal BM, Kravit NG, Pfister KK, Vallee RB. 1991. Homology of a 150 K cytoplasmic dynein-associated polypeptide with the *Drosophila* gene *Glued*. *Nature* 351:579–83

83. Holzbaur ELF, Vallee RB. 1994. Dyneins: molecular structure and cellular function. *Annu. Rev. Cell Biol.* 10:339–72

84. Hoyt MA. 1994. Cellular roles of kinesin and related proteins. *Curr. Opin. Cell Biol.* 6:63–68

85. Hoyt MA, He L, Loo KK, Saunders WS. 1992. Two *Saccharomyces cerevisiae* kinesin-related gene products required for mitotic spindle assembly. *J. Cell Biol.* 118:109–20

86. Hoyt MA, He L, Totis L, Saunders WS.

1993. Loss of function of *Saccharomyces cerevisiae* kinesin-related *CIN8* and *KIP1* is suppressed by *KAR3* motor domain mutations. *Genetics* 135:35–44

87. Huang B, Ramanis Z, Luck DJL. 1982. Suppressor mutations in Chlamydomonas reveal a regulatory mechanism for flagellar function. *Cell* 28:115–24

88. Huang TG, Suhan J, Hackney DD. 1994. *Drosophila* kinesin motor domain extended to amino acid position 392 is dimeric when expressed in *Escherichia coli*. *J. Biol. Chem.* 269:16502–7

89. Ikebe M, Hinkins S, Hartshorne DJ. 1983. Correlation of enzymatic properties and conformation of smooth muscle myosin. *Biochemistry* 22:4580–87

90. Ikebe M, Ikebe R, Kamisoyama H, Reardon S, Schwonek JP, et al. 1994. Function of the $NH_2$-terminal domain of the regulatory light chain on the regulation of smooth muscle myosin. *J. Biol. Chem.* 269:28173–80

91. Ikebe M, Morita J. 1991. Identification of the sequence of the regulatory light chain required for the phosphorylation-dependent regulation of actomyosin. *J. Biol. Chem.* 266:21339–42

92. Ikebe M, Reardon S, Mitani Y, Kamisoyama H, Matsuura M, Ikebe R. 1994. Involvement of the C-terminal residues of the 20,000-dalton light chain of myosin on the regulation of smooth muscle actomyosin. *Proc. Natl. Acad. Sci. USA* 91:9096–100

93. Itakura S, Yamakawa H, Toyoshima YY, Ishijima A, Kojima T, et al. 1993. Force-generating domain of myosin motor. *Biochem. Biophys. Res. Commun.* 196:1504–10

94. Jansco A, Szent-Gyorgyi AG. 1994. Regulation of scallop myosin by the regulatory light chain depends on a single glycine residue. *Proc. Natl. Acad. Sci. USA* 91:8762–66

95. Jay PY, Elson EL. 1992. Surface particle transport mechanism independent of myosin II in *Dictyostelium*. *Nature* 356:438–40

96. Jay PY, Pham PA, Wong SA, Elson EL. 1995. A mechanical function of myosin II in cell motility. *J. Cell Sci.* 108:387–93

97. Johnson KA. 1983. The pathway of ATP hydrolysis by dynein. *J. Biol. Chem.* 258:13825–32

98. Johnson KA, Wall JS. 1983. Structure and molecular weight of the dynein ATPase. *J. Cell Biol.* 96:669–78

99. Johnston GC Prendergast JA, Singer RA. 1991. The *Saccharomyces cervisiae MYO2* gene encodes an essential myosin for vectorial transport of vesicles. *J. Cell Biol.* 113:539–51

100. Jung G, Hammer JA III. 1990. Generation and characterization of *Dictyostelium* cells deficient in a myosin I heavy chain isoform. *J. Cell Biol.* 110:1955–64

101. Jung G, Korn ED, Hammer JA III. 1987. The heavy chain of *Acanthamoeba* myosin IB is a fusion of myosin-like and non-myosin-like sequences. *Proc. Natl. Acad. Sci. USA* 84:6720–24

102. Kagami O, Kamiya R. 1992. Translocation and rotation of microtubules caused by multiple species of *Chlamydomonas* inner-arm dynein. *J. Cell Sci.* 103:653–64

103. Kamisoyama H, Araki Y, Ikebe M. 1994. Mutagenesis of the phosphorylation site (serine 19) of smooth muscle myosin regulatory light chain and its effects on the properties of myosin. *Biochemistry* 33:840–47

104. Kamiya R. 1988. Mutations at twelve independent loci result in absence of outer dynein arms in *Chlamydomonas reinhardtii*. *J. Cell Biol.* 107:2253–58

105. Karess RE, Chang X, Edwards KA, Kulkarni S, Aguilera I, Kiehart DP. 1991. The regulatory light chain of nonmuscle myosin is encoded by *spaghetti-squash*, a gene required for cytokinesis in Drosophila. *Cell* 65:1177–89

106. Karki S, Holzbaur ELF. 1995. Affinity chromatography demonstrates a direct binding between cytoplasmic dynein and the dynactin complex. *J. Biol. Chem.* 270:28806–11

107. Kendrick-Jones J, Lehman W, Szent-Gyorgyi AG. 1970. Regulation in molluscan muscles. *J. Mol. Biol.* 54:313–26

108. King SM, Wilkerson CG, Witman GB. 1991. The $M_r$ 78,000 intermediate chain of *Chlamydomonas* outer arm dynein interacts with α-tubulin in situ. *J. Biol. Chem.* 266:8401–7

109. King SM, Witman GB. 1990. Localization of an intermediate chain of outer arm dynein by immunoelectron microscopy. *J. Biol. Chem.* 265:19807–11

110. Komma DJ, Horne AS, Endow SA. 1991. Separation of meiotic and mitotic effects of claret non-disjunctional on chromosome segregation in *Drosophila*. *EMBO J.* 10:419–24

111. Kronert WA, O'Donnell PT, Bernstein SI. 1994. A charge change in an evolutionarily-conserved region of the myosin globular head prevents myosin and thick filament accumulation in *Drosophila*. *J. Mol. Biol.* 236:697–702

112. Kubalek EW, Uyeda TQP, Spudich JA. 1992. A *Dictyostelium* myosin II lacking

a proximal 58-KDa portion of the tail is functional in vivo and in vitro. *Mol. Cell Biol.* 3:1455–62

113. Labbé J-P, Audemard E, Bertrand R, Kassab R. 1986. Specific interactions of the alkali light chain 1 in skeletal myosin heads probed by chemical cross-linking. *Biochemistry* 25:8325–30

114. Lankford E, Epstein N, Fananapazir L, Sweeney HL. 1995. Abnormal contractile properties of muscle fibers expressing beta-myosin heavy chain gene mutations in patients with hypertrophic cardiomyopathy. *J. Clin. Invest.* 95:1409–14

115. LeBlanc-Straceski JM, Fukui Y, Sohn RL, Spudich JA, Leinwand LA. 1994. Functional analysis of a cardiac myosin rod in *Dictyostelium discoideum. Cell Motil. Cytoskelet.* 27:313–26

116. Lee RJ, Egelhoff TT, Spudich JA. 1994. Molecular genetic truncation analysis of filament assembly and phosphorylation domains of *Dictyostelium* myosin heavy chain. *J. Cell Sci.* 107:2875–86

117. Lees-Miller JP, Helfman DM, Schroer TA. 1992. A vertebrate actin-related protein is a component of a multisubunit complex involved in microtubule-based vesicle motility. *Nature* 359:244–46

118. LeGuellec R, Paris J, Couturier A, Roghi C, Philippe M. 1991. Cloning by differential screening of a *Xenopus* cDNA that encodes a kinesin-related protein. *Mol. Cell. Biol.* 11:3395–98

119. Levine BA, Griffiths HS, Patchell VB, Perry SV. 1988. Study of the phosphorylatable light chains of skeletal and gizzard myosins by nuclear magnetic resonance spectroscopy. *Biochem. J.* 254:277–86

120. Levine RJ, Chantler PD, Kensler RW, Woodhead JL. 1991. Effects of phosphorylation by myosin light chain kinase on the structure of Limulus thick filaments. *J. Cell Biol.* 113:563–72

121. L'heureux K, Forne T, Chaussepied P. 1993. Interaction and polymerization of the G-actin—myosin head complex: effect of DNase I. *Biochemistry* 32:10005–14

122. Li YY, Yeh E, Hays T, Bloom K. 1993. Disruption of mitotic spindle orientation in a yeast dynein mutant. *Proc. Natl. Acad. Sci. USA* 90:10096–100

123. Liao H, Li G, Yen TJ. 1994. Mitotic regulation of microtubule cross-linking activity of CENP-E kinetochore protein. *Science* 265:394–98

124. Lillie SH, Brown SS. 1992. Suppression of a myosin defect by a kinesin-related gene. *Nature* 356:358–61

125. Lillie SH, Brown SS. 1994. Immuno-fluorescence localization of the unconventional myosin, Myo2p, and the putative kinesin-related protein, Smy1p, to the same regions of polarized growth in *Saccharomyces cerevisiae. J. Cell Biol.* 125:825–42

126. Lin SXH, Collins CA. 1992. Immunolocalization of cytoplasmic dynein to lysosomes in cultured cells. *J. Cell Sci.* 101:125–37

127. Lin SXH, Ferro KL, Collins CA. 1994. Cytoplasmic dynein undergoes intracellular redistribution concomitant with phosphorylation of the heavy chain in response to serum starvation and okadaic acid. *J. Cell Biol.* 127:1009–19

128. Lowey S, Waller GS, Trybus KM. 1993. Skeletal muscle myosin light chains are essential for physiological speeds of shortening. *Nature* 365:454–56

129. Luck DJL, Piperno G. 1989. Dynein arm mutants of *Chlamydomonas. Cell Mov.* 1:49–60

130. Lye RJ, Porter ME, Scholey JM, McIntosh JR. 1987. Identification of a microtubule-based cytoplasmic motor in the nematode C. elegans. *Cell* 51:309–18

131. MacLeod AR, Waterston RH, Brenner S. 1977. An internal deletion mutant of a myosin heavy chain in *C. elegans. Proc. Natl. Acad. Sci. USA* 74:5336–40

132. Manstein DJ, Titus MA, De Lozanne A, Spudich JA. 1989. Gene replacement in *Dictyostelium:* generation of myosin null mutants. *EMBO J.* 8:923–32

133. Marian AJ, Kelly D, Mares A Jr, Fitzgibbons J, Caira T, et al. 1994. A missense mutation in the β myosin heavy chain gene is a predictor of premature sudden death in patients with hypertropic cardiomyopathy. *J. Sports Med. Phys. Fit.* 34:1–10

134. Marian AJ, Yu Q-T, Mares A Jr, Hill R, Roberts R, Perryman MB. 1992. Detection of a new mutation in the beta-myosin heavy chain gene in an individual with hypertrophic cardiomyopathy. *J. Clin. Invest.* 90:2156–65

135. Mastronarde DN, O'Toole ET, McDonald KL, McIntosh JR, Porter ME. 1992. Arrangement of inner dynein arms in wild-type and mutant flagella of *Chlamydomonas. J. Cell Biol.* 118:1145–62

136. Matsuura M, Ikebe M. 1995. Requirement of the two-headed structure for the phosphorylation-dependent regulation of smooth muscle myosin. *FEBS Lett.* 363:246–50

137. Mazumdar M, Mikami A, Gee M, Vallee RB. 1994. In vitro expression of cytoplasmic dynein heavy chain and its

functional characterization. *Mol. Biol. Cell* 5:131 (Abstr.)

138. McDonald HB, Goldstein LSB. 1990. Identification and characterization of a gene encoding a kinesin-like protein in Drosophila. *Cell* 61:991–1000

139. McDonald HB, Stewart RJ, Goldstein LS. 1990. The kinesin-like ncd protein of Drosophila is a minus end-directed microtubule motor. *Cell* 63:1159–65

140. McGrail M, Gepner J, Silvanovich A, Lidmann S, Serr M, Hays TS. 1995. Regulation of cytoplasmic dynein function in vivo by the *Drosophila* Glued complex. *J. Cell Biol.* 131:411–25

141. Meluh PB, Rose MD. 1990. *KAR3*, a kinesin-related gene required for yeast nuclear fusion. *Cell* 60:1029–41

142. Mercer JA, Seperack PK, Strobel MC, Copeland NG, Jenkins NA. 1991. Novel myosin heavy chain encoded by murine *dilute* coat colour locus. *Nature* 349:709–13

143. Metzger JM, Greaser ML, Moss RL. 1989. Variations in cross-bridge attachment rate and tension with phosphorylation of myosin in mammalian skinned skeletal muscle fibers: implications for twitch potentiation in intact muscle. *J. Gen. Physiol.* 93:855–83

144. Milligan RA, Whittaker M, Safer D. 1990. Molecular structure of F-actin and location of surface binding sites. *Nature* 348:217–21

145. Mitchell DR, Brown KS. 1994. Sequence analysis of the *Chlamydomonas* alpha and beta dynein heavy chain genes. *J. Cell Sci.* 107:635–44

146. Mitchell DR, Kang Y. 1991. Identification of *oda6* as a *Chlamydomonas* dynein mutant by rescue with the wild-type gene. *J. Cell Biol.* 113:835–42

147. Mocz G, Gibbons IR. 1993. ATP-insensitive interaction of the amino-terminal region of the β heavy chain of dynein with microtubules. *Biochemistry* 32:3456–60

148. Moerman DG, Plurad S, Waterston RH, Baillie DL. 1982. Mutations in the *unc-54* myosin heavy chain gene of Caenorhabditis elegans that alter contractility but not muscle structure. *Cell* 29:773–81

149. Montell C, Rubin GM. 1988. The Drosophila *ninaC* locus encodes two photoreceptor cell specific proteins with domains homologous to protein kinases and the myosin heavy chain head. *Cell* 52:757–72

150. Muhua L, Karpova TS, Cooper JA. 1994. A yeast actin-related protein homologous to that in vertebrate dynactin complex is important for spindle orientation and nuclear migration. *Cell* 78:669–79

151. Nangaku M, Sato-Yoshitake R, Okada Y, Noda Y, Takemura R, et al. 1994. KIF1B, a novel microtubule plus end-directed monomeric motor protein for transport of mitochondria. *Cell* 79:1209–20

152. Nishi H, Kimura A, Harada H, Adachi K, Koga Y, et al. 1994. Possible gene dose effect of a mutant cardiac β-myosin heavy chain gene on the clinical expression of familial hypertrophic cardiomyopathy. *Biochem. Biophys. Res. Commun.* 200:549–56

153. Nishi H, Kimura A, Harada H, Toshima H, Sasazuki T. 1992. Novel missense mutation in cardiac β myosin heavy chain gene found in a Japanese patient with hypertrophic cardiomyopathy. *Biochem. Biophys. Res. Commun.* 188:379–87

154. O'Connell MJ, Meluh PB, Rose MD, Morris NR. 1993. Suppression of the *bimC4* mitotic spindle defect by deletion of *klpA*, a gene encoding a KAR3-related kinesin-like protein in *Aspergillus nidulans*. *J. Cell Biol.* 120:153–62

155. Ogawa K. 1991. Four ATP binding sites in the midregion of the β heavy chain of dynein. *Nature* 352:643–45

156. Onishi H, Wakabayashi T. 1982. Electron microscopic studies of myosin molecules from chicken gizzard muscle I: the formation of the intramolecular loop in the myosin tail. *J. Biochem.* 92:871–79

157. Ostrow BD, Chen P, Chisholm RL. 1994. Expression of a myosin regulatory light chain phosphorylation site mutant complements the cytokinesis and developmental defects of *Dictyostelium* RMLC null cells. *J. Cell Biol.* 127:1945–55

158. Page BD, Satterwhite LL, Rose MD, Snyder M. 1994. Localization of the Kar3 kinesin heavy chain-related protein requires the CIK1 interacting protein. *J. Cell Biol.* 124:507–19

159. Page BD, Snyder M. 1992. CIK1: a developmentally regulated spindle pole body-associated protein important for microtubule functions in *Saccharomyces cerevisiae*. *Genes Dev.* 6:1414–29

160. Paschal BM, Holzbaur ELF, Clark S, Meyer D, Vallee RB. 1993. Characterization of a 50-kDa polypeptide in cytoplasmic dynein preparations reveals a complex with p150^Glued and a novel actin. *J. Biol. Chem.* 268:15318–23

161. Paschal BM, Mikami A, Pfister KK, Vallee RB. 1992. Homology of the 74-kD cytoplasmic dynein subunit with a

flagella dynein polypeptide suggests an intracellular targeting function. *J. Cell Biol.* 118:1133–43

162. Paschal BM, Shpetner HS, Vallee RB. 1987. MAP 1C is a microtubule-activated ATPase which translocates microtubules in vitro and has dynein-like properties. *J. Cell Biol.* 105:1273–82

163. Paschal BM, Vallee RB. 1987. Retrograde transport by the microtubule-associated protein MAP 1C. *Nature* 330: 181–83

164. Patel N, Thierry-Mieg D, Mancillas JR. 1993. Cloning by insertional mutagenesis of a cDNA encoding *Caenorhabditis elegans* kinesin heavy chain. *Proc. Natl. Acad. Sci. USA* 90:9181–85

165. Perryman MB, Yu Q-T, Marian AJ, Mares A Jr, Czernuszewicz G, et al. 1992. Expression of a missense mutation in the messenger RNA for β-myosin heavy chain in myocardial tissue in hypertrophic cardiomyopathy. *J. Clin. Invest.* 90:271–77

166. Piperno G, Mead K, LeDizet M, Moscatelli A. 1994. Mutations in the "dynein regulatory complex" alter the ATP-insensitive binding sites for inner arm dyneins in *Chlamydomonas* axonemes. *J. Cell Biol.* 125:1109–17

167. Piperno G, Ramanis Z, Smith EF, Sale WS. 1990. Three distinct inner dynein arms in *Chlamydomonas* flagella: molecular composition and location in the axoneme. *J. Cell Biol.* 110:379–89

168. Plamman M, Minke PF, Tinsley JH, Bruno KS. 1994. Cytoplasmic dynein and actin-related protein Arp1 are required for normal nuclear distribution in filamentous fungi. *J. Cell Biol.* 127: 139–49

169. Plough HH, Ives PT. 1935. Induction of mutations by high temperature in *Drosophila. Genetics* 20:42–69

170. Pollard TD, Korn ED. 1973. *Acanthamoeba* myosin I: isolation from *Acanthamoeba castellanii* of an enzyme similar to muscle myosin. *J. Biol. Chem.* 248:4682–90

171. Pollenz RS, Chen T-LL, Trivinos-Lagos L, Chisholm R. 1992. The Dictyostelium essential light chain is required for myosin function. *Cell* 69:951–62

172. Porter JA, Hicks JL, Williams DS, Montell C. 1992. Differential localizations of and requirements for the two *Drosophila ninaC* kinase/myosins in photoreceptor cells. *J. Cell Biol.* 116:683–93

173. Porter JA, Montell C. 1993. Distinct roles of the *Drosophila ninaC* kinase and myosin domains revealed by systematic mutagenesis. *J. Cell Biol.* 122: 601–12

174. Porter JA, Mujun Y, Doberstein SK, Pollard TD, Montell C. 1993. Dependence of calmodulin localization in the retina on the ninaC unconventional myosin. *Nature* 262:1038–42

175. Porter ME, Knott JA, Gardner LC, Mitchell DR, Dutcher SK. 1994. Mutations in the *SUP-PF-1* locus of *Chlamydomonas reinhardtii* identify a regulatory domain in the β-dynein heavy chain. *J. Cell Biol.* 126:1495–507

176. Prince HP, Trayer HR, Henry GD, Trayer IP, Dalgarno DC, et al. 1981. Proton nuclear-magnetic resonance spectroscopy of myosin subfragment 1 isoenzymes. *Eur. J. Biochem.* 121:213–19

177. Rajasekharan KN, Morita J-I, Mayadevi M, Ikebe M, Burke M. 1991. Formation and properties of smooth-muscle myosin 20-kDa light chain skeletal-muscle myosin hybrids and photo-cross-linking from the maleimidylbenzophenone-labeled light chain to the heavy chain. *Arch. Biochem. Biophys.* 288:584–90

178. Rasmusson K, Serr M, Gepner J, Gibbons I, Hays TS. 1994. A family of dynein genes in *Drosophila melanogaster. Mol. Biol. Cell* 5:45–55

179. Rasooly RS, New CM, Zhang P, Hawley RS, Baker BS. 1991. The *lethal(1)TW-6cs* mutation of *Drosophila melanogaster* is a dominant antimorphic allele of *nod* and is associated with a single base change in the putative ATP-binding domain. *Genetics* 129:409–22

180. Rasooly RS, Zhang P, Tibolla AK, Hawley RS. 1994. A structure-function analysis of NOD, a kinesin-like protein from *Drosophila melanogaster. Mol. Gen. Genet.* 242:145–51

181. Rayment I, Holden HM, Sellers JR, Fananapazir L, Epstein ND. 1995. Structural interpretation of the mutations in the β-cardiac myosin that have been implicated in familial hypertrophic cardiomyopathy. *Proc. Natl. Acad. Sci. USA* 92:3864–68

182. Rayment I, Holden HM, Whittaker M, Yohn CB, Lorenz M, et al. 1993. Structure of the actin-myosin complex and its implications for muscle contraction. *Science* 261:58–65

183. Rayment I, Rypniewski WR, Schmidt-Bäde K, Smith R, Tomchick DR, et al. 1993. Three-dimensional structure of myosin subfragment-1: a molecular motor. *Science* 261:50–58

184. Reinach FC, Nagai K, Kendrick-Jones J. 1986. Site directed mutagenesis of the regulatory light-chain $Ca^{+2}/Mg^{+2}$ binding sites and its role in hybrid myosins. *Nature* 322:80–83

185. Reinhard J, Scheel AA, Diekmann D, Hall A, Ruppert C, Bähler M. 1995. A novel type of myosin implicated in signalling by rho family GTPases. *EMBO J.* 14:697–704

186. Reiser PJ, Moss RL, Giulian GG, Greaser ML. 1985. Shortening velocity in single fibers from adult rabbit soleus muscles is correlated with myosin heavy chain composition. *J. Biol. Chem.* 260:9077–80

187. Rindt H, Bauer BJ, Robbins J. 1993. In vitro production of enzymatically active myosin heavy chain. *J. Muscle Res. Cell Motil.* 14:26–34

188. Roof DM, Meluh PB, Rose MD. 1992. Kinesin-related proteins required for assembly of the mitotic spindle. *J. Cell Biol.* 118:95–108

189. Rovner AS, Freyzon Y, Trybus KM. 1995. Chimeric substitutions of the actin-binding loop disrupt regulation of smooth muscle heavy meromyosin. *J. Biol. Chem.* In press

190. Rowe T, Kendrick-Jones J. 1993. The C-terminal helix in subdomain 4 of the regulatory light chain is essential for myosin regulation. *EMBO J.* 12:4877–84

191. Ruppel KM, Uyeda TQ, Spudich JA. 1994. Role of highly conserved lysine 130 of myosin motor domain. *J. Biol. Chem.* 269:18773–80

192. Sakakibara H, Mitchell DR, Kamiya R. 1991. A *Chlamydomonas* outer arm dynein mutant missing the α-heavy chain. *J. Cell Biol.* 113:615–22

193. Sakakibara H, Takada S, King SSM, Witman GB, Kamiya R. 1993. A *Chlamydomonas* outer arm dynein mutant with a truncated β-heavy chain. *J. Cell Biol.* 122:653–61

194. Saunders WS, Hoyt MA. 1992. Kinesin-related proteins required for structural integrity of the mitotic spindle. *Cell* 70:451–58

195. Saunders WS, Koshland D, Eshel D, Gibbons IR, Hoyt MA. 1995. *Saccharomyces cerevisiae* kinesin- and dynein-related proteins required for anaphase chromosome segregation. *J. Cell Biol.* 128:617–24

196. Saxton WM, Hicks J, Goldstein LSB, Raff EC. 1991. Kinesin heavy chain is essential for viability and neuromuscular functions in Drosophila, but mutants show no defects in mitosis. *Cell* 64:1093–102

197. Schafer DA, Gill SR, Cooper JA, Heuser JE, Schroer TA. 1994. Ultrastructural analysis of the dynactin complex: an actin-related protein is a component of a filament that resembles F-actin. *J. Cell Biol.* 126:403–12

198. Schnapp BJ, Reese TS. 1989. Dynein is the motor for retrograde axonal transport of organelles. *Proc. Natl. Acad. Sci. USA* 86:1548–52

199. Sinard JH, Rimm DL, Pollard TD. 1990. Identification of functional regions on the tail of *Acanthamoeba* myosin-II using recombinant fusion proteins. II. Assembly properties of tails with $NH_2$- and COOH-terminal deletions. *J. Cell Biol.* 111:2417–26

200. Smith CA, Rayment I. 1995. X-ray structure of the magnesium(II)-pyrophosphate complex of the truncated head of *Dictyostelium discoideum* myosin to 2.7Å resolution. *Biochemistry* 34:8973–81

201. Smith EF, Sale WS. 1992. Regulation of dynein-driven microtubule sliding by the radial spokes in flagella. *Science* 257:1557–59

202. Solomon SD, Simonetta W, Watkins H, Ridker PM, Come P, et al. 1993. Left ventricular hypertrophy and morphology in familial hypertrophic cardiomyopathy associated with mutations of the beta-myosin heavy chain gene. *J. Am. Coll. Cardiol.* 22:498–505

203. Sprang SR, Acharya KR, Goldsmith EJ, Stuart DI, Varvill K, et al. 1988. Structural changes in glycogen phosphorylase induced by phosphorylation. *Nature* 336:215–21

204. Springer ML, Patterson B, Spudich JA. 1994. Stage-specific requirement for myosin II during *Dictyostelium* development. *Development* 120:2651–60

205. Stewart RJ, Thaler JP, Goldstein LSB. 1993. Direction of microtubule movement is an intrinsic property of the motor domains of kinesin heavy chain and *Drosophila* ncd protein. *Proc. Natl. Acad. Sci. USA* 90:5209–13

206. Straceski AJ, Geisterfer-Lowrance A, Seidman CE, Seidman JG, Leinwand LA. 1994. Functional analysis of myosin missense mutations in familial hypertrophic cardiomyopathy. *Proc. Natl. Acad. Sci. USA* 91:589–93

207. Sutoh K. 1982. Identification of myosin-binding sites on the actin sequence. *Biochemistry* 21:3654–61

208. Sweeney HL. 1995. Function of the N-terminus of the myosin essential light chain of vertebrate striated muscle. *Biophys. J.* 68:S112–19

209. Sweeney HL, Bowman BF, Stull JT. 1993. Myosin light chain phosphorylation in vertebrate striated muscle: regulation and function. *Am. J. Physiol.* 264:C1085–95

210. Sweeney HL, Kushmerick MJ, Mabuchi K, Sreter FA, Gergeley J. 1988. Myosin

alkali light chain and heavy chain variations correlate with altered shortening velocity of isolated skeletal muscle fibers. *J. Biol. Chem.* 263:9034–39

211. Sweeney HL, Straceski A, Leinwand L, Tikunov B, Faust L. 1994. Heterologous expression and characterization of a cardiac myosin mutant that causes hypertrophic cardiomyopathy. *J. Biol. Chem.* 269:1603–5

212. Sweeney HL, Yang Z, Zhi G, Stull JT, Trybus KM. 1994. Charge replacement near the phosphorylatable serine of the myosin regulatory light chain mimics aspects of phosphorylation. *Proc. Natl. Acad. Sci. USA* 90:1490–94

213. Theurkauf WE, Hawley RS. 1992. Meiotic spindle assembly in *Drosophila* females: behavior of nonexchange chromosomes and the effects of mutations in the *ncd* kinesin-like protein. *J. Cell Biol.* 116:1167–80

214. Thierfelder L, Watkins H, MacRae C, Lamas R, McKenna W, et al. 1994. Alpha-tropomyosin and cardiac troponin T mutations cause familial hypertrophic cardiomyopathy: a disease of the sarcomere. *Cell* 77:701–12

215. Titus MA, Wessels D, Spudich JA, Soll DR. 1993. The unconventional myosin encoded by the *myo* A gene plays a role in *Dictyostelium* motility. *Mol. Biol. Cell* 4:233–46

216. Tohtong R, Yamashita H, Graham M, Haeberle J, Simcox A, Maghan D. 1995. Impairment of muscle function caused by mutations of phosphorylation sites in myosin regulatory light chain. *Nature* 374:650–53

217. Trayer IP, Trayer HR, Levine BA. 1987. Evidence that the N-terminal region of A1-light chain of myosin interacts directly with the C-terminal region of actin. *Eur. J. Biochem.* 164:259–66

218. Trybus KM. 1989. Filamentous smooth muscle myosin is regulated by phosphorylation. *J. Cell Biol.* 109:2887–94

219. Trybus KM. 1991. Regulation of smooth muscle myosin. *Cell Motil. Cytoskelet.* 18:81–85

220. Trybus KM. 1994. Regulation of expressed truncated smooth muscle myosins. *J. Biol. Chem.* 269:20819–22

221. Trybus KM, Chatman TA. 1993. Chimeric regulatory light chains as probes of smooth muscle myosin function. *J. Biol. Chem.* 168:4412–19

222. Trybus KM, Waller GS, Chatman TA. 1994. Coupling of ATPase activity and motility in smooth muscle myosin is mediated by the regulatory light chain. *J. Cell Biol.* 124:963–69

223. Uyeda TQP, Ruppel KM, Spudich JA. 1994. Enzymatic activities correlate with chimaeric substitutions at the actin-binding face of myosin. *Nature* 368:567–69

224. Uyeda TQP, Spudich JA. 1993. A functional recombinant myosin II lacking a regulatory light chain binding site. *Science* 262:1867–70

225. Vaisberg EA, Koonce MP, McIntosh JR. 1993. Cytoplasmic dynein plays a role in mammalian mitotic spindle formation. *J. Cell Biol.* 123:849–58

226. Vale RD, Reese TS, Sheetz MP. 1985. Identification of a novel force-generating protein, kinesin, involved in microtubule-based motility. *Cell* 42:39–50

227. Vallee RB, Wall JS, Paschal BM, Shpetner HS. 1988. Microtubule-associated protein 1C from brain is a two-headed cystolic dynein. *Nature* 332:561–63

228. VanBuren P, Waller GS, Harris DE, Trybus KM, Warshaw DM, Lowey S. 1994. The essential light chain is required for full force production in skeletal muscle myosin. *Proc. Natl. Acad. Sci. USA* 91:12403–7

229. Vaughan KT, Vallee RB. 1995. Cytoplasmic dynein binds dynactin through a direct interaction between the intermediate chain and p150^Glued. *J. Cell Biol.* In press

230. Vybiral T, Deitiker PR, Roberts R, Epstein HF. 1992. Accumulation and assembly of myosin in hypertrophic cardiomyopathy with the 403 Arg to Gln β-myosin heavy chain mutation. *Circulation* 71:1404–9

231. Walczak CE, Nelson DL. 1994. Regulation of dynein-driven motility in cilia and flagella. *Cell Motil. Cytoskelet.* 27:101–7

232. Walker JE, Saraste M, Runswick MJ, Gay NJ. 1982. Distantly related sequences in the α- and β-subunits of ATP synthase, myosin, kinases and other ATP-requiring enzymes and a common nucleotide binding fold. *EMBO J.* 1:945–51

233. Walker RA, Salmon ED, Endow SA. 1990. The *Drosophila claret* segregation protein is a minus-end directed motor molecule. *Nature* 347:780–82

234. Walther Z, Vashishta M, Hall JL. 1994. The *Chlamydomonas* FLA10 gene encodes a novel kinesin-homologous protein. *J. Cell Biol.* 126:175–88

235. Warmke J, Yamakawa M, Molloy J, Falkenthal S, Maughan D. 1992. Myosin light chain-2 mutation affects flight, wing beat frequency, and indirect flight muscle contraction kinetics in *Drosophila*. *J. Cell Biol.* 119:1523–39

236. Waterman-Storer CM, Holzbaur ELF. 1996. The product of the *Drosophila* gene *Glued* is a functional homologue of the component of the vertebrate dynactin complex p150^Glued. *J. Biol. Chem.* In press

237. Waterman-Storer CM, Karki S, Holzbaur ELF. 1995. p150^Glued binds directly to both microtubules and centractin. *Proc. Natl. Acad. Sci. USA* 92: 1634–38

238. Watkins H, Rosenzweig A, Hwang DS, Levi T, McKenna W, et al. 1992. Characteristics and prognostic implications of myosin missense mutations in familial hypertrophic cardiomyopathy. *N. Engl. J. Med.* 326:1108–14

239. Well D, Blanchard S, Kaplan J, Guilford P, Gibson F, et al. 1995. Defective myosin VIIA gene responsible for Usher syndrome type 1B. *Nature* 374:60–61

240. Wessels D, Murray J, Jung G, Hammer JA III, Soll DR. 1991. Myosin IB null mutants of *Dictyostelium* exhibit abnormalities in motility. *Cell Motil. Cytoskelet.* 20:301–15

241. Whitaker M, Faust L, Smith J, Milligan RA, Sweeney HL. 1995. A 35 Å movement of smooth muscle myosin upon ADP release. *Nature.* In press

242. Wordeman L, Mitchison TJ. 1995. Identification and partial characterization of mitotic centromere-associated kinesin, a kinesin-related protein that associates with centromeres during mitosis. *J. Cell Biol.* 128:95–104

243. Xiang X, Beckwith SM, Morris NR. 1994. Cytoplasmic dynein is involved in nuclear migration in *Aspergillus nidulans. Proc. Natl. Acad. Sci. USA* 94: 2100–4

244. Xie X, Harrison DH, Schlichting I, Sweet RM, Kalabokis VN, et al. 1994. Structure of the regulatory domain of scallop myosin at 2.8 Å resolution. *Nature* 368:306–12

245. Yang JT, Laymon RA, Goldstein LSB. 1989. A three domain structure of kinesin heavy chain revealed by DNA sequence and microtubule binding analyses. *Cell* 56:879–89

246. Yang JT, Saxton WM, Stewart RJ, Raff EC, Goldstein LSB. 1990. Evidence that the head of kinesin is sufficient for force generation and motility in vitro. *Science* 249:42–47

247. Yang Z, Sweeney HL. 1995. Restoration of phosphorylation-dependent regulation to the skeletal muscle myosin regulatory light chain. *J. Biol. Chem.* 270: 24646–49

248. Yen TJ, Li G, Schaar BT, Szilak I, Cleveland DW. 1992. CENP-E is a putative kinetochore motor that accumulates just before mitosis. *Nature* 359: 536–39

249. Young PE, Richman AM, Ketchum AS, Kiehart DP. 1993. Morphogenesis in *Drosophila* requires nonmuscle myosin heavy chain function. *Genes Dev.* 7:29–41

250. Yu Q-T, Ifegwu J, Marlan AJ, Mares A Jr, Hill R, et al. 1993. Hypertrophic cardiomyopathy mutation is expressed in messenger RNA of skeletal as well as cardiac muscle. *Circulation* 87:406–12

251. Zhang P, Knowles BA, Goldstein LSB, Hawley RS. 1990. A kinesin-like protein required for distributive chromosome segregation in Drosophila. *Cell* 62: 1053–62

# SUBJECT INDEX

# CUMULATIVE INDEXES

## CONTRIBUTING AUTHORS, VOLUMES 54–58

# CHAPTER TITLES, VOLUMES 54–58